University of Michigan

Physics 235

Fall 2013 / Winter 2014

Physics for the Life Sciences II

University of Michigan Ann Arbor

Wiley Custom Learning Solutions

Cover Image © Sebastian Kaulitzki /Shutterstock

Printing identification and country of origin will either be included on this page and/or the end of the book. In addition, if the ISBN on this page and the back cover do not match, the ISBN on the back cover should be considered the correct ISBN.

To order books or for customer service, please call 1(800)-CALL-WILEY (225-5945).

Printed in the United States of America.

ISBN 978-1-118-81212-9

Printed and bound by Quad/Graphics

V10002725_073018

Contents

Equalities denoted by $\equiv$ are exact.

Length

1 metre $\equiv$ 39.37 inches = 3.281 feet
1 inch $\equiv$ 2.54 centimetres
1 foot $\equiv$ 30.48 centimetres
1 kilometre $\equiv 10^3$ metres = 0.6214 miles
1 mile $\equiv$ 5280 feet = 1.609 kilometres
1 angstrom $\equiv 10^{-10}$ metres
1 nanometre $\equiv 10^{-9}$ metres
1 micrometre = 1 micron = 10^{-6} metres

Area

1 in.^{2} $\equiv$ 6.4516 cm^2
1 ft^2 = 9.29×10^{-2} m^2
1 cm^2 $\equiv 10^{-4}$ m^2 = 0.155 in.^{2} = 1.076×10^{-3} ft^2
1 m^2 $\equiv 10^4$ cm^2 = 10.76 ft^2

Volume

1 in.^{3} = 16.39 cm^3
1 ft^3 = 2.832×10^{-2} m^3
1 cm^3 $\equiv 10^{-6}$ m^3 = 6.102×10^{-2} in.^{3}
= 3.531×10^{-5} ft^3
1 m^3 $\equiv 10^6$ cm^3 = 35.31 ft^3
1 litre $\equiv 10^{-3}$ m^3 = 0.264 gallons
1 gallon = 3.786 liters = 231 in.^{3}

Time

1 hour $\equiv$ 60 minutes $\equiv$ 3600 seconds
1 day $\equiv$ 24 hours $\equiv$ 1440 minutes
$\equiv 8.64 \times 10^4$ seconds
1 year = 365.24 days = 3.156×10^7 seconds

Mass

1 gram $\equiv 10^{-3}$ kilograms = 6.852×10^{-5} slugs
= 6.024×10^{23} u
1 kilogram $\equiv 10^3$ grams = 6.852×10^{-2} slugs
= 6.024×10^{26} u
1 slug = 14.59 kilograms
1 u = 1.66×10^{-27} kilograms

Mass density

1 gm cm^{-3} $\equiv 10^3$ kg m^{-3} = 1.94 slug ft^{-3}
1 slug ft^{-3} = 0.5153 gm cm^{-3}
= 5.153×10^2 kg m^{-3}

Speed

1 cm s^{-1} $\equiv 10^{-2}$ m s^{-1} $\equiv 3.6 \times 10^{-2}$ km h^{-1}
1 m s^{-1} $\equiv$ 3.6 km h^{-1} = 2.24 mi h^{-1}
1 ft s^{-1} $\equiv$ 30.48 cm s^{-1} $\equiv$ 0.3048 m s^{-1}
= 1.097 km h^{-1}
1 mi h^{-1} = 0.447 m s^{-1} = 1.609 km h^{-1}
= 1.467 ft s^{-1}
1 km h^{-1} = 0.2778 m s^{-1} = 0.6214 mi h^{-1}

Angle and Angular Speed

180 degrees $\equiv \pi$ radians
1 radian = 57.3 degrees
1 degree = $1.745 \chi 10^{-2}$ radians
1 rad s^{-1} = 0.159 rev s^{-1} = 9.549 rev min^{-1}
1 rev min^{-1} = 0.0167 rev s^{-1} = 0.1047 rad s^{-1}

Force

1 pound = 4.448 newtons = 4.448×10^5 dynes
1 newton $\equiv 10^5$ dynes = 0.2248 pounds
1 dyne $\equiv 10^{-5}$ newtons = 2.248×10^{-6} pounds

Pressure

1 atmosphere = 1.013×10^5 pascals
= 14.7 lb in.$^{-2}$
1 pascal $\equiv$ 10 dyn cm^{-2} = 1.450×10^{-4} lb in.$^{-2}$
= 7.501×10^{-4} cm Hg
1 cm Hg = 1.333×10^4 dyn cm^{-2}
=1.316×10^{-2} atmosphere
= 1.333×10^3 pascals
1 in. H_2O = 1.868 mm Hg = 249.1 pascals
1 lb in.$^{-2}$ = 6.895×10^3 pascals
= 6.805×10^{-2} atmosphere
1 lb ft^{-2} = 47.88 pascals
1 torr $\equiv$ 1 mm Hg = 133.3 pascals
1 bar = 10^5 pascals

Viscosity and Flow Resistance

1 Pa s $\equiv$ 10 poise
1 Pa s m^{-3} = 0.750×10^{-8} torr s cm^{-3}

Energy

1 joule $\equiv 10^7$ ergs = 0.2390 calorie = 0.7376 ft lb
1 calorie = 4.184 joules
1 kcal $\equiv 10^3$ calories
1 joule = 6.24×10^{18} electron volts
1 electron volt = 1.602×10^{-19} joule
1 kWh $\equiv 3.6 \times 10^6$ joules
1 BTU = 1.054×10^3 joules
1 ft lb = 1.356 joules

Mass Energy Conversion

1 u = 931×10^6 electron volts $\equiv$ 931 MeV

Power

1 watt $\equiv 10^{-3}$ kilowatts = 0.7376 ft lb s^{-1}
= 1.341×10^{-3} horsepower
1 horsepower $\equiv$ 550 ft lb s^{-1} = 7.457×10^2 watts
1 kilowatt $\equiv 10^3$ watts = 1.341 horsepower

Magnetic Field

1 gauss = 10^{-4} tesla

Prefixes used to define multiples of S.I. units. These may be used with any of the basic S.I. units or with units derived from them

Fraction	*Prefix*	*Symbol*	*Example*
10^{-18}	atto	a	
10^{-15}	femto	f	
10^{-12}	pico	p	
10^{-9}	nano	n	1 nanosecond = 1 ns $= 10^{-9}$ seconds
10^{-6}	micro	μ	
10^{-3}	milli	m	1 millimetre = 1 mm $= 10^{-3}$ metres
10^{-2}	centi	c	1 centimetre = 1 cm $= 10^{-2}$ metres
10^{-1}	deci	d	
10	deka	da	
10^{2}	hecto	h	
10^{3}	kilo	k	1 kilogram = 1 kg $= 10^{3}$ grams
10^{6}	mega	M	
10^{9}	giga	G	
10^{12}	tera	T	

Motion with Constant Acceleration

$v = v_0 + a\Delta t$

$\Delta x = v_0 \Delta t + \frac{1}{2}a(\Delta t)^2$

$\bar{v} = \frac{1}{2}(v_0 + v)$

$\Delta x = \frac{1}{2}(v_0 + v)\Delta t$

$v^2 = v_0^2 + 2a\Delta x$

The Greek Alphabet

Α	α	alpha
Β	β	beta
Γ	γ	gamma
Δ	δ	delta
Ε	ε	epsilon
Ζ	ζ	zeta
Η	η	eta
Θ	θ	theta
Ι	ι	iota
Κ	κ	kappa
Λ	λ	lambda
Μ	μ	mu
Ν	ν	nu
Ξ	ξ	xi
Ο	o	omicron
Π	π	pi
Ρ	ρ	rho
Σ	σ	sigma
Τ	τ	tau
Υ	υ	upsilon
Φ	ϕ	phi
Χ	χ	chi
Ψ	ψ	psi
Ω	ω	omega

GENERAL PHYSICS

SUPPLEMENTS

Student Study Guide and Solutions Manual for General Physics 2nd Edition
Morton M. Sternheim, University of Massachusetts, Amherst
Joseph W. Kane, University of Massachusetts, Amherst

Developed for student use with this text, including objectives, reviews, examples, new concepts and terms, quizzes and exams, as well as solutions for approximately 25% of the problems in the text.

Experiments in Physics—A Laboratory Manual for Scientists and Engineers
Daryl W. Preston, California State University at Hayward

A laboratory manual designed to be used in the calculus-based general physics course. The experiments follow the order of topics in traditional texts. Optional material is provided as well as flexibility in the choice of experiments.

For The Instructor
Instructor's Manual for *Physics 2nd Edition, includes solutions to all exercises and problems* and *transparency masters from which overhead transparencies may be made, in the text. A computerized text bank is also available, for MACINTOSH and IBM compatible computers.*

GENERAL PHYSICS

SECOND EDITION

MORTON M. STERNHEIM

Department of Physics and Astronomy
University of Massachusetts
Amherst, Massachusetts

JOSEPH W. KANE

Digital Equipment Corporation

WILEY

JOHN WILEY & SONS

Cover Photo: @ Michael Melford / Getty Images, Inc
Cover Design: Laura Nicholls

Acquisitions Editor: Cliff Mills
Managing Editor: Joan Kalkut
Production Manager: Katy Rubin
Production Supervisor: Nancy Prinz
Manufacturing Manager: Lorraine Fumoso
Photo Research Manager: Stella Kupferberg

Library of Congress Cataloging in Publication Data:

Sternheim, Morton M., 1933-
General physics/Morton M. Sternheim, Joseph W. Kane. —2nd ed.
Includes bibliographical references.
ISBN 9780471522782
1. Physics. I. Kane, Joseph W., 1938-. II. Title.
QC23.S84 1991
530—dc20 90-40174
CIP

Printed in the United States of America

To Suzy, Laura, Bill, and Pat. JWK

To my wife, Helen, and my children, Laura, Amy, and Jeffrey. MMS

PREFACE

General Physics is an introduction to physics for science majors with some background in calculus. Like our earlier text, *Physics*, it is intended to appeal to students with a wide range of interests and needs. However, it differs in that we have rewritten and added numerous topics which can most effectively be presented and understood with the aid of somewhat more advanced mathematical tools.

Ideally, students using this text will have completed at least one semester of calculus at the outset, but this is not essential. The derivative is introduced in discussing kinematics in Chapter One. Integrals are used only sparingly until Electricity and Magnetism is reached near the middle of the book. Calculations involving calculus are carried out with a good deal of detail and discussion. A few minor omissions may be appropriate if the students begin their calculus along with the physics.

Both our books differ in several ways from many other physics texts. First, the specific needs of science majors, including those in the life sciences, have influenced which physics topics are included or emphasized. Thus we cover some topics no longer of great current interest to many physicists, such as geometric optics, the mechanics of fluids, and acoustics, and minimize historical material and contemporary physics areas with little impact on other sciences. Second, we make extensive use of examples involving biological, chemical, geophysical, and astronomical systems, as well as alternative energy sources. Finally, we devote entire sections and chapters to applications of physics, covering subjects such as nerve conduction, ionizing radiation, and nuclear magnetic resonance. These features help to motivate students while demonstrating the widespread utility of physics and the unity of science.

General Physics contains 31 chapters, grouped into nine units. To accommodate varying needs and tastes, there is more material than can usually be covered in a two-semester or three-quarter course. Chapters that may be treated lightly or omitted entirely include Chapter Eight, Elastic Properties of Materials; Chapter Eighteen, Nerve Conduction; Chapter Twenty-Five, Special Relativity; Chapter Twenty-Nine, The Structure of Matter; and Chapter Thirty-One, Ionizing Radiation. Most of the chapters end with Supplementary Topics sections containing either applications of physics or traditional topics that can be omitted without loss of continuity. This arrangement assists the instructor in selecting what to include or to emphasize and also helps the student to distinguish the basic principles of physics from more peripheral material.

The changes made in the units of mechanics, thermal physics, and fluids in the present book are relatively minor. We use calculus in our discussions of kinematics, the center of gravity, moments of inertia, work and energy, area and polar moments of inertia, simple harmonic motion, the adiabatic expansion of an ideal gas, and Poiseuille's law. In Electricity and Magnetism, a significant amount of new material has been added, including finding fields and potentials by integration. Gauss' and Ampere's laws are present as Supplementary Topics. In Wave Motion, we use trigonometric functions to represent waves. In Chapter Twenty-Eight, Quantum Mechanics and Atomic Structure, we introduce and solve the Schrödinger equation in one dimension, and consider the hydrogen atom wave functions.

Throughout *General Physics,* we present the appropriate calculus-based derivations within the main discussion; the few such derivation included in *Physics* are located in the Supplementary Topics. SI units are used exclusively. Each chapter has a checklist of terms to define or explain, and exercises keyed to the sections. There are also problems, which are unkeyed; occasional more difficult ones are preceded by an asterisk. Exercises and problems involving calculus are preceded by a ^{c}. There are also exercises and problems for the Supplementary Topics.

This second edition of *General Physics* incorporates the improvements we made in the recent third edition of *Physics*. We have strengthened the pedagogic aspects wherever possible by clarifying our developments, adding examples, exercises, and problems. We have also kept the book up to date and have sought to increase its appeal for students with a wide range of interests. This has meant revising or adding many sections and subsections devoted to topics in basic physics and to applications of the fundamental principles in science and technology. Much of this new material is based on very recent developments or events. We think that both students and teachers will find it very stimulating.

In improving the pedagogy, we looked carefully at each section to make sure that there were varied examples, exercises, and problems at different levels of difficulty. We have added more than 50 examples and nearly 300 exercises and problems, as well as revising some of the older items. We also rewrote sections and paragraphs scattered throughout the book where we thought we could improve the discussion or could clarify topics that are difficult for students.

Clearly physics underlies much of what is happening today in other sciences and in technology. In keeping with our basic philosophy, the additions are aimed at making the book interesting and useful for students majoring in all areas of the biological and physical sciences. We have expanded and updated some earlier discussions of applications such as tomography, NMR, and PET scans (Chapters 23, 29, 31), and of nuclear safety and accidents (Chapter 30). Completely new materials include Coriolis forces and wind patterns (Chapter 7); large-scale atmospheric motions and monsoons (Chapter 12); models for the earth's crust (Chapter 13); hysteresis and magnetic disk-storage (Chapter 20); auditory localization by barn owls (Chapter 22); reflectance, rainbows (Chapter 23); direct observations of quantum jumps, barrier penetration and tunneling, scanning tunneling electron microscope (Chapter 28); superconductivity (Chapters 17, 29); superstrings (Chapter 30); and radon in the home (Chapter 31).

We thank the students and faculty colleagues who have helped us in so many ways. Kandula S. R. Sastry (University of Massachusetts) and Elizabeth P. Nickles (Albany College of Pharmacy) made many valuable suggestions. We are also grateful to H. Michael Sommermann (Westmont College, Santa Barbara, CA), Mildred Moe (University of California—Irvine), Frances Anderson (College of St. Thomas, St. Paul, MN), James A. Coleman (American International College, Springfield, MA), D. Harrison (University of Toronto, Toronto, Ontario), and Dennis Collins (Grossmont College, El Cajon, CA) for their comments. We are indebted to the competent and cooperative editorial and production staffs at John Wiley & Sons for their valuable assistance. Most of all, we thank our families for their ongoing patience, help, and encouragement.

MORTON M. STERNHEIM

JOSEPH W. KANE

PROLOGUE PHYSICS AND THE SCIENCE STUDENT

"Why should I study physics?" Sometimes asked with emotional overtones ranging from anguish to anger, this is one of the questions most frequently heard by physics teachers. It seems appropriate therefore to begin this book by attempting an answer.

One reason this question is asked so often is that many people who have not studied physics—and some who have—lack a clear notion of what physics is. Dictionaries are not much help. A typical short dictionary definition says that physics is the branch of science that deals with matter, energy, and their interactions. This is vague and general enough to include what is usually considered to be chemistry; in any case, it does not give any real feeling for what is involved. Longer dictionary entries usually expand the definition by noting that physics includes subfields such as mechanics, heat, electricity, and so forth. They give no clues as to why some subfields of science are included and others are not.

A better approach to defining physics is to ask what physicists are concerned about. Physicists attempt to understand the basic rules or *laws* that govern the operation of the natural world in which we live. Since their activities and interests evolve with time, the basic science called physics also changes with time. Many of the most active contemporary subfields of physics were undreamed of a generation or two ago. On the other hand, some parts of what are now considered to be chemistry or engineering were once considered to be physics. This is because physicists sometimes gradually abandon a field once the basic principles are known, leaving further developments and practical applications to others.

The fact that physics deals with the basic rules governing how the world works lets us see why people with varied interests may find the study of physics interesting and useful. For example, a historian who wants to understand the origins of our contemporary society will find significance in the story of the development of physics and its relationship to other human activities. Similarly, a philosopher concerned about concepts of space and time will profit greatly from understanding the revolutionary twentieth-century advances in physics. However, since we have written this book primarily for students majoring in the sciences, we have not stressed the historical or philosophical aspects of physics. Instead, we have tried to make clear in every chapter the connection between physics and other areas of science. We have learned that science majors find this approach more appropriate, since it makes clear the relevance and usefulness of studying physics.

An obvious impact of physics on both the life and physical sciences is in the area of instrumentation. Physical principles underlie the operation of light and electron microscopes, of X-ray machines and nuclear magnetic resonance spectrometers, of oscilloscopes and nuclear radiation monitors. Physics is also fundamental to a true understanding of chemistry, biology, and the earth sciences. The physical laws governing the behavior of molecules, atoms, and nuclei are the basis for all of chemistry and biochemistry. At the macroscopic level, the effects of forces of various types strongly influence the shapes of anatomical and human-built structures. Physiology offers many examples of physical processes and principles; diffusion within cells, the regulation of body temperature, the motion of fluids within the circulatory system, and electrical signals in nerves are just a few. In exercise science, activities ranging from running and jumping to karate can be analyzed and sometimes optimized by the application of physical principles. In the course of developing and illustrating the basic principles of physics, we discuss these applications and many others.

A few remarks about how one studies physics may be helpful. More than any other science, physics is a logical and deductive discipline. In any subfield of physics, there are just a few fundamental concepts or laws derived from experimental measurements. Once one has mastered these basic ideas, the applications are usually straightforward conceptually, even though the details may sometimes become complicated. Consequently, it is important to focus one's attention on the basic principles and to avoid memorizing a mass of facts and formulas.

Most of the basic laws of physics can be expressed rather concisely in the form of mathematical equations. This is a great convenience, since a tremendous amount of information is implicitly contained in a single equation. However, this also means that any serious attempt to learn or apply physics necessitates using a certain amount of mathematics. *General Physics* assumes a reasonable level of facility with high school algebra and basic geometry. Also, students should ideally have had some calculus before starting to use this text, although they may take it concurrently. An understanding of what derivatives and integrals mean is important, although not a great deal of skill in applying these concepts is needed. A mathematical review in Appendix B reviews key algebra and geometry topics and also lists the derivatives and integrals required for the examples and problems.

In summary, we believe that science majors will benefit in two major ways from studying physics. They will gain an understanding of the basic laws that govern everything in our world, from the subatomic to the cosmic scale, and will also learn much that will be important in their later work. The study of physics as a basic science is not particularly easy, but we believe it is rewarding, particularly for students planning further training in related sciences. We hope that all who use this book will agree.

M. M. S.

J. W. K.

CONTENTS

UNIT FIVE

CHAPTER 16 ELECTRIC FORCES, FIELDS, AND POTENTIALS

We have already touched lightly upon electric charges and forces (Chapter Five) and on the electric potential energy (Chapter Six). In this chapter, we explore these and related concepts in more depth, so that we have a better understanding of how charges interact. We frequently employ the ideas developed here in later chapters.

16.1 | ELECTRIC FORCES

Coulomb's law states that the force between two electric charges is proportional to the product of the charges and inversely proportional to their separation squared. If a charge q is at a distance r from a second charge Q in air or vacuum, then the force on q (Fig. 16.1) is

$$\mathbf{F} = \frac{kqQ}{r^2}\,\hat{\mathbf{r}} \qquad (16.1)$$

where, $\hat{\mathbf{r}}$ is a unit vector directed toward q. In S.I. units, the charge is measured in coulombs, and k has the experimentally determined value

$$k = 9.0 \times 10^9 \text{ N m}^2 \text{ C}^{-2} \qquad (16.2)$$

The force is attractive if q and Q have opposite signs, and it is repulsive if they have like signs.

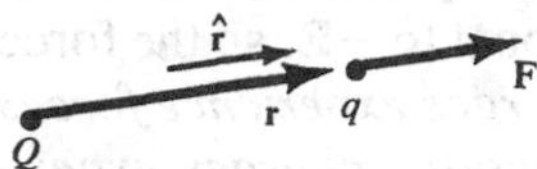

Figure 16.1. The force $\mathbf{F}$ between the two charges has a magnitude kqQ/r^2. When the charges have like signs, the force on q is repulsive or away from Q.

When a charge q is near two or more additional charges, the net force on q is the vector sum of the forces due to each of the other charges. The following example illustrates this point.

Example 16.1

A positive charge q is near a positive charge Q and a negative charge $-Q$ (Fig. 16.2). (a) Find the magnitude and direction of the force on q. (b) If $q = 10^{-6}$ C, $Q = 2 \times 10^{-6}$ C, and $a = 1$ m, find the force on q.

(a) Probably the easiest way to find the directions of the forces on q is to remember that like charges repel and opposites attract. Since q is positive, it is repelled by the positive charge Q. Thus the force $\mathbf{F}_+$ on q due to Q is directed away from Q, or in the $\hat{\mathbf{y}}$ direction. Similarly, q is attracted toward $-Q$, so the force $\mathbf{F}_-$ due to $-Q$ also points upward or in the $\hat{\mathbf{y}}$ direction.

These directions can also be found by keeping track of the signs in Coulomb's law, Eq. 16.1. The distance from Q to q is a, and the unit vector $\hat{\mathbf{r}}$ directed from Q

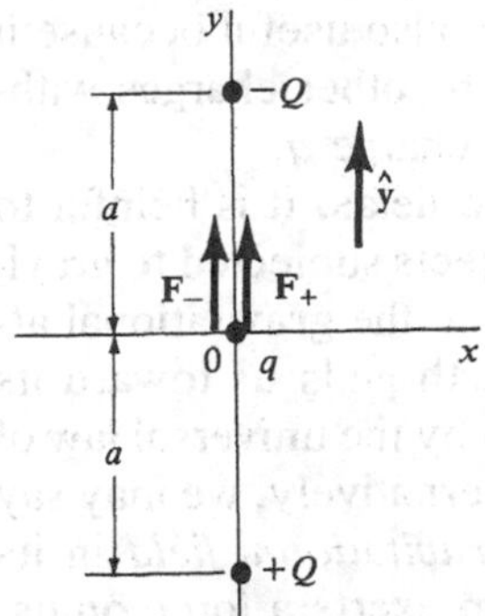

Figure 16.2. Both q and Q are positive. The force $\mathbf{F}_+$ on q due to the charge Q is repulsive, so it is directed upward in the direction of $\hat{\mathbf{y}}$. The force $\mathbf{F}_-$ on q due to $-Q$ is attractive and is also directed upward.

toward q is $\hat{\mathbf{y}}$. Thus the force on q due to this charge is

$$\mathbf{F}_+ = \frac{kqQ}{a^2}\,\hat{\mathbf{y}}$$

Since both q and Q are positive, the force is parallel to $\hat{\mathbf{y}}$, or upward. Similarly, the distance from $-Q$ to q is a, and here $\hat{\mathbf{r}}$ is along the $-y$ direction. Thus $\hat{\mathbf{r}} = -\hat{\mathbf{y}}$, and the force on q due to $-Q$ is

$$\mathbf{F}_- = \frac{kq(-Q)}{a^2}(-\hat{\mathbf{y}}) = \frac{kqQ}{a^2}\,\hat{\mathbf{y}}$$

Again the force is parallel to $\hat{\mathbf{y}}$. Since $\mathbf{F}_+$ and $\mathbf{F}_-$ are parallel, the net force on q is

$$\mathbf{F} = \mathbf{F}_+ + \mathbf{F}_- = \frac{2kqQ}{a^2}\,\hat{\mathbf{y}}$$

(b) Substituting the numerical values given, the net force on q is

$$\begin{aligned}\mathbf{F} &= \frac{2kqQ}{a^2}\,\hat{\mathbf{y}}\\ &= \frac{2(9 \times 10^9\ \mathrm{N\ m^2\ C^{-2}})(10^{-6}\ \mathrm{C})(2 \times 10^{-6}\ \mathrm{C})}{(1\ \mathrm{m})^2}\,\hat{\mathbf{y}}\\ &= 3.6 \times 10^{-2}\,\hat{\mathbf{y}}\ \mathrm{N}\end{aligned}$$

The force is directed upward.

16.2 | THE ELECTRIC FIELD

We have seen that when two or more charges exert forces on a given charge q, the net force is the vector sum of the forces. When there are many charges, it is often more convenient to do this sum indirectly by introducing a quantity called the *electric field*. The electric field is also useful because it characterizes the effects of the other charges without explicit reference to the charge q.

Before considering electric fields, it is helpful to look at some examples of objects subjected to gravitational forces. We experience the gravitational attraction of the earth: the earth pulls us toward its center with a force described by the universal law of gravitation $F = GmM/r^2$. Alternatively, we may say that the earth produces a *gravitational field* in its vicinity, and that field in turn exerts a force on us. Similarly, a spaceship sent to Mars experiences gravitational forces due to the sun, earth, Mars, and the other planets. The net gravitational force on the spaceship at any point will be determined by the net gravitational field there. This field is produced by the sun, earth, and so on (Fig. 16.3). The gravitational force on the spaceship is proportional to its mass: the larger the ship, the larger the gravitational force. It is also proportional to the strength of the gravitational field, which is determined by the masses and locations of the sun and planets.

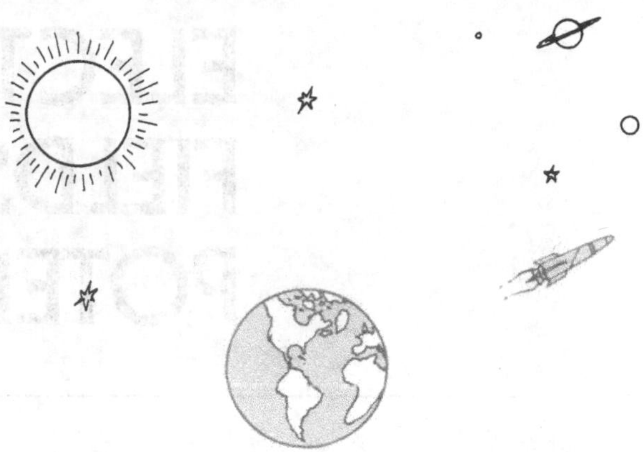

Figure 16.3. A spaceship encounters gravitational forces due to the sun and the planets. Equivalently, it encounters a force proportional to its mass and to the net gravitational field produced by the sun and planets.

For the applications considered in this text, the concept of a gravitational field is not particularly useful, and we will not pursue it in detail. However, we shall find electric and magnetic fields quite important.

When we have one or more electric charges, we may say that they produce an electric field in their vicinity. If another charge q is present, it experiences a force proportional to the electric field $\mathbf{E}$ and to q itself:

$$\mathbf{F} = q\mathbf{E} \qquad (16.3)$$

Since the force $\mathbf{F}$ is a vector, the electric field $\mathbf{E}$ must also be a vector. If q is a positive charge, the force due to the electric field is parallel to the field. If q is negative, $\mathbf{F}$ is proportional to $-\mathbf{E}$, so the force is opposite to $\mathbf{E}$. *Positive charges experience forces parallel to the field, and negative charges experience forces opposite to the field.*

From Eq. 16.3 it follows that the units of the electric field are those of force divided by charge. Thus in S.I. units, the electric field has units of newtons per coulomb (N C^{-1}).

The expression for the field due to a single point charge can be deduced from Coulomb's law. As we saw, the force on a charge q due to a charge Q at a distance r is

$$\mathbf{F} = \frac{kqQ}{r^2}\hat{\mathbf{r}}$$

where $\hat{\mathbf{r}}$ is a unit vector directed from the charge Q toward the point P where q is located (Fig. 16.4). The electric force on q can also be written as $\mathbf{F} = q\mathbf{E}$. Thus, it follows that at point P the field due to Q is $\mathbf{E} = \mathbf{F}/q$ or

$$\mathbf{E} = \frac{kQ}{r^2}\hat{\mathbf{r}} \tag{16.4}$$

If Q is positive, $\mathbf{E}$ points along $\hat{\mathbf{r}}$ or away from Q; if Q is negative, $\mathbf{E}$ points along $-\hat{\mathbf{r}}$ or toward Q. *The electric field due to a charge points away from the charge if it is positive, and toward it if the charge is negative.*

When there are several charges Q_1, Q_2, . . . at various positions, the electric field $\mathbf{E}$ at a point P is the vector sum of the individual electric fields $\mathbf{E}_1$, $\mathbf{E}_2$, . . . due to all the charges. If a charge q is placed at P, then the force on it is again given by $\mathbf{F} = q\mathbf{E}$. This is equivalent to the statement that the total force on q is the sum of the forces due to the individual charges.

Once we have measured the electric field at a point, we can immediately find the force on any charge placed there. It is not necessary to know the magnitude or location of the charges producing the field. For example, a Na^+ ion has a charge $q = e = 1.6 \times 10^{-19}$ C. If the field in a cell membrane is 10^6 N C^{-1}, the force on the ion has a magnitude $F = qE = (1.6 \times 10^{-19}\text{ C})(10^6\text{ N C}^{-1}) = 1.6 \times 10^{-13}$ N and is directed along the electric field. (Fig. 16.5).

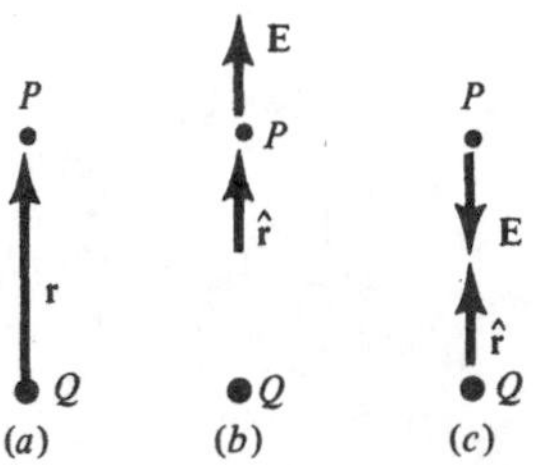

Figure 16.4. (*a*) A point P is at a distance **r** from a charge Q. (*b*) If the charge Q is positive, the electric field **E** at P is away from Q or along $\hat{\mathbf{r}}$. (*c*) If Q is negative, the field is along $-\hat{\mathbf{r}}$.

The following example demonstrates the calculation of the electric field due to two point charges and the force exerted by this field on another charge.

Example 16.2

The charges Q and $-Q$ of the preceding example are shown again in Fig. 16.6. (a) If $Q = 2 \times 10^{-6}$ C and $a = 1$ m, find the electric field at the origin. (b) Find the force on the charge $q = 10^{-6}$ C placed at the origin.

(a) As before, the distance from the charge Q to the origin is a, and $\hat{\mathbf{r}} = \hat{\mathbf{y}}$. Using Eq. 16.4, the field at the origin due to this charge is

$$\mathbf{E}_+ = \frac{kQ}{a^2}\hat{\mathbf{y}}$$

The field points upward, *away from the positive charge*. Also, the distance from the charge $-Q$ to the

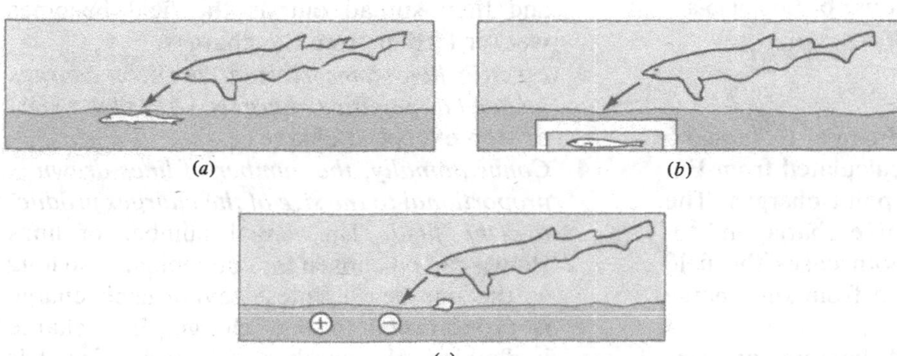

Figure 16.5. Sharks are sensitive to the minute electric fields produced by charges in a body. (*a*) The shark attacks a fish hidden beneath the sand. (*b*) A chamber blocks all but electrical stimuli, and the shark still attacks. (*c*) An artificially produced electric field elicits the same response. Here the shark is ignoring an obvious piece of food to follow the electrical stimulus.

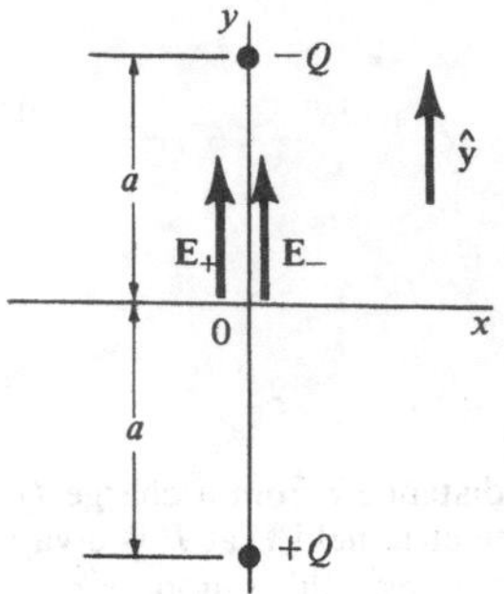

Figure 16.6. The electric field due to a positive charge is directed away from the charge, while the field due to a negative charge is directed toward the charge. Hence both contributions to the total field at the origin point along the $+y$ direction.

origin is a, and $\hat{\mathbf{r}} = -\hat{\mathbf{y}}$, so its field there is

$$\mathbf{E}_- = \frac{k(-Q)}{a^2}(-\hat{\mathbf{y}}) = \frac{kQ}{a^2}\,\hat{\mathbf{y}}$$

This field points upward as well; *it is pointed toward the negative charge*. The net electric field at the origin is the sum:

$$\begin{aligned}\mathbf{E} = \mathbf{E}_+ + \mathbf{E}_- &= \frac{2kQ}{a^2}\,\hat{\mathbf{y}} \\ &= \frac{2(9 \times 10^9\ \text{N m}^2\ \text{C}^{-2})(2 \times 10^{-6}\ \text{C})}{(1\ \text{m})^2}\,\hat{\mathbf{y}} \\ &= 3.6 \times 10^4\,\hat{\mathbf{y}}\ \text{N C}^{-1}\end{aligned}$$

The net field is directed upward.

(b) The force on a charge $q = 10^{-6}$ C at the origin is

$$\begin{aligned}\mathbf{F} = q\mathbf{E} &= (10^{-6}\ \text{C})(3.6 \times 10^4)\hat{\mathbf{y}}\ \text{N C}^{-1} \\ &= 3.6 \times 10^{-2}\,\hat{\mathbf{y}}\ \text{N}\end{aligned}$$

As expected, this is identical to the force calculated in the previous example by the direct use of Coulomb's law.

Electric Field Diagrams

Figures 16.7*a* and *b* show the electric field vectors calculated from Eq. 16.4 for several locations near point charges. The field points away from the positive charge and toward the negative charge. In both cases the field becomes weaker as the distance from the charge increases, since it varies as $1/r^2$.

Another kind of electric field diagram, or map, may be drawn by joining the vectors with continuous *lines* or *lines of force* (Figs. 16.7*c* and *d*). Electric field lines have the following properties:

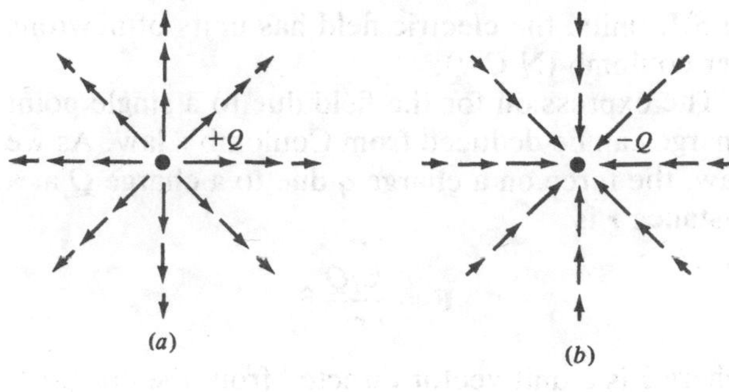

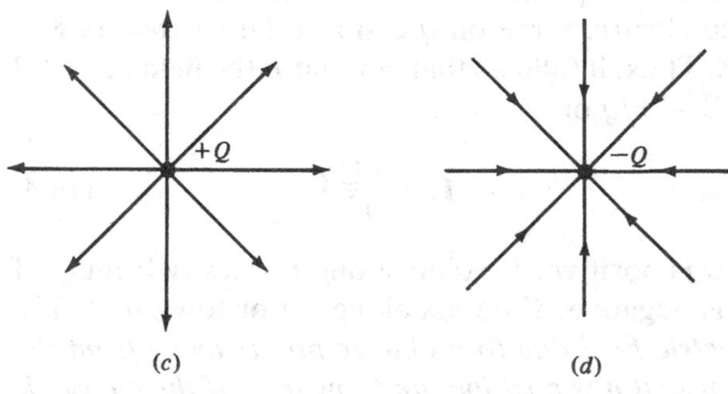

Figure 16.7. (*a*) and (*b*) Electric field vectors at locations near charges that are (*a*) positive, (*b*) negative. The corresponding electric field lines are shown in (*c*) and (*d*).

1. *At any point on an electric field line, its direction indicates the field direction at that point.* The lines never cross, since there is a unique field direction everywhere.
2. *The closer the lines, the larger the electric field.* The field lines are very close to each other near the charges where the field is large, and they spread out as the field becomes weaker farther from the charges.
3. *Electric field lines start at positive charges and end at negative charges.* They never start or stop except at charges.
4. *Conventionally, the number of lines drawn is proportional to the size of the charges producing the field.* The actual number of lines shown can be chosen for convenience, so long as the number of lines leaving each charge is proportional to that charge. If a charge is doubled, the number of lines leaving it is doubled.

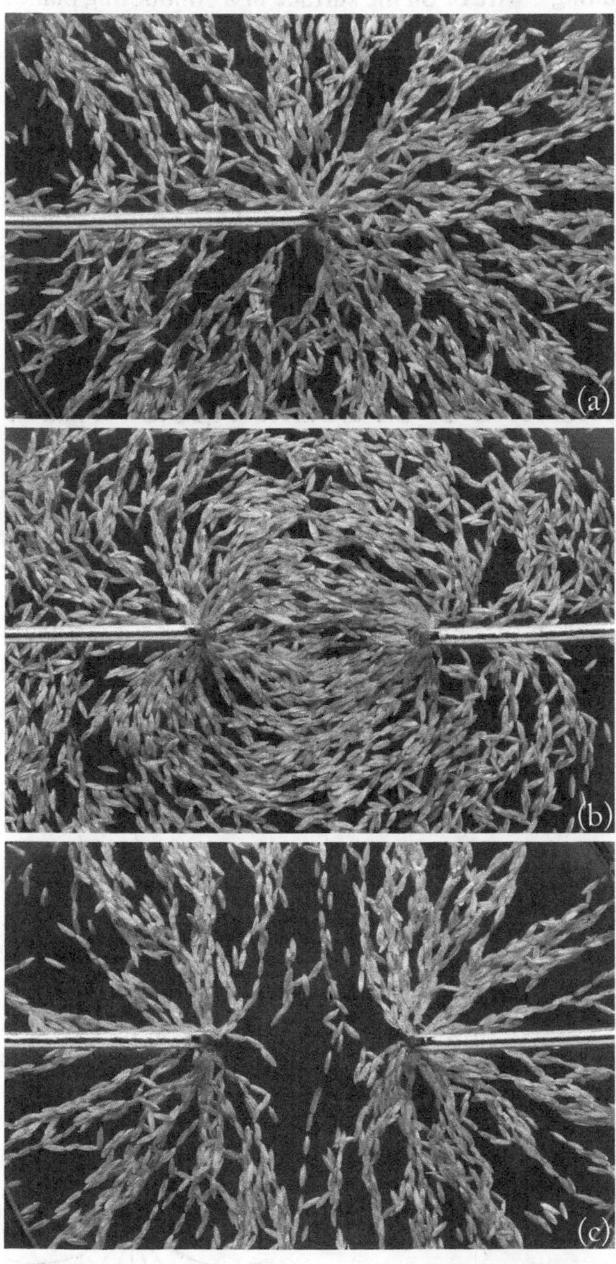

Figure 16.8. Photographs of patterns formed by grass seeds in a liquid near various charge arrangements. (*a*) A point charge. (*b*) Two point charges, opposite signs. (*c*) Two point charges, like signs. (Richard Megna / Fundamental Photographs)

Electric field line drawings present a great deal of information in a concise graphical form that is easy to understand with the aid of these four properties. The diagrams are especially useful in describing the fields produced by complex arrangements of charges. In such situations, one picture replaces a great many words!

We can actually make the field lines visible by exploiting the fact that when suspended in a liquid oblong objects, such as grass seeds, tend to line up along the field lines (Fig. 16.8). The pattern formed near a single point charge is strikingly similar to that in Fig. 16.7. We will see corresponding similarities shortly for more complex charge arrangements.

Significance of the Electric Field | Now let's discuss the basic concept of an electric field more fully. When there is a charge at rest at some point, we say that it produces an electric field in its vicinity. This field in turn exerts a force on any other charge that may be present. So far, this field approach is really equivalent to Coulomb's law, but it is useful because the electric field can often be conveniently measured or calculated. Also, the electric field diagrams convey information about the effects of a charge or set of charges on *any* other charges brought into their field. *Specifically, positive charges will experience forces along (or, more precisely, tangent to) the field lines. Negative charges will experience forces in the opposite direction.*

However, the electric field and the Coulomb law or "action-at-a-distance" descriptions of electrical forces are *not* equivalent for charges in motion. Electric fields are not merely a bookkeeping device for keeping track of electric forces. Suppose a charge Q is moved so its field changes. The effect of relocating Q is not felt immediately by a nearby charge q, because the change in the field does not propagate instantaneously. Instead, it travels at the speed of light, $c = 3 \times 10^8$ m s^{-1}. The force on q changes only when the changed field has reached it. Coulomb's law implies an instantaneous change in this force, contrary to what is observed.

To make this point more concrete, consider a television transmitter. Charges oscillating back and forth in its antenna produce an *electromagnetic wave* that carries the programming in coded form. In the antenna of a distant receiver, electric charges respond to the wave as it passes by a fraction of a second later. Similarly, electromagnetic waves from distant stars reach us and have an effect only after many years. Thus a full description of electrical forces requires a careful study of the electric field, and involves physical principles not contained in Coulomb's law. These ideas will be explored further in Chapter Twenty.

16.3 | THE ELECTRIC FIELD DUE TO ARRANGEMENTS OF CHARGES

The total electric field due to two or more charges is the vector sum of their individual electric fields. When charges are distributed continuously, say, along a wire or on the surface of a conducting plane, this sum can sometimes be found using symmetry arguments. Using integration to find the fields of continuous charge distributions is discussed in the next section.

If the individual fields point in different directions, cancellations will occur in the sum, or integral. As a result, the field may change with distance in a way that is quite different from the $1/r^2$ variation of the individual point charge fields. We shall see, for example, that the field may vary as $1/r^3$ or as $1/r$, or it may even be constant.

The Field of an Electric Dipole | A pair of charges with equal magnitudes and opposite signs, $+q$ and $-q$, is called an *electric dipole*. We see later in this chapter that dipoles are useful in characterizing atoms and molecules and in discussing the effect of an electric field on an insulator.

Consider the electric dipole in Fig. 16.9. At the point P, the fields $\mathbf{E}_+$ due to $+q$ and $\mathbf{E}_-$ due to $-q$ are

$$\mathbf{E}_+ = \frac{kq}{(r-a)^2}\,\hat{\mathbf{y}}, \qquad \mathbf{E}_- = \frac{-kq}{(r+a)^2}\,\hat{\mathbf{y}}$$

The total field at P is

$$\mathbf{E} = \mathbf{E}_+ + \mathbf{E}_- = kq\left[\frac{1}{(r-a)^2} - \frac{1}{(r+a)^2}\right]\hat{\mathbf{y}}$$

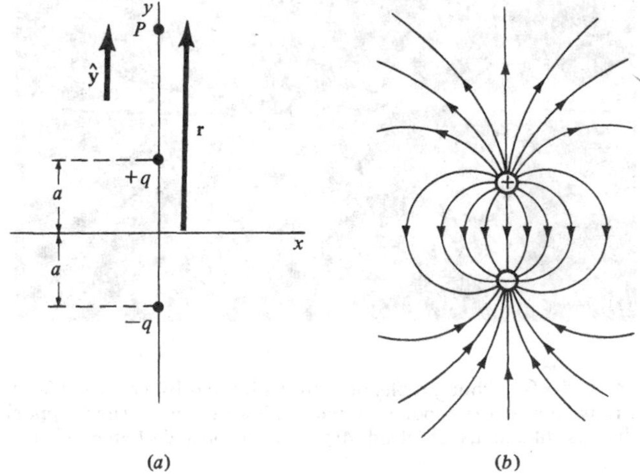

Figure 16.9. (*a*) A dipole is a pair of equal but opposite charges. (*b*) The field due to a dipole. Note that the lines go from the positive to the negative charge. Note also the similarity with Fig. 16.8*b*.

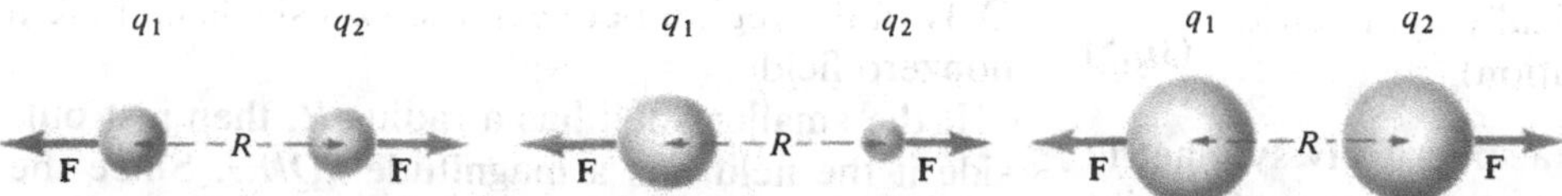

Figure 16.10. The forces between two pith balls depend only on their charges and on the distance R between their centers. All three pairs experience the same electrical forces even though their radii are different.

If r is large compared to a, the total field **E** is quite small, since the fields due to the two charges nearly cancel. Rewriting **E** by putting both terms over a common denominator, some terms cancel in the numerator, and we find

$$\mathbf{E} = \frac{4kqar}{(r^2 - a^2)^2} \hat{\mathbf{y}}$$

When r is much greater than a, we can neglect a in the denominator. Then

$$\mathbf{E} = \frac{4kqa}{r^3} \hat{\mathbf{y}}$$

Thus the field diminishes as $1/r^3$ at large distances, which is a faster rate of decrease than the $1/r^2$ associated with a single charge. If we repeat this calculation for a distant point on the x axis or somewhere else, the overall numerical factor and the direction of the field will vary, but the field will again diminish as $1/r^3$.

Spherically Symmetric Charge Distributions

Continuous charge distributions are very common. They occur, for example, on the surfaces of metallic objects and in the intracellular fluids of living organisms. There are so many electrons or ions in these situations that the charge distribution appears to be continuous when viewed from the macroscopic level.

We saw in Chapter Three that the gravitational force law applies to point masses and to spheres. Similarly, Coulomb's law holds for both point charges and for spheres with charges spread uniformly over their surfaces or within them. For example, the force between two pith balls depends only on their charges and on the distance between their centers; their radii do not matter (Fig. 16.10). Since a very small sphere is effectively a point, Coulomb's law holds also for a point charge and a sphere.

Now suppose a point charge q is placed a distance r from the center of a uniformly charged sphere with a total charge Q. It experiences the same force **F** as it would at a distance r from a point charge Q. Since $\mathbf{E} = \mathbf{F}/q$, the electric field produced by the sphere must be the same as that of the point charge, Q. This is true everywhere outside the sphere (Fig. 16.11).

This simple property holds for any *spherically symmetric* charge distribution: a distribution with charges arranged in a manner that depends only on the distance from its center. *The field outside a spherically symmetric charge distribution is identical to that of a point charge*:

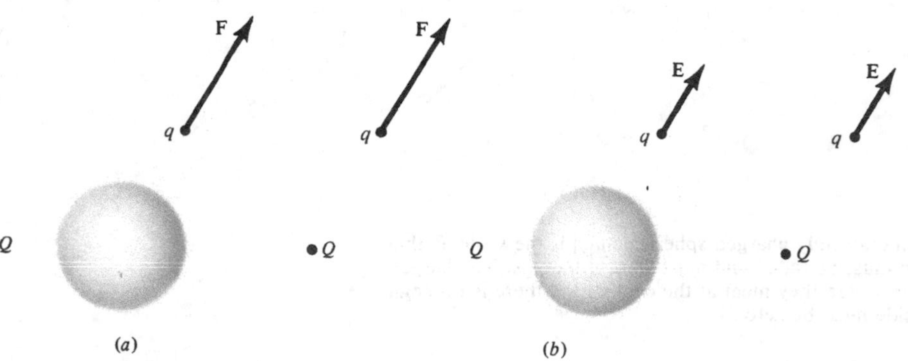

Figure 16.11. (*a*) The force on q is the same for a sphere of total charge Q and for a point charge, Q. (*b*) The field $\mathbf{E} = \mathbf{F}/q$ at q is the same in both cases.

$$\mathbf{E} = \frac{kQ}{r^2}\hat{\mathbf{r}} \quad \text{(outside spherically symmetric charge distribution)} \tag{16.5}$$

Note that the field *inside* a spherically symmetric charge distribution is not the same as that of a point charge. This field depends on where the charges are actually located. For example, consider a thin hollow spherical shell with a charge Q spread uniformly over its surface (Fig. 16.12*a*). The field outside is $kQ\hat{\mathbf{r}}/r^2$. What is the field inside? Because of the symmetry, if there is a field inside, it must be radial. If we draw lines starting at the positive charges on the shell and directed inward, they all meet at the center. This can only happen if there is a negative charge at the center, which is not true. *Thus the field inside a uniformly charged spherical shell must be zero* (Fig. 16.12*b*). This occurs because the fields produced by the individual charges exactly cancel.

What happens if we have two concentric shells (Fig. 16.13) with equal but opposite uniformly distributed charges, $+Q$ and $-Q$? At each point the net field is the sum of the fields due to the two shells. The field due to either shell is zero inside it and equal to that of a point charge outside. Thus inside the smaller sphere of charge $+Q$, the field is zero. Between the two, the field is $kQ\hat{\mathbf{r}}/r^2$. Outside the larger one, the fields cancel, and $\mathbf{E} = 0$ again. Only in the region between the two shells is there a nonzero field.

If the smaller shell has a radius R, then just outside it the field has a magnitude kQ/R^2. Since the surface area of this sphere is $A = 4\pi R^2$, we may rewrite this as $E = 4\pi kQ/A$. Note that E contains the *charge per unit area* σ, defined by

$$\sigma = \frac{Q}{A} \tag{16.6}$$

Thus the field is

$$\mathbf{E} = 4\pi k\sigma\hat{\mathbf{r}} \quad \text{(field just outside sphere)} \tag{16.7}$$

When the two shells are very close, r^2 does not vary appreciably between them, and Eq. 16.7 gives the approximate field magnitude everywhere between the shells. We use this result below in discussing uniformly charged planes.

Uniformly Charged Planes | A metal plate and the membrane of a cell are examples of plane surfaces that may carry uniformly distributed charges. Except near its edges, the field close to such a plane is almost constant in magnitude and direction (Fig. 16.14*a*). This is due to cancellations among the fields due to the various charges. For example, in Fig. 16.14*b*, the fields at point P due to

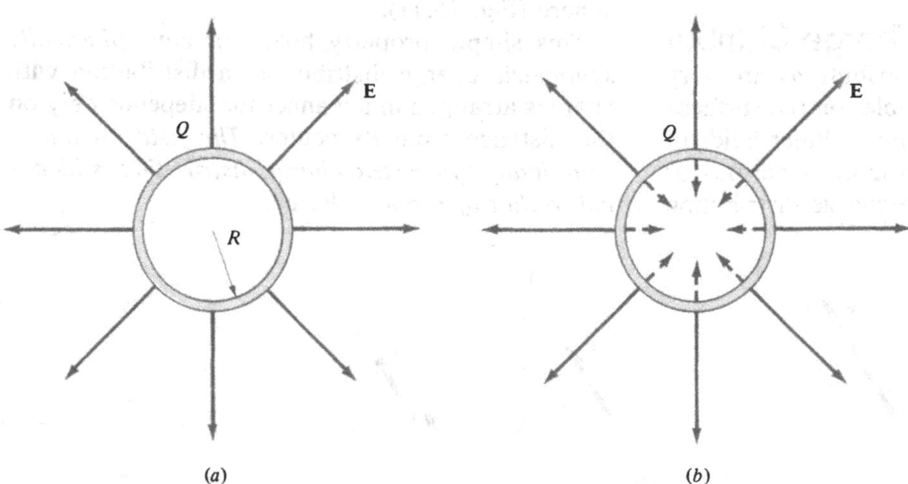

Figure 16.12. (*a*) The field outside a uniformly charged spherical shell is the same as that of a point charge. (*b*) The lines inside must be radial and must start at the positive charges. Because they would have to terminate where they meet at the center, and there is no negative charge at that point, the field inside must be zero.

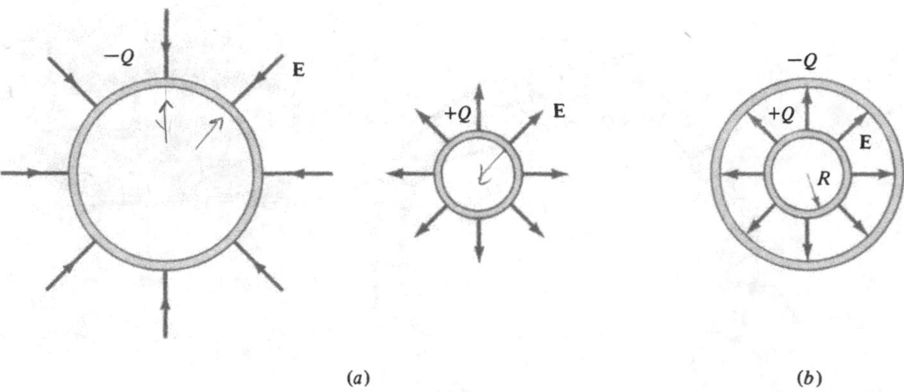

Figure 16.13. (*a*) Two uniformly charged spherical shells with charges $+Q$ and $-Q$ each have no field inside and a point charge field outside. (*b*) When one is inside the other, the fields cancel outside the larger, and between the two, the field is that of a point charge $+Q$ at the center.

charges at A and B have canceling vertical components, so their vector sum is horizontal. All other pairs of charges located symmetrically about point C produce a net horizontal field, so the total field at P is horizontal. If P is not opposite the midpoint of the plane, there are unpaired charges left over at one edge. However, if P is much closer to the plane than to an edge, the fields of these distant charges are unimportant.

Actually summing the fields due to all the charges on a uniformly charged plane involves integration. However, we can find the formula for the total field if we first consider *two* planes of area A with opposite charges $+Q$ and $-Q$ (Fig. 16.15). The fields E_+ and E_- are equal in magnitude. They *add* between the planes and *cancel* everywhere else. This is similar in some ways to the example of two uniformly charged spherical shells discussed above. In fact, a small section of two closely spaced shells is almost flat, and it looks much like two parallel planes (Fig.

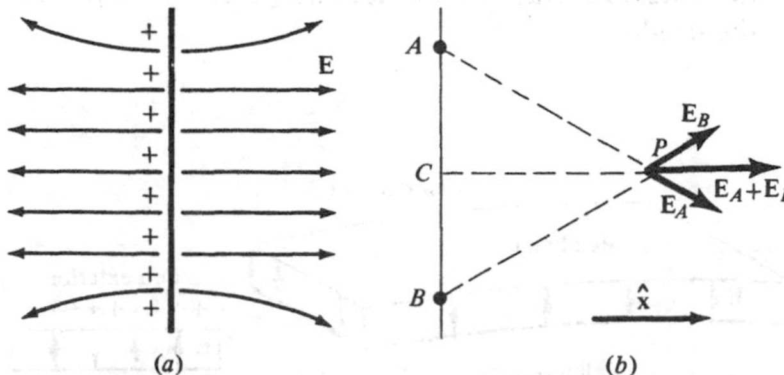

Figure 16.14. (*a*) The electric field close to a uniformly charged plane is uniform except near the edges. Note the similarity with Fig. 16.8*e*. (*b*) The fields at point P due to a pair of charges located symmetrically about point C have canceling vertical components.

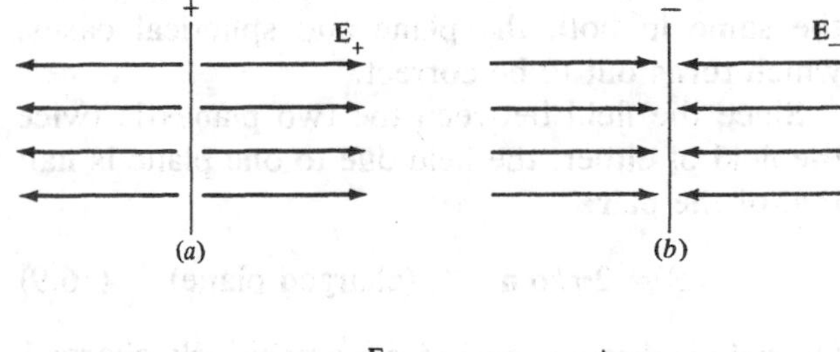

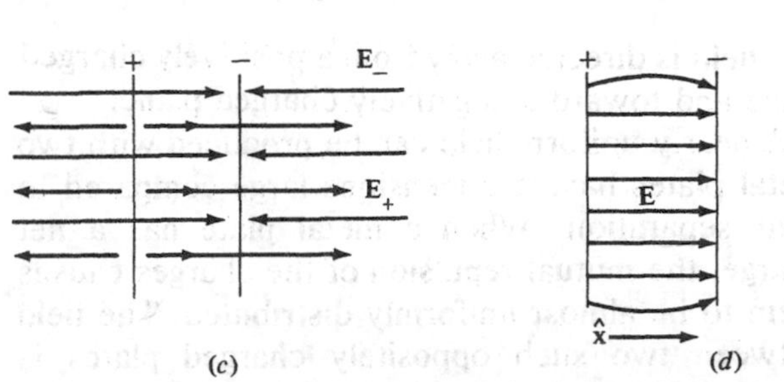

Figure 16.15. (*a*) The field of a positively charged plane. (*b*) The field of a negatively charged plane shown in color for clarity. (*c*) The field lines due to the two planes when they are close together. (*d*) The total field due to the two charged planes. Note the similarity with Fig. 16.8*d*. The field is not quite uniform at the edges. The effects of these *fringing fields* at the edges may often be neglected.

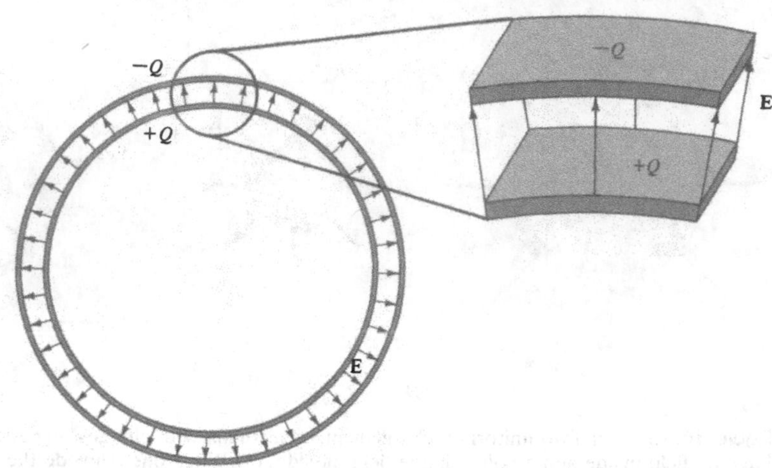

Figure 16.16. A small section of two closely spaced spherical shells looks like a pair of parallel plane surfaces.

16.16). Hence we may conclude that the field magnitude is the same in both cases and that, with $\sigma = Q/A$,

$$\mathbf{E} = 4\pi k\sigma\hat{\mathbf{n}} \quad \text{(between oppositely charged planes)} \qquad (16.8)$$

where $\hat{\mathbf{n}}$ is a unit vector directed away from the positive plane and toward the negative. This argument assumes that the effects of distant charges are the same in both the plane and spherical cases, which turns out to be correct.

Since the field between the two planes is twice the field of either, the field due to one plane is half that of the pair:

$$\mathbf{E} = 2\pi k\sigma\hat{\mathbf{n}} \quad \text{(charged plane)} \qquad (16.9)$$

The field is directed away from a positively charged plane and toward a negatively charged plane.

A nearly uniform field can be produced with two metal plates having dimensions large compared to their separation. When a metal plate has a net charge, the mutual repulsion of the charges causes them to be almost uniformly distributed. The field between two such oppositely charged plates is nearly uniform. A charged particle, such as an electron, moving through the uniform field experiences a constant acceleration. We see later how this is put to use in an oscilloscope (Section 16.8) and in other kinds of apparatus employing charged particle beams (Chapter Nineteen). The electric fields in a cell membrane are also approximately uniform, as seen in the next example.

Example 16.3

A thin, flat membrane separates a layer of positive ions outside a cell from a layer of negative ions inside (Fig. 16.17). If the electric field due to these charges is 10^7 N C^{-1}, find the charge per unit area Q/A in the layers on either side of the membrane.

Since the membrane is flat, the charges form uniformly charged planes on either side. Using $E = 4\pi kQ/A$, we have

$$\frac{Q}{A} = \frac{E}{4\pi k} = \frac{10^7 \text{ N C}^{-1}}{4\pi(9 \times 10^9 \text{ N m}^2 \text{ C}^{-1})}$$
$$= 88.4 \times 10^{-6} \text{ C m}^{-2} = 88.4\ \mu\text{C m}^{-2}$$

using 1 microcoulomb = 1 μC = 10^{-6} C. Thus 1 m^2 of membrane will have a net charge of +88.4 μC along the outside surface and a net charge of −88.4 μC on the inside.

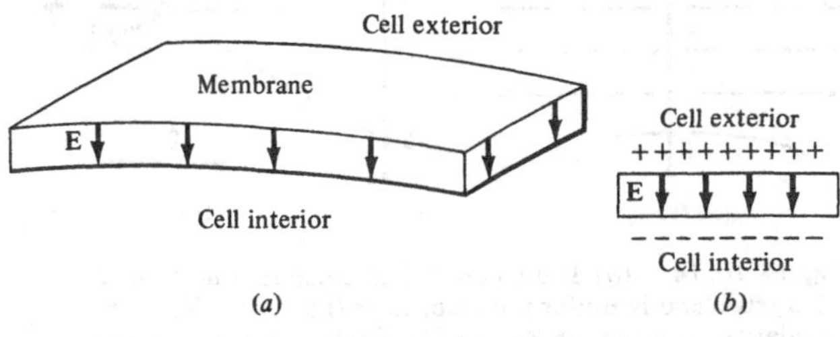

Figure 16.17. (*a*) A portion of a cell membrane seen in perspective. (*b*) A cross-sectional view showing the charge layers.

16.4 | THE ELECTRIC FIELDS OF CONTINUOUS CHARGE DISTRIBUTIONS

Integration provides a tool for finding the field produced by a continuous charge distribution. We first illustrate the procedure with a long straight wire and then again consider a uniformly charged plane.

The Field of a Long Charged Wire | A long, uniformly charged straight wire provides one of the simplest illustrations of a continuous distribution of electric charges. Such a wire might be found in an electrical device or in an antenna. Although any real wire has a finite length, for simplicity we consider the idealized case of an infinitely long wire (Fig. 16.18a). The result will be accurate for a real wire at points that are located much closer to the wire than to its ends (Exercise 16-23).

We will specify the charge on the wire in terms of its *charge per unit length* λ (lambda). Suppose a length L of the wire has a charge Q. Then the charge per unit length is

$$\lambda = \frac{Q}{L} \tag{16.10}$$

For a segment of the wire of length dx, the charge is $\lambda\, dx$.

In Fig. 16.18a, the distance to an arbitrary point P is R, where

$$R^2 = r^2 + x^2 \qquad R = (r^2 + x^2)^{1/2}$$

Thus the magnitude of the field due to the charge $\lambda\, dx$ is

$$dE = \frac{k\lambda\, dx}{R^2} = \frac{k\lambda\, dx}{r^2 + x^2}.$$

The total field due to a charge distribution is found by adding up the fields due to all the charges. Here this means integrating the fields due to all the segments. To do this, we first find the horizontal and vertical components of $\mathbf{dE}$,

$$dE_x = dE \cos\theta \qquad dE_y = dE \sin\theta$$

Now we can see immediately that the net horizontal field component E_x is zero. This is because the segments located symmetrically on either side of the origin have canceling dE_x contributions (Fig. 16.18b). Thus we need only consider E_y. Since

$$\sin\theta = \frac{r}{R} = \frac{r}{(r^2 + x^2)^{1/2}}$$

$dE_y = dE \sin\theta$ becomes

$$dE_y = \frac{k\lambda\, dx}{(r^2 + x^2)} \frac{r}{(r^2 + x^2)^{1/2}}$$

$$= \frac{kr\lambda\, dx}{(r^2 + x^2)^{3/2}}$$

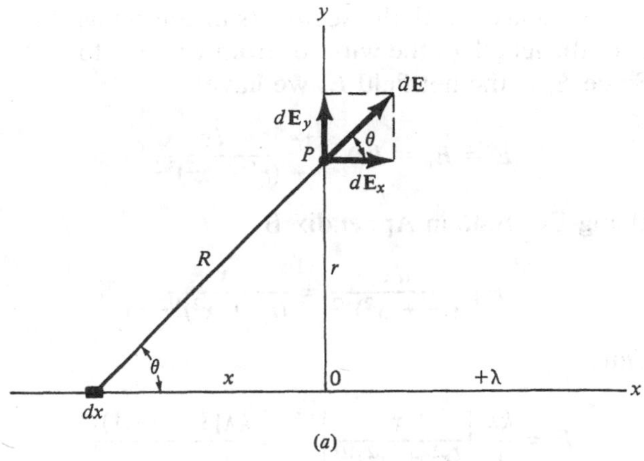

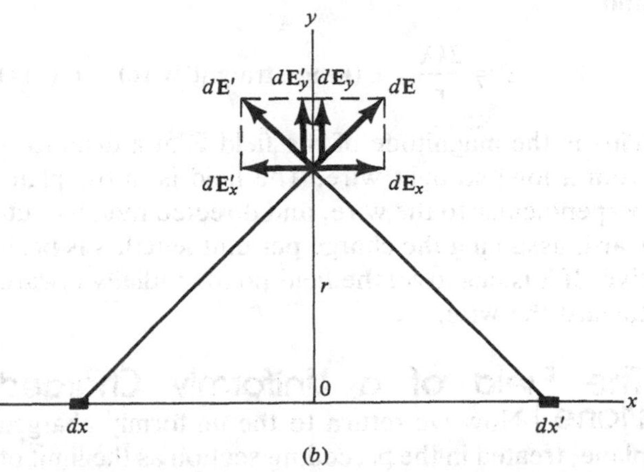

Figure 16.18. (a) The field due to one segment of an infinitely long uniformly charged wire. (b) Two equally long segments dx and dx' located symmetrically about the origin produce fields with horizontal components $d\mathbf{E}_x$, that are equal in magnitude but opposite in direction.

Summing over all the segments means integrating over the length of the wire, or from $x = -\infty$ to $+\infty$. Since E_y is the net field E, we have

$$E = E_y = kr\lambda \int_{-\infty}^{+\infty} \frac{dx}{(r^2 + x^2)^{3/2}}$$

Using Eq. B.46 in Appendix B,

$$r^2 \int \frac{dx}{(r^2 + x^2)^{3/2}} = \frac{x}{(r^2 + x^2)^{1/2}}$$

Thus

$$E = \frac{k\lambda}{r} \left[\frac{x}{(r^2 + x^2)^{1/2}} \right]_{-\infty}^{+\infty} = \frac{k\lambda[1 - (-1)]}{r}$$

and

$$E = \frac{2k\lambda}{r} \quad \text{(long straight wire)} \quad (16.11)$$

This is the magnitude of the field $\mathbf{E}$ at a distance r from a long straight wire. The field is in the plane perpendicular to the wire, and directed radially outward, assuming the charge per unit length λ is positive. If λ is negative, the field points radially inward toward the wire.

The Field of a Uniformly Charged Plane | Now we return to the uniformly charged plane, treated in the preceding section as the limit of a large sphere. Again, we consider an idealized case, an infinitely large plane. The results hold for a finite plane at points much closer to the plane than to the edges.

The electric field due to a uniformly charged plane can be found by cutting it into many thin strips and applying our result for a long straight wire to each strip (Fig. 16.19). As in the long straight wire calculation, the symmetry simplifies our work. The strip shown at a positive value of z produces an electric field with a component parallel to the plane along the $-z$ direction. The strip located equally far from the origin at a negative value of z (shown dotted) has an electric field with an equally large component parallel to the plane pointing in the $+z$ direction. These two contributions to the field cancel, as do those of all the other pairs of strips drawn on either side of the origin. Thus there is no component of $\mathbf{E}$ parallel to the plane, and we need only evaluate E_y, the component normal to the plane.

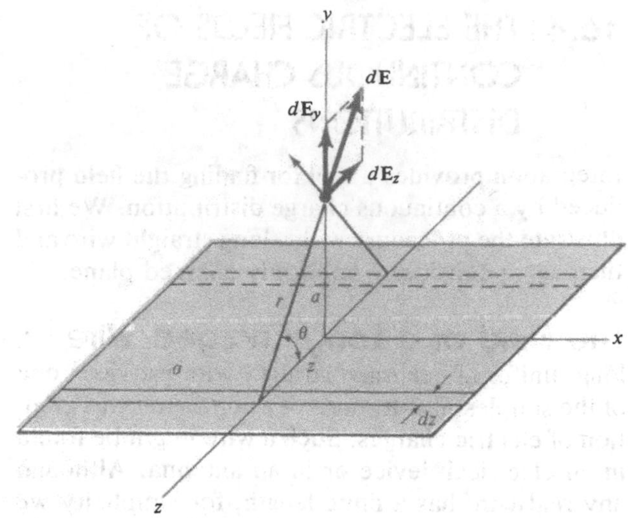

Figure 16.19. A uniformly charged infinite plane can be broken up into many narrow strips. The strips on opposite sides of the origin produce fields with components parallel to the plane that cancel. The resulting field is normal to the plane and is uniform.

If the plane has a charge per unit area σ, then a strip of width dz and length L has an area $dA = L\,dz$, and a charge $\sigma\,dA = \sigma L\,dz$. Dividing by the length L gives its charge per unit length, $d\lambda = \sigma\,dA/L = \sigma\,dz$. Using the result for an infinite wire (Eq. 16.11), the magnitude of the field the strip or "wire" produces at P is

$$dE = \frac{2k\,d\lambda}{r} = \frac{2k\sigma\,dz}{r}$$

The vertical component of $d\mathbf{E}$ is $dE_y = dE \sin\theta$, where $\sin\theta = a/r$. Thus with $r^2 = a^2 + z^2$,

$$dE_y = \frac{2k\sigma\,dz}{r}\frac{a}{r} = \frac{2k\sigma a\,dz}{a^2 + z^2}$$

We can now sum over all the strips by integrating over z. Replacing dE_y by dE and using Eq. B.44 to evaluate the integral

$$E = 2k\sigma a \int_{-\infty}^{+\infty} \frac{dz}{(a^2 + z^2)}$$

$$= 2k\sigma a \left[\frac{1}{a} \tan^{-1} \frac{z}{a} \right]_{-\infty}^{+\infty} = 2k\sigma \left[\frac{\pi}{2} - \frac{(-\pi)}{2} \right] = 2k\sigma\pi$$

In vector form, we can write this result as

$$\mathbf{E} = 2\pi k\sigma\hat{\mathbf{n}}$$

where $\hat{\mathbf{n}}$ is a unit vector normal to the plane. This agrees with the earlier result, Eq. 16.9.

With two parallel planes having charges per unit area that are equal in magnitude but opposite in sign, the fields add between them and cancel elsewhere (Fig. 16.15). Hence we recover Eq. 16.8, $\mathbf{E} = 4\pi k\sigma\hat{\mathbf{n}}$.

16.5 | THE ELECTRIC POTENTIAL

In Chapter Six, we noted that the electric forces among charges at rest are conservative, so that their effects can be included in the potential energy of a system. Here we introduce a related concept, the *electric potential*, which is the potential energy per unit charge. Like the electric field, it permits us to characterize the effects of one or more charges without specifying the magnitude or sign of a charge located at the position of interest.

Suppose that at a certain position a charge q has an electric potential energy $\mathcal{U}$. *Then the electric potential* V *at that position is defined to be the potential energy divided by the charge,*

$$V = \frac{\mathcal{U}}{q} \tag{16.12}$$

The unit of potential is the volt (V), where from this definition 1 volt = 1 joule per coulomb. (The standard abbreviation V for the volt should not be confused with the symbol V for the potential.) Colloquially, potential differences are often referred to as *voltages*. We see in the next chapter that it is the potentials rather than the fields that are most useful in discussing electric circuits.

We saw in Chapter Six that many problems in mechanics can be solved quite readily if the potential energies at two points are known. Similarly, given the potential difference between two points, we can say many things about the motion of charged particles without using detailed information about the electric forces or fields. This is illustrated by the next example.

Example 16.4

In the cathode-ray tube of an oscilloscope or a television picture tube, electrons are accelerated from rest through a potential difference of +20,000 V. What is their velocity? (The electron mass is 9.11×10^{-31} kg, and the charge is $-e = -1.6 \times 10^{-19}$ C.)

From the definition of the electric potential, the change in potential energy is $\Delta\mathcal{U} = q\,\Delta V = (-e)\Delta V$, where $\Delta V = 20{,}000$ V. Then from energy conservation,

$$\tfrac{1}{2}mv^2 = e\,\Delta V$$

Hence

$$\begin{aligned} v &= \sqrt{\frac{2e\,\Delta V}{m}} \\ &= \sqrt{\frac{2(1.60 \times 10^{-19}\ \text{C})(20{,}000\ \text{V})}{9.11 \times 10^{-31}\ \text{kg}}} \\ &= 8.38 \times 10^{7}\ \text{m s}^{-1} \end{aligned}$$

Often, energies of electrons or other atomic particles are most conveniently expressed in units of *electron volts* (eV). An electron volt is the kinetic energy acquired when a charge e is accelerated by a potential difference of 1 volt,

$$\begin{aligned} 1\ \text{eV} &= (1.60 \times 10^{-19}\ \text{C})(1\ \text{V}) \\ &= 1.60 \times 10^{-19}\ \text{J} \end{aligned}$$

For example, when an electron is accelerated by a 20,000-V potential difference, it acquires a kinetic energy of 20,000 eV, or

$$(20{,}000\ \text{eV})\frac{(1.60 \times 10^{-19}\ \text{J})}{1\ \text{eV}} = 3.2 \times 10^{-15}\ \text{J}$$

We make extensive use of the electron volt and multiples of this unit in our discussions of atomic and molecular phenomena in later chapters.

Relation Between Electric Fields and Potentials

If we know the electric field in a region, we can use it to calculate the potential differences between various points. We show how this is done in general and illustrate the result for a uniform field, a point charge, and a uniformly charged wire.

Consider a positive charge q in an electric field $\mathbf{E}$ (Fig. 16.20). We suppose a force $\mathbf{F}$ equal in magnitude but opposite in direction to the electric force $q\mathbf{E}$ is applied, so that the charge moves at a constant velocity over a short distance $d\mathbf{l}$. Then the work done (Chapter Six) by the applied force $\mathbf{F}$ is $\mathbf{F} \cdot d\mathbf{l} = -q\mathbf{E} \cdot d\mathbf{l}$. Since the kinetic energy remains constant, this work must equal the change in the potential energy of the charge

$$d\mathcal{U} = -q\mathbf{E} \cdot d\mathbf{l} \tag{16.13}$$

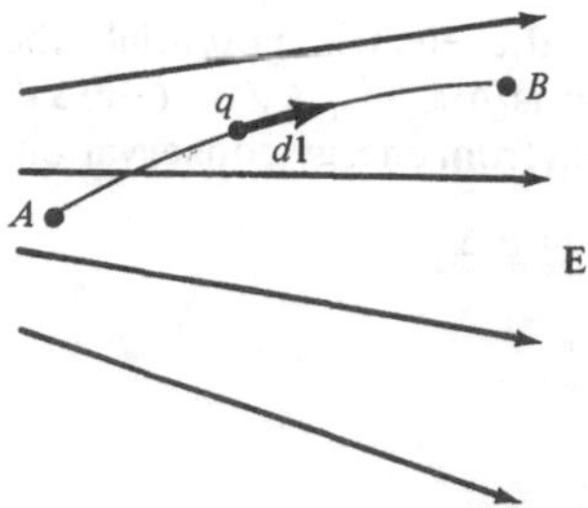

Figure 16.20. When a charge q is moved a distance $d\mathbf{l}$, its electric potential energy changes by $-q\mathbf{E} \cdot d\mathbf{l}$. For a positive charge, the increase is greatest when $d\mathbf{l}$ is opposite to $\mathbf{E}$.

Dividing by q, we obtain the change in the electric potential

$$dV = -\mathbf{E} \cdot d\mathbf{l} \tag{16.14}$$

If we move the charge a finite distance from A to B, then the change in the potential is found by summing the dV's from each small displacement. This requires carrying out the integral

$$\Delta V = -\int_A^B \mathbf{E} \cdot d\mathbf{l} \tag{16.15}$$

This integral is evaluated along any convenient path from point A to point B, because changes in $\mathcal{U}$ and V depend only on the initial and final positions, and not on the path. This is a consequence of the fact that the electric force is a conservative force.

Equation 16.15 is the general formula for the difference in the potential between two points in an electric field. A charge q displaced from A to B would have a potential energy change $\Delta\mathcal{U} = q\,\Delta V$. We now illustrate the use of this result.

Uniform Field | We saw in the preceding sections that the field is uniform in the region between two closely spaced large metal plates with opposite charges (Fig. 16.21). If we move in a direction opposite to a uniform field, then the scalar product simplifies to

$$\mathbf{E} \cdot d\mathbf{l} = E\,dl \cos 180° = -E\,dl$$

E is constant, so it can be taken out of the integral, and Eq. 16.15 becomes

$$\Delta V = E \int_A^B dl = El \quad \text{(uniform field)} \tag{16.16}$$

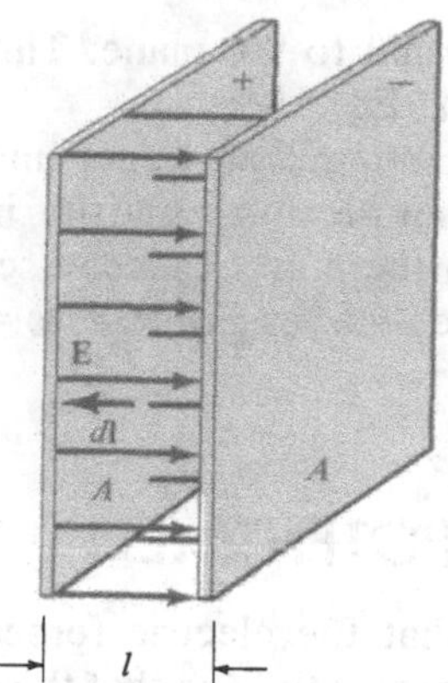

Figure 16.21. The potential different between the parallel plates is $\Delta V = El$. The positively charged plate is at the higher potential, since work must be done against the field to move a positive charge $+q$ from the negative plate to the positive plate.

The field between two plates with charges per unit area $+\sigma$ and $-\sigma$ is $E = 4\pi k\sigma$. Thus for plates a distance l apart, the potential difference has a magnitude

$$\Delta V = 4\pi k\sigma l \quad \text{(oppositely charged plates)} \tag{16.17}$$

The positive plate is at the higher potential. This result is illustrated by the following example.

Example 16.5

Two oppositely charged parallel plates have an area of 1 m^2 and are separated by 0.01 m. The potential difference between the plates is 100 V. Find (a) the field between the plates; (b) the magnitude of the charge on a plate.

(a) Since the field is uniform, $\Delta V = El$ can be used, and

$$E = \frac{\Delta V}{l} = \frac{100\text{ V}}{0.01\text{ m}} = 10^4\text{ V m}^{-1}$$

The field is directed from the positive plate at the higher potential toward the negative plate.

(b) Using Eq. 16.17, and the definition $\sigma = Q/A$, the charge on a plate has a magnitude

$$Q = \sigma A = \frac{A\,\Delta V}{4\pi kl} = \frac{(1\text{ m}^2)(100\text{ V})}{4\pi(9 \times 10^9\text{ N m}^2\text{ C}^{-2})(10^{-2}\text{ m})}$$
$$= 8.84 \times 10^{-8}\text{ C}$$

Note that a small charge is sufficient to produce a 100-V potential difference.

Potential energy of any kind depends only on the position of an object and not on how it arrived there. Stated somewhat differently, the work done by the conservative electric force is independent of the path followed between the initial and final positions. Therefore, we may obtain the difference in potential between two points using any convenient path to find the work per unit charge done against the electric field. For example, if we wish to know the difference in potential between points A and C in Fig. 16.22, we can choose the path ABC. Path AB is a displacement opposite to the field, so $\Delta V = El$. Path BC is perpendicular to the field, so no work is done, and the potential is the same at B as at C. Using the dashed path AC, we would find the same potential difference. However, the calculation would be slightly more complicated.

Point Charge | Finding the potential of a point charge $+Q$ is a bit more complicated since $E = kQ/r^2$ is not constant. If we move radially outward, or away from the charge, then the displacement is parallel to the field (Fig. 16.23*a*). Thus writing $d\mathbf{l} = dr$,

$$\mathbf{E} \cdot d\mathbf{l} = E\,dr = \frac{kQ}{r^2}\,dr$$

Suppose we move a finite distance from point A along this line at a distance r_1 from Q to point B at a distance r_2. Then Eq. 16.15 gives, with $\int dr/r^2 = -1/r$,

$$\Delta V = V(r_2) - V(r_1) = -\int_{r_1}^{r_2} E\,dr = -\int_{r_1}^{r_2} \frac{kQ\,dr}{r^2} = \frac{kQ}{r_2} - \frac{kQ}{r_1}$$

Because only potential differences can be measured, we can define the potential to be zero at any convenient point. It is customary to choose the potential at $r = \infty$ to be zero. With this assignment, putting $r_2 = \infty$ and $r_1 = r$ leads to

$$V(r) = \frac{kQ}{r} \quad \text{(point charge)} \qquad (16.18)$$

$V(r)$ is the amount of work we must do per unit charge to move a second charge from infinity to a point a distance r from Q. To restate this, suppose there is a charge q at a distance r. Then from the definition of the potential, $V = \mathcal{U}/q$, the potential energy of the two charges (q and Q) is $\mathcal{U} = qV = kqQ/r$. This is the formula obtained in Chapter Six for the potential energy of two point charges.

One other point should be noted. We assumed that the points A and B were on the same radial line directed outward from Q. However, the potential is the same everywhere on the sphere of radius r_2 centered at Q, because no work is required to move at right angles to the field (Fig. 16.23*b*). We return to this point in the next section.

The field outside a spherically symmetric charge distribution is the same as that for a point charge, so the work needed to move a charge q closer to it is the same as for a point charge. Thus the potential outside is the same as that of a point charge located at its center. We use this in the next example.

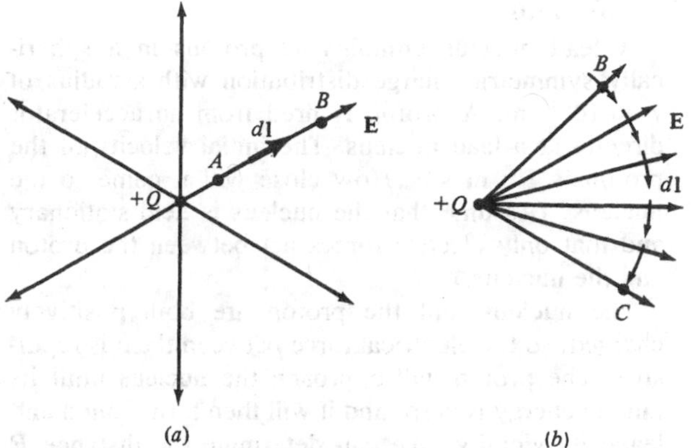

Figure 16.23. (*a*) Moving a charge from A to B can be broken up into infinitesimal steps $d\mathbf{l}$ that are parallel to the field $\mathbf{E}$ for the case shown. (*b*) If we move a charge from B to a point C equally far from the charge Q, the displacement can be made in steps perpendicular to the field, so no work is required. Thus the potential at B and at C is the same, and V depends only on the distance from the charge.

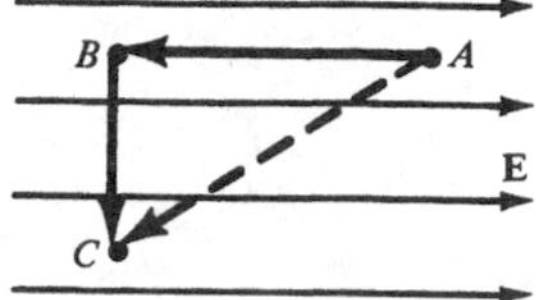

Figure 16.22. The work done by the conservative electric force is the same for the paths ABC and AC.

Example 16.6

A lead nucleus contains 82 protons in a spherically symmetric charge distribution with a radius of 7×10^{-15} m. A proton is fired from an accelerator directly at a lead nucleus. The initial velocity of the proton is 10^7 m s^{-1}. How close will it come to the nucleus? (Assume that the nucleus is held stationary and that only electric forces act between the proton and the nucleus.)

The nucleus and the proton are both positively charged, so the electrical force between them is repulsive. The proton will approach the nucleus until its kinetic energy is zero, and it will then turn around and leave its vicinity. We can determine the distance R where this will occur using energy conservation.

At a distance r from the center of the nucleus, since its charge is $Q = +82e$, its potential is

$$V = \frac{kQ}{r} = \frac{82ke}{r}$$

The potential energy of the proton is $\mathcal{U} = qV = e(82ke)/r$. At infinity, the potential energy is zero; at the point of closest approach, the kinetic energy is zero. Since the total energy is constant,

$$\frac{mv^2}{2} = \frac{82ke^2}{R}$$

Solving for R, we have

$$\begin{aligned} R &= \frac{164ke^2}{mv^2} \\ &= \frac{164(9 \times 10^9 \text{ N m}^2 \text{ C}^{-2})(1.6 \times 10^{-19} \text{ C})^2}{(1.673 \times 10^{-27} \text{ kg})(10^7 \text{ m s}^{-1})^2} \\ &= 2.26 \times 10^{-13} \text{ m} \end{aligned}$$

This is about 30 times larger than the nuclear radius, which is 7×10^{-15} m. Thus the proton never comes close enough to the nucleus to experience the strong nuclear force.

If there are several charges, or several charge distributions, we can use either of two equivalent procedures to find the potential. We can calculate the total electric field of the system, and then find the potential difference associated with moving a charge from one point to another in this field. This is effectively how we found the potential difference between two plates. Alternatively, we can add the potentials due to the various charges. Potentials are scalars, ordinary positive and negative numbers, and adding them is a simpler task than the vector summation required when combining electric fields.

Again cancellations between the contributions of various charges can lead to varied dependences on the distance. We see such a cancellation in the following example of a dipole.

Example 16.7

For the dipole in Fig. 16.24, find the electric potential at (a) point P_1 on the y axis; (b) at point P_2 on the x axis. (c) How much work is required to move a charge q from infinitely far away to point P_1 if $r = 3a$? (d) How much work is needed to move q from infinity to P_2?

(a) At P_1, the potentials due to the two charges are

$$V_+ = \frac{kq}{r - a}, \qquad V_- = \frac{-kq}{r + a}$$

The total electric potential is then

$$V = V_+ + V_- = kq\left[\frac{1}{r - a} - \frac{1}{r + a}\right] = \frac{2kqa}{r^2 - a^2}$$

If r is large compared to a, then a can be neglected in the denominator, so

$$V = \frac{2kqa}{r^2}$$

Thus even though the potential due to a single point charge varies as $1/r$, this combination of two point charges of equal magnitude and opposite sign has a potential that diminishes as $1/r^2$.

(b) The two charges are equally distant from *any* point on the x axis. Therefore, at P_2 the two potentials will have the same magnitude but opposite signs, and their sum will be zero. The net potential of the dipole is zero everywhere on the x axis.

(c) Using the result for V in part (a) with $r = 3a$, the potential at P_1 is

$$V = \frac{2kqa}{(3a)^2 - a^2} = \frac{2kqa}{8a^2} = \frac{kq}{4a}$$

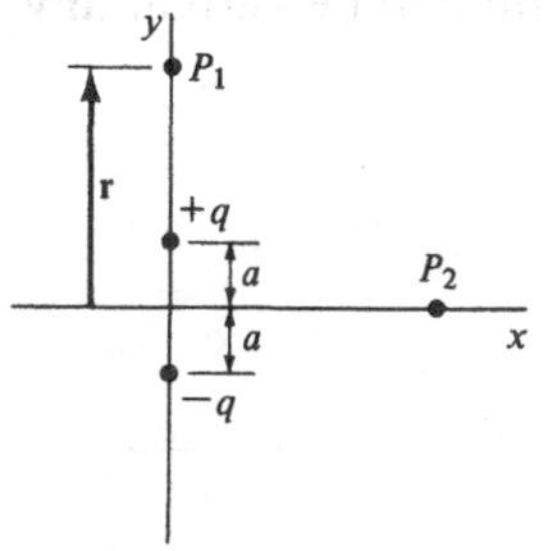

Figure 16.24. Example 16.7.

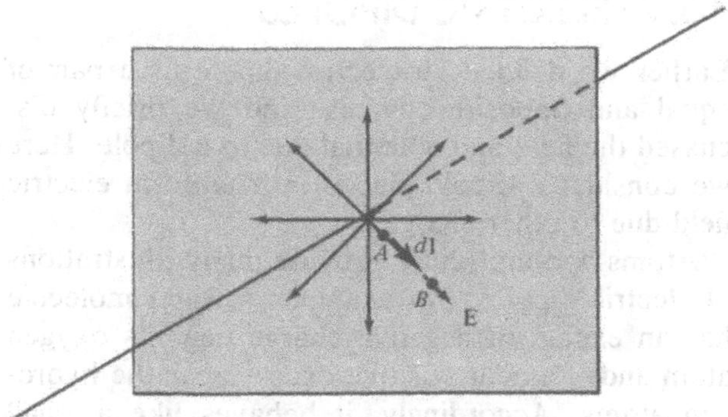

Figure 16.25. The field of an infinitely long straight wire carrying a uniform positive charge is directed radially outward. A displacement $d\mathbf{l} = d\mathbf{r}$ is parallel to the field.

Thus the potential energy of the system consisting of the dipole and the charge q is $\mathcal{U} = qV = kq^2/4a$. This is the amount of work needed to move q from infinity to P_1.

(d) Since $V = 0$ at point P_2, $\mathcal{U} = qV = 0$, and no work is needed to move the charge from infinity to P_2.

Long Straight Wire | The calculation of the potential of a uniformly charged infinitely long straight wire is very similar to that for a point charge. Here the field is radially outward in the plane perpendicular to a wire carrying a positive charge per unit length λ. If we go radially outward from the wire, then $d\mathbf{l} = d\mathbf{r}$ is parallel to $\mathbf{E}$, and $\mathbf{E} \cdot d\mathbf{l} = E dr$ (Fig. 16.25). Suppose point A is at a distance r_1 from the wire, and B is at a distance r_2. Then, with $E = 2k\lambda/r$,

$$\Delta V = V(r_2) - V(r_1) = -\int_{r_1}^{r_2} E\, dr$$

$$= -2k\lambda \int_{r_1}^{r_2} \frac{dr}{r} = -2k\lambda \ln r \Big|_{r_1}^{r_2}$$

and

$$V(r_2) - V(r_1) = -2k\lambda \ln \frac{r_2}{r_1} \quad \text{(long straight wire)} \qquad (16.19)$$

Here ln is the natural logarithm (see Appendix B.10). Again, as in the case of a point charge, the potential difference depends only on the distance from the wire, and not on the direction.

Note that when $r_2/r_1 > 1$, the logarithm is positive. This means that the potential decreases as we go away from a positively charged wire, as would be expected. However, here we cannot conveniently assign the potential a value of zero at infinity, since $\ln (r_2/r_1)$ is infinite when $r_2 = \infty$. This behavior is related to the artificial nature of an infinitely long charged wire, and disappears when a finite wire is considered.

16.6 | EQUIPOTENTIAL SURFACES

At any point on the surface of an imaginary sphere of radius r centered on a point charge Q, the potential has the same value, $V = kQ/r$. A surface on which the potential is the same everywhere is called an *equipotential surface*. Thus for a point charge the equipotential surfaces are concentric spheres (Fig. 16.26). The equipotential surfaces for a uniform electric field are planes normal to the field.

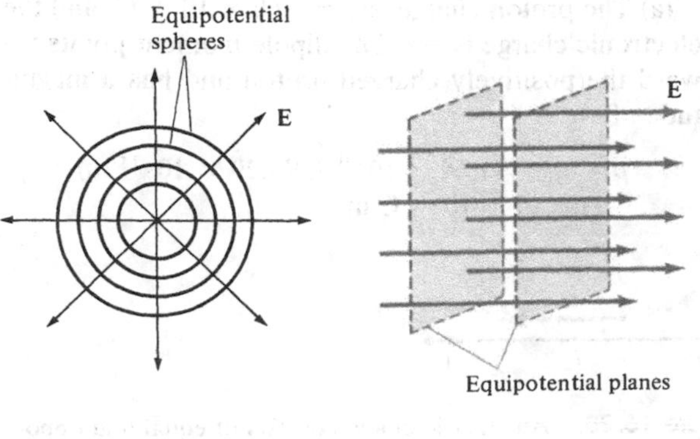

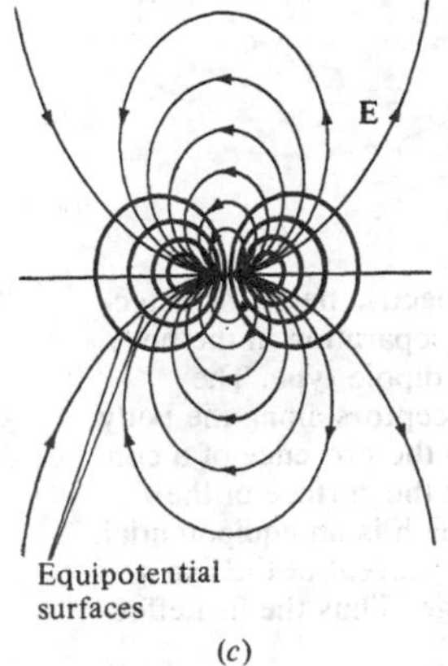

Figure 16.26. Equipotential surfaces for (*a*) a point charge; (*b*) a uniform electric field; (*c*) a dipole. Note that the equipotential surfaces and the electric field lines are always mutually perpendicular.

When a charge moves at right angles to the electric field, no work is done against electrical forces, so its potential energy remains constant. For this reason, *the equipotential surfaces are always perpendicular to the electric field lines*. Charges may move along an equipotential surface with no change in potential energy.

Conductors and Insulators | Most materials may be considered either electrical *conductors* or *insulators*. A conductor is a material, such as a metal or an ionic solution, in which some charges are relatively free to move about. In an insulator, such as paper or glass, all the charges are relatively immobile.

Conductors have the important property of being equipotential objects when there are no charges in motion. To see this, we note that if all the charges that can move are at rest, the electric field must be zero everywhere in the conductor. Alternatively, only if the field is zero everywhere will the charges stop moving. Consequently the potential is the same at all points.

The effect of a conductor on an electric field is illustrated in Fig. 16.27.

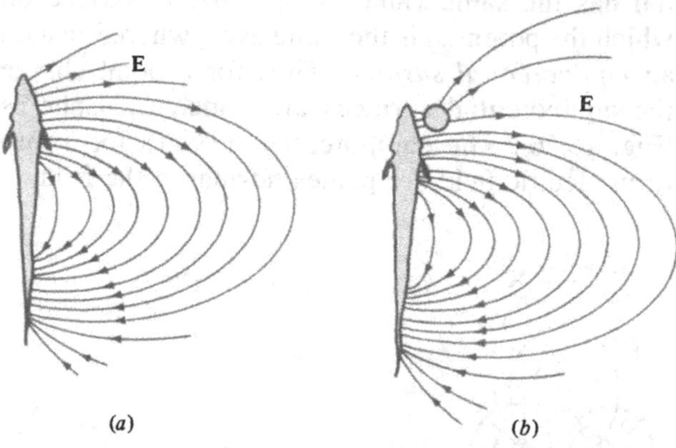

Figure 16.27. A number of fish use electric fields for detection and communication. (*a*) A charge separation in the body of the fish produces electric fields of a dipole type. The strength of the field is monitored by receptors along the body of the fish. (*b*) The field is distorted by the presence of a conducting object. The field lines intersect the surface of the object perpendicular to the surface, which is an equipotential. The resulting distortion of the field is apparent at the fish's body and the receptors sense the change. Thus the fish effectively "sees" using electric fields.

16.7 | ELECTRIC DIPOLES

Earlier we defined an electric dipole as a pair of equal and opposite charges, and we briefly discussed the field and potential due to a dipole. Here we consider a dipole placed in a uniform electric field due to other charges.

Atoms and molecules provide many illustrations of electric dipoles. For example, a water molecule has an excess of negative charge near its oxygen atom and a similar positive excess near the hydrogen atoms. Accordingly, it behaves like a small electric dipole, and many of its physical and chemical properties are related to its dipole character. Also, atoms and molecules can develop *induced* dipoles in response to an electric field. This is one way in which insulators are affected by electric fields.

A dipole is characterized by its *electric dipole moment* (Fig. 16.28). If $\mathbf{l}$ is the distance vector from $-q$ to $+q$, then the electric dipole moment is defined by

$$\mathbf{p} = q\mathbf{l} \tag{16.20}$$

This is the definition usually given in physics books. Chemistry books often define $\mathbf{p}$ so that it points from $+q$ to $-q$. The calculation of the electric dipole moment is illustrated by the following example.

Example 16.8

In a hydrogen atom the electron and proton are separated by 5.29×10^{-11} m. (a) Find the electric dipole moment at one instant in time. (b) The electron moves in a circular path about the proton. Find the average of the electric dipole moment vector over one full orbit.

(a) The proton charge is $e = 1.60 \times 10^{-19}$ C, and the electronic charge is $-e$. The dipole moment points toward the positively charged proton and has a magnitude of

$$\begin{aligned} p = ql &= (1.60 \times 10^{-19}\text{ C})(5.29 \times 10^{-11}\text{ m}) \\ &= 8.46 \times 10^{-30}\text{ C m} \end{aligned}$$

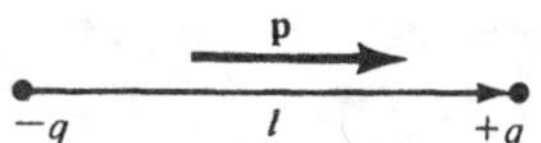

Figure 16.28. An electric dipole consists of equal and opposite charges, $+q$ and $-q$. The electric dipole moment is $\mathbf{p} = q\mathbf{l}$.

(b) If the electric dipole initially points in one direction, half an orbit later it will point in the opposite direction. The average of two vectors equal in magnitude but opposite in direction is zero. Thus the average of the electric dipole moment vector over a complete circular orbit must be zero. For this reason the hydrogen atom has no permanent electric dipole moment.

Figure 16.29 shows an electric dipole in a uniform field **E**. The force on the positive charge is $q\mathbf{E}$, and the force on the negative charge is $-q\mathbf{E}$. Their sum is zero, so *the net force on an electric dipole in a uniform electric field is zero.*

However, the net torque on the dipole is not zero, because the equal but opposite forces have different lines of action and form a couple. The torque due to a couple is the same relative to any point, so we may choose to compute torques about the charge $-q$. The force on $-q$ then has no lever arm, and it produces no torque. The charge $+q$ is subjected to a force $q\mathbf{E}$ and acts at a distance $\boldsymbol{l}$. Thus the torque $\boldsymbol{\tau} = \mathbf{r} \times \mathbf{F}$ becomes

$$\boldsymbol{\tau} = \boldsymbol{l} \times (q\mathbf{E}) = \mathbf{p} \times \mathbf{E} \qquad (16.21)$$

The magnitude of the torque is $pE \sin \theta$, and it is directed so that the dipole tends to line up with the field. When the dipole is oriented as in Fig. 16.29*a*, the torque is directed into the page, tending to rotate the dipole clockwise. The torque is directed out of the page in Fig. 16.29*b* and tends to rotate the dipole counterclockwise. The torque is zero, and the dipole is in stable equilibrium when it is directed along the field (Fig. 16.29*c*).

Conventionally the potential energy $\mathcal{U}$ of a dipole in a uniform field is taken to be zero when $\theta = 90°$; the dipole is then perpendicular to the field (Fig. 16.30*a*). The energy is a minimum when the dipole is parallel to the field. Thus, when the dipole is in the position shown in Fig. 16.30*b*, its potential energy must be negative. We can find an expression for $\mathcal{U}$ by imagining that the dipole is rotated from $\theta = 90°$, where $\mathcal{U} = 0$, to θ. If the rotation is performed with $-q$ held in place, the energy of the negative charge remains unchanged. The displacement of the positive charge along the field is $l \cos \theta$, so the work done against the electrical force $q\mathbf{E}$ is $-qE(l \cos \theta)$. Equating this work to the change in potential energy, we find

$$\mathcal{U} = -qEl \cos \theta = -pE \cos \theta = -\mathbf{p} \cdot \mathbf{E} \qquad (16.22)$$

These ideas are illustrated by the following example.

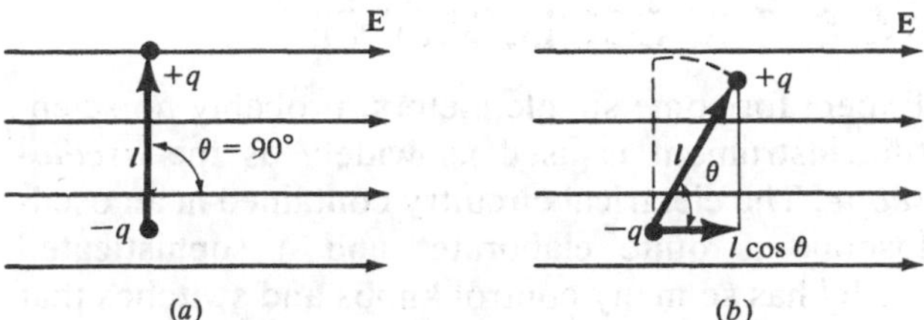

Figure 16.30. The energy of the dipole $\mathcal{U}$ is zero in (*a*), negative in (*b*).

Example 16.9

An atom with an electric dipole moment of 8.46×10^{-30} C m is in a uniform electric field of 10^4 N C^{-1}. If the angle between **p** and **E** is 30°, find (a) the magnitude of the torque; (b) the potential energy.

(a) When $\theta = 30°$, $\sin \theta = 0.5$, and the torque has a magnitude

$$\begin{aligned}\tau &= pE \sin \theta \\ &= (8.46 \times 10^{-30}\ \text{C m})(10^4\ \text{N C}^{-1})(0.5) \\ &= 4.23 \times 10^{-26}\ \text{N m}\end{aligned}$$

(b) At $\theta = 30°$, $\cos \theta = 0.866$, and the potential energy is

$$\begin{aligned}\mathcal{U} &= -pE \cos \theta \\ &= -(8.46 \times 10^{-30}\ \text{C m})(10^4\ \text{N C}^{-1})(0.866) \\ &= -7.33 \times 10^{-26}\ \text{J}\end{aligned}$$

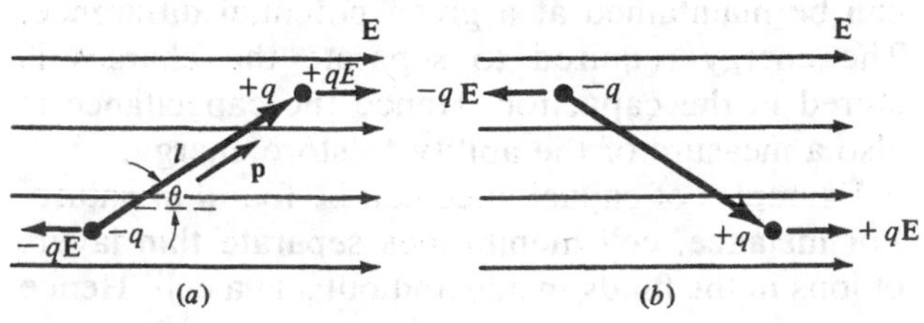

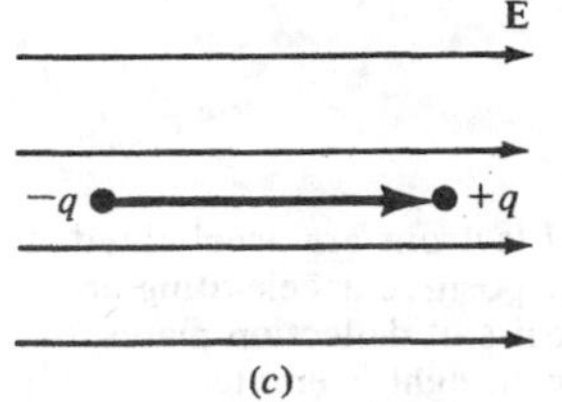

Figure 16.29. The torque on the dipole tends to produce rotations that are (*a*) clockwise; (*b*) counterclockwise. (*c*) The dipole is in equilibrium.

16.8 | THE OSCILLOSCOPE

Except for some simple meters, probably no scientific instrument is used as widely as the *oscilloscope*. The electrical circuitry contained in an oscilloscope is quite elaborate, and a sophisticated model has so many control knobs and switches that it takes some time to become acquainted with its operation. Nevertheless, the basic principles of its major component, the *cathode-ray tube*, can be understood fully with the ideas developed in this chapter.

In the first part of the tube, which is the electron gun, a constant potential difference accelerates electrons emitted from a hot filament (Fig. 16.31). If there are no other forces on the electron, they travel along a straight line and strike the center of the fluorescent screen, producing a bright spot. Horizontal deflections can be produced with horizontal electric fields between the parallel plates marked 1 in Fig. 16.31. These plates have a separation l. If they are at a potential difference V_1, there is a uniform horizontal electric field between them, $E_1 = V_1/l$. This field accelerates the electrons, which then strike the screen at a horizontal distance from the center, which is proportional to V_1. If V_1 is gradually increased, the spot gradually moves or *sweeps* across the screen; when V_1 returns to its original value, the spot returns to its starting point. If this sweep is repeated at a high enough frequency, the persistence of the image on the screen and in the eye conceals the motion, and a straight line is seen (Fig. 16.32*b*).

In the same way, a potential difference V_2 applied to the plates marked 2 in Fig. 16.31 will cause vertical deflections. For example, a constant V_2 will shift the line as in Fig. 16.32*c*. Usually an unknown potential difference V_2, varying at some frequency f, produces the vertical deflection. The horizontal sweep frequency is adjusted until it is equal to f (or f divided by some integer), so every time the vertical signal V_2 repeats itself the horizontal sweep is at the same point in its cycle. Thus the beam repeatedly hits the same points on the screen, and a stable pattern is seen (Fig. 16.32*d*, *e*). Accurate measurements of both the frequency and the magnitude of the unknown potential difference can readily be made in this way.

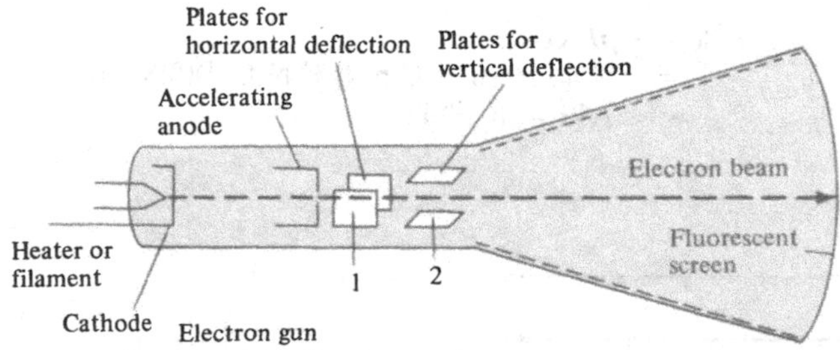

Figure 16.31. A cathode-ray tube. Electrons are accelerated from the negative cathode toward the positive accelerating anode and then pass between the two pairs of deflection plates. When they strike the fluorescent screen, light is emitted.

Since almost any type of information can be converted into electric potential differences, oscilloscopes are used in laboratories of virtually every kind. They are extremely valuable in qualitative and quantitative studies, not only of electrical variables but also of mechanical, acoustical, and other quantities. Microphones and television cameras are examples of devices that convert energy from other forms into varying electrical potentials. In general, devices that convert energy from one form to another are called *transducers*.

16.9 | CAPACITANCE

Suppose that two conductors are initially electrically neutral and that we then take small amounts of charge from one and place them on the other. As this process continues, a potential difference develops. The ratio of the amount of charge transferred to the potential difference resulting is defined to be the *capacitance* of the two conductors and turns out to be independent of the charge transferred. An arrangement of two conductors separated by a vacuum or an insulator is called a *capacitor*.

As our description suggests, the capacitance is a measure of the amount of charge separation that can be maintained at a given potential difference. The energy required to separate the charges is stored in the capacitor. Hence the capacitance is also a measure of the ability to store energy.

Examples of capacitance can be found in nature. For instance, cell membranes separate thin layers of ions in the fluids inside and outside a cell. Hence

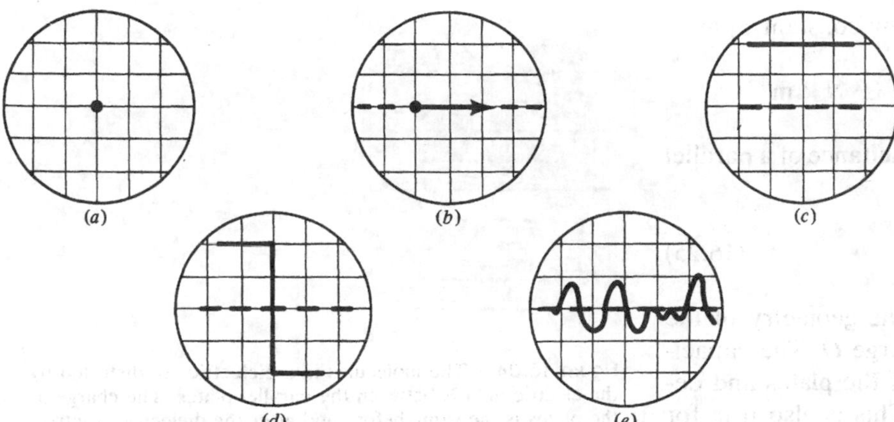

Figure 16.32. (a) If there are no deflecting fields, a bright spot is seen at the center of the oscilloscope screen. (b) Gradually changing the horizontal potential difference causes the beam spot to move steadily across the screen. If this sweep is repeated rapidly enough, a continuous line is perceived. (c) A constant vertical field displaces the line. (d) If the vertical field quickly reverses after each half sweep, this pattern is seen. (e) Complex variations of the vertical field with time can be displayed if they repeat at the sweep frequency.

the membrane and the adjacent fluids are considered to have capacitance.

Capacitors are widely used in electrical circuits. They are used in radio and television tuners, in automobile ignition systems, and in the starting circuits of electric motors. Capacitors also influence the way currents change in time. In nerve cells the rate of transmission of a nerve pulse depends on the membrane capacitance. Some of these applications are discussed in later chapters.

If two conductors have equal and opposite charges $\pm Q$ and a corresponding potential difference V, the ratio Q/V is usually found to be a constant independent of Q. The ratio is the capacitance,

$$C = \frac{Q}{V} \tag{16.23}$$

Note that V is defined to be the potential of the positive plate less that of the negative plate, so C is positive.

The unit of capacitance is the *farad* (F); 1 F = 1 C V^{-1}. Because the coulomb is a large unit, the farad is also large, and most capacitors have small values in terms of the farad. Hence we define the microfarad and picofarad by

$$1\ \mu\text{F} = 10^{-6}\ \text{F}, \qquad 1\ \text{pF} = 10^{-12}\ \text{F}$$

These ideas are illustrated by the next example.

Example 16.10

A 1-μF capacitor is connected to a 12-V battery. What are the charges on its plates?

From the defintion of the capacitance, $C = Q/V$, we have

$$Q = CV = (10^{-6}\ \text{F})(12\ \text{V}) = 1.2 \times 10^{-5}\ \text{C}$$

There is a charge of $+1.2 \times 10^{-5}$ C on the plate connected to the positive terminal of the battery and a charge of -1.2×10^{-5} C on the other plate.

The Parallel Plate Capacitor | The simplest capacitor is composed of two parallel plates in a vacuum. The plates have surface area A, charges $\pm Q$, and a separation l (Fig. 16.33). From Eq. 16.17, $V = 4\pi k\sigma l = 4\pi kQl/A$. Thus the capacitance $C = Q/V$ is

$$C = \frac{A}{4\pi kl} \tag{16.24}$$

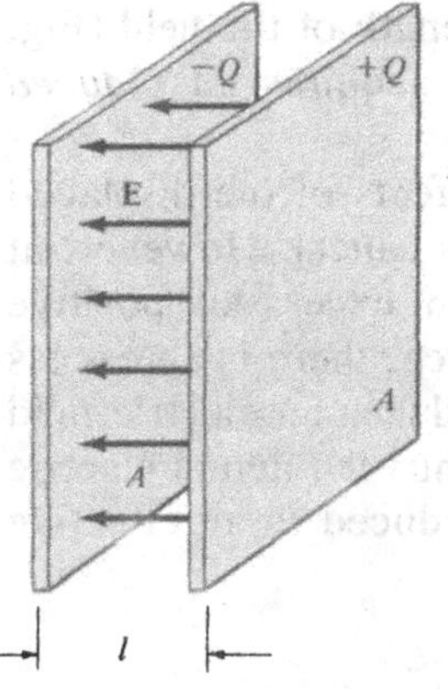

Figure 16.33. A parallel plate capacitor.

It is conventional to define a new constant ε_0 as

$$\varepsilon_0 = \frac{1}{4\pi k} = 8.85 \times 10^{-12}\ \mathrm{C^2\ N^{-1}\ m^{-2}}$$

Our final expression for the capacitance of a parallel plate capacitor is then

$$C = \frac{\varepsilon_0 A}{l} \tag{16.25}$$

Note that C depends only on the geometry of the arrangement and not on the charge Q. The capacitance increases with the area of the plates and decreases with their separation. This is also true for capacitors with more complicated shapes. Numerical examples of parallel plate capacitors are given in the next section.

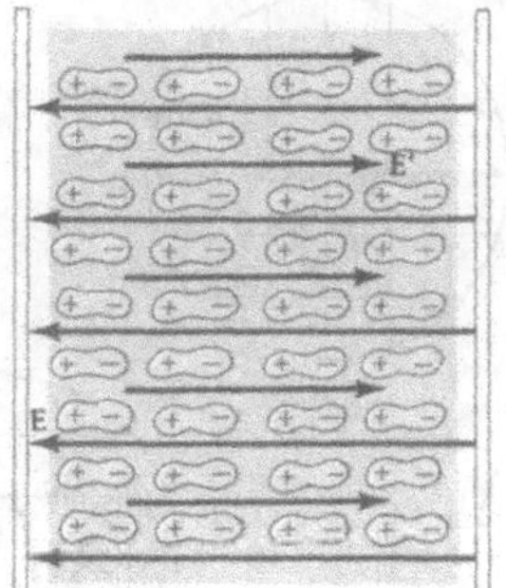

Figure 16.34. The molecules in a dielectric are distorted by the electric field **E** between the parallel plates. The charge on the plates is the same before and after the dielectric is introduced.

16.10 | EFFECTS OF DIELECTRICS

If an insulator or *dielectric* is introduced between the plates of a parallel plate capacitor with fixed charges, the capacitance is increased. This occurs because the electric field due to the charges on the plates distorts the charge distributions of the molecules in the dielectric, giving each molecule a small *induced* electric dipole moment. These dipoles, in turn, reduce the overall electric field and hence the potential difference between the plates.

To study this in detail, consider a neutral molecule that normally has its centers of positive and negative charge coincident so that it has no permanent dipole moment. When an external electric field is applied, it separates the charge centers by a distance proportional to the strength of the field (Fig. 16.34). Thus each molecule acquires an *induced* electric dipole moment.

Inside the dielectric the effects of the displaced positive and negative charges cancel. However, at the left surface, there is an excess of positive charge, and at the right surface, there is an excess of negative charge. This produces an electric field **E**′ directed opposite to **E**. Thus the actual electric field between the plates is reduced to an effective value,

$$E_{\text{eff}} = E - E'$$

Since the separation of the charges increases with **E**, the field **E**′ they produce is also proportional to **E**. Thus we can write

$$\mathbf{E}_{\text{eff}} = \frac{1}{K}\mathbf{E} \tag{16.26}$$

The *dielectric constant* K is a dimensionless number that indicates the reduction of the field due to the dielectric. K is one for a vacuum, and greater than one for a dielectric.

Table 16.1 lists representative dielectric constants. In some substances, such as water, the molecules have permanent electric dipole moments that tend to line up with the field. The degree of alignment increases with the field but decreases as the

TABLE 16.1

Dielectric constants of several common insulators. Note that for air we can usually use $K = 1$, the value for a vacuum.

Material	Temperature (°C)	Dielectric Constant K
Air (dry, at 1 atm)	20	1.00059
Glass	25	5–10
Water	25	78
	80	61
Plastics	20	3–20
Titanium dioxide	20	100
Axon membrane (unmyelinated)	37	8
Paper	20	3.5

temperature rises due to thermal disordering. Thus K depends on temperature.

The potential difference between the plates is $V = E_{\text{eff}}l = El/K$. Since K is greater than one for a dielectric, V is reduced when a dielectric is inserted. Consequently, the *capacitance* $C = Q/V$ *increases by the factor* K. An increase in C occurs for any capacitor, not just a parallel plate arrangement. In a parallel plate capacitor, the capacitance changes from $\varepsilon_0 A/l$ to

$$C = \frac{K\varepsilon_0 A}{l} \qquad (16.27)$$

The following examples illustrate the effects of dielectrics on the capacitance.

Example 16.11

A capacitor is made of two foils, each of surface area 1 m², separated by paper 0.05 mm = 5×10^{-5} m thick. What is its capacitance?

According to Table 16.1, $K = 3.5$ for paper. Thus the capacitance is

$$C = \frac{K\varepsilon_0 A}{l}$$

$$= \frac{(3.5)(8.85 \times 10^{-12}\ \text{C}^2\ \text{N}^{-1}\ \text{m}^{-2})(1\ \text{m}^2)}{5 \times 10^{-5}\ \text{m}}$$

$$= 6.19 \times 10^{-7}\ \text{F} = 0.619\ \mu\text{F}$$

Example 16.12

The ions inside and outside a cell are separated by a flat membrane 10^{-8} m thick with a dielectric constant $K = 8$. Find the capacitance of 1 cm² of membrane (Fig. 16.35).

For an area $A = 1\ \text{cm}^2 = 10^{-4}\ \text{m}^2$, the capacitance is

$$C = \frac{K\varepsilon_0 A}{l} = \frac{8(8.85 \times 10^{-12}\ \text{C}^2\ \text{N}^{-1}\ \text{m}^{-2})(10^{-4}\ \text{m}^2)}{10^{-8}\ \text{m}}$$

$$= 7.08 \times 10^{-7}\ \text{F} = 0.708\ \mu\text{F}$$

When the electric field in a dielectric becomes sufficiently strong, large numbers of free electrons and ions are produced, and the material becomes an excellent conductor. This *breakdown* occurs at a critical electric field called the *dielectric strength*. Lightning is a spectacular example of this phenomenon in which the air becomes a conductor (Fig. 16.36). Commercial capacitors are marked with the maximum voltage that can be applied without risk of exceeding the dielectric strength and damaging the capacitor or other parts of a circuit.

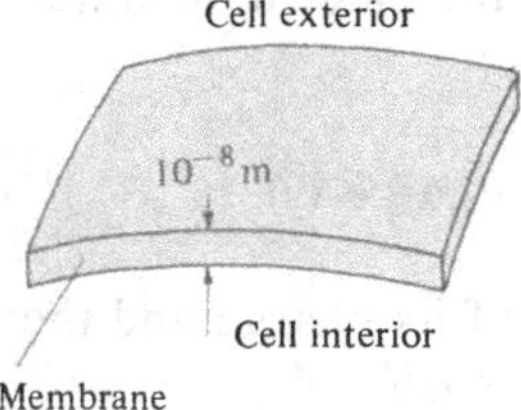

Figure 16.35. A small section of a cell membrane.

Figure 16.36. When low-lying clouds accumulate a charge, there is a potential difference between the cloud and the ground. If this potential difference is large enough, the electric field exceeds the dielectric strength of the air. The air then ionizes and becomes a good electrical conductor. (Kent Wood / Photo Researchers, INC.)

16.11 | ENERGY STORED IN A CAPACITOR

A charged capacitor stores electrical energy. If its plates are connected by conducting wire, electrons will move in the wire from the negative plate to the positive plate. This charge flow or *current* continues until the plates are neutralized and can be used to operate an electronic flash gun or trigger an artificial heart pacemaker. Thus stored electrical energy can be transformed into other forms of energy.

The energy stored in a capacitor may initially be supplied by a battery, which maintains a potential difference between its two terminals. When the plates of an uncharged capacitor are connected by two wires to the terminals, electrons flow in the wires from one plate through the battery to the other until the potential difference across the capacitor reaches a maximum value. We can find the energy stored in the capacitor by calculating the work that must be done by the battery in building up this charge from zero to the final value Q.

To avoid minus signs, we suppose that positive charges are gradually transferred from one plate to the other. (The final result is independent of the sign of the moving charges.) As one plate acquires an increasingly large positive charge and the other a corresponding negative charge, the potential difference between them increases. If at some instant the charges are $+q$ and $-q$, then from the definition of capacitance, $C = q/v$, we have $v = q/C$. Transferring a small additional amount of charge therefore requires that work dW be done by the battery, where

$$dW = v\,dq = \frac{q}{C}\,dq$$

Since the electric force is conservative, the work done by the battery dW must equal the increase $d\mathcal{U}$ in the stored energy of the capacitor, so

$$d\mathcal{U} = \frac{q}{C}\,dq$$

To find the total energy stored in the capacitor, we integrate from 0 to the final charge Q:

$$\mathcal{U} = \int_0^Q \frac{q}{C}\,dq = \frac{1}{2}\frac{Q^2}{C}$$

Using $C = Q/V$, the energy can be expressed in three equivalent forms,

$$\mathcal{U} = \frac{1}{2}QV = \frac{1}{2}\frac{Q^2}{C} = \frac{1}{2}CV^2 \qquad (16.28)$$

The perhaps surprising factor of $\frac{1}{2}$ reflects the fact that, on the average, during the charging process the potential is just half its final value.

The energy stored in a cell membrane is calculated in the following example.

Example 16.13

One square centimetre of membrane has a capacitance of 7.08×10^{-7} F. If the potential difference across the membrane is 0.1 V, find the electrical energy stored in 1 cm^2 of membrane.

Since we know C and V, we write the energy as $\frac{1}{2}CV^2$. Then

$$\mathcal{U} = \tfrac{1}{2}CV^2 = \tfrac{1}{2}(7.08 \times 10^{-7}\ \text{F})(0.1\ \text{V})^2 = 3.54 \times 10^{-9}\ \text{J}$$

Several important concepts are reviewed in our last example.

Example 16.14

The separation between the plates of a parallel plate capacitor is doubled while the charge on them is held constant. What happens to the (a) electric field between the plates; (b) potential difference; (c) capacitance; (d) stored energy?

(a) The electric field between two oppositely charged parallel plates is $4\pi kQ/A$. Since neither the charge nor the plate area changes when the plate separation is increased, the field E is unchanged.

(b) The potential difference between the plates is the work per unit charge needed to move charge from one plate to the other, or $V = El$. Since l has been doubled, V is doubled.

(c) The capacitance is defined as the ratio $C = Q/V$. Here Q is constant and V is doubled, so C is halved.

(d) The stored energy can be written as $\mathcal{U} = \frac{1}{2}QV$. Since Q is constant and V is doubled, the energy $\mathcal{U}$ is doubled. The two plates are oppositely charged and attract each other. The mechanical work we do against this force when we increase their separation is the source of the increased energy stored by the capacitor.

SUMMARY

A charge Q exerts an electric force on a second charge q, which is given by Coulomb's law:

$$\mathbf{F} = \frac{kqQ}{r^2}\hat{\mathbf{r}} \qquad \text{(Coulomb's law)}$$

Alternatively, we can say that the electric field due to a point charge Q is

$$\mathbf{E} = \frac{kQ}{r^2}\hat{\mathbf{r}} \qquad \text{(point charge } Q\text{)}$$

The force on q is the product of its charge and the electric field at its location, $\mathbf{F} = q\mathbf{E}$.

The field due to a system of charges is found by summing or integrating their individual fields. The resulting field may vary with position in many ways. The field of an infinitely long uniformly charged straight wire is radial and has a magnitude

$$E = \frac{2k\lambda}{r} \quad \text{(long straight wire)}$$

A uniformly charged infinite plane produces a uniform field. A pair of oppositely charged plates has a field between them which is normal to the plates and has a magnitude

$$E = 4\pi k\sigma \quad \text{(parallel plates)}$$

Outside the plates, the field is zero.

The electric potential is the potential energy of a charge divided by that charge,

$$V = \frac{\mathcal{U}}{q}$$

Moving a distance $d\mathbf{l}$ in an electric field $\mathbf{E}$ changes the potential by

$$dV = -\mathbf{E} \cdot d\mathbf{l}$$

Summing or integrating over such small displacements, the potential change is

$$\Delta V = -\int \mathbf{E} \cdot d\mathbf{l}$$

This equation can be used to find formulas for some simple situations:

$$V = \frac{kQ}{r} \quad \text{(point charge)}$$

$$\Delta V = 4\pi k\sigma l \quad \text{(parallel plates)}$$

$$\Delta V = -2k\lambda \ln\frac{r_2}{r_1} \quad \text{(long straight wire)}$$

Two charges $+q$ and $-q$ separated by a distance $\mathbf{l}$ have a dipole moment $\mathbf{p} = q\mathbf{l}$. In a uniform electric field, there is no net force on a dipole, but there is a torque tending to align it with the field. The torque on the dipole is

$$\boldsymbol{\tau} = \mathbf{p} \times \mathbf{E}$$

and its potential energy is

$$\mathcal{U} = -pE\cos\theta = -\mathbf{p} \cdot \mathbf{E}$$

A capacitor is a pair of conductors separated by a vacuum or an insulator. If the conductors are given equal but opposite charges, the ratio $C = Q/V$ of the charge to the resulting potential difference is the capacitance. Other arrangements of conductors and insulators, such as those in living cells, can also be regarded as having capacitance.

When an insulator is placed between the plates of a charged capacitor, electric dipoles are induced in the material. The dipole fields oppose the applied field and reduce the potential difference between the plates, thereby increasing the capacitance. Capacitors store electrical energy according to the relationship $\mathcal{U} = \frac{1}{2}QV$.

Checklist

Define or explain:

Coulomb's law	insulator
electric field	cathode-ray tube
electric field lines	capacitance
electric dipole	dielectric
electric potential	induced dipole moment
voltage	dielectric constant
equipotential surface	dielectric strength
conductor	

REVIEW QUESTIONS

Q16-1 The force between two charges of opposite sign is _____.

Q16-2 The force on a charge q in an electric field $\mathbf{E}$ is _____.

Q16-3 The electric force on a positive charge is _____ to the field; the electric force on a negative charge is _____ to the field.

Q16-4 The electric field due to a positive charge points _____ the charge; the field due to a negative charge points _____ the charge.

Q16-5 The spacing of electric field lines indicates the _____, and their direction gives the _____.

Q16-6 The field between two oppositely charged metal plates is nearly _____.

Q16-7 The change in potential energy of a charge q moved through a potential difference ΔV is _____.

Q16-8 The equipotential surfaces near a point charge are _____.

Q16-9 Two charges $+q$ and $-q$ a distance l apart have a dipole moment of magnitude _____ directed toward _____.

Q16-10 The potential energy of a dipole is least when it points _____.

Q16-11 If a capacitor has a capacitance C and its plates have charges $\pm Q$, the potential difference across it is _____.

Q16-12 Inserting a dielectric between two charged plates _____ the field, _____ the potential difference, and _____ the capacitance.

Q16-13 If the voltage across a capacitor is doubled, the energy stored changes by a factor of _____.

EXERCISES

Several of the following exercises involve atomic quantities. The magnitude of the charge on an electron or a proton is $e = 1.60 \times 10^{-19}$ C, the electron mass is 9.11×10^{-31} kg, and the proton mass is 1.673×10^{-27} kg.

Section 16.1 | Electric Forces

16-1 Find the magnitude and direction of the force on the charge Q in Fig. 16.37.

16-2 If $Q = 10^{-6}$ C and $b = 0.1$ m, what is the magnitude and direction of the force on the charge $2Q$ in Fig. 16.37?

16-3 An additional charge Q is placed at the origin in Fig. 16-37. What is the force on this charge?

16-4 Find the magnitude and direction of the force on the charge $-Q$ in Fig. 16.38.

16-5 In a NaCl molecule, a Na^+ ion with charge e is 2.3×10^{-10} m from a Cl^- ion with charge $-e$. What is the magnitude of the force between them?

in Fig.

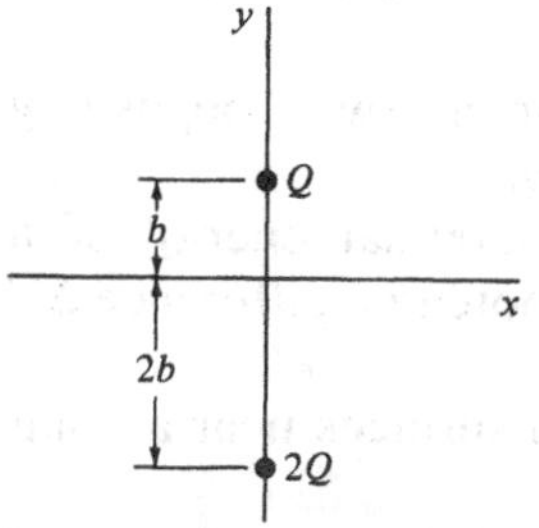

Figure 16.37. Exercises 16-1, 16-2, 16-3, 16-13, 16-14, and 16-17.

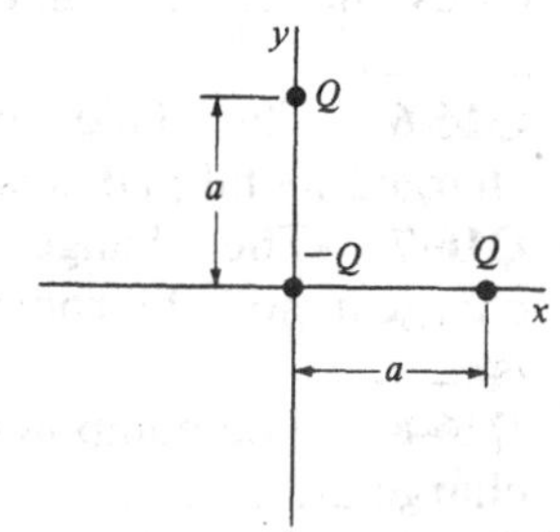

Figure 16.38. Exercise 16-4, Problem 16-71.

16-6 A cell membrane 10^{-8} m thick has positive ions on one side and negative ions on the other. What is the force between two ions with charges $+e$ and $-e$ at this separation?

16-7 According to the quark model, a proton consists of two u (up) quarks, each with a charge $+2e/3$, and one d (down) quark, with a charge $-e/3$. (a) What is the total charge of the proton in this model? (b) If the u quarks are separated by a distance of 4×10^{-16} m, how large is the electric force between them?

16-8 The distance between two charges is increased by a factor of 10. By what factor does the force change?

Section 16.2 | The Electric Field
Section 16.3 | The Electric Field Due to Arrangements of Charges

16-9 A uranium nucleus has a charge of $92e$. (a) What is the direction and magnitude of the electric field due to the nucleus at a distance of 10^{-10} m from the nucleus? (b) What is the direction and magnitude of the force on an electron at this distance?

16-10 What is the force on an electron in a field of 10^5 N C^{-1}?

16-11 An electron is accelerated at 10^8 m s^{-2} by an electric field. What is the direction and magnitude of the field?

16-12 Find the magnitude and direction of the electric field 0.1 m from a charge of -10^{-4} C.

16-13 In Fig. 16-37, find the electric field at the origin.

16-14 In Fig. 16.37, find the electric field at $x = 0$, $y = -b$.

16-15 The electric field near a uniformly charged circular plate of area 0.1 m^2 is directed toward the plate and has a magnitude of 10^4 N C^{-1}. Find the charge on the plate.

16-16 Two square plates of side 0.1 m have equal and opposite charges of $\pm 10^{-6}$ C, which are uniformly distributed. The plates are separated by 10^{-2} m. (a) What is the magnitude and direction of the electric field? (b) What is the magnitude and direction of the force on an electron placed in this field? (c) How much work must be done against the field to move an electron from the positive plate to the negative plate?

16-17 In Fig. 16-37, find a point where $E = 0$.
16-18 A thundercloud has a charge distribution that attracts positive charge to the surface of the earth below it. If this induced charge is 2×10^{-6} C m^{-2}, find the field produced by it.
16-19 Can electric field lines cross? (*Hint*: What would be the direction of the force on a charge placed at the crossing point?)
16-20 Show that the electric field at the center of a uniformly charged circular ring is zero.

Section 16.4 | The Electric Fields of Continuous Charge Distributions

16-21 A 10-m straight line has a total charge of 10^{-5} C. (a) Find the charge per unit length, assuming the charge is uniformly distributed. (b) What is the field 0.1 m from the wire at a point near its center?
c**16-22** (a) Suppose that in Fig. 16.18 the wire is not infinite but rather extends from $-L$ to $+L$. Show that the field at P is normal to the wire and has a magnitude

$$E = \frac{2k\lambda L}{r(r^2 + L^2)^{1/2}}$$

(b) Show that this formula reduces to Eq. 16.11 in the limit of an infinitely long wire.
16-23 The fractional error Δ in a formula for the field **E** is defined as

$$\Delta = \frac{|E(\text{exact}) - E(\text{approx})|}{E(\text{exact})}$$

(a) If $r = L/10$, what is the fractional error Δ produced by using the formula for the field due to an infinitely long straight wire instead of the equation in the preceding exercise? (b) Find the corresponding fractional error when $r = L$.
16-24 The electric field at a distance of 0.01 m from a long straight wire is directed toward the wire and has a magnitude of 10^6 N C^{-1}. What is the charge per unit length on the wire?

Section 16.5 | The Electric Potential

16-25 A carbon nucleus has a charge of $+6e$. At a distance of 10^{-10} m from a carbon nucleus, find (a) the electric potential; (b) the potential energy of an electron in electron volts and joules.

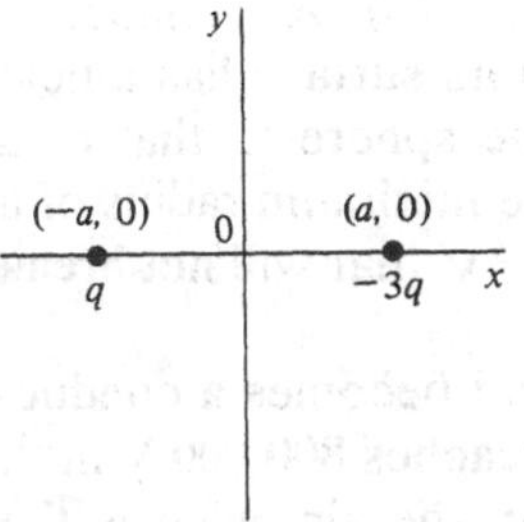

Figure 16.39. Exercise 16-26.

16-26 In Fig. 16.39, what is the potential at (a) the origin; (b) $x = 3a$, $y = 0$? (c) At what points on the x axis is the potential zero?
16-27 Two uniformly charged metal plates separated by 0.04 m produce a uniform field between them of 10^4 N C^{-1}. Find (a) the charge per unit area Q/A on the plates; (b) the potential difference between the plates.
16-28 At the center of the square in Fig. 16.40, find (a) the electric field; (b) the potential.
16-29 An electron and a proton are separately placed at rest midway between two oppositely charged metal plates. (a) Which way will the electron accelerate? (b) Which way will the proton accelerate? (c) Which particle, if either, will acquire more kinetic energy just before striking a plate? (d) What is the ratio of their velocities just before they strike the plates?
16-30 In Bohr's model of the hydrogen atom, the electron moves in a circle of radius 5.29×10^{-11} m. Find (a) the electric potential due to the proton at that circle; (b) the potential energy of the electron in electron volts and joules.
16-31 Air breaks down and becomes a conductor when the electric field reaches 800,000 V m^{-1}. (a) How far from a point charge of 10^{-5} C does the

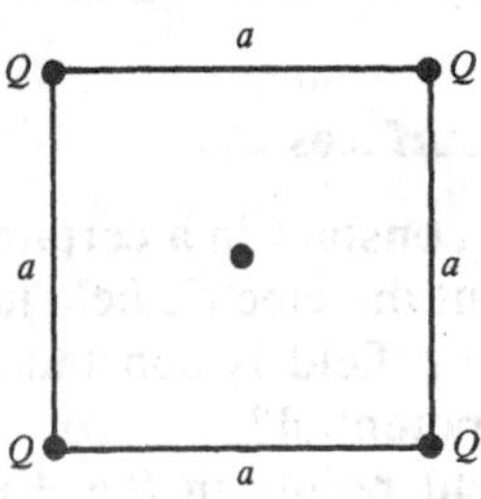

Figure 16.40. Exercise 16-28.

field have this magnitude? (b) A conducting sphere with a charge Q on its surface has a field that is identical outside the sphere to that of a point charge Q. What is the minimum radius of a sphere with a charge of 10^{-5} C that will not break down the air?

16-32 Air breaks down and becomes a conductor when the electric field reaches 800,000 V m^{-1}. (a) If a large flat plate is in the air, what is the maximum charge per unit area it can have without breaking down the air? (b) How many excess electrons per square metre does such a plate have?

16-33 Charged particles such as protons are accelerated to high velocities and allowed to collide with atomic nuclei to probe their internal structure. The electric potential outside of a nucleus with Z protons is equal to that of a point charge Ze. (a) A lead nucleus ($Z = 82$) is approximately described as a sphere of radius 7×10^{-15} m. How much kinetic energy in megaelectron volts (1 MeV = 10^6 electron volts) must a proton have initially to overcome the electrical repulsion and reach its surface? (b) What is the corresponding initial velocity?

16-34 A uniformly charged thin ring of radius a has a total charge Q. Find the potential at the center of the ring.

16-35 An infinitely long straight wire has a charge per unit length of 10^{-4} C m^{-1}. (a) If a proton moves from a distance of 0.01 m from the wire to a distance of 0.5 m, by how much will its kinetic energy increase? (b) If the proton was initially at rest 0.01 m from the wire, what is its speed when it is 0.5 m away?

16-36 The potential changes by V_0 going from a distance a to a distance b from a long uniformly charged wire. How far from the wire must one go for the potential to change by $2V_0$ from its value at a?

Section 16.6 | Equipotential Surfaces

16-37 (a) If the potential is constant in a certain region, what can be said about the electric field in that region? (b) If the electric field is constant, what can be said about the potential?

16-38 (a) If the electric field points in the $+x$ direction, in what direction is the most rapid increase in the electric potential observed? (b) How does V change as we move in the $-y$ direction?

16-39 A long, uniformly charged wire has an electric field that points directly outward from the wire, or along the radial direction. Describe the corresponding equipotential surfaces.

16-40 In an electric field diagram, some lines stop and other lines start on the surface of a sphere. If the number of lines stopping equals the number starting, what can be said about the net charge on the sphere?

Section 16.7 | Electric Dipoles

16-41 The NH_3 molecule has a permanent electric dipole moment of 5.0×10^{-30} C m. If this arises from net charges of $+e$ and $-e$ in two regions of the molecule, what is their separation?

16-42 Although a neutron has no net charge, it has a charge distribution consisting of spherical layers of positive and negative charge. Its electric dipole moment has not been detected; if it has one, the moment must be less than 10^{-45} C m according to recent experiments. The diameter of a neutron is about 10^{-15} m. How large must equal and opposite charges at a distance of 10^{-15} m be to produce an electrical dipole moment of 10^{-45} C m? Express your result in multiples of e.

16-43 What energy is required to "flip" an electric dipole **p** from its position parallel to an electric field **E** to the antiparallel position?

16-44 An electric dipole consists of two charges of $\pm 10^{-4}$ C separated by 10^{-5} m. (a) What is the magnitude of the electric dipole moment? (b) If the dipole is in a field of 10^3 N C^{-1}, find its minimum and maximum potential energies.

16-45 An electric dipole consists of charges $\pm e$ separated by 10^{-10} m. It is in a field of 10^6 N C^{-1}. Find the magnitude of the torque on the dipole when it is (a) parallel to the field; (b) at right angles to the field; (c) opposite to the field.

Section 16.9 | Capacitance

16-46 What is the charge on a 100-μF capacitor when its potential difference is 1000 V?

16-47 A capacitor has a potential difference of 100 V when its plates have charges of magnitude 10^{-5} C. What is its capacitance?

16-48 Two square metal plates with sides of length 0.1 m are separated in vacuum by 10^{-3} m. Find their capacitance.

16-49 A 1-μF capacitor is charged to a potential difference of 1000 V. How many excess electrons are there on its negatively charged plate?

16-50 Two metal plates of area A are separated by a distance d and connected to the terminals of a battery with a potential difference V. (a) How much charge is on each plate? (b) If the plate separation is doubled, and the potential difference is kept fixed, by what factor is the charge changed? (c) If instead the plate separation is doubled but the charge is to be kept constant, by what factor must the potential difference be changed?

Section 16.10 | Effects of Dielectrics

16-51 A capacitor made of thin foils of aluminum separated by paper 10^{-4} m thick is found to have a capacitance of 1 μF. What is the area of the foil?

16-52 Metal plates are placed on either side of a sheet of glass, and their capacitance is measured to be 10^{-5} F. If they are kept at the same separation in air, their capacitance is found to be 2×10^{-6} F. What is the dielectric constant of the glass?

16-53 A lightning bolt travels 500 m from a cloud to a mountain top. What is the potential difference between the cloud and the peak? (Assume that the electric field is uniform and that the air breaks down and becomes a conductor when the field reaches 8×10^5 V m^{-1}.)

16-54 A parallel plate capacitor has a capacitance of 2 μF when the plates are separated by a vacuum. The plates are 10^{-3} m apart, and they are connected to a battery that maintains a 50-V potential difference between them. (a) What is the charge on the plates? (b) What is the electric field between the plates? (c) If a slab with dielectric constant equal to 5 is inserted between the plates, what is the new charge? (d) What is the electric field with the slab in place?

16-55 A capacitor is made of metal foils 5×10^{-5} m thick separated by paper 10^{-4} m thick. (a) How large an area of foil is needed to make a 0.1-μF capacitor? (b) If the capacitor is tightly rolled into a cylinder 10 cm long, what is its radius?

Section 16.11 | Energy Stored in a Capacitor

16-56 A 50-μF capacitor in an electronic flash gun supplies an average power of 10^4 W for 2×10^{-3} s. (a) To what potential difference must the capacitor initially be charged? (b) What is its initial charge?

16-57 An electronic flash gun uses energy stored in a capacitor. (a) How large a capacitor is needed to provide 30 J of energy if it is charged to 1000 V? (b) How much charge is on its plates?

16-58 Can you run a car on energy stored in a capacitor? Make a rough estimate to support your answer.

16-59 Two parallel metal plates of area 0.1 m^2 are separated in air by 0.01 m. Their potential difference is 1000 V. Find (a) the charge on the plates; (b) the stored energy. (c) A slab of dielectric with $K = 10$ is inserted so that it fills the space between the plates. The charge on the plates remains the same. Find the new potential difference and stored energy. (d) Explain the change, if any, in the stored energy.

16-60 A 500-μF capacitor is connected to a 100-V potential difference. How much energy is stored in the capacitor?

16-61 An insulating membrane separates conducting fluids inside and outside an unmyelinated axon, a type of nerve fiber. A certain unmyelinated axon has a capacitance of 0.01 F per square metre of surface area and is a cylinder 2.5×10^{-6} m in radius and 0.1 m long. (a) Find the surface area and capacitance of the axon. (b) If the potential difference across the membrane is 0.09 V, how much electrical energy is stored in the axon?

16-62 The separation between the plates of a parallel plate capacitor is halved while the charge on them is held constant. What will happen to the (a) electric field; (b) potential difference; (c) capacitance; (d) stored energy?

16-63 The separation between the plates of a parallel plate capacitor is doubled while the potential difference between them is held constant.

What will happen to the (a) electric field; (b) charge; (c) capacitance; (d) stored energy?

PROBLEMS

16-64 An electron is accelerated by a constant electric field from rest to a velocity of 10^6 m s^{-1}. If the accelerating region is 0.2 m long, what is the magnitude of the electric field?

16-65 In his oil-drop measurements of the electronic charge (1900–1913), R. A. Millikan suspended small, charged oil droplets by adjusting a vertical electric field to balance their weight. The size of a droplet was measured by observing its terminal velocity in the air with the field turned off. Millikan found that the droplets always had charges that were integer multiples of a basic unit, which he identified with the electronic charge e. (a) If a droplet had a radius of 1.2×10^{-6} m, and the field required to balance it was 1.26×10^5 N C^{-1}, what was the charge on the droplet? (The density of the oil was 851 kg m^{-3}.) (b) What is the ratio of this charge to the magnitude of the charge e on an electron? (c) If the field was produced by a pair of metal plates 0.015 m apart, what potential difference was required to produce this field?

16-66 A charge of -10^{-6} C is placed at the origin of an x–y plane. Find the magnitude and direction of the electric field at (a) $x = 1$ m, $y = 0$; (b) $x = 0$, $y = -2$ m; (c) $x = 2$ m, $y = 2$ m.

16-67 A circular metal plate of radius 0.2 m has 10^{10} excess electrons uniformly distributed over its surfaces. What is the magnitude and direction of the field just outside the plate near its center?

16-68 Estimate the magnitude and direction of the field at a distance of 10 m from the center of the plate in the preceding problem.

16-69 An electron is projected with a velocity v_0 into a uniform electric field (Fig. 16.41). (Neglect the gravitational force on the electron.) (a) Find the direction and magnitude of its acceleration. (b) How long will it be in the field? (c) How far will it be deflected vertically as it leaves the field? (d) Find the angle between its velocity as it leaves the field and its original direction.

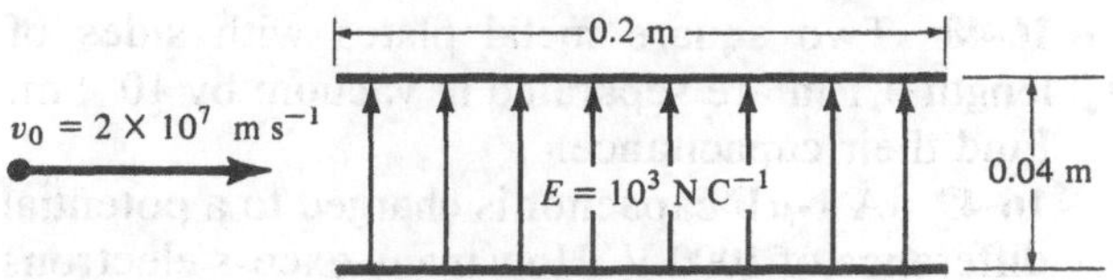

Figure 16.41. Problem 16-69.

16-70 A charge q is placed at the origin and a charge $2q$ is placed at $x = a$, $y = 0$. Find the potential at $x = a$, $y = a$.

16-71 In Fig. 16.38, find the direction and magnitude of the field at $x = -a$, $y = 0$.

16-72 Electrostatic precipitators can remove up to 99 percent of the small particles from the smoke of coal-burning electrical power plants and other industrial sources of air pollution. In a typical precipitator, a conducting wire located on the axis of a cylindrical chamber is at a potential of 40,000 to 100,000 V below that of the outer walls. (a) What is the general direction of the electric field lines in the device? (b) Where is the field largest? Explain. (c) The field near the wire ionizes some of the gas molecules. In which direction do the electrons and negative ions move? (d) As the exhaust gases move through the precipitator, collisions with the electrons and negative ions cause the particles to become negatively charged. Which way will the particles move?

16-73 In a *Xerox* photocopying machine, positive charge is sprayed onto a plate with a *photoconducting surface*, one that becomes a conductor when light strikes it. (a) The image of the document to be copied is projected onto the plate. Which parts of the plate will still be positively charged after light hits it, the light or dark areas? (b) A negatively charged toner powder is next sprayed onto the plate. Where will it adhere? (The toner is then transferred from the plate to the paper and fixed to it by heating.)

16-74 A model of a typical thundercloud has a +50-C charge 10 km above the earth's surface and a −20-C charge 2 km above the earth (Fig. 16.42*a*). (a) What is the magnitude and direction of the field due to these charges at the surface of the earth just below the cloud? (b) A charge out-

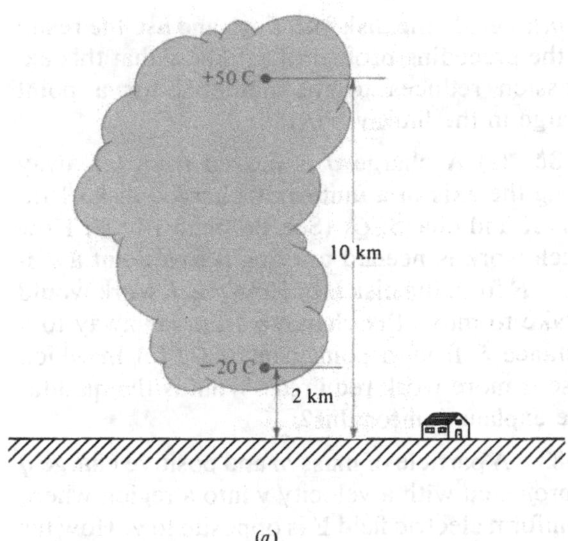

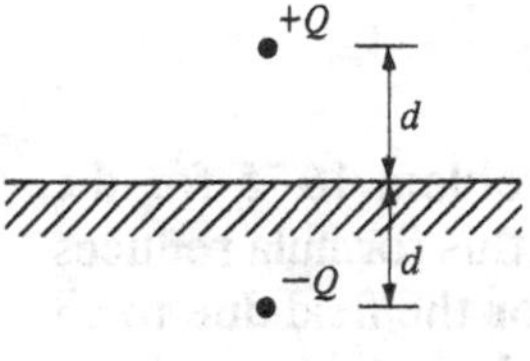

Figure 16.42. Problem 16-74.

side a conducting object induces charges in its surface by attracting opposite charges to the surface and repelling like charges. If a charge Q is a distance d from a large conductor, the field outside the conductor due to the induced charges can be found by considering a single equivalent "image charge." Thus one imagines a charge $-Q$ located a distance d below the surface and ignores the effects of the conductor (Fig. 16.42*b*). What are the locations and values of the image charges corresponding to the +50-C and −20-C charges? (c) What is the total electric field due to all the charges at the surface of the earth just below the cloud? (d) Air becomes a conductor when the electric field reaches 800,000 V m^{-1}. Will lightning from this cloud strike the ground? Explain.

16-75 A thin ring of radius a has a total charge Q distributed uniformly around it (Fig. 16.43). Show that the electric field on the axis at a distance y from the center of the ring is directed along the axis and has a magnitude

$$E = \frac{kQy}{(y^2 + a^2)^{3/2}}$$

16-76 A uniformly charged ring with a radius a has a total charge Q (Fig. 16.43). Show that the potential at a point on its axis a distance y from its center is

$$V = \frac{kQ}{(y^2 + a^2)^{1/2}}$$

16-77 (a) Find the magnitude and direction of the electric field at a point on the x axis for the dipole in Fig. 16.9. (b) For $x \gg a$, find the ratio of the magnitude of this field to that of the field at a point equally far from the origin on the y axis.

c16-78 A disk of radius R has a uniform charge per unit area σ (Fig. 16.44). (a) Show that the electric field on the axis at a distance y from the center of the disk has a magnitude

$$E = 2\pi k\sigma \left[1 - \frac{y}{(y^2 + R^2)^{1/2}}\right]$$

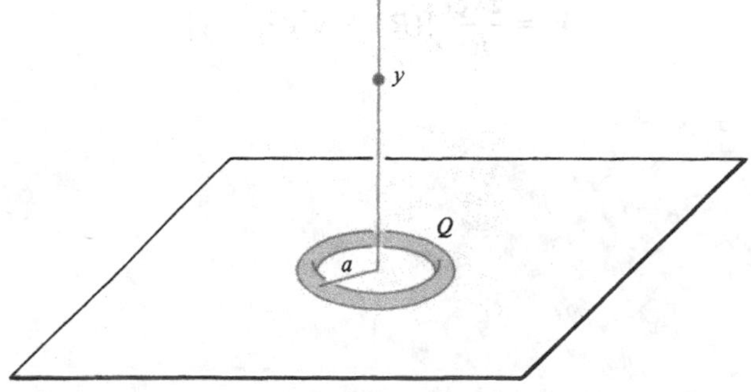

Figure 16.43. Problems 16-75 and 16-76.

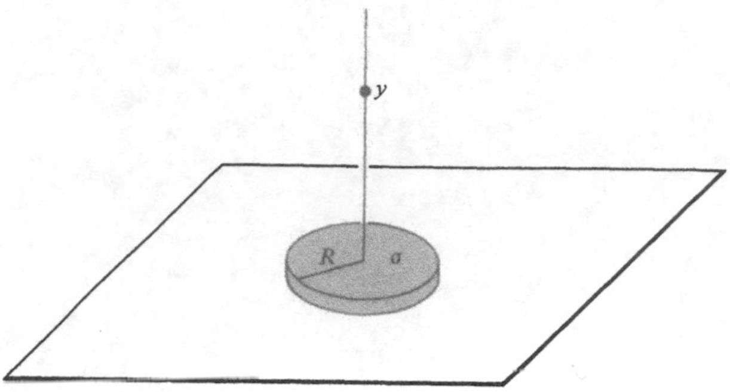

Figure 16.44. Problems 16-78, 16-81.

[*Hint*: Use the result of Problem 16-75 for the field of a ring.] (b) Show that this formula reduces to Eq. 16.9, the expression for the field due to an infinite plane, when the disk becomes very large compared to y ($R \gg y$). (c) Show that in the limit $y \gg R$, the formula reduces to the usual field for a point charge.

[c]**16-79** A wire is bent into a semicircle of radius R and has a uniform charge per unit length λ (Fig. 16.45). Find the electric field at its center. [*Hint*: Write the length of a segment as $R\,d\theta$ and integrate over θ.]

16-80 When an electron is 2 cm from a long wire carrying a uniform positive charge, its speed is 10^4 m s^{-1}. When it is 1 cm from the wire, its speed is 2×10^4 m s^{-1}. At what distance from the wire will its speed be 4×10^4 m s^{-1}?

[c]**16-81** A uniformly charged disk with a radius R has a total charge Q. (Fig. 16.44). (a) Show that the potential at a point on its axis a distance y from its center is

$$V = \frac{2kQ}{R^2}\left[(R^2 + y^2)^{1/2} - y\right]$$

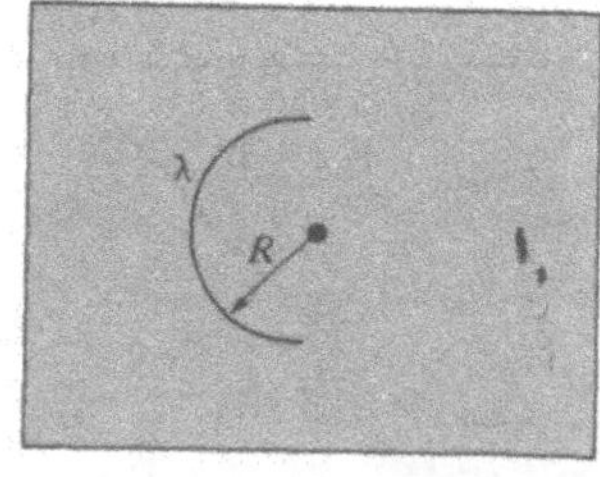

Figure 16.45. Problem 16-79.

[*Hint*: Divide the disk into rings and use the result of the preceding problem.] (b) Show that this expression reduces to the potential for a point charge in the limit $y \gg R$.

16-82 (a) A charge q is moved from far away along the axis of a uniformly charged disk of radius R and charge Q. (See Problem 16-81.) How much work is needed to bring it to a point a distance R from the disk? (b) How much work would it take to move the charge q from far away to a distance R from a point charge Q? (c) In which case is more work required? What is the qualitative explanation for this?

16-83 A particle of mass m and positive charge q is projected with a velocity $\mathbf{v}$ into a region where a uniform electric field $\mathbf{E}$ is opposite to $\mathbf{v}$. How far will the particle travel before it comes momentarily to rest?

16-84 If an atom is placed in an electric field $\mathbf{E}$, its charge distribution will be distorted so that an induced electric dipole moment $\mathbf{p} = \alpha\mathbf{E}$ is produced, where α is the *polarizability* of the atom. (a) An atom of polarizability α is a distance r from an ion with charge $+e$, where r is large compared to the size of the atom. What is the induced dipole moment? (b) What is the potential energy of the atom and ion?

***16-85** Two dipoles $\mathbf{p}_1$ and $\mathbf{p}_2$ are a distance R apart, which is large compared to their charge separation. Find the total electrical energy of the dipoles when they are oriented as in Fig. 16.46*a* and *b*. (A dipole at the origin directed along the y axis has an electric field at a distant point on the x axis that is $\mathbf{E} = -kp\hat{\mathbf{y}}/x^3$, and on the y axis the field is $\mathbf{E} = 2kp\hat{\mathbf{y}}/y^3$.

16-86 The electric dipole moment of a water molecule is 6.13×10^{-30} C m. (a) If this dipole moment is due to a pair of point charges $\pm e$, how far apart must they be? Find the ratio of this

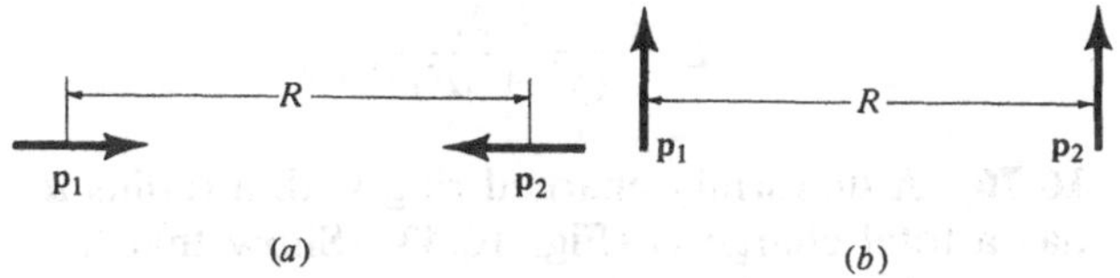

Figure 16.46. Problem 16-85.

distance to the radius of a hydrogen atom, 5.29×10^{-11} m. (b) If the dipole is parallel to an electric field of 10^6 V m^{-1}, how much energy is needed in joules and in electron volts to "flip" the dipole so that it is opposite to the field? (c) At room temperature, the average kinetic energy of a molecule is about 0.04 eV. What implication does this have for the orientation of water molecules in the relatively strong field of 10^6 V m^{-1}?

***16-87** Figure 16.47 shows a model of a water molecule. Each hydrogen atom has a net positive charge q, and the oxygen atom has a net charge $-2q$. The distance l is 9.65×10^{-11} m. The positive charge on a hydrogen atom and half the negative charge on the oxygen atom form a dipole. The total molecular electric dipole moment **p** is the vector sum of the two H—O dipole moments. (a) What is the direction of **p**? (b) If $p = 6.0 \times 10^{-30}$ C m, what is the charge q in multiples of the proton charge e?

16-88 A certain nerve fiber (axon) is a cylinder 10^{-4} m in diameter and 0.1 m long. Its interior has a potential 0.09 V below that of the surrounding fluid; it is separated from that fluid by a thin membrane. Na^+ ions are transported by a chemical reaction out of the fiber at the rate of 3×10^{-11} moles per second per square centimeter of membrane. (a) How many coulombs of charge per hour are transported out of the fiber? (b) How much work per hour must be done against the electrical forces?

***16-89** The two capacitors in Fig. 16-48 are said to be connected in *parallel*. They are connected to a battery so the potential difference across each is V. Show that a single capacitor C_p will

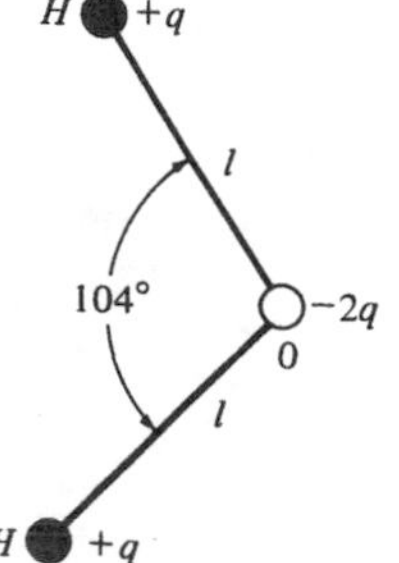

Figure 16.47. Problem 16-87.

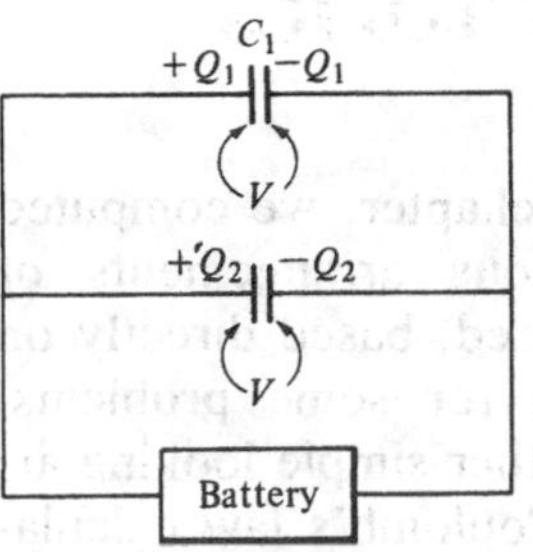

Figure 16-48. Problems 16-89 and 16-90.

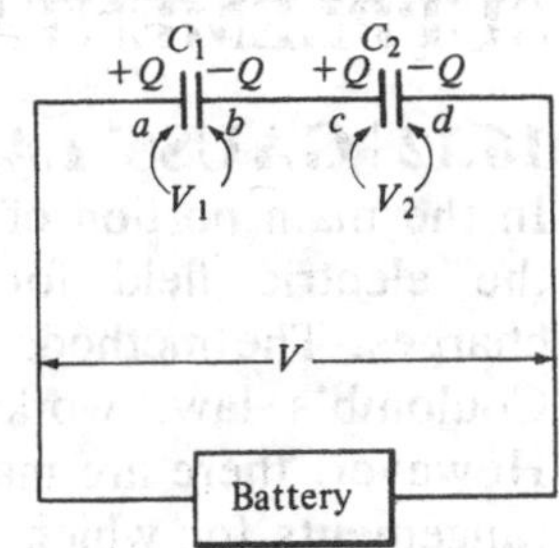

Figure 16-49. Problems 16-92 and 16-93.

store the same amount of charge if $C_p = C_1 + C_2$. (C_p is called the *equivalent capacitance*.)

16-90 In Fig. 16.48, $C_1 = 2\ \mu$F and $C_2 = 4\ \mu$F. Using the result of the preceding problem, find the equivalent single capacitance that would have the same charge when connected to the battery.

16-91 Using the result of Problem 16-89, show how an equivalent capacitance of 10 μF can be assembled from a supply of 2-μF capacitors.

16-92 The capacitors in Fig. 16.49 are said to be in *series*. When they are connected to the battery as shown, the charge Q on each is the same. Show that a single capacitor C_s with charge Q will have a potential difference $V = V_1 + V_2$ if

$$\frac{1}{C_s} = \frac{1}{C_1} + \frac{1}{C_2}$$

(C_s is called the equivalent capacitance.)

16-93 In Fig. 16-49, $C_1 = 2\ \mu$F and $C_2 = 4\ \mu$F. Using the result of the preceding problem, find the equivalent single capacitance that would maintain the same potential difference $V = V_1 + V_2$ with the same charge Q.

ANSWERS TO REVIEW QUESTIONS

Q16-1, attractive; **Q16-2**, q**E**; **Q16-3**, parallel, opposite; **Q16-4**, away from, toward; **Q16-5**, magnitude of the electric field, direction of the electric field; **Q16-6**, uniform; **Q16-7**, $\Delta\mathcal{U} = q\,\Delta V$; **Q16-8**, concentric spheres; **Q16-9**, ql, $+q$; **Q16-10**, along the field; **Q16-11**, Q/C; **Q16-12**, decreases, decreases, increases; **Q16-13**, 4.

SUPPLEMENTARY TOPICS

16.12 | GAUSS' LAW

In the main portion of this chapter, we computed the electric field for various arrangements of charges. The methods we used, based directly on Coulomb's law, work well for some problems. However, there are many other simple looking arrangements for which the Coulomb's law calculations turn out to be very complex. We see in this section that Gauss' law offers a useful alternative approach to finding the electric fields for certain important types of charge distributions.

For many situations, Gauss' law is just another formulation of the information contained in Coulomb's law. However, in the presence of time-varying magnetic fields, Gauss' law correctly describes the entire electric field, while Coulomb's law does not. We will not prove nor use this fact. Instead we will use Gauss' law as a tool to investigate some charge configurations that we cannot deal with so readily in any other way.

Our description of Gauss' law has a very strong geometric basis, as does our use of it. We will obtain the integral form of Gauss' law with the aid of some geometric ideas and the concept of electric

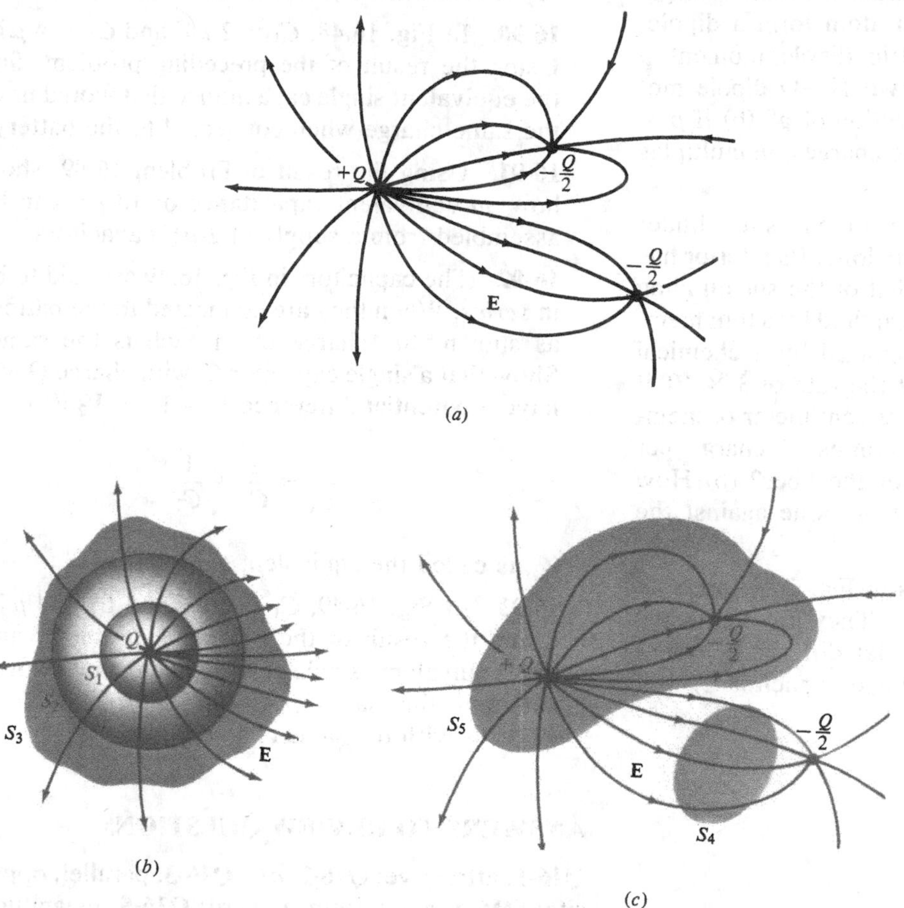

Figure 16.50. Approximate field line pattern for charges $+Q$, $-Q/2$, and $-Q/2$. (*a*) All the field lines start at $+Q$. Half end at each negative charge. (*b*) The same number of lines passes through the spheres S_1 and S_2 with different radii and also through the irregular surface S_3. (*c*) As many lines enter as leave S_4, so the net number leaving is zero. There is no net charge inside S_4. Half as many lines leave S_5 as leave the surfaces in (*b*); S_5 encloses half as much charge.

field lines. There is also a differential form of Gauss' law that we will not discuss. It is equivalent in content to the integral form, and it is useful in more advanced applications.

Our analysis relies on the fact that electric field lines begin at positive charges and end at negative charges. Conventionally, the number of electric field lines drawn is proportional to the number and size of the charges producing the field. Thus if we have one positive charge Q and two negative charges of $-Q/2$ each, then all the electric field lines begin at the lone positive charge and half end at each of the negative charges (Fig. 16.50*a*).

In Fig. 16.50*b*, we have focused on the positive charge Q and have drawn three *closed surfaces* around it. A closed surface is one where we cannot pass from the inside to the outside without passing through the surface. For example, a complete sphere is a closed surface, but one with a hole in it is not. Note in Figure 16.50*b* that the net number of electric field lines passing through each of the three closed surfaces is the same. Since the number of such lines is proportional to the positive charge shown, we conclude that the number of lines leaving a closed surface is proportional to the total amount of charge inside that surface.

This general statement can be verified by trying several surfaces other than those shown. For example, in Fig. 16.50*c*, the surface *S*4 has as many lines leaving it as entering it. The net number of lines passing through the surface (the number leaving minus the number entering) is zero, and so is the charge enclosed by it. *S*5 in Fig. 16.50*c* has half as many net lines passing through it as does *S*3 in Fig. 16.50*b*, and it encloses a total charge half as large, namely, $Q-(Q/2) = Q/2$.

We can now make these observations more quantitative. The number of electric field lines crossing a surface ΔA depends on how **E** is oriented relative to ΔA. For example, in Fig. 16.51*a*, several lines cross ΔA, but none do so in Fig. 16.51*b*. The area that is effective in intercepting the field lines is the projection of ΔA onto the plane perpendicular to the field lines. In Fig. 16.51*c*, θ is the angle between **E** and the unit vector $\hat{\mathbf{n}}$ drawn normal to the area ΔA. The projection of ΔA on the plane normal to **E** is $\Delta A \cos\theta$. Note, for example, in Fig. 16.51*a*, the normal to the plane is parallel to **E**, so that $\cos\theta = \cos 0° = 1$, and $\Delta A \cos\theta = \Delta A$ there. Similarly, the normal is perpendicular to **E**, and $\Delta A \cos\theta = \Delta A \cos 90° = 0$ in Fig. 16.51*b*.

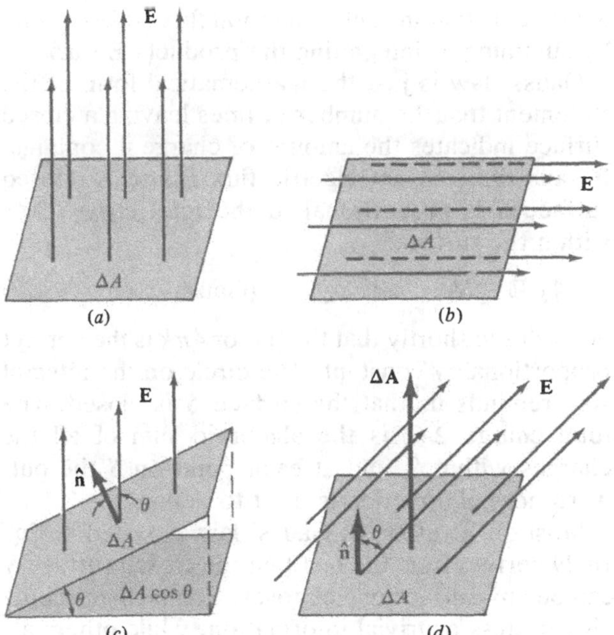

Figure 16.51. (*a*) The number of field lines passing through is a maximum when **E** is perpendicular to the surface. (*b*) No field lines pass through the surface when **E** is parallel to it. (*c*) The projection of ΔA on the plane perpendicular to **E** determines how many lines cross ΔA. $\hat{\mathbf{n}}$ is a unit vector normal or perpendicular to the surface, and θ is the angle between **E** and $\hat{\mathbf{n}}$. (*d*) $\Delta\mathbf{A}$ is a vector of magnitude ΔA directed along $\hat{\mathbf{n}}$. The electric flux is $\mathbf{E}\cdot\Delta\mathbf{A} = \mathbf{E}\cdot\hat{\mathbf{n}}\Delta A = E\Delta A\cos\theta$.

We see then that the number of lines crossing the surface is proportional to the magnitude of the field E, to the area ΔA, and to $\cos\theta$. Thus it is proportional to $E\,\Delta A \cos\theta$. We can define an *area vector* by $\Delta\mathbf{A} = \hat{\mathbf{n}}\Delta A$; ΔA is equal in magnitude to the area and directed normal to it. Then the number of lines is proportional to the scalar product $\mathbf{E}\cdot\Delta\mathbf{A}$, since

$$\mathbf{E}\cdot\Delta\mathbf{A} = \mathbf{E}\cdot\hat{\mathbf{n}}\,\Delta A = E\,\Delta A\cos\theta$$

$\mathbf{E}\cdot\Delta\mathbf{A}$ is called the *electric flux* (Fig. 16.51*d*).

The flux though a surface is a quantity that provides a numerical way of discussing the pictorial concept of the number of field lines crossing the surface. If the field varies, then the surface is broken up into infinitesimal areas $d\mathbf{A}$ such that **E** is nearly constant in each. The total flux is then found by summing or integrating the products $\mathbf{E} \cdot d\mathbf{A}$.

Gauss' law is just the mathematical form of the statement that the number of lines leaving a closed surface indicates the amount of charge it contains. It says that the net electric flux leaving a closed surface S is proportional to the total charge ΣQ_i within the surface:

$$\oint_S \mathbf{E} \cdot d\mathbf{A} = 4\pi k \Sigma Q_i \qquad \text{(Gauss' law)} \quad (16.29)$$

We will see shortly that the factor $4\pi k$ is the correct proportionality constant. The circle on the integral sign reminds us that the surface S is closed. The total charge ΣQ_i is the algebraic sum of all the charges within S, and at each point on S the outward normal direction is used to define $\hat{\mathbf{n}}$.

Most of the utility of Gauss' law as stated in Eq. 16.29 derives from the fact that the closed surface S can be any surface one chooses. Some choices provide useless or trivial information, while others allow one to reach conclusions or calculate fields in cases where the use of Coulomb's law is very difficult or not helpful. It is this judicious choice of surfaces to use in Gauss' law that the reader should focus on in the remainder of this section and the next.

We can demonstrate the equivalence of Gauss' law and Coulomb's law and the correctness of the $4\pi k$ factor by considering the field of a point positive charge $+Q$ (Fig. 16.52). This demonstration also illustrates how we exploit geometry in using Gauss' law.

By symmetry, since no direction is different from any other, and because the lines must start at the positive charge, the field of the point charge $+Q$ can

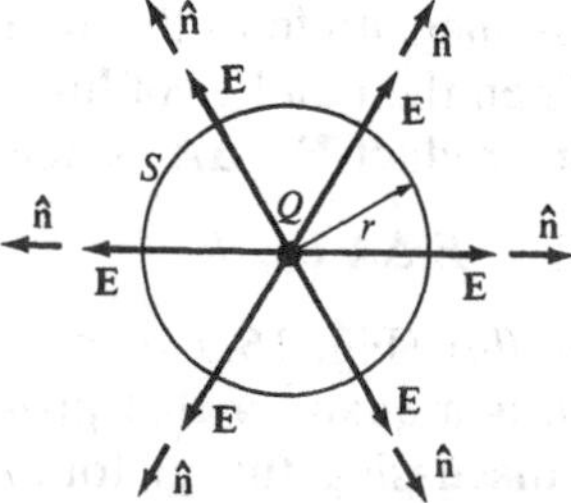

Figure 16.52. By symmetry, the field of a point charge in use be radial, and its magnitude is the same at all points a distance r from the charge.

only be radial. Then everywhere on the surface of a sphere S centered at Q, $\mathbf{E}$ must be perpendicular to the sphere, that is, along its normal $\hat{\mathbf{n}}$. Thus $\cos\theta = 1$, and $\mathbf{E} \cdot d\mathbf{A} = E\, dA$. Also, the same symmetry requires that $\mathbf{E}$ have the same magnitude *everywhere on this sphere;* otherwise, all directions would not be the same. Since E is constant, we can take it out of the integral sign. The total charge inside the sphere is $+Q$, so Gauss' law reduces to

$$E \oint_S dA = 4\pi k Q$$

Now the integral $\int dA$ over the surface of a sphere gives us its area, $4\pi r^2$. Thus this equation becomes $E(4\pi r^2) = 4\pi k Q$, or

$$E = \frac{kQ}{r^2}$$

If there is a second charge q in this field, it will experience a force $F = qE = kqQ/r^2$. This is precisely Coulomb's law, Eq. 16.1.

Besides showing the equivalence of Gauss' law and Coulomb's law, this calculation illustrates how to find electric fields using Gauss' law. If the geometric symmetry of a situation can be used to define surfaces called *Gaussian surfaces* on which $\mathbf{E}$ is constant in magnitude, E can be taken out of the integral. The integral then reduces to a surface area. However, when there isn't enough symmetry to do this, even though Gauss' law as stated in Eq. 16.29 is still correct, it is not sufficient to determine $\mathbf{E}$. The equivalent form of Gauss' law involving derivatives of the field components can then be used, but such calculations are beyond the level of this text.

The use of Gauss' law to solve problems involving symmetrical charge distributions is further illustrated in the next two examples. In both we rederive results found earlier by using Coulomb's law, while in the second we also obtain a new result. Notice carefully that the key point in both examples is that we are able to exploit Gauss' law because the symmetry enable us to find Gaussian surfaces on which the electric field has a constant magnitude.

Example 16.15

Use Gauss' law to find the field of a uniformly charged infinite plane with a charge per unit area $+\sigma$.

The field lines start at the charges and must be perpendicular to the charged plane, since any other direction would not be consistent with the symmetry (Fig.

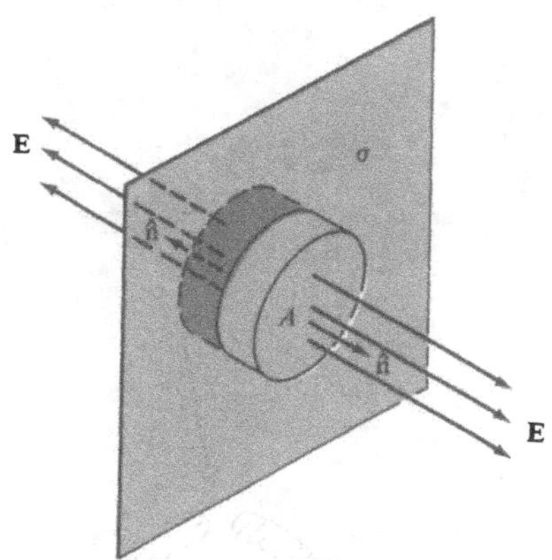

Figure 16.53. Part of a uniformly charged infinite plane. By symmetry, the field is perpendicular to the plane. Thus $\mathbf{E} \cdot d\mathbf{A} = \mathbf{E} \cdot \hat{\mathbf{n}}\, dA$ is zero except on the two ends of the Gaussian cylinder.

16.53). We draw a Gaussian surface in the form of a circular cylinder, so that **E** is parallel to its sides and normal to both of its ends. Then the Gauss' law integral can be divided into three parts: the integral over the sides of the cylinder, and the integrals over each of the two ends. The field is constant on each of these three surfaces. At each end it has some constant value E, and it is perpendicular to the area. Hence $\int \mathbf{E} \cdot d\mathbf{A} = E\int dA = EA$ on each of the ends; the integrals total $2EA$ for the two ends. On the sides, **E** is parallel to $d\mathbf{A}$, so $\mathbf{E} \cdot d\mathbf{A} = 0$, and the integral over the sides is zero. The total charge inside the cylinder is $Q = \sigma A$. Thus Gauss' law becomes

$$2EA = 4\pi k\sigma A \quad \text{or} \quad E = 2\pi k\sigma$$

This agrees with Eq. 16.9.

Example 16.16

Find the electric field (a) outside and (b) inside a uniformly charged sphere of radius R and total charge Q.

(a) To find the field outside the sphere, we choose as our Gaussian surface a sphere S of radius $r > R$ (Fig. 16.54*a*). As in the case of a point charge, the symmetry demands that **E** be radial and constant in magnitude on the Gaussian surface. The charge inside S is the total charge on the sphere, Q. Thus Gauss' law gives

$$E \oint_S dA = 4\pi kQ$$

Since the surface area of the sphere is $4\pi r^2$, we find

$$E = \frac{kQ}{r^2}$$

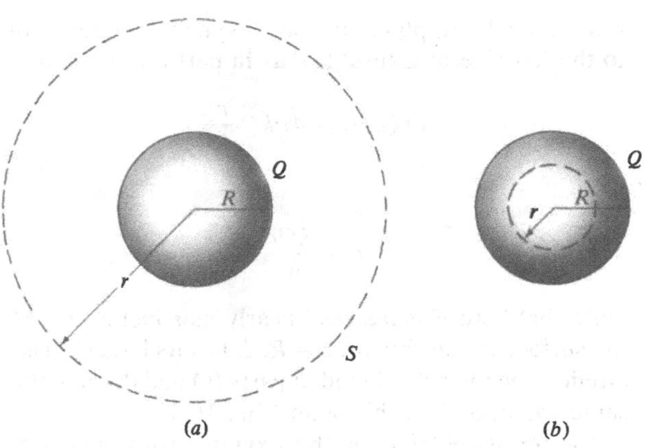

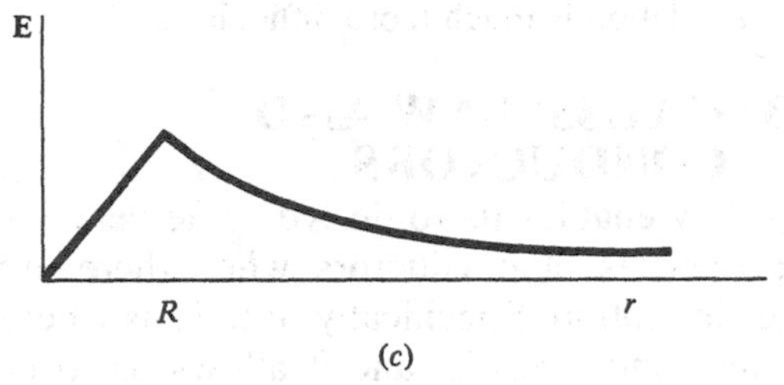

Figure 16.54. (*a*) A Gaussian sphere larger than the uniformly charged sphere encloses the full charge Q. (*b*) A sphere of radius $r < R$ contains only part of the charge. (*c*) The field increases linearly inside the charged sphere. Outside it is identical to the field of a point charge.

This result means that the field outside the sphere is idential to that of a point charge. This would also be the case if the sphere carried a uniformly distributed surface charge or any other spherically symmetric charge distribution. We made this observation earlier by noting that Coulomb's law applies to a pair of point charges or to a pair of spherical charges. We see now that Gauss' law determines the field of a spherically symmetric charge, without assuming explicitly that Coulomb's law applies to spheres. From the field outside the charge, we cannot tell whether its source is a point charge or a more complicated spherically symmetric distribution. Similarly, the field *outside* a cylindrically symmetric distribution is identical to that of a uniformly charged long straight wire.

(b) To find the field inside the sphere, we choose a spherical Gaussian surface S' with $r < R$ (Fig. 16.54*b*). The portion of the charge inside S' is the total charge Q times the ratio of the volumes of the Gaussian sphere and the entire charged sphere of radius R. Since the volume of a sphere of radius a is $4\pi a^3/3$, this volume ratio is r^3/R^3. Applying the same symmetry argument to the left side of Gauss' law as in part (a), we find

$$E(4\pi r^2) = 4\pi kQ \frac{r^3}{R^3}$$

or

$$E = \frac{kQr}{R^3}$$

Note that here E increases linearly as r increases. At the surface of the sphere, $r = R$, E has its largest magnitude. The formulas found in parts (a) and (b) give the same value for E at this point (Fig. 16.54*c*).

The results obtained in this example with the aid of Gauss' law can also be found from Coulomb's law, but the calculation is much more difficult.

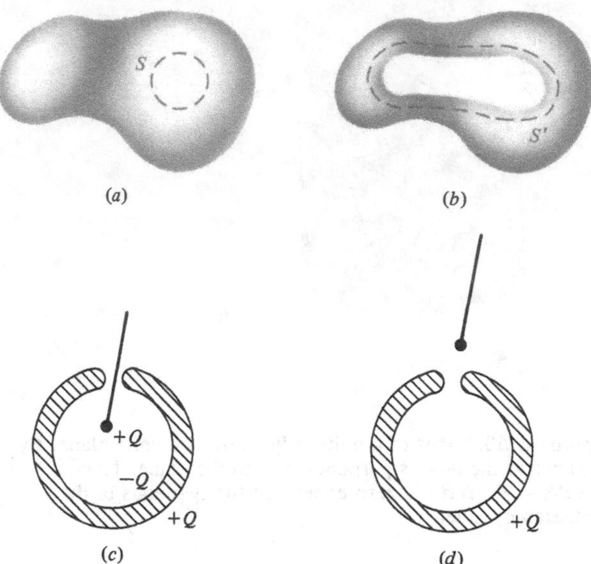

Figure 16.55. A conductor with no charges in motion must have $E = 0$ inside of it. (*a*) The net charge inside any surface S is zero, so the charge is zero everywhere in the conductor. (*b*) S' includes the cavity and contains no net charge, so there is no charge on the interior of the cavity. (*c*) Introducing a charge $+Q$ through a small hole in the cavity causes a charge $-Q$ to be induced on the interior of the conductor. This leaves a charge $+Q$ on its outside, since the conductor has no net charge. (*d*) If the object is touched to the inner surface, the charges $+Q$ and $-Q$ cancel. All the charge is then on the outer surface of the conductor.

16.13 | GAUSS' LAW AND CONDUCTORS

Gauss' law enables us to derive some very important properties of conductors when there are no charges in motion. Specifically, it tells us where the net charge must reside, and it allows us to determine the field near the surface.

We noted in Section 16.6 that inside a conductor the electric field must be zero when there are no charges in motion. Thus if we consider a solid conductor, the field must vanish everywhere within it (Fig. 16.55*a*). Also, if we draw any closed surface S inside the conductor, $\mathbf{E} \cdot d\mathbf{A}$ is zero everywhere on S because $\mathbf{E}$ is zero, and the integral in Gauss' law is zero. Accordingly, the net charge contained within S is also zero. Since this is true for any closed surface within the metal, it must be true that there is no net charge anyplace inside the metal. *Any net charge at rest on any solid conductor must therefore reside on its surface.*

Suppose now that the conductor is hollow rather than solid. Again the field within the conductor itself is zero, so that $\mathbf{E} \cdot d\mathbf{A}$ vanishes everywhere on the Gaussian surface S' that encloses the cavity. Thus there can be no net charge within S' (Fig. 16.55*b*).

A simple experiment using a hollow conductor shows some interesting consequences of this fact. When we introduce an object carrying a charge $+Q$ through a small opening into a cavity, an opposite charge $-Q$ must appear on the inner surface of the conductor to balance or neutralize it. (This must happen or the field in the conductor would be nonzero, since the Gaussian surface surrounding the cavity would contain a net, nonzero charge). If the conductor as a whole was initially electrically neutral, it follows that a charge $+Q$ will now be present on its outer surface (Fig. 16.55*c*). If we finally touch the object carrying the charge $+Q$ to the inside of the conductor, the charges $+Q$ and $-Q$ exactly neutralize. When the object is withdrawn, all the charge $+Q$ will reside on the outside of the conductor (Fig. 16.55*d*).

Field Near a Conductor | The field at the surface of a conductor must be perpendicular to the surface when all the charges are at rest. This follows because if the field had a component parallel to the surface, electrons would tend to move. The field is zero inside the conductor. Thus if we draw a small, flat Gaussian cylinder as in Fig. 16.56, the field is zero on its inner end, normal to its outer end,

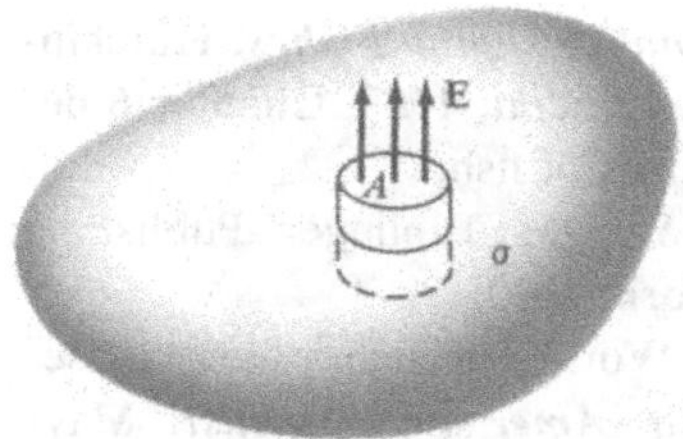

Figure 16.56. The field at the surface of a conductor is perpendicular to the surface on the outside and zero inside. Shown is a tiny cylindrical Gaussian surface. The cylinder is supposed to be small enough so that no matter what the actual shape of the surface, the field is perpendicular to the outer surface and parallel to the sides.

and parallel to its sides. The charge contained in the cylinder is σA, so Gauss' law becomes

$$EA = 4\pi k \sigma A$$

$$E = 4\pi k \sigma \quad \text{(field just outside conductor)} \quad (16.30)$$

This is the field just outside a charged conductor of any shape. It is exactly *double* the field $2\pi k\sigma$ derived for a uniformly charged plane. The difference is that here all the field lines go through a single end of the Gaussian cylinder, rather than just half of the lines. The field is zero inside the conductor, and twice as large outside.

EXERCISES ON SUPPLEMENTARY TOPICS

Section 16.12 | Gauss' Law

16-94 A hollow metallic sphere has an outer radius b and an inner radius a. The total charge on the sphere is Q. Find the electric field for (a) $r > b$; (b) $a < r < b$; (c) $r < a$.

16-95 Two concentric thin conducting spherical shells have radii a and $2a$. The inner sphere has a charge $-Q$ and the outer has a charge $+Q$. Find the magnitude and direction of the field for (a) $r > 2a$; (b) $a < r < 2a$; (c) $r < a$.

16-96 According to the modern view of the atom, its positive charge is contained in a small nucleus. A lead nucleus contains 82 protons and is a sphere of radius 7×10^{-15} m. (a) What is the electric field at the surface of the nucleus? (b) The early Thomson model assumed the positive charge was spread over the entire atom, or over a sphere of radius 10^{-10} m. Ignoring the effects of the electrons, what would the field be at the suface of the atom according to this model?

16-97 A sphere of radius 0.1 m is uniformly charged. Its total charge is 10^{-4} C. (a) Where does the electric field have its greatest magnitude? (b) How large is that maximum field? (c) At what two distances from the center is the field half its maximum magnitude?

16-98 A long thin cylindrical metallic shell has a radius R. It has a charge per unit area σ. (a) What is the charge per unit length on the cylinder? (b) What is the electric field outside the cylinder? (c) What is the field inside the cylinder?

16-99 A cube of side a has a cube of side $a/2$ centered within it. The inner cube has a total charge Q that is uniformly distributed over its surface. (a) For the surface of the outer cube, find

$$\oint_S \mathbf{E} \cdot d\mathbf{A}$$

(b) Is this sufficient information to find the electric field at points on the surface of the outer cube? Explain.

16-100 A thin spherical shell of radius r_1 has a net charge per unit area σ_1. A larger concentric spherical shell of radius r_2 has a net charge per unit area σ_2. If the field outside the larger shell is zero, what is the ratio of σ_2 to σ_1?

Section 16.13 | Gauss' Law and Conductors

16-101 Show that Eq. 16.30 for the field just outside a charged conductor agrees with the formula for the field of a charged conducting sphere, kQ/r^2.

16-102 A hollow metal sphere has radii a and $0.8a$ and has no net charge. A charge Q is introduced through a small hole and placed at the center of the sphere. Find the charge per unit area on (a) the inner surface of the sphere; (b) the outer surface. (c) If Q were placed not in the center but elsewhere within the cavity, what can be said about the induced charge distribution on each surface?

16-103 When a conducting wire is connected to the terminals of a battery, there is a current in the wire. Do the remarks in Section 16.13 concerning the fields and charge distributions in conductors apply? Explain.

PROBLEMS ON SUPPLEMENTARY TOPICS

[c]**16-104** A thin metallic sphere has an outer radius R_1 and a total charge Q. A larger concentric metallic sphere has an inner radius R_2 and a total charge $-Q$. (a) Show that the magnitude of the potential difference between them is

$$V = kQ\left[\frac{1}{R_1} - \frac{1}{R_2}\right]$$

(b) Find the capacitance of the two spheres.

[c]**16-105** Find the potential at the center of a uniformly charged solid sphere of radius R and total charge Q.

[c]**16-106** A thin metallic cylinder has an outer radius R_1 and a charge per unit length λ. A larger concentric metallic cylinder has an inner radius R_2 and a charge per unit length $-\lambda$. (a) Show that the magnitude of the potential difference between them is $V = 2k\lambda\ln(R_2/R_1)$. (b) Find the capacitance per unit length of the cylinders, $C = \lambda/V$.

[c]**16-107** An infinitely long uniformly charged cylinder has a charge per unit length λ and a radius R. (a) Find the electric field outside the cylinder. (b) Show that inside the cylinder $E = 2k\lambda r/R^2$. [*Hint*: Use a concentric cylinder as a Gaussian surface.]

*[c]**16-108** A sphere of radius R has a charge distribution that is linear in the distance from the center. This means that its charge per unit volume ρ is given by $\rho = Cr$. (a) Find the total charge inside the sphere. (b) Find the electric field inside the sphere.

Additional Reading

R. E. Orville, The Lightning Discharge, *Physics Teacher*, vol. 14, 1976, p. 7.

R. M. Alexander, *Functional Design in Fishes*, Hutchinson University Library, London, 1967. Chapter 6 describes the electrical senses of fish.

Robert Burton, *Animal Senses*, Taplinger Publishing Company, Inc., New York, 1970.

R. H. Bullock, Seeing the World Through a New Sense: Electroreception in Fish, *American Scientist*, May/June 1973, p. 316.

Carl D. Hopkins, Electric Communication in Fish, *American Scientist*, July/August 1974, p. 426.

R. T. Cox, Electric Fish, *American Journal of Physics*, vol. 11, 1943, p. 13.

Russell K. Hobbie, The Electrocardiogram as an Example of Electrostatics, *American Journal of Physics*, vol. 41, 1973, p. 824.

Donald M. Burland and Lawrence B. Schein, Physics of Electrophotography, *Physics Today*, May 1986, p. 46.

Scientific American articles:

George Shiers, Ferdinand Brown and the Cathode Ray Tube, March 1974, p. 92.

H. Kondo, Michael Faraday, October 1953, p. 90.

A. D. Moore, Electrostatics, March 1972, p. 46.

Donald M. Trotter, Jr., Capacitors, July 1988, p. 86.

Herbert A. Pohl, Nonuniform Electric Fields, December 1960, p. 106.

C. Andrave Bassett, Electrical Effects in Bone, October 1965, p. 18.

L. B. Loeb, The Mechanism of Lightning, January 1949, p. 22.

Earle R. Williams, The Electrification of Thunderstorms, November 1988, p. 88.

A. A. Few, Thunder, July 1975, p. 80.

J. E. McDonald, The Earth's Electricity, April 1953, p. 32.

Harry Grundfest, Electric Fishes, October 1960, p. 115.

H. W. Lissman, Electric Location by Fishes, March 1963, p. 50.

H. B. Steinback, Animal Electricity, February 1950, p. 40.

CHAPTER 17
DIRECT CURRENTS

Most applications of electricity and magnetism involve moving charges, or *electric currents*, in conductors. Direct currents (dc) are produced when a conducting path exists between the terminals of a battery or a dc generator. These devices tend to maintain a constant potential difference between their terminals and convert other kinds of energy, such as chemical or mechanical energy, into electrical energy. An alternating current (ac) is produced by an ac generator, which has a terminal potential difference that alternates in sign at some characteristic frequency. Many of the ideas we consider in this chapter can be applied immediately or with minor changes to alternating currents as well as to direct currents.

We begin this chapter by defining *electric current* and *resistance*. We then consider sources of energy and the transformation of energy in circuits. In the remaining sections, we discuss methods of analyzing complex circuits, electrical meters, the charging of a capacitor through a resistor, and electrical safety.

17.1 | ELECTRIC CURRENT

The *electric current* in a wire is the rate at which charge moves in the wire. For example, in Fig. 17.1, charges move through a conducting wire under the influence of an applied electric field. If a net charge ΔQ crosses the shaded cross-sectional area in a time Δt, the *average current* is

$$\bar{I} = \frac{\Delta Q}{\Delta t} \tag{17.1}$$

and the *instantaneous current* is

$$I = \frac{dQ}{dt} \tag{17.2}$$

The S.I. current unit is the *ampere* (A). Often it is convenient to use the *milliampere* (mA); 1 mA = 10^{-3} A. From the definition, it follows that an ampere is a coulomb per second. (The ampere is defined by the magnetic force between two currents under specified conditions. This, in turn, defines the coulomb. See Section 19.8.) The definition of current is used in the following example taken from electrochemistry.

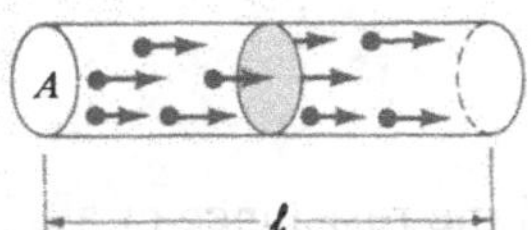

Figure 17.1. A segment of a conducting wire. Charges enter through the left end and leave through the right end.

Example 17.1

An electrochemical cell consists of two silver electrodes placed in an aqueous solution of silver nitrate. A constant 0.5-A current is passed through the cell for 1 hour. (a) Find the total charge transported through the cell in coulombs and in multiples of the electronic charge. (b) Each electron reaching the cell discharges one positively charged silver ion, which is then deposited on the negative electrode (cathode). What is the total mass of the deposited silver? (The atomic mass of silver is 107.9 u.)

(a) Since the current is constant,

$$\Delta Q = I\,\Delta t = (0.5\text{ A})(1\text{ h}) = (0.5\text{ C s}^{-1})(3600\text{ s}) = 1800\text{ C}$$

The ratio of ΔQ to the electronic charge is

$$N = \frac{\Delta Q}{e} = \frac{1800\ \text{C}}{1.60 \times 10^{-19}\ \text{C}} = 1.13 \times 10^{22}$$

This is the number of silver ions transported through the cell and deposited in 1 hour.

(b) The mass of the deposited silver is the number of atoms N times the mass of an atom. Using $1\ \text{u} = 1.66 \times 10^{-27}$ kg,

$$\begin{aligned} m &= (1.13 \times 10^{22})(107.9\ \text{u})(1.66 \times 10^{-27}\ \text{kg u}^{-1}) \\ &= 2.02 \times 10^{-3}\ \text{kg} \end{aligned}$$

Conventionally, the current in a conductor is assumed to be in the direction of motion of positive charges. However, in metallic conductors the moving charges are electrons. In metals, some of the electrons become detached, leaving behind positively charged ions. The heavy ions form a regularly spaced crystalline lattice and vibrate about their equilibrium positions with an energy and an amplitude that increases with the temperature. The detached *conduction electrons* move randomly among the ions. In the absence of an applied electric field, the average charge flow in any direction is zero. When an electric field is applied, the electrons acquire an average *drift velocity* opposite to the field, and there is a net current.

We can relate the current in a wire to the density of conduction electrons and their drift velocity v. If there are n electrons per unit volume, the total number of electrons in a volume V is nV. The segment of wire in Fig. 17.1 has length ℓ and cross-sectional area A, so its volume is $V = \ell A$. Hence there are $n\ell A$ electrons in the wire, with a total charge of magnitude $en\ell A$. The time needed for all of them to pass through the end of the segment shown is $\Delta t = \ell/v$, so the magnitude of the current is

$$I = \frac{\Delta Q}{\Delta t} = \frac{en\ell A}{\ell/v} = enAv \qquad (17.3)$$

The current is the product of the electronic charge, the density of conduction electrons, the area, and the average drift velocity. Note that a positive charge flow in one direction is equivalent to a negative flow in the opposite direction. The following example shows that the drift velocity in a typical metal is surprisingly small.

Example 17.2

Number 12 copper wire is often used to wire household electrical outlets. Its radius is 1 mm = 10^{-3} m. If it carries a current of 10 A, what is the drift velocity of the electrons? (Metallic copper has one conduction electron per atom, the atomic mass of copper is 64 u, and the density of copper is 8900 kg m^{-3}.)

From Eq. 17.3, the drift velocity is $v = I/neA$. We are given the current I, and we can immediately find the area A from the radius of the wire, leaving only the electron density to be found. Since copper has one conduction electron per atom, n equals the number of atoms per unit volume. The number of atoms per unit volume times the mass of one atom M equals the mass of a unit volume of copper, which is its density d. (We will use d here for density rather than ρ as in Chapter Three to avoid confusion with the resistivity ρ defined later.) Thus $nM = d$, or

$$\begin{aligned} n &= \frac{d}{M} = \frac{8900\ \text{kg m}^{-3}}{(64\ \text{u})(1.66 \times 10^{-27}\ \text{kg u}^{-1})} \\ &= 8.38 \times 10^{28}\ \text{m}^{-3} \end{aligned}$$

The drift velocity is then

$$\begin{aligned} v &= \frac{I}{neA} = \frac{I}{ne\pi r^2} \\ &= \frac{10\ \text{A}}{(8.38 \times 10^{28}\ \text{m}^{-3})(1.6 \times 10^{-19}\ \text{C})\pi(10^{-3}\ \text{m})^2} \\ &= 2.37 \times 10^{-4}\ \text{m s}^{-1} \end{aligned}$$

Thus the electrons move very slowly, contrary to what one might have supposed; it takes about 4200 s, or over an hour, for them to move a metre! The average electron thermal velocity at room temperature is about 10^5 m s^{-1}, which is about 10^{10} times the drift velocity. On the other hand, changes in the electric field travel in a wire at nearly the speed of light. This is analogous to the situation in a fluid such as air or water, where the effects of pressure changes travel much faster than the fluid itself.

17.2 | RESISTANCE

In Chapter Fourteen, we defined the resistance of a section of pipe to the flow of a fluid as the pressure difference divided by the flow rate. Similarly, the *electrical resistance R* of a conductor is the poten tial difference V between its ends divided by the current I,

$$R = \frac{V}{I} \qquad (17.4)$$

The S.I. unit for resistance is the *ohm*; an ohm is a volt per ampere.

For many materials, the potential difference and the current are directly proportional, so the resistance is a constant independent of the current. This is illustrated in Fig. 17.2 for a length of copper wire with its ends at an adjustable potential difference V. The current increases linearly with V and reverses direction when V is reversed, so the ratio $R = V/I$ is constant. Materials with a constant resistance are said to obey *Ohm's law* and are called *ohmic conductors*.

The resistance of some conductors varies with the magnitude or direction of the applied potential difference. The operation of many electronic devices, such as vacuum tubes and transistors, is based on their *nonohmic* character (Fig. 17.3). The calculation of the resistance from the definition $R = V/I$ for an ohmic conductor is illustrated by the following example.

Example 17.3

Find the resistance of the wire in Fig. 17.2.

The potential difference and current are proportional, so the resistance is a constant. When the current is 10 A, the potential difference is 1 V, and

$$R = \frac{V}{I} = \frac{1\text{ V}}{10\text{ A}} = 0.1\text{ ohm}$$

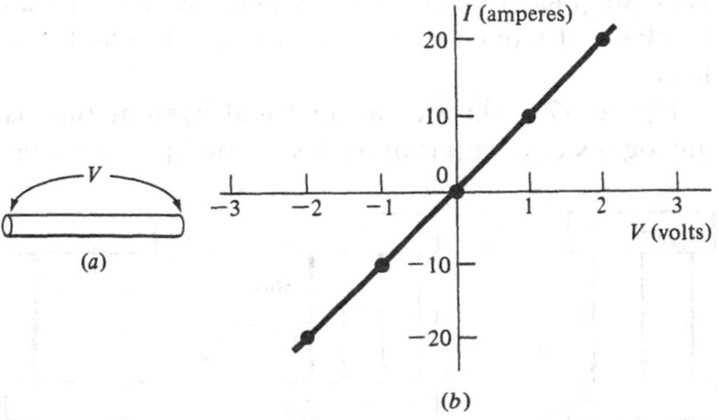

Figure 17.2. (*a*) A copper wire has a variable potential difference V between its ends. (*b*) The current varies linearly with the potential difference in the wire, so it is an ohmic conductor.

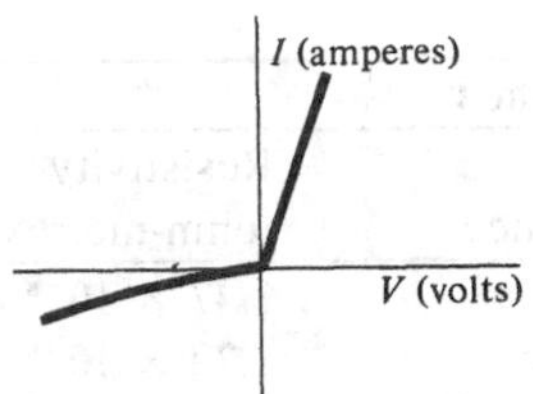

Figure 17.3. The current-versus-potential difference graph for a rectifying transistor. An applied voltage, which produces a large current in one direction, produces only a small current in the opposite direction. This is an example of a conductor that does not satisfy Ohm's law.

The resistance of a conductor depends on its size, shape, and composition. We can understand the size and shape dependence with the following argument. If we put two identical wires side by side, the current doubles and hence the resistance is halved. Thus, R must vary inversely with the cross-sectional area A. Now if we halve the length ℓ, the potential change and hence the resistance are also halved, so R must be proportional to ℓ. Thus we can write the resistance in terms of geometric factors and a constant as

$$R = \frac{\rho \ell}{A} \qquad (17.5)$$

The proportionality constant ρ (rho) depends only on the properties of the material and is called the *resistivity*. The S.I. unit for resistivity is the ohm metre. The *conductivity* σ (Greek letter "sigma"), defined by

$$\sigma = \frac{1}{\rho} \qquad (17.6)$$

is sometimes used instead of the resistivity to characterize conductors. The S.I. unit of conductivity is the $\text{ohm}^{-1}\text{ m}^{-1}$.

Some representative resistivities are listed in Table 17.1. Note the huge range of values: the best insulators have resistivities more than 20 orders of magnitude (powers of 10) greater than the resistivities of good conductors. Very few physical quantities have such enormous variability.

TABLE 17.1
Resistivities at 20°C in ohm-metres

	Substance	Resistivity (ohm-metres)
Conductors	Silver	1.47×10^{-8}
	Copper	1.72×10^{-8}
	Aluminum	2.63×10^{-8}
Semiconductors	Germanium	0.60
	Silicon	2300
Insulators	Sulfur	10^{15}
	Glass	10^{10}–10^{14}
Ionic conductors	Body fluids	approx. 0.15

The calculation of the resistance of a wire is illustrated by the following example.

Example 17.4

Find the room temperature resistance of a copper wire 100 m long with a radius of 1 mm = 10^{-3} m.

According to Table 17.1, the resistivity of copper at room temperature (20° C) is 1.72×10^{-8} ohm m. Hence the resistance of this wire is

$$R = \frac{\rho \ell}{A} = \frac{\rho \ell}{\pi r^2}$$

$$= \frac{(1.72 \times 10^{-8}\text{ ohm m})(100\text{ m})}{\pi (10^{-3}\text{ m})^2}$$

$$= 0.547\text{ ohm}$$

17.3 | ENERGY SOURCES IN CIRCUITS

A nonelectrical source of energy, such as a battery or a generator, is needed to maintain a continuous current in a closed conducting path, or *circuit*. Such an energy source is called a *source of EMF*, which is short for the archaic term electromotive force. EMF, as we define it below, has the dimensions of potential, not force.

To clarify the role of an EMF in a circuit, consider the analogous situation of water moving under the influence of gravitational forces. Figure 17.4 shows an artificial stream and waterfall constructed for decorative purposes in a garden. Water drops over the falls a vertical distance h, so that the gravitational potential energy of a mass m decreases by mgh. This energy is converted into kinetic energy as the water accelerates and is then transformed into heat $Q = mgh$ as the water splashes among the rocks in the falls. If no water is supplied to the beginning of the stream, the flow stops almost immediately. However, water is returned to the stream by a pump, which does work $W = mgh$ on the water against the gravitational force. The conservative gravitational force does positive work equal to mgh on the water as it falls and negative work $-mgh$ as it rises. These exactly cancel, so the conservative gravitational force does no net work when the water goes completely around the system. The energy W supplied by the pump exactly equals the heat energy Q generated in the falls. Note that if we introduced a waterwheel connected to a machine into the falling stream, then some of the energy supplied by the pump would be used to do mechanical work rather than being converted into heat.

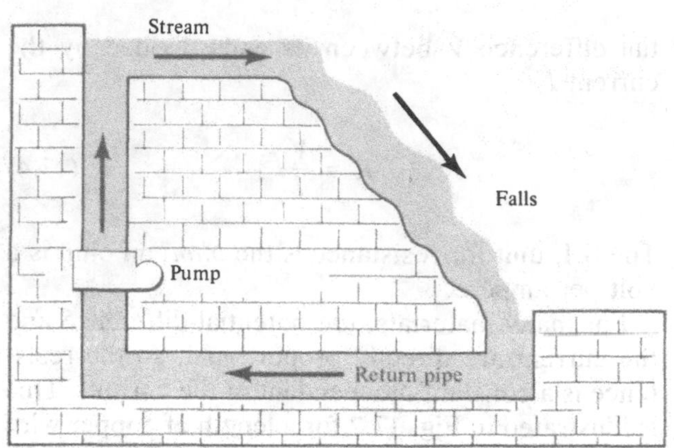

Figure 17.4. The work done by the pump equals the energy dissipated as heat in the falls. The conservative gravitational force does no net work on water that goes completely around the system.

Figure 17.5 shows an electrical system that is analogous to a waterfall *without* a pump. Two con-

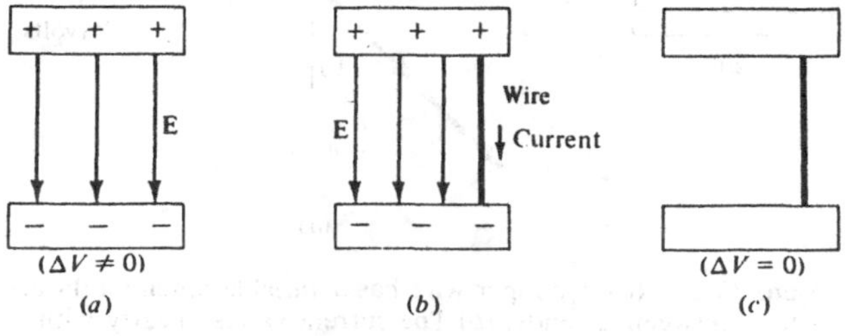

Figure 17.5. The electrical analog to a falls without a pump.

ductors have equal and opposite charges, so there is a potential difference between them. When they are connected by a metal wire, there is a brief charge flow, which stops when the charges are neutralized and the potential difference is reduced to zero.

To maintain a steady current, a *pump* or source of EMF must supply energy. In Fig. 17.6, a battery is connected to a resistor by wires that are perfect conductors. As a charge goes through the battery, it is *pumped* by nonelectric forces to a position of higher potential energy. The energy required for this is supplied by chemical reactions occurring in the battery. In the resistor, the charge moves in the direction of the electric force, and the kinetic energy it acquires is transformed into heat. The conservative electric field does positive work in the resistor, negative work in the battery, and zero net work when a charge goes completely around the circuit. The net effect of the various energy transfers is that stored chemical energy in the battery is transformed into heat in the resistor. This is completely analogous to the energy supplied by the pump, which is converted into heat in the waterfall.

Two other aspects of the analogy should be noted. The resistor can be replaced in the circuit by some other *load*, such as an electric motor. Then the chemical energy of the battery is converted into mechanical energy, just as the energy supplied by the pump is used to do mechanical work if a waterwheel is introduced. Also, just as the pump supplied energy but did not alter the original supply of water, the battery cannot produce or destroy charge. Whatever current enters the battery in Fig. 17.6 must leave it, and the current in the resistor and in the connecting wires must also be the same. *A battery or generator converts some other kind of energy into electrical energy, but it is not a source of charge.*

The EMF $\mathscr{E}$ of a battery or generator is defined as the *work done per unit charge by the nonelectric forces*. Its S.I. unit is a joule per coulomb or volt, which is also the unit of the electric potential.

For the circuit of Fig. 17.6, we can relate the current I to the battery EMF $\mathscr{E}$ and to the resistance R by using the potential changes observed as we go completely around the circuit. This is equivalent to finding the potential energy changes for a unit positive charge. Proceeding clockwise, these changes are

From a to b: V *increases* by $\mathscr{E}$ ($\Delta V = \mathscr{E}$); the potential increase in the battery is equal to the EMF.

From b to c: V is constant ($\Delta V = 0$); the potential difference is IR, the current times the resistance, and the resistance is zero for a perfect conductor.

From c to d: V *decreases* by IR ($\Delta V = -IR$).

From d to a: V is constant ($\Delta V = 0$); again, no potential change occurs in a perfect conductor.

When a charge goes around a closed path and returns to the starting point, its potential energy must return to its original value, since the conservative electric forces do no net work. Thus the sum of

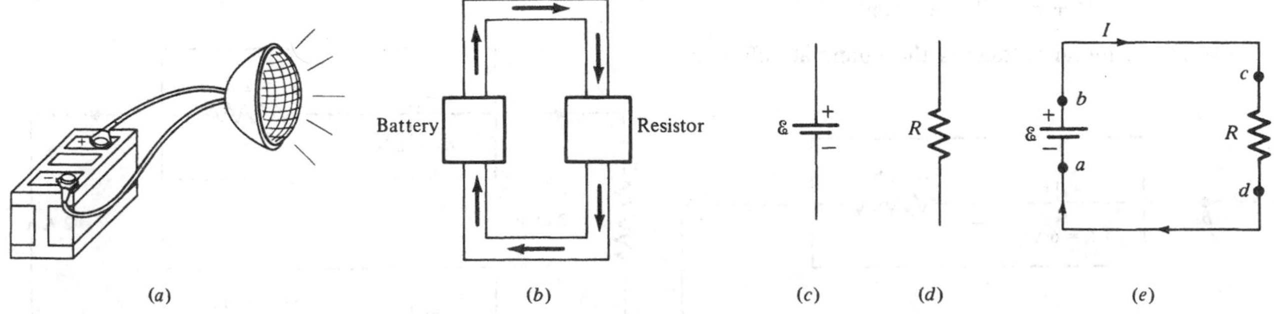

Figure 17.6. (*a*) An automobile battery connected to a headlight by low-resistance wires. (*b*) This circuit can be idealized as a battery connected to a resistor by perfectly conducting wires. (*c*) The symbol for an EMF used in circuit diagrams. The longer line and + symbol indicate the higher-potential terminal. (*d*) The symbol for a resistance. (*e*) The circuit redrawn using the conventional symbols.

the potential changes must be zero, or $\mathscr{E} - IR = 0$. Equivalently, the potential increase in the battery must equal the decrease in the resistor:

$$\mathscr{E} = IR \tag{17.7}$$

This result is illustrated by the following example.

Example 17.5

A dry cell with an EMF of 6 V is connected to a light bulb with resistance 4 ohms. Find the current.

With $\mathscr{E} = IR$, the current is

$$I = \frac{\mathscr{E}}{R} = \frac{6 \text{ V}}{4 \text{ ohm}} = 1.5 \text{ A}$$

Real batteries and generators usually have various dissipative effects associated with them that can be thought of as *internal resistances*. These cause the terminal voltages to be different from the EMFs and can result in substantial heat being produced. For example, the electrolytic fluid in storage batteries will boil if the current is large enough. These effects are illustrated in the next two examples.

Example 17.6

A battery with an EMF of 6 V and an internal resistance $r = 2$ ohms is connected to an R = 4-ohm lightbulb (Fig. 17.7). Find (a) the current; (b) the terminal potential difference of the battery.

(a) The potential increase due to the EMF must equal the total of the potential decreases in the resistances, so

$$\mathscr{E} = IR + Ir$$

and

$$I = \frac{\mathscr{E}}{R + r} = \frac{6 \text{ V}}{(2 + 4) \text{ ohm}} = 1 \text{ A}$$

(b) The terminal voltage is the potential difference V_{ab} between points a and b. It equals the EMF minus the potential drop associated with the internal resistance, so

$$V_{ab} = \mathscr{E} - Ir = 6 \text{ V} - (1 \text{ A})(2 \text{ ohm}) = 4 \text{ V}$$

Alternatively, we can obtain the same result from

$$V_{ab} = IR = (1 \text{ A})(4 \text{ ohm}) = 4 \text{ V}$$

We see that the terminal potential difference of a real battery is different from its EMF when there is a current.

Example 17.7

Two batteries are connected to a resistor as shown in Fig. 17.8. Find (a) the current; (b) the terminal potential difference of each battery.

(a) Since the batteries are connected so that their polarities are opposite, the direction of the current is determined by the larger EMF and is counterclockwise in Fig. 17.8. As we follow the current through the larger EMF, the potential *increases* by $\mathscr{E}_2$, and in the other EMF the potential *decreases* by $\mathscr{E}_1$. The current is found from

$$\mathscr{E}_2 - \mathscr{E}_1 = I(r_1 + r_2 + R)$$

Thus

$$I = \frac{\mathscr{E}_2 - \mathscr{E}_1}{r_1 + r_2 + R} = \frac{(18 - 6) \text{ V}}{(2 + 1 + 3) \text{ ohm}} = 2 \text{ A}$$

(b) The potential differences across the batteries are

$$V_{ab} = \mathscr{E}_2 - Ir_2 = 18 \text{ V} - (2 \text{ A})(1 \text{ ohm}) = 16 \text{ V}$$
$$V_{dc} = \mathscr{E}_1 + Ir_1 = 6 \text{ V} + (2 \text{ A})(2 \text{ ohm}) = 10 \text{ V}$$

Note that the terminal potential difference V_{dc} is greater than the EMF in this case. In calculating the potential difference between points c and d, we are

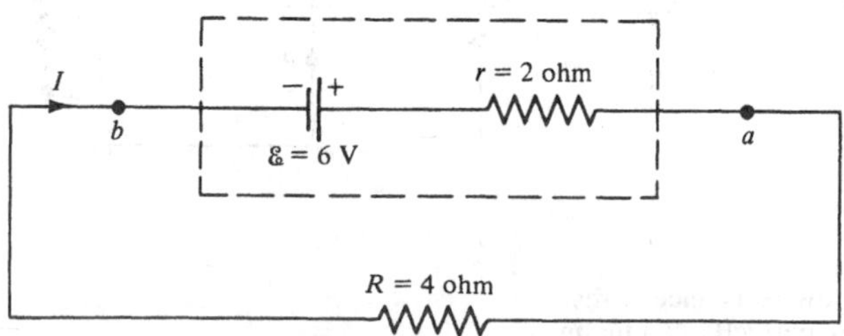

Figure 17.7. The terminal voltage of the battery is less than the EMF here because of the internal resistance.

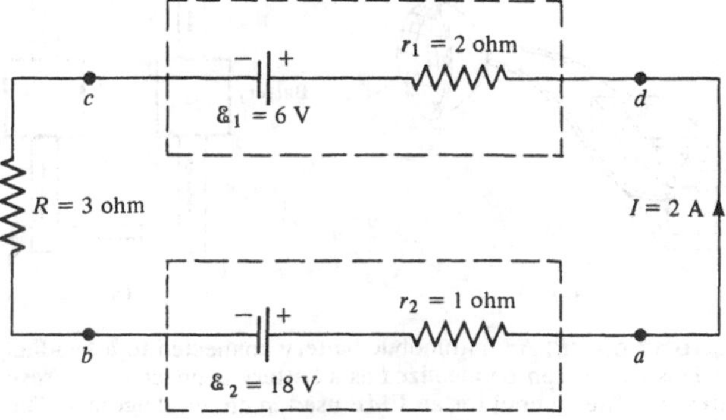

Figure 17.8. Examples 17.7 and 17.8.

proceeding opposite to the current. Thus we see a potential *rise* in the resistance as well as in the EMF. The terminal potential difference exceeds the EMF only when the current is driven "backward" through the battery by another larger EMF.

17.4 | POWER IN ELECTRICAL CIRCUITS

In a circuit, energy is initially converted from some other form by a battery or a generator into electrical potential energy. It is then transformed in the load into heat, mechanical work, or some other kind of energy. In this section, we calculate the power or rate of energy conversion for various parts of a circuit.

Figure 17.9 shows a *circuit element* (one part of a circuit) with a potential difference V across its terminals and a current I through it. If the element is a battery, V is the terminal voltage; if it is a resistance R, then V is equal to IR in magnitude. In a time Δt, a charge $\Delta Q = I\,\Delta t$ passes through the element. Its change in potential energy is $V\,\Delta Q = VI\,\Delta t$, which must equal the work ΔW done by the element on the charge. Dividing this work by the time Δt and taking the limit as Δt approaches zero, the power in any circuit element is

$$\mathcal{P} = \frac{dW}{dt} = IV \qquad \text{(any circuit element)} \qquad (17.8)$$

If the current is in the direction of increasing potential, the circuit element supplies energy. When the current is in the direction of decreasing V, as in a resistor or a motor, the element receives or dissipates energy. For an EMF, the potential difference is $\mathscr{E}$, so

$$\mathcal{P} = I\mathscr{E} \qquad \text{(EMF)} \qquad (17.9)$$

For a resistor, $V = IR$, and

$$\mathcal{P} = I^2R \qquad \text{(resistor)} \qquad (17.10)$$

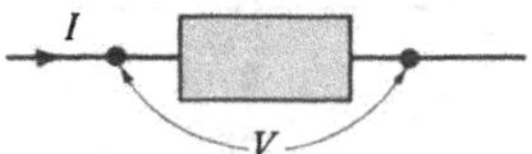

Figure 17.9. A circuit element is one part, such as a battery or resistor, of a complete circuit.

In any electrical circuit, the power supplied is always equal to the power dissipated, unless a capacitor or other device that can store energy is present. These ideas are illustrated by the following example.

Example 17.8

Calculate the power supplied to or by each element in the circuit of Fig. 17.8.

In the larger battery, the EMF supplies power $I\mathscr{E}_2$, and the internal resistance dissipates heat at the rate I^2r_2. Thus the net power *supplied* by this battery is

$$\begin{aligned}\mathcal{P}_2 &= I\mathscr{E}_2 - I^2r_2\\ &= (2\text{ A})(18\text{ V}) - (2\text{ A})^2(1\text{ ohm})\\ &= 32\text{ W}\end{aligned}$$

The other battery has *work done on it* by the current, since the charge is moving from the high-potential terminal to the low-potential side. Thus the power *absorbed* by this battery is

$$\begin{aligned}\mathcal{P}_1 &= I\mathscr{E}_1 + I^2r_1\\ &= (2\text{ A})(6\text{ V}) + (2\text{ A})^2(2\text{ ohm})\\ &= 20\text{ W}\end{aligned}$$

Finally the resistor R generates heat at the rate

$$\mathcal{P}_R = I^2R = (2\text{ A})^2(3\text{ ohm}) = 12\text{ W}$$

Note that the power supplied by the larger battery equals the power dissipated in R plus the power absorbed by the smaller battery. This is just the energy conservation law in another form.

Electric utilities charge their customers for the electrical energy used, which is the product of the electrical power and the time. Electrical energy is usually sold by the kilowatt-hour (kW h). This is a kilowatt of power for 1 hour, so

$$\begin{aligned}1\text{ kW h} &= (10^3\text{ W})(3600\text{ s})\\ &= 3.6 \times 10^6\text{ J}\end{aligned} \qquad (17.11)$$

Most household electrical power in North America is equivalent to 120 V dc, but is actually alternating current at a frequency of 60 Hz. As we see in Chapter Twenty, for resistive current and power calculations, an *effective* voltage of 120 V ac is the same as 120 V dc. The calculation of the cost of operating a typical electrical device is illustrated by the following example.

Example 17.9

For a household 60-W light bulb operated at 120 V, find (a) the current; (b) the resistance; (c) the 24-hour operating cost, if energy costs 10 cents per kilowatt hour.

(a) Since the power $\mathcal{P}$ in any circuit element equals VI,

$$I = \frac{\mathcal{P}}{V} = \frac{60 \text{ W}}{120 \text{ V}} = 0.5 \text{ A}$$

(b) The resistance is

$$R = \frac{V}{I} = \frac{120 \text{ V}}{0.5 \text{ A}} = 240 \text{ ohm}$$

(c) The bulb uses power at the rate of 60 W, or 0.060 kW. Thus the cost of operating it for 24 hours is

$$(0.06 \text{ kW})(24 \text{ h})[10¢ \text{ (kW h)}^{-1}] = 14.4¢$$

17.5 | SERIES AND PARALLEL RESISTORS; KIRCHHOFF'S RULES

Looking inside a television set or stereo, one quickly discovers that circuits are often quite complex. Nevertheless, the most complex dc circuit can be analyzed to find the currents and voltages at each point using two basic rules formulated by Kirchhoff. These rules can also be generalized to deal with ac circuits. Here we show how they can be used to simplify the discussion of circuits containing certain combinations of resistors.

The first rule is already familiar, and follows from the conservative nature of electric forces:

(*1*) *The sum of the potential changes around any closed path is zero.*

The second rule is a restatement of another basic idea, charge conservation. Suppose a current divides into two or more currents at a point where a number of wires come together. No charge can be lost or created nor can it collect at that point. Consequently,

(2) *The current entering any point must equal the current leaving.*

We can use Kirchhoff's rules to discuss series and parallel combinations of resistors. Two or more

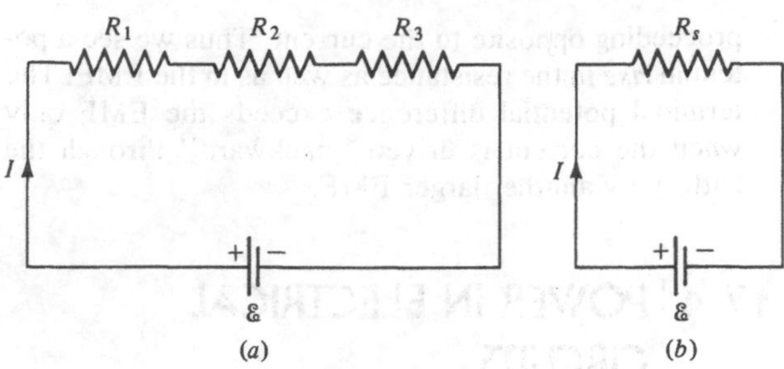

Figure 17.10. (*a*) Three resistors in series. (*b*) The equivalent resistance R_s leads to the same current I.

resistors are in *series* if the same current goes through each (Fig. 17.10). According to the first rule, the sum of the potential changes around the circuit is zero, or

$$\mathcal{E} - IR_1 - IR_2 - IR_3 = 0$$

Thus

$$I = \frac{\mathcal{E}}{R_1 + R_2 + R_3}$$

A single *equivalent resistance* R_s connected to the battery will produce the same current if $I = \mathcal{E}/R_s$, or

$$R_s = R_1 + R_2 + R_3 + \cdots \qquad (17.12)$$

Two or more resistors are in *parallel* if they have a common potential difference (Fig. 17.11.) According to the second rule, the current entering point a must equal that leaving, or

$$I = I_1 + I_2 + I_3$$

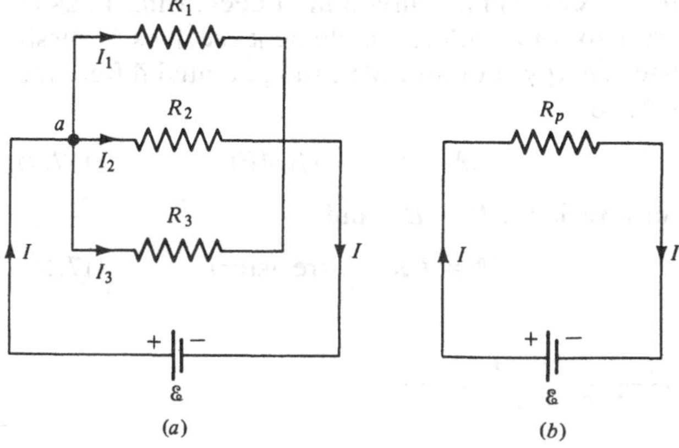

Figure 17.11. (*a*) Three resistors in parallel. (*b*) The equivalent single resistance R_p produces the same current I.

Applying $I = \mathscr{E}/R$ to each resistor,

$$I_1 = \frac{\mathscr{E}}{R_1}, \quad I_2 = \frac{\mathscr{E}}{R_2}, \quad \text{and} \quad I_3 = \frac{\mathscr{E}}{R_3}$$

Hence

$$I = \frac{\mathscr{E}}{R_1} + \frac{\mathscr{E}}{R_2} + \frac{\mathscr{E}}{R_3}$$

A single equivalent resistance R_p will produce the same current I if

$$I = \frac{\mathscr{E}}{R_p}$$

Comparing, we see that

$$\frac{1}{R_p} = \frac{1}{R_1} + \frac{1}{R_2} + \frac{1}{R_3} + \cdots \qquad (17.13)$$

The following example illustrates how the series and parallel formulas may sometimes be used together in analyzing a complex arrangement of resistors.

Example 17.10

(a) Find the equivalent resistance of the resistors in Fig. 17.12*a*. (b) Find the current in each resistor.

(a) The current I splits at point a into two currents, I_1 and I_2. I_1 goes through each of the 1-ohm resistors, so they are in series. Their equivalent resistance is then

$$R_s = 1 \text{ ohm} + 1 \text{ ohm} + 1 \text{ ohm} = 3 \text{ ohm}$$

This reduces the circuit to two parallel 3-ohm resistors (Fig. 17.12*b*). The effective resistance of the entire system is found from

$$\frac{1}{R_p} = \frac{1}{3 \text{ ohm}} + \frac{1}{3 \text{ ohm}} = \frac{2}{3 \text{ ohm}}$$

Thus

$$R_p = 1.5 \text{ ohm}$$

as shown in Fig. 17.12*c*.

(b) The current I in the battery is found using the equivalent resistance of the system, 1.5 ohm. Thus

$$I = \frac{\mathscr{E}}{R} = \frac{6 \text{ V}}{1.5 \text{ ohm}} = 4 \text{ A}$$

In Fig. 17.12*b*, the voltage drop across each resistor must be the same. Since their resistances are equal, the current in each must also be the same. Hence each current is half the total, or

$$I_1 = I_2 = \tfrac{1}{2}I = \tfrac{1}{2}(4 \text{ A}) = 2 \text{ A}$$

The current in each resistor is 2 A.

Some circuits cannot be analyzed by use of the series and parallel formulas, and Kirchhoff's rules must be applied directly. We show how this is done in Section 17.12.

17.6 | VOLTMETERS AND AMMETERS

The most basic dc measuring instruments are the *voltmeter* and the *ammeter*, which measure potential differences and currents, respectively. Each of these contains a *galvanometer*, which consists of a coil of wire suspended near a magnet. The coil is attached to a spring, which opposes rotational motion. When there is a current in the coil, the magnetic force on the moving charges causes the coil to rotate by an amount proportional to the current. Typically, a few milliamperes will cause full-scale deflection, and the resistance of the coil is about 10 to 100 ohms.

Figure 17.13 illustrates how a voltmeter and an ammeter are used. To measure the potential difference across a circuit element, the *voltmeter is connected in parallel* with that element. According to the parallel resistance formula, the voltmeter resistance must be large compared to that of the element

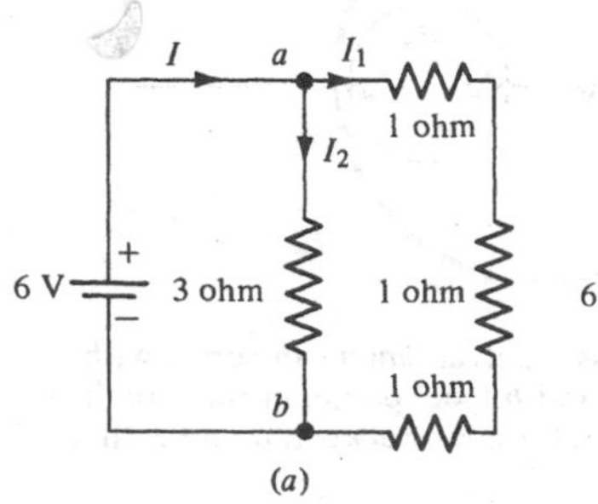

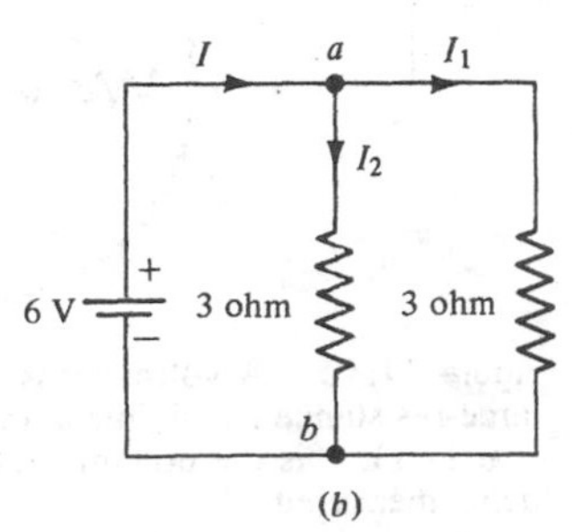

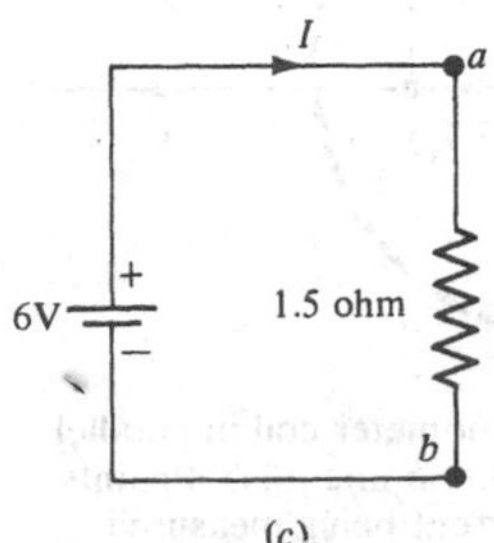

Figure 17.12. (*a*) The complete network. (*b*) The simplified equivalent network obtained using the series resistance formula. (*c*) The final equivalent network obtained with the parallel resistance formula.

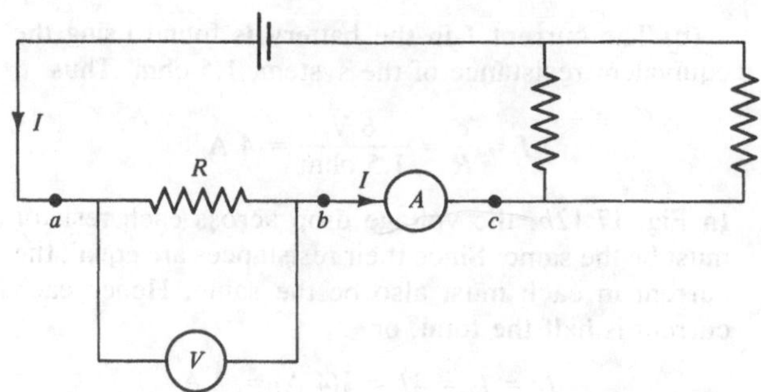

Figure 17.13. The voltmeter V is placed in parallel with the resistor R and indicates the potential difference across R. The ammeter A is in series with R and gives the current through R.

to avoid large changes in the current in the circuit. To measure the current in an element, the *ammeter is inserted in series* with the element. Consequently, from the series resistance formula, the ammeter resistance must be small to minimize current changes.

To construct an ammeter, we connect a small resistance r in parallel with a galvanometer coil (Fig. 17.14). If the circuit has a current I, only a small part of the current, I_g, goes through the relatively high-resistance galvanometer coil. The remaining current, $I - I_g$, goes through r. Since the potential drop across the galvanometer and the parallel resistor must be the same, it follows that

$$I_g R_g = (I - I_g)r \tag{17.14}$$

The choice of r is determined by the desired range of the ammeter. This is illustrated in the following example.

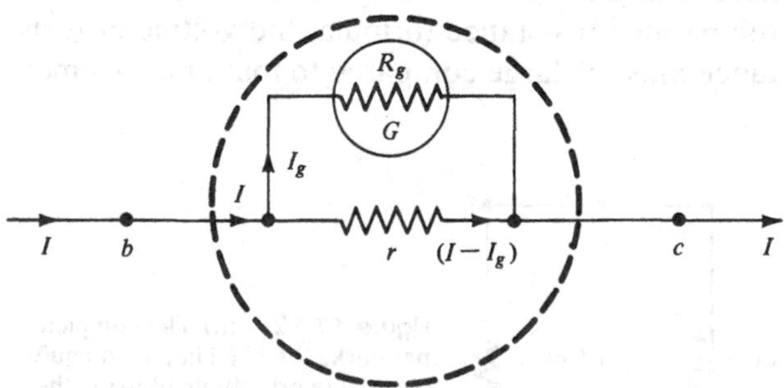

Figure 17.14. An ammeter is a galvanometer coil in parallel with a small resistance r. The two points b and c label points in the circuit of Fig. 17.13. I is the current being measured.

Example 17.11

A galvanometer with a resistance of 100 ohms gives a full-scale deflection for a current of 1 mA. (a) How large a parallel resistor is needed to convert it into an ammeter with a 20-A range? (b) What is the ammeter resistance?

(a) Using Eq. 17.14,

$$r = \frac{R_g I_g}{I - I_g} = \frac{(100 \text{ ohm})(0.001 \text{ A})}{20 \text{ A} - 0.001 \text{ A}}$$

Since we are working to three significant figures, the 0.001 A in the denominator can be neglected. Thus

$$r \simeq \frac{(100 \text{ ohm})(0.001 \text{ A})}{20 \text{ A}} = 0.005 \text{ ohm}$$

($\simeq$ means approximately equal.)

(b) Since r is much smaller than R_g, the resistance of the ammeter is very close to r:

$$\frac{1}{R_A} = \frac{1}{r} + \frac{1}{R_g}$$

$$= \frac{1}{0.005 \text{ ohm}} + \frac{1}{100 \text{ ohm}} \simeq \frac{1}{0.005 \text{ ohm}}$$

and $R_A = 0.005$ ohm.

To construct a voltmeter, a large resistance R_s is placed in series with the galvanometer coil (Fig. 17.15). The potential difference V across the voltmeter is

$$V = I_g(R_g + R_s)$$

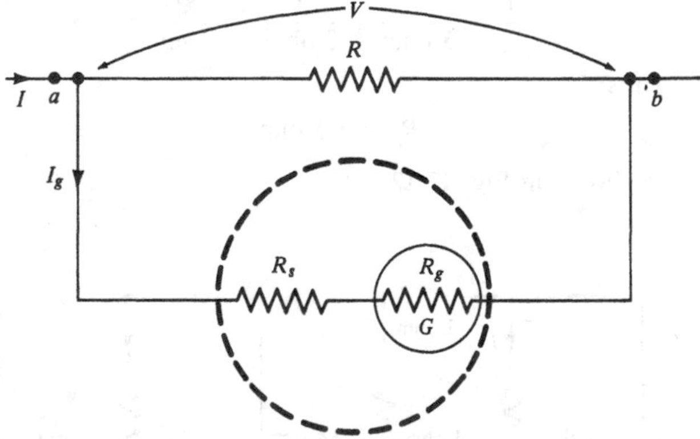

Figure 17.15. A voltmeter is a galvanometer in series with a large-resistance R_s. Points a and b label points in the circuit of Fig. 17.13. V is the potential difference between a and b that is being measured.

so

$$R_s = \frac{V}{I_g} - R_g \tag{17.15}$$

Again the desired range of the meter determines R_s, as is seen in the next example.

Example 17.12

The galvanometer of Example 17.11 has a resistance of 100 ohms and gives a full-scale deflection for a current of 1 mA. (a) How can it be converted into a voltmeter with a 100-V range? (b) What is the voltmeter resistance?

(a) The series resistance needed is

$$R_s = \frac{V}{I_g} - R_g = \frac{100\text{ V}}{0.001\text{ A}} - 100\text{ ohm}$$
$$= (100{,}000 - 100)\text{ ohm} = 99{,}900\text{ ohm}$$

(b) The total voltmeter resistance is

$$R_V = R_s + R_g = 99{,}990\text{ ohm} + 100\text{ ohm}$$
$$= 100{,}000\text{ ohm}$$

17.7 | CIRCUITS CONTAINING RESISTANCE AND CAPACITANCE

If we connect an uncharged capacitor to a battery, charge moves from one capacitor plate to the other through the battery and the connecting wires. This current stops once the potential difference across the capacitor equals the EMF of the battery. Similarly, if the plates of a charged capacitor are connected by a wire, there will be a current in the wire until the capacitor is fully discharged. These short-lived currents are referred to as *transients*. The constant currents we have been discussing until now are referred to as *steady* currents.

We first consider the transient currents associated with charging a capacitor. Fig. 17.16*a* shows a circuit containing an initially uncharged capacitance C, a resistance R, and an EMF $\mathscr{E}$. If at time $t = 0$ the switch is closed, the charge q on the capacitor and the current i in the circuit vary with time as in Fig. 17.16*b* and *c*. As we show below, the time required for either q or i to reach a specific fraction of its final value is proportional to the time constant T given by

$$T = RC \tag{17.16}$$

The greater the resistance or the capacitance, the longer it takes to charge the capacitor. This is physically reasonable, since a larger capacitance requires a larger final charge, and a larger resistance leads to smaller charging currents.

To study this in more detail, we calculate the potential differences across the circuit elements during the charging process. Suppose at time t the charge on the capacitor is q and the current in the circuit is i. Proceeding counterclockwise, there is a potential rise, $\mathscr{E}$, in the EMF, and a drop, iR, in the resistor. For the capacitor, $C = q/V$, so the potential drop is q/C. The sum of these changes is zero. Thus

$$\mathscr{E} - iR - \frac{q}{C} = 0$$

or

$$i = \frac{\mathscr{E}}{R} - \frac{q}{RC} \tag{17.17}$$

This equation directly gives the current i at $t = 0$ and at $t = \infty$. At $t = 0$, when the switch has just been closed, the charge q on the capacitor is its initial value, zero. Thus the current i_0 at $t = 0$ is

$$i_0 = \frac{\mathscr{E}}{R} \quad (t = 0) \tag{17.18}$$

This equals the constant current that would occur if only the resistance and the EMF were connected in

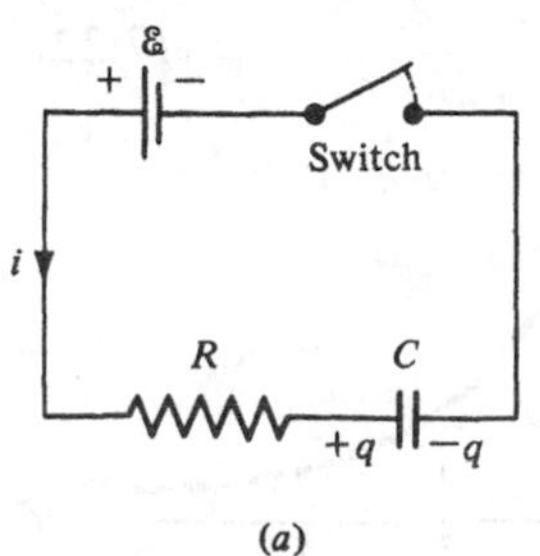

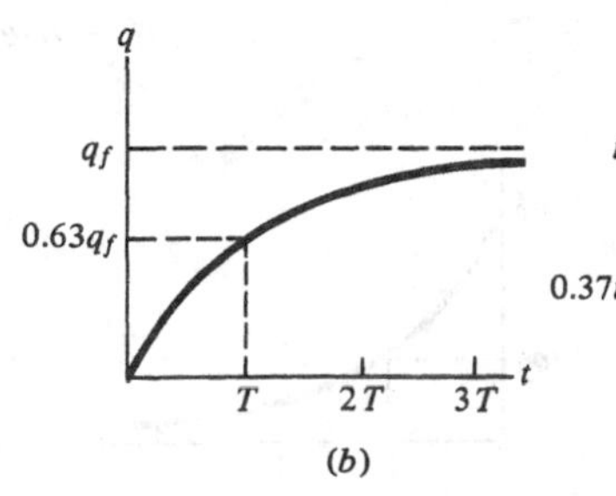

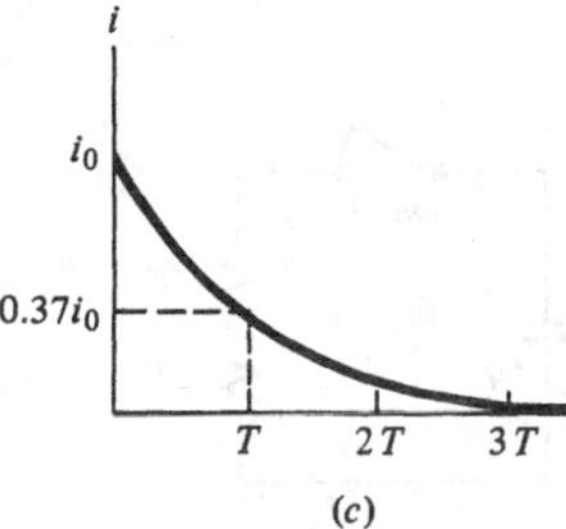

Figure 17.16. (*a*) A circuit containing a resistance, a capacitance, and an EMF. (*b*) and (*c*) If the capacitor is initially uncharged and the switch is closed at time $t = 0$, the charge q and current i vary with the time t as shown. The time constant T is equal to RC.

series. If we wait a long time, the capacitor will be fully charged, and its potential difference must equal the EMF $\mathscr{E}$. The charge q is then

$$q_f = \mathscr{E}C \qquad (t = \infty) \tag{17.19}$$

If we substitute q_f for q in Eq. 17.17, we find that the current is zero. As expected, once the capacitor is fully charged, the current ceases.

We now find the charge and current as functions of time. First, using $i = dq/dt$, we rewrite Eq. 17.17 as

$$RC\frac{dq}{dt} - \mathscr{E}C + q = 0 \tag{17.20}$$

The simplest way to solve this equation is to write down the solution for q and verify that it is correct. Thus we take

$$q(t) = \mathscr{E}C(1 - e^{-t/RC})$$

Here e is the base of natural logarithms, and has the value 2.718. . . (see Appendix B for a discussion of the exponential function). Note that at $t = 0$, $q = 0$, and that when $t = \infty$, $q = \mathscr{E}C$, as required. Now according to Eq. B.25 from Appendix B, $(d/dt)e^{-at} = -ae^{-at}$. Thus differentiating the charge, we obtain the current

$$i = \frac{dq}{dt} = \mathscr{E}C\frac{1}{RC}e^{-t/RC} = \frac{\mathscr{E}}{R}e^{-t/RC}$$

Now if we substitute these expressions for q and dq/dt into the left side of Eq. 17.20, we obtain

$$\mathscr{E}Ce^{-t/RC} - \mathscr{E}C + \mathscr{E}C\,(1 - e^{-t/RC})$$

Since these add up to zero, we have found a correct solution.

Using $i_0 = \mathscr{E}R$, $q_f = \mathscr{E}C$, and $T = RC$, our formulas for q and i can be rewritten as

$$q(t) = q_f(1 - e^{-t/T})$$
$$i(t) = i_0e^{-t/T} \tag{17.21}$$

Note that when $t = T$, $e^{-t/T} = e^{-1} = 1/2.718\ldots = 0.37\ldots$ Thus, after one time constant has elapsed, the current has dropped to about 37 percent of its initial value i_0. Also, since

$$1 - e^{-1} = 1 - 0.37\ldots = 0.63\ldots$$

after a time T has elapsed, $q = 0.63q_f$. That means the capacitor charge is equal to approximately 63 percent of its final charge q_f. Alternatively, we can say it is within 37 percent of its final value. When the elapsed time is equal to twice the time constant, $e^{-t/T} = e^{-2} = 0.14\ldots$ At this time the charge is $(1 - 0.14)q_f = 0.86q_f$, and the current is $0.14i_0$. After a time equal to several time constants, the charge q and current i are very close to their final values, as is seen in Fig. 17.16. The calculation of some of these quantities is illustrated by the following example.

Example 17.13

In Fig. 17.16, $C = 2\ \mu$F, $R = 1000$ ohm, and $\mathscr{E} = 6$ V. Find (a) the final charge on the capacitor; (b) the initial current; (c) the time constant.

(a) The final charge is

$$q_f = \mathscr{E}C = (6 \text{ V})(2 \times 10^{-6} \text{ F}) = 1.2 \times 10^{-5} \text{ C}$$

(b) The initial current is

$$i_0 = \frac{\mathscr{E}}{R} = \frac{6 \text{ V}}{1000 \text{ ohm}} = 6 \times 10^{-3} \text{ A}$$

(c) The time constant is

$$T = RC = (1000 \text{ ohm})(2 \times 10^{-6} \text{ F}) = 2 \times 10^{-3} \text{ s}$$

We have seen that the time constant $T = RC$ determines the rate at which the charge on a capacitor increases. The time constant also determines the rate at which the charge *decreases*. For example, in Fig. 17.17 a capacitor discharges through a resistance R when the switch is closed. If initially it has a charge q_0, after a time t the charge q is reduced to

$$q = q_0e^{-t/T} \tag{17.22}$$

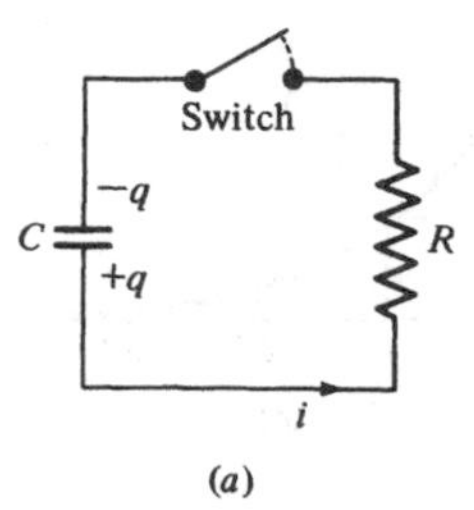

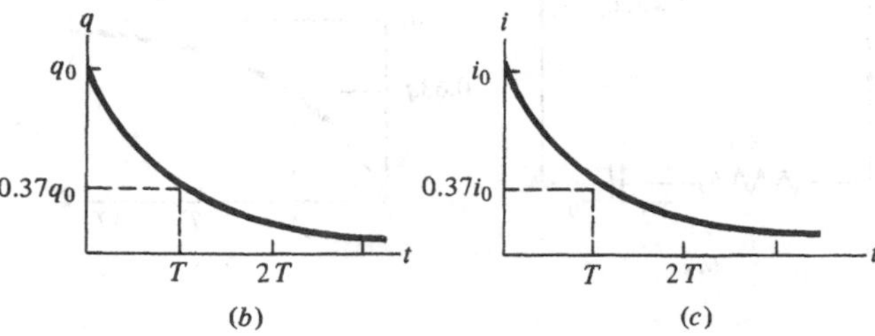

Figure 17.17. (*a*) An initially charged capacitor discharging through a resistor. (*b*) The charge on the capacitor versus time. (*c*) The current in the circuit versus time.

The initial potential difference across the capacitor is $V_0 = q_0/C$, and the initial current is directed away from the positive plate and has a magnitude of $i_0 = V_0/R$. The current after a time t is

$$i = i_0 e^{-t/T} \tag{17.23}$$

Thus both the charge on the capacitor and the current in the circuit steadily diminish, reaching very small values after a few time constants. Verifying that these are the correct expressions for q and i is left as a problem.

The artificial pacemaker provides an example of a circuit in which a capacitor is repeatedly charged and discharged.

r
"Switch"
+
$\mathcal{E}$
−
C
R
T
To heart
(a)

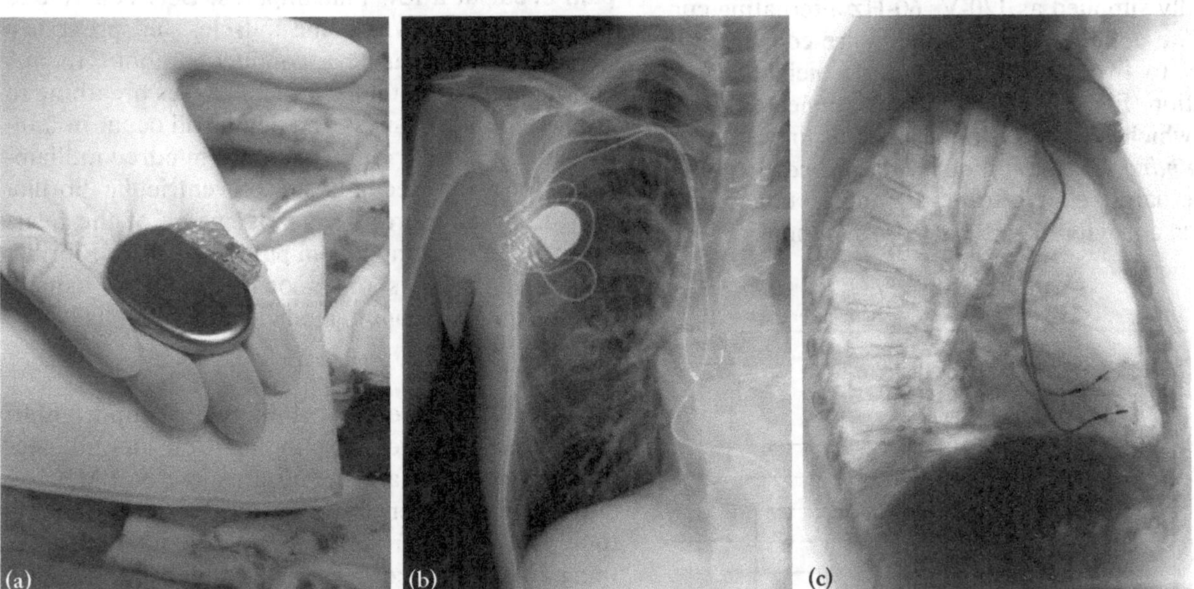

Figure 17.18. (*a*) The basic pacemaker timing circuit. The capacitor C charges quickly through the small resistance r. The "switch," which is actually a transistor, then changes position, and the capacitor slowly discharges through the large-resistance R. When the voltage across R reaches a preset level, the triggering circuit T sends a pulse to the heart. (*b*) If a patient's heart fails to initiate a pulse, this artificial pacemaker provides both atrial and ventricular stimulation. (c) The implanted pacemaker and leads. [(a) AJ Photo / Photo Researchers, Inc. (b) PDSN / Phototake (c) Scott Camazine / Phototake.]

Example 17.14

Each cycle in the human heart begins with an electrical *pacemaker* pulse from a group of nerve fibers. Some heart patients are now being helped by surgically implanted *artificial pacemakers*, which are battery-powered circuits that pulse if the person's pacemaker fails to do so. One model has pulses triggered 75 times per minute by a 0.4-μF capacitor, which rapidly charges through a very small resistance r and then slowly discharges through a large resistance R (Fig. 17.18). When the charge drops to $e^{-1} = 0.37$ times its initial value, transistors deliver a short pulse to the heart and then recharge the capacitor almost immediately through r. (a) Find the time constant of the discharging RC circuit, neglecting the small time needed to recharge the capacitor through r. (b) Find the resistance R.

(a) There are 75 pulses per minute, $75/60 = 1.25$ per second, or one pulse each $1/1.25 = 0.8$ s. This equals the time for the capacitor charge to drop to e^{-1} times its initial value, since the recharging time is negligible. Such a decrease in the charge requires one time constant to elapse, so $T = 0.8$ s.

(b) From $T = RC$, using $C = 0.4\ \mu$F,

$$R = \frac{T}{C} = \frac{0.8 \text{ s}}{0.4 \times 10^{-6} \text{ F}} = 2 \times 10^6 \text{ ohm}$$

The artificial pacemaker in this example stimulates the heart at a fixed frequency. More advanced demand pacemakers trigger only if the patient's natural pacemaker fails to operate within a specified time.

17.8 | ELECTRICAL SAFETY

Electrical equipment must be designed and used with care to avoid possible fire and electrocution hazards. In this section, we consider these hazards and the means of reducing them.

Electrical power in American homes and offices is usually supplied as 120-V, 60-Hz alternating current. The outlets in each building are connected in parallel to two power lines from a neighborhood substation (Fig. 17.19). One line is connected to the earth, which is a good conductor. This line is said to be *grounded*. The other line is *hot,* or *live*; its potential alternates relative to that of the grounded line, which is considered to be at zero potential.

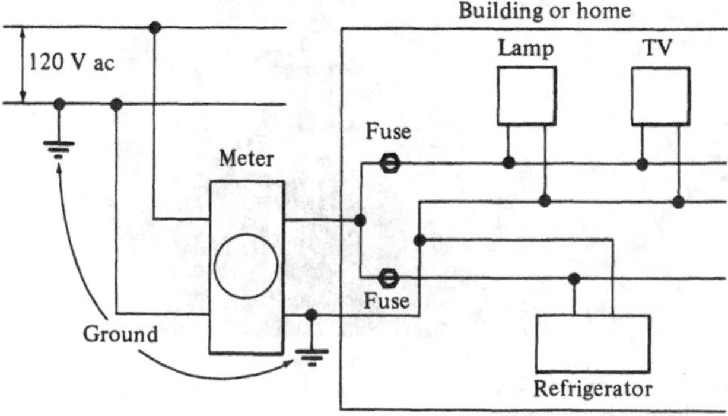

Figure 17.19. Each circuit in every house in a neighborhood is connected in parallel to the power lines. Each circuit contains a fuse or a circuit breaker. The meter is normally placed in series with the lines that enter the building.

Each circuit in a building is protected by a *fuse* or a *circuit breaker*. If the current exceeds a conservatively chosen maximum, the fuse melts or the breaker trips, opening the circuit. This reduces the danger of a fire starting because of the heat generated by excessive currents. One cause of excess currents is an *overload*: too many electrical devices in operation on one circuit at the same time. Another cause is a *short circuit*: a very-low-resistance path between the two power lines leading to a very large current. This sometimes occurs when electrical insulation becomes defective as a result of wear or gradual deterioration.

Electrocution is a serious hazard, since relatively small currents through the human torso can cause injury or death. The average adult can detect a current as small as 1 mA = 10^{-3} A; a direct current produces slight warmth, and a 60-Hz alternating current causes a tingling sensation. Someone reacting involuntarily to a small, unexpected current might drop a hot pan or fall from a ladder, so the maximum allowable leakage currents are set at less than 1 mA. Considerable muscular reaction and pain occur at a few milliamperes. Between 10 and 20 mA will paralyze some muscles and prevent a person from releasing a conductor; about 18 mA contracts the chest muscles and causes breathing to stop. Unconsciousness and death will occur in minutes unless the current stops. One hundred milliamperes for a few seconds causes ventricular fibrillation, rapid uncoordinated movements of the heart muscle that prevent it from pumping blood. Fibrillation rarely stops spontaneously, so death usually results unless prompt medical treatment is available.

Grounding | In electrical safety, it is important to understand the role of grounding. Consider an electrical fence on a farm. Here a source of EMF has either one of its terminals attached to a wire that is totally insulated from electrical contact with anything else. The other terminal is attached to a metal rod driven into the earth and is said to be grounded (Fig. 17.20). If an animal standing on the ground touches the wire, it will complete a conducting path from the EMF through the wire and the ground back to the EMF. Thus a current will pass through the animal, and it will experience a shock. On the

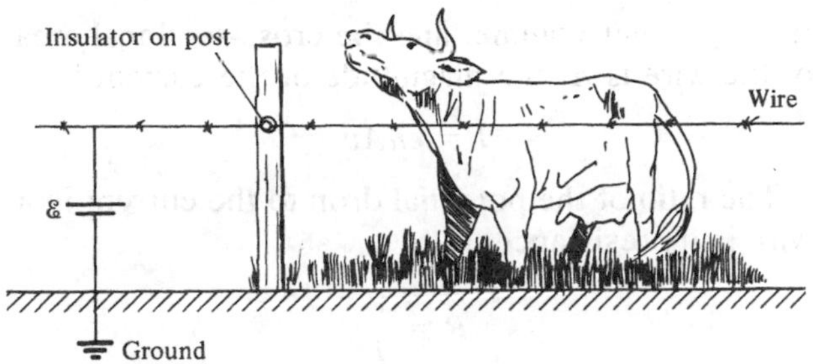

Figure 17.20. A person or animal touching the fence completes a path to ground and receives a mild shock.

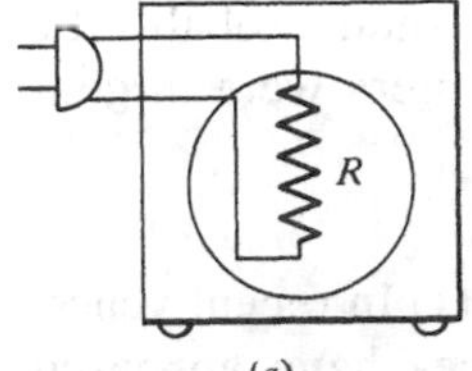

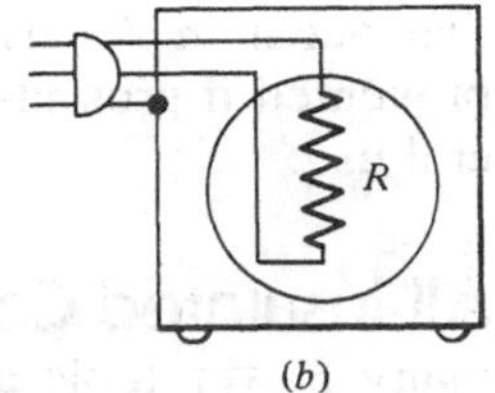

Figure 17.21. An electrical clothes dryer. (*a*) In a two-wire circuit the cabinet is not grounded. A defect in the wiring can therefore make the cabinet "hot." (*b*) In a three-wire circuit the cabinet is connected directly to ground.

other hand, if a bird sits on the wire, its body is at the potential of the wire. It does not receive a shock, because it does not form part of a closed conducting path.

The point of this example is that electrical power lines usually have one wire grounded. If anything is simultaneously in contact with the ground and with a part of the circuit not at ground potential, charge will flow through that object.

Electrical accidents usually occur when a person comes into contact with both a live power line and a good path to ground. The current through the body is determined by its electrical resistance, which is highly variable. Dry skin has a resistance of 10^5 ohms per square centimetre or greater, but the resistance may decrease by a factor of 100 when the skin is wet. A person standing in water in a bathtub is in excellent electrical contact with the ground via the water pipes. If this person grasps a defective electrical appliance, the resistance of the body can be as small as 500 ohms. At 120 V, the resulting current is $I = V/R = 120$ V/500 ohms = 0.240 A = 240 mA, which is lethal. The resistance between the two hands of a person perspiring slightly is roughly 1500 ohms, corresponding to an 80-mA current at 120 V. Again this current may be fatal if it persists for a few seconds.

The way shock hazards can arise is illustrated in Fig. 17.21*a*. The heating coil in a clothes dryer, represented by the resistor R, is connected to the power line with a common two-prong plug. Consequently, the ground and hot lines are determined by which way the plug is inserted into the outlet. Since the plug can usually be inserted in either of two ways, no wire in the dryer may be permitted to touch the metal cabinet. If a wire does come into contact with the cabinet, it will be either at ground or at the hot line voltage, depending on how the plug is inserted into the outlet. A person simultaneously touching a live cabinet and a water faucet or a concrete floor could receive a lethal shock.

To minimize this hazard, electrical devices such as laundry appliances or power tools should be grounded. This is sometimes done by connecting their metal housings or cabinets to water pipes or other grounded conductors. A more reliable way to ground devices is provided by modern household wiring, which has a third, separate wire. This wire is grounded and is connected to the third prong of the electrical outlets. Thus when an electrical device with a three-prong plug is plugged into such an outlet, its housing is automatically grounded (Fig. 17.21*b*). When the housing is grounded, accidental contact between the live wire and the housing will result in a short circuit, and the fuse or circuit breaker will open the circuit. Once this happens, there is no danger of a shock.

Ground-Fault-Interrupters | If the failure of some component in an electrical appliance or instrument leads to large enough currents leaking to ground, the fuse or circuit breaker opens the circuit, eliminating any shock hazard. However, if an electrical device fails in such a way that smaller currents leak to ground, then a person touching a component not quite at ground potential may receive a severe shock.

A device called a *ground-fault-interrupter* is now sometimes installed in the ground wire of three-wire circuits. If the current in the ground wire exceeds some very small preset limit, say 5 mA, this device opens the circuit. The majority of the electrocutions that occur in American homes could probably be prevented if ground-fault-interrupters were in general use.

All-Insulated Construction | In recent years, many power tools and appliances have appeared with *all-insulated* or *double-insulated* construction. They are designed so that, in the event of an insulation failure, no exposed metal part will become electrically live. These devices do not require grounding and represent a useful advance in electrical safety.

Hospitals | The electrical shock hazards in hospitals are generally similar to those in homes and offices, although the use of electrical devices near grounded metal beds and in the presence of water or other liquids does pose potential problems. However, a patient with catheters, probes, and needles inserted in the body is highly vulnerable to very small electric currents, since 0.02 mA applied directly to the heart is sufficient to produce ventricular fibrillation. Since deaths due to such small current are indistinguishable from those due to natural causes, there is some dispute over how often they occur. The special hazards associated with patients connected directly to electrical circuits have led to recommendations that their beds be specially insulated so that they are not grounded and that no other objects within reach of the patient be grounded. Then, like the bird on the fence wire, these patients cannot complete a conducting path to ground. Chapter Twenty discusses how devices called transformers can also be used to reduce shock hazards.

SUMMARY

If an amount of charge ΔQ passes through a cross section of a wire in a time Δt, the average current is

$$\bar{I} = \frac{\Delta Q}{\Delta t}$$

The instantaneous current is $I = dq/dt$.

In a metallic conductor, conduction electrons can move readily among the positive lattice ions, When there is an electric field in a wire, the electrons acquire a small net drift velocity v in the direction of the electric force. If there are n conduction electrons per unit volume, and the cross-sectional area of the wire is A, the magnitude of the current is

$$I = enAv$$

The ratio of the potential drop to the current in a wire is its resistance,

$$R = \frac{V}{I}$$

Materials in which the resistance is independent of the current are said to obey Ohm's law. The resistance is determined by the geometry and by the resistivity ρ of the material according to

$$R = \rho \frac{\ell}{A}$$

In an electrical circuit a continuous current can exist only if energy is supplied by an EMF. The power supplied by or to any circuit element is VI, where I is the current in the element and V is the potential change across the element. This power is I^2R for a resistor and $I\mathscr{E}$ for an EMF.

Kirchhoff's rules state that the sum of the potential changes around any closed path is zero and that the current entering any point must equal the current leaving. These rules, can be used to analyze any dc circuit and lead to formulas for series and parallel resistors,

$$R_s = R_1 + R_2 + R_3 + \cdots$$

$$\frac{1}{R_p} = \frac{1}{R_1} + \frac{1}{R_2} + \frac{1}{R_3} + \cdots$$

A galvanometer is a device for measuring currents. A voltmeter is made by adding a large-series resistance to a galvanometer; it measures the voltage across a circuit element when it is placed in parallel with that element. An ammeter is constructed by placing a small resistance in parallel with a galvanometer. Placed in series in a circuit, the ammeter measures the current through that part of the circuit.

When the plates of a capacitance C are connected to an EMF through a resistance R, the rate at which its charge changes is determined by the time constant

$$T = RC$$

When a time equal to T has elapsed, an initially

uncharged capacitor is within 37 percent of its final charge. Similarly, an initially charged capacitor being discharged through a resistance will lose all but 37 percent of its charge in one time constant.

Checklist

Define or explain:

electric current	series, parallel resistors
ampere	voltmeter
conduction electrons	ammeter
drift velocity	galvanometer
resistance	transient, steady currents
Ohm's law	
resistivity	time constant
conductivity	overload
EMF	short circuit
kilowatt hour	ground
Kirchhoff's rules	

REVIEW QUESTIONS

Q17-1 If 3 C of charge passes a point in a wire in 10 s, the current is _____.

Q17-2 The resistance of a wire is the ratio of the voltage difference across the wire to the _____.

Q17-3 In an ohmic conductor, the resistance is independent of the _____.

Q17-4 If a material is a good conductor, its resistivity is _____.

Q17-5 A battery converts _____ energy into _____ energy.

Q17-6 Electrical energy is sold by the _____.

Q17-7 The power supplied to or by a circuit element is the product of the _____ and _____.

Q17-8 If two identical resistances R are connected in series, the equivalent resistance is _____; if they are connected in parallel, the equivalent resistance is _____.

Q17-9 A voltmeter is used in _____ with the circuit element whose potential difference is being measured.

Q17-10 An ammeter must have a _____ resistance to avoid disturbing the circuit it is placed in.

Q17-11 When a resistor and capacitor are connected in series to a battery, the current has its greatest value at _____ and drops to $1/e$ = 0.37 . . . times its peak value after a time _____.

Q17-12 Appliances should be _____ to minimize the risk of _____.

EXERCISES

Resistivities needed in some of the exercises are given in Table 17.1

Section 17.1 | Electric Current

17-1 The current in a toaster is 12 A. (a) How much charge passes through the toaster in 1 min? (b) How many electrons pass through the device in 1 min?

17-2 A heavy-ion accelerator produces a beam of 10^{15} oxygen nuclei per second. The charge on an oxygen nucleus is $+8e$. Find the beam current in amperes.

17-3 (a) Can there be a steady current in a conducting wire without an electric field? (b) Can there be an electric field in a conducting wire without a current? Explain.

17-4 In an electrochemical experiment, a current of 0.5 A passes through a cell for 1 hour. If two electrons are needed to discharge an ion, how many ions are discharged?

17-5 Silver has 5.8×10^{28} free electrons per cubic metre. If the current in a silver wire is 10 A and the wire has a radius of 10^{-3} m, what is the drift velocity of the electrons?

17-6 In a hydrogen discharge tube positive hydrogen ions (protons) and negative electrons travel in opposite directions under the influence of an electric field. Find the direction and magnitude in amperes of the current if in 1 second 8×10^{18} electrons and 3×10^{18} protons reach the electrodes.

17-7 Two copper plates are immersed in a copper sulfate solution and connected to a battery. If there is a 0.4-A current for 1 hour, how much copper is deposited on the plates? (The atomic mass of copper is 63.6 u, and two electrons are needed to discharge one copper ion.)

17-8 The conduction electrons in a metal can be considered for some purposes as an ideal gas. (a) What is the average thermal kinetic energy $\frac{3}{2}k_BT$ of an electron at 300 K? (b) What is the corresponding velocity? (c) Calculate the ratio of this velocity to the drift velocity found in Example 17.2.

Section 17.2 | Resistance

17-9 A wire has a 10-V potential difference

across its end when it carries a 4-A current. What is its resistance?

17-10 A 10-A current in a wire results in a potential difference of 2 V across its ends. If it is an ohmic conductor, what current will produce a 6-V potential difference?

17-11 The thinnest copper wire normally manufactured has a radius of 4×10^{-5} m. Find the resistance of a 10-m long segment.

17-12 A nerve fiber (axon) may be approximated as a long cylinder. If its diameter is 10^{-5} m and its resistivity is 2 ohm m, what is the resistance of a 0.3-m-long fiber?

17-13 A 2-m long copper wire has a resistance of 0.01 ohms. Find its radius.

17-14 The resistivity of copper increases approximately 0.39 percent if the temperature rises 1°C. A copper wire has a resistance of 10 ohms at 20°C. Estimate its resistance at 50°C.

17-15 How does the mass of a fixed length of wire vary with (a) its radius; (b) its resistance?

17-16 Find the resistance of a 10-m length of aluminum wire with a radius of 0.002 m.

17-17 The voltage–current relationship for a certain wire is $\Delta V = 3$ V, $I = 1$ A; $\Delta V = 6$ V, $I = 2.2$ A; $\Delta V = 9$ V, $I = 4$ A; $\Delta V = 12$ V, $I = 8$ A. (a) Is the resistance constant? If not, how does it vary with the current? (b) Is this an ohmic material? Explain.

17-18 The voltage difference across a resistor is varied, and the current is measured. The results are $\Delta V = 2$ V, $I = 0.4$ A; 4 V, 0.8 A; 6 V, 1.2 A; 8 V, 1.6 A. (a) What resistance is implied by the measurement at 2 V? (b) What resistance is implied by the measurement at 8 V? (c) Is the resistor an ohmic conductor? Explain.

Section 17.3 | Energy Sources in Circuits

17-19 The heating element in a hot-water heater has a current of 20 A when connected to a 230-V line. What is its resistance?

17-20 An automobile lamp draws 1.2 A when connected to a 12-V battery. What is its resistance?

17-21 An electrical iron draws 6 A when plugged into a 120-V outlet. What is its resistance?

17-22 A 120-V power line contains a fuse that will open when the current exceeds 15 A. What is the minimum resistance of an appliance operated by this circuit?

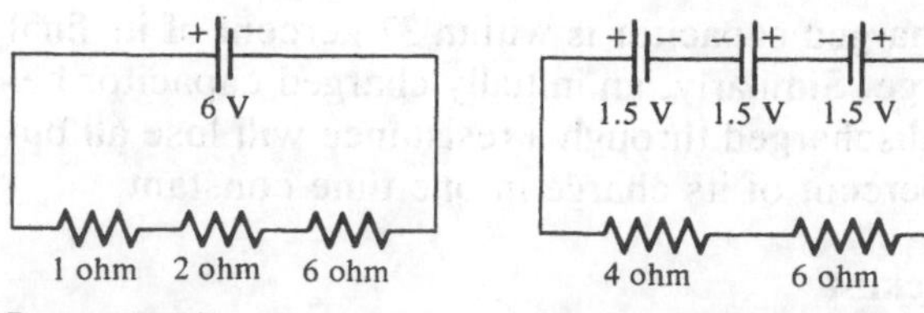

Figure 17.22. Exercises 17-24 and 17-26.

Figure 17.23. Exercise 17-25.

17-23 A 12-V battery is connected to a 2-ohm resistor. (a) What is the current? (b) How much charge is transported through the circuit in 10 seconds? (c) How much work is done on the charge by electric fields in the battery? (d) How much work is done on the charge by electric fields in the resistor? (e) What is the total work done by the electric fields on the charge? (f) How much energy is converted into heat? (g) What is the source of that energy?

17-24 For the circuit in Fig. 17.22, find (a) the current; (b) the potential difference across each resistance.

17-25 (a) Find the current in the circuit of Fig. 17.23. (b) Find the potential difference across each circuit element.

Section 17.4 | Power in Electrical Circuits

17-26 Find the power supplied to or by each circuit element in Fig. 17.22.

17-27 (a) A 12-V automobile storage battery has an internal resistance of 0.004 ohm. Find the current and power dissipation when the terminals are connected by a conductor of negligible resistance. (b) The battery delivers 80 A to the starter motor. What resistance would draw the same current? (c) How much power is supplied to the motor? What happens to that power? (d) How much power is dissipated in the battery?

17-28 A toaster uses 1500 W when plugged into a 120-V line. It takes 1 min to toast a slice of bread. If electrical energy costs 6 cents per kilowatt-hour, how much does it cost to do this?

17-29 (a) What is the resistance of a 100-W light bulb designed for use in 120-V circuits? (b) What current will it draw?

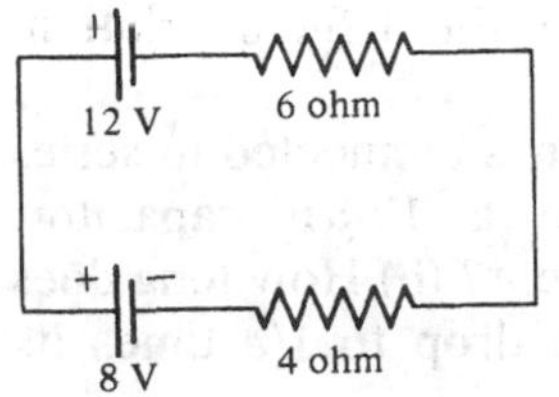

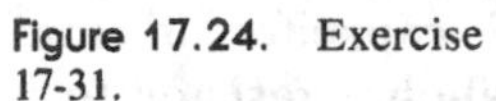

Figure 17.24. Exercise 17-31.

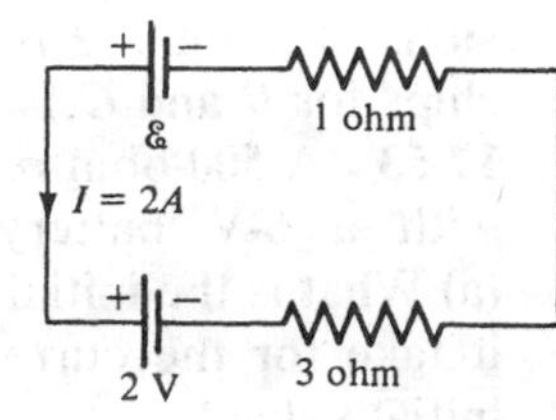

Figure 17.25. Exercise 17-32.

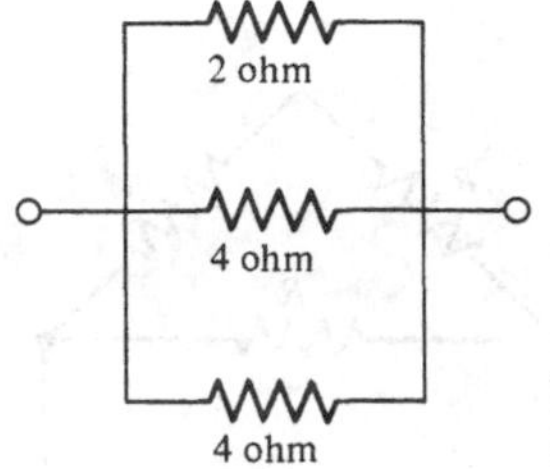

Figure 17.26. Exercise 17-43.

17-30 A 20-A circuit in a home is wired with No. 12 copper wire. A single No. 12 wire 1 m long has a resistance of 5.2×10^{-3} ohm. If a two-wire cable carries 20 A for 30 m, find (a) the potential drop along each wire; (b) the total power dissipated.

17-31 For the circuit in Fig. 17.24, find (a) the current; (b) the power supplied by each battery; (c) the power dissipated by each resistor.

17-32 (a) In Fig. 17.25, what is the EMF $\mathscr{E}$? (b) Find the power supplied to each of the two resistors. (c) Find the power supplied to or by each EMF. Compare the results with those in part (b).

17-33 A room air conditioner uses 900 W of electrical power. If it operates an average of 12 hour per day, find the daily operating cost at 6 cents per kilowatt-hour.

17-34 A heater uses 1400 W of power when connected to a 120-V line. (a) What is its resistance? (b) What current does it draw? (c) If the line voltage is reduced to 112 V, how much power does the heater use? (Assume that the resistance remains constant.)

17-35 According to its manufacturer, a "super-size" 12-V auto battery can supply a current of 25 A for 6.5 hours. (a) How much energy does the battery supply in that time? (b) Because of the internal resistance, the terminal voltage is only 10.5 V. How much heat is produced in the battery during the 6.5-hour interval?

17-36 Show that I^2R has the dimensions of power.

Section 17.5 | Series and Parallel Resistors; Kirchhoff's Rules

17-37 A string of 25 Christmas tree lights wired in series uses 500 W when connected to a 120-V line. (a) What is the current in the lights? (b) What is the resistance of a single bulb?

17-38 Some strings of Christmas lights are connected in series, and others are connected in parallel. Which is less affected by the burning out of one light bulb? Explain your reasoning.

17-39 An electrically heated home is supplied with 200 A at 230 V. How many 100-W appliances could be operated simultaneously in this home?

17-40 An electrical heater uses 1800 W when connected to a 120-V source. (a) What is the resistance of the heater? (b) The heater is plugged into a 10-m long extension cord made of No. 18 wire, which is intended only for lamps and small-wattage appliances. One metre of a single No. 18 wire has a resistance of 0.021 ohm. How much power is dissipated in the cord?

17-41 Six 60-W light bulbs are used in parallel in a lighting fixture connected to a 120-V power line. (a) What is the resistance of one bulb? (b) What is the effective resistance of the six bulbs?

17-42 Two light bulbs use 100 W each when separately connected to a 120-V line. (a) If they are connected in series to this line, how much power will they draw? (Assume that the resistance of a bulb does not change when it is used in this way.) (b) Will the bulbs be brighter or dimmer? Explain.

17-43 Find the equivalent resistance for the network in Fig. 17.26.

17-44 Find the equivalent resistance for the network in Fig. 17.27.

17-45 For the circuit in Fig. 17.28, find (a) the current through the 2-ohm resistance; (b) the

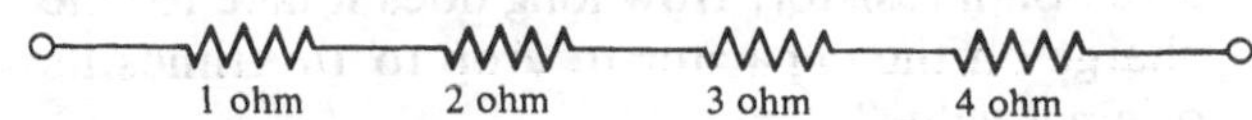

Figure 17.27. Exercise 17-44.

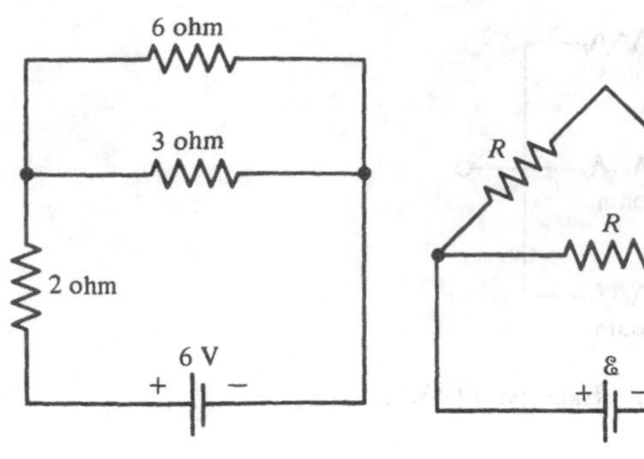

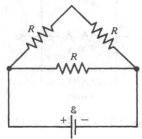

Figure 17.28. Exercise 17-45.

Figure 17.29. Exercise 17-46.

voltage difference across the 3-ohm resistance; (c) the current through the 3-ohm resistance.

17-46 Find the current through the battery in Fig. 17.29.

Section 17.6 | Voltmeters and Ammeters

17-47 A galvanometer has a resistance of 10 ohms and gives full-scale deflection with a current of 10^{-3} A. How can one convert it into a voltmeter with a 0.1-V range?

17-48 A galvanometer has an internal resistance of 100 ohms and has full-scale deflection for a current of 10^{-5} A. (a) Design a voltmeter with full-scale deflection for 10 V. (b) Design an ammeter with full-scale deflection for 10 A.

Section 17.7 | Circuits Containing Resistance and Capacitance

17-49 A 1-μF capacitor is connected with copper wires to a 12-V battery. The initial current is 120 A. (a) What is the total resistance of the wires and the battery? (b) What is the time constant for the circuit?

17-50 A 1000-ohm resistor and a 10^{-5}-F capacitor are connected in series to a 100-V EMF. (a) Find the time constant. (b) What is the final charge on the capacitor?

17-51 A 10^{-4}-F capacitor is discharged through a 100-ohm resistor. How long does it take for the charge on the capacitor to drop to $1/e^2$ times its original value?

17-52 Verify that the product RC has the dimensions of a time. (*Hint*: Use the defining relationships for R and C.)

17-53 A 500-ohm resistor is connected in series with a 6-V battery and a 10-μF capacitor. (a) What is the initial current? (b) How long does it take for the current to drop to $1/e$ times its initial value?

17-54 An uncharged 1-μF capacitor is connected in series with a 1000-ohm resistor to a 100-V EMF. The switch has been closed 0.001 s. Find (a) the voltage across the capacitor; (b) the voltage across the resistor.

17-55 A 100-μF capacitor is connected in series with a 10,000-ohm resistor to a 100-V EMF for a long time. A switch is then flipped, replacing the EMF by a perfectly conducting wire and discharging the capacitor. (a) What is the charge on the capacitor after it has been attached to the battery for a long time? (b) One second after the switch has been flipped, what is the charge on the capacitor?

Section 17.8 | Electrical Safety

17-56 A bird stands on one foot on a high-voltage power line. What happens when it puts the other foot down on the same line? What would happen if the bird put this foot instead on a grounded conductor?

17-57 (a) If a person with wet hands grasps two conductors and has a resistance of 1000 ohms, how large a potential difference is needed to produce a 10-mA current that may freeze the hands to the conductors? (b) How large a potential difference is needed to produce a 100-mA current that will cause ventricular fibrillation in a second or so?

17-58 (a) Is one likely to get a dangerous electrical shock from a 12-V automobile battery? (b) What other possible hazards are associated with such batteries?

17-59 An electrical shaver plugged into an electric outlet is accidentally dropped into a sink full of water. Is it safe to reach into the water and remove the shaver? Does it matter whether it is turned on? Explain.

17-60 Why is it especially important to ground appliances properly when used outdoors or in basements?

PROBLEMS

17-61 In a determination of Avogadro's number, a constant 4-A current is passed for 30 min through a cell consisting of two silver electrodes in a silver nitrate solution. (a) How many coulombs of charge are transported through the system? (b) How many electrons are transported? (c) If 7.84 g of silver are found to be deposited on the plates, what value of Avogadro's number is obtained? (Each electron discharges one ion, and the atomic mass of silver is 107.9 u.)

17-62 The resistivity of body fluids is about 0.15 ohm m. Estimate the resistance of a finger end to end, ignoring the resistance of the skin.

17-63 (a) What is the room temperature resistance of a 1-m long aluminum wire of radius 0.002 m? (b) What is the radius of a 1-m-long copper wire with the same resistance? (c) Compare the weights of the two wires. (The density of copper is 8900 kg m^{-3}, and the density of aluminum is 2700 kg m^{-3}.)

17-64 When the terminals of a dry cell are connected by a wire, the current is 2.2 A and the terminal voltage is 1.4 V. When the circuit is opened, the terminal voltage is 1.52 V. Find the internal resistance and the EMF, neglecting any error due to the meters.

17-65 An electrical dryer connected to a 230-V power line draws 20 A. (a) How much power does it use? (b) If it takes 2600 J to evaporate 1 g of water, how long will it take to dry a load of wet laundry containing 4 kg of water? (Assume that no heat is lost to the surroundings.)

17-66 A motor is driven by a 12-V battery. This load is equivalent to a 0.2-ohm resistor. (a) What is the current? (b) What is the power supplied to the motor? (c) If the motor operates at 80 percent efficiency, at what rate can it lift a 100-N weight?

17-67 In a student laboratory experiment to measure the mechanical equivalent of heat, a resistor immersed in 0.7 kg of water carries a current of 4.2 A and a potential difference of 12 V. (a) How much energy is supplied in 5 min? (b) If no heat is lost to the surroundings, what is the temperature change of the water?

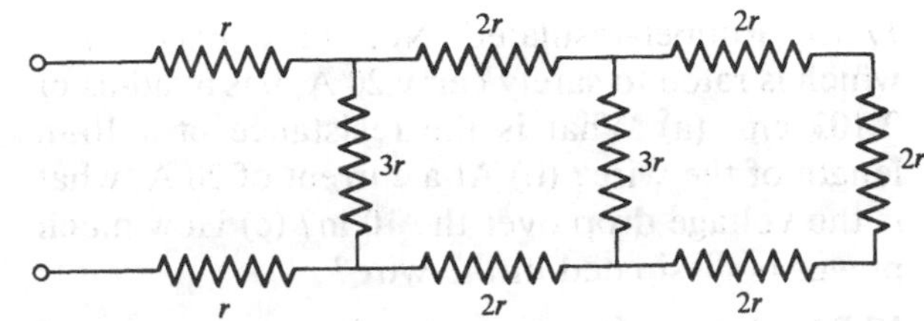

Figure 17.30. Problem 17-70.

17-68 A calorimeter is used to measure the latent heat of fusion of a material. The calorimeter has a 50-ohm resistor connected to a 120-V dc power line. Once the sample reaches the melting point, it takes 2 min to melt 0.3 kg. What is the latent heat of fusion of the material?

17-69 A 12-V storage battery with an internal resistance of 0.003 ohms is charged by a generator at a rate of 20 A. (a) Which terminal of the battery is connected to the high-potential side of the generator? (b) How much power is supplied by the generator? (c) What is the terminal voltage of the battery while it is being charged?

17-70 Find the equivalent resistance for the network in Fig. 17.30.

17-71 If an EMF $\mathscr{E}$ is connected to the terminals of the network shown in Fig. 17.31, what is the current in (a) the EMF; (b) the lower $\frac{3}{2}r$ resistor?

17-72 A large supply of 20-ohm resistors is available. What are the simplest ways to combine several such resistors so as to produce an equivalent resistance of (a) 60 ohms; (b) 70 ohms; (c) 75 ohms?

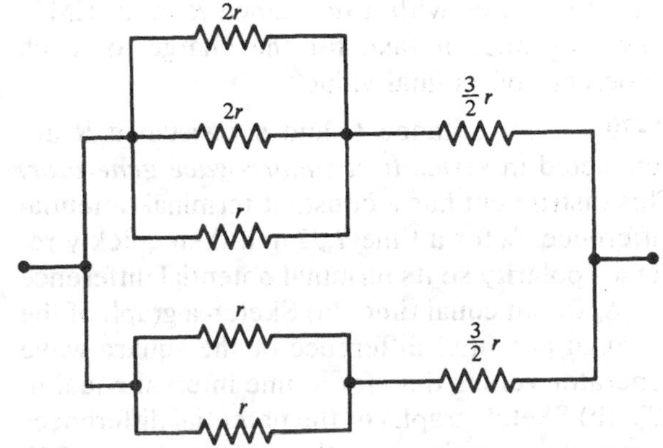

Figure 17.31. Problem 17-71.

17-73 Rubber-insulated No. 12 copper wire, which is rated to safely carry 20 A, has a radius of 0.103 cm. (a) What is the resistance of a 10-m length of the wire? (b) At a current of 20 A, what is the voltage drop over the 10 m? (c) How much power is dissipated in the wire?

17-74 A capacitor consists of two square metal plates of side 0.02 m separated by a 0.0002-m thick polyethylene sheet. The resistivity of polyethylene is 2×10^{11} ohm m. How much current will leak through the polyethylene if the applied potential difference is 1000 V?

17-75 A 50-m long copper extension cord is needed for use with an electrical lawn mower. If the current is 20 A and the maximum allowable voltage drop is 5 V, what is the minimum radius of the wire? (*Hint*: Remember the current must travel both ways.)

***17-76** An initially uncharged 100-μF capacitor is connected in series with a 1000-ohm resistor to a 100-V EMF. The current is 0.05 A. How long has the switch been closed?

17-77 The capacitor in an electronic flash gun has a capacitance of 100 μF and is charged so that its potential difference is 1000 V. (a) What is the charge on the capacitor plates? (b) The capacitor is discharged through the flashbulb, and 0.001 s after the switch is closed, the charge remaining is 0.37 times the initial charge. What is the resistance of the circuit? (c) What is the current after 0.001 s?

***17-78** If an uncharged capacitance C is connected in series with a resistance R to an EMF, how long does it take for the charge to reach 99 percent of its final value?

***17-79** A capacitance C and a resistance R are connected in series to a *square-wave generator*. This instrument has a constant terminal potential difference $\mathscr{E}_0$ for a time $T_0/2$ and then quickly reverses polarity so its terminal potential difference is $-\mathscr{E}_0$ for an equal time. (a) Sketch a graph of the terminal potential difference of the square-wave generator versus time for a time interval equal to $3T_0$. (b) Sketch graphs of the potential differences across the capacitor and the resistor if $T_0 \gg RC$. (c) Repeat part (b) assuming $T_0 = RC$.

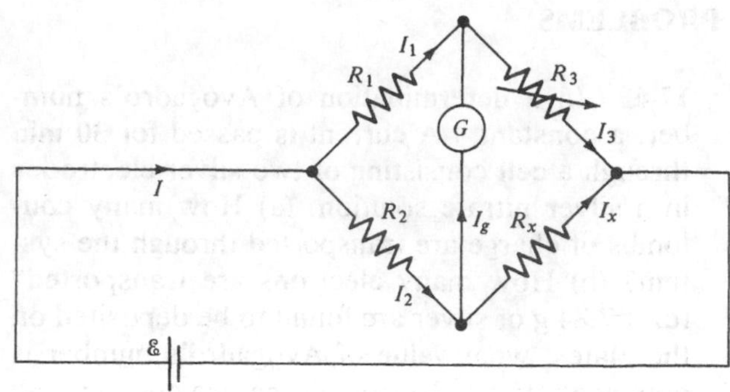

Figure 17.32. A Wheatstone bridge. Problem 17-80.

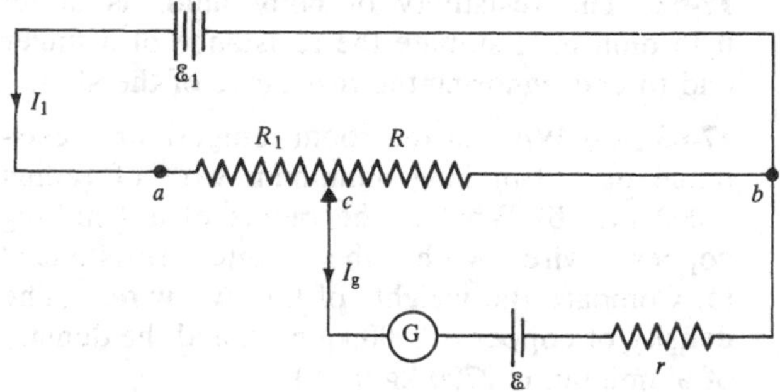

Figure 17.33. A potentiometer. Problem 17-81.

17-80 Figure 17.32 shows a *Wheatstone bridge*, an instrument used to measure resistance. R_1 and R_2 are 10 ohms, and R_3 is adjusted until the galvanometer current I_g is zero. If R_3 is then 98.2 ohms, find the unknown resistance R_x.

***17-81** Figure 17.33 shows a *potentiometer*, which is used to measure the EMF of a battery without drawing any current from it. The contact c is moved along the resistive wire ab until the galvanometer current is zero. When this happens, how is the unknown EMF $\mathscr{E}$ related to $\mathscr{E}_1$, R, and R_1?

c17-82 Show that Eqs. 17.22 and 17.23 for q and i satisfy Eq. 17.17 for the case where $E = 0$ and $q = q_0$ at time $t = 0$.

17-83 When a capacitor is discharged, how many time constants are required for its stored energy to decrease to half its initial value?

ANSWERS TO REVIEW QUESTIONS

Q17-1, 0.3 A; **Q17-2**, current; **Q17-3**, current; **Q17-4**, small; **Q17-5**, chemical, electrical;

Q17-6, kilowatt hour; **Q17-7**, current, potential difference; **Q17-8**, $2R$, $R/2$; **Q17-9**, parallel; **Q17-10**, small; **Q17-11**, $t = 0$, $t = RC$; **Q17-12**, grounded, electrical shock.

SUPPLEMENTARY TOPICS

17.9 | ATOMIC THEORY OF RESISTANCE

We now discuss a simple atomic model that gives some insight into the physical origin of electrical resistance. The model assumes that the conduction electrons in a metal move freely among the positive ions with an average *thermal velocity u* determined by the temperature. Their directions are frequently changed by collisions with the ions. The average distance between collisions is called the *mean free path* λ (Greek letter "lambda") and plays a key role in determining the resistance.

In the absence of an applied electric field, the electrons move randomly, and there is no net charge flow in any direction. When an electric field **E** is maintained in the metal, the negatively charged electrons experience a force opposite to **E**, and they acquire an average drift velocity along the force. Although this drift velocity v is very small compared to the thermal velocity u, it is responsible for the current (Fig. 17.34).

Suppose an electric potential difference V is maintained between the ends of a wire of length ℓ. If the field is uniform, then $E = V/\ell$. The force on an electron has a magnitude $eE = eV/\ell$, and the acceleration is

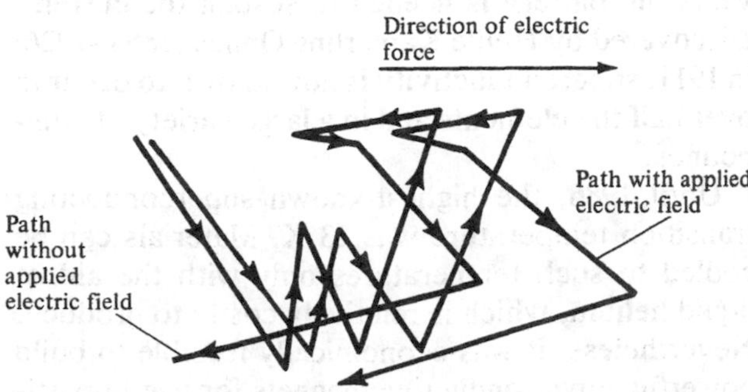

Figure 17.34. A typical random electron path with and without an applied electric field. An electric force produces a small net draft velocity in the direction of the electric force. Note how the field steadily deflects the electron toward the right.

$$a = \frac{eV}{m\ell}$$

Every time an electron collides with an ion, it is deflected randomly and loses its tendency to drift with the electric force. Its next collision will occur after a time t that satisfies $ut = \lambda$ or $t = \lambda/u$. Between the collisions, it will acquire a velocity at. The average drift velocity v is half this, so

$$v = \frac{1}{2}\frac{eV}{m\ell}\frac{\lambda}{u}$$

If the wire has a cross-sectional area A and there are n conduction electrons per unit volume, then the net current is

$$I = envA = \frac{ne^2\lambda}{2mu}\frac{A}{\ell}V$$

This result states that the current and the potential difference are proportional. Thus the model has led to Ohm's law, which is found experimentally to describe correctly the behavior of most metals. Now using $R = \rho\ell/A$, the current $I = V/R$ is

$$I = \frac{V}{\rho\ell/A} = \frac{VA}{\rho\ell}$$

Comparing the two previous equations for I, we find that in this atomic model the resistivity is given by

$$\rho = \frac{2mu}{ne^2\lambda} \tag{17.24}$$

Only the factors n and λ in this formula for the resistivity depend on the choice of the material, since the electron charge e and mass m are constants, and the thermal speed u is determined by the temperature. For a metal, the number of conduction electrons is typically one or two per atom. Estimating the mean free path λ is a little more difficult. Classical mechanics suggests that λ is comparable to the interatomic spacing, but this value leads to overestimating the room temperature resistivity by a factor of 100 or more. Modern atomic theory leads to the remarkable but experimentally correct result that the electrons travel completely unimpeded in the crystal lattice until they encounter a deviation from the regular lattice structure (Fig. 17.35). Such an imperfection can be an impurity or a lattice ion located some distance from its equilibrium position

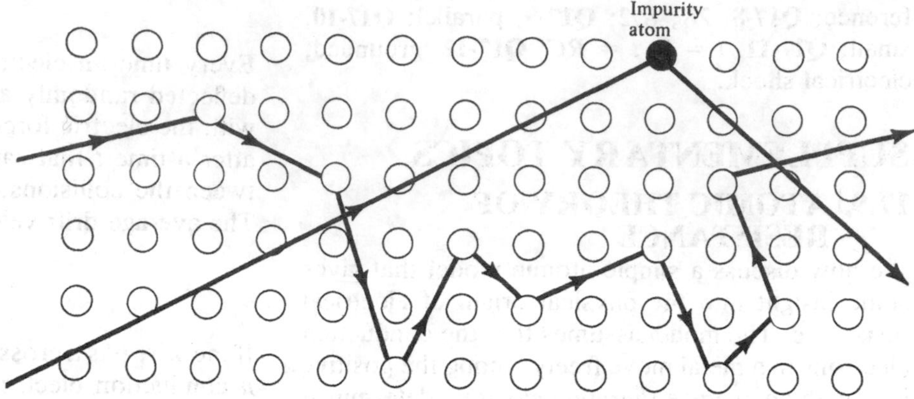

Figure 17.35. Classical mechanics suggests that the mean free path for an electron in a crystal lattice is comparable to the interatomic spacing (black path). According to modern atomic theory, collisions occur only when an electron encounters an imperfection in the lattice, such as the impurity atom in the top row (colored path). The modern theory is in agreement with measured resistivities.

because of its thermal vibrational motion. At very low temperatures, the amplitude of the lattice ion vibrations is very small, so in very pure metals the mean free path of an electron may be thousands of interatomic spacings.

As noted earlier, the resistivities of electrical insulators are larger than those of conductors by a factor of up to 10^{22}. This is much larger than the variation of 10^4 between good thermal conductors and thermal insulators. Materials that are good electrical conductors are usually good thermal conductors, because the free electrons transport both charge and thermal energy. Insulators have very few free electrons, so they do not readily conduct either electricity or heat. Some materials called *semiconductors* have resistivities that are intermediate between those of conductors and insulators. They have only a few charge carriers, which can be either electrons or missing electrons (holes). These materials are employed in the manufacture of transistors and other solid-state electronic components.

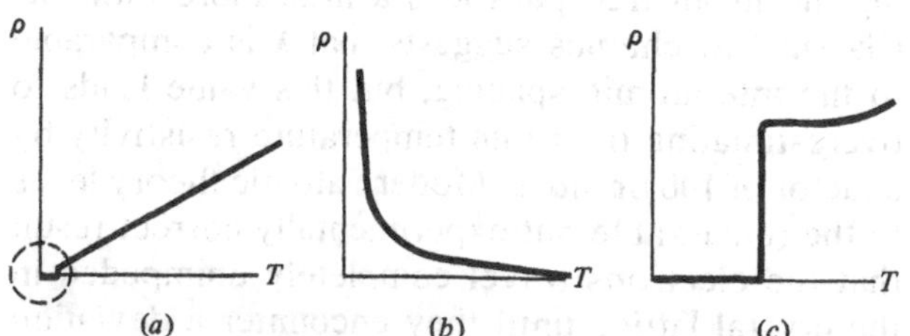

Figure 17.36. Resistivity versus temperature for (*a*) a conductor; (*b*) a semiconductor. (*c*) At very low temperatures, many materials become superconducting. This graph is an expanded view of the circled part of (*a*) for such a material.

As the temperature rises, the average electron velocity increases. Also, the mean free path decreases, since the lattice ion vibrational amplitude increases. Thus, Eq. 17.24 predicts that the resistivity will also increase, as is observed experimentally in metals (Fig. 17.36*a*). However, the resistivity of a semiconductor decreases as the temperature rises (Fig. 17.36*b*), because the number of charge carriers rises rapidly with the temperature, more than offsetting the changes in the path length λ and velocity u in Eq. 17.24.

At very low temperatures, many materials become *superconducting*. As the material is cooled to its characteristic transition temperature, the resistance suddenly drops to zero. Once a current is started in a superconducting loop, it will persist for years; no battery is needed to sustain the current! Discovered by Heike Kamerling Onnes (1853–1926) in 1911, superconductivity is now known to occur in over half the elements and in a large variety of compounds.

Until 1986, the highest-known superconducting transition temperature was 23 K. Materials can be cooled to such temperatures only with the aid of liquid helium, which is relatively costly to produce. Nevertheless, it was economically feasible to build powerful superconducting magnets for use in particle accelerators, nuclear fusion research machines, and nuclear magnetic resonance (NMR) scanners used in hospitals. However, in 1986, the record high-transition temperature was raised to 30 K and then to 39 K, causing a great deal of excitement. By early 1987, a large number of materials were found that become superconducting at over 90 K, and there were preliminary indications of possible superconducting materials at or near room temperature.

Even at 90 K, many new applications become feasible, since materials can be cooled to this level using liquid nitrogen, which liquifies at 77 K and costs less than milk or soft drinks. Very fast computers, loss-free electric transmission lines, huge magnets for electric energy storage, and magnetically levitated trains are just a few of the possibilities. Furthermore, if room temperature superconductors that can be made into practical devices are actually discovered, our entire electrical technology will be completely transformed.

17.10 | APPLICATIONS OF RESISTANCE MEASUREMENTS

Resistance measurements often provide very useful information. The resistance of some semiconductors varies as much as 5 percent if the temperature changes by 1°C. A small semiconducting bead or *thermistor* can rapidly detect temperature changes as small as 10^{-3} degrees over large temperature ranges (Fig. 17.37).

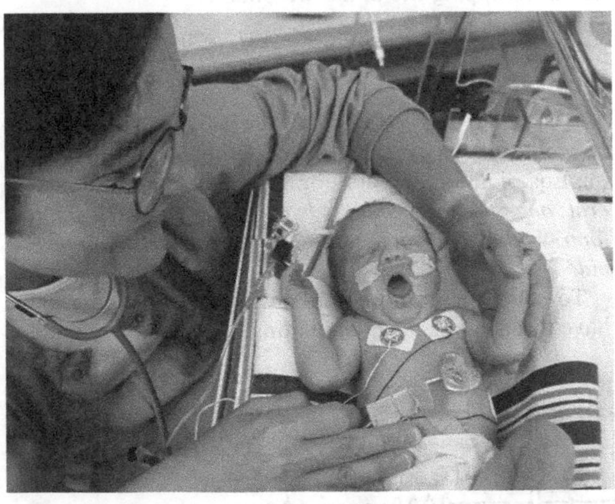

Figure 17.37. The resistance of the thermistor taped to the abdomen of the infant changes rapidly with the temperature. This provides information to an electronic circuit that controls the incubator temperature, compensating for the baby's erratic temperature control system. (David Joel / Getty Images, Inc.)

A *strain gauge* exploits the dependence of the resistance of a wire on its geometry. A small wire grid is bonded to a flexible backing material, which is attached to a flexible diaphragm; the entire unit is covered with rubber. If the diaphragm flexes, the wire grid is distorted, and its resistance changes. This strain gauge and its attached wires can be swallowed by a patient to measure pressures within the digestive tract or inserted with a catheter into veins or arteries to measure blood pressures.

Resistance measurements are useful in chemistry and biochemistry laboratories. The resistivity of a conducting or *electrolytic* solution is measured with a *conductivity cell*, which consists of two metal plates immersed in the solution. The cell is calibrated by using it to measure the resistance of a solution of known resistivity. For example, strongly acidic or basic solutions have many free ions and therefore have a low resistivity or high conductivity. If one gradually adds measured amounts of a basic solution to an acidic solution of unknown concentration, the conductivity of the sample drops sharply as the point of exact acid–base neutralization is approached, and the number of free ions becomes very small. This procedure is called *titration* and can be used to find the concentration of the acid (Fig. 17.38).

Resistance measurements are also used to study changes in living cells. A decrease in the cell resistance means that ions can more easily pass through the cell membrane. Therefore the changes in the resistance that occur when various materials are added to the cellular environment give clues to their effects on the membrane.

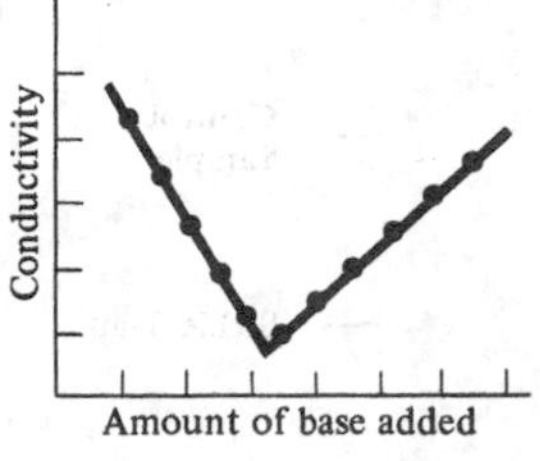

Figure 17.38. The conductivity of a solution is smallest at the point of exact acid–base neutralization. (The conductivity σ is the inverse of the resistivity ρ.)

17.11 | ELECTROPHORESIS

Electrophoresis is an efficient technique for separating and analyzing the mixtures of proteins found in human blood and in other biological materials. It is based on the fact that the drift velocities of molecules in an electric field depend on their masses. When a solution is placed in an electric field, large protein molecules with a net charge of a few times the electronic charge but with masses of thousands of atomic mass units experience small accelerations. Thus, they drift much more slowly than do small ions, such as Na^+ or Cl^-.

In an electrophoretic technique commonly used for medical diagnostic studies, one end of a moistened filter paper strip is placed in the protein solution. A potential difference is applied across the ends of the strip, and the protein molecules of various sizes migrate at different rates along the strip. If the process is stopped after a while, the various proteins have traveled different distances and are separated into several components (Fig. 17.39). Comparison with standard electrophoresis patterns then indicates whether certain abnormalities are present. More elaborate electrophoretic techniques can separate as many as 40 proteins in human blood plasma.

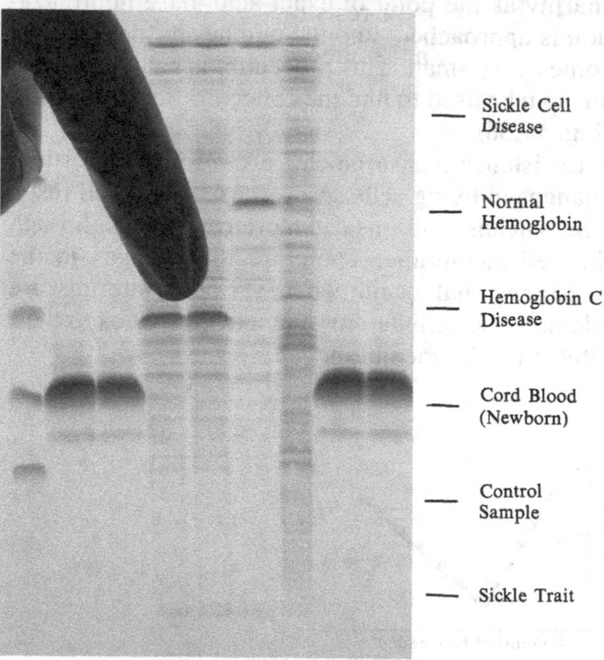

Figure 17.39. Electrophoretic separation of blood samples can be used to help diagnose many disorders. (Jean Claude Revy - ISM / Phototake.)

17.12 | KIRCHHOFF'S RULES IN COMPLEX CIRCUITS

We noted in Section 17.5 that Kirchhoff's rules permit us to analyze any dc circuit, including circuits too complex for the parallel and series formulas to apply. The procedure is simple in principle, but one has to be careful to get all the signs right in constructing the equations, and the algebra rapidly gets messy.

Recall the two rules: (1) the sum of the potential drops around any closed path is zero; (2) the current entering any point must equal the current leaving. We apply these in the following example.

Example 17.15

Find the currents in the circuit in Fig. 17.40.

We start by applying the second rule to point d, where I_1 and I_3 enter and I_2 leaves. According to the rule,

$$I_1 + I_3 = I_2 \quad \text{(i)}$$

We can also apply this rule at point a, but the same equation results with an overall minus sign. *In general, if there are* n *points where currents branch, the second rule can give us* n − 1 *independent equations.*

We now apply the first rule to the loops $abcda$ and $adefa$. Dropping the units, we obtain

$$-2I_1 + 6 - 8 + 12I_3 = 0 \quad \text{(ii)}$$

$$-12I_3 + 8 - 4I_2 = 0 \quad \text{(iii)}$$

We can also apply the first rule to the larger loop $abcdefa$; this yields the same equation we get by adding Eqs. ii and iii, so nothing new is obtained. *In general, once the first rule has been applied to each small loop, we have extracted all the information it can provide.*

To solve for the three unknown currents, we must have three independent equations; we have now found

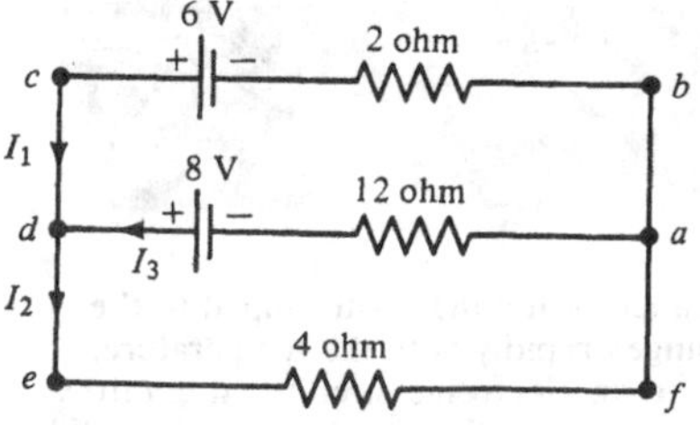

Figure 17.40. Example 17.15.

three such equations. Solving three linear equations for three unknowns is straightforward if you know how to use determinants. Alternatively, the equations can be combined two at a time to eliminate one unknown, reducing the problem to two equations in two unknowns. These are then solved as in Appendix B.4.

The set of equations we have here is relatively simple to solve. From Eq. ii, we find immediately

$$I_1 = 6I_3 - 1 \qquad \text{(iv)}$$

Also, from Eq. iii, we have

$$I_2 = 2 - 3I_3 \qquad \text{(v)}$$

If we substitute these expressions for I_1 and I_2 into Eq. i, we get

$$(6I_3 - 1) + I_3 = 2 - 3I_3$$

Solving for I_3,

$$I_3 = 0.3 \text{ A}$$

Substituting this result into Eqs. iv and v, we obtain

$$I_1 = 0.8 \text{ A}, \qquad I_2 = 1.1 \text{ A}$$

EXERCISES ON SUPPLEMENTARY TOPICS

Section 17.9 | Atomic Theory of Resistance

17-84 At room temperature the average random thermal speed of a conduction electron in copper is about 10^5 m s^{-1}, and there are approximately 10^{29} conduction electrons per cubic metre. (a) Using the measured resistivity, what is the mean free path of an electron in the copper? (b) Find the ratio of this distance to the interatomic spacing, 4.2×10^{-10} m.

Section 17.10 | Applications of Resistance Measurements

17-85 The two parallel electrodes in a conductivity cell each have an area of 1.4×10^{-4} m^2, and they are separated by 4×10^{-2} m. The cell has a resistance of 370 ohms when filled with a particular electrolytic solution. Find the resistivity of the solution.

17-86 A conductivity cell is calibrated by filling it with a solution of known conductivity σ and measuring its resistance R. The *cell constant* k is defined as $R\sigma$. (a) When a cell is filled with an aqueous solution of potassium chloride with conductivity 0.277 ohm^{-1} m^{-1}, the resistance is 190 ohms. What is the cell constant? (b) If the area of each plate is 1.2×10^{-4} m^2, what is their average separation?

17-87 The resistance R and resistivity ρ of a sample in a conductivity cell are related by $\rho = R/k$, where k is the *cell constant*. The cell constant for a particular cell is 42 m^{-1}. (a) When the cell is filled with a potassium sulfate solution, the resistance is 570 ohms. What is the resistivity of the solution? (b) What is the conductivity of the solution?

17-88 A conductivity cell has a resistance of 156 ohms when filled with a potassium chloride solution with conductivity 0.277 ohm^{-1} m^{-1}. Its resistance is 755 ohms when it is filled with a sodium chloride solution. Find the conductivity of the sodium chloride solution.

PROBLEMS ON SUPPLEMENTARY TOPICS

17-89 In Fig. 17.41, find (a) I_2; (b) r; (c) $\mathscr{E}$.

17-90 Find I_1, I_2, and I_3 in Fig. 17.42.

17-91 Two batteries with EMFs of 6 V and internal resistances of 0.5 ohm are connected in parallel to a 10-ohm resistor. How much power is dissipated in the resistor?

17-92 When the direction of a current is guessed incorrectly, its value turns out to be negative; this

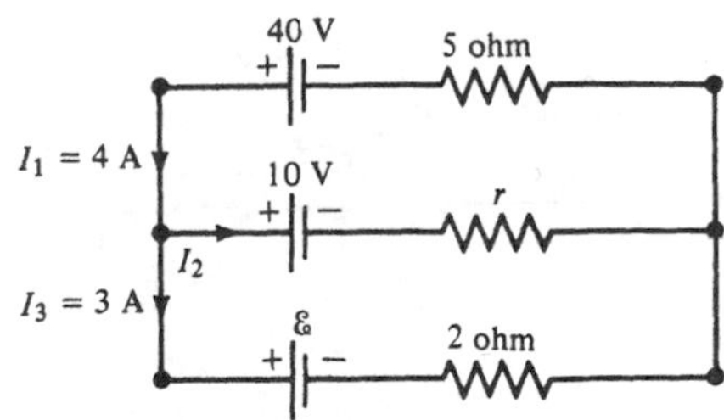

Figure 17-41. Problem 17-89.

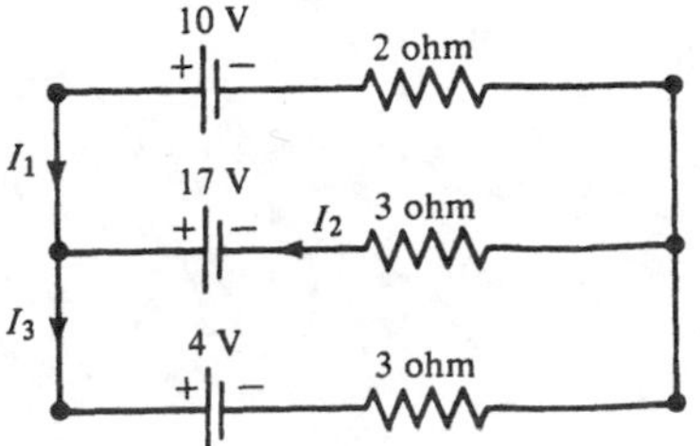

Figure 17-42. Problem 17-90.

tells us that the current is in the opposite direction. Repeat Example 17.15 assuming I_3 is in the opposite direction (to the right), and show that the results have the same physical meaning.

Additional Reading

O. H. Smith, An Inexpensive High Resistance Voltmeter, *American Journal of Physics*, vol. 19, 1951, p. 224.

Charles F. Dalziel, Electric Shock Hazard, *IEEE Spectrum*, vol. 7, February 1972, p. 41.

G. D. Friedlander, Electricity in Hospitals, Elimination of Lethal Hazards, *IEEE Spectrum*, vol. 8, September 1971, p. 40.

B. N. Turman, Is a Swimmer Safe in a Lightning Storm? *The Physics Teacher*, May 1980, p. 388.

Brian B. Schwartz and Simon Foner, Large Scale Applications of Superconductivity, *Physics Today*, vol. 30, July 1977, p. 34.

Barry N. Taylor, New Measurement Standards of 1990, *Physics Today*, August 1989, p. 23. Standards for the volt and ohm.

Scientific American articles:

Giorgio de Sautillana, Alessandro Volta, January 1965, p. 82.

Henry Ehrenreich, The Electrical Properties of Materials, September 1967, p. 194.

Werner Rieder, Circuit Breakers, January 1971, p. 76.

L. O. Barthold and H. G. Pfeiffer, High Voltage Transmission, May 1964, p. 3.

Curtis A. Williams, Jr., Immunoelectrophoresis, March 1960, p. 130.

R. T. Mattias, Superconductivity, November 1957, p. 92.

W. A. Little, Superconductivity at Room Temperature, February 1965, p. 21.

N. B. Brandt and N. I. Ginzberg, Superconductivity at High Pressure, April 1971, p. 83.

T. H. Geballe, New Superconductors, November 1971, p. 22.

Donald P. Snowden, Superconductors for Power Transmission, April 1972, p. 84.

T. H. Geballe and J. K. Hulm, Superconductors in Electric-Power Technology, November 1980, p. 138.

Juri Matisoo, The Superconducting Computer, May 1980, p. 50.

CHAPTER 18 NERVE CONDUCTION

In the preceding chapter, we applied the concepts of electric potential, current, resistance, and capacitance to electrical circuits and instruments. These concepts can also be applied to the biological phenomenon of nerve conduction.

Information is transmitted in the human body by electrical pulses in nerve fibers called *axons*. These pulses differ greatly from pulses in copper telephone wires because an axon is a complex structure in which biochemical processes play an important role. An axon has a very high resistance and is poorly insulated from its surroundings, so after a very short distance nerve pulses become very weak and must be amplified. By comparison, telephone messages need to be amplified only after traveling many kilometres. Also, the velocity of a nerve pulse is only about one millionth that of a pulse in a wire; the latter travels with nearly the speed of light.

Our discussion in this chapter centers on understanding two electric potentials observed in nerves. In its undisturbed or *resting state*, the interior of an axon is at a lower potential than the surrounding *interstitial fluid*. This is the *resting potential*. When a nerve is suitably stimulated, a current pulse travels along the axon. The associated transient potential change is termed the *action potential*.

18.1 | THE STRUCTURE OF NERVE CELLS

Like other cells, a nerve cell is separated from its surroundings by a membrane that restricts the flow of materials. However, it is atypical in shape (Fig. 18.1). Protuberances called *dendrites*, as well as a long thin structure, the *axon*, are attached to the central core of the cell, the *cell body*. Axons are typically 1 to 20 micrometres in diameter (1 micrometre = 1 μm = 10^{-6} m) and may be quite long. For example, nerves controlling the muscles have their cell bodies in the spinal column. Since some axons

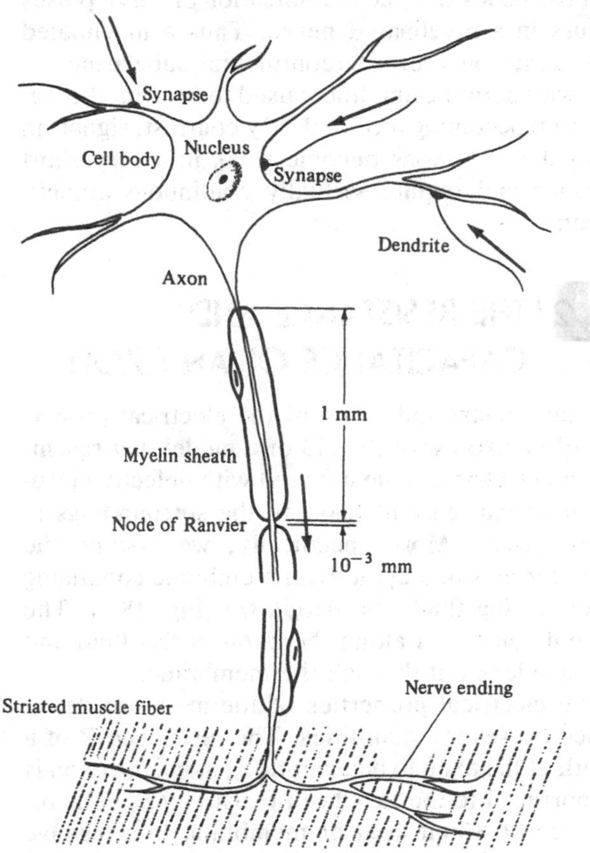

Figure 18.1. A typical nerve. Arrows indicate the direction of nerve impulse conduction.

reach as far as the foot, a human axon may be 1 m long. The dendrites are typically shorter and thinner, but like the axon, they may have several branches. One nerve cell can influence another at points called *synapses* where dendrites make functional contact.

Wrapped around some axons of higher animals are *Schwann cells*, which form a multilayered *myelin sheath*, reducing the membrane capacitance and increasing its electrical resistance. This sheath allows a nerve pulse to travel farther without amplification, reducing the metabolic energy required by the nerve cell. Each Schwann cell is about 1 mm = 10^{-3} m long, but the distance between successive Schwann cells is only about 1 μm = 10^{-6} m. In these short spaces between successive cells, called the *nodes of Ranvier*, the axon is in close contact with the surrounding interstitial fluid. We will see that it is at the nodes that the amplification of nerve pulses occurs in a myelinated nerve. Thus a myelinated axon resembles an intercontinental submarine cable, with periodic amplifiers used to prevent the signal from becoming too weak. By contrast, signals in unmyelinated axons become weak in a very short distance and require virtually continuous amplification.

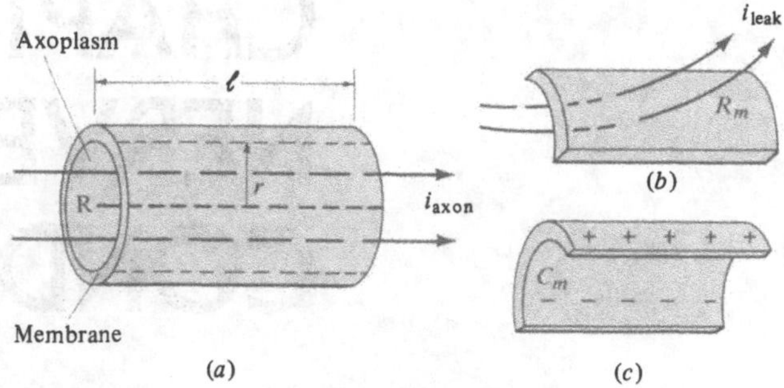

Figure 18.2. (*a*) The conducting axoplasm has a resistance R to a current i_{axon} along the axon. (*b*) The resistance of a unit area of membrane to a leakage current i_{leak} is R_m. (*c*) Charges can accumulate on the two sides of the membrane. The capacitance of a unit area is C_m.

18.2 | THE RESISTANCE AND CAPACITANCE OF AN AXON

We can understand many of the electrical properties of an axon with the aid of a model that resembles an electrical cable covered with defective insulation so that current leaks to the surroundings in many places. More specifically, we assume the axon consists of a cylindrical membrane containing a conducting fluid, the *axoplasm* (Fig. 18.2). The current can travel along the axon in this fluid and can also leak out through the membrane.

The electrical properties of the axon are determined by several quantities. The resistance R of a length of the axon to a current i_{axon} along the axon is proportional to the axoplasm resistivity ρ_a. The resistance of a unit area of membrane to a leakage current i_{leak} is labeled R_m. The membrane also has capacitance, since charges of opposite signs accumulate on the two sides of the membrane. The charge per unit area divided by the resulting potential difference is the capacitance of a unit area C_m.

From Eq. 17.5, the resistance of a wire of length ℓ, cross-sectional area $A = \pi r^2$, and resistivity ρ_a is $R = \rho_a \ell / A$. Using the typical axon parameters given in Table 18.1, a 1-cm = 10^{-2}-m length of axon has a resistance

$$R = \frac{\rho_a \ell}{\pi r^2} = \frac{(2 \text{ ohm m})(0.01 \text{ m})}{\pi (5 \times 10^{-6} \text{ m})^2} = 2.5 \times 10^8 \text{ ohm} \qquad (18.1)$$

This is a huge resistance! It equals that of 70,000 kilometres of No. 40 copper wire, the thinnest wire normally manufactured, with a diameter of 0.08 mm. Nature has paradoxically devised an efficient communication system using a "wire" that would usually be considered a good insulator.

The membrane is quite thin, so a small section appears nearly flat. This permits us to use the parallel plate capacitance formula, Eq. 16.25, which states that the capacitance is proportional to the plate area A. A length ℓ of membrane has a surface area $A = 2\pi r \ell$. Since the capacitance per unit area is C_m, the capacitance of the length ℓ of axon is

$$C = C_m(2\pi r \ell) \qquad (18.2)$$

Using the data of Table 18.1, a 1-cm length of an unmyelinated axon of radius 5 μm has a capacitance of 3.1×10^{-9} F. A similar myelinated axon segment has a much larger distance between the interstitial fluid and the axoplasm. Its capacitance is therefore

TABLE 18.1

Values of axon parameters used in examples. Measured values vary somewhat with the type of axon. (The resistivity of the interstitial fluid is small and can be neglected.)

Quantity	Myelinated Axon	Unmyelinated Axon
Axoplasm resistivity ρ_a	2 ohm m	2 ohm m
Capacitance per unit area of membrane C_m	5×10^{-5} F m^{-2}	10^{-2} F m^{-2}
Resistance of a unit area of membrane R_m	40 ohm m^2	0.2 ohm m^2
Radius r	5 μm = 5×10^{-6} m	5 μm = 5×10^{-6} m

smaller by a factor of about 200, because the capacitance of any capacitor diminishes as its two conductors are separated.

Because a membrane is not a perfect insulator, charge leaks from the axoplasm through the membrane into the interstitial fluid. The resistance of a conductor is inversely proportional to its cross-sectional area. If the resistance to leakage currents through a unit surface area of membrane is R_m, then a portion of the membrane with surface area A has a resistance $R' = R_m/A$. For a length ℓ of axon, the surface area of the membrane is $2\pi r\ell$, and the membrane leakage resistance is

$$R' = \frac{R_m}{2\pi r\ell} \tag{18.3}$$

Using the values in Table 18.1, a 1-cm length of unmyelinated axon has a leakage resistance $R' = 6.4 \times 10^5$ ohms, which is less than 1 percent of the axoplasm resistance R. Hence most of a current entering an axon segment leaks out through the walls in much less than 1 cm.

According to our model, the axoplasm resistance R is proportional to the length ℓ of the axon segment, and the leakage resistance R' is proportional to $1/\ell$. Thus there is a characteristic distance λ, called the *space parameter,* at which R and R' are equal. At that distance, there is as much resistance to the flow of charge along the axon as through the walls. If you go further than λ, the axoplasm resistance is greater than the leakage resistance, and most of the current has leaked out through the membrane.

Using Eqs. 18.1 and 18.3 for R and R', respectively, λ must satisfy $R = R'$ or

$$\frac{\rho_a \lambda}{\pi r^2} = \frac{R_m}{2\pi r\lambda}$$

Solving, the space parameter is

$$\lambda = \sqrt{\frac{R_m r}{2\rho_a}} \tag{18.4}$$

The values in Table 18.1 give $\lambda = 0.05$ cm for a typical unmyelinated axon and 0.7 cm for a myelinated axon. Thus a current pulse can travel much farther without amplification in a myelinated nerve.

18.3 | IONIC CONCENTRATIONS AND THE RESTING POTENTIAL

So far, we have considered the capacitance and the resistances associated with an axon. In this section, we consider some additional information that is needed to understand the behavior of an axon in its undisturbed or resting state: the differences in the ionic concentrations and potentials inside and outside the axon.

Figure 18.3 lists the concentrations of various ions inside, c_i, and outside, c_o, a resting axon. Of the ions that can pass through the membrane, sodium (Na^+) and chlorine (Cl^-) are much more numerous outside, while potassium (K^+) has a larger concentration inside. Conventionally, the electric potential V_o in the fluid outside the cell is taken to be zero. The potential inside the axon is found to be

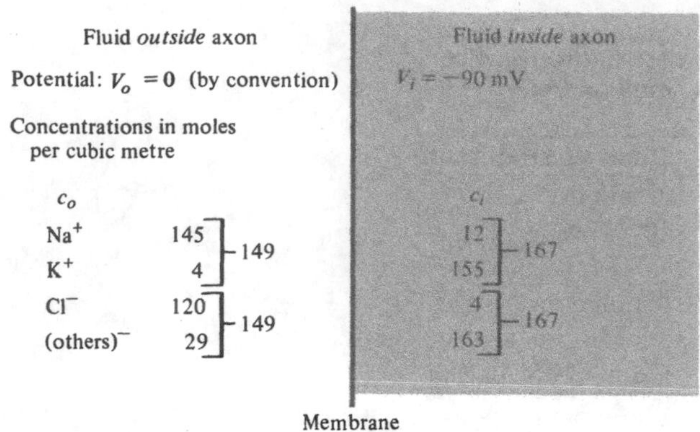

Figure 18.3. Concentrations and potentials inside and outside a typical mammalian axon in the resting state.

90 mV lower, so $V_i = -90$ mV. A number of important consequences follow from these observations, as we see shortly.

According to Fig. 18.3, there are equal numbers of positive and negative ions inside and outside the cell. However, there is a potential difference across the membrane, so there must be small net charges $\pm Q$ on either side of the membrane. These can be calculated from $Q = CV$, using the capacitance found earlier and the measured resting potential. The excess of negative ions over positive ions inside the cell turns out to be only about 1/100,000 times the number of negative ions in the cell. An equal number of excess positive ions is present in the interstitial fluid. The excess ions form thin charge layers on either side of the membrane.

Let us now consider the effects arising from the fact that the concentration of Na^+ is much higher outside the cell than inside. We saw in Chapter Ten that because of their random thermal motion, particles tend to diffuse from regions where their concentrations are high to regions where they are lower. The permeability of a cell membrane is a measure of the ease with which a given molecule or ion can pass through the membrane. Sodium ions will diffuse *into* the cell at a rate proportional to the Na^+ concentration difference $c_o - c_i$ and to the permeability of the membrane to Na^+ (Fig. 18.4). The resting potential is negative, so the electric field is directed into the cell, and it drives additional positive Na^+ ions through the membrane *into* the cell. Since the Na^+ concentration remains much larger outside, *sodium must be continually brought back out against both the electrical forces and the effects of the concentration differences*. This return process requires an ongoing expenditure of metabolic energy.

The discussion of the Cl^- and K^+ flows is more complicated. There are more Cl^- ions outside, so diffusion produces a net flow into the cell. However, the electric force on negative ions is opposite to the field, so the electric field draws some Cl^- ions outward. Conversely, K^+ ions diffuse outward because of the concentration difference, but they also flow inward under electric forces. Thus Cl^- and K^+ each have flows in both directions across the membrane (Fig. 18.4). In a resting axon, the effect of the K^+ concentration difference exceeds that of the potential difference, and there is a net outward movement of K^+ ions. As in the case of sodium, there must be a mechanism that returns potassium into the cell and maintains the imbalanced concentrations. There is no net movement of Cl^- ions, since the effect of the Cl^- concentration difference is exactly balanced by the effect of the resting potential difference.

Figure 18.4. Ionic currents I_c due to concentration differences and I_p due to potential differences. (*a*) Both Na^+ flows are into the cell. (*b*) The flows exactly balance for Cl^-. (*c*) For K^+, I_c is slightly larger than I_p, and there is a slight outward flow.

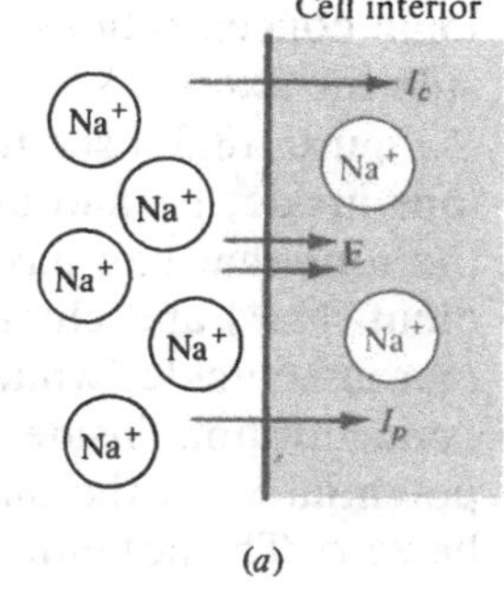

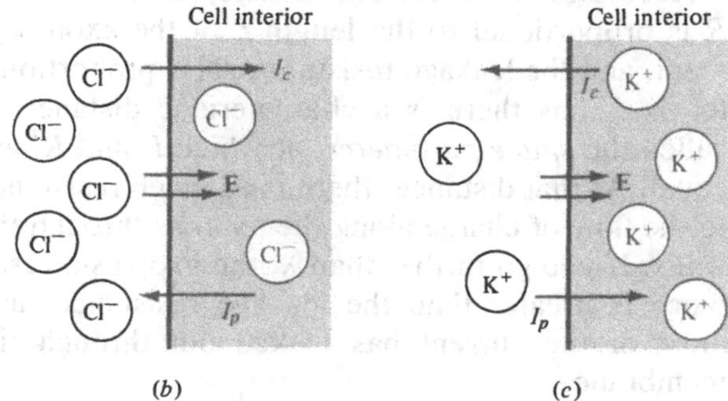

Nernst Equation | We can determine whether an ion is in equilibrium by calculating a theoretical resting potential for which there would be no net flow of that ion across the cell membrane. At this *equilibrium potential difference* across the cell membrane, the flows due to the concentration and potential differences are exactly balanced.

The equilibrium potential difference for an ion can be found from the *Nernst equation*. Although its derivation involves mathematics beyond the level of this textbook, it is based on a model that treats ions in a dilute solution as an ideal gas. A potential difference across a membrane will produce a concentration imbalance on the two sides of the membrane. Equilibrium occurs when the potential energy of one ion with charge q, $q(V_i - V_o)$, is equal to the work necessary to transfer it to the region of higher concentration. According to the model, this work is $k_B T \ln(c_o/c_i)$, where k_B is the Boltzmann constant, T is the Kelvin temperature, and $\ln(c_o/c_i)$ is the natural logarithm (to the base e) of the concentration ratio. (Logarithms are reviewed in Appendix B.10.) Hence the ion is in equilibrium if the concentrations satisfy the Nernst equation,

$$q(V_i - V_o) = k_B T \ln \frac{c_o}{c_i} \qquad (18.5)$$

Example 18.1 illustrates the use of the Nernst equation by considering the K^+ concentrations.

Example 18.1

Compare the equilibrium potential difference for K^+ with the observed resting potential, −90 mV. (Use the data in Fig. 18.3 and assume a temperature of 37°C = 310 K.)

The charge e on a K^+ ion is $q = e = 1.60 \times 10^{-19}$ C, and $k_B = 1.38 \times 10^{-23}$ J K^{-1}. From Fig. 18.3, $\ln c_o/c_i = \ln 4/155 = -\ln 155/4$. Hence the Nernst equation gives the equilibrium potential difference

$$\begin{aligned} V_i - V_o &= \frac{k_B T}{q} \ln \frac{c_o}{c_i} \\ &= \frac{(1.38 \times 10^{-23}\ \text{J K}^{-1})(310\ \text{K})}{(1.60 \times 10^{-19}\ \text{C})} \left(-\ln \frac{155}{4}\right) \\ &= -98\ \text{mV} \end{aligned}$$

This is slightly larger in magnitude than the resting potential, −90 mV. Therefore, in the resting axon the inward flow due to the potential difference is not quite as large as the outward flow due to the concentration difference. If $V_i - V_o$ were −98 mV, the two flows would balance exactly.

If we apply the Nernst equation to Cl^-, we find that the equilibrium potential difference is −90 mV. This is equal to the resting potential, so the Cl^- flows are balanced as noted before. The equilibrium potential difference for Na^+ is +66 mV, which is opposite in sign to the resting potential. In other words, if enough positive charge entered the axon to reverse its polarity and change the axon potential to +66 mV, the outward flow of Na^+ due to the potential difference would balance the inward flow due to the concentration difference. One way to visualize this situation is to think of the concentration difference as producing the same inward flow as a 66-mV battery. When the charge inside the axon builds up enough so that it produces a 66-mV axon potential, there will be no net flow of Na^+ ions.

The Sodium–Potassium Pump | The net flows of Na^+ into the cell and of K^+ out of the cell due to diffusion and to the electric forces are referred to as *passive flows*, because energy does not have to be supplied for them to occur. Some as yet undetermined process returns the Na^+ and K^+ across the membrane and maintains the nonequilibrium ionic concentrations. This energy expending process is called the *active Na–K transport* or the *Na–K pump*.

In the resting state, the axon membrane is about 100 times more permeable to K^+ than to Na^+. This means that equal concentration or potential differences would produce much larger flows of potassium ions than of sodium ions. However, the net passive sodium and potassium flows are about equal, because the resting potential is much closer to the equilibrium potential for K^+ than for Na^+. It is thought that the pump transports one K^+ ion into the cell for each Na^+ ion it removes.

The Na–K pump is responsible for the establishment and maintenance of the resting potential and the concentration imbalances. We can see this explicitly if we suppose that initially the potentials V_i inside the cell and V_o outside are both zero and that the concentrations of Na^+, K^+, and Cl^- are the same on both sides of the membrane. In a short time the pump transports a few K^+ ions into the cell and as many Na^+ ions out of the cell. Since the permeability of the membrane to K^+ ions is relatively large, some K^+ ions diffuse back out of the cell. A smaller number of Na^+ ions diffuse into the cell, since the membrane is less permeable to Na^+ ions. Thus a net positive charge has developed outside the cell, even though the pump has not transferred any net charge across the membrane. This positive charge attracts negative ions from inside the cell. The only negative ion inside the cell that can readily pass through the membrane is Cl^-, so some Cl^- ions move out of the cell, reducing but not quite eliminating the excess of positive ions outside the cell. Since the total system is electrically neutral, there is then an equal slight excess of negative ions inside the cell. The excess charges on either side of the membrane produce a potential difference across it, and now V_i is negative if V_o is defined to be zero.

As the pumping continues, the outside Na^+ and Cl^- concentrations, the inside K^+ concentration, and the magnitude of V_i all gradually increase. Eventually, equilibrium is reached and the concentrations stop changing when the passive Na^+ and K^+ flows due to diffusion and to the electrical forces exactly balance the active transport due to the pump. Because the membrane is much more permeable to K^+ ions than to Na^+ ions, the resting potential $V_i = -90$ mV, at which equilibrium occurs, is much closer to the −98-mV K^+ equilibrium than to the +66-mV Na^+ equilibrium potential.

It is important to note that if the membrane were suddenly to become much more permeable to Na^+, the balance would be upset briefly by an increased flow of Na^+ ions into the axon. A small increase in the number of sodium ions entering the cell would substantially modify V_i without significantly altering the ionic concentrations. We see in Section 18.5 that such a change of permeability is believed to occur when the nerve is stimulated and an action potential is produced.

In summary, the observed resting state potential and ionic concentrations imply a passive flow of Na^+ ions into the axon and of K^+ ions out of the axon due to diffusion and electrical forces. The continued existence of these imbalances is due to the Na–K pump, which actively transports Na^+ out of the cell and K^+ into the cell, expending metabolic energy in the process. The magnitude and sign of the potential of the cell, in turn, is largely determined by the ratio of the permeabilities of the membrane for K^+ and Na^+.

18.4 | THE RESPONSE TO WEAK STIMULI

Having considered the resting state of the axon, we now examine the response of an axon to a weak stimulus. In most experiments, the stimuli are electrical, since these are easily controlled and do not injure the cell if they are sufficiently mild. For an electrical stimulus smaller than a critical threshold value, the response of the axon is similar to that of an analog network of resistors and capacitors. Specifically, if a weak stimulus is applied at some point on an axon, no significant axon potential changes occur beyond a few millimetres from that point. By contrast, a stimulus *above* the threshold level produces a current pulse that travels the length of the axon without attenuation. This current pulse and the associated action potential are discussed in the next section.

We can develop the analog circuit for the axon by dividing the axon into many short segments. The interstitial fluid surrounding the axon has very little resistance and may be represented by a perfect conductor. Each axon segment has a resistance R to a current i_{axon} along its length. The membrane has a resistance R' to a leakage current i_{leak} plus a capacitance C (Figs. 18.5*a*, *b*). A series of several segments is then analogous to the complex network of resistors and capacitors in Fig. 18.5*c*. The EMF shown there represents an applied stimulus.

The behavior of this complex axon analog circuit is more readily understood if we first consider the simplest RC network in Fig. 18.6*a*. Suppose that the initial charge q on C is zero, and the switch is closed at $t = 0$. The charge q and the potential difference $v = q/C$ will gradually increase. As we saw in Chapter Seventeen, the time needed to reach a characteristic fraction of the final values of q and v is determined by the time constant, $T = RC$.

When there are two resistors and two capacitors, as in Fig. 18.6*b*, the charging process is more com-

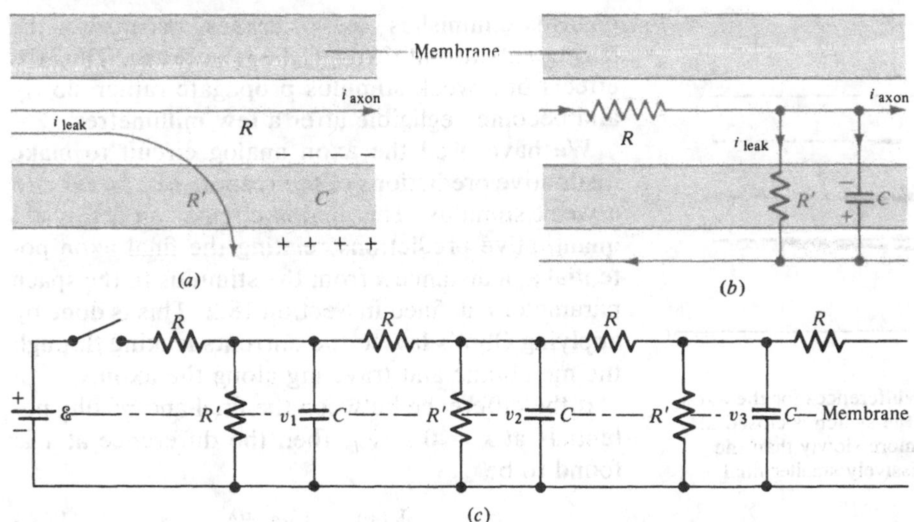

Figure 18.5. (*a*) A short segment of an axon. (*b*) The equivalent analog circuit for the segment. (*c*) The analog circuit for several axon segments. The EMF $\mathscr{E}$ represents the stimulus.

plicated. The potential difference v_2 across C_2 must increase more slowly than the potential difference v_1 across C_1, since the path from the battery to C_2 and back has resistance $2R$. As more and more RC pairs are added, the potential difference across each added capacitor rises ever more slowly. Consequently, in the axon analog circuit (Fig. 18.5*c*), v_2 will change more slowly than v_1, v_3 still more slowly, and so on.

The effect of a leakage resistor can be seen in Fig. 18.6*c*. There is always some current in the conducting path through R and R'. Thus there is a corresponding potential drop across R, and the final potential difference across the capacitor is less than the EMF. In the axon analog circuit, the final potential differences steadily diminish as we move to the right because of the current lost through the leakage resistors R'.

To summarize, when the switch is closed or a "stimulus" is applied in the axon analog circuit, the potential differences across the capacitors gradually change. As one goes farther from the stimulus, the

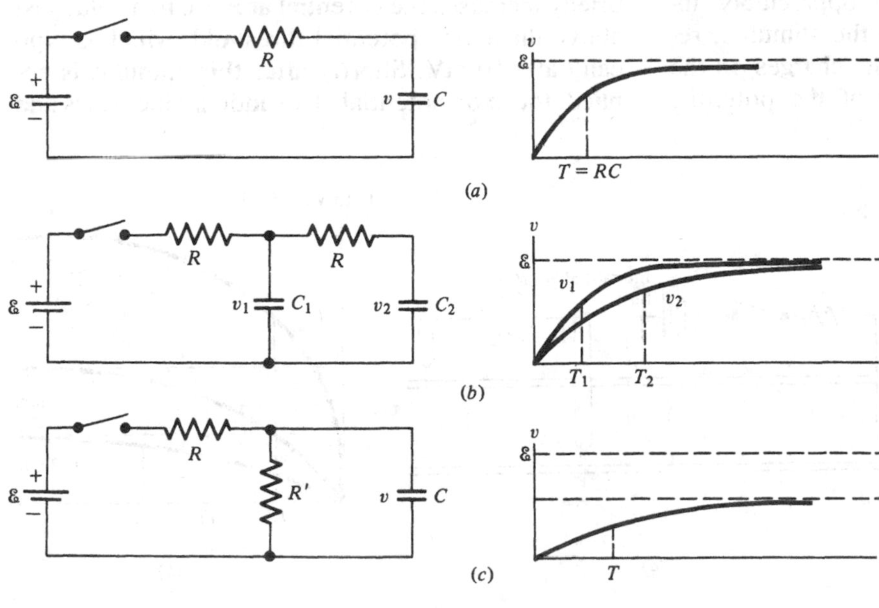

Figure 18.6. Circuit diagrams and capacitor potential differences versus time. The capacitors are initially uncharged, and the switch is closed at $t = 0$. (*a*) Simplest RC circuit. (*b*) v_2 rises more slowly than v_1, but ultimately reaches the same final value, the battery EMF $\mathscr{E}$. (*c*) If a leakage resistor is placed in parallel with the capacitor, the final potential difference v is less than $\mathscr{E}$.

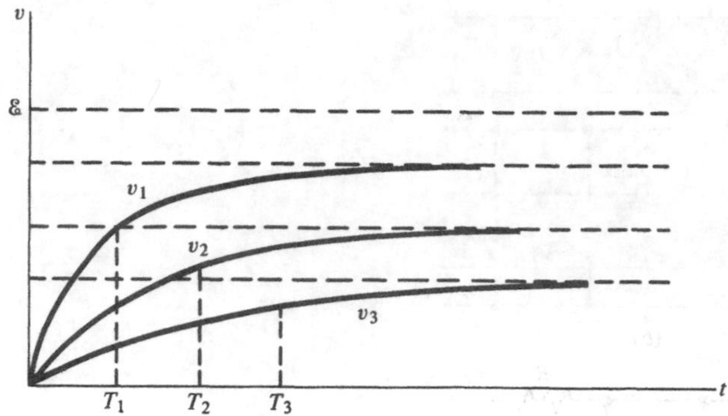

Figure 18.7. The capacitor potential differences for the axon analog circuit of Fig. 18.5*c*, assuming the switch is closed at $t = 0$. Each potential difference rises more slowly than the preceding one and approaches a successively smaller final value.

changes occur more slowly, and their final magnitudes diminish (Fig. 18.7).

Very similar behavior is observed when an unmyelinated axon is stimulated weakly, as in Fig. 18.8. A probe connected to a battery is inserted at $x = 0$, and gradually the axon potential V_i at that point changes from -90 to -60 mV. The time required for this change to occur is determined by the membrane capacitance and the external series resistance r. At other values of x, the potentials change more slowly, reaching a final potential between -90 and -60 mV. As in the axon analog circuit, the time needed to change the potential appreciably increases with the distance x from the stimulus, reflecting the time needed to alter the charges on the membrane. The final magnitude of the potential changes diminishes as x increases, because of the leakage of current through the membrane. Thus the effects of a weak stimulus propagate rather slowly and become negligible after a few millimetres.

We have used the axon analog circuit to make qualitative predictions of the response of an axon to a weak stimulus. The analog circuit can also yield quantitative predictions relating the final axon potential at a distance x from the stimulus to the space parameter λ defined in Section 18.2. This is done by applying Ohm's law to the currents leaking through the membrane and traveling along the axon.

If the difference between the final and resting potentials at $x = 0$ is V_d, then the difference at x is found to be

$$V(x) = V_d e^{-x/\lambda} \tag{18.6}$$

If λ is 0.05 cm, a typical value for an unmyelinated axon, then $V(x)$ diminishes to $V_d e^{-1} = 0.37 V_d$ after 0.05 cm, to $V_d e^{-2} = 0.135 V_d$ after 0.1 cm, and so on. This predicted dependence on x agrees with the experimental data.

18.5 | THE ACTION POTENTIAL

We have seen that when a weak electrical stimulus is applied to an axon, the potential changes are proportional to the stimulus. The situation is very different if a battery such as that shown in Fig. 18.8 briefly increases the potential at $x = 0$ to a value just above the action potential threshold, which is typically at -50 mV. Shortly after this stimulus is applied, the axon potential at x suddenly increases and

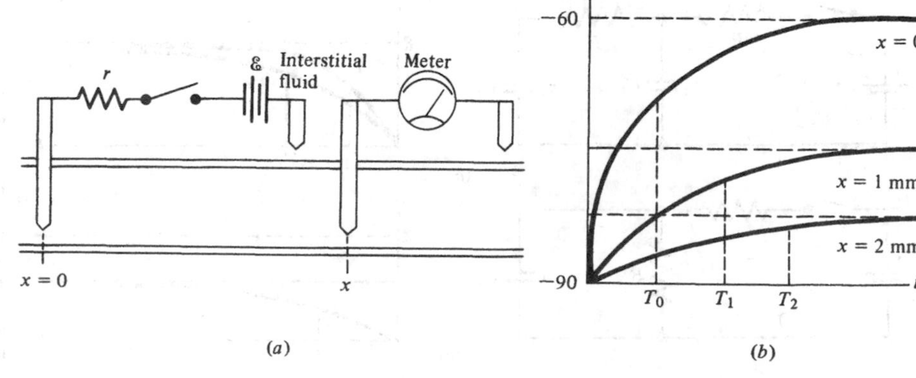

Figure 18.8. (*a*) Apparatus for changing the axon potential at $x = 0$ and observing the resulting change at position x. The "meter" is usually a cathode-ray oscilloscope. (*b*) The axon potential versus time at $x = 0$, 1, and 2 mm. Note the similarities with Fig. 18.7.

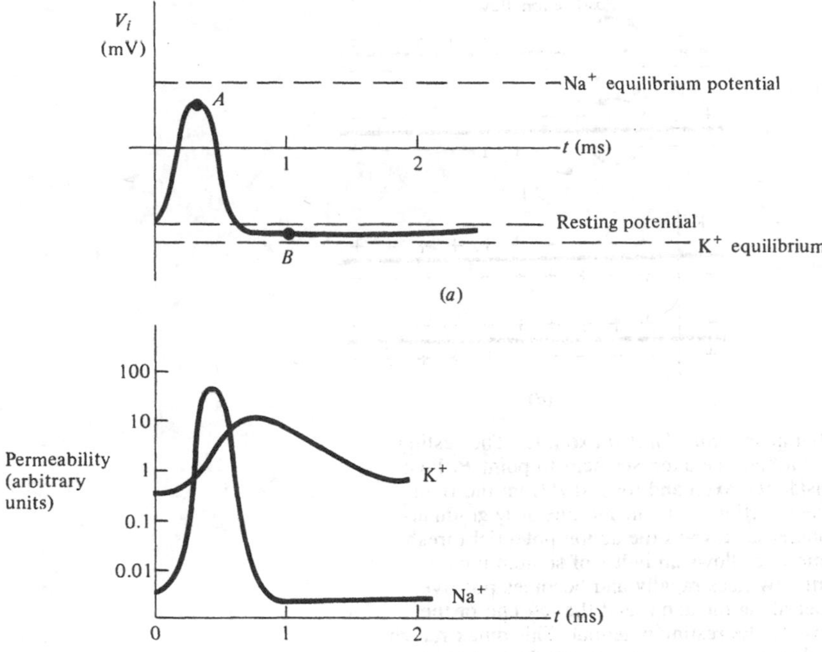

Figure 18.9. (*a*) The axon potential at a point some distance from the stimulus. (*b*) The associated changes in the membrane permeabilities. Note that the vertical scale is logarithmic.

becomes positive, reaching a value as high as +50 mV for some axons (Fig. 18.9*a*). The potential then gradually returns to its resting value. For a particular axon, the shape and peak size of the action potential curve are *independent of the strength of the initial above-threshold stimulus* or the distance x from the stimulus except very near $x = 0$. Thus the action potential is not proportional to the stimulus. Instead, it is a transient *all-or-nothing* response.

In an unmyelinated axon, the action potential is accompanied by dramatic changes in the permeability of the membrane to Na^+ and K^+ (Fig. 18.9*b*). When the axon potential V_i in an unmyelinated axon rises above the action potential threshold at some point, the Na^+ permeability there suddenly increases by a factor of more than 1000. This causes a rapid influx of positive sodium ions, which changes the sign of V_i from negative to positive. After about 0.3 ms, the potential approaches the Na^+ equilibrium potential (point A in Fig. 18.9*a*) as determined from the Nernst equation, and the sodium influx diminishes. Also the sodium permeability begins to decrease toward its normal low level. Meanwhile the potassium permeability has gradually risen by about a factor of 30. Consequently, potassium ions now begin to flow rapidly out of the cell, and V_i again becomes negative. V_i actually reaches a value below the resting potential (point B in Fig. 18.9*a*), close to the K^+ equilibrium potential, which, as we saw before, is slightly more negative than the resting potential. This return over about 1 ms to a potential close to the resting potential is due to the changes in the K^+ permeability and *not* to the effects of the Na–K pump, which acts much more slowly. The pump does gradually reestablish the resting Na^+ and K^+ concentrations that were altered slightly during the action potential pulse; this process takes about 50 ms.

We now see how this mechanism amplifies a pulse and permits an action potential to travel the length of an axon without attenuation. Figure 18.10 shows an unmyelinated axon segment that has been excited at one end, so that V_i is positive at this point. Positive ions move toward this end on the outside of the membrane and away from it inside. This decreases the charge on the adjacent portion of the membrane, so that the axoplasm potential there becomes less negative and rises to the action potential threshold. This triggers an increased sodium

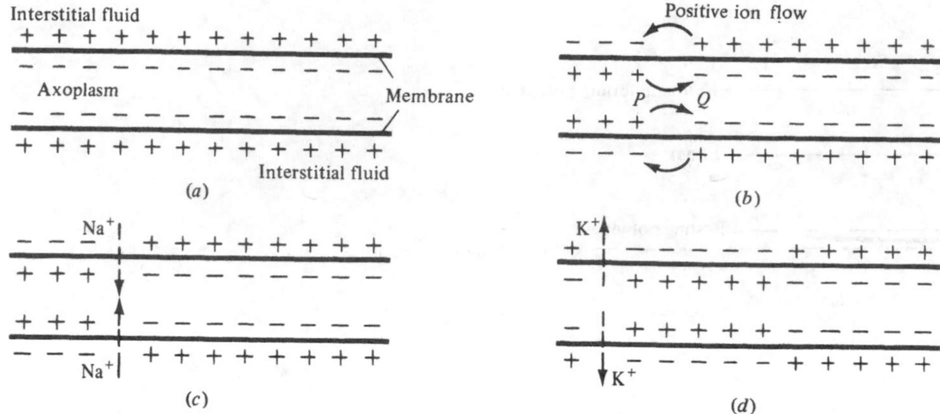

Figure 18.10. Propagation of an action potential in an *unmyelinated* axon. (*a*) The resting state. (*b*) An action potential pulse has traveled through the axon segment to point *P*. Positive ions move away from *P* toward the right inside the axon and toward *P* from the right outside. The charges on either side of the adjacent portion of the membrane at *Q* gradually diminish in magnitude, and the potential there increases toward the action potential threshold. (*c*) Once that threshold is reached, the membrane allows an influx of sodium ions (dashed arrows). The axon potential at this point now rises rapidly and becomes positive. (*d*) The action potential pulse has traveled farther along the axon, and the left end of the segment has returned to a negative potential close to the resting potential. This quick return to a negative axon potential is due to an outward flow of potassium ions (dashed arrows) caused by an increase in the K^+ permeability. The resting state potential and ionic concentrations are restored over a much longer interval by the active Na–K pump.

permeability, leading to a sodium influx and an action potential at the adjacent portion of the membrane. In this way the action potential proceeds from point to point along the entire length of the axon.

The term "amplification" is applied to the process that occurs each time an action potential is generated at some point along an axon, because it is here that energy is expended. The Na–K pump is continually maintaining both the resting potential and the ionic imbalances of Na^+ and K^+ ions across the membrane. In so doing, considerable electric potential energy is stored in the membrane, much like water is stored above a dam. An action potential occurs because of the increases that occur in the permeability of the membrane to Na^+ and K^+ ions. The increases of permeability are analogous to opening a floodgate in the dam. There is a sudden flow of ions through the cell membrane due to the large concentration differences, and it is this flow of ions that provides the current of an action potential. The Na–K pump then acts analogously to a pump at the dam, which redeposits the water above the dam for the next flow. Like the pump at the dam, the Na–K pump requires much more time to restore the ions than elapses during an action potential.

Myelinated Axon | In a myelinated nerve, relatively few ions pass through the myelin sheath except at the nodes of Ranvier, which are about 1 mm apart (Fig. 18.11). At the nodes the membrane responds to an above-threshold stimulus much as in an unmyelinated axon: the Na^+ permeability increases rapidly, producing an influx of Na^+ and the characteristic action potential pulse. This, in turn, produces flows of positive ions away from the node inside the axon and toward the node outside. Some of the axon current leaks through the membrane, but most of it reaches the next node, since the 1-mm internodal distance is small compared to the space parameter λ, which is equal to several millimetres in a typical myelinated axon. The axon current reduces the charges on the membrane and increases the potential at the next node to the action potential threshold level. Consequently, this next node is

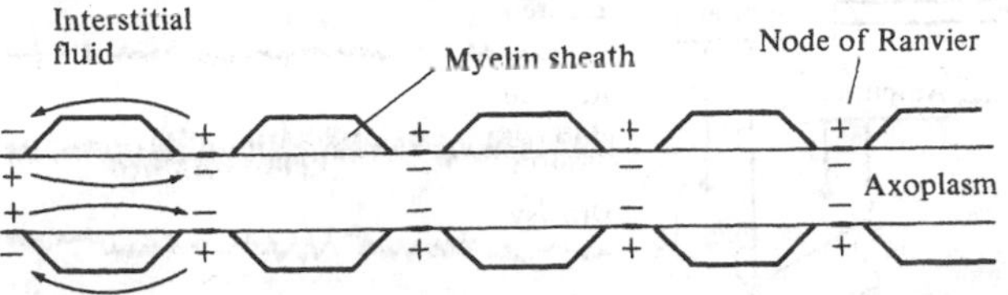

Figure 18.11. Propagation of an action potential in a *myelinated* axon. An above-threshold axon potential at one node triggers an influx of sodium and an action potential pulse, which in turn triggers the next node.

triggered, and the action potential travels along the axon.

Because the amplification and the associated ionic transfers occur only at the nodes, less metabolic energy is needed to restore a myelinated axon to its resting state after an action potential pulse than is required for an unmyelinated axon. The propagation of an action potential is also faster in a myelinated axon. Thus such axons are better suited to transmit rapidly the large amounts of information required by more advanced animals and represent an important evolutionary step.

The velocity of propagation of an action potential between two nodes in a myelinated axon can be predicted with the simple axon model because amplification occurs only at the nodes. Although a rigorous derivation involves advanced mathematics, we can quickly obtain the correct formula for the velocity using plausible physical arguments. This formula is interesting because it indicates some compromises that have been made in the process of evolution.

The action potential velocity v is the distance X between two nodes divided by the time T needed to reduce the charge on the membrane and increase the potential at the second node to the threshold level. This time must be comparable to the time constant RC of the series circuit containing the axoplasm resistance R and membrane capacitance C. R is the resistance from the first node to $X/2$, or to the midpoint of the "capacitor" being charged. Using $\ell = X/2$ in Eq. 18.1 for R and $\ell = X$ in Eq. 18.2 for C gives, for an axon of radius r,

$$T = RC = \left(\frac{\rho_a X}{2\pi r^2}\right)(2\pi r X C_m) = \rho_a C_m \frac{X^2}{r}$$

and

$$v = \frac{X}{T} = \frac{r}{\rho_a C_m X} = 10r \text{ m s}^{-1}\ \mu\text{m}^{-1} \qquad (18.7)$$

This last expression is obtained using $X = 1$ mm and the values of ρ_a and C_m in Fig. 18.3. Measured values of v in metres per second are usually between $12r$ and $17r$, so the simple axon model gives reasonable results.

Equation 18.7 shows that nerve pulses travel rather slowly. For example, if $r = 5\ \mu$m, v is 50 m s^{-1}, and it takes 0.08 s to send messages from a toe stepping on a sharp object to the brain and back again. Increasing the radius of an axon increases the velocity, but it also increases the metabolic energy requirements, so that a compromise must be made. Clearly, long axons that transmit information requiring rapid responses must have large radii, but other axons need not. Accordingly, many, but by no means all, long axons have large radii. For example, about 60 percent of the axons going to muscles are 6 to 10.5 μm in radius. By contrast, in parts of the brain where the nerves are very short, 90 percent of the axons are 2 μm or less in radius.

A subtle process is also involved in choosing the optimum internode spacing, since the velocity varies as $1/X$. If X is increased, the velocity decreases, which is undesirable, but the metabolic energy requirements are also reduced. Thus again, a compromise between high velocity and low energy usage must be made. In nature, X varies over the relatively small range of 1 to 2 mm, suggesting that deviations from this range render the axon less useful in carrying out its function.

18.6 | ELECTROENCEPHALOGRAPH AND ELECTROCARDIOGRAPH

Direct observations of nerve pulses require inserting a probe into a nerve and are impractical for routine medical diagnostic studies. Fortunately, electrodes placed on the skin can pick up small signals related to large-scale electrical activity within the body. This makes possible the *electroencephalograph (EEG)* and *electrocardiograph (EKG)*, instruments that are useful aids in studying brain and heart disorders, respectively.

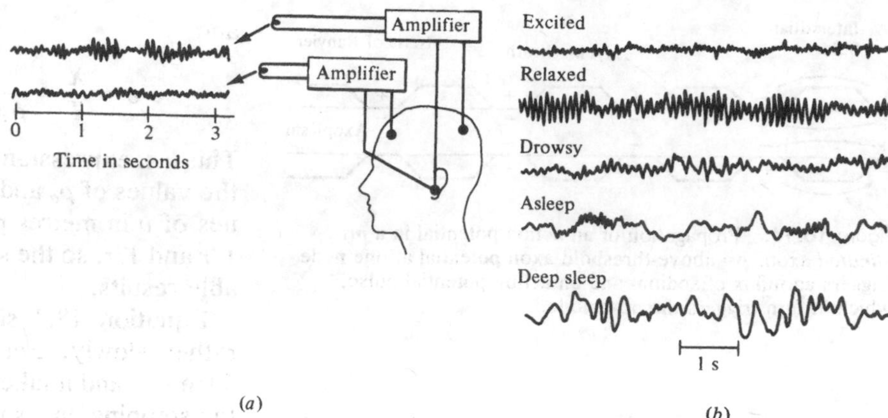

Figure 18.12. Electroencephalograph. (*a*) An electrode attached to the ear provides the reference potential. The two recordings are typical of the response from different areas. (*b*) EEG patterns typical of different states of awareness of a patient.

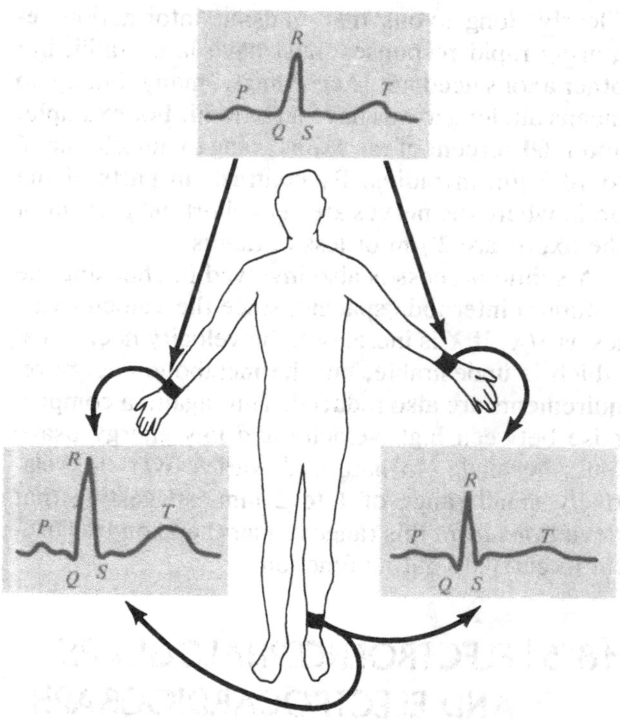

Figure 18.13. The standard limb leads of the electrocardiogram and normal patterns recorded from these leads. The *P* peak corresponds to the initial electrical pulse that triggers a heart cycle. The interval from *P* to *Q* lasts about 0.12 to 0.20 s in a normal person and corresponds to the spread of the pulse over the atria (the upper heart chambers.) The *QRS* interval lasts about 0.06 to 0.10 s and corresponds to the spread of the pulse over the ventricles (lower chambers). The *T* peak is associated with the return of the heart to its normal unstimulated state after a pulse.

Electrical signals arising within the body reach the surface because the resistance of the interstitial fluid is not quite zero. If many axons are simultaneously active, then the potential of the body nearby changes relative to the potential elsewhere in the body. Although the changes observed at the surface are at most 50 μV, or about 0.1 percent of the full action potential changes, they can be amplified and measured or recorded.

An *electroencephalograph* is shown in Fig. 18.12, along with EEGs typical of various states of awareness. Electrodes are placed at standardized locations on the head, and the signals are recorded. Deviations from the norm can aid in the diagnosis of epilepsy, tumors, accidental brain damage, and other disorders.

An *electrocardiograph* records electrical activity associated with the heart. The usual positions for the electrodes are shown in Fig. 18.13 along with typical EKG patterns.

SUMMARY

An axon resembles a poorly insulated electrical cable. Many of its electrical properties can be understood using this model or an equivalent *RC* network.

A resting axon has a potential below that of the surrounding interstitial fluid. The resting potential and nonequilibrium concentrations of Na^+ and K^+ ions are maintained by the active Na–K pump mechanism, which offsets passive ionic flows due to diffusion and to electric forces.

Weak electrical stimuli produce proportional axon responses that are similar to those of the analog *RC* circuit and diminish rapidly with distance. A stimulus that raises the axon potential above a critical threshold triggers a current pulse and an associated action potential. These travel without attenuation along the entire length of the axon, amplified by processes associated with changes in the ionic permeabilities of the membrane.

The velocity of nerve pulses in a myelinated axon is proportional to the axon radius and inversely proportional to the distance between the nodes of Ranvier where amplification occurs. Thus there is a delicate evolutionary compromise between speed and economy of energy usage.

Checklist

Define or explain:

axon	Nernst equation
myelin sheath	Na–K pump
nodes of Ranvier	axon analog circuit
leakage resistance	action potential
space parameter	amplification
equilibrium potential difference	EEG
	EKG

REVIEW QUESTIONS

Q18-1 Compared to a telephone cable, an axon has much ______ resistance, is much more ______ insulated, and needs much ______ frequent amplification.

Q18-2 A myelinated axon is surrounded by ______.

Q18-3 The distance a current can travel without amplification is characterized by the ______.

Q18-4 In the resting state of an axon, there are far more ______ ions on the outside of the membrane than inside and far more ______ ions on the inside than outside.

Q18-5 The Nernst equation relates the potential difference across a membrane to the equilibrium ratio of ______.

Q18-6 When an axon is subjected to a weak stimulus, the potential differences change at a ______ rate and with a ______ final magnitude as one goes farther from the stimulus.

Q18-7 The action potential involves a sudden increase in the membrane permeability to ______ ions.

Q18-8 In a myelinated axon, amplification occurs at the ______.

Q18-9 If the radius of a myelinated axon is doubled, the velocity of the action potential changes by a factor of ______.

Q18-10 Axons with larger radii require more ______ than those with smaller radii.

EXERCISES

When numerical values are required that are not given in the exercise, the data in Table 18.1 and Fig. 18.3 should be used.

Section 18.1 | The Structure of Nerve Cells

18-1 Estimate the number of axons in the human spinal column if the average axon is 10 μm in diameter and the spinal column is 1 cm in diameter.

18-2 An axon 1 m long has nodes of Ranvier every 10^{-3} m. How many times is a nerve pulse amplified when it is transmitted along this axon?

Section 18.2 | The Resistance and Capacitance of an Axon

18-3 Calculate the axoplasm resistance of a 1-cm-long segment of unmyelinated axon of radius 2 μm.

18-4 Calculate the axoplasm resistance of a 1-cm long segment of myelinated axon of radius 2 μm.

18-5 An unmyelinated segment of axon has a radius of 2 μm and a length of 1 cm. Find its (a) membrane capacitance; (b) membrane leakage resistance.

18-6 A myelinated segment of axon has a radius of 2 μm and a length of 1 cm. Find its (a) membrane capacitance; (b) membrane leakage resistance.

18-7 An axon membrane is 7.5×10^{-9} m thick. (a) In the resting state the axon potential is -90 mV. What is the direction and magnitude of the electric field in the membrane? (b) If the membrane has a capacitance of 0.01 F m^{-2}, what is its dielectric constant?

18-8 Find the space parameter for an axon of radius 0.2 μm if it is (a) myelinated; (b) unmyelinated.

18-9 A membrane has a potential difference of 90 mV across it. How much charge per square metre is located on either side if it is (a) myelinated; (b) unmyelinated?

18-10 What is the space parameter for an axon of radius 3 μm if it is (a) unmyelinated; (b) myelinated?

18-11 A myelinated axon has a space parameter of 1 cm. Find its radius.

18-12 A myelinated axon and an unmyelinated axon have the same space parameter. Find the ratio of their radii.

18-13 Find the radius of an unmyelinated axon with a space parameter of 2×10^{-4} m.

Section 18.3 | Ionic Concentrations and the Resting Potential

18-14 How many potassium ions are there inside a 1-cm-long segment of an axon of radius 2 μm?

18-15 How many sodium ions are there in a 1-cm length of an axon of radius 6 μm?

18-16 The concentration of an ion is 100 moles m^{-3}. How many ions are there in 1 m^3?

18-17 Find the equilibrium potential at 37°C for an ion with charge $+e$ if its concentration outside the axon is 160 moles m^{-3} and inside is 10 moles m^{-3}.

18-18 The equilibrium potential at 37°C for Cl^- ions in a particular axon is -80 mV. If the Cl^- concentration outside the cell is 110 moles m^{-3}, what is the concentration inside?

18-19 The active sodium transport due to the Na-K pump occurs at the rate of 3×10^{-7} moles m^{-2} s^{-1}. For 1 m^2 of membrane, find (a) the current in amperes due to the sodium ions; (b) the power expended against electric forces if the resting potential is -90 mV.

18-20 The K^+ concentration inside an axon is 165 moles m^{-3} and outside it is 8 moles m^{-3}. (a) What is the equilibrium potential at 37°C? (b) In which directions are the potassium flows due to diffusion and to the electric field if the axon potential is -90 mV? Which flow is greater?

Section 18.4 | The Response to Weak Stimuli

18-21 Estimate the space parameter for the axon in Fig. 18.8*b*.

18-22 A myelinated axon of radius 3 μm is stimulated so that the potential at $x = 0$ is -100 mV, which is 10 mV below the resting potential. (a) What is the space parameter? (b) Sketch the axon potential-versus-distance graph when the potential has achieved its final steady-state value.

18-23 A myelinated nerve with a space parameter of 0.5 cm is disturbed at a point so that its potential is raised from the resting value of -90 mV to -80 mV. Find the steady-state potential at distances from this point of (a) 0.5 cm; (b) 1 cm.

Section 18.5 | The Action Potential

18-24 A probe with a resistance of 10^7 ohms connects an electrical circuit to an axon. Estimate the time constant for charging a 1-cm long axon segment assuming $C_m = 10^{-2}$ F m^{-2}, $\rho_a = 0$, $R_m = \infty$, and a radius of 5 μm.

18-25 Find the velocity of propagation for an action potential and the time required for it to travel 2 m in a myelinated nerve (a) with a radius of 1 μm; (b) with a radius of 20 μm.

18-26 A nerve pulse can travel the length of a 0.5-m long myelinated axon in 0.05 s. What is its radius?

PROBLEMS

Use the data in Table 18.1 and Fig. 18.3 when numerical values are required that are not given in the problem.

18-27 A square metre of axon membrane has a resistance of 0.2 ohm. The membrane is 7.5×10^{-9} m thick. (a) What is the resistivity of the membrane? (b) Suppose the membrane resistance is due to fluid-filled cylindrical pores through the membrane. The pores have a radius of 3.5×10^{-10} m and a length equal to the membrane thickness, 7.5×10^{-9} m. The fluid in the pores has a resistivity of 0.15 ohm m, and the remainder of the membrane is assumed to be a perfect insulator. How many pores must there be in 1 m^2 to account for the observed resistance?

(c) If the pores are in a square pattern, how far apart are they?

***18-28** If an ion in an electric field E has a drift velocity v, then the *mobility* of the ion is $\mu = v/E$. (a) Show that the resistivity of a fluid containing a single type of ion is $(qn\mu)^{-1}$, where q is the magnitude of the charge on an ion and n is the number of ions per unit volume. (b) Show that if there are m different kinds of ions in a solution, the resistivity is $(q_1n_1\mu_1 + q_2n_2\mu_2 + \cdots + q_mn_m\mu_m)^{-1}$.

18-29 Using the relationship between mobility and resistivity given in the preceding problem and the ionic concentrations in Fig. 18.3, estimate the resistivities of axoplasm and interstitial fluid. Explain any difference between the calculated result for ρ_a and the value in Table 18.1. (The mobilities of Na^+, K^+, and Cl^- are 5.20×10^{-8}, 7.64×10^{-8}, and 7.91×10^{-8} m^2 V^{-1} s^{-1}, respectively. Neglect the effects of the "other" ions.)

18-30 A 1-cm-long segment of myelinated axon has a radius of 10^{-5} m. Its capacitance is 6×10^{-9} F, and the resting potential is -90 mV. (a) The resting potential is due to an excess of positive ions along the membrane outside the axon and an equal negative excess inside. How much excess charge is there on either side? (b) If these excesses are due to singly charged ions, how many excess ions are there on either side? (c) Find the ratio of this number of ions to the total number of negative ions inside the segment.

18-31 A 1-cm long segment of unmyelinated axon has a capacitance of 3×10^{-9} F. (a) If the axoplasm potential changes from -90 to $+40$ mV, by how much do the excess charges on either side of the membrane change? (b) If this change is due to an influx of sodium ions, how many sodium ions enter the axon?

18-32 A 1-cm long segment of unmyelinated axon has a radius of 5×10^{-6} m and a capacitance of 3×10^{-9} F. (a) If the axoplasm potential changes from $+40$ to -96 mV, by how much do the excess charges on either side of the membrane change? (b) If this change is due to an outflow of potassium ions, how many ions must leave the axon segment? (c) If the original potassium concentration inside the axon is 155 moles m^{-3}, what fraction of the potassium ions leave the axon?

18-33 The axon analog network in Fig. 18.5*c* can be made more complete by adding EMFs that simulate the resting potential. Show how this may be done.

18-34 The *Goldman* equation

$$V_i - V_o = \frac{k_B T}{e} \ln \left[\frac{c_{oNa} + c_{oK}(P_K/P_{Na})}{c_{iNa} + c_{iK}(P_K/P_{Na})} \right]$$

gives the net equilibrium potential difference for an axon, where P_K/P_{Na} is the ratio of the membrane permeabilities for potassium and sodium, the c's are the ionic concentrations, and e is the proton charge. Assume $T = 310$ K. (a) If the resting potential is -90 mV, what is the permeability ratio? (b) An above-threshold stimulus alters the permeabilities so the potential jumps to $+40$ mV. What is the new ratio? (c) Explain to what extent it is correct to use the same concentrations in parts (a) and (b).

***18-35** Draw a rough graph of the equilibrium potential versus the permeability ratio using the Goldman equation given in Problem 18-34.

***18-36** Using the Goldman equation in Problem 18-34, find the resting potential of an axon if the concentrations are as in Fig. 18.3 and the potassium to sodium permeability ratio is 100.

18-37 The total influx of Na^+ during the transmission of a single action potential pulse is 4×10^{-8} moles m^{-2} of active axon surface. (a) How many pulses may be transmitted in an unmyelinated nerve of radius 5 μm before the Na^+ concentration within the axon is increased by 10 percent? (Neglect the effects of the Na–K pump.) (b) How many pulses in a myelinated axon of radius 5 μm are required to increase the Na^+ concentration by 10 percent? (Assume that the active surface is only at the nodes, which are 1 μm long and 1 mm apart. Again neglect the effects of the Na–K pump.)

ANSWERS TO REVIEW QUESTIONS

Q18-1, more, poorly, more; **Q18-2**, Schwann cells; **Q18-3**, space parameter; **Q18-4**, sodium, potassium; **Q18-5**, ionic concentrations; **Q18-6**, slower, smaller; **Q18-7**, sodium; **Q18-8**, nodes of Ranvier; **Q18-9**, two; **Q18-10**, metabolic energy.

Additional Reading

Bernard Katz, *Nerve, Muscle, and Synapse*, McGraw-Hill Book Co., New York, 1966. Paperback.

Arthur C. Guyton, *Textbook of Medical Physiology*, 4th ed., W. B. Saunders Co., Philadelphia, 1971, Chapters 4 and 5. More advanced but quite readable.

Theodore C. Ruch, Harry D. Patton, J. Walter Woodbury, and Arnold L. Towe, *Neurophysiology*, W. B. Saunders Co., Philadelphia, 1965. A very complete discussion is given in Chapters 1 and 2.

D. V. Aidley, *Physiology of Excitable Cells*, Cambridge University Press, Cambridge, 1971.

John R. Cameron and James G. Skofronick, *Medical Physics*, John Wiley & Sons, Inc. New York, 1978. Chapter 9 is an introduction to electrocardiograms, electroencephalograms, and other aspects of electricity in the body.

Russell K. Hobbie, *Intermediate Physics for Medicine and Biology*, John Wiley & Sons, Inc., New York, 1978. Chapter 6 is a more mathematical introduction to the electrical properties of nerves than that presented in this textbook.

Scientific American articles:

C. L. Stong, How to Make an Electrocardiogram of a Water Flea and Investigate Other Bioelectric Effects, *The Amateur Scientist*, January 1962, p. 145. Description of a demonstration apparatus for nerve and muscle potentials in aquatic animals.

Arthur K. Solomon, Pumps in the Living Cell, August 1962, p. 100.

Peter F. Baker, The Nerve Axon, March 1966, p. 74.

Sir John Eccles, The Synapse, January 1965, p. 56.

Bernard Katz, The Nerve Impulse, November 1952, p. 55.

Werner R. Lowenstein, Biological Transducers, August 1960, p. 98.

Graham Hoyle, How Is Muscle Turned On and Off? April 1970, p. 85.

H. E. Huxley, The Contraction of Muscle, November 1958, p. 66.

Allen M. Scher, The Electrocardiogram, November 1961, p. 132.

Bruce I. H. Scott, Electricity in Plants, October 1962, p. 107.

Keir Pearson, The Control of Walking, December 1976, p. 72.

CHAPTER 19
MAGNETISM

Most of us have had the opportunity to observe some of the fascinating properties of permanent magnets. The north pole of one magnet attracts the south pole and repels the north pole of another magnet. Either pole of a magnet attracts unmagnetized iron or steel objects, and when such objects are in contact with a magnet, they can attract other iron or steel objects.

It has been known since antiquity that *lodestones*, pieces of the mineral *magnetite* (iron oxide), are able to attract iron objects. Also, the fact that the earth is a large magnet was long known from its orienting effect on compass needles. However, it was only in 1820 that Hans Christian Oersted (1777–1851) discovered that an electric current in a wire can deflect a compass needle. Electric currents in wires, as well as charges moving in a vacuum, produce magnetic effects indistinguishable from those due to permanent magnets. Since currents exert forces on magnets, we would expect from Newton's third law relating action and reaction forces that magnets also exert forces on currents. Such forces are indeed observed.

In discussing electric forces, we found it advantageous to avoid the direct use of Coulomb's law for the force between two charges. Instead, we said that one charge produces an electric field **E**, which in turn exerts a force on a second charge. Similarly, we will consider that a magnet or moving charge produces a magnetic field **B**. The magnetic field exerts a force on another magnet or moving charge.

We begin this chapter by describing magnetic fields. We then discuss the forces on moving charges and currents, along with some applications. Finally we show how the fields due to currents can be calculated.

19.1 | MAGNETIC FIELDS

The direction and magnitude of the magnetic field **B** produced by a magnet can be determined with the aid of a compass, a permanently magnetized steel needle pivoted at its center. The equilibrium orientation of the needle gives the direction of the field, and the torque tending to align the needle is proportional to its magnitude (Fig. 19.1).

Magnetic fields are represented by diagrams or maps similar to those used for electric fields. Again the lines indicate the field direction, and the field is strongest where the lines are closest together (Figs. 19.2 and 19.3). *Note that by convention the magnetic field lines are always directed from the north*

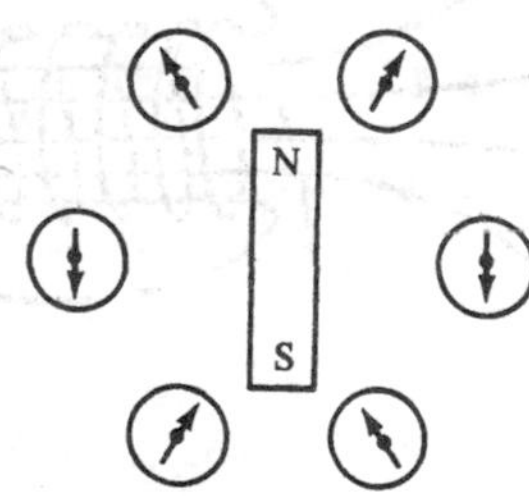

Figure 19.1. The equilibrium orientation of a compass needle indicates the direction of the magnetic field.

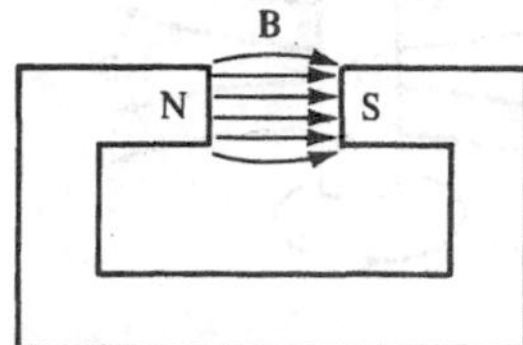

Figure 19.2. If the pole faces of a magnet are closely spaced, the field between them is nearly uniform.

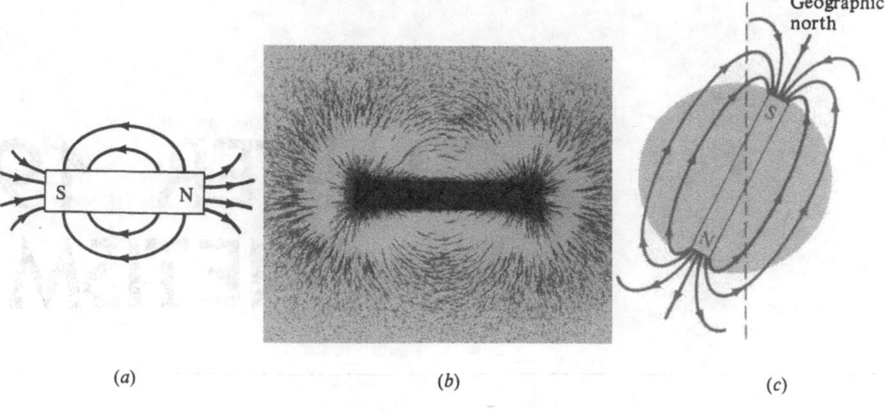

Figure 19.3. (*a*) Magnetic field of a bar magnet. (*b*) The pattern formed by iron filings near a bar magnet. (*c*) The magnetic field of the earth resembles that of a bar magnet. The *magnetic* south pole is located near the *geographic* north pole; it attracts the north pole of a compass needle. [Part (*b*) Cordelia Molloy / Photo Researchers, Inc.]

pole to the south pole outside a magnet. The field lines around a magnet can be made visible by sprinkling iron filings on a sheet of paper. The filings become magnetized and tend to align themselves with the field (Fig. 19.3).

As we noted earlier, electric currents also produce magnetic fields (Figs. 19.4, 19.5, and 19.6). The field due to a current in a long coil of wire looks much like that of a long bar magnet, and the field of a single current turn is similar to that of a short bar magnet. A current in a long straight wire produces circular magnetic field lines.

A convenient rule aids in remembering the observed relationship between the directions of the magnetic field and the current. We may use the long straight wire as an example. If the right thumb is placed along the wire in the direction of the current, the fingers curl in the direction of the field (Fig. 19.7*a*). Similarly, for the circular current loop in Fig. 19.7*b*, this rule indicates that inside the loop, **B** points out of the page; outside the loop, **B** points into the page.

The close similarity between the magnetic fields of currents and permanent magnets led André

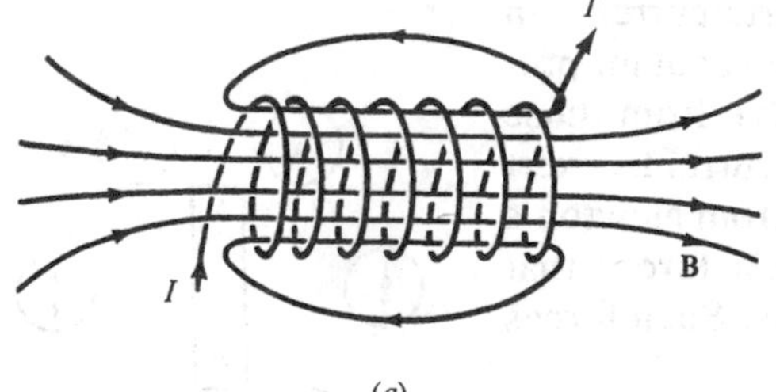

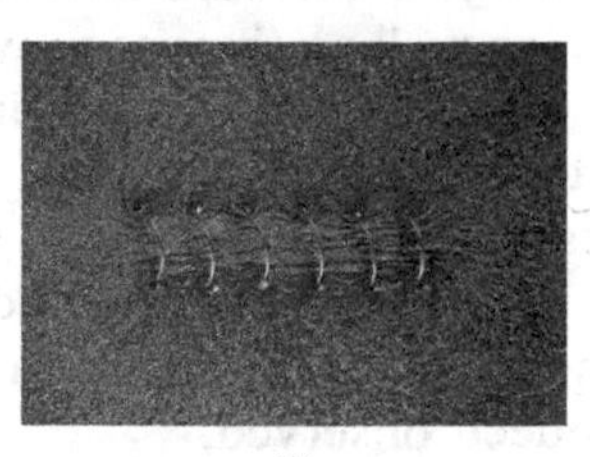

Figure 19.4. (*a*) Magnetic field lines and (*b*) iron filing patterns due to a current in a long coil of wire. Note the similarities to the field lines and patterns for the long bar magnet in Fig. 19.3. [Part (*b*) Richard Megna / Fundamental Photographs]

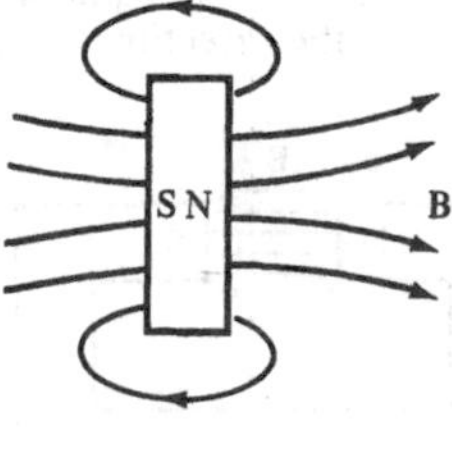

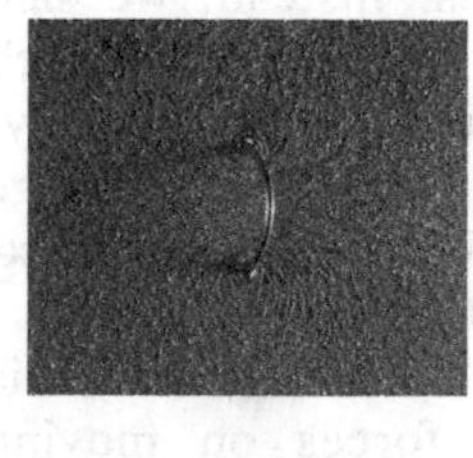

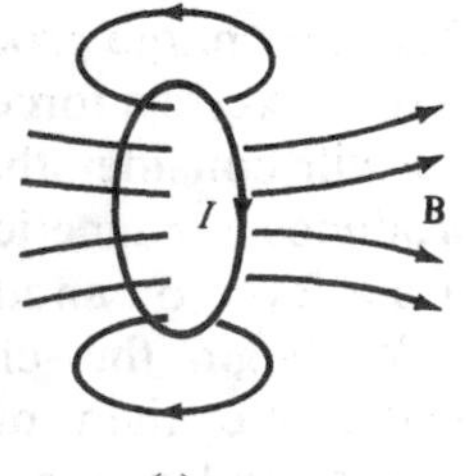

Figure 19.5. (*a*) Magnetic field lines for a short permanent bar magnet. (*b*) Iron filing patterns. (*c*) Magnetic field lines due to a single current turn. [Part (*b*) Richard Megna / Fundamental Photographs]

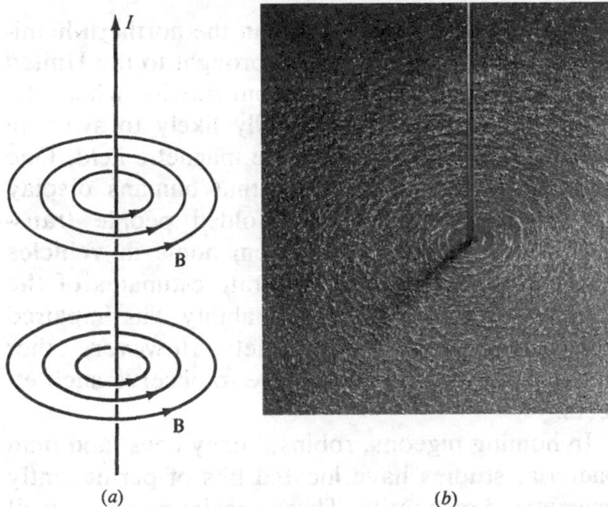

Figure 19.6. (*a*) Magnetic field lines and (*b*) iron filing patterns due to a current in a long straight wire. [Part (*b*) Richard Megna / Fundamental Photographs.]

Marie Ampère (1775–1836) to realize that microscopic currents in atoms or molecules are responsible for the fields of permanent magnets. Within a permanent magnet, the atoms are aligned so that their currents are in the same direction (Fig. 19.8*a*). In the interior of the material the currents occur in opposing pairs, so their fields exactly cancel. The net field is then due to the currents around the edge

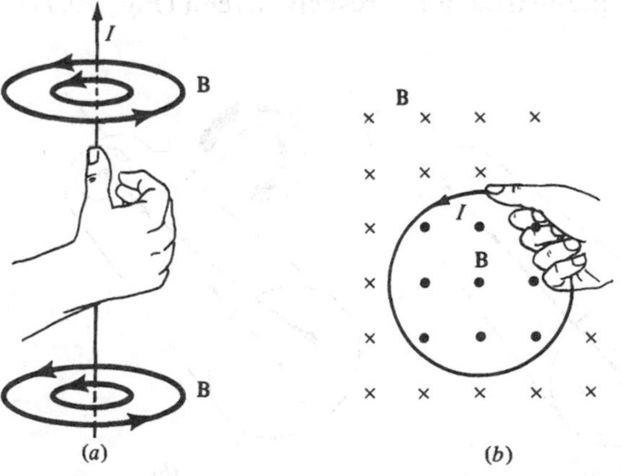

Figure 19.7. (*a*) With the right thumb along the direction of the current, the fingers curl in the direction of the magnetic field. (*b*) Inside the loop, **B** points out of the page; outside the loop, **B** points into the page.

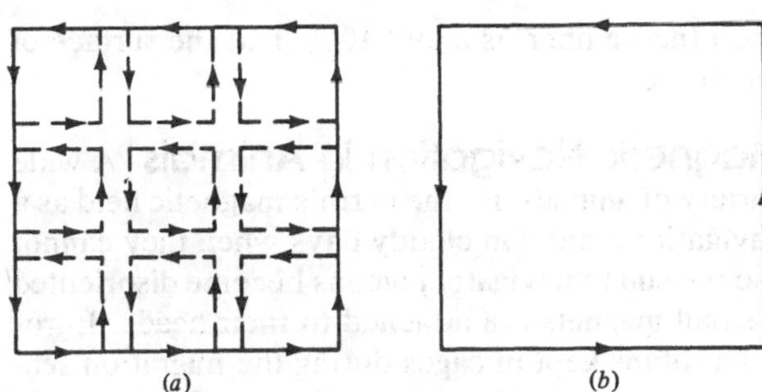

Figure 19.8. (*a*) The microscopic currents in a permanent magnet. (*b*) Since the effects of the opposing pairs of currents cancel in the interior, the net field produced is the same as for a current around the edge.

of the material and is identical to that produced by an electric current in a wire with the same shape (Fig. 19.8*b*).

The S.I. magnetic field unit, the *tesla* (T), is a rather large unit. The largest fields produced in the laboratory for an extended time are about 10 T; fields up to about 100 T can be produced very briefly. The earth's magnetic field at the surface of the earth is about 10^{-4} T. One centimetre away from a long straight wire carrying the relatively large current of 100 A, the field is only 2×10^{-3} T. The small electric currents associated with the human nervous system produce very weak magnetic fields. These fields are about 10^{-11} T near the chest (Fig. 19.9). The magnetic field due to a current pulse in a single

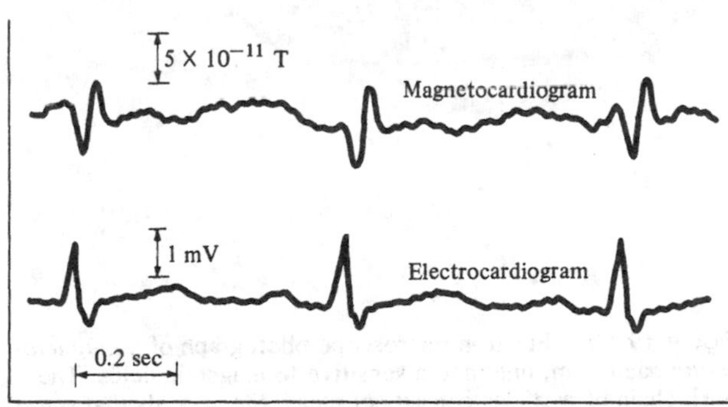

Figure 19.9. Magnetic fields near the human chest vary in time much like the electric potential differences measured with an electrocardiagraph. Possible diagnostic uses of magnetic field measurements near the heart and brain are under investigation. (From Alexander Kolin, *Physics Today*, November 1968, p. 39 © American Institute of Physics.)

axon (nerve fiber) is about 10^{-10} T at the surface of the nerve.

Magnetic Navigation in Animals | A wide variety of animals use the earth's magnetic field as a navigational aid. On cloudy days when they cannot use the sun to navigate, pigeons become disoriented if small magnets are attached to their heads. European robins kept in cages during the migration season orient themselves according to the magnetic field in the cage. Honey bees display several behavioral patterns correlated with the direction of the local magnetic field. Mud bacteria normally swim downward, seeking the soft mud that is their habitat; when magnets are used to cancel out and reverse the magnetic field of the earth, they swim upward. Also, mud bacteria from the southern hemisphere—where the vertical component of the magnetic field is opposite to that in the northern hemisphere—swim upward when brought to the United States, while mud bacteria from Brazil—where the field is horizontal—are equally likely to swim in either direction relative to the magnetic field. One scientist has even reported that humans display some homing ability; blindfolded people transported several kilometres from home in vehicles could make moderately accurate estimates of the direction toward home. This ability was impaired when the subject wore magnets. However, other investigators have been unable to observe such effects.

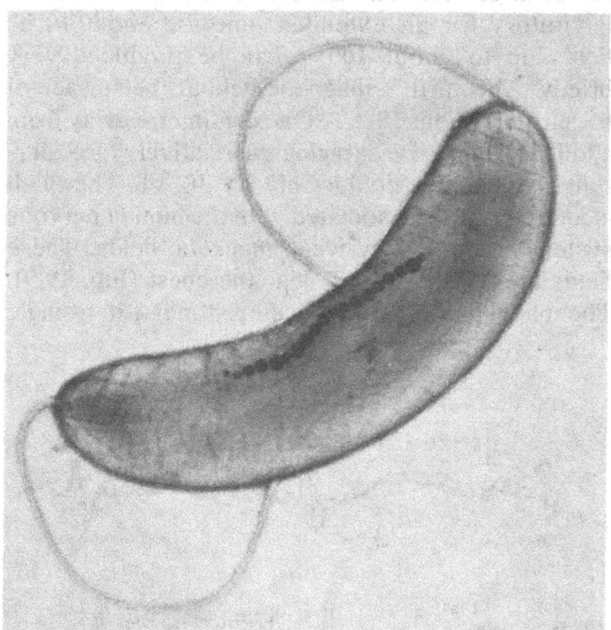

Figure 19.10. Electron microscope photograph of a *magnetotactic* bacterium, one that is sensitive to magnetic fields. The dark chain of particles consists of magnetite crystals that serve as a compass, tending to align the bacterium along the earth's magnetic field. The existence of magnetotactic bacteria was discovered in 1975 by Richard P. Blakemore, then a graduate student at the University of Massachusetts in Amherst. Many different types of magnetotactic bacteria have since been found. (Photo courtesy of Richard P. Blakemore and Nancy Blakemore.)

In homing pigeons, robins, honey bees, and mud bacteria, studies have located bits of permanently magnetized magnetite. These species possess small permanent magnets that apparently behave like compass needles and experience torques when placed in a magnetic field (Fig. 19.10). Just how this information is sensed and processed is a tantalizing question currently under investigation by many scientists.

19.2 | THE MAGNETIC FORCE ON A MOVING CHARGE

Electric charges in motion near a magnet experience forces that can readily be demonstrated. For example, a magnet brought near a cathode-ray tube will deflect a beam of electrons and alter the places where they strike a fluorescent screen (Fig. 19.11).

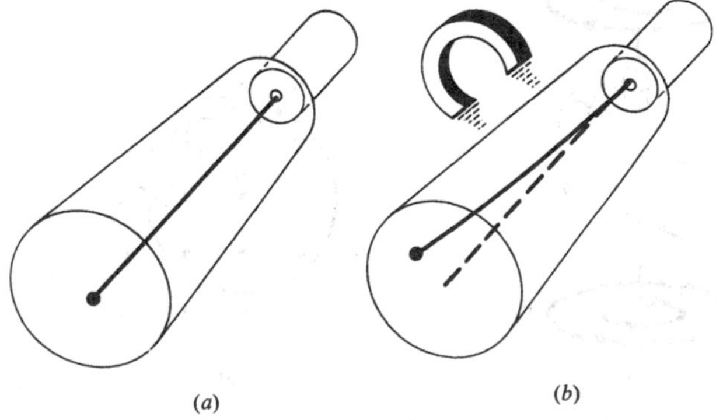

Figure 19.11. (*a*) Electrons in a cathode-ray tube strike a fluorescent screen. (*b*) The electrons are deflected by a magnet.

The magnetic force law is more complicated in form than is the electric force law, $\mathbf{F} = q\mathbf{E}$. A charge q moving with velocity $\mathbf{v}$ in a magnetic field $\mathbf{B}$ experiences a force perpendicular to $\mathbf{v}$ and to $\mathbf{B}$. The magnitude of this force is the product of q, v, and the component of $\mathbf{B}$ perpendicular to $\mathbf{v}$. Using the cross-product notation introduced in Chapter Four, the magnetic force $\mathbf{F}$ is given (Fig. 19.12) by

$$\mathbf{F} = q\mathbf{v} \times \mathbf{B} \quad (19.1)$$

The magnitude of this force is

$$F = |q|vB \sin \theta \quad (19.2)$$

where θ is the angle between $\mathbf{v}$ and $\mathbf{B}$. The force is greatest when $\sin \theta = 1$ or when the velocity is at right angles to the field. It is zero when $\sin \theta = 0$ or when the velocity is parallel or opposite to $\mathbf{B}$ (Fig. 19.13). Note that a charge at rest experiences no force; magnetic fields exert forces only on moving charges. The following example illustrates the calculation of the magnetic force on a moving charge.

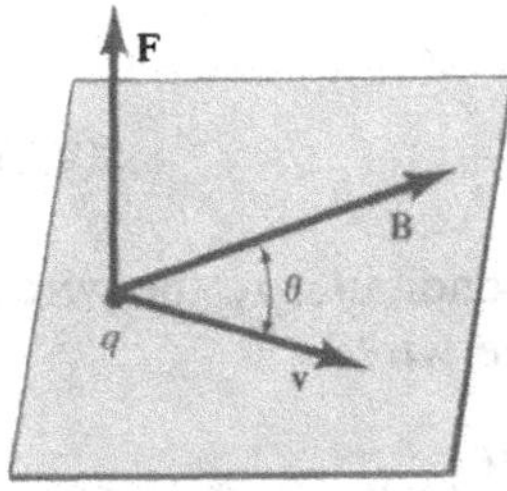

Figure 19.12. The magnetic force **F** on a positive charge q has a magnitude $qvB \sin \theta$ and is directed as shown.

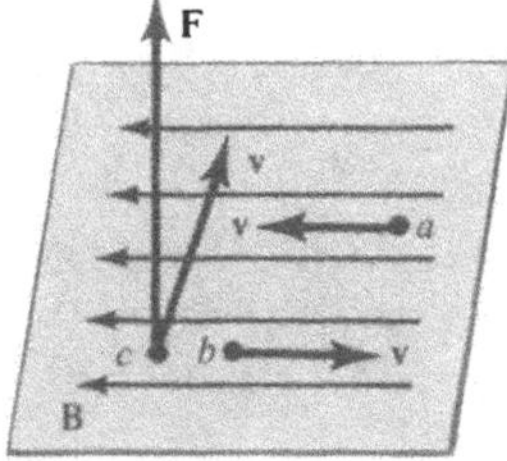

Figure 19.13. Positively charged particles in a magnetic field experience no force if the velocity is parallel (a) or opposite (b) to the field. The force has its maximum magnitude qvB when **v** is perpendicular to the field (c).

Example 19.1

At Boston, Massachusetts, the magnetic field due to the earth is at 17° to the vertical direction and has a magnitude of 5.8×10^{-5} T (Fig. 19.14). (a) Find the force $\mathbf{F}$ on an electron moving straight down at 10^5 m s^{-1}. (b) Find the ratio of F to the weight mg.

(a) With $q = -e = -1.6 \times 10^{-19}$ C and $\sin 17° = 0.292$, the magnitude of the magnetic force is

$$\begin{aligned} F &= evB \sin \theta \\ &= (1.6 \times 10^{-19}\text{ C})(10^5\text{ m s}^{-1})(5.8 \times 10^{-5}\text{ T})(0.292) \\ &= 2.71 \times 10^{-19}\text{ N} \end{aligned}$$

Since $\mathbf{F} = -e\mathbf{v} \times \mathbf{B}$, the force is opposite to $\mathbf{v} \times \mathbf{B}$ or into the page in Fig. 19.14.

(b) The mass of an electron is 9.1×10^{-31} kg, so

$$\begin{aligned} \frac{F}{mg} &= \frac{2.71 \times 10^{-19}\text{ N}}{(9.1 \times 10^{-31}\text{ kg})(9.8\text{ m s}^{-2})} \\ &= 3.04 \times 10^{10} \end{aligned}$$

The force on the electron due to the relatively weak magnetic field of the earth is larger than its weight by a factor of more than 10^{10}. For this reason the motion of charged cosmic ray particles entering the upper atmosphere is determined primarily by the earth's magnetic field and not by gravitational forces.

The magnetic force $q\mathbf{v} \times \mathbf{B}$ is perpendicular to the velocity, so it can change the direction in which a particle is moving but not its speed. Magnetic forces never change the kinetic energy, since they are always perpendicular to the motion and hence do no work.

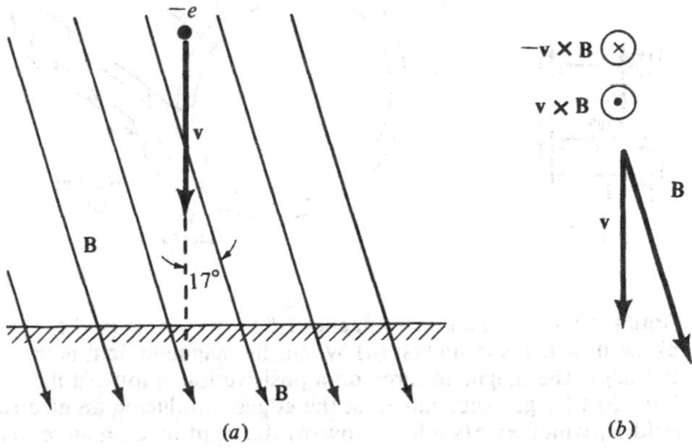

Figure 19.14. (a) The magnetic field of the earth varies in strength and direction. At Boston, it is at 17° to the vertical. (b) **v** × **B** is out of the page. The force on an electron is $\mathbf{F} = -e\mathbf{v} \times \mathbf{B}$ and is opposite to **v** × **B** or into the page.

19.3 | ELECTROMAGNETIC FLOW METERS

Electromagnetic flow meters, which employ the force on charges moving in a magnetic field, provide an excellent way to measure blood flow rates in patients undergoing heart or arterial surgery. Unlike the flow meters discussed in Chapter Thirteen, they do not require the insertion of a probe into a vessel and may be used even if the flow is not laminar but turbulent.

Figure 19.15*a* illustrates the principle of this device. A magnetic field is applied perpendicular to the motion of the blood. This produces magnetic forces to the left on positive ions in the blood and to the right on negative ions. Thus, charges accumulate at the edges of the vessel. Equilibrium occurs when the electric field due to these accumulations produces a force qE on an ion of charge q, which exactly balances the magnetic force qvB, that is, when $E = vB$ (Fig. 19.15*b*). The potential difference associated with the electric field is then proportional to the average velocity v of the blood and can be measured with a sensitive voltmeter.

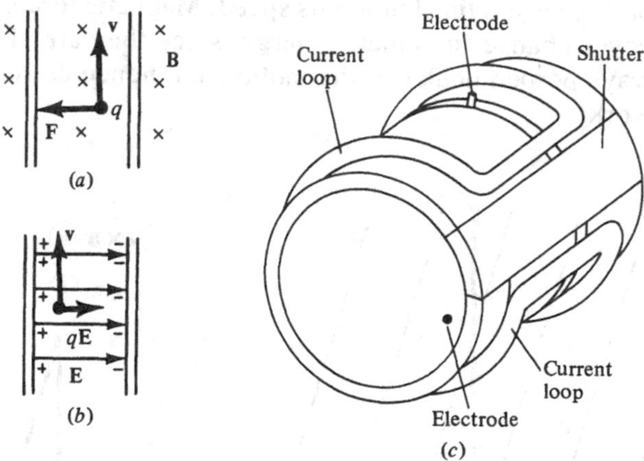

Figure 19.15. The electromagnetic flow meter as used for blood flow measurements. (*a*) When the magnetic field is into the page, the magnetic force on a positive ion is toward the left. (*b*) Charges accumulate at the edges, producing an electric field **E**, which exerts a force toward the right on a positive ion. In equilibrium the electric force balances the magnetic force. (*c*) In one apparatus the artery is inserted into a metal sleeve by opening a shutter. The magnetic field is provided by a single current loop. The voltage between the electrodes is proportional to the flow rate.

In a version of this instrument used for arteries 4 mm or larger in diameter, a closely fitting metal sleeve is placed around the artery to assure that its diameter remains constant (Fig. 19.15*c*). A current in a single loop of wire provides a small magnetic field that is rapidly alternated in direction to avoid *polarization*, the formation of an insulating gas layer. Voltmeter leads are attached to electrodes on opposite sides of the sleeve. The meter is calibrated by making measurements on an artery with a known flow rate.

19.4 | THE MAGNETIC FORCE ON A CURRENT-CARRYING WIRE

We can find the expression for the magnetic force on a current-carrying wire directly from the force $\mathbf{F} = q\mathbf{v} \times \mathbf{B}$ on a moving charge. Consider a straight segment of wire of length ℓ, which is part of a closed circuit carrying a current I (Fig. 19.16). If the moving charges in the wire have a velocity v, they travel the length of the segment in a time $t = \ell/v$. The total moving charge q is the product of the current and the time,

$$q = It = \frac{I\ell}{v} \qquad (19.3)$$

If the magnetic field **B** is perpendicular to the wire, then the magnetic force on the wire is

$$F = qvB = \left(\frac{I\ell}{v}\right) vB$$

or

$$F = I\ell B \qquad (\ell \text{ perpendicular to } \mathbf{B}) \qquad (19.4)$$

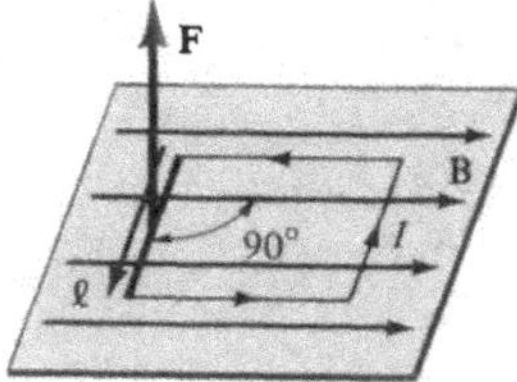

Figure 19.16. When the segment of wire carrying the current is perpendicular to the field, the force has a magnitude $F = I\ell B$.

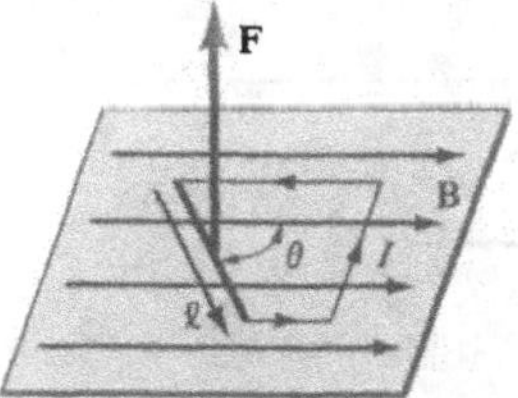

Figure 19.17. If the segment is at an angle θ to the field, the magnitude of the force is $F = I\ell B \sin\theta$.

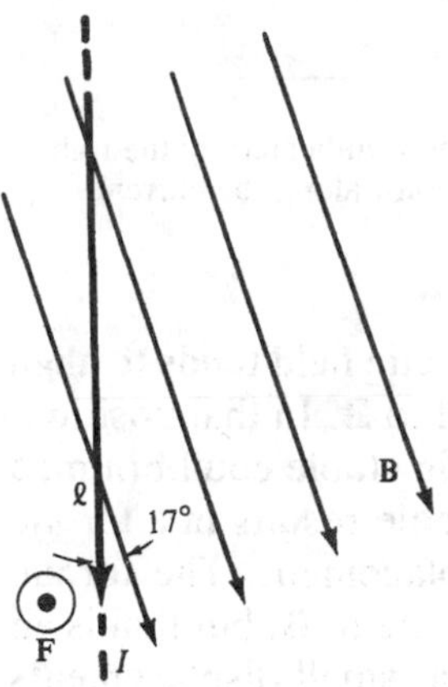

Figure 19.18. The force on the current-carrying wire is directed out of the page.

If the wire and the field are not perpendicular, $\mathbf{F} = q\mathbf{v} \times \mathbf{B}$ leads to

$$\mathbf{F} = I\boldsymbol{\ell} \times \mathbf{B} \tag{19.5}$$

where $\boldsymbol{\ell}$ is directed along the wire in the direction of the current (Fig. 19.17). If the wire is not straight, or if $\mathbf{B}$ varies with position, the wire may be regarded as having many small segments so that Eq. 19.5 holds true for each. The total force on the wire is then the vector sum of the forces on each segment.

In the next example, we see that the force due to the earth's magnetic field on a current-carrying wire is relatively small.

Example 19.2

The magnetic field of the earth at Boston, Massachusetts, is at 17° to the vertical and has a magnitude of 5.8×10^{-5} T (Fig. 19.18). A vertical wire carries a current of 10 A. Find the force on a 2-m length of the wire.

The magnitude of the force is

$$\begin{aligned} F &= I\ell B \sin\theta \\ &= (10\text{ A})(2\text{ m})(5.8 \times 10^{-5}\text{ T})(\sin 17°) \\ &= 3.39 \times 10^{-4}\text{ N} \end{aligned}$$

With the right-hand rule for cross products, the force is out of the page in Fig. 19.18.

19.5 | MAGNETIC DIPOLES

In Chapter Sixteen, we discussed the electric dipole, two neighboring electric charges $+q$ and $-q$. A loop of wire carrying a current behaves in a magnetic field much as an electric dipole does in an electric field and is called a *magnetic dipole*. Magnetic dipoles associated with orbiting and spinning charges are important in discussions of the magnetic properties of atoms and molecules, including many molecules of importance in biochemistry.

We saw in Chapter Sixteen that an electric dipole in a uniform electric field experiences no net force, but it does experience a torque. We now show that a magnetic dipole in a uniform magnetic field also experiences no net force but experiences a torque. The rectangular current loop in Fig. 19.19 is an example of a magnetic dipole. The uniform magnetic field is parallel to sides 1 and 3, so no forces are

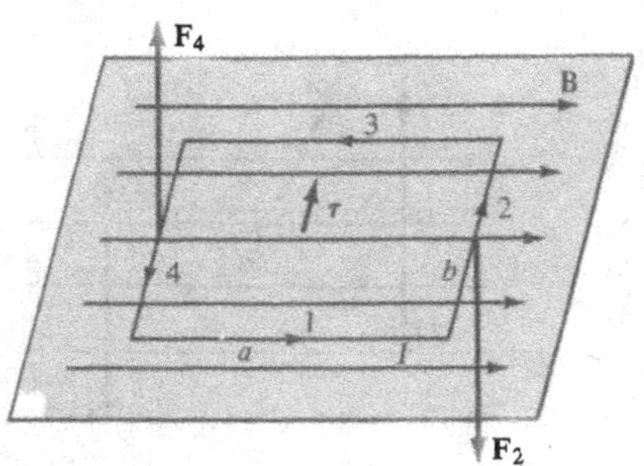

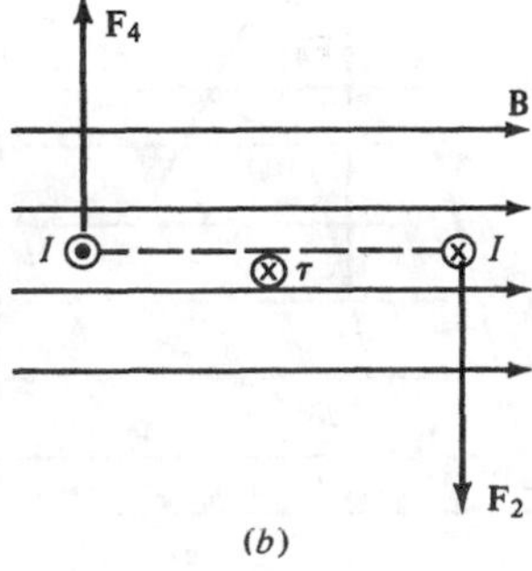

Figure 19.19. A magnetic dipole in a uniform magnetic field experiences no net force, but it does experience a torque. (*a*) A current loop with its plane parallel to the field. (*b*) The same loop seen in cross section. The dashed line indicates the plane of the loop.

exerted on them. Using $\mathbf{F} = I\boldsymbol{\ell} \times \mathbf{B}$, the forces on sides 2 and 4 are

$$F_2 = IbB \text{ (downward)}, \qquad F_4 = IbB \text{ (upward)}$$

These are equal but opposite, so the net force on the loop is zero. However, the net torque on the loop is not zero, since $\mathbf{F}_2$ and $\mathbf{F}_4$ have different lines of action and form a couple.

We found in Chapter Four that the torque due to a couple is independent of the position of the axis of rotation. With the convenient choice of an axis along side 4, the torque due to $\mathbf{F}_4$ is zero. The lever arm for $\mathbf{F}_2$ is a, so its torque, $\boldsymbol{\tau} = \mathbf{r} \times \mathbf{F}$, is equal in magnitude to $\tau = a(IbB)$. Since $ab = A$ is the area of the loop, $\tau = IAB$ and is directed as shown.

If the loop is oriented as in Fig. 19.20, then the torque has a magnitude of $aF \sin\theta = IAB \sin\theta$. This can be rewritten in vector form as

$$\boldsymbol{\tau} = IA\hat{\mathbf{n}} \times \mathbf{B}$$

Here $\hat{\mathbf{n}}$ is a unit vector perpendicular or *normal* to the plane of the loop; its direction can be found using the right-hand rule as in Fig. 19.21. The *magnetic dipole moment* $\boldsymbol{\mu}$ (Greek letter "mu") is defined by

$$\boldsymbol{\mu} = IA\hat{\mathbf{n}} \tag{19.6}$$

With this definition, the torque on a magnetic dipole in a uniform magnetic field is

$$\boldsymbol{\tau} = \boldsymbol{\mu} \times \mathbf{B} \tag{19.7}$$

This result is correct for a current loop of *any* shape. It is identical in form to the torque $\mathbf{p} \times \mathbf{E}$ on an electric dipole in a uniform electric field.

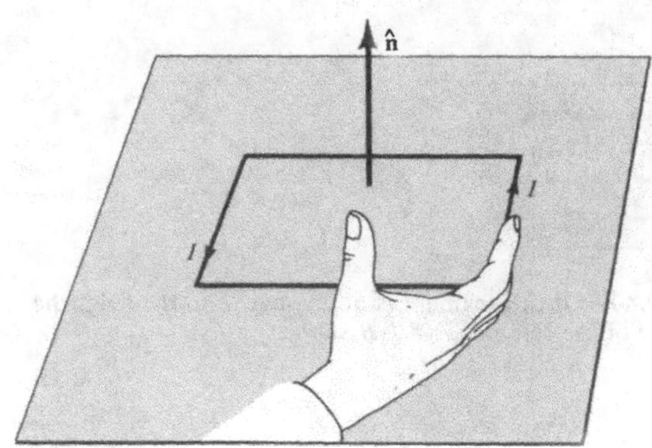

Figure 19.21. The normal direction $\hat{\mathbf{n}}$ indicated by the right thumb is upward when the fingers point along the current direction.

The torque due to the magnetic field tends to align the dipole so that $\boldsymbol{\mu}$ is parallel to $\mathbf{B}$. In that position, $\boldsymbol{\mu} \times \mathbf{B} = 0$, and the dipole is in stable equilibrium; a slight displacement of the dipole results in a torque tending to decrease the displacement. The torque also vanishes when $\boldsymbol{\mu}$ is opposite to $\mathbf{B}$, but that is an unstable equilibrium situation; small displacements produce torques tending to increase the displacements.

The potential energy $\mathcal{U}$ of an electric dipole moment $\mathbf{p}$ at an angle θ to a uniform electric field $\mathbf{E}$ is $-pE\cos\theta = -\mathbf{p}\cdot\mathbf{E}$. Similarly, a magnetic dipole moment $\boldsymbol{\mu}$ at an angle θ to a uniform magnetic field has a potential energy

$$\mathcal{U} = -\mu B \cos\theta = -\boldsymbol{\mu}\cdot\mathbf{B} \tag{19.8}$$

The potential energy has its minimum value $-\mu B$ at $\cos\theta = 1$ or $\theta = 0°$, which is its stable equilibrium

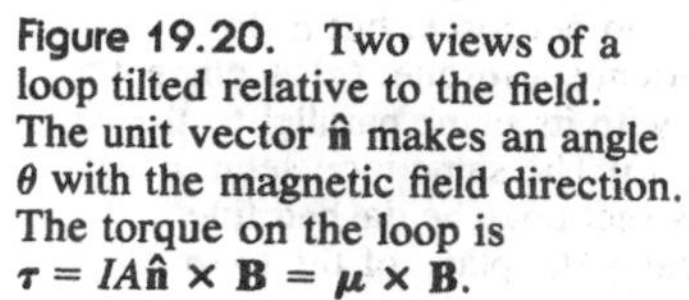

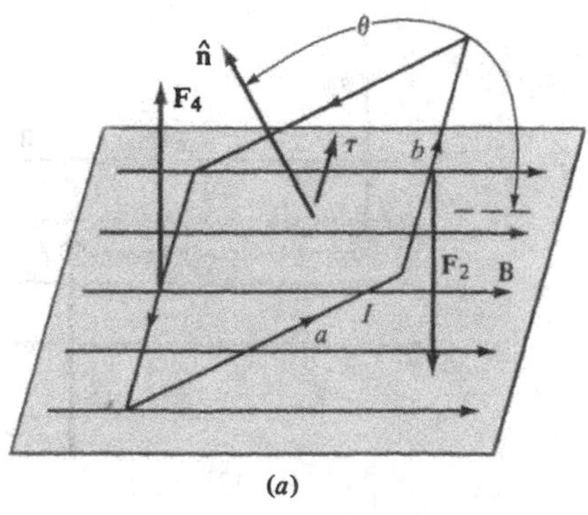

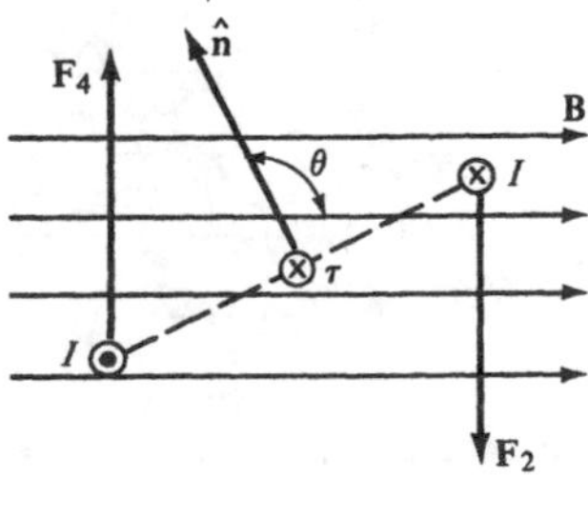

Figure 19.20. Two views of a loop tilted relative to the field. The unit vector $\hat{\mathbf{n}}$ makes an angle θ with the magnetic field direction. The torque on the loop is $\boldsymbol{\tau} = IA\hat{\mathbf{n}} \times \mathbf{B} = \boldsymbol{\mu} \times \mathbf{B}$.

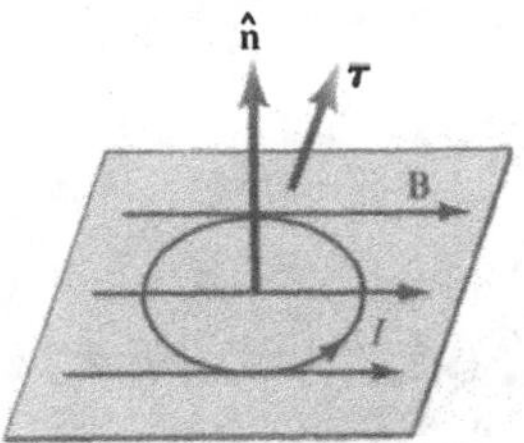

Figure 19.22. Example 19.3.

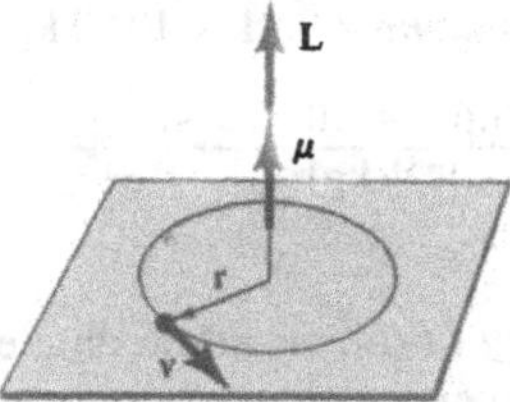

Figure 19.23. The magnetic moment due to an orbiting positive charge is parallel to its angular momentum.

orientation. It has the greatest value $+\mu B$ when $\cos\theta = -1$ or $\theta = 180°$.

These results are illustrated in the following example.

Example 19.3

A circular turn of wire of radius 0.5 m carries a current of 4 A. (a) What is its magnetic moment? (b) If the normal to the loop is at 90° to a field of 2 T, what is the magnitude of the torque? (c) What is its potential energy at this angle?

(a) The area of the loop is πr^2, so its magnetic moment is

$$\mu = IA = I\pi r^2 = (4\text{ A})\pi(0.5\text{ m})^2 = 3.14\text{ A m}^2$$

(b) With $\sin 90° = 1$,

$$\tau = \mu B \sin\theta = (3.14\text{ A m}^2)(2\text{ T})(1) = 6.28\text{ N m}$$

The direction of the torque is shown in Fig. 19.22.

(c) Since $\cos 90° = 0$, the potential energy of the loop is $\mathcal{U} = -\mu B\cos\theta = 0$.

Magnetic Moment of an Orbiting Charge

When an electron moves around an atomic nucleus, there is a flow of charge, or a current, around the nucleus. The corresponding magnetic dipole moment determines how an electron interacts with an applied magnetic field. We now obtain a formula for the dipole moment of an orbiting charge, which we use in later chapters.

Suppose a particle of mass m and charge q (Fig. 19.23) moves in a circular orbit. To find the magnetic moment $\mu = IA$, we need the current I and the area A. The time t required for the charge to complete one orbit of radius r at a speed v satisfies $vt = 2\pi r$ or $t = 2\pi r/v$. The magnitude of I is then

$$I = \frac{q}{t} = \frac{q}{2\pi r/v} = \frac{qv}{2\pi r}$$

Since the area A of the orbit is πr^2, the magnetic moment is

$$\mu = IA = \frac{qv}{2\pi r}\pi r^2 = \frac{qrv}{2}$$

This result can be put into another form involving the angular momentum of the particle. We saw in Chapter Seven that the angular momentum of a particle is $\mathbf{L} = \mathbf{r} \times \mathbf{p}$ and that, when the linear momentum $\mathbf{p} = m\mathbf{v}$ is perpendicular to the distance vector $\mathbf{r}$, the magnitude of the angular momentum is $L = mvr$. Hence $rv = L/m$ and the magnetic dipole moment can be rewritten in vector form as

$$\boldsymbol{\mu} = \frac{q}{2m}\mathbf{L} \tag{19.9}$$

The magnetic moment of a charged particle is proportional to its angular momentum; it is parallel to the angular momentum for a positive charge and opposite for a negative charge (Fig. 19.23). This result is illustrated by the next example.

Example 19.4

In the Bohr model of the hydrogen atom, the electron moves in circular orbits for which the angular momentum $L = nh/2\pi$, where n is an integer and h is Planck's constant; $h = 6.63 \times 10^{-34}$ J s. (a) Find the magnetic moment due to the orbital motion in the lowest ($n = 1$) orbit. (b) Suppose an electron in the $n = 1$ orbit has its moment parallel to a magnetic field of magnitude 10 T. How much energy in electron volts must be supplied to reverse the orientation of the moment?

(a) With $n = 1$, the angular momentum is $L = h/2\pi$. Since $q = -e$, the magnetic moment has a magnitude

$$\mu = \frac{e}{2m}L = \frac{eh}{4\pi m}$$

Substituting $e = 1.6 \times 10^{-19}$ C and $m = 9.11 \times 10^{-31}$ kg,

$$\mu = \frac{(1.60 \times 10^{-19}\text{ C})(6.63 \times 10^{-34}\text{ J s})}{4\pi(9.11 \times 10^{-31}\text{ kg})}$$
$$= 9.26 \times 10^{-24}\text{ A m}^2$$

(b) Since the potential energy of the magnetic dipole is $\mathcal{U} = -\mu B \cos\theta$, the potential energy is $-\mu B$ when μ is along the field and $+\mu B$ when μ is opposite to the field. Hence the energy needed to reverse the direction of the dipole is

$$2\mu B = 2(9.26 \times 10^{-24}\text{ A m}^2)(10\text{ T})$$
$$= 1.85 \times 10^{-22}\text{ J}\left(\frac{1\text{ eV}}{1.60 \times 10^{-19}\text{ J}}\right)$$
$$= 1.16 \times 10^{-3}\text{ eV}$$

We use the relationship between the magnetic dipole moment and the angular momentum of a particle in atomic and molecular applications in Chapters Twenty-eight and Twenty-nine. There we see that the energy needed to reorient the dipole moment as in the previous example can be supplied by a time-varying magnetic field.

19.6 | MOTORS; GALVANOMETERS

The magnetic force on a current-carrying wire has many useful applications. Two of the most important ones are electric motors and galvanometers.

Figure 19.24 illustrates the principle of the dc motor. A loop connected to an EMF is mounted so that it can rotate in a magnetic field that is produced either by a permanent magnet or by an electromagnet. When the normal to the loop becomes parallel to the field, the *split ring*, or *commutator*, reverses the current direction. As a result the torque on the loop is always in the same direction. This causes the loop to rotate and enables it to do work on a load. Practical dc motors have many turns with each successive turn rotated slightly, so that the net torque is nearly constant as the motor turns. Alternating current motors of various types are also widely used. In these, no commutator is needed, since an alternating current is supplied to the electromagnet in such a way that the field reverses along with the current in the coil.

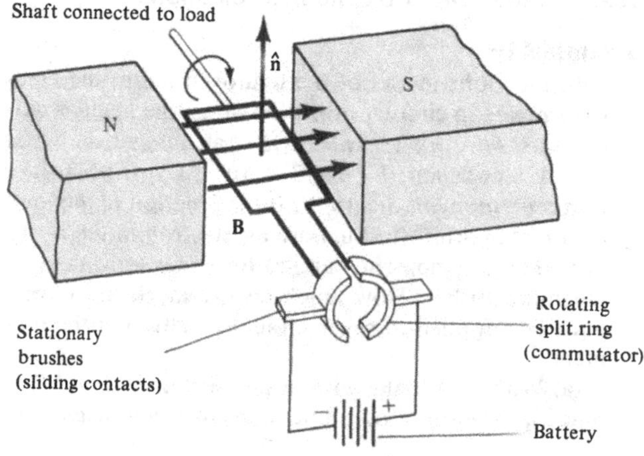

Figure 19.24. Elements of a dc motor.

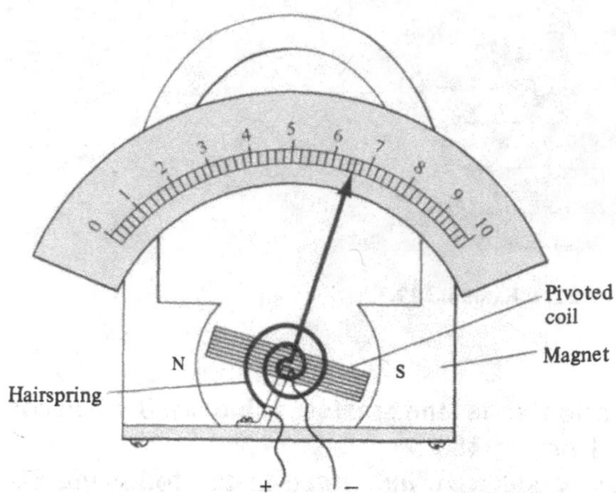

Figure 19.25. A galvanometer.

The pivoted coil galvanometer used in voltmeters and ammeters has a coil suspended in a radial magnetic field (Fig. 19.25). Hairsprings provide restoring torques proportional to the angular displacement. When there is a current in the coil, the torque due to the magnetic field causes it to rotate until equilibrium is established. A pointer is used to indicate the deflection of the coil, and a calibrated scale gives the corresponding current.

19.7 | MAGNETIC FIELDS PRODUCED BY CURRENTS

We saw in Chapter Sixteen how to calculate the electric field due to an arrangement of charges. We now discuss the analogous procedure for finding the magnetic field due to a current.

The basic law for the magnetic field is an expression for the field due to a short current segment. It is named the *Biot-Savart law*, after the two physicists who deduced it from experimental studies soon after Oersted discovered that currents produce magnetic fields. Consider a short segment of length $d\ell$ in a closed circuit with a current I (Fig. 19.26). At point P, a distance $\mathbf{r}$ from the segment, the magnetic field due to the segment is

$$d\mathbf{B} = k'I\frac{d\boldsymbol{\ell} \times \hat{\mathbf{r}}}{r^2} \tag{19.10}$$

where $\hat{\mathbf{r}}$ is a unit vector directed along $\mathbf{r}$. The net magnetic field $\mathbf{B}$ at P is the sum of the fields due to all the elements in the complete circuit. In S.I. units, the proportionality constant k' has the exact value

$$\begin{aligned} k' &= 10^{-7}\ \mathrm{T\ m\ A^{-1}} \\ &= 10^{-7}\ \mathrm{N\ A^{-2}} \end{aligned} \tag{19.11}$$

Like Coulomb's law for the electric field of a point charge, the Biot–Savart law is an inverse square law. However, it is more complex, since it involves a vector cross product. Also, we can never directly observe the field $d\mathbf{B}$ at P due to the single element in Fig. 19.26, because only the net field $\mathbf{B}$ due to the complete circuit can be measured.

Magnetic Field of a Circular Current Loop | To illustrate the use of the Biot–Savart law, we calculate the field at the center of a circular wire loop of radius a carrying a current I (Fig. 19.27). We divide the loop into many small segments. For any one segment $d\ell$, the distance r to the center is a. Since $d\ell$ is perpendicular to the unit vector $\hat{\mathbf{r}}$, $|d\boldsymbol{\ell} \times \hat{\mathbf{r}}| = d\ell$; $d\boldsymbol{\ell} \times \hat{\mathbf{r}}$ is directed out of the page. Thus the field due to the one segment is directed out of the page and has a magnitude

$$dB = \frac{k'I\,d\ell}{a^2}$$

Because $d\mathbf{B}$ is out of the page for all the $d\ell$'s, summing or integrating over the segments just replaces $d\ell$ by the circumference $2\pi a$, and the net field has a magnitude

$$B = \frac{2\pi k'I}{a} \tag{19.12}$$

Thus at the center of the circle, $\mathbf{B}$ varies inversely with the first power of the radius, even though the fundamental Biot–Savart law varies as $1/r^2$. (The complete field was shown in Fig. 19.5.)

A single loop carrying a relatively large current produces a fairly weak field. For this reason, many turns of wire are needed to produce even modest sized fields. This is illustrated by the following example.

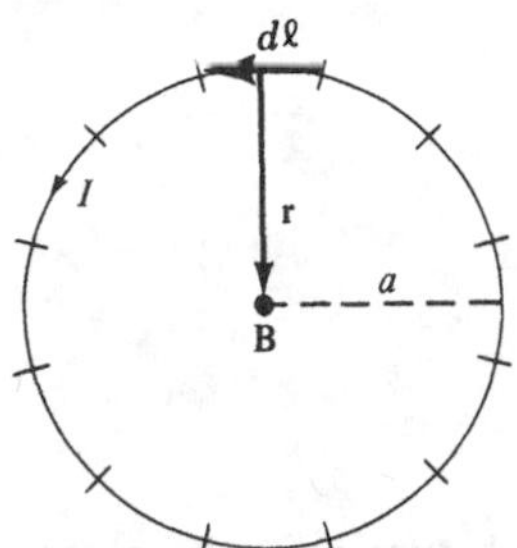

Figure 19.27. A circular current loop is divided into many small segments to calculate the magnetic field. The field is directed out of the page at the center of the circle.

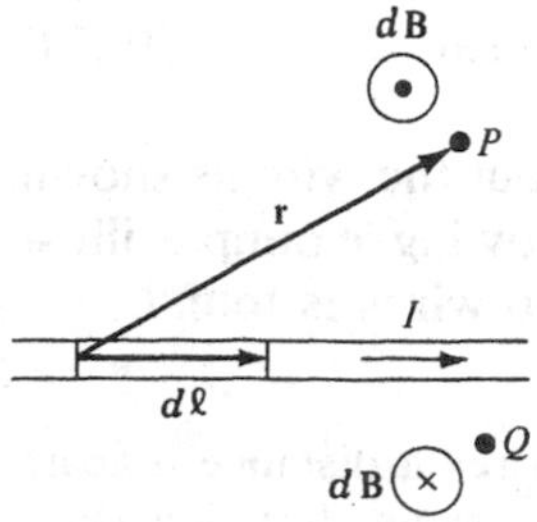

Figure 19.26. The field dB due to the current through $d\ell$ is out of the page at P and into the page at Q.

Example 19.5

A coil consists of 1000 circular turns of thin wire with an average radius of 0.1 m (Fig. 19.28). If the current in the coil is 10 A, find the magnetic field at its center due to (a) one turn; (b) the entire coil.

(a) For any one turn, the field has a magnitude

$$\begin{aligned} B = \frac{2\pi k'I}{a} &= \frac{2\pi(10^{-7}\ \mathrm{T\ m\ A^{-1}})(10\ \mathrm{A})}{0.1\ \mathrm{m}} \\ &= 6.28 \times 10^{-5}\ \mathrm{T} \end{aligned}$$

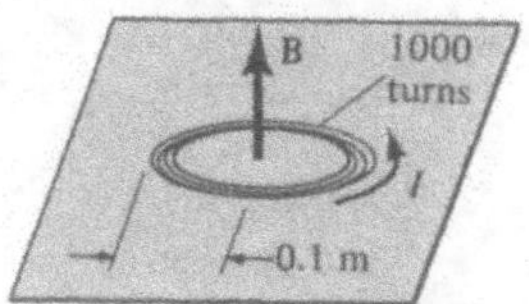

Figure 19.28. Example 19.5.

(b) Since the field due to each turn is in the same direction, the net field is 1000 times the field of one turn or $(1000) \times (6.28 \times 10^{-5}\text{ T}) = 0.0628\text{ T}$.

We will see in the next chapter that larger fields can be obtained if materials such as iron are present in the coil.

Magnetic Field of a Solenoid

A long coil with many circular turns placed next to each other is called a *solenoid*. It is a particularly useful device because within the solenoid the magnetic field is nearly uniform (Fig. 19.29). A solenoid with length ℓ and N turns has $n = N/\ell$ turns per unit length. The field inside the solenoid is

$$B = 4\pi k'In \quad \text{(solenoid)} \qquad (19.13)$$

This formula is exact for an infinitely long solenoid, and it is a good approximation near the center of a long thin solenoid. It will be derived in Section 19.12 in the Supplementary Topics.

Example 19.6

A person studying magnetic bacteria wishes to have a uniform field of 0.01 T inside a solenoid of length 0.2 m. The maximum current is to be 2 A. How much wire is required to construct a suitable solenoid if the average radius of a turn is 0.01 m?

We must first find N, the number of turns required. The length of wire needed is then N times the average circumference of a turn.

The field satisfies $B = 4\pi k'In$, so the number of turns per unit length is $n = B/4\pi k'I$. The total number of turns is found from $n = N/\ell$ or $N = \ell n$. Thus

$$N = \frac{\ell B}{4\pi k'I} = \frac{(0.2\text{ m})(0.01\text{ T})}{4\pi(10^{-7}\text{ T m A}^{-1})(2\text{ A})} = 796$$

If the average radius is r, the average circumference is $2\pi r$, and the length of wire required is

$$L = 2\pi rN = 2\pi(0.01\text{ m})(796) = 50\text{ m}$$

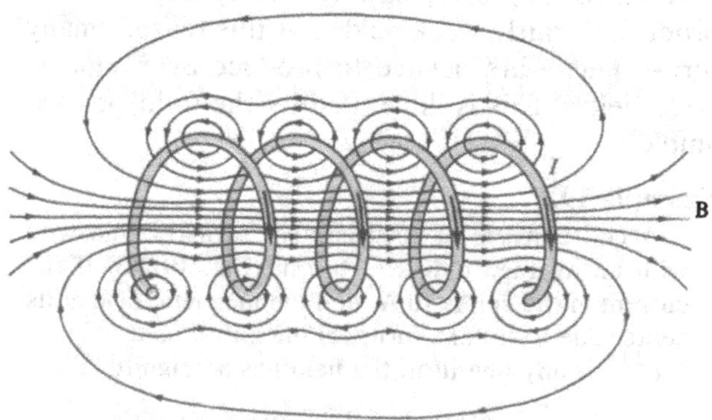

Figure 19.29. The field of a loosely wound solenoid. Inside the solenoid the field is nearly uniform.

Magnetic Field of a Long, Straight Wire

A current in an infinitely long straight wire is an idealized situation which cannot really occur. Its field, however, is a good approximation to the actual field at points near a long straight wire which are far from its ends and from other currents.

For a long straight wire along the x axis (Fig. 19.30), we replace $d\ell$ by dx in the Biot–Savart law. Point P is a perpendicular distance r to the wire, and it is a distance R from dx. The field due to this segment, $d\mathbf{B}$, is out of the page no matter where dx is on the axis. Thus summing (integrating) the $d\mathbf{B}$ vectors means adding their magnitudes.

Since $d\ell$ is at an angle θ with respect to $\mathbf{R}$, the magnitude of $d\mathbf{B}$ is

$$dB = \frac{k'Idx\sin\theta}{R^2}$$

Now $\sin\theta = r/R$, and $R^2 = r^2 + x^2$, so integrating from $-\infty$ to $+\infty$ yields

$$B = \int_{-\infty}^{+\infty} \frac{k'Ir\,dx}{(r^2 + x^2)^{3/2}} = k'Ir\frac{1}{r^2}\left[\frac{x}{(r^2 + x^2)^{1/2}}\right]_{-\infty}^{+\infty}$$

$$= \frac{2k'I}{r} \quad \text{(long straight wire)} \qquad (19.14)$$

The lines of $\mathbf{B}$ form circles about the wire as shown before in Fig. 19.6. The following example illustrates how the field due to two wires is found.

Example 19.7

Two parallel long straight wires a distance d apart each carry a current I in the same direction (Fig. 19.31*a*). Find the net magnetic field (a) midway between the wires; (b) at points P and Q in Fig. 19.31*a*.

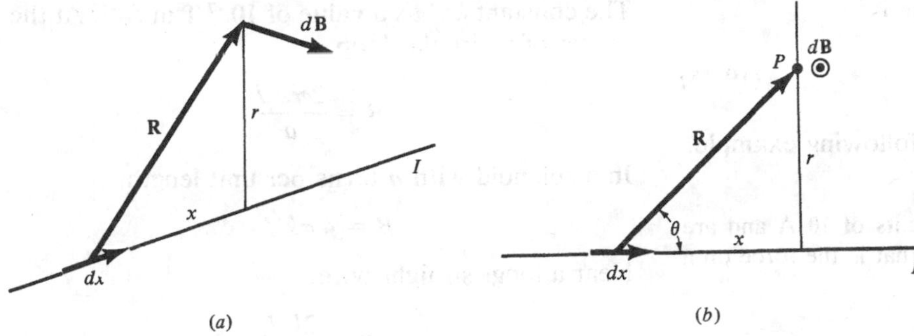

Figure 19.30. (*a*) The field at P due to one segment of a current in an infinitely long wire. (*b*) The fields at P due to all the segments point out of the page.

(a) According to the right-hand rule, the field $\mathbf{B}_l$ due to the left-hand wire points into the page in the region between the wires. Similarly, the field $\mathbf{B}_r$ due to the right-hand wire points out of the page in this region. At the midpoint, the distance to either wire is the same, so $\mathbf{B}_l$ and $\mathbf{B}_r$ are equal in magnitude. Since they are oppositely directed, their vector sum is zero.

(b) At point P, the fields due to both wires point out of the page. Using $B = 2k'I/r$, we have

$$B_l = \frac{2k'I}{d} \qquad B_r = \frac{2k'I}{2d}$$

Hence

$$B = B_l + B_r = \frac{2k'I}{d} + \frac{2k'I}{2d} = \frac{3k'I}{d}$$

At point Q, the field has the same magnitude, but it points into the page.

19.8 | THE FORCE BETWEEN TWO PARALLEL CURRENT-CARRYING WIRES

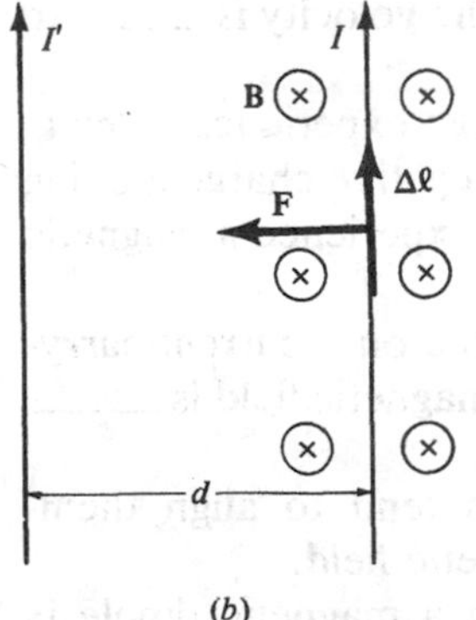

Figure 19.31. (*a*) The fields due to the two currents are opposite in the region between the two wires and in the same directions elsewhere, in the plane of the wires. (*b*) Two currents in the same direction attract each other. **B** is the field due to I'.

Two long, parallel wires attract each other when their currents are in the same direction and repel when the currents are opposite. The force between them can be found using $B = 2k'I/r$ for the field of a straight wire. In Fig. 19.31*b*, I and I' are in the same direction, and their separation is d. The field **B** due to I' at the segment $\Delta\ell$ is into the page, and its magnitude is $2k'I'/d$. The force **F** on the segment is $I\,\Delta\boldsymbol{\ell} \times \mathbf{B}$. By the right-hand rule for cross products, **F** is directed to the left or toward the other wire, so the force is attractive as anticipated. Since $\Delta\boldsymbol{\ell}$ is perpendicular to **B**,

$$F = I\,\Delta\ell B = I\,\Delta\ell\,\frac{2k'I'}{d}$$

The *force per unit length* of wire is

$$\frac{F}{\Delta \ell} = \frac{2k'II'}{d} \qquad (19.15)$$

This result is illustrated by the following example.

Example 19.8

Two parallel wires carry currents of 10 A and are separated by 1 mm = 10^{-3} m. What is the force on a 2-m long portion of a wire?

The force per unit length is

$$\frac{F}{\Delta \ell} = \frac{2k'II'}{d} = \frac{2(10^{-7}\ \mathrm{T\ m\ A^{-1}})(10\ \mathrm{A})(10\ \mathrm{A})}{10^{-3}\ \mathrm{m}}$$

$$= 0.02\ \mathrm{N\ m^{-1}}$$

Thus the force on a 1-m segment of the wire is 0.02 N. The force on a 2-m segment is twice this force, or 0.04 N.

A standard arrangement of this type is used to define the ampere as the current that gives rise to a stated force between the two wires. The unit of charge, the coulomb, is defined as the charge carried by an ampere of current in 1 s.

SUMMARY

Magnetic fields are established by permanent magnets and by moving charges. These fields, in turn, exert forces on other permanent magnets and on moving charges. The magnetic force on a charge q moving with velocity $\mathbf{v}$ in a magnetic field $\mathbf{B}$ is

$$\mathbf{F} = q\mathbf{v} \times \mathbf{B}$$

From the expression for the magnetic force on a moving charge it follows that the magnetic force on a wire segment of length ℓ carrying a current I is

$$\mathbf{F} = I\,\boldsymbol{\ell} \times \mathbf{B}$$

In a uniform magnetic field, a current loop experiences a torque but no net force. Such a loop is called a magnetic dipole, and its dipole moment is $\boldsymbol{\mu} = IA\hat{\mathbf{n}}$. Its behavior in a magnetic field is very similar to that of an electric dipole in an electric field.

Given a current, the magnetic field it produces can be found by applying the Biot–Savart law,

$$d\mathbf{B} = k'I\frac{d\boldsymbol{\ell} \times \hat{\mathbf{r}}}{r^2}$$

The constant k' has a value of 10^{-7} T m A^{-1}. At the center of a circular loop,

$$B = \frac{2\pi k'I}{a}$$

In a solenoid with n turns per unit length,

$$B = 4\pi k'In$$

Near a long, straight wire,

$$B = \frac{2k'I}{r}$$

Two long, parallel wires attract each other when their currents are in the same direction and repel when they are opposite. The force per unit length has a magnitude

$$\frac{F}{\Delta \ell} = \frac{2k'II'}{d}$$

Checklist

Define or explain:

magnetic field	magnetic dipole
magnetic force on a moving charge	motor
magnetic force on a current-carrying wire	galvanometer
	Biot–Savart law
	solenoid

REVIEW QUESTIONS

Q19-1 The magnetic field is largest where the field lines are ______.

Q19-2 The force on a charge moving in a magnetic field is largest when the velocity is ______ to the magnetic field.

Q19-3 If a positive charge experiences a magnetic force straight up, a negative charge moving in the same direction will experience a magnetic force ______.

Q19-4 The magnetic force on a current-carrying wire is zero when the magnetic field is ______ or ______ to the current.

Q19-5 Magnetic dipoles tend to align themselves ______ to the magnetic field.

Q19-6 The net force on a magnetic dipole is ______ when it is in a uniform magnetic field.

Q19-7 In a galvanometer, the deflection is proportional to the ______ and ______.

Q19-8 The magnitude of the magnetic field due

to a short segment of a circuit varies as the ____ of the distance.

Q19-9 A nearly uniform magnetic field can be found inside a ____.

Q19-10 The field due to a long straight wire varies ____ with the distance.

EXERCISES

Section 19.1 | Magnetic Fields

19-1 Consider the magnetic field in Fig. 19.32 at points P_1, P_2, P_3, P_4. (a) At which point is the field largest? (b) At which point is it smallest?

19-2 In the magnetic field shown in Fig. 19.32, near which point is the field most nearly uniform?

Section 19.2 | The Magnetic Force on a Moving Charge

19-3 An electron passing through an apparatus is undeflected. Does that imply that the apparatus has no magnetic field? Explain.

19-4 A particle with charge 10^{-6} C is moving in the $+y$ direction at 10^4 m s^{-1} at right angles to a magnetic field of 2 T (Fig. 19.33). (a) Find the magnitude and direction of the force on the particle. (b) What would the force be if the velocity were in the $-y$ direction?

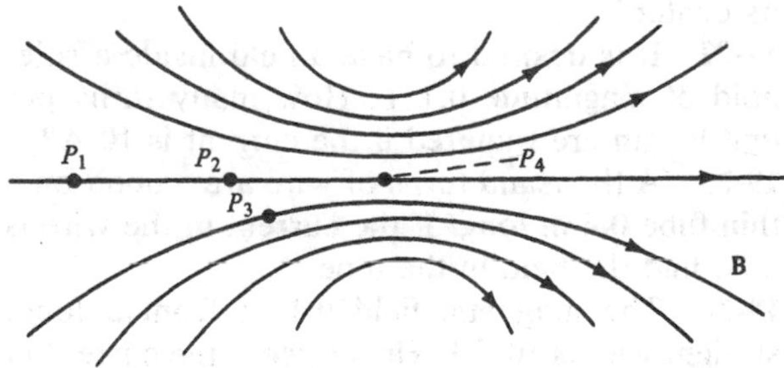

Figure 19.32. Exercises 19-1 and 19-2.

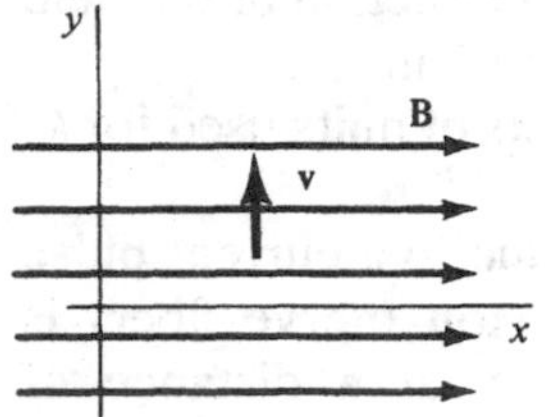

Figure 19.33. Exercises 19-4, 19-5, and 19-6.

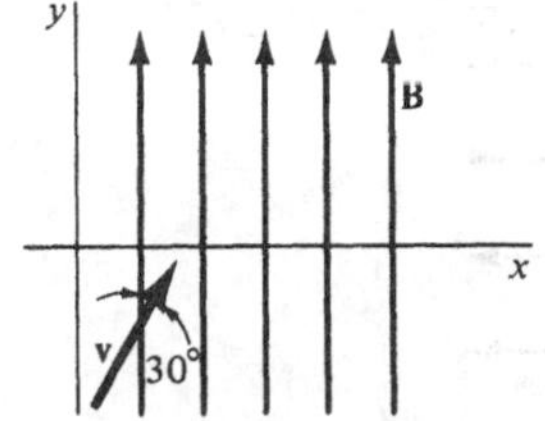

Figure 19.34. Exercise 19-7.

19-5 A particle of charge $+q$ and mass m moves with a velocity **v** in a magnetic field **B** (Fig. 19.33). Find the magnitude and direction of the acceleration if **v** is (a) in the $+x$ direction; (b) $-x$ direction; (c) $+y$ direction; (d) $-y$ direction; (e) out of the page; (f) into the page.

19-6 A negatively charged particle moves in a uniform magnetic field (Fig. 19.33). Find the direction of the force on the particle if it is moving (a) in the $+x$ direction; (b) $+y$ direction; (c) $-y$ direction; (d) out of the page; (e) into the page.

19-7 An object of mass 0.01 kg moves at 100 m s^{-1} at an angle of 30° to a magnetic field of 10^{-2} T (Fig. 19.34). If its charge is -10^{-3} C, find the magnitude and direction of (a) the magnetic force; (b) the acceleration.

19-8 The velocity of a typical hydrogen ion (proton) at room temperature is about 3000 m s^{-1}. (a) If the magnetic field of the earth is 10^{-4} T, what is the maximum magnetic force on the hydrogen ion? (b) Find the ratio of this force to the electric force between two protons 10^{-10} m apart, a typical interatomic distance. (c) Is the earth's magnetic field likely to affect most biochemical processes? Explain.

Section 19.4 | The Magnetic Force on a Current-Carrying Wire

19-9 A 0.5-m long segment of a wire carrying a 20-A current experiences a force of 5 N when it is perpendicular to a magnetic field. What is the magnitude of the field?

19-10 A horizontal wire experiences a 10-N force directed straight up when it carries a 5-A current toward the right. What will the force be if the current is reversed and its magnitude is doubled?

19-11 A straight 2-m long segment of a circuit is

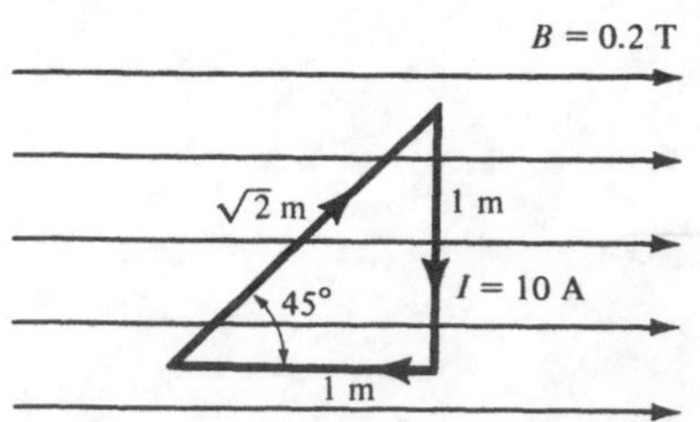

Figure 19.35. Exercises 19-13 and 19-14.

at 30° to a magnetic field. (a) If the field is 3 T and the current is 10 A, find the magnitude of the force on the segment. (b) Indicate the force direction with the aid of a sketch.

19-12 A power line carries a current of 1000 A. The earth's magnetic field makes an angle of 73° with the line and has a magnitude of 7×10^{-5} T. Find the magnitude of the magnetic force on a 100-m-long section of the line.

19-13 (a) Find the magnitude and direction of the force on each of the three straight segments in Fig. 19.35. (b) What is the net force on the circuit?

Section 19.5 | Magnetic Dipoles

19-14 What is the torque on the circuit in Fig. 19.35?

19-15 A square wire loop with sides 0.1 m and a current of 10 A is placed in a magnetic field of magnitude 0.1 T. (a) What is magnetic dipole moment of the loop? (b) What is the largest torque the loop can experience in this field? (c) For what orientation of the loop will this torque occur?

19-16 What orientation of a magnetic dipole in a magnetic field will result in (a) zero energy; (b) maximum torque?

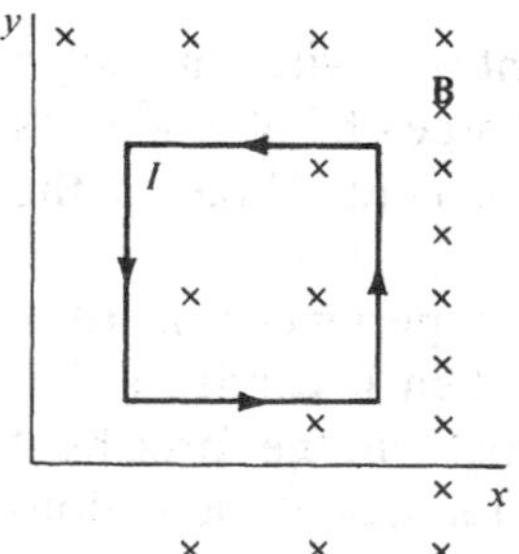

Figure 19.36. Exercise 19-17.

19-17 A square current loop is placed in a magnetic field directed into the page (Fig. 19.36). The magnitude of **B** increases as x increases. Is there a net force on the loop? If there is, what is its direction? Explain.

19-18 The z component of the magnetic dipole moment due to the spin of an electron about its axis is $\mu_z = \pm eh/4\pi m$, where $h = 6.63 \times 10^{-34}$ J s is Planck's constant. (a) If μ_z is parallel to a magnetic field of 10 T, how much energy in electron volts must be supplied to reverse its direction so that it is opposite to the field? (b) Find the ratio of this energy to the 13.6 eV needed to remove an electron from a normal hydrogen atom.

Section 19.7 | Magnetic Fields Produced by Currents

19-19 A circular current loop of radius 0.2 m has a resistance of 100 ohms and is connected to a 12-V battery. What is the magnetic field at the center of the loop?

19-20 The magnetic field at the center of a circular current loop is 0.05 T. If the radius of the loop is 1.2 m, find the current.

19-21 Fifty circular turns of wire are wound closely together, so that all of them have a radius of close to 0.05 m. If the wire carries a current of 2 A, what is the magnitude of the magnetic field at its center?

19-22 It is desired to have a field inside a solenoid of magnitude 0.1 T. How many turns per unit length are required if the current is 10 A?

19-23 A thousand turns of wire are wound on a thin tube 0.4 m long. If the current in the wire is 2 A, find the field in the tube.

19-24 The magnetic field 0.1 m from a long, straight wire is 10^{-4} T. How large is the current in the wire?

19-25 A long straight wire carries a current of 4 A. Find the magnitude and direction of the field at a distance of (a) 0.1 m; (b) 1 m.

19-26 Show that the two sets of units used for k' in Eq. 19.11 are equivalent.

19-27 The magnetic field due to a current pulse in a single long, straight axon (nerve fiber) is found to be 1.2×10^{-10} T at a distance of 1.3 mm = 0.0013 m from the axon. How large is the current in the axon?

Section 19.8 | The Force Between Two Parallel Current-Carrying Wires

19-28 Two long straight parallel wires 0.1 m apart each carry a current of 10 A. Find the direction and magnitude of the force on a 0.5-m long segment of one of the wires if the currents are (a) in the same direction; (b) in opposite directions.

19-29 A 10-m long segment of wire carries a 5-A current and has a weight of 0.5 N. It is constrained so that it can move vertically but not horizontally above another wire carrying a current of 10 A in the opposite direction. (a) At what separation would the weight of the wire be supported by the magnetic forces? (b) If the wires each have a radius of 1 mm = 10^{-3} m, will they be in contact?

19-30 Three parallel wires lie in a plane. The separation between adjacent wires is 0.1 m, and each wire carries a 10-A current in the same direction. Find the magnitude of the net force per unit length on (a) the central wire; (b) one of the outer wires.

19-31 Two parallel wires attract each other with a force of 10^{-4} N per metre of length. The wires are 0.01 m apart. The current in one wire is 20 A. What is the magnitude and relative direction of the current in the other wire?

PROBLEMS

19-32 An electron is moving at 10^5 m s^{-1} directly toward a long straight wire that carries a 50-A current. (a) Find the force on the electron when it is 0.5 m from the wire. (Using a sketch, indicate the direction of the force.) (b) Find the resulting acceleration.

19-33 In Fig. 19.37, electrons in a conductor are moving into the page with a drift velocity $\mathbf{v}_d$. A magnetic field **B** is perpendicular to $\mathbf{v}_d$. (a) Find the magnitude and the direction of the magnetic force on the electrons. (b) Find the direction and magnitude of the electric field **E** that would exert an equal but opposite force on the electrons. (c) What potential difference would have to be applied across the conductor to produce this electric field? (d) If no external electric field is applied, then electrons will tend to move toward one side of the conductor until a constant potential difference is established across the conductor. How large is this potential difference? (The establishment of a potential difference across a conductor in a magnetic field is called the *Hall effect*.) (e) Find the Hall potential difference if $v_d = 10^{-3}$ m s^{-1}, $B = 2$ T, and $a = 10^{-2}$ m. (f) What is the direction of the current? (g) In some conductors, the charge carriers are missing electrons, or "holes," which behave as positive charges. Will the Hall potential difference be the same as when the carriers are negative? Explain.

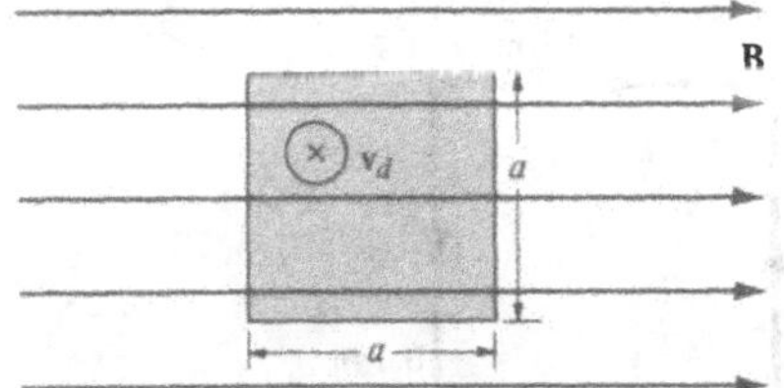

Figure 19.37. Problem 19-33.

19-34 It has been proposed to build huge magnets using superconducting wires to store energy for periods of peak electrical power demands. In one design, turns of radius 100 m carry 150,000 A. The average field due to this current is 5 T. The magnet is placed in a tunnel cut into bedrock to obtain the necessary structural support, since each portion of the wire is subjected to large forces due to the field. (a) If the magnetic field is parallel to the coil axis and perpendicular to the wires, what is the force on 1 m of wire? (b) Show that the force is radially outward. (c) If there are 10 turns per metre of length in the coil, what is the average outward pressure on the bedrock?

19-35 A wire with a resistance of 10 ohms is bent into a rectangle 0.5 m by 0.8 m and connected to a 6-V battery. (a) What is the dipole moment of the loop? (b) The loop is placed in a magnetic field of 0.5 T. What is the maximum torque on the loop? (c) How is it oriented when the torque is a minimum?

19-36 Suppose that the wire in the preceding problem is bent to obtain the maximum magnetic dipole moment. (a) What is the shape of the wire? (b) What is the dipole moment?

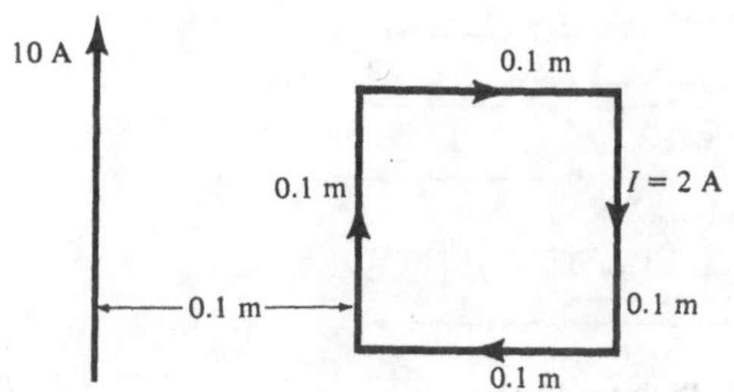

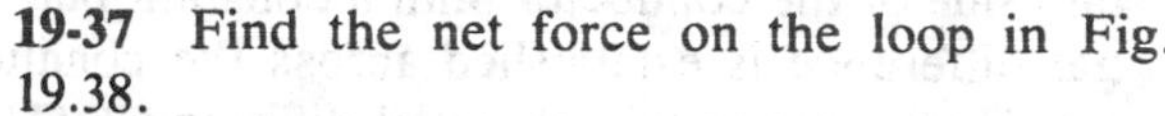

Figure 19.38. Problem 19-37.

19-37 Find the net force on the loop in Fig. 19.38.

***19-38** In Fig. 19.39, $I = I'$. Show that the field between the wires at a distance x from the origin is $4k'Ix/(a^2 - x^2)$ if $|x| < a$. (Positive B values are out of the page, and negative values are into the page.)

19-39 In Fig. 19.39, $I = 10$ A, $I' = 5$ A, and $a = 0.1$ m. Find the magnitude and direction of **B** at (a) $x = 0$; (b) $x = 0.2$ m; (c) $x = -0.2$ m. (d) Where is the field zero?

19-40 The coil of a galvanometer has 100 turns, each with an area of 10^{-3} m^2. The magnetic field is 0.02 T and is arranged so that it is always in the plane of the coil. A current of 1 mA = 10^{-3} A produces a rotation of $\theta = 10°$. If the torque due to the hairspring equals $k\theta$, find the spring constant k in newton metres per radian.

19-41 Five hundred metres of wire are wound on a tube 0.5 m long and 0.2 m in circumference. How large a current is needed to produce a field inside the tube of 0.1 T?

***19-42** (a) Show that the magnetic field along the axis of a circular loop of radius a carrying a current I at a distance y from its center is equal in magnitude to $2\pi Ik'a^2/(a^2 + y^2)^{3/2}$ (Fig. 19.40).

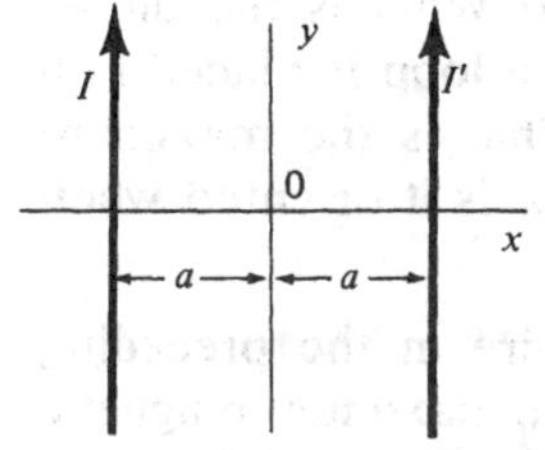

Figure 19.39. Problems 19-38 and 19-39.

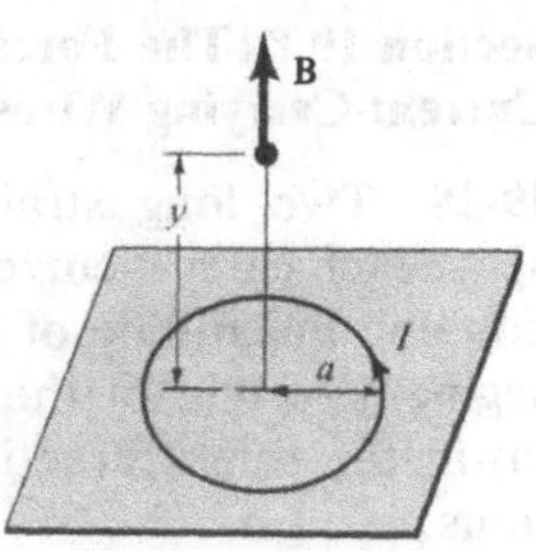

Figure 19.40. Problem 19-42.

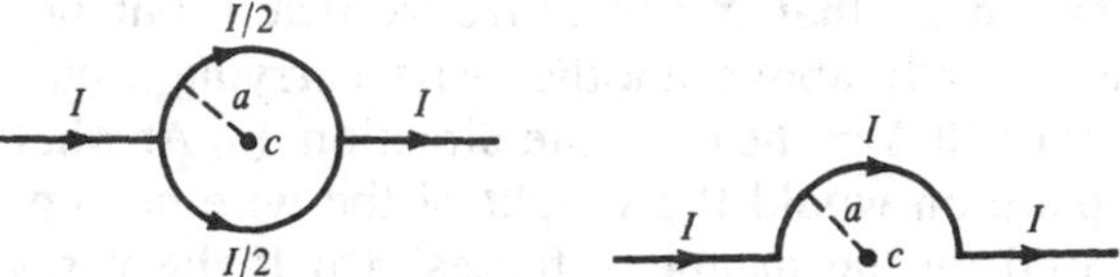

Figure 19.41. Problem 19-44. Figure 19.42. Problem 19-45.

(b) Find an approximate expression for the field in terms of the dipole moment and y when y is large compared to a. (c) Compare this result to the corresponding formula for the electric field due to an electric dipole (Chapter Sixteen).

***19-43** According to the Bohr model, in the normal hydrogen atom the electron orbits the proton in a circle of radius 5.1×10^{-11} m at a frequency of 6.8×10^{15} Hz. (a) What is the current due to the orbital motion of the electron? (b) What is the magnetic field at the proton due to this current?

***19-44** A current splits into two equal currents in Fig. 19.41. What is the magnetic field at the center c of the circle?

***19-45** What is the magnetic field at the center c of the semicircle in Fig. 19.42?

19-46 In a laboratory, the magnetic field of the earth has a magnitude of 6×10^{-5} T and is 20° to the vertical; its vertical component is downward. It is desired to reverse this field in an experiment to study the magnetic senses of bacteria. (a) If a solenoid with 1000 turns per metre is used, how large a current is required? (b) How should the solenoid and current be oriented?

ANSWERS TO REVIEW QUESTIONS

Q19-1, closest; **Q19-2**, perpendicular; **Q19-3**, straight down; **Q19-4**, parallel, opposite; **Q19-5**, parallel; **Q19-6**, zero; **Q19-7**, current, magnetic field; **Q19-8**, inverse square; **Q19-9**, solenoid; **Q19-10**, inversely.

SUPPLEMENTARY TOPICS

19.9 | MEASUREMENT OF CHARGE-TO-MASS RATIOS

In this and the following two sections, we consider some applications of the magnetic force on a moving charge. Here we discuss an arrangement of electric and magnetic fields that can be used to measure the charge-to-mass ratio of a charged particle.

Figure 19.43 shows a particle of mass m and charge q accelerated from rest by a known potential difference V. Since the sum of the kinetic and potential energies must remain constant, the resulting velocity $\mathbf{v}$ satisfies $\frac{1}{2}mv^2 = qV$, and the charge to mass ratio is

$$\frac{q}{m} = \frac{v^2}{2V} \tag{19.16}$$

Thus the charge-to-mass ratio q/m of the particle can be found if the velocity is measured. This is accomplished with the aid of the *crossed* or perpendicular electric and magnetic fields shown in the center of Fig. 19.43. The magnetic force on the particle is $q\mathbf{v} \times \mathbf{B}$, and the electric force in $q\mathbf{E}$. Since $\mathbf{v} \times \mathbf{B}$ points upward or opposite to $\mathbf{E}$, these forces exactly balance when $qvB = qE$ or

$$v = \frac{E}{B} \tag{19.17}$$

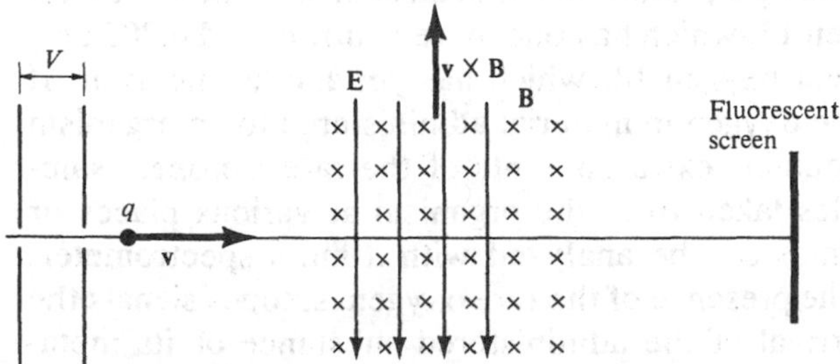

Figure 19.43. The charged particle is accelerated from rest to a velocity $\mathbf{v}$ by a potential difference V. The magnetic field $\mathbf{B}$ is directed into the page. The vector $\mathbf{v} \times \mathbf{B}$ is opposite to $\mathbf{E}$, so the net force $\mathbf{F} = q\mathbf{E} + q\mathbf{v} \times \mathbf{B}$ is zero for some value of E/B.

This means the velocity may be determined by adjusting the crossed fields until the beam spot on the fluorescent screen is undeflected from its position when there are no crossed fields.

J. J. Thomson (1856–1940) used an arrangement of this kind in 1897 to measure the charge to mass ratio for the negative cathode rays in a cathode-ray tube. He concluded that these cathode rays were negatively charged particles (electrons). He also found that their velocity in his apparatus was about one tenth of the velocity of light, which was much greater than any velocity previously observed.

One other feature of this apparatus is significant. The crossed $\mathbf{E}$ and $\mathbf{B}$ fields permit charged particles to travel through them without deflection whenever the condition $v = E/B$ is satisfied, no matter what the charge or mass of the particles. If a beam of several kinds of charged particles with various velocities passes through such a crossed field region, the particles emerging undeflected all have the same velocity. Thus perpendicular electric and magnetic fields act as a *velocity selector*. One use of such an arrangement is seen in the next section.

19.10 | MASS SPECTROMETERS

The *mass spectrometer* was originally developed as a nuclear physics research tool. Today, mass spectrometers are widely used in many kinds of laboratories to measure and identify minute quantities of various substances.

The principle of the mass spectrometer can be understood by considering a particle with positive charge q and mass m moving perpendicular to a uniform magnetic field $\mathbf{B}$ (Fig. 19.44). The magnetic force $\mathbf{F} = q\mathbf{v} \times \mathbf{B}$ is perpendicular to the velocity $\mathbf{v}$, so it changes direction but not magnitude. The mag-

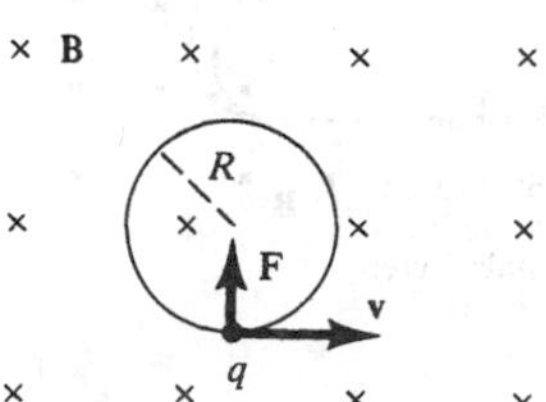

Figure 19.44. A charged particle moves with velocity $\mathbf{v}$ perpendicular to a uniform magnetic field $\mathbf{B}$ directed into the page. Since the force and the acceleration are always perpendicular to $\mathbf{v}$ and are constant in magnitude, the particle moves in a circular orbit with constant speed.

nitude of the force qvB does not change, because **v** and **B** remain constant in magnitude and perpendicular to each other.

Since the acceleration $\mathbf{a} = \mathbf{F}/m$ is constant in magnitude and always perpendicular to **v**, the particle moves in a circular orbit with constant speed. The centripetal acceleration $a_r = v^2/R$ is produced by the magnetic force. Thus the radius R of the orbit must satisfy $qvB = mv^2/R$, and

$$R = \frac{mv}{qB} \tag{19.18}$$

The use of this result is illustrated by the following example.

Example 19.9

How large a magnetic field is needed to cause an O_2^+ ion to move in a circular orbit of radius 2 m at 10^6 m s^{-1}? (The mass of the O_2^+ ion is approximately 32 u, where 1 u = 1.66×10^{-27} kg.)

The charge on the ion is $e = 1.60 \times 10^{-19}$ C. Using $R = mv/qB$, the magnetic field required is

$$B = \frac{mv}{qR}$$

$$= \frac{(32 \times 1.66 \times 10^{-27}\ \text{kg})(10^6\ \text{m s}^{-1})}{(1.60 \times 10^{-19}\ \text{C})(2\ \text{m})}$$

$$= 0.167\ \text{T}$$

Figure 19.45 shows the major parts of the mass spectrometer. In the ion source, molecules are ionized by bombarding them with electrons, and the ions are extracted by an electric field. Crossed electric and magnetic fields in the velocity selector only permit ions with a velocity $v = E_1/B_1$ to proceed without deflection through the slits into the uniform magnetic field **B**. There the ions move in circular paths of radius $R = mv/qB$ until they strike the photographic plate at a distance proportional to their mass, since the radius of curvature increases with the mass. This allows one to separate ions with the same charges but different masses.

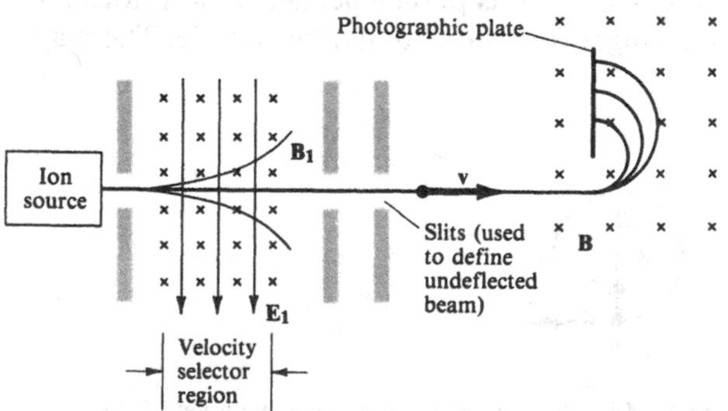

Figure 19.45. A mass spectrometer. Crossed fields $\mathbf{E}_1$ and $\mathbf{B}_1$ select only those particles that have the same velocity. The radius of the circular path in the **B** field then determines m/q.

Historically the mass spectrometer made possible the systematic study of *isotopes*. Isotopes are forms of an element with very nearly the same chemical properties but different numbers of neutrons in their nuclei and hence different atomic masses. Later the mass spectrometer was also used to separate the fissionable uranium 235 isotopes from the more abundant ^{238}U in the World War II development of nuclear weapons.

The ability of the mass spectrometer to distinguish among nuclear isotopes makes it invaluable in situations involving *stable* rather than *radioactive* isotopes. The latter spontaneously transform into other nuclear species, emitting ionizing radiation in the process. If a radioactive material is administered to a plant or animal, its motion within the organism may be observed by detecting the ionization due to the radiation. Such *radioactive tracers* are widely used in biological research and medical diagnosis. However, some biologically important elements, such as nitrogen and oxygen, lack suitable radioactive isotopes, although they do have stable isotopes. For example, oxygen normally has 99.756 percent oxygen 16, which is a nucleus containing 8 protons and 8 neutrons; 0.039 percent oxygen 17, which has one more neutron; and 0.205 percent oxygen 18, which has yet another neutron. If the oxygen in material administered to an organism contains extra amounts of the rare isotopes, samples taken from the organism at various places or times can be analyzed with a mass spectrometer. The presence of the rare oxygen isotopes signals the arrival of the administered substance or its metabolic derivatives. Thus the mass spectrometer makes possible the use of stable isotopes as tracers. It is also used to identify the ratios of the abundances of stable isotopes in geological samples to aid in determining their source or age.

Because the masses of different isotopes of an element differ by a considerable percentage in the lighter elements, small but sometimes significant variations occur in the rates of chemical reactions, evaporation, and so on. As a result, measurable variations arise in the ratios of the hydrogen, carbon, and oxygen isotopes, among others, in minerals, bodies of water, and organisms. A vast amount of contemporary research in biology, planetary science, oceanography, and archaeology is made possible by using mass spectrometers to study these minute isotopic ratio variations. For example, investigators traced the source of the carbon used by plankton in a lake, and fragments of several Greek columns bearing inscriptions were sorted out in this way.

Mass spectrometers are sometimes employed in situations where one is not concerned about the isotopic composition. They have been used to analyze the respiratory gases of patients with various disorders, and to study the composition of the gas surrounding plants during photosynthesis. Also, they are used in the petroleum industry to distinguish among complex compounds having identical chemical compositions but different molecular configurations, and a mass spectrometer was one of the instruments carried by the space ships that landed on Mars and Venus.

19.11 | CYCLOTRONS

The *cyclotron*, invented by Ernest O. Lawrence (1901–1958) in 1930, was the first machine developed to accelerate charged particles to high velocities by causing them to pass repeatedly through the same accelerating region. Its operation depends on the remarkable fact that the period or the time required for a charged particle to complete one circular orbit in a uniform magnetic field **B** is independent of the speed of the particle v.

For a particle of charge q and mass m, the radius R of the orbit was shown in the preceding section to be $R = mv/qB$. The period T satisfies $vT = 2\pi R$, or

$$T = \frac{2\pi R}{v} = \frac{2\pi m}{qB} \tag{19.19}$$

Thus increasing the velocity increases the radius of the orbit but has no effect on the period T or the orbital frequency $f = 1/T$.

A cyclotron consists of two evacuated hollow metal *dees* in a uniform magnetic field perpendicular to their plane (Fig. 19.46). Protons or other positive ions are injected near the center. An electric generator reverses the potential difference between the dees at the orbital frequency of the ions, so they are accelerated each time they pass through the gap between the dees. This increases their velocity and consequently their orbital radius $R = mv/qB$ but does not alter their period.

The operation of the cyclotron depends on the fact that the period is independent of the velocity. However, it is found that the inertial mass of a particle increases rapidly as its velocity approaches the speed of light. This was originally predicted by Einstein's special theory of relativity in 1905 and has been well confirmed. This mass increase causes the period to increase and sets a limit to the velocity and kinetic energy attainable with a cyclotron. Higher energies can be achieved in more complex accelerators that gradually vary the magnetic field or the generator frequency as the ions accelerate.

Originally developed for nuclear physics research, cyclotrons have largely been replaced in

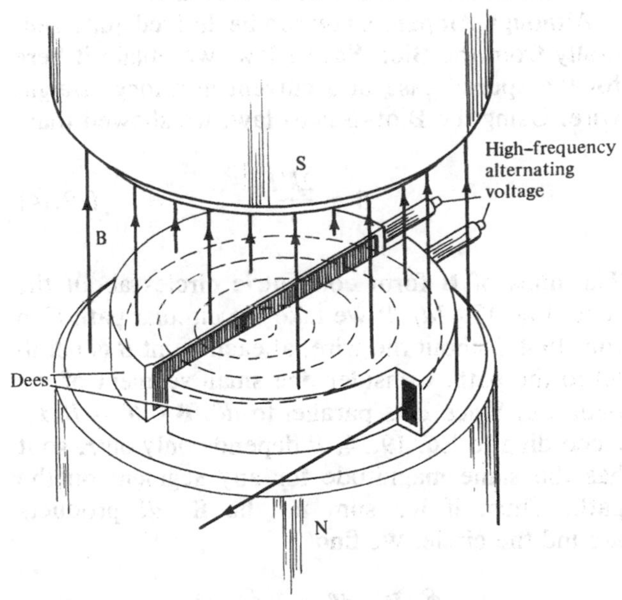

Figure 19.46. The principle of the cyclotron. A magnetic field perpendicular to the plane of the dees maintains the ions in circular orbits. The orbital radius increases as the ions are accelerated by the potential difference between the dees, which reverses at the orbital frequency of the ions.

that area by newer machines. However, they are sometimes used today in hospitals to bombard various targets, inducing nuclear reactions that produce medically useful radioactive materials. Most radioactive materials are supplied to hospitals by nuclear reactor facilities, but some are so short-lived that they cannot be transported, and others can only be made in cyclotrons.

19.12 | AMPÈRE'S LAW

The Biot–Savart law permits us to find the magnetic field by summing the fields due to small current segments. A different looking but equivalent way of finding magnetic fields is provided by Ampère's law.

Like Gauss' law in electrostatics, Ampère's law involves integrals that we can evaluate when there is sufficient geometric symmetry to determine the field direction. Also, it has a differential form that is useful in more advanced applications. Both forms of Ampère's law contain precisely the same physical information as the Biot–Savart law.

Although Ampère's law can be derived quite generally from the Biot–Savart law, we obtain it here for the special case of a current in a long straight wire. Using the Biot–Savart law, we showed that

$$B = \frac{2k'I}{r} \qquad (19.14)$$

The lines of **B** form concentric circles about the wire (Fig. 19.47*a*). If we take the circular path C in Fig. 19.47*b* about the wire, at each point B is parallel to the path. Consider one small segment of the path, $d\ell$. Since $\mathbf{B}$ is parallel to $d\ell$, $\mathbf{B} \cdot d\ell = B\, d\ell$. According to Eq. 19.14, B depends only on r, so it has the same magnitude for any segment on the path. Thus, if we sum up the $\mathbf{B} \cdot d\ell$ products around the circle, we find

$$\oint_C \mathbf{B} \cdot d\ell = B \oint_C d\ell$$

The circle on the integral sign indicates a closed path C. Since $\oint d\ell$ is the circumference of the circle $2\pi r$, with Eq. 19.14 we have

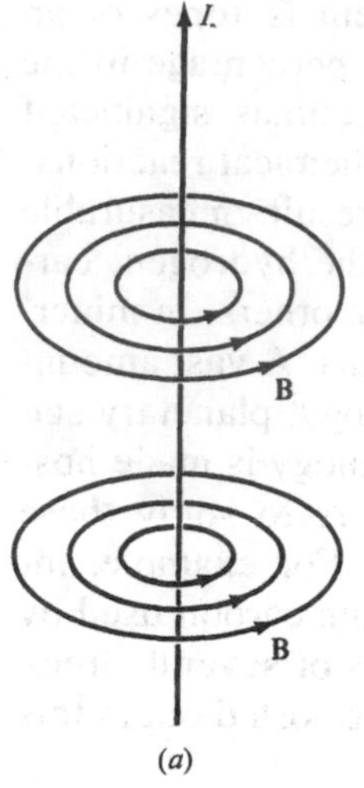

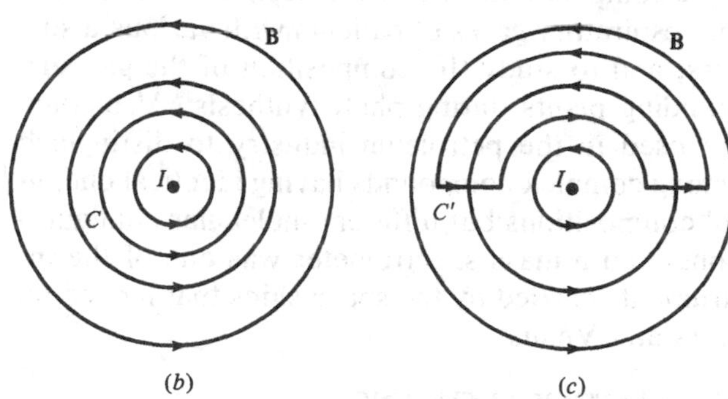

Figure 19.47. (*a*) A current in a long straight wire, perpendicular to the page, has magnetic field lines that are concentric circles. (*b*) The current crossing the surface within the circle C is I. (*c*) There is no current crossing the surface within C'.

$$\oint_C \mathbf{B} \cdot d\ell = \frac{2k'I}{r} 2\pi r = 4\pi k'I$$

Note that the factors of r have canceled; the result is independent of the radius of the circle. This cancellation would also have occurred if we had integrated over a semicircle or some other fraction of a circle.

It is left as a problem to show that the integral is zero for a path such as C' in Fig. 19.47*c* that does not encircle the wire. Therefore, our result, which is known as Ampere's law, is

$$\oint_C \mathbf{B} \cdot d\ell = 4\pi k'I \quad \text{(Ampère's law)} \qquad (19.20)$$

Here I is the current passing through the surface enclosed by the closed path C. When there are two or more currents, I is their algebraic sum. If, as in Fig. 19.47*a*, you can put your fingers on your right hand around the curve, and your thumb is approximately in the direction of the current, the current is positive. Your thumb will be opposite to a negative current.

Despite the lack of generality of our derivation, Ampère's law is, in fact, equivalent to the Biot–Savart law for any path and current distribution. However, when there are time-varying electric fields present, neither law as presented here corrected predicts the entire magnetic field. This will be discussed further in the next chapter.

The fact that Ampère's law holds for any closed path we wish to choose is what makes it useful in finding magnetic fields. Much as with Gauss' law, the judicious choice of integration paths and the exploitation of the geometric symmetrics are the keys to its applications.

We now illustrate the use of Ampère's law by considering a current in a long cylindrical conductor and in a solenoid. In both caşes the direct application of the Biot–Savart law would involve very difficult calculations.

Field of a Long Cylindrical Conductor | In Fig. 19.48*a*, a current I is distributed uniformly across a long cylindrical conductor of radius R. In the simpler case of a long straight wire, the Biot–Savart law showed the field lines are circles centered at the wire. The same symmetry is present here; nothing changes when we move about the wire at a fixed radius. We still have a current with symmetry about the axis, so we again expcct to find circular field lines. Thus our task is to determine how the magnitude of **B** depends on r.

First consider a circular path C inside the wire, $r < R$ (Fig. 19.48*b*). The current in Ampère's law is the total current I times the fraction of the cross-sectional area of the wire enclosed by C, or

$$i = \frac{I\pi r^2}{\pi R^2} = \frac{Ir^2}{R^2}$$

B is tangent to the path C, so $\mathbf{B} \cdot d\boldsymbol{\ell} = B\, d\ell$. Since **B** is constant in magnitude for a fixed r

$$\oint_C \mathbf{B} \cdot d\boldsymbol{\ell} = B \oint_C d\ell$$

The integral is just the circumference $2\pi r$. Thus Ampère's law gives

$$B(2\pi r) = 4\pi k' I\left(\frac{r^2}{R^2}\right)$$

$$B = \frac{2k'Ir}{R^2} \qquad r < R \qquad (19.21)$$

The field inside the wire increases in magnitude linearly with r.

To find the field outside the wire, consider a circle with radius $r > R$ (Fig. 19.48*c*). Then the entire current I passes through the circle. The left side of Ampère's law is again $B(2\pi r)$. Hence we have

$$B(2\pi r) = 4\pi k' I$$

$$B = \frac{2k'I}{r} \qquad r > R \qquad (19.22)$$

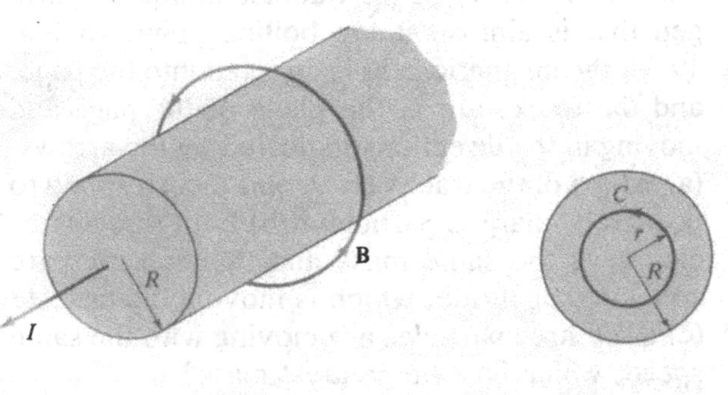

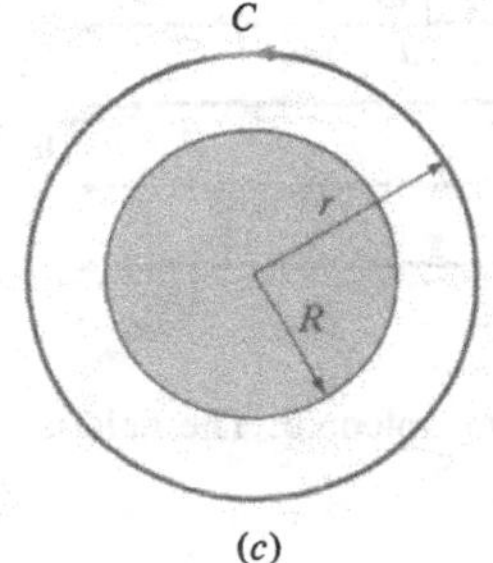

Figure 19.48. (*a*) An infinitely long cylinder with a current I uniformly distributed over its cross section. The symmetry indicates that the lines of B are circles centered at the axis. (*b*) A circular path within the cylinder is parallel to B and encloses part of the current. (*c*) A path outside the wire encloses all the current.

This result for the field is identical to that of a long straight wire (Eq. 19.14). Measurements of the field outside the wire give no clue as to whether its source is a thin wire, a current uniformly distributed in a wire of finite radius, or any other current distribution with circular symmetry about the axis. Note that the results for $r < R$ and for $r > R$ agree at $r = R$, as expected.

Field of a Solenoid | We now derive Eq. 19.13 for the field of a solenoid. As the turns of a solenoid come closer together, and the number of turns becomes very large, the cancellations among the separate turns produce a field that is along the axis within the solenoid and very small outside it (Fig. 19.29). The field lines outside become further and further apart as the solenoid is increased in size. In the limit of an infinitely long solenoid, the symmetry of the current leads to the field in Fig. 19.49. In this idealized case, **B** is uniform and directed along the axis inside the coil, and it is zero outside the coil.

Suppose now we apply Ampère's law to the rectangular path C. The integral splits into four parts, corresponding to the sides of the rectangle. The field is zero along the top side, so this integral is zero. Also, **B** is perpendicular to the short sides, so $\mathbf{B} \cdot d\ell$ is zero everywhere on these sides. Finally, along the bottom side, **B** is parallel to $d\ell$, so $\mathbf{B} \cdot d\ell = B\,d\ell$. Also, B is constant along this side, so it can be taken out of the integral. Hence, if the length of the rectangle is h, we find

$$\oint_C \mathbf{B} \cdot d\ell = B \oint d\ell = Bh$$

If a length L of the solenoid has N turns, there are $n = N/L$ turns per unit length. The number of turns crossing the rectangle is nh, and the total current through it is nhI. Hence Ampère's law becomes

$$Bh = 4\pi k' nhI$$
$$B = 4\pi k' nI$$

This is Eq. 19.13.

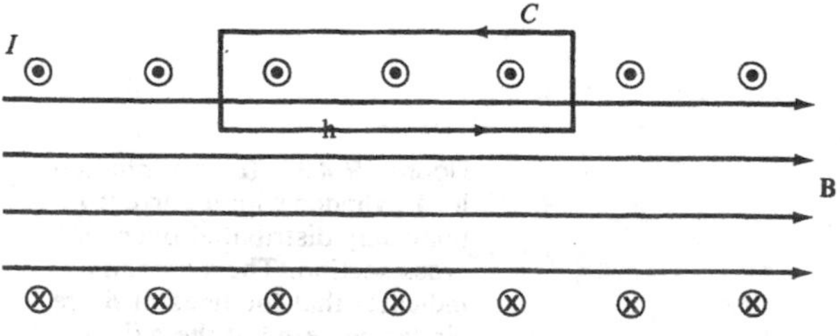

Figure 19.49. Part of an infinitely long solenoid. The field is parallel to the axis.

EXERCISES ON SUPPLEMENTARY TOPICS

Section 19.10 | Mass Spectrometers

19-47 A beam of particles with charge $+e$ moves in a circle of radius 3 m in a magnetic field of magnitude 0.2 T. (a) What is the momentum of the particles? (b) If the particles are protons, what is their velocity? (The proton mass is 1.67×10^{-27} kg.)

19-48 An electron moves at a speed of 10^7 m s^{-1} in a circle of radius 2 m in a magnetic field. (a) How large is the field? (b) How large is the acceleration? (c) Draw a sketch showing the directions of the electron path and the field.

19-49 Protons with a kinetic energy of 5 MeV = 5×10^6 eV move along a circular path in a magnetic field. Alpha particles, which are helium nuclei, have twice the charge and about four times the mass of a proton. How much energy must they have to move along the same path?

19-50 A beam of ions passes through a velocity selector in a mass spectrometer that has an electric field of 1.4×10^5 N C^{-1}. (a) If the ions emerging from the selector have a velocity of 2×10^5 m s^{-1}, what is the magnetic field in the selector? (b) The magnetic field in the bending region is 1 T. What is the radius of the path followed by a He$^+$ ion with charge e and a mass 6.68×10^{-27} kg?

19-51 Charged particles passing through a bubble chamber leave visible tracks that consist of very small hydrogen gas bubbles in liquid hydrogen that is almost at the boiling point. In Fig. 19.50, the magnetic field is directed into the page, and the tracks are in the plane of the page and moving in the directions indicated by the arrows. (a) Which of the tracks C, D, and E correspond to positively charged particles? (b) If all three particles have the same mass and their charges are equal in magnitude, which is moving the fastest? (c) If all three particles are moving with the same speed, which has the greatest mass?

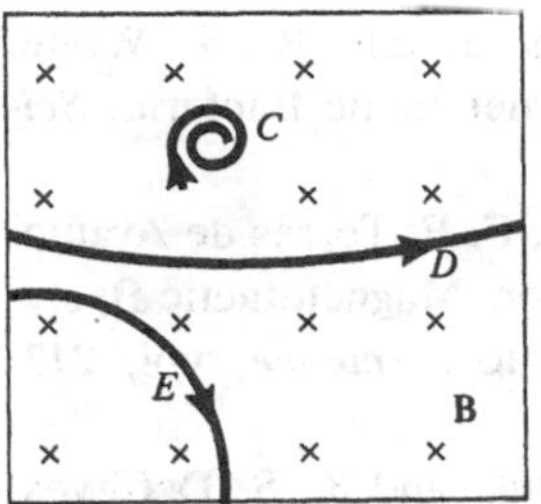

Figure 19.50. Exercise 19-51.

Section 19.11 | Cyclotrons

19-52 Helium nuclei with mass 6.68×10^{-27} kg and charge $2e$ are accelerated in a cyclotron. The period of their orbit is 10^{-7} s. (a) What is the magnetic field? (b) If the maximum orbital radius is 2 m, what is the maximum velocity attained?

PROBLEMS ON SUPPLEMENTARY TOPICS

19-53 A mass spectrometer has an electric field of 10^5 N C^{-1} and a magnetic field of 0.6 T in its velocity selector and a magnetic field of 0.8 T in its bending region. (a) What is the velocity of the ions passing through the velocity selector? (b) Find the spatial separation of singly ionized neon 20 and neon 22 isotopes with charges $+e$ after they have been bent through a half circle. (Neon 20 has a mass of approximately 20 u, and neon 22 has a mass of approximately 22 u. 1 u = 1.66×10^{-27} kg.)

19-54 A cyclotron accelerates protons of mass 1.67×10^{-27} kg to a velocity 3×10^7 m s^{-1}, a tenth that of light. The magnetic field is 1.5 T. Find the maximum orbital radius and the orbital frequency.

***19-55** An electron is projected with velocity $\mathbf{v}$ at an angle of 30° into a uniform magnetic field $\mathbf{B}$. (a) Find the magnitude and direction of the acceleration. (b) Find the component of the velocity along the magnetic field. What is its rate of change? (c) Find the component of the velocity perpendicular to the field. Show that this component rotates about the field and find the associated radius. (d) How far does the electron move along the field direction during one full rotation? (e) Sketch the trajectory of the electron.

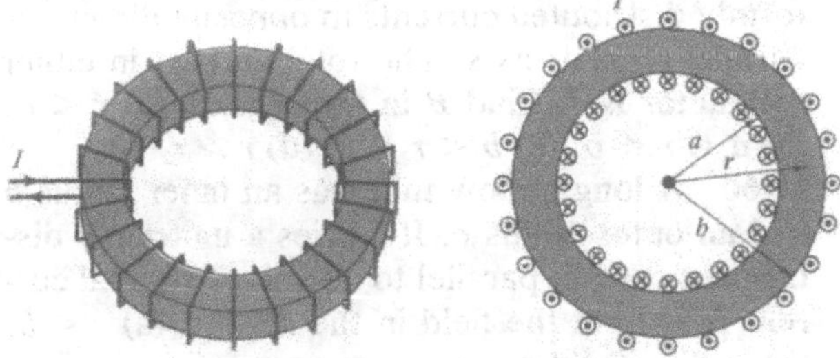

Figure 19.51. A toroid. Problem 19-57.

***19-56** (a) Electrons in a television picture tube are accelerated from rest by a potential difference of 2×10^4 V. What is their speed? (b) If the earth's magnetic field is at right angles to the electron beam and its magnitude is 6×10^{-5} T, what is the magnetic force on an electron? (c) Estimate the displacement resulting from this force when the beam travels 0.15 m through the tube.

[c]19-57 A solenoid of finite length bent into a circular or doughnut shape is a *toroid* (Fig. 19.51). If it has N turns and a current I in its windings, using Ampère's law show that B is (a) zero for $r < a$; (b) $2k'IN/r$ for $a < r < b$; (c) zero for $r > b$.

[c]19-58 Two long parallel plates of width a are separated by a distance small compared to a (Fig. 19.52). The plates carry uniformly distributed currents in opposite directions along their length. The total current in either plate is I. Show that the field between them is given approximately by $4\pi k'I/a$.

[c]19-59 A coaxial cable has a solid central conductor of radius a separated by insulators from an outer concentric tube with inner radius b and outer radius c. The two conductors carry uni-

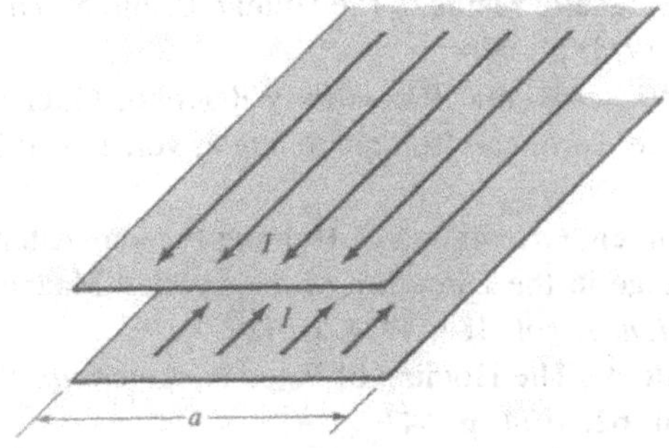

Figure 19.52 Problem 19-58.

formly distributed currents in opposite directions parallel to their axis. The total current in either conductor is I. Find B in the regions (a) $r < a$; (b) $a < r < b$; (c) $b < r < c$; (d) $r > c$.

[c]**19-60** A long hollow tube has an inner radius b and an outer radius c. It carries a uniformly distributed current parallel to its axis. The total current is I. Find the field in the regions (a) $r < b$; (b) $b < r < c$; (c) $r > c$.

[c]**19–61** Show that the integral of $\mathbf{B} \cdot d\boldsymbol{\ell}$ around path C' in Fig. 19.47c is zero along the radial lines, positive on the outer semicircle, negative on the inner semicircle, and zero for the complete path.

Additional Reading

Francis Bitter, *Magnets: The Education of a Physicist*, Science Study Series, Doubleday and Co., Garden City, N.Y., 1959. Paperback.

Louis W. McKeehan, *Magnets*, Momentum Series, D. Van Nostrand and Co., Princeton, N.J., 1967. Paperback.

Lawrence G. Rubin and Peter A. Wolff, High Magnetic Fields for Physics, *Physics Today*, August 1984, p. 24.

David Larbalestier, Gene Fisk, Bruce Montgomery, and David Hawksworth, High-Field Superconductivity, *Physics Today*, March 1986, p. 24. High-field magnets and applications in physics and medicine.

Alexander Kolin, Magnetic Fields in Biology, *Physics Today*, November 1968, p. 39.

David Cohen, Magnetic Fields of the Human Body, *Physics Today*, vol. 29, August 1975, p. 34.

Richard Blakemore, Magnetotactic Bacteria, *Science*, vol. 190, 1975, p. 377.

D. Brenner, S. J. Williamson, and L. Kaufman, Visually Evoked Magnetic Fields of the Human Brain, *Science*, vol. 190, 1975, p. 480.

Wolfgang Wiltschko and Roswitha Wiltschko, Magnetic Compass of European Robins, *Science*, vol. 176, 1972, p. 62.

Robert P. Green, Orientation of Homing Pigeons Altered by a Change in the Direction of an Applied Magnetic Field, *Science*, vol. 184, 1974, p. 180.

Charles Walcott, The Homing of Pigeons, *American Scientist*, vol. 62, 1974, p. 542.

J. P. Wikswo, Jr., J. P. Barach, and J. A. Freeman, Magnetic Field of a Nerve Impulse: First Measurements, *Science*, vol. 208, 1980, p. 53.

R. B. Frankel, R. P. Blakemore, and R. S. Wolfe, Magnetite in Freshwater Magnetotactic Bacteria, *Science*, vol. 203, 1979, p. 1355.

R. B. Frankel, R. P. Blakemore, F. F. Torres de Araujo, D. M. S. Esquival, and J. Danon, Magnetotactic Bacteria at the Geomagnetic Equator, *Science*, vol. 212, 1981, p. 1269.

James L. Gould, J. L. Kirschvink, and K. S. Deffeyes, Bees Have Magnetic Remanence, *Science*, vol. 201, 1978, p. 1026.

Charles Wolcott, James L. Gould, and J. L. Kirschvink, Pigeons Have Magnets, *Science*, vol. 205, 1979, p. 1027.

James L. Gould and Kenneth P. Able, Human Homing: An Elusive Phenomenon, *Science*, vol. 212, 1981, p. 1961.

R. R. Baker, Goal Orientation by Blindfolded Humans After Long-Distance Displacement: Possible Involvement of a Magnetic Sense, *Science*, vol. 210, 1980, p. 555.

Samuel Epstein, Peter Thompson, and Crayton J. Yapp, Oxygen and Hydrogen Isotopic Ratios in Plant Cellulose, *Science*, vol. 198, 1977, p. 1209.

Norman Herz and David B. Wenner, Assembly of Greek Marble Inscriptions by Isotopic Methods, *Science*, vol. 199, 1978, p. 1070.

Greg Rau, Carbon-13 Depletion in a Subalpine Lake; Carbon Flow Implications, *Science*, vol. 201, 1978, p. 901.

Richard A. Kerr,. Isotopic Anomalies of Meteorites: Complications Multiply, *Science*, vol. 202, 1978, p. 203.

Roger Lewin, Isotopes Give Clues to Past Diets, *Science*, vol. 220, 1983, p. 1369.

Woodfin V. Ligon, Jr., Molecular Analysis by Mass Spectrometry, *Science*, vol. 205, 1979, p. 151.

W. H. Berger and J. S. Killingley, Migrations of California Gray Whales Tracked by Oxygen-18 Variations in Their Epizoic Barnacles, *Science*, vol. 207, 1980, p. 759.

F. W. McLafferty, Tandem Mass Spectrometry, *Science*, vol. 214, 1981, p. 280.

R. Thompson et al., Environmental Applications of Magnetic Measurements, *Science*, vol. 207, 1980, p. 481.

Scientific American articles:

L. Pearce Williams, André-Marie Ampère, January 1989, p. 90.

M. Wilson, Joseph Henry, July 1954, p. 72.

Joseph J. Becker, Permanent Magnets, December 1970, p. 92.

H. P. Furth, Strong Magnetic Fields, February 1958, p. 28.

Henry H. Kolm and Arthur J. Freeman, Intense Magnetic Fields, April 1965, p. 66.

Francis Bitter, Ultrastrong Magnetic Fields, July 1965, p. 64.

Alfred O. C. Nier, The Mass Spectrometer, March 1953, p. 68.

A. B. Benfield, The Earth's Magnetism, June 1950, p. 20.

S. K. Runcorn, The Earth's Magnetism, September 1955, p. 152.

W. M. Elsasser, The Earth on a Dynamo, May 1958, p. 44.

Charles R. Carrigan and David Gubbins, The Source of the Earth's Magnetic Field, February 1979, p. 118.

S. W. Angrist, Galvanomagnetism and Thermomagnetism, December 1961, p. 124.

Raymond Wolfe, Magnetothermoelectricity, June 1964, p. 70.

Laurence L. Cahill, Jr., The Magnetosphere, March 1965, p. 58.

Allen Cox et al., Reversals of the Earth's Magnetic Field, February 1967, p. 44.

Palmer Dyal and Curtis W. Parkin, The Magnetism of the Moon, August 1971, p. 62.

J. E. Kurszler and M. Tanenbaum, Superconducting Magnets, June 1962, p. 60.

W. B. Sampson et al., Advances in Superconducting Magnets, March 1967, p. 114.

John H. Reynolds, The Age of the Solar System, November 1960, p. 171.

Kenneth W. Ford, Magnetic Monopoles, December 1963, p. 122.

Henry Koln, John Oberteuffer, and David Kelland, High-Gradient Magnetic Separation, November 1975, p. 46.

R. R. Wilson, The Batavia Accelerator, February 1974, p. 72.

William T. Keeton, The Mystery of Pigeon Homing, December 1974, p. 96.

Richard P. Blakemore and Richard B. Frankel, Magnetic Navigation in Bacteria, December 1981, p. 58.

R. K. O'Nions, P. J. Hamilton, and N. M. Evensen, The Chemical Evolution of the Earth's Mantle, May 1980, p. 120. Applications of mass spectrometers.

Robert R. Wilson, The Next Generation of Particle Accelerators, January 1980, p. 42.

Richard A. Carrigan, Jr., and Peter W. Trower, Superheavy Magnetic Monopoles, April 1982, p. 106.

Ronald E. Rosenzweig, Magnetic Fluids, October 1982, p. 136. The strange properties of a liquid with magnetic particles in suspension.

Richard A. Mewalt, Edward C. Stone, and Mark E. Wiedenbeck, Samples of the Milky Way, December 1982, p. 108. Mass spectrometers and cosmic rays.

Jearl Walker, Motors in Which Magnets Attract Other Magnets in Apparent Perpetual Motion, *The Amateur Scientist*, May 1983, p. 162.

CHAPTER 20 INDUCED CURRENTS AND FIELDS

We have seen that charged objects at rest may experience electric forces and that moving charged objects may experience electric and also magnetic forces. However, we have not yet encountered any situations in which the electric and magnetic forces are related; electricity and magnetism have appeared to be essentially distinct phenomena. We see in this chapter that when electric and magnetic fields are changing in time, they are, in fact, related to each other in a remarkable fashion. A changing magnetic field produces an *induced* electric field, and a changing electric field produces an *induced* magnetic field. One major consequence of these effects is the existence of *electromagnetic waves*, which travel with the speed of light.

20.1 | FARADAY'S LAW

As we saw in the preceding chapter, Oersted discovered in 1820 that electric currents produce magnetic fields. Michael Faraday (1791–1867), a self-educated English physicist and chemist, guessed that magnetic fields might also produce electric currents. He found that this did not happen if a wire loop and a magnet were both stationary. However, he discovered in 1831 that when the magnetic field through a loop is changing, a current is *induced* in the loop.

This phenomenon, called Faraday's law, can be illustrated with a coil of wire connected to a battery and a second separate loop of wire attached to an ammeter (Fig. 20.1). When the switch is closed, the ammeter indicates that a current occurs momentarily in the second loop; when it is reopened, a current in the opposite direction is briefly observed. Moving the loop farther away from the coil or reducing its area by bending the wires produces a current in the same direction, as does opening the switch. Rotating the loop so that its plane is not horizontal also induces a current.

Faraday's studies led him to observe that the single common feature in these and related phenomena was the occurrence of a change in the "amount" of the magnetic field passing through the loop in which the current is induced. Suppose, for example, that we count the number of magnetic field lines that pass through the loop of Fig. 20.1. Then a current will be induced in the loop when any change occurs in the number of lines intersecting the loop area. Such a change occurs in each of the situations we just described.

To make this idea more precise, we define the *magnetic flux*. We will see shortly that the magnetic flux is proportional to the number of lines that pass through an area. Suppose a loop of area A has its normal vector $\hat{\mathbf{n}}$ at an angle θ to a uniform magnetic field $\mathbf{B}$ (Fig. 20.2). The vector area $\mathbf{A}$ is defined then as $\mathbf{A} = A\hat{\mathbf{n}}$; the magnitude of $\mathbf{A}$ is equal to the area, and it is directed perpendicular to the surface. The magnetic flux Φ (Greek capital phi) through the loop is a scalar quantity defined by

$$\Phi = BA\cos\theta = B_n A = \mathbf{B}\cdot\mathbf{A} \qquad (20.1)$$

Thus the magnetic flux is the product of the area and the component B_n *of the magnetic field normal to the loop*. Note that the flux is proportional to the area, since a larger area has more lines passing through it. The $\cos\theta$ factor indicates that the maxi-

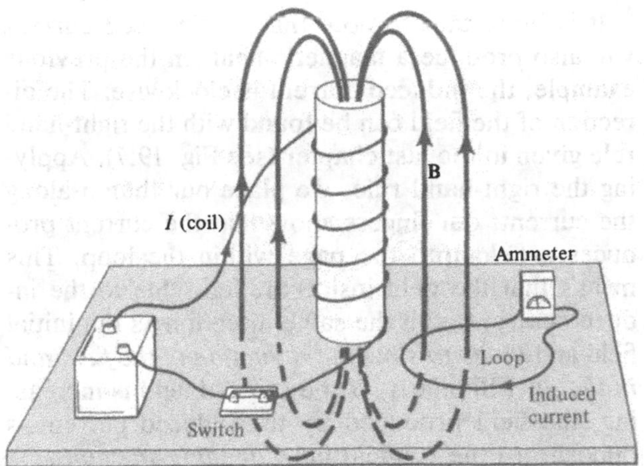

Figure 20.1. When the switch is closed, a current is temporarily produced in the loop in the indicted direction; a current in the opposite direction occurs when the switch is opened. If the switch is left closed so that a constant magnetic field is present, moving the loop or changing its size or orientation will also produce a current.

mum number of lines of **B** will pass through the area when **n̂** and **B** are parallel, and this number decreases until no lines pass through the loop when $\theta = 90°$. We will see shortly that it is the changes in the magnetic flux that are most directly related to the induced currents.

The definition we have given above for the magnetic flux holds true only when the magnetic field is constant over the loop. If **B** varies, the loop must be subdivided into areas small enough so that the field is nearly constant in each. The total flux is then the sum of the fluxes through the small areas, or the integral over the area of the loop:

$$\Phi = \int \mathbf{B} \cdot d\mathbf{A} \tag{20.2}$$

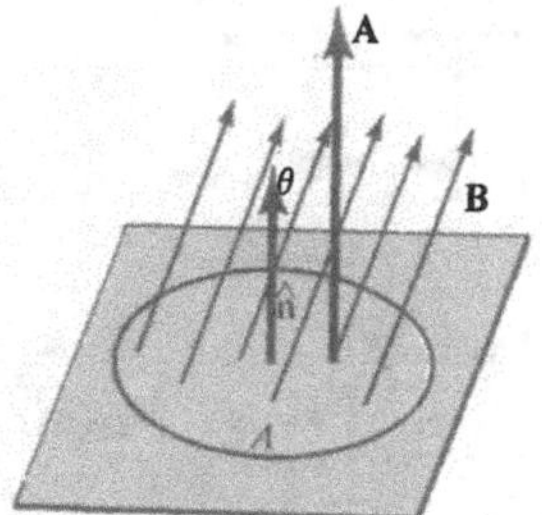

Figure 20.2. $\mathbf{A} = A\hat{\mathbf{n}}$ is a vector equal in magnitude to the area of the loop and directed parallel to the normal vector **n̂**. The magnetic flux through the loop is $\Phi = BA \cos \theta = B_n A = \mathbf{B} \cdot \mathbf{A}$.

In S.I. units, magnetic flux is measured in *webers* (Wb). Since the field **B** is measured in teslas and the area A in square metres, $\Phi = \mathbf{B} \cdot \mathbf{A}$ implies

$$1 \text{ weber} = 1 \text{ tesla (metre)}^2 = 1 \text{ T m}^2$$

Magnetic fields are sometimes given in webers per square metre (Wb m^{-2}) instead of in teslas.

The calculation of the flux is illustrated by the following example.

Example 20.1

The loop in Fig. 20.3 has an area of 0.1 m^2. The magnetic field is perpendicular to the plane of the loop and has a constant magnitude of 0.2 T. Find the magnetic flux through the loop.

The normal vector **n̂** must be perpendicular to the loop, but it may be chosen to be either into or out of the page in Fig. 20.3. If we choose **n̂** to be into the page, then by the convention discussed in the preceding chapter, clockwise currents will be positive, and counterclockwise currents will be negative. (See Section 19.5.) Since **B** is parallel to **n̂**, $B_n = B$, and

$$\Phi = \mathbf{B} \cdot \mathbf{A} = BA$$
$$= (0.2 \text{ T})(0.1 \text{ m}^2) = 0.02 \text{ Wb}$$

Faraday's law can now be written in terms of the magnetic flux. Suppose that the magnetic flux through a loop is changed by an amount $\Delta\Phi$ in a time Δt.

Faraday's law states that the average EMF induced in the circuit equals the average rate of change of the flux:

$$\bar{\mathscr{E}} = -\frac{\Delta\Phi}{\Delta t} \tag{20.3a}$$

The instantaneous EMF is

$$\mathscr{E} = -\frac{d\Phi}{dt} \tag{20.3b}$$

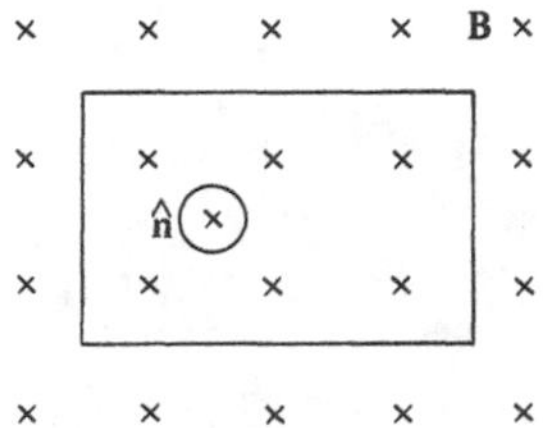

Figure 20.3. **n̂** is chosen to be directed into the page. (With this choice, clockwise currents are positive, counterclockwise currents are negative.) Hence **B** is parallel to **n̂** and $B_n = B$.

The minus signs indicate the direction of the induced EMF and current, as can be seen in the following examples. *Note that Faraday's law contains only the rate of change of the flux and does not depend on how that rate is achieved.* This is consistent with the observation that moving the loop away in Fig. 20.1, reducing the loop area, or rotating the loop, all produce the same qualitative effect as reducing the field; all of these result in a reduction in the flux. Calculation of the induced EMF and the resulting current is illustrated by the next example.

Example 20.2

A wire loop of area 0.1 m² has a resistance of 10 ohms (Fig. 20.4). A magnetic field **B** normal to the loop initially has a magnitude of 0.2 T and is reduced to zero at a uniform rate in 10^{-4} s. Find the induced EMF and the resulting current.

Since the flux changes at a uniform rate, the average EMF and the instantaneous EMF are the same. Let us take $\hat{\mathbf{n}}$ parallel to the field or into the page, so that clockwise currents are positive. The initial flux is $\Phi_i = BA$ and the final flux Φ_f is zero, so $\Delta\Phi = \Phi_f - \Phi_i = -BA$. Thus

$$\mathscr{E} = \overline{\mathscr{E}} = -\frac{\Delta\Phi}{\Delta t} = -\frac{-BA}{\Delta t} = \frac{BA}{\Delta t}$$

$$= \frac{(0.1 \text{ m}^2)(0.2 \text{ T})}{10^{-4} \text{ s}} = 200 \text{ V}$$

and

$$I = \frac{\mathscr{E}}{R} = \frac{200 \text{ V}}{10 \text{ ohm}} = 20 \text{ A}$$

Since I is positive, the current is clockwise.

Note that $\hat{\mathbf{n}}$ can be chosen to be out of the page, so that counterclockwise currents are positive. With this choice of $\hat{\mathbf{n}}$, $\Delta\Phi$ is positive, and the induced EMF and the current are negative. Since with this convention a negative current is clockwise, we have the same result as before.

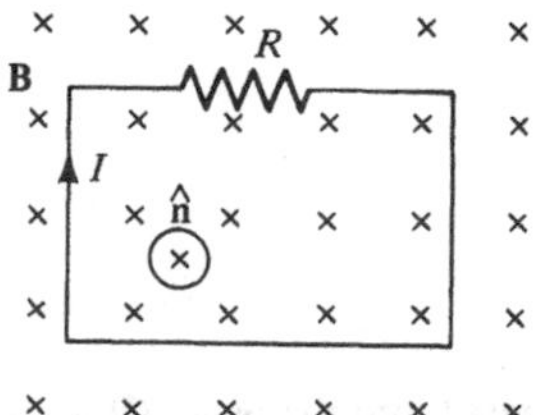

Figure 20.4. Example 20.2.

It is important to note that the induced current will also produce a magnetic field. In the previous example, the induced current is clockwise. The direction of the field can be found with the right-hand rule given in the last chapter (see Fig. 19.7). Applying the right-hand rule, we place our thumb along the current; our fingers show that the current produces a field into the page within the loop. This means that the field inside the loop due to the induced current is in the same direction as the initial field and *tends to slow the reduction in the field and in the flux*. Similarly, if the original field is increasing, the field produced by the induced current is opposite to the original field, *tending to retard its increase*. For example, if in Fig. 20.4, **B** is into the page and increasing, then the induced current will produce a field out of the page, so the current must be counterclockwise.

The observation that the field due to the induced current always opposes the change in flux is called Lenz's law.

In solving problems, it is often easier to use Lenz's law to find the direction of the induced current than to carefully keep track of the minus signs in applying Faraday's law. However, we must remember that it is the *change* in flux, not the flux, that is opposed. This is seen again in the next example.

Example 20.3

According to Faraday's law, an EMF is induced when the flux through a loop is changed by varying its area. To illustrate this, consider a metal bar of length l sliding with a velocity **v** along two conducting rails that form a closed circuit (Fig. 20.5). A uniform magnetic

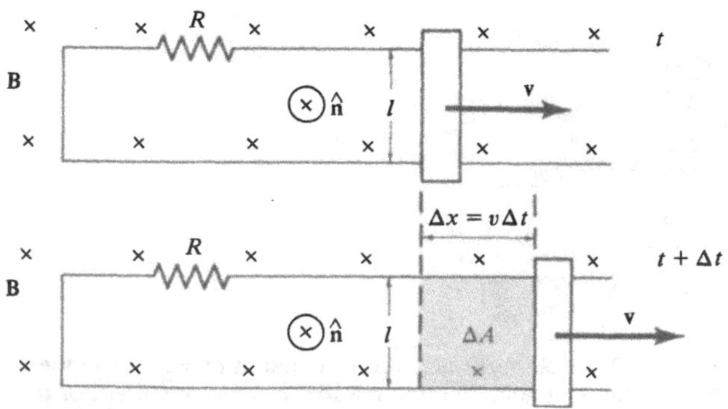

Figure 20.5. Example 20.3.

field is directed into the page. What is the induced EMF?

We choose the normal vector $\hat{\mathbf{n}}$ into the page or parallel to **B**; with this choice, clockwise currents are positive. If the area of the circuit is A, then the flux is $\Phi = BA$. A short time Δt later, the bar will have moved a distance $\Delta x = v\,\Delta t$. Hence the area will have increased by $\Delta A = l\,\Delta x = lv\,\Delta t$, and the flux will have increased by $\Delta\Phi = B\,\Delta A = Blv\,\Delta t$. The instantaneous induced EMF is therefore

$$\mathscr{E} = -\lim_{\Delta t \to 0} \frac{\Delta\Phi}{\Delta t} = \lim_{\Delta t \to 0} \frac{Blv\,\Delta t}{\Delta t} = -Blv$$

The minus sign indicates that the induced current $I = \mathscr{E}/R$ will be negative, or counterclockwise. Using the right-hand rule, we see that the field within the loop due to this current will be out of the page, or opposite to **B**. This opposes the increase in the flux that occurs as the area increases, and again our result is in accordance with Lenz's law.

20.2 | EDDY CURRENTS

So far, we have considered examples of currents induced in circuits with a single current path. However, whenever the magnetic flux through a conducting object changes, EMFs and currents are induced in that object. Such *eddy currents* occur, for example, in electrical machinery. As we see in Section 20.6, iron has the property of greatly increasing an applied magnetic field. For this reason, motors and generators usually have large amounts of iron in magnetic fields. Since the flux through the iron is continually changing, eddy currents are produced that generate heat and reduce the efficiency of the machine. This effect is minimized by using thin iron sheets separated by insulating coatings rather than large solid pieces. This increases the resistance of the iron and decreases the eddy currents and hence the power loss (Fig. 20.6).

Eddy currents also arise when the flux through a conductor changes because of its motion. For example, if a metal pendulum swings between the poles of a strong magnet, it rapidly comes to rest (Fig. 20.7). This happens because the changing flux induces a current, and the magnetic force on that current is opposite to the motion of the pendulum. The kinetic energy lost by the pendulum is dissipated as heat by the eddy currents.

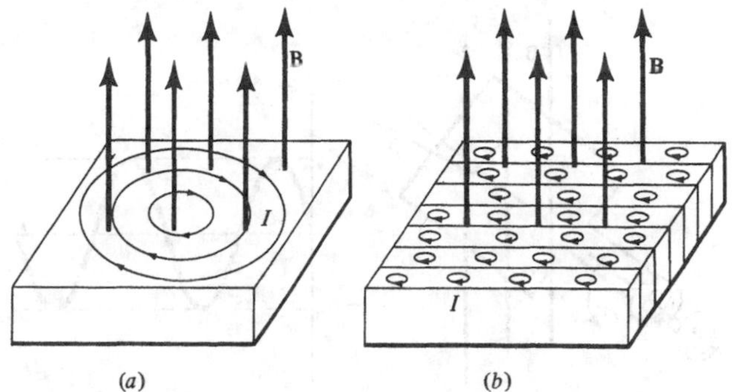

Figure 20.6. (*a*) An increasing magnetic field will induce eddy currents in a conducting object. (*b*) If the object is made of thin conducting sheets separated by insulating layers, the induced currents are confined to the individual sheets. The average current is smaller than in (*a*) and less power is dissipated as heat.

Eddy currents can also be induced in nonmetallic conductors, such as biological tissues. For example, a field of about 1 T alternating at 60 Hz will induce a large enough current in the retina of a human eye to produce a sensation of intense brightness.

20.3 | ELECTRIC GENERATORS

Faraday's law is the basic physical principle underlying electrical power generators. To understand their operation, consider a wire loop of area A rotated by some power source at an angular velocity ω in a magnetic field (Fig. 20.8*a*). Its ends slide along

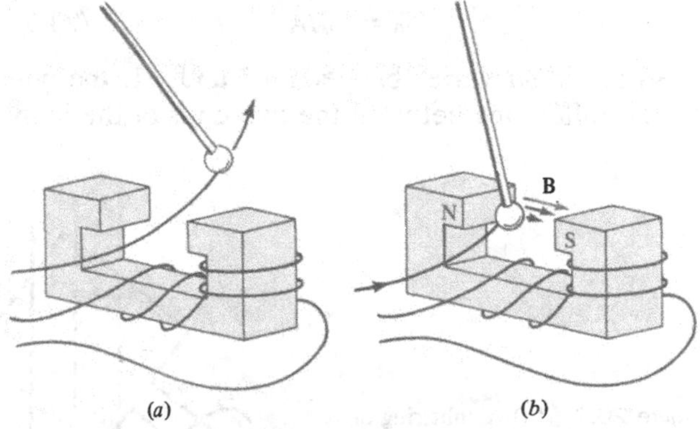

Figure 20.7. (*a*) If the magnet is turned off, the metal pendulum swings freely between the poles. (*b*) When the magnet power is on, the pendulum slows abruptly as it enters the magnetic field due to the magnetic forces on the eddy currents induced in the pendulum.

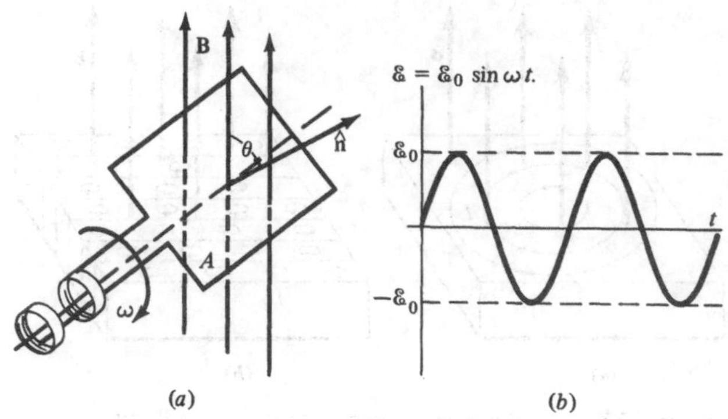

Figure 20.8. (*a*) A simplified ac generator consists of a coil rotating in a magnetic field. (*b*) The potential difference between the rings.

two fixed rings. If at some instant the angle between the normal vector $\hat{\mathbf{n}}$ and the field $\mathbf{B}$ is $\theta = \omega t$, then the flux through the loop is

$$\Phi = \mathbf{B} \cdot \mathbf{A} = BA \cos \omega t$$

Since the flux is continually changing, there is an EMF induced in the loop, which is the generator voltage. According to Eq. B.27 in Appendix B,

$$\frac{d}{dt}(\cos \omega t) = -\omega \sin \omega t$$

Thus $\mathscr{E} = -d\Phi/dt = -BA(-\omega \sin \omega t)$, or

$$\mathscr{E} = \mathscr{E}_0 \sin \omega t \tag{20.4}$$

where the *amplitude* $\mathscr{E}_0$ is

$$\mathscr{E}_0 = \omega BA \tag{20.5}$$

Since $\sin \omega t$ varies between $+1$ and -1, the potential difference between the two ends of the loop varies between $+\mathscr{E}_0$ and $-\mathscr{E}_0$ with a frequency $f = \omega/2\pi$ (Fig. 20.8*b*). Hence this rotating loop is an alternating current (ac) generator.

Direct current or dc generators supply an EMF that does not reverse polarity. The two rings of the ac generator are replaced by a single *split ring* or *commutator* (Fig. 20.9*a*). This reverses the connectors every half-turn and produces the EMF plotted in Fig. 20.9*b*. A practical dc generator has many loops each at slightly different angles, so the resulting total EMF is nearly constant (Fig. 20.9*c*).

20.4 | TRANSFORMERS

The fact that an ac voltage can efficiently be increased or decreased with a *transformer* is of great practical importance to the transport and distribution of electrical power. To see why, we recall that the rate at which electrical energy is lost as heat in a power line of resistance R carrying a current i is i^2R. Since the power supplied by a pair of lines with a potential difference v is iv, choosing the largest feasible voltage and a correspondingly small current minimizes the heat losses. For example, power is sent hundreds of kilometres from hydroelectric plants to cities at some hundreds of thousands of volts. The power lines used are of moderate size. By contrast, if power were transported over such distances at a low voltage, huge amounts of copper would be needed to build lines with acceptable losses. However, safety and insulation limitations require that electricity be supplied to consumers at low voltages. This requirement is satisfied by using transformers to reduce the voltage in several steps in the local transmission system.

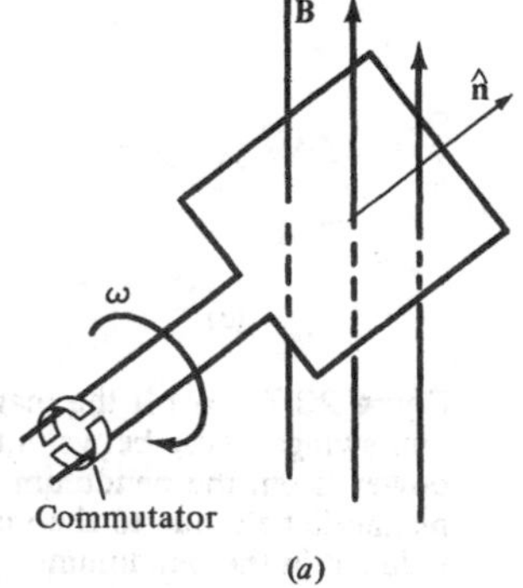

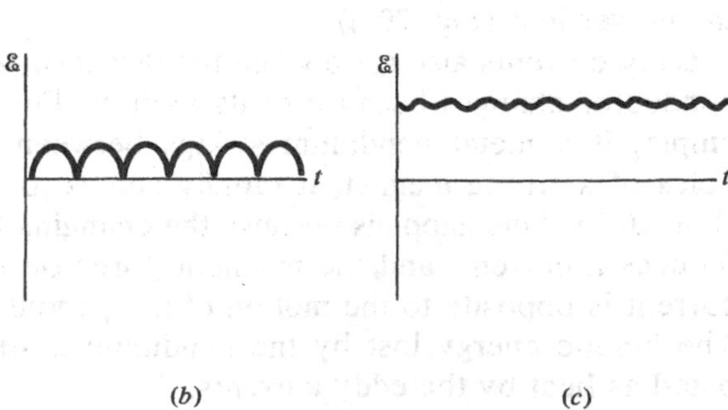

Figure 20.9. (*a*) A split ring or commutator reverses the connections each half turn. (*b*) The terminal voltage measured at the split ring. (*c*) The total EMF due to a large number of turns, each at slightly different angles.

MICHAEL FARADAY (1791–1867)

Michael Faraday discovered many of the fundamental laws of physics and chemistry, despite the fact that he had virtually no formal education. The son of an English blacksmith, he was apprenticed at the age of 14 to a bookseller and bookbinder. He read every book on science in the bookshop and attended lectures given at the Royal Institute by various scientists, including Sir Humphrey Davy, the discoverer of 12 chemical elements. In 1812, he applied to Davy for a job, citing his interest in science and showing Davy the extensive lecture notes he had taken. Davy hired Faraday to assist with his research and lecture demonstrations.

Within a few years, Faraday began to do original research on his own, submitting two papers on chemistry to the Royal Society in 1820. In that same year, Oersted discovered that a current in a wire will deflect a compass needle. Faraday repeated Oersted's experiments and found that a magnet also exerts a force on a wire carrying an electric current. Soon afterward, he also showed how to liquefy chlorine, and he isolated benzene, a compound now widely used in chemical products.

Faraday's important discoveries brought him considerable fame, much to the discomfort of Davy, who felt he should have shared the credit for some of the advances. Davy preferred to regard Faraday as a technical assistant and even forced him to serve as a valet on an extended tour of European research centers. Despite Davy's objections, Faraday was elected to the Royal Society in 1824 and was made director of the laboratory at the Royal Institute in 1825.

After Faraday discovered, in 1831, that a changing magnetic field can induce a current, he performed a series of experiments that showed clearly that the induced EMF is equal to the rate of change of magnetic flux. Also, generalizing from the patterns formed by iron filings around magnets, he invented the concepts of magnetic and electric field lines. Faraday knew little mathematics and found this concrete approach to electricity and magnetism much more useful than equations giving the forces between charges or currents. He also suggested that the propagation of light through space consisted of vibrations of these lines. His concepts of electric and magnetic fields were put into a mathematical form a generation later by Maxwell, who showed that light is, in fact, an oscillatory electromagnetic disturbance.

Faraday made many other notable contributions. He devised the first electric generator, which consisted of a copper disk rotating between the poles of a magnet. He discovered the correct laws of electrochemistry after proving that earlier theories disagreed with experiments. He studied optical phenomena and found that when light passes through a medium, a magnetic field will rotate the direction of the oscillating electric field. Ignoring scorn from his contemporaries, he attempted unsuccessfully in laboratory experiments to find a link between gravitation and electromagnetism. Such a link was observed 70 years later in a test of Einstein's general theory of relativity, when light rays passing near the sun were found to be deflected.

Despite his achievements, Faraday remained a modest and humble person. He declined to be knighted or to receive honorary degrees and only reluctantly accepted a small pension on his retirement in 1858.

Figure 20.10 illustrates the principle of a transformer. *Primary* and *secondary* coils with N_1 and N_2 turns, respectively, are wound around an iron core. A variable current i_1 in the primary produces a magnetic field through both coils. The iron serves to increase the field and the flux. The induced EMF in any one turn of either coil is $-\Delta\Phi/\Delta t$; the total induced EMF in a coil is this times the number of turns. Since $\mathscr{E}_1 = -N_1(\Delta\Phi/\Delta t)$ and $\mathscr{E}_2 = -N_2(\Delta\Phi/\Delta t)$, it follows that

$$\frac{\mathscr{E}_2}{\mathscr{E}_1} = \frac{N_2}{N_1} \tag{20.6}$$

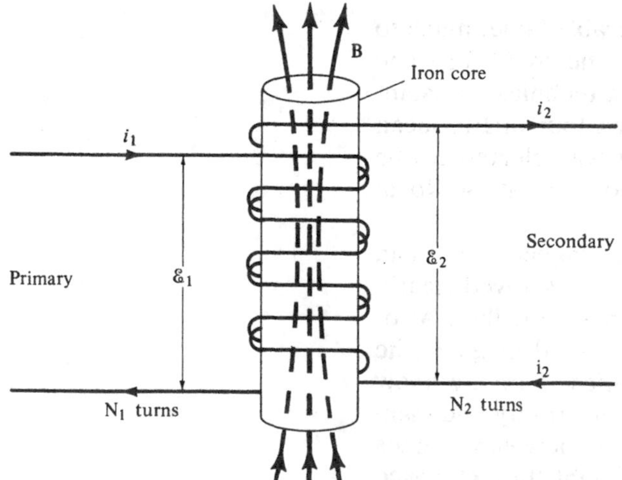

Figure 20.10. A transformer consists of a primary coil and a secondary coil wound around a core that is usually made of iron to increase the field and the flux.

If the secondary coil has fewer turns than the primary, the EMF is reduced by the transformer.

Transformers are very efficient devices. In many large transformers, over 99 percent of the power $\mathscr{E}_1 i_1$ supplied by the primary coil is transferred to the secondary circuit. For an ideal, loss-free transformer, we have exactly

$$\mathscr{E}_1 i_1 = \mathscr{E}_2 i_2 \tag{20.7}$$

This relationship is used in the following example.

Example 20.4

A transformer reduces the voltage supplied to a nearby house from 480 V ac to 120 V. (a) What is the ratio of the turns in the secondary and primary circuits? (b) If the current in the primary is 20 A, how large is the current in the secondary?

(a) The ratio of the turns is

$$\frac{N_2}{N_1} = \frac{\mathscr{E}_2}{\mathscr{E}_1} = \frac{120 \text{ V}}{480 \text{ V}} = \frac{1}{4}$$

There is one turn in the secondary coil for every four in the primary.

(b) Since $\mathscr{E}_1 i_1 = \mathscr{E}_2 i_2$, we have

$$i_2 = i_1 \frac{\mathscr{E}_1}{\mathscr{E}_2} = (20 \text{ A}) \frac{(480 \text{ V})}{(120 \text{ V})} = 80 \text{ A}$$

The current is 80 A, or four times as large as the current supplied to the transformer. Use of such a transformer minimizes the power losses in supplying power to the house.

Transformers are useful in increasing electrical safety. Since the primary and secondary coils are not directly connected to each other, the secondary is electrically "*isolated*," and its potential relative to ground is independent of that in the primary. If a person simultaneously touches a wire in the secondary circuit and a ground, this will ground the wire, but no current will pass through the person. This is especially useful in reducing the risk associated with high voltages. Also, the extreme vulnerability of patients wired into EKGs, pacemakers, and other devices has led to the proposal that hospital units serving such people should have all their instrumentation supplied with power via carefully designed isolation transformers.

20.5 | INDUCED FIELDS AND ELECTROMAGNETIC WAVES

We have seen that a varying magnetic field induces an EMF in a wire loop. This EMF, in turn, does work on the charges in the conductor and sustains a current. Alternatively, we may say that the *changing magnetic field* **B** *produces an induced electric field* **E** in the loop, and this electric field exerts an electric force on the charges.

Since an induced electric field *does net work* on a charge as it goes around a closed path, *an induced electric field is not conservative*. In this respect, an induced electric field due to a changing magnetic field is quite different from the conservative electrostatic field produced by electric charges, which does no net work around a closed path.

It is not necessary to have a conductor present in the changing magnetic field in order to observe the effects of the induced electric fields. One example of this provided by the *betatron*, which accelerates electrons to energies of about 100 MeV = 10^8 eV. If the electrons are allowed to strike a target, they produce highly penetrating X rays that can be used for cancer therapy. In a betatron, a magnetic field maintains the electrons in circular orbits, just as in the cyclotron (Chapter Nineteen). However, the magnetic field is not kept constant. Instead, it is gradually increased with time, and the resulting induced electric field accelerates the electrons. With proper shaping of the magnetic field, the radius of the electronic orbits remains constant as the electronic speed and the field increase. Thus the electrons can be confined to a narrow doughnut-shaped tube instead of requiring a large chamber as in a cyclotron.

With the introduction of the idea of an induced electric field resulting from a changing magnetic field, there is a fundamental connection between electrical and magnetic phenomena. However, the situation is not symmetric unless we suppose that a changing electric field can also induce a magnetic field.

Maxwell's Hypothesis and Electromagnetic Waves | James Clerk Maxwell (1831–1879) made the brilliant hypothesis in 1864 that *changing electric fields do indeed induce magnetic fields*. He was led to this idea by considering the relationships between the basic laws of electromagnetism, which had been discovered decades before. These were

1 Coulomb's law for the force between two charges, or equivalently, for the electric field due to a point charge.
2 The Biot–Savart law for the magnetic field due to a current.
3 Faraday's law, which states that a changing magnetic field induces an electric field.
4 The conservation of electric charge.

Maxwell showed that these laws were not mathematically consistent when the electric fields were changing in time. However, if one hypothesized that a changing electric field could induce a magnetic field, the inconsistency was removed.

Although it was based on purely theoretical reasoning, Maxwell's hypothesis led immediately to the prediction that *electromagnetic waves* can be produced by oscillating charges or currents. For example, suppose a current oscillates (reverses direction) at some frequency. The current produces a magnetic field nearby that also oscillates at this frequency. According to Faraday's law, the magnetic field induces an oscillatory electric field in its vicinity. Maxwell's hypothesis provides the critical next step: *the changing electric field induces a magnetic field*. This magnetic field in turn induces an electric field, and so on (Fig. 20.11).

Maxwell showed that this electromagnetic disturbance would travel away from the oscillating current with a velocity equal to $(k/k')^{1/2}$ = 3.00 ×

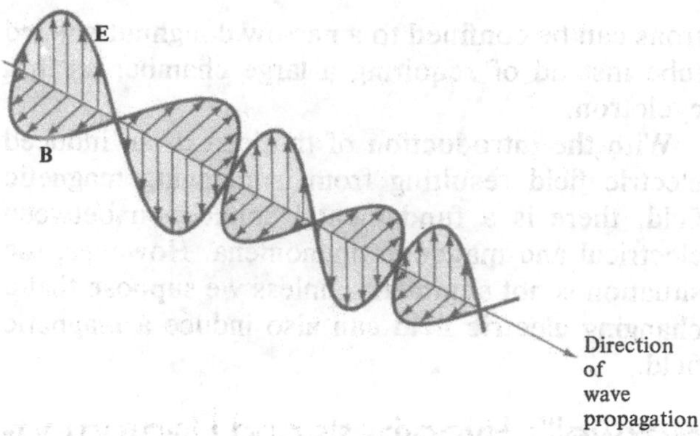

Figure 20.11. An electromagnetic wave. An oscillating magnetic field induces an oscillating electric field, which in turn induces an oscillating magnetic field, and so on. This disturbance travels at the speed of light.

10^8 m s^{-1}, where k and k' are the constants in the electric and magnetic force laws, respectively. Since this velocity was equal to the velocity of light to the accuracy then known, he inferred that light is an electromagnetic wave.

The first experimental verification of Maxwell's prediction of electromagnetic waves came nearly a quarter century after he had published his work and several years after his death. In 1887, Heinrich Hertz (1857–1894) constructed two circuits that tended to oscillate at the same frequency. He found that if one circuit was connected to an EMF so that it had a current, the other circuit located some distance away would also have a current.

The "technological fallout" from this demonstration of electromagnetic waves quickly followed. In 1890, Guglielmo Marconi (1874–1937) became interested in wireless telegraphy, and by 1901 he succeeded in transmitting signals across the Atlantic. Today, we enjoy the benefits of radio, television, and other communications systems based on electromagnetic waves produced by oscillating currents.

The wavelength of the radiation produced by electrical circuits ranges from millimetres to kilometres or longer, while visible light has a wavelength of 4×10^{-7} to 7×10^{-7} m. It has been verified to a very high accuracy that all the waves produced by oscillating currents have the same velocity as that of visible light. Thus Maxwell's remarkable theoretical predictions have been fully verified.

20.6 | MAGNETIC MATERIALS

We saw in Chapter Sixteen that the introduction of a dielectric into an applied electric field $\mathbf{E}$ reduces the field to $\mathbf{E}/K$, where K is the dielectric constant. Similarly, the introduction of materials into an applied magnetic field $\mathbf{B}$ changes that field to $K_m\mathbf{B}$, where K_m is the *magnetic constant.*

There are three major kinds of magnetic materials. In *diamagnetic* materials, K_m is slightly less than 1. In *paramagnetic* materials, K_m is slightly greater than 1. Finally, in *ferromagnetic* materials, K_m varies with the applied field and with the way the material has been treated, but it is typically very large compared to 1.

When a diamagnetic material is placed in a changing applied magnetic field, changes are induced in the electron currents in the atoms. When the applied field is increasing, the field due to the induced currents opposes the applied field, in accordance with Lenz's law, so the net field is smaller than the applied field. Diamagnetism is a weak effect; typically, K_m is less than 1 by 0.001 to 0.01 percent in diamagnetic materials. Diamagnetism is present in all materials, although it is sometimes masked by other effects.

In many materials, when there is no applied field, the magnetic effects associated with the orbital and spin motions of the atomic electrons cancel exactly. However, in some materials, which are called paramagnetic, there is a permanent residual magnetic dipole moment associated with the individual atoms. In the absence of an applied field, thermal agitation will cause these dipoles to be randomly aligned, and no macroscopic magnetic field will be observed. However, when such a paramagnetic substance is placed in a magnetic field, the dipoles tend to align themselves with their moments along the field, increasing the total field inside the material. Since the effects of the permanent dipoles are usually larger than those of induced currents, paramagnetism, when present, will mask diamagnetic effects. Paramagnetic materials typically have values of K_m that are larger than 1 by about 0.01 percent.

Five elements (Fe, Co, Ni, Gd, and Dy) are ferromagnetic, as are many alloys. Ferromagnets are characterized by strong interactions between neighboring atomic dipoles that are sufficiently strong to cause a spontaneous alignment of the dipoles, even in the absence of an applied magnetic field.

Although the dipoles align themselves without an applied field, the fields produced outside the material are often very small. This is associated with the behavior of *magnetic domains*, regions in which all of the dipoles have the same alignment. If the directions of the domains are sufficiently varied, their net field will be small. These domains are rather stable, but when an external magnetic field is applied, the domains most nearly parallel with the field grow in size at the expense of others. The domains may also rotate into alignment with the field. In both cases the ordering of the dipoles may enhance the field by a factor of 1000 or more. For this reason, ferromagnetic materials play an important role in transformers and other devices requiring large magnetic fields. When the applied field is removed the domains in a ferromagnet may retain some order. In this case the sample is a permanent magnet (Fig. 20.12).

Ferromagnetic materials exhibit a behavior called *hysteresis*: the state of the material depends on its history. We discuss this property and its application to magnetic disk storage in Section 20.9 in the Supplementary Topics.

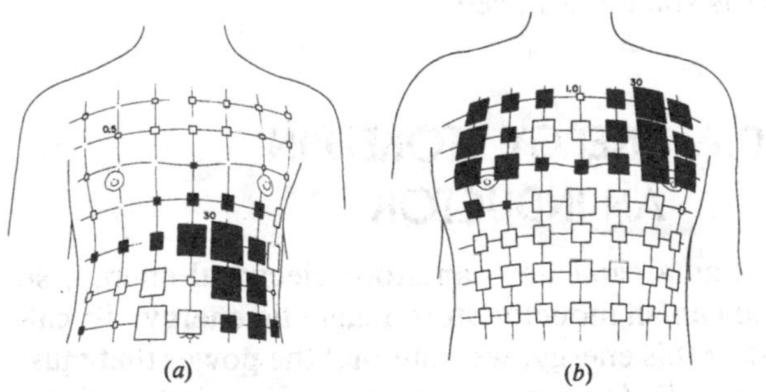

Figure 20.12. Ferromagnetic particles in the body can be detected by magnetizing them with a strong magnetic field and observing the fields they produce afterward. (*a*) This man has eaten beans from a can, and his stomach contains about 10^{-4} g of iron oxide. The areas of the squares are proportional to the field at their centers; the largest and smallest nonzero values are indicated in units of 10^{-11} T. Solid squares indicate fields in one direction, and open squares show fields in the opposite direction. (*b*) A similar plot for a man with 5×10^{-4} g of iron oxide in his lungs inhaled while doing arc welding. Since asbestos has small amounts of iron oxide adhering to its fibers, measurements of this type can also be used to determine the amount of the dangerous asbestos dust inhaled by workers. (D. Cohen, *Physics Today*, August 1975, p. 41. © American Institute of Physics.)

20.7 | INDUCTANCE

A current in a circuit always produces a magnetic field and a magnetic flux through that circuit. If this current changes, so does the flux, and this causes a *self-induced* EMF $\mathscr{E}$ in the circuit. According to Lenz's law, the induced current opposes the change in the flux and therefore also opposes the change in the current. ***Thus self-induced EMFs tend to prevent rapid current changes in circuits.***

One familiar example of the effect of self-induced EMFs in limiting current changes is the flash seen when a high-current appliance, such as a toaster, is on and its plug is pulled out of the electric outlet. This flash or arc occurs because the sudden current change induces a large EMF, which produces an electric field strong enough to ionize the air and permit current to pass through it briefly.

The self-induced EMF in a circuit can be related as follows to the rate of change of the current in that circuit. The EMF is proportional to the rate of change of flux. The flux, in turn, is proportional to the field and therefore to the current. Thus the EMF is proportional to the rate of change of current, and the average induced EMF is

$$\overline{\mathscr{E}} = -L \frac{\Delta i}{\Delta t} \tag{20.8a}$$

The constant L is called the *inductance* of the circuit. The minus sign indicates that the induced EMF opposes the current change. The instantaneous EMF is

$$\mathscr{E} = -L \frac{di}{dt} \tag{20.8b}$$

The inductance depends on the geometry of the circuit and on the magnetic materials present in its vicinity. In S.I. units, L is measured in ***henries*** (H). This unit is named after Joseph Henry (1797–1878), an American contemporary of Faraday, who independently discovered induced EMFs.

We can calculate L if the flux Φ through the circuit is known. In a coil with a flux Φ through each of N turns, the total average induced EMF is

$-N(\Delta\Phi/\Delta t)$. Comparing this with Eq. 20.8, we have

$$Li = N\Phi \qquad (20.9)$$

Consider, for example, a coil with n turns per unit length, length ℓ, and cross-sectional area A wound on a core with magnetic constant K_m (Fig. 20.13). From Chapter Nineteen, the field in the coil is $B = 4\pi K_m k' in$, where we have added a factor K_m to the earlier formula to account for the core. The inductance is then $L = N\Phi/i = (n\ell)(BA)/i$ or

$$L = 4\pi K_m k' n^2 A\ell \quad \text{(long thin coil)} \qquad (20.10)$$

Note that the inductance is proportional to K_m and to the coil volume $A\ell$. Such a coil is referred to as an *inductor*. Its effect is seen in the next example.

Example 20.5

A coil with 1000 turns has a cross section of 1 cm^2 = 10^{-4} m^2 and a length of 0.1 m. (a) If K_m is 1, find the inductance. (b) The current increases from 0 to 1 A in 10^{-3} s. Find the average EMF in the coil (c) Suppose the current in the coil varies as $i = i_0 \cos \omega t$, where i_0 = 10 A, and ω = 1000 rad s^{-1}. Find the induced EMF as a function of time.

(a) Using Eq. 22.10, the inductance is

$$L = 4\pi K_m k' n^2 A\ell$$
$$= 4\pi(1)(10^{-7}\text{ T m A}^{-1})\left(\frac{1000}{0.1\text{ m}}\right)^2(10^{-4}\text{ m}^2)(0.1\text{ m})$$
$$= 1.26 \times 10^{-3}\text{ H} = 1.26\text{ mH}$$

Note that this relatively large coil has an inductance of only a small fraction of a henry. The henry is a comparitively large unit.

(b) The average EMF induced in the coil is

$$\bar{\mathscr{E}} = -L\frac{\Delta i}{\Delta t} = -(1.26 \times 10^{-3}\text{ H})\frac{1\text{ A}}{10^{-3}\text{ s}} = -1.26\text{ V}$$

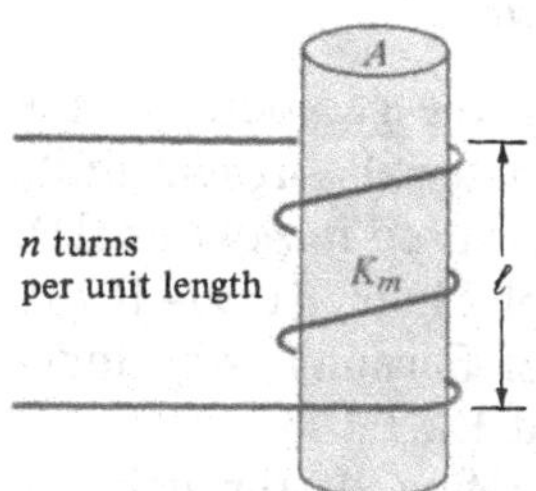

Figure 20.13. A solenoid wound on a core with magnetic constant K_m.

The minus sign indicates that the EMF opposes the current change.

(c) The instantaneous induced EMF is

$$\mathscr{E} = -L\frac{di}{dt} = -Li_0(-\omega)\sin\omega t = \text{L}i_0\,\omega\sin\omega t$$
$$= (1.26 \times 10^{-3}\text{ H})(10\text{ A})(1000\text{ s}^{-1})\sin(1000t\text{ s}^{-1})$$
$$= 12.6\sin(1000t\text{ s}^{-1})\text{ V}$$

The EMF varies from −12.6 V to +12.6 V during each cycle.

A current in one circuit can produce a magnetic flux through another circuit. If that is the case, then a change in the current will induce an EMF in the second circuit. The ratio of the EMF induced in the second circuit to the rate of change of the current in the first is the *mutual inductance* of the two circuits (see Problem 20-40). This phenomenon provides a way to transfer power and information from one circuit to another. It also represents a potential problem in complex electronic systems, since unwanted signals from one part of the device can be picked up elsewhere. These effects are minimized by the careful placement of components. Also, magnetic fields will not penetrate far into metals except at very low frequencies, so metallic shielding is sometimes used.

20.8 | ENERGY STORED IN AN INDUCTOR

Just as a capacitor can store electrical energy, so also can an inductor store magnetic energy. To calculate this energy, we note that the power that must be *supplied* to change a current i in an inductor at a rate di/dt is $\mathscr{P} = -\mathscr{E}i = L(di/dt)i$. In a time dt, the work done *against* the induced EMF $\mathscr{E}$ is

$$dW = \mathscr{P}\,dt = \left(Li\frac{di}{dt}\right)dt = Li\,di$$

Now the energy stored in an inductor with current I equals the work done in increasing the current from 0 to I. Thus

$$\mathscr{U} = \int_0^I Li\,di = \tfrac{1}{2}L\left[i^2\right]_0^I$$

or

$$\mathcal{U} = \tfrac{1}{2}LI^2 \qquad (20.11)$$

For example, if a 10^{-2}-H inductor carries a current of 1 A, the energy stored is $\frac{1}{2}LI^2 = \frac{1}{2}(10^{-2}\text{ H})(1\text{ A})^2 = 5 \times 10^{-3}$ J.

The quantitative effects of inductances on circuits are considered in the supplementary topics at the end of this chapter.

SUMMARY

In a uniform magnetic field, the magnetic flux through a loop of area A is $\Phi = B_nA$, where B_n is the normal component of the field. Whenever the flux is changing, Faraday's law states that there is an induced EMF in the loop equal to the time rate of change of the flux:

$$\mathcal{E} = -\frac{d\Phi}{dt}$$

Lenz's law states that the current due to an induced EMF always has a magnetic field that tends to retard the change in the flux. The induced EMF is determined only by the flux change; it does not matter whether it is the magnetic field or the area of the loop in the field that is changing.

When the magnetic flux through a conducting object changes, eddy currents are induced. The changing magnetic flux through the coil of a generator is the source of its EMF. In a transformer, a changing flux due to the current in the primary coil induces an EMF in the secondary coil. The ratio of the EMFs equals the ratio of the number of turns,

$$\frac{\mathcal{E}_1}{\mathcal{E}_2} = \frac{N_1}{N_2}$$

Also, $\mathcal{E}_1 i_1 = \mathcal{E}_2 i_2$.

A changing magnetic field will induce an EMF even if no conducting loop is present, as is illustrated by the betatron. This is equivalent to stating that the changing magnetic field induces a nonconservative electric field. Since changing electric fields also induce magnetic fields, oscillating charges or currents produce electromagnetic waves that travel with the speed of light.

The self-induced EMF in a circuit slows current changes. It is proportional to the inductance and to the rate of change of the current,

$$\mathcal{E} = -L\frac{di}{dt}$$

The energy stored in an inductor is

$$\mathcal{U} = \tfrac{1}{2}LI^2$$

Checklist

Define or explain:

induced current	induced electric field
Faraday's law	induced magnetic field
magnetic flux	electromagnetic waves
weber	diamagnetism
Lenz's law	paramagnetism
eddy currents	ferromagnetism
amplitude	magnetic domains
generator	inductance
transformer	henry
primary, secondary coils	

REVIEW QUESTIONS

Q20-1 The flux through a loop is the product of its area and the _____.

Q20-2 The induced EMF is equal to the _____.

Q20-3 Magnetic flux is measured in _____.

Q20-4 The induced current produces a magnetic field that tends to _____ the change in flux.

Q20-5 In the design of machinery, eddy currents are minimized in order to reduce _____.

Q20-6 In a dc generator, the connections are reversed every _____.

Q20-7 If the secondary coil in a transformer has more turns than the primary coil, the EMF will be _____ in the secondary.

Q20-8 Maxwell proposed that a changing _____ field induces a _____ field.

Q20-9 Maxwell predicted the existence of _____ that travel at the speed of _____.

Q20-10 Diamagnetic materials slightly _____ magnetic fields, while paramagnetic materials slightly _____ magnetic fields.

Q20-11 The strong magnetic effects in ferromagnetic materials arise from the alignment of _____.

Q20-12 Self-induced EMFs tend to prevent _____ in circuits.

Q20-13 If the current in an inductor is doubled, the stored energy increases by a factor of _____.

EXERCISES

Section 20.1 | Faraday's Law

20-1 In Fig. 20.14, the magnetic field is uniform in the region shown and is into the page. A wire loop is in the plane of the page. State whether there is an induced current when the loop is removed from (a) P_1 to P_2; (b) P_2 to P_3; (c) P_3 to P_1. Give reasons for your answers.

20-2 The wire loop in Fig. 20.14 is moved in the plane of the page from position P_1 to P_2. Find the direction of the induced current, if any.

20-3 A copper loop and a rubber loop of the same size and shape are placed in a uniform magnetic field perpendicular to the plane of the loops, which is gradually increased. Discuss (a) the EMFs induced in the two loops; (b) the currents induced in the two loops.

20-4 In Fig. 20.15, (a) what is the direction of the field inside the rectangular wire loop due to the current I in the long straight wire? (b) If I is increasing, what is the direction of the current induced in the loop? (c) If I is constant and the loop is moved toward the right, what is the direction of the induced current?

20-5 A wire loop of radius 0.1 m has a 2-ohm resistance. A uniform magnetic field perpendicular to the plane of the loop increases from zero to 2 T in 0.01 s. Find the average induced current.

20-6 A circular wire loop has a resistance of 10 ohms and a radius of 0.1 m. Its normal is parallel to a uniform magnetic field of magnitude 3 T. If the loop is rotated so that in 0.3 s its normal is perpendicular to the field, find (a) the average induced EMF; (b) the average induced current.

20-7 A loop of area 0.1 m^2 is at right angles to a uniform magnetic field. The field alternates direction at 60 Hz and has a peak magnitude of 2 T.

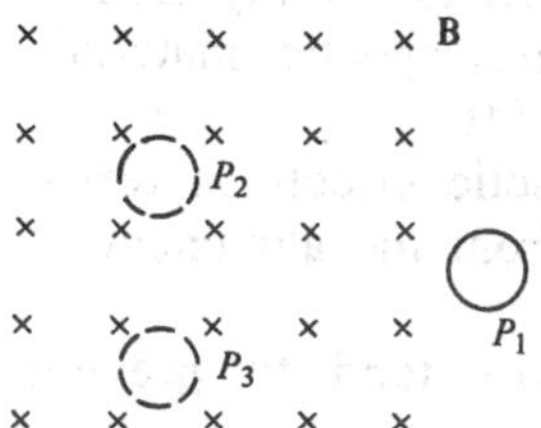

Figure 20.14. Exercises 20-1 and 20-2.

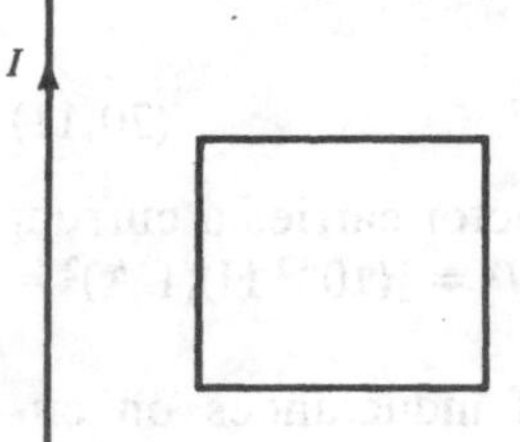

Figure 20.15. Exercise 20-4.

(a) What is the average induced EMF during one half-cycle when the field varies from normal to the loop to zero and to normal again, but in the opposite direction? (b) What is the average EMF over a full cycle?

20-8 In Fig. 20.5, the resistance of the loop is 100 ohms, the velocity of the moving conductor is 0.7 m s^{-1}, its length is 0.05 m, and B is 0.5 T. Find the induced current.

Section 20.2 | Eddy Currents

20-9 In Fig. 20.16, the field through a conductor is upward and increasing in magnitude. What is the direction of the eddy currents?

20-10 Suppose the field in Fig. 20.16 is constant and the conductor is gradually removed to the left. What is the direction of the eddy currents induced?

Section 20.3 | Electric Generators

20-11 Find the average EMF induced during the one-quarter cycle it takes for the normal vector in Fig. 20.8 to rotate from parallel to the field to perpendicular to the field. (Express the result in terms of A, B, and ω.)

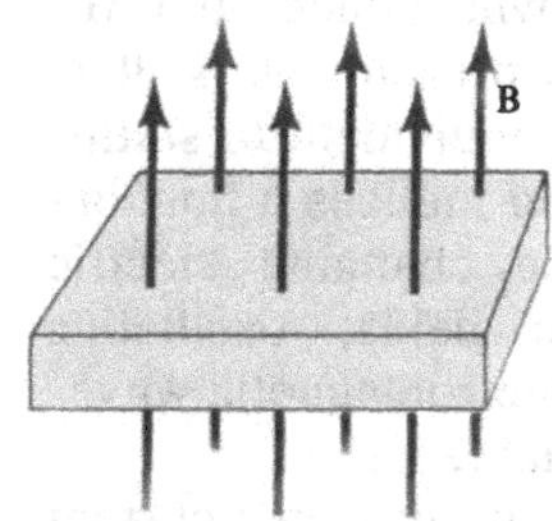

Figure 20.16. Exercises 20-9 and 20-10.

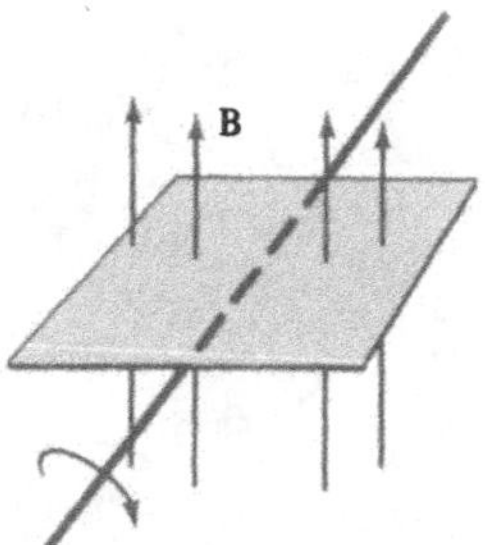

Figure 20.17. Exercise 20-12.

20-12 A square wire loop of resistance 10 ohms with sides 0.2 m rotates 100 times per second about a horizontal axis (Fig. 20.17). The magnetic field is vertical and has a magnitude of 0.5 T. Find the amplitude of the induced current.

20-13 When a generator turns at 60 Hz, the amplitude of the induced EMF is 50 V. What is its amplitude when it turns at 180 Hz if the magnetic field remains the same?

Section 20.4 | Transformers

20-14 The tube of an X-ray machine requires an ac voltage of 50,000 V. If this is obtained from a 120-V line, what is the ratio N_2/N_1 of the number of turns in the secondary and primary coils of the transformer?

20-15 In a transformer used with a set of toy trains, the 120-V ac line voltage is stepped down to 9 V. What is the ratio N_2/N_1 of the turns?

20-16 A transformer has 100 turns in one coil and 500 in the other. It is connected to a 120-V ac power line. What is the voltage across the secondary if (a) the 100-turn coil is connected to the power line; (b) the 500-turn coil is connected to the power line?

Section 20.5 | Induced Fields and Electromagnetic Waves

20-17 Find the ratio of $(k/k')^{1/2}$ to the speed of light in a vacuum, c. (Using the best experimental values of the constants involved gives agreement to better than one part per million.)

Section 20.6 | Magnetic Materials

20-18 The field in a solenoid is 0.5 T when it is in a vacuum. A rod is placed inside the solenoid, and the field drops to 0.498 T. (a) What is the magnetic constant of the material? (b) What kind of magnetic material is the rod made of?

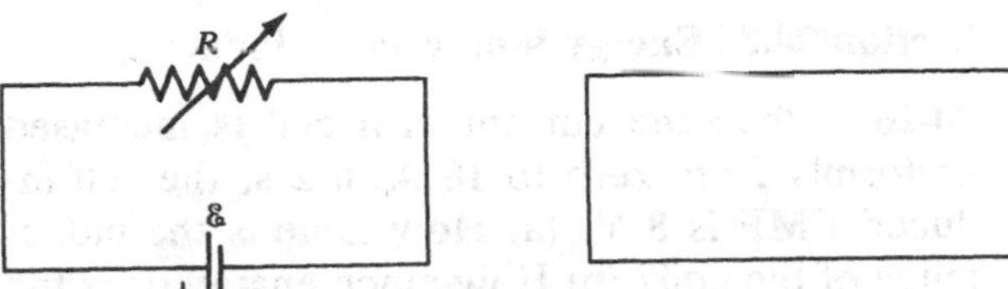

Figure 20.18. Exercise 20-21.

Section 20.7 | Inductance

20-19 Why is it important that the materials used in or near electrical switches and outlets be fireproof?

20-20 How can one make a variable inductance?

20-21 The variable resistance in the left-hand loop of Fig. 20.18 is increased. Find the direction of the current induced in the (a) left-hand loop; (b) right-hand loop.

20-22 The current in a 0.2-H inductor is increased from zero to 10 A in 0.1 s. Find the induced EMF.

20-23 Figure 20.19 shows the current in a solenoid during some time interval. Sketch how the voltage drop across the solenoid varies during that interval.

20-24 A solenoid with 1000 turns is wound on a core of radius 0.01 m and length 0.2 m. The magnetic constant of the core is 1000. Find the inductance of the coil.

20-25 Show that 1 henry = 1 ohm second = 1 weber ampere^{-1}.

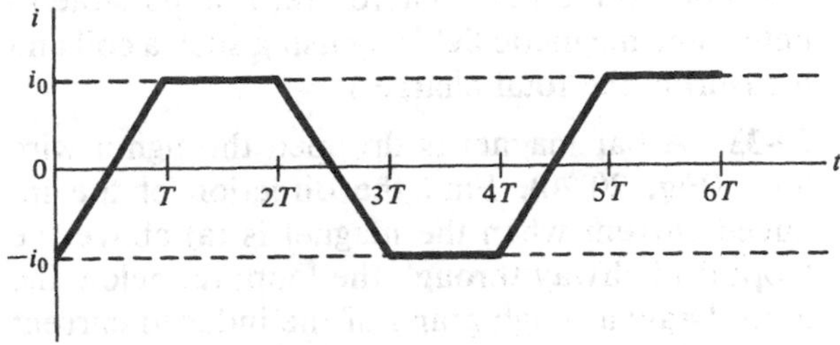

Figure 20.19. Exercise 20-23.

Section 20.8 | Energy Stored in an Inductor

20-26 When the current in a coil is increased uniformly from zero to 10 A in 2 s, the self-induced EMF is 8 V. (a) How large is the inductance of the coil? (b) How much energy does the coil store when the current is 10 A?

20-27 An inductance stores 4 J of energy when the current is 5 A. How large is it?

20-28 A coil stores 50 J of energy when the current is 10 A. How much current is required for it to store 450 J?

20-29 Show that 1 henry = 1 joule ampere^{-2}.

PROBLEMS

20-30 Suppose the opposite to Lenz's law were true, so that induced currents would tend to increase changes in flux instead of opposing them. Would this be consistent with the energy conservation principle? Explain.

20-31 (a) In Fig. 20.5, what is the magnetic force on a charge q in the moving conductor? (b) If this charge moves the length l of the moving conductor, how much work W is done on it? (c) The EMF is defined as the work done per unit charge, W/q. Compare this result with the EMF obtained in Example 20.3

20-32 A wire loop of resistance R and area A has its normal along the direction of a uniform magnetic field, **B**. The loop is then flipped over in a time Δt so that its normal is opposite to the field. (a) Calculate the average induced EMF. (b) Find the average induced current. (c) If the field is out of the page, what is the direction of the induced current? (d) What is the total charge transported through the circuit in the time interval Δt? (This charge turns out to be independent of Δt and proportional to the field. Therefore, it is possible to determine magnetic fields by using such a coil and measuring the total charge.)

20-33 A bar magnet is dropped through a wire loop (Fig. 20.20). Find the direction of the induced current when the magnet is (a) above the loop; (b) halfway through the loop; (c) below the loop. Draw a rough graph of the induced current versus time, assuming the velocity of the magnet is constant.

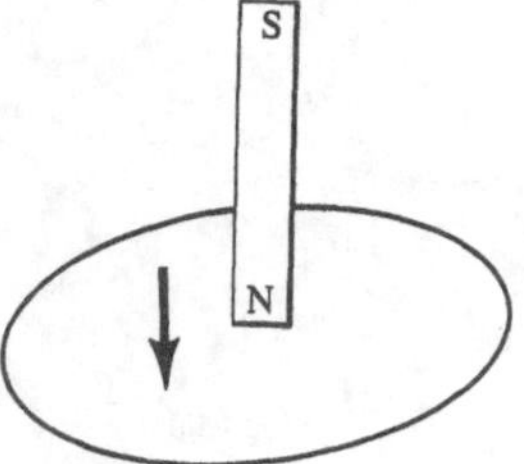

Figure 20.20. Problem 20-33.

20-34 In Fig. 20.21, a metal pendulum is moving into a uniform magnetic field. (a) Are the induced eddy currents generally clockwise or counterclockwise? (b) What is the direction of the magnetic force on the pendulum? (Explain your answers in both parts.)

20-35 When a motor coil turns, the magnetic field in the motor induces a *back EMF* in its coil that opposes the current. (a) How does the back EMF depend upon the speed of the motor? (b) How does the EMF affect the current? (c) When a motor is connected to a large load, its speed decreases. What effect will this have on the current in the motor? (d) Why is there a danger that an excessive load will burn out a motor?

20-36 The ratio of the power transmitted into the secondary of a transformer to that supplied to the primary is usually over 90 percent, but it is never 100 percent. Suggest some reasons for the power losses.

20-37 Explain why the magnetic constant of a diamagnetic material does not change as the temperature is increased. Would a paramagnetic material have the same temperature dependence? Explain.

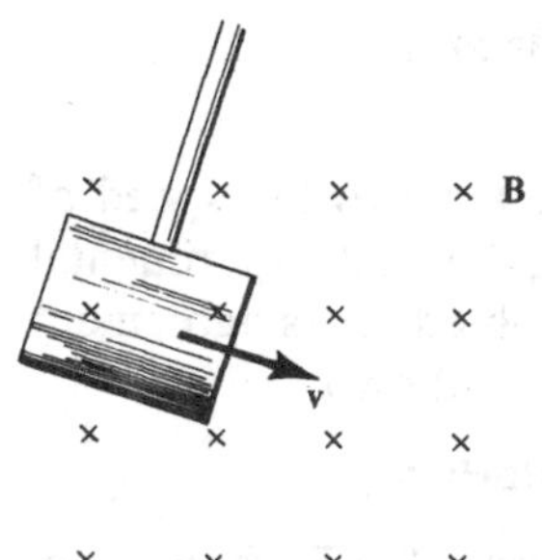

Figure 20.21. Problem 20-34.

20-38 It has been proposed to build very large magnets using superconducting wires that have no resistance and therefore dissipate no heat. In one proposed design, 1000 turns of radius 100 m form a coil of height 100 m in rock ($K_m = 1$). (a) Using the formula for the inductance of a solenoid, estimate the inductance of this coil. (This is only a rough estimate since this coil is not long in relation to its width). (b) Estimate the energy stored if the current is 1.5×10^5 A. (c) A very large nuclear reactor or fossil fuel electric power plant produces 10^9 W of power. For how long can the superconducting magnet supply energy at this rate if its current is initially 1.5×10^5 A?

20-39 A solenoid carrying a current I has N turns, area A, length ℓ, and magnetic constant K_m. (a) What is the magnetic field B inside the solenoid? (b) How much energy is stored per unit volume of the solenoid? (c) The energy stored per unit volume in a magnetic field is a constant times B^2/K_m. Use your result in part (b) to find that constant.

***20-40** A change in the current i_1 in a loop (1) will induce an EMF $\mathscr{E}_2$ in a second loop (2) nearby. The *mutual inductance M* is defined by $\mathscr{E}_2 = -M\, di_1/dt$. Two solenoids with N_1 and N_2 turns, respectively, are wound on a common core of area A, length ℓ, and magnetic constant K_m. Show that the mutual inductance is

$$M = 4\pi K_m k' \frac{N_1 N_2}{\ell} A.$$

***20-41** Show that two inductances L_1 and L_2 connected in series have an equivalent inductance equal to $L_1 + L_2$.

***20-42** Show that two inductances L_1 and L_2 in parallel are equivalent to a single inductance L, where

$$\frac{1}{L} = \frac{1}{L_1} + \frac{1}{L_2}$$

20-43 Using the results of Problems 20-41 and 20-42, find the equivalent inductance of a 2-H and a 4-H inductor connected (a) in parallel; (b) in series.

***c20-44** In Fig. 20.22, the current in the long straight wire is i. (a) What is the flux due to this current through a strip of width dr in the rectangular loop if the strip is at a distance r from the wire? (b) What is the total flux due to i through the loop? (c) If i is changing at a known rate di/dt, what is the EMF induced in the loop? (d) The rectangular loop has a resistance R. What is the current i_1 induced in this loop? (e) If i is increasing, what is the direction of i_1?

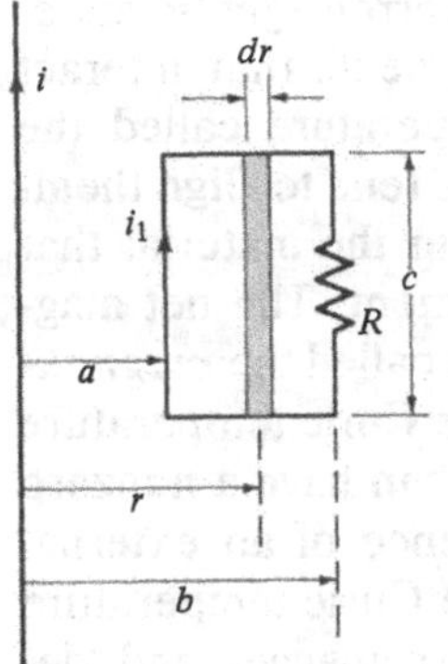

Figure 20.22. Problem 20-44.

c20-45 The current through a coil with inductance L is $i_0 e^{-t/T}$. (a) Find the EMF induced in the coil at time t. (b) Find the energy stored in the coil at t.

ANSWERS TO REVIEW QUESTIONS

Q20-1, normal component of the magnetic field; **Q20-2**, rate of change of magnetic flux; **Q20-3**, webers; **Q20-4**, oppose; **Q20-5**, power losses; **Q20-6**, half cycle; **Q20-7**, greater; **Q20-8**, electric, magnetic; **Q20-9**, electromagnetic waves, light; **Q20-10**, decrease, increase; **Q20-11**, magnetic domains; **Q20-12**, rapid current changes; **Q20-13**, 4.

SUPPLEMENTARY TOPICS

20.9 | HYSTERESIS; MAGNETIC DISK STORAGE

Ferromagnetic materials exhibit a behavior referred to as *hysteresis*, meaning a lagging behind. One can also think of the history of the material as having an influence on its state later on when certain things happen. In this section we discuss hysteresis and show how it is used to store information on magnetic disks.

As we noted in Section 20.6, ferromagnetic materials contain atomic dipole moments that interact strongly. Below a certain temperature called the *Curie temperature*, these dipoles tend to align themselves and to produce regions in the material that have a net magnetic dipole moment. The net magnetic moment per unit volume is called the *magnetization*. A ferromagnet below the Curie temperature may be a permanent magnet: it can have a nonzero magnetization even in the absence of an external magnetic field. The value of the Curie temperature varies from ferromagnet to ferromagnet and depends on the detailed interactions of the dipoles. In the remainder of this section, we only consider ferromagnets below their Curie temperature.

If, in the absence of an external magnetic field, the temperature of a ferromagnetic substance is lowered through the Curie temperature, the magnetization of the object is zero. However, within small regions or domains the dipoles are aligned. If an external magnetic field is applied to a ferromagnet that initially has zero magnetization, the small randomly oriented magnetic domains begin to become aligned (Fig. 20.23*a*) and the material acquires a corresponding magnetization parallel to the applied field. As the external field increases further, the magnetization eventually increases less rapidly until finally an increase in the field produces no increase in the magnetization. All the dipoles are completely aligned, and the magnetization is said to be *saturated* (point *c* in Fig. 20.23*a*).

Now, if the external field is reduced to zero, the magnetization decreases somewhat but does *not* become zero (point *d*, Fig. 20.23*b*). We have a permanent magnet; the material itself produces a magnetic field. The decrease in the magnetization from the saturation value reflects some disordering of the magnetic regions. In Chapter Ten we noted that the temperature of a material is an indication of the kinetic energy of its molecules. In ferromagnets, it is also an indication of random motions of the individual dipole moments. This random thermal motion works against the alignment of the dipoles and hence reduces the magnetization.

If the external magnetic field is now increased, but opposite to its original direction, the domains begin to reorient themselves with the new direction of the field. At some value of the field (point *e* in Fig. 20.23*b*), the domains are effectively randomly ordered again and the net magnetization is zero.

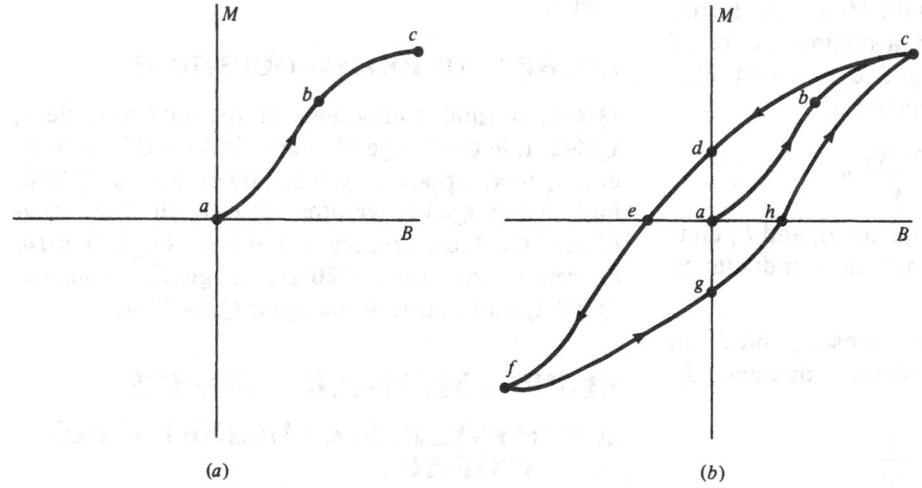

Figure 20.23. (*a*) As an applied magnetic field *B* increases from zero, the magnetization *M* of a ferromagnetic object increases almost linearly between points *a* and *b*. For larger values of *B*, *M* increases less rapidly and finally the curve becomes flat; the magnetization is saturated at *c*. (*b*) If the applied field is reduced to zero, point *d*, the magnetization does not become zero. As the applied field increases in the opposite direction, the magnetization decreases and finally becomes zero, point *e*. A further increase in *B* in this direction causes the magnetization to increase in this direction until it again becomes saturated, but in the opposite direction.

The value of the field that causes the magnetization to return to zero is determined by the properties of the material and is called the *coercive force*, even though it is not a force but a magnetic field magnitude. A *hard* ferromagnet has a relatively large coercive force. As the field is increased further, the magnetization grows in this new direction until it saturates again with all the domains aligned in the new direction (point *f* in Fig. 20.23*b*).

A similar sequence of events is observed if the external field is reduced to zero and increased again in the original direction (points *f*, *g*, *h*, and *c* in Fig. 20.23*b*). Notice that again the magnetization is not zero when the external field is zero. Thus the state of zero magnetization at zero external magnetic field is not recovered. This is *hysteresis*: the magnetization lags behind the external field, and it depends on the past history of the material.

The width of the hysteresis loop (the difference in field values between points *e* and *h* in Fig. 20.23*b*) characterizes the coercive force. In practical applications, ferromagnets used for speaker coils and motors have large coercive forces because a persistent magnetization (and resultant field) is required. Small coercive force ferromagnets are used in transformers (Section 20.4) so that the magnetization changes rapidly in response to changes in the external fields.

Magnetic Disk Storage | The storage and retrieval of data from magnetic disks and tapes provides an interesting demonstration of the role of magnets and hysteresis in a practical device. We will concentrate on magnetic disk storage. This has become a key element in modern computers because it provides rapidly accessible data storage that is secure and reliable.

The advances being made in disk storage technology cause any detailed descriptions to become dated rapidly. However, the basic principles of magnetic disk storage are much the same for many types of devices.

During the manufacturing process, a disk is coated with a liquid suspension of small magnetized iron oxide particles that are typically a micrometre in length and a tenth as wide. These particles are permanent magnets and have a large coercive force. The suspension is dried in the presence of an external magnetic field so that the particles are aligned in the plane of the disk perpendicular to its radius. When the suspension is dry and the external field is removed, the particles remain aligned. Thus the collection of particles also forms a ferromagnet. Its coercive force is large enough so that the magnetization at any point on the disk remains constant even when it is subjected to minor disturbances.

Data are stored in narrow circular tracks on the disk as local regions magnetized either parallel or antiparallel to the tangent to the tracks. This is accomplished by using a read/write head on which there is an electromagnet (Fig. 20.24). The magnet in the read/write head has a small coercive force because its magnetization needs to be altered rapidly and easily by the field due to the current in the coil and by the field due to the magnetized regions on the disk.

Pairs of adjacent magnetic regions are used to encode the data as a sequence of binary numbers. When the magnetization changes as the disk rotates under the read/write head, a current is induced briefly in a coil in the head. A common data encoding scheme represents a binary 1 by a magnetization reversal across the boundary between two regions. A 0 is represented by no magnetization reversal at a region boundary. The encoded 1's and 0's are called *bits*. Each eight bits is called a *byte* (Fig. 20.25). Each data bit is followed by a boundary across which there is always a magnetization reversal. Note that each bit is defined by two magnetic regions and that magnetization changes rather than magnetization states are used to represent 1 and 0.

The amount of data that can be stored on disks depends in detail on the mechanical, electrical, and magnetic properties of all the parts of the system. If the magnetization regions are too small, their magnetization may be changed too easily by unwanted influences, the fields they produce may be too weak to give proper definition to magnetization changes, and the magnetization may reverse too quickly to be sensed by the read/write head.

Small computers often use flexible, or "floppy," magnetic disks. The heads actually touch the disk surface when reading or writing data, so the rotation rate is low. A common floppy disk produced by one major manufacturer is 13.33 cm ($5\frac{1}{4}$ in.) in diameter and is spun at 300 rev min^{-1}. It holds 409 kilo-

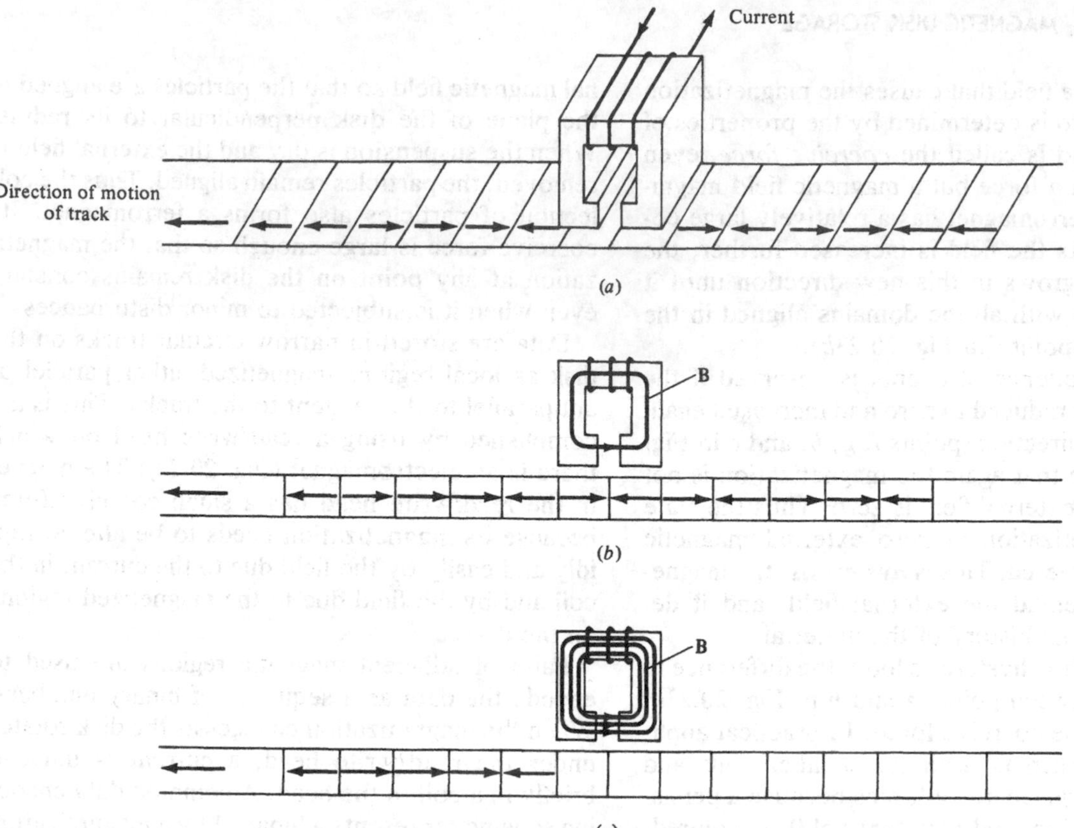

Figure 20.24. (*a*) Schematic view of the read/write head of a magnetic disk drive. The encoded data for one track on the disk are shown as regions of alternating magnetization. (*b*) The head is used to read data. The magnetic region boundaries cause a change in the magnetic field in the coils of the head. This change in flux in the coil produces an induced EMF in the coil and a detectable current. (*c*) Data are written to the disk by applying a current to the head coils, producing a strong enough magnetic field in the gap to cause the particles on the disk to be aligned with the field.

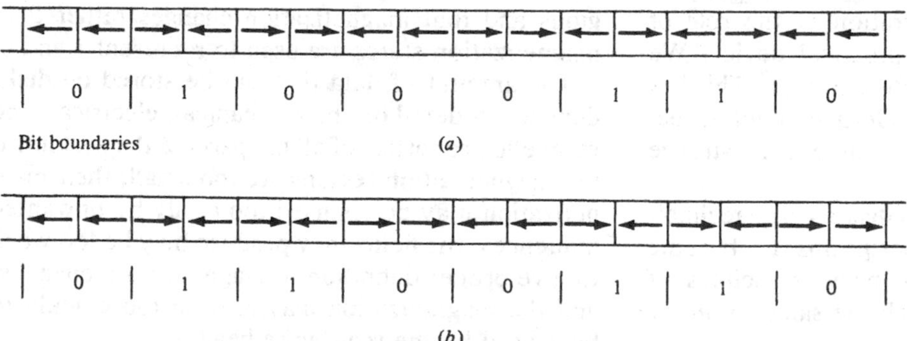

Figure 20.25. (*a*) A section of a track on a magnetic data storage disk. The rectangular blocks represent the individual magnetic regions and the arrows represent the direction of magnetization. Each bit consists of two magnetized regions. If the magnetization in the two regions is opposite, the bit is a 1. If the two regions have the same direction, the bit is a 0. Note that a magnetization reversal always occurs at the boundaries between bits. Data are commonly stored using a coding scheme called the American Standard Code for Information Exchange, or ASCII. The eight bits shown here, 01000110, represent the character F in ASCII. (*b*) A section of a track showing the pattern 01100110 that represents the character f in the ASCII scheme.

bytes (kb) of data on 80 tracks, all on one side of the disk. A large disk system from the same manufacturer has a pack of nine rigid aluminum disks, about 30.5 cm in diameter. It spins at 3633 rev min^{-1} and can store 516 megabytes (Mb) of data using 16 of the disk surfaces. The read/write head is separated by a thin air layer from the disk and never touches it.

The data transfer rates of these two disks are very different. When data are needed, the read/write head moves to the proper track and then waits an average of a half turn for the desired data to move under it. Access times average 264 ms for the floppy drive and 31.5 ms for the larger system. Once the start of the data is found, the rate at which they are read or written is determined by the spin rate and the density of the data. The maximum transfer rate is 250 kilobits per second for the floppy drive and 17.6 megabits per second for the large system. Thus the larger, rigid-disk multiplatter system has a much larger capacity and also permits much faster data transfers.

Smaller hard disk systems have become economical enough for small computers. With the same dimensions as floppy drives, they are in sealed enclosures and typically spin at 3600 rev min^{-1}. Their access time is between 20 and 85 ms, and the maximum data transfer rate is about 5 megabits per second. Capacities range from 10 to 600 megabytes and are rapidly increasing.

20.10 | *RL* CIRCUITS

We saw in Section 20.7 that any circuit always has some inductance. The inductance retards current changes, but it has no effect on a current that is constant. We now examine this in more detail for a series circuit consisting of a resistance R, an EMF $\mathscr{E}$ provided by a battery, and an inductance L (Fig. 20.26).

When the switch is closed in the circuit, the inductance prevents a sudden change in the current. Instead, the current gradually increases from zero toward the current predicted by Ohm's law,

$$i_f = \frac{\mathscr{E}}{R} \tag{20.12}$$

The *time constant* T_L, which characterizes this buildup, is proportional to L, since the greater the inductance, the longer it takes to achieve the final current. If the resistance R is large, then the magni-

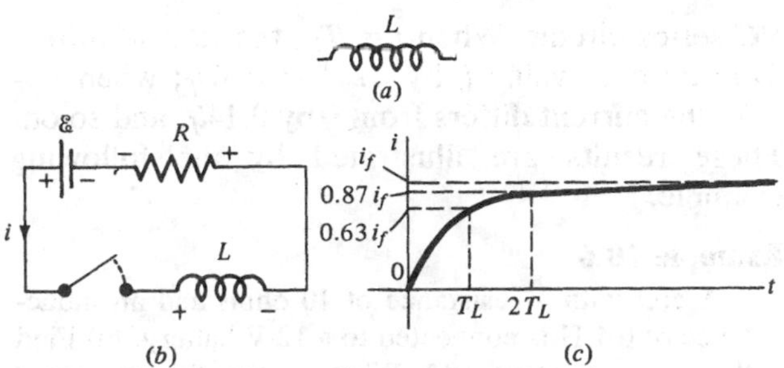

Figure 20.26. (*a*) The symbol for an inductor. (*b*) An *RL* series circuit. The switch is closed at $t = 0$. (*c*) The current in the circuit versus time.

tude of the overall current change is small, and the final current may be achieved more rapidly. Thus, we also expect T_L to be proportional to $1/R$, and the time constant is

$$T_L = \frac{L}{R} \tag{20.13}$$

To see how the current changes in detail, we suppose that in Fig. 20.26 the switch is closed at $t = 0$. Since the current was zero before the switch was closed, it is zero immediately after because the inductance prevents sudden current changes. At a later time t, there is a current i and a corresponding potential drop iR across the resistor. Because the current is increasing, there is an induced EMF in the inductance equal in magnitude to $L\, di/dt$. The voltage drops by this amount as we go through the inductance with the current. Also, the voltage rises by $\mathscr{E}$ in the EMF. Setting the algebric sum of the voltage changes around the circuit to zero,

$$-iR - L\frac{di}{dt} + \mathscr{E} = 0 \tag{20.14}$$

The solution to this equation is

$$i = i_f(1 - e^{-t/T_L}) \tag{20.15}$$

where the final current $i_f = \mathscr{E}/r$ and the time constant $T_L = L/R$ are as defined above. Note that at $t = 0$, $i = 0$ as required. Also, when $t/T_L \gg 1$, i approaches i_f and di/dt approaches zero, as we anticipated. It is left as an exercise to verify by differentiating that Eq. 20.15 does satisfy Eq. 20.14.

It is clear from the equation for i that the time constant T_L plays a role in the *RL* series circuit that closely parallels that of the time constant RC in an

RC series circuit. When $t = T_L$, the current differs from its final value i_f by $i_f e^{-1} = 0.37 i_f$; when $t = 2T_L$, the current differs from i_f by $0.14 i_f$, and so on. These results are illustrated by the following example.

Example 20.6

A coil with a resistance of 10 ohms and an inductance of 0.1 H is connected to a 12-V battery. (a) Find the time constant. (b) What is the final current? (c) Find the current after 0.03 s.

(a) The time constant is

$$T_L = \frac{L}{R} = \frac{0.1 \text{ H}}{10 \text{ ohm}} = 0.01 \text{ s}$$

(b) From Ohm's law, the final current is

$$i_f = \frac{\mathscr{E}}{R} = \frac{12 \text{ V}}{10 \text{ ohm}} = 1.2 \text{ A}$$

(c) Since 0.03 s is equal to $3T_L$, the current at that time is

$$i = i_f(1 - e^{-t/T_L}) = (1.2 \text{ A})(1 - e^{-3}) = 1.14 \text{ A}$$

The current is within a few percent of its final value.

20.11 | EFFECTIVE OR ROOT MEAN SQUARE ALTERNATING CURRENTS AND VOLTAGES

In the remainder of this chapter, we discuss some basic features of alternating currents, beginning here with the concept of *effective* or *root mean square (rms) currents* and *voltages*. Alternating currents are important in many applications. As we noted earlier, electrical power is normally supplied as 60 Hz ac. Higher-frequency currents are present in the circuits used to produce radio waves with an antenna or sound waves with a loudspeaker. Combinations of currents with many frequencies can also occur. For example, to reproduce a musical sound or a human voice, a loudspeaker is supplied with a complex current that is a sum of many small currents with various frequencies. Such complex currents can be discussed by analyzing each small current separately.

In discussing ac circuits, it is customary to use effective or rms currents and voltages, since these are convenient for power calculations. Alternating current ammeters and voltmeters are normally calibrated to read these quantities, rather than the amplitudes or peak values.

To define the effective current, consider a circuit connected to an ac generator. The current varies with the generator frequency $f = \omega/2\pi$ (Section 20.3) and has the form $i = i_0 \sin \omega t$, where i_0 is the amplitude of the current. Since $\sin \omega t$ is positive for one-half cycle and negative for the other, the current averages to zero over a full cycle. Nevertheless, the current still has some effects; for example, it heats a resistance R at an instantaneous rate $\mathscr{P} = i^2 R$ (Fig. 20.27). Since i^2 is never negative, its average cannot be zero. According to Eq. B.13 in Appendix B, the average of $\sin^2 \omega t$ over a full cycle is 1/2. Hence the average value of $i^2 = i_0^2 \sin^2 \omega t$ is $i_0^2/2$, and the average power dissipated in a resistor is

$$\overline{\mathscr{P}} = \frac{i_0^2}{2} R = i_e^2 R \qquad (20.16)$$

Here the *effective* or *root mean square (rms) current* i_e is defined by

$$i_e = \frac{i_0}{\sqrt{2}} \qquad (20.17)$$

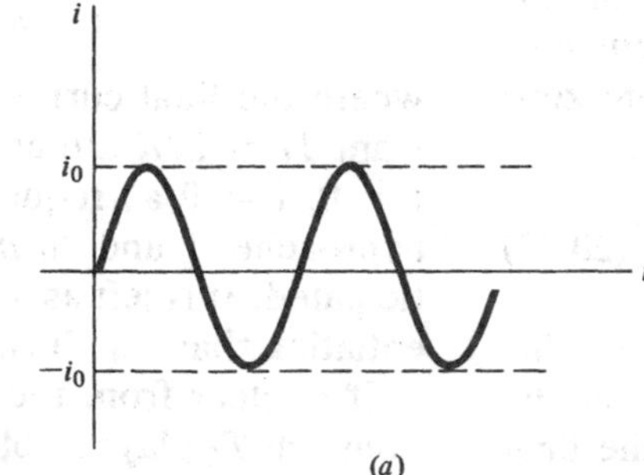

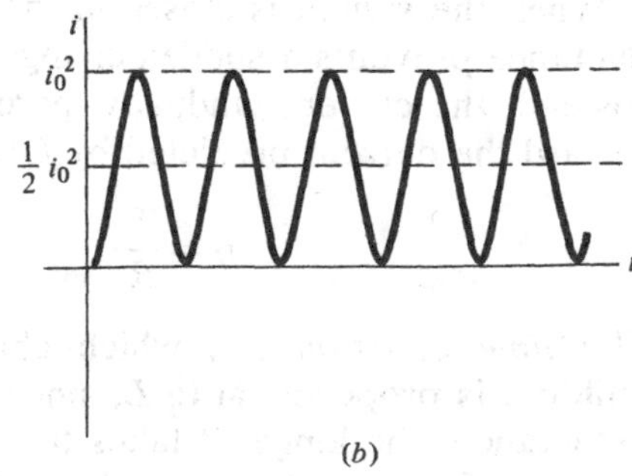

Figure 20.27. (*a*) An alternating current $i = i_0 \sin \omega t$ has an average value of zero. (*b*) The average of $\sin^2 \omega t$ over a full cycle is $\frac{1}{2}$, so the average value of i^2 is $i_0^2/2$.

Thus an effective current of 1 ampere in an ac circuit produces exactly as much heat in a resistor as a 1-ampere dc current. Note that both i_0 and i_e are defined as positive quantities.

Effective ac voltages are defined in an analogous fashion. If the voltage amplitude is v_0, the *effective or rms voltage* is

$$v_e = \frac{v_0}{\sqrt{2}} \tag{20.18}$$

Again v_0 and v_e are always positive.

The effective voltage across a resistor v_e^R can be related to the current using Ohm's law, $v = iR$. At any instant, the voltage and current are related by

$$v^R = (i_0 \sin \omega t)R \tag{20.19}$$

Squaring and averaging, we find $(v_e^R)^2 = \frac{1}{2}i_0^2R^2$, or

$$v_e^R = i_eR \tag{20.20}$$

The average power dissipated in a resistor can then be expressed as

$$\overline{\mathcal{P}} = \frac{(v_e^R)^2}{R} = i_e v_e^R \tag{20.21}$$

Thus with effective quantities, we have exactly the same formulas as for the power dissipation in a dc circuit. These quantities are used in the following example.

Example 20.7

A broiler draws 1000 W from a 120-V rms power line. Find (a) the amplitude of the power line voltage; (b) the rms current; (c) the amplitude of the current.

(a) Since the rms voltage is 120 V, $v_e = v_0/\sqrt{2}$ gives for the amplitude or peak voltage

$$v_0 = \sqrt{2}v_e = 1.414(120 \text{ V}) = 170 \text{ V}$$

(b) Using $\overline{\mathcal{P}} = i_e v_e^R$, with v_e^R equal to the rms line voltage, the rms current is

$$i_e = \frac{\overline{\mathcal{P}}}{v_e^R} = \frac{1000 \text{ W}}{120 \text{ V}} = 8.33 \text{ A}$$

(c) From $i_e = i_0/\sqrt{2}$, the current amplitude is

$$i_0 = \sqrt{2}i_e = 1.414(8.33 \text{ A}) = 11.8 \text{ A}$$

20.12 | REACTANCE

In an ac circuit, the rms current and the potential drop across a resistor are related by the resistance R. The analogous quantities for inductances and capacitances are called *reactances*. They can be used to determine the effective and instantaneous potential differences in an ac circuit.

Inductive Reactance | Suppose the current in an inductance is $i = i_0 \sin \omega t$. Then the induced EMF is $\mathcal{E} = -L\, di/dt$, and the voltage drop is $-\mathcal{E}$, or

$$v^L = L\frac{di}{dt} = Li_0\frac{d}{dt}\sin \omega t$$

Now $(d/dt) \sin \omega t = \omega \cos \omega t$. Thus defining the *inductive reactance* X_L by

$$X_L = \omega L \tag{20.22}$$

we have $v^L = Li_0(\omega \cos \omega t)$, or

$$v^L = i_0 X_L \cos \omega t \tag{20.23}$$

This is the instantaneous potential drop across the inductor. To find the effective or rms voltage, we must square this equation and average over a full cycle. By definition, the square of the left side averages to $(v_e^L)^2$. Now $\cos^2 \omega t$, like $\sin^2 \omega t$, averages to 1/2. Hence we find $(v_e^L)^2 = i_0^2X_L^2/2 = i_e^2X_L^2$, and the rms voltage drop across an inductance carrying an effective current i_e is

$$v_e^L = i_e X_L \tag{20.24}$$

This is similar in form to the voltage drop across a resistor, $v_e^R = i_eR$. The resistance R determines the effective voltage across a resistor, and the inductive reactance X_L determines the effective voltage across an inductor. Resistors, inductors, and capacitors are referred to as *impedances*. From the definition of the inductive reactance, $X_L = \omega L$, we see that for $\omega = 0$, a constant current, an inductor does not impede the current at all; there is no voltage drop across the inductor. On the other hand, as ω becomes large, the inductive reactance X_L becomes large. An inductor opposes changes in the current, and the more rapidly one attempts to change the current in an inductor, the more it opposes that change.

The reactance of an inductor is calculated and used in the following example.

Example 20.8

A 5-mH = 5×10^{-3}-H inductor is connected to a 120-V rms 60-Hz power line. Find (a) the inductive reactance, and (b) the rms current.

(a) Since the frequency f is 60 Hz, the inductive reactance is

$$X_L = \omega L = 2\pi f L = 2\pi(60\ \text{s}^{-1})(5 \times 10^{-3}\ \text{H})$$
$$= 1.88\ \text{ohm}$$

(b) Since the rms voltage across the inductor is 120 V, $v_e^L = i_e X_L$ gives

$$i_e = \frac{v_e^L}{X_L} = \frac{120\ \text{V}}{1.88\ \text{ohm}} = 63.8\ \text{A}$$

Capacitive Reactance | The charge on a capacitor is related to the current entering it by $i = dq/dt$. With $\int \sin \omega t\, dt = (-1/\omega) \cos \omega t$, we have

$$q = \int i\, dt = \int i_0 \sin \omega t$$
$$= -\frac{i_0}{\omega} \cos \omega t$$

Hence the voltage drop across the capacitor at time t is

$$v^C = \frac{q}{C} = -\frac{i_0}{\omega C} \cos \omega t$$

If we define the *capacitive reactance* X_C by

$$X_C = \frac{1}{\omega C} \tag{20.25}$$

we have the instantaneous potential drop across the capacitor

$$v^C = -i_0 X_C \cos \omega t \tag{20.26}$$

As with the inductive reactance, squaring and averaging gives the rms voltage drop across the capacitor

$$v_e^C = i_e X_C \tag{20.27}$$

Note that the capacitive reactance $X_C = 1/\omega C$ *decreases* with the frequency. This happens because the voltage drop q/C is proportional to the charge, and the charge has less and less time to built up as the frequency increases. Since the inductive reactance increases with the frequency, circuits containing both capacitors and inductors ,can exhibit complicated frequency variations.

If a resistor, inductor, and capacitor are connected in series to a generator which supplies a current $i_0 \sin \omega t$, their voltage maximum and minima occur at different times (Fig. 20.28). The potential drops across the three elements vary with time as

$$v^R = i_0 R \sin \omega t \tag{20.19}$$
$$v^L = i_0 X_L \cos \omega t \tag{20.23}$$
$$v^C = -i_0 X_C \cos \omega t \tag{20.26}$$

These potential differences and the current are plotted in Fig. 20.28*c*. The drop v^R across the resistor is always proportional to the instantaneous current, but this is not true for the other two voltages. For example, at $t = 0$, the current is zero, but its rate of change is a maximum. Since the induced EMF is proportional to di/dt, v^L has its maximum positive value. Also, at $t = 0$, the current has just completed a negative half cycle. Hence the capacitor charge q and its potential drop $v^C = q/C$ have their most negative values. These concepts are illustrated by the next example.

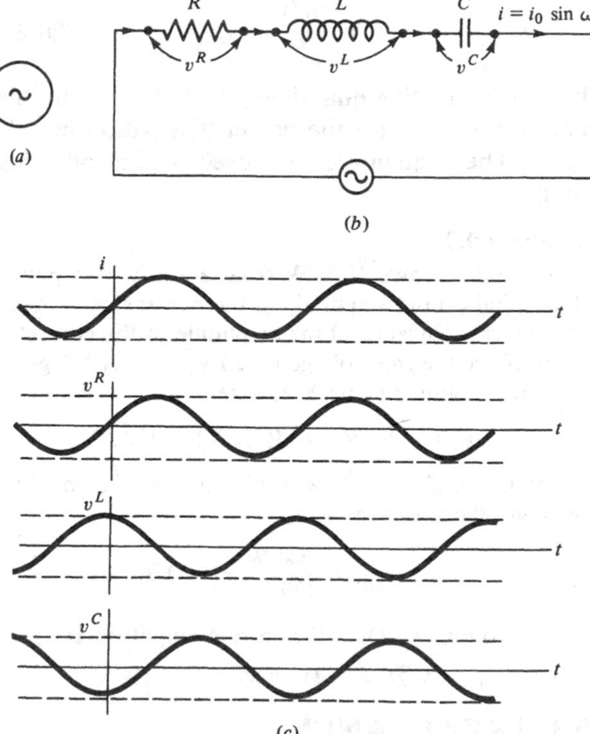

Figure 20.28. (*a*) Symbol for an ac generator. (*b*) An *RLC* series circuit. (*c*) The potential drops across each of the elements and the current versus time.

Example 20.9

The current in Fig. 20.29 has an amplitude of 0.5 A and a frequency $f = \omega/2\pi = 159$ Hz, so $\omega = 1000\ \text{s}^{-1}$. (a) Find the instantaneous voltage drop across each circuit element at $t = 0$. (b) Find the potential difference v between points a and b at an arbitrary time t and the effective voltage between these points. (c) Find the effective voltages across the reactances, X_L and X_C.

(a) At $t = 0$, $\sin \omega t = \sin 0 = 0$, and $\cos \omega t = \cos 0 = 1$. With $X_L = X_C = 20$ ohms, the voltage drops are

$$v^R = i_0 R \sin \omega t = 0$$
$$v^L = i_0 X_L \cos \omega t = (0.5\ \text{A})(20\ \text{ohm})(1) = 10\ \text{V}$$
$$v^C = -i_0 X_C \cos \omega t = -(0.5\ \text{A})(20\ \text{ohm})(1) = -10\ \text{V}$$

Thus at this instant, if we proceed along the circuit in the direction of positive currents, we see no voltage drop across the resistor, a 10-V drop across the inductor, and a 10-V *rise* across the capacitor.

(b) Since X_L and X_C are equal, $v^L = -v^C$ at all times. Thus the sum $v^R + v^L + v^C$ of the voltage drop across the three circuit elements equals v^R, and with $R = 10$ ohms, the total drop from point a to point b is

$$\begin{aligned} v = v^R &= i_0 R \sin \omega t \\ &= (0.5\ \text{A})(10\ \text{ohm}) \sin (1000\ t) \\ &= 5 \sin(1000\ t)\ \text{V} \end{aligned}$$

Since the voltage amplitude is 5 V, the effective voltage is

$$v_e = v_e^R = \frac{v_0}{\sqrt{2}} = \frac{5\ \text{V}}{1.414} = 3.54\ \text{V}$$

(c) The potential differences across the inductor and the capacitor each have an amplitude $v_0 = i_0 X_L = i_0 X_C = (0.5\ \text{A})(20\ \text{ohms}) = 10$ V, so

$$v_e^L = v_e^C = \frac{v_0}{\sqrt{2}} = \frac{10\ \text{V}}{1.414} = 7.07\ \text{V}$$

From this example, we can see that it is *not* correct to proceed in analogy with dc circuits and simply add rms ac voltages. Alternating current voltmeters connected to the terminals of the resistor, inductor, and capacitor will give rms voltages of

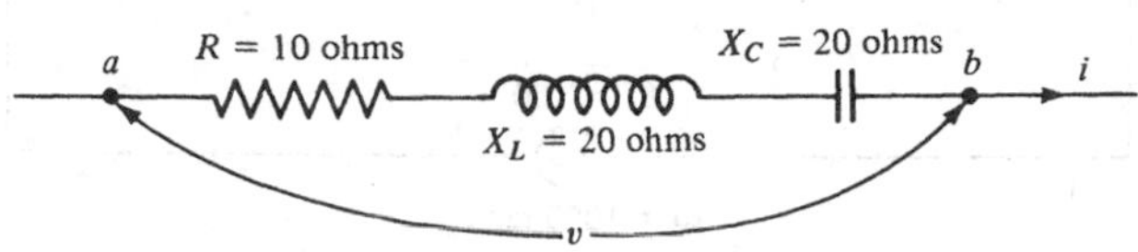

Figure 20.29. Example 20.9.

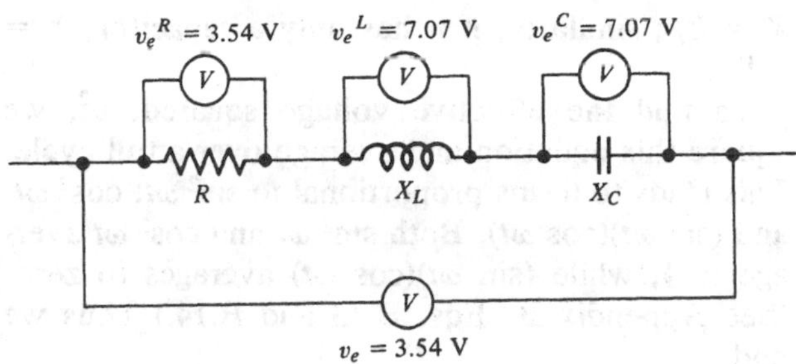

Figure 20.30. Effective voltages are *not* additive.

3.54, 7.07, and 7.07 V, respectively. These add up to 17.68 V, but the rms voltage across the three elements according to part (b) is 3.54 V (Fig. 20.30). The procedure for combining ac voltages is considered in the next section.

20.13 | IMPEDANCE

The current in a network of resistors connected to a dc EMF can be found by calculating the equivalent resistance of the network and using Ohm's law. Similarly, the current in a network of resistors, inductors, and capacitors can be found by calculating the equivalent *impedance Z* of the network and using an analog to Ohm's law.

As we saw in the preceding section, the instantaneous potential drop v from point a to point b in Fig. 20.31 is the sum of the individual voltage drops,

$$\begin{aligned} v &= v^R + v^L + v^C \\ &= i_0 R \sin \omega t + i_0 X_L \cos \omega t - i_0 X_C \cos \omega t \\ &= i_0 (R \sin \omega t + X \cos \omega t) \end{aligned}$$

Here the *net reactance* is

$$X = X_L - X_C = \omega L - \frac{1}{\omega C} \tag{20.28}$$

If a circuit contains an inductor but no capacitor,

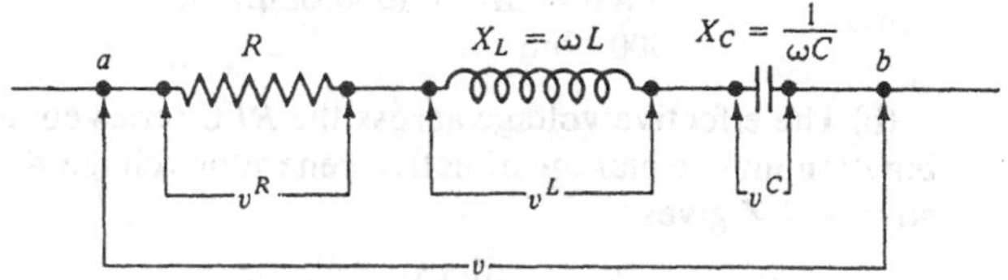

Figure 20.31. Reactances and voltages in an *RLC* circuit.

$X = X_L$; similarly, if it has only a capacitor, $X = -X_C$.

To find the effective voltage squared, v_e^2, we square this equation and average over a full cycle. This leads to terms proportional to $\sin^2 \omega t$, $\cos^2 \omega t$, and $(\sin \omega t)(\cos \omega t)$. Both $\sin^2 \omega t$ and $\cos^2 \omega t$ average to $\frac{1}{2}$, while $(\sin \omega t)(\cos \omega t)$ averages to zero. (See Appendix B, Eqs. B.13 and B.14.) Thus we find

$$v_e^2 = \left(\frac{i_0^2}{2}\right)(R^2 + X^2)$$

The impedance Z is defined as

$$Z = (R^2 + X^2)^{1/2} \qquad (20.29)$$

Equivalently, with $X = X_L - X_C$,

$$Z = [R^2 + (X_L - X_C)^2]^{1/2} \qquad (20.30)$$

With this definition and $i_e^2 = i_0^2/2$, v_e satisfies

$$v_e = i_e Z \qquad (20.31)$$

This equation is very similar to Ohm's law, $v = iR$. However, it relates effective or rms voltages and currents, rather than instantaneous quantities. Also, the impedance, unlike the resistance, depends on the frequency. These results are used in the next example.

Example 20.10

An *RLC* series circuit is connected to an ac generator (Fig. 20.31). If $\omega = 1000$ rad s^{-1}, find (a) the impedance, and (b) the effective current.

(a) The net reactance is

$$X = X_L - X_C = \omega L - \frac{1}{\omega C}$$

$$= (1000 \text{ rad s}^{-1})(0.4 \text{ H}) - \frac{1}{(1000 \text{ rad s}^{-1})(10^{-5} \text{ C})}$$

$$= 400 \text{ ohm} - 100 \text{ ohm} = 300 \text{ ohm}$$

Hence the impedance is

$$Z = (R^2 + X^2)^{1/2} = [(400 \text{ ohm})^2 + (300 \text{ ohm})^2]^{1/2} = 500 \text{ ohm}$$

(b) The effective voltage across the *RLC* series combination must equal the effective generator voltage $\mathscr{E}_e$, so $v_e = i_e Z$ gives

$$i_e = \frac{\mathscr{E}_e}{Z} = \frac{100 \text{ V}}{500 \text{ ohm}} = 0.2 \text{ A}$$

In the preceding section, we also saw that the sum of the rms ac voltages is *not* equal to the rms potential difference v_e across two or more circuit elements. The correct procedure for combining these voltages can be found from Eq. 20.30 for the impedance. If we multiply this by i_e, then we have

$$i_e Z = [(i_e R)^2 + (i_e X_L - i_e X_C)^2]^{1/2}$$

Now, $i_e Z = v_e$, $i_e R = v_e^R$, $i_e X_L = v_e^L$, and $i_e X_C = v_e^C$, so

$$v_e = [(v^R)^2 + (v^L - v^C)^2]^{1/2} \qquad (20.32)$$

These ideas are illustrated by the next two examples.

Example 20.11

(a) Find the rms voltage drops across each of the elements in the preceding example, where $i_e = 0.2$ A, $X_L = 400$ ohms, $X_C = 100$ ohms, and $R = 400$ ohms. (b) Calculate the rms voltage drop across the three elements, and show it is equal to the generator rms EMF, 100 V.

(a) The rms drops across the three elements are

$$v_e^R = i_e R = (0.2 \text{ A})(400 \text{ ohm}) = 80 \text{ V}$$
$$v_e^L = i_e X_L = (0.2 \text{ A})(400 \text{ ohm}) = 80 \text{ V}$$
$$v_e^C = i_e X_C = (0.2 \text{ A})(100 \text{ ohm}) = 20 \text{ V}$$

(b) Using Eq. 20.32,

$$v_e = [(80 \text{ V})^2 + (80 \text{ V} - 20 \text{ V})^2]^{1/2} = [10{,}000 \text{ V}^2]^{1/2} = 100 \text{ V}$$

Example 20.12

Suppose the frequency of the generator in Fig. 20.32 is varied. (a) At what value of $\omega = 2\pi f$ will the impedance be smallest? (b) Find the effective current at that value of ω.

(a) Since $Z = [R^2 + (X_L - X_C)^2]^{1/2}$, its minimum value occurs when $X_L - X_C = \omega L - 1/\omega C = 0$, or when

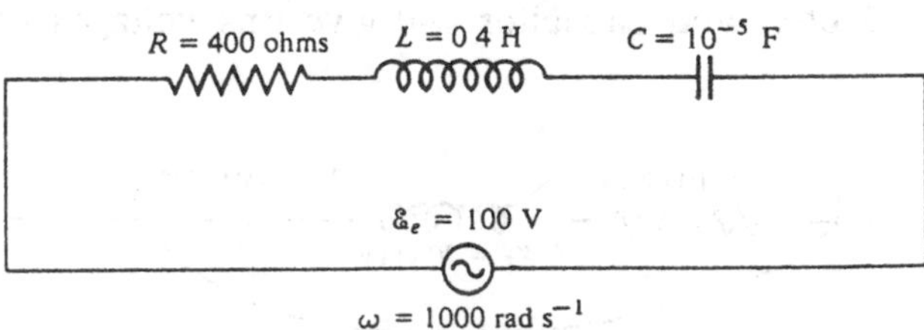

Figure 20.32. Examples 20.10, 20.11, and 20.12.

$\omega L = 1/\omega C$. Thus $\omega^2 = 1/LC$, or

$$\omega = \sqrt{\frac{1}{LC}}$$

$$= \sqrt{\frac{1}{(0.4 \text{ H})(10^{-5} \text{ F})}} = 500 \text{ rad s}^{-1}$$

(b) Since X is zero, $Z = R$, and the effective current is

$$i_e = \frac{v_e}{Z} = \frac{v_e}{R} = \frac{100 \text{ V}}{400 \text{ ohm}} = 0.25 \text{ A}$$

This last example illustrates the phenomenon called *resonance*. At a frequency below or above the resonance frequency, the impedance is greater, so the current for a given applied generator EMF is smaller (Fig. 20.33). This is very similar to the behavior of a mechanical oscillator. We found in Chapter Nine that an oscillating object will have its greatest amplitude if the driving force is applied at the characteristic frequency of the oscillator. The similarity in the behavior of the *RLC* circuit and the mechanical oscillator reflects the fact that the two systems satisfy the same equation of motion, except for a relabeling of the variables.

Resonant ac circuits have many applications. For example, in a television or radio antenna, currents are produced by the electromagnetic waves broadcast at different frequencies by many stations. A tuner in the receiver contains an inductor and a variable capacitor adjusted so that the resonant frequency corresponds to the desired station. Since the resistance of the tuner is small, the impedance rises rapidly as the frequency varies from the resonant frequency, and therefore only one station will normally be received.

20.14 | POWER IN ALTERNATING CURRENT CIRCUITS

The equation for the power dissipated in an ac circuit differs somewhat from the dc formula. During half of each cycle, the capacitor charge is increasing, so the capacitor is absorbing energy. However, this stored electrical energy is released when the capacitor discharges during the other half cycle. Similarly, the inductor temporarily stores and releases magnetic energy. Neither of these circuit elements absorbs any *net* energy over a full cycle. However, as we have seen in Section 20.11, a resistor dissipates energy as heat at the average rate $\overline{\mathcal{P}} = i_e^2 R$. Since $v_e = i_e Z$, this can be rewritten as $\overline{\mathcal{P}} = i_e(v_e/Z)R$, or

$$\overline{\mathcal{P}} = i_e v_e \left(\frac{R}{Z}\right) \qquad (20.33)$$

The power dissipation in a dc circuit is iv, so this result has an extra factor (R/Z) called the *power factor*. It is always less than 1 if there is any reactance. If R is small compared to Z, then very little power is dissipated by the circuit, even though i_e is large; energy is absorbed and released by the inductor and the capacitor, but little heating occurs in the resistor. The power factor is less than 1 for ac motors, as in the next example.

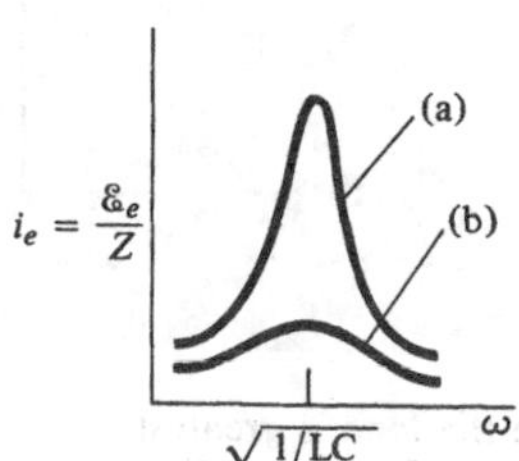

Figure 20.33. Effective current versus frequency for two circuits with the same EMF and resonant frequency. The narrow curve (*a*) corresponds to a circuit with a small resistance. The broad flat curve (*b*) corresponds to a circuit with a large resistance.

Example 20.13

An ac motor connected to a 120-V rms power line is equivalent in the circuit to a 80-ohm resistor and a 60-ohm inductive reactance in series. Find (a) the effective current; (b) the power supplied to the motor.

(a) To find the effective current, we first calculate the impedance:

$$Z = [R^2 + X^2]^{1/2}$$
$$= [(80 \text{ ohm})^2 + (60 \text{ ohm})^2]^{1/2}$$
$$= 100 \text{ ohm}$$

Then

$$i_e = \frac{v_e}{Z} = \frac{120 \text{ V}}{100 \text{ ohm}} = 1.2 \text{ A}$$

(b) The power supplied to the motor is

$$\overline{\mathcal{P}} = i_e v_e \left(\frac{R}{Z}\right) = (1.2 \text{ A})(120 \text{ V})\left(\frac{80 \text{ ohm}}{100 \text{ ohm}}\right)$$
$$= 115 \text{ W}$$

20.15 | IMPEDANCE MATCHING

It is often desirable to arrange that the maximum possible power transfer occurs between a power source and a load. These could be a battery and a resistor, respectively, as in the example we discuss

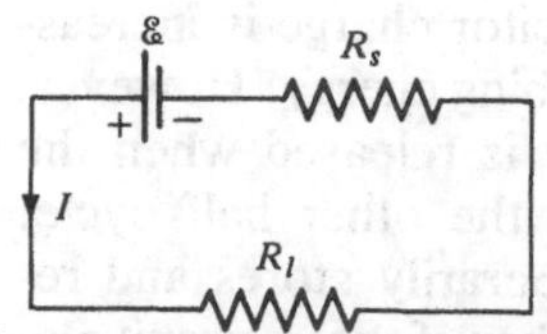

Figure 20.34. The power transfer to R_l is greatest if the resistances are matched ($R_l = R_s$).

shortly. They could also be an amplifier and a loudspeaker or probes connected to a person and an EKG recorder. *In general, the maximum power transfer occurs when the impedances of a source and a load are matched.*

We begin by considering the dc case. Figure 20.34 shows a battery with EMF $\mathscr{E}$ and internal resistance R_s connected to a load that is a resistance R_l. With Ohm's law, the current is

$$I = \frac{\mathscr{E}}{R_s + R_l}$$

The power supplied to the load is then

$$\mathscr{P} = I^2 R_l = \frac{R_l}{(R_l + R_s)^2}\mathscr{E}^2$$

To see how this varies with the ratio $x = R_l/R_s$ of the load and source resistances, we divide out a factor of R_s^2 in the denominator and rewrite $\mathscr{P}$ as

$$\mathscr{P} = \frac{\mathscr{E}^2}{R_s}\frac{x}{(1 + x)^2} \qquad (20.34)$$

The factor $\mathscr{E}^2/R_s$ is the power that would be dissipated in the battery if the load resistance R_l were equal to zero, or if the battery were short-circuited. The second factor is proportional to x, when x is small compared to 1 (Fig. 20.35). It is left as a problem to show that its maximum occurs when $x = 1$, or $R_l = R_s$.

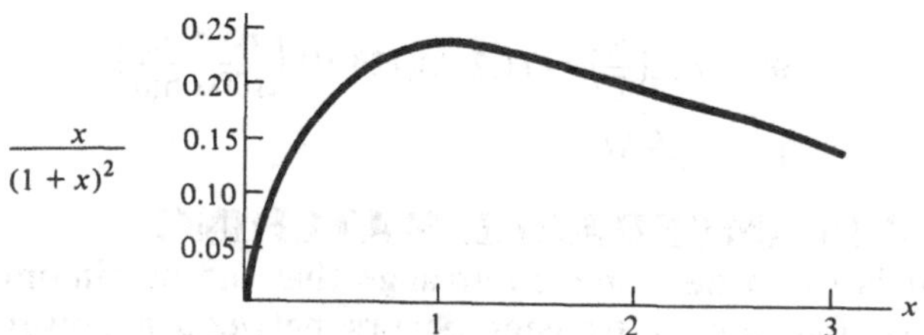

Figure 20.35. The peak power transfer to the load is at $x = R_l/R_s = 1$.

Thus the maximum dc power transfer occurs when the load and source resistances are equal.

Note that when $x = 1$, the power supplied to R_l is $(1/4)(\mathscr{E}^2/R_s)$, or one fourth the power dissipated in a short-circuited source.

Now let us consider, instead, an ac generator with effective EMF $\mathscr{E}_e$, internal resistance R_s, and internal reactance X_s connected to a load with resistance R_l and net reactance X_l (Fig. 20.36). Again we want to know what load will receive the maximum power transfer. If the previous analysis is repeated using the formulas appropriate to alternating currents, the result is that the maximum power transfer occurs if

$$R_l = R_s \quad \text{and} \quad X_l = -X_s \qquad (20.35)$$

This means that the maximum power transfer in an ac circuit occurs when the source and load resistances are equal and the reactances cancel, so that the total reactance $X_l + X_s$ *of the circuit is zero.*

We recall that the net reactance is $X = X_L - X_C$, which may be positive or negative. For example, if the source has a resistance of 50 ohms and an inductive reactance of 100 ohms, then to be matched the load must have a resistance of 50 ohms and a capacitive reactance of 100 ohms.

Impedance matching is important whenever "black boxes" are assembled in a laboratory. Even though we can often ignore the internal details of complex electronics instruments, we must be sure that the input and output electrical impedances of

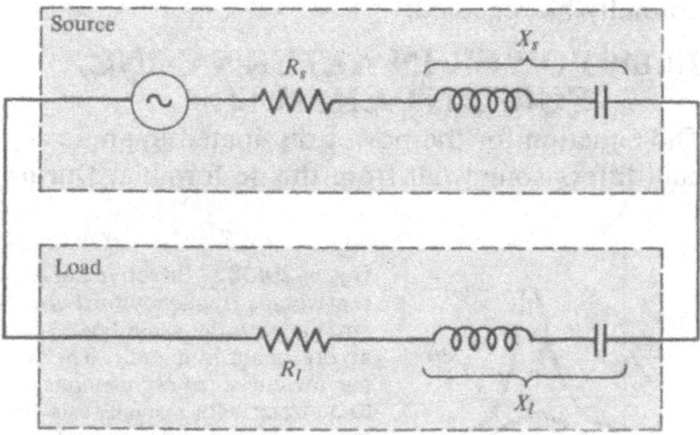

Figure 20.36. The power transfer to the load is greatest when the impedances are matched. ($R_l = R_s$, $X_l = -X_s$.)

two interconnected instruments are not badly mismatched. Impedance matching also is important in applications other than electrical circuits. For example, if sound is to be transferred efficiently without reflections from one medium to another, then the *acoustical impedances* must be matched. Thus, impedance matching is a concept with wide applicability.

EXERCISES ON SUPPLEMENTARY TOPICS

Section 20.9 | Hysteresis; Magnetic Disk Storage

20-46 The *seek time* is the time a read/write head needs to reach a track. The *latency time* is the time required for a specific point on a track to swing under the head, or half the rotational period on the average. The access time is the sum of the seek and latency times. (a) A floppy disk system has an average access time of 264 ms and rotates at 300 rev min^{-1}. What is its average latency time? (b) What is its average seek time? (c) A hard-disk storage system has an average access time of 31.3 ms and rotates at 3633 rev min^{-1}. Find its average latency and seek times.

20-47 (a) A floppy disk system has a maximum data transfer rate of 250 kilobits s^{-1} and a spin rate of 300 rev min^{-1}. How many bits per centimetre are stored on a track 10 cm in diameter? (b) A large hard disk storage system has a maximum data transfer rate of 17.6 megabits s^{-1} and a spin rate of 3633 rev min^{-1}. How many bits per cm are stored on a track 21 cm in diameter?

20-48 A word processing program reads a screenful (2000 bytes) of a document into the computer's memory. (a) A floppy drive has an average access time of 264 ms and a transfer rate of 250 kilobits s^{-1}. From the time the location of the data on the disk is determined, what is the minimum time required to read the data? (b) If instead a hard disk is used with an average access time of 85 ms and a transfer rate of 5 megabits s^{-1}, what is the corresponding time?

20-49 A small hard magnetic disk storage system has an average access time of 85 ms and rotates at 3600 rev min^{-1}. If data are stored at a density of 3572 bits cm^{-1} on a track of diameter 7.5 cm, what is the maximum data transfer rate?

20-50 How many different characters can be represented by 1 byte (8 bits)?

20-51 Some early computer terminals used only 64 characters, not enough to represent all the upper- and lowercase letters, numerals, punctuation symbols, and control characters such as line feeds. How many bits are needed to represent 64 different characters?

Section 20.10 | RL Circuits

20-52 Using the definitions of the inductance and resistance, show that L/R has the units of time.

20-53 A 10-ohm resistor and a 0.2-H inductor are connected in series to a 12-V battery. (a) What is the final current? (b) What is the time constant? (c) What is the current after one time constant? (d) What is the current after 4 s?

20-54 A coil of wire connected to a 6-V battery has a current of 0.063 A after 0.01 s and a current of 0.1 A after a few seconds. (a) What is its resistance? (b) What is its time constant? (c) What is its inductance?

20-55 An RL circuit has a time constant of 4 s and a final current of 8 A. The inductance is 0.1 H. How much energy is stored in the inductor 8 s after the switch is closed?

20-56 A coil with a resistance of 10 ohms and an inductance of 0.5 H is attached to a 12 V battery. (a) What is the final current? (b) How much energy is stored in the coil when this current is reached? (c) At what rate is power dissipated in the coil due to its resistance once the final current is reached?

c20-57 Verify by differentiating that Eq. 20.15 for i is a correct solution of Eq. 20.14.

c20-58 Suppose the switch in Fig. 20.37 has been closed in position 1 for a long time, so that $i = \mathscr{E}/R$. At $t = 0$, the switch is suddenly shifted to position 2. (a) Show that the equation satisfied by the current for $t > 0$ is $-iR - L\,di/dt = 0$. (b) Show that for $t > 0$, the current is

$$i = \left(\frac{\mathscr{E}}{R}\right) e^{-t/T_L}$$

(c) Show that this formula for the current is also correct at $t = 0$.

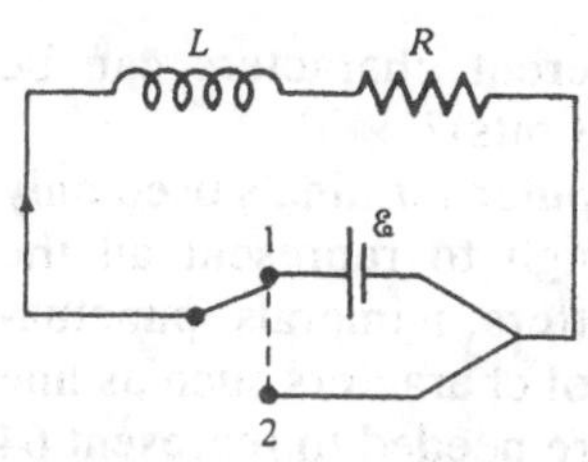

Figure 20.37. Exercise 20-58.

Section 20.11 | Effective or Root Mean Square Alternating Current and Voltages

20-59 A fuse is designed to open if the current exceeds 20 A rms. What is the peak current allowed if this fuse is used in an ac circuit?

20-60 A light bulb draws 60 W from a 120-V rms 60-Hz line. (a) What is the rms current? (b) What is the peak current? (c) How many times per second does this peak current occur?

20-61 A light bulb draws 1.67 A from a 120-V dc line. (a) How much power does the light bulb use? (b) If it is used with a 120-V rms ac line, what is the rms current? (c) What is the peak current when it is used with the ac line?

20-62 An electrical heater is designed to use 1500 W of power when connected to a 120-V rms ac line. It is accidentally connected to a 240-V rms ac line. Assuming its resistance does not change and that it does not burn out, how much power will it use?

20-63 Homes are often supplied with 240-V rms alternating current to provide the power for high-wattage appliances or electric heat. The lines coming into the home include a ground and two "hot" lines, which have voltages equal in magnitude but opposite in sign at all times. Explain how 120-V rms alternating current can be obtained from these lines.

20-64 Number 14 wire is rated to carry 15 A rms safely. How much power can this wire supply at (a) 120-V rms alternating current; (b) 240-V rms alternating current?

20-65 The EMF of a generator is given by $\mathscr{E} = 100 \sin(1000t)$ V, where t is in seconds. (a) What is the frequency f of the generator? (b) What is its rms voltage?

20-66 A generator rotates at 400 Hz and has an rms EMF of 1000 V. Find the formula for the EMF versus time.

Section 20.12 | Reactance

20-67 A capacitor has a reactance of 10 ohms at 400 Hz. (a) Find the capacitance. (b) What is the reactance at 60 Hz? (c) What will be the rms voltage drop across the capacitor if it is connected to a 240-V 60-Hz line?

20-68 At 60 Hz, find the reactance of a (a) 0.05-H inductor; (b) a 1-μF = 10^{-6}-F capacitor. (c) At what frequency will the inductive and capacitive reactances be equal?

20-69 At 1000 Hz, an inductor and a capacitor have equal reactances. What is the ratio of the capacitive reactance to the inductive reactance at 100 Hz?

20-70 A 10^{-4}-F capacitor is connected to a 120-V, 60-Hz ac line. Find (a) the rms current; (b) the peak current.

20-71 When a 0.4-H inductor is connected to a 120-V, 60-Hz ac line, what are (a) the rms current; (b) the peak current?

20-72 A 2-H inductor is connected to a 120-V rms, 60-Hz power line. (a) Find its reactance. (b) Find the rms potential difference across the inductor. (c) What is the peak voltage drop across the inductor?

Section 20.13 | Impedance

20-73 A 100-ohm resistance and a 0.2-H inductance are connected in series to a 240-V rms 60-Hz generator. (a) Find the reactance of the inductor. (b) Find the impedance of the circuit. (c) Find the rms current.

20-74 For the circuit in the preceding exercise, draw sketches showing how the following quantities vary with time: (a) the current; (b) the potential difference across the resistor; (c) the potential difference across the inductor.

20-75 A 100-ohm resistor, a 10^{-4}-F capacitor, and a 0.1-H inductor are connected in series to a 120-V rms generator. If the generator frequency is 60 Hz, find (a) the impedance; (b) the effective current.

20-76 A 30-ohm resistor and a capacitor with a reactance of 40 ohms are connected in series to a 50-V rms ac generator. (a) What is the rms current? (b) What is the peak current?

20-77 A tuning circuit in a radio transmitter has a 10^{-6}-H inductance in series with a 10^{-12}-F capacitance. Find (a) the frequency of the waves transmitted; (b) their wavelength.

20-78 A tuning circuit in a radio has a coil of inductance 2×10^{-5} H in series with a variable capacitor. What is the capacitance if the radio is tuned to receive a station at $f = \omega/2\pi = 10^6$ Hz?

20-79 Alternating current voltmeters are connected across the terminals of an inductance, a capacitance, and a resistance connected in series. Their readings are 100 V, 300 V, and 150 V, respectively. What is the rms voltage across the three circuit elements?

Section 20.14 | Power in Alternating Current Circuits

20-80 An air conditioner connected to a 120-V rms ac line is equivalent to a 10-ohm resistance and a 1-ohm inductive reactance in series. (a) What is its impedance? (b) What is the power supplied to the air conditioner?

20-81 A 5-ohm resistor, a 10-ohm inductive reactance, and a 22-ohm capacitive reactance are connected in series to a 120-V rms ac generator. (a) Find the impedance. (b) How much power is dissipated in the resistor?

20-82 A 5-ohm resistor, a 0.01-H inductor, and a 10^{-4}-F capacitor are connected in series to a power supply with a variable frequency. (a) At what value of ω is the current the greatest? (b) What is the corresponding frequency f? (c) How much power is dissipated at this frequency if the effective EMF of the power supply is 10 V?

20-83 For the circuit in the preceding exercise, find (a) the impedance at $\omega = 2000$ rad s^{-1}; (b) the power supplied to the resistor if the effective EMF is 10 V.

Section 20.15 | Impedance Matching

20-84 It is more economical to extract energy from a battery by using a load resistance that is larger than the internal source resistance rather than a load resistance equal to the source resistance. Explain why.

20-85 Why is impedance matching *not* desirable when using a voltmeter to measure a potential difference?

20-86 A 12-V battery has an internal resistance of 0.005 ohms. A resistance R is connected across its terminals. (a) If $R = 0.005$ ohm, find the ratio of the power dissipated in the internal resistance to that dissipated in R. (b) Find this ratio when $R = 0.05$ ohm.

20-87 A dc generator has an internal resistance of 10^{-4} ohm. It is desired that no more than 1 percent of the total power generated to be dissipated in the generator itself. What is the minimum resistance one can connect to the generator?

PROBLEMS ON SUPPLEMENTARY TOPICS

20-88 A 10-ohm resistor and a 0.1-H inductor are connected in series to a battery. (a) What is the time constant? (b) How long will it take for the current to reach 99 percent of its final value?

20-89 A coil with a resistance R and inductance L is connected to a battery with an EMF $\mathscr{E}$ and a negligible internal resistance. Show that when the current has reached its final value, the energy stored in the coil is $\frac{1}{2}\mathscr{E}^2 T_L/R$.

20-90 (a) Show that the initial rate of change of the current in an RL circuit when it is connected to a battery is $i_f R/L$. (b) If the current continued to increase at this initial rate, how long would it take to reach i_f?

20-91 The current in an RL circuit reaches half its final value in 4 s. What is the time constant of the circuit?

20-92 Suppose a light bulb and a variable inductance are connected in series to an ac power line. (a) How would the brightness of the bulb vary as the inductance is increased? (b) One can also vary the brightness by replacing the inductor with a variable resistance. Why is that less satisfactory?

***20-93** A tuning circuit in a radio receiver consists of a coil with an inductance of 10^{-5} H and a variable capacitor. (a) What is the capacitance if the receiver is tuned to $f_0 = 1.4 \times 10^6$ Hz? (b) Find the reactance at a frequency 1 percent above f_0. (c) At this higher frequency, the impedance is larger than at f_0 by a factor of 4. Find the resistance of the circuit.

ᶜ20-94 Show by differentiating Eq. 20.34 and setting $d\mathscr{P}/dx = 0$ that the maximum power transfer occurs in a dc circuit when the load and source resistances are equal.

20-95 A battery with EMF $\mathscr{E}$ and internal resistance R_s is connected to a resistance R_l. Compare the power dissipated in the battery and in the load if (a) $R_l = R_s$; (b) R_l is much larger than R_s.

Additional Reading

E. Schlömann, Recovery of Nonmagnetic Metals from Municipal Wastes, *Physics Teacher*, vol. 14, 1976, p. 116. The process uses eddy currents.

Kurt S. Lion, Elements of Electrical and Electronic Instrumentation, McGraw-Hill Book Co., New York, 1975.

E. B. Forsyth, The Brookhaven Superconducting Power Transmission Line, *The Physics Teacher*, vol. 21, 1983, p. 285.

Chris A. Kapetanakos and Phillip Sprangle, Ultra-high-current Electron Induction Accelerators, *Physics Today*, February 1985, p. 58.

Mark H. Kryder and Alfred B. Bortz, Magnetic Information Technology, *Physics Today*, December 1984, p. 20.

James E. Brittain, The Magnetron and the Beginning of the Microwave Age, *Physics Today*, July 1985, p. 60.

Joseph F. Mulligen, Heinrich Hertz and the Development of Physics, *Physics Today,* March 1989, p. 50. Hertz confirmed Maxwell's theory of electromagnetic waves and made many other contributions.

Scientific American articles:

Herbert Kondo, Michael Faraday, October 1953, p. 90.

J. R. Newman, James Clerk Maxwell, June 1955, p. 58.

P. Morrison and E. Morrison, Heinrich Hertz, December 1957, p. 98.

H. L. Sharlin, From Faraday to the Dynamo, May 1961, p. 107.

G. Shiers, The Induction Coil, May 1971, p. 80.

John W. Coltman, The Transformer, January 1988, p. 86.

James R. Heirtzler, The Longest Electromagnetic Waves, March 1962, p. 128.

E. N. Parker, Magnetic Fields in the Cosmos, August 1983, p. 44.

Praveen Chaudhari, Electronic and Magnetic Materials, October 1986, p. 137.

Edward W. Homes, Jr., The Earth's Magnetotail, March 1986, p. 40.

Robert M. White, Disk-Storage Technology, August 1980, p. 138.

Mark H. Kryder, Data Storage Technologies for Advanced Computing, October 1987, p. 117.

UNIT SIX

WAVE MOTION

Most of the wave motions with which we are familiar involve a large-scale coordinated disturbance of many particles or objects. While the individual particles do not move far, the disturbance may travel great distances, carrying with it energy and momentum. The motions of the particles vary with the type of wave. For example, in a water wave, the water molecules move in small, approximately circular paths; in a sound wave, molecules move back and forth; and in a wave on a string, the parts of the string move up and down.

Light waves are also coordinated disturbances involving changing electric and magnetic fields. Here no particles move, but the waves nevertheless carry energy and momentum, and the mathematical description of these waves is nearly identical to the mechanical examples just given.

All waves have a number of characteristics in common. Many of these are described in the first chapter of this unit (Chapter Twenty-one), where we mainly use strings and springs for illustration. The special features of sound waves are described in Chapter Twenty-two, and the properties of light are covered in Chapters Twenty-three and Twenty-four.

The importance of waves in physics derives from the transmission of energy and momentum from one place to another or from a source to a detector. These wave motions are described using the ideas of mechanics or electromagnetic theory. Their properties follow from the ideas presented earlier in this book and merely represent cooperative or coordinated motions in systems we have already studied.

A severe jolt to physics in the early twentieth century was the realization that the sharp distinction between wave and individual particle motions was not valid when studying atoms and molecules. In the years since, a dramatic revolution in our description of nature has taken place. Modern quantum physics, which was developed to describe the microscopic properties of molecules, atoms, and nuclei, has forced us to regard particles as having some wave properties and to regard waves as though they are composed of particles, or *quanta*. This wave—particle duality of our present description of nature may be due to our lack of a true understanding of nature or of our inability to express our understanding clearly. Nevertheless, with the language we do have, we must, for example, regard an electron as an entity with both particle- and wavelike characteristics.

This revolution of modern physics does not mean that all of our studies have been for naught. It simply means that when very small dimensions are involved, we must further refine our understanding. The remaining units of this book are devoted to those refinements.

CHAPTER 21 THE DESCRIPTION OF WAVE MOTION

In this chapter, concepts common to all kinds of wave phenomena are developed. We primarily use the readily visualized waves along strings and springs as examples and analogies for other types of wave motion that are more difficult to observe.

When a stone is dropped into a lake or when a string is wiggled briefly at an end, a single wave *pulse* travels away from the disturbance. However, waves also occur in a regular continuing series; they are then said to be *periodic*. For example, a vibrating tuning fork produces alternate compressions and rarefactions of the air nearby. These disturbances, which are perceived as sound, occur at the frequency of the tuning fork.

When a string is disturbed, its particles move at right angles to the string. Waves with displacements perpendicular to the direction of the wave are called *transverse waves*. Light is a transverse wave. Waves that have displacements along the wave direction are termed *longitudinal*. Examples of this latter type are sound waves and compressional waves in coiled springs.

All the waves we consider have the important property of *linearity*. Linearity means that when two or more waves pass the same point, the resulting wave is the sum of the individual waves, and after passing, the waves continue along their paths as if no encounter had occurred. If one observes the circular waves traveling outward from separate points where two pebbles are dropped in still water, the peaks add up when they meet. Afterward, they travel along undisturbed. The description of such linear behavior is called the *principle of superposition*.

21.1 | THE REPRESENTATION OF WAVES

Figure 21.1 shows single wave *pulses* on a string and in a spring produced by a disturbance at their left ends and traveling toward the right. Figure 21.2 shows *periodic waves* produced by oscillatory motion of the left ends. The waves on the string are transverse, and the waves in the spring are longitudinal. Nevertheless, both types of waves can be represented symbolically by similar graphs.

Many kinds of wave phenomena occur in nature. Light is a transverse electromagnetic wave, with changing electric and magnetic fields at right angles to each other and to the direction of the light wave. Sound is an alternate compression and rarefaction of the medium along the direction of motion, so it is a longitudinal wave. Water waves are a mixture of longitudinal and transverse waves, with water molecules moving in roughly circular paths. All these wave phenomena can be represented by graphs similar to those for strings and springs and share many common properties (Fig. 21.3).

Periodic waves of any type are characterized by several quantities. The *frequency* f is the number of waves passing a point per second and is determined by the source of the waves. For example, in the string and spring of Fig. 21.2, the frequency is the rate at which the oscillations occur at the left end. The *period* T is the time between successive wave crests, or the inverse of the frequency $T = 1/f$. The *velocity* c of a wave is the speed at which a wave peak travels. The *wavelength* λ of a periodic wave is the distance between successive wave peaks. Fi-

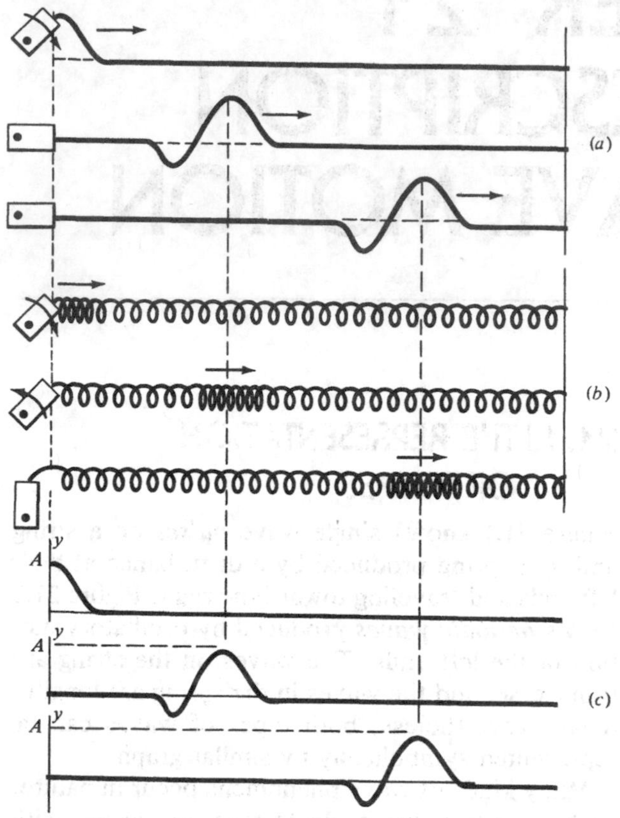

Figure 21.1. (*a*) A single wave pulse is produced at the left end of a string. The appearance of the string is shown at three successive times. Note that the motion of the particles is transverse to the motion of the wave. (*b*) A similar wave pulse on a coiled spring. The spring is alternately compressed and extended along the direction of motion, so the wave is longitudinal. (*c*) Either wave pulse can be represented symbolically by the same graph. For the string, *y* is the displacement of the string from its undisturbed position; displacements above the equilibrium position are positive. For the spring, *y* is a measure of the compression or extension of the spring; a compression is regarded as a positive displacement.

nally, the *amplitude* *A* is the maximum magnitude of the displacement; the displacement of a periodic wave varies back and forth between A and $-A$. Most of the periodic waves we consider are *sinusoidal* waves, and their graphs look like sine or cosine graphs.

The relationships among the frequency, wavelength, and velocity of a periodic wave can be found from Fig. 21.4. In one period T, the time required for one complete wave oscillation, the wave travels

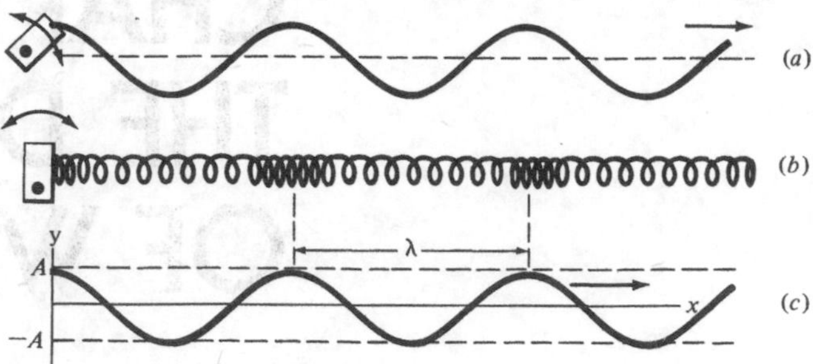

Figure 21.2. (*a*) A periodic disturbance produced in a string by an oscillating lever travels toward the right. The dashed line indicates the undisturbed position of the string. (*b*) A spring is alternately compressed and extended. (*c*) The same graph can represent either wave.

one wavelength λ. The velocity of the wave c is the distance traveled divided by the time, so $c = \lambda/T$. Since $T = 1/f$, this implies

$$f\lambda = c \tag{21.1}$$

The following examples illustrate these relationships.

Example 21.1

A wave pulse on a string moves a distance of 10 m in 0.05 s. (a) What is the velocity of the pulse? (b) What is the frequency of a periodic wave on the same string if its wavelength is 0.8 m?

(a) The velocity of the pulse is $c = \Delta x/\Delta t$, where $\Delta x = 10$ m and $\Delta t = 0.05$ s, so

$$c = \frac{10 \text{ m}}{0.05 \text{ s}} = 200 \text{ m s}^{-1}$$

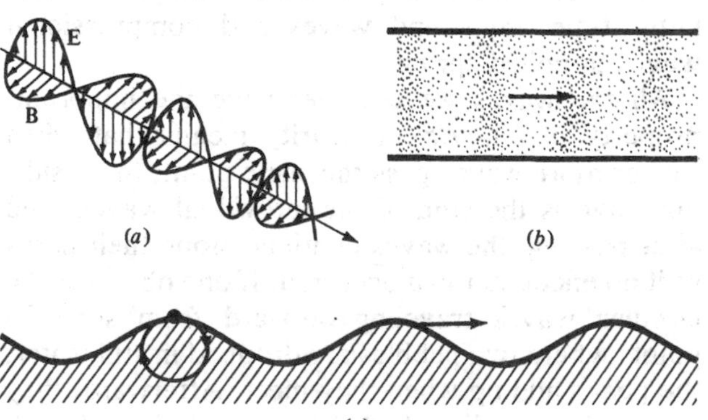

Figure 21.3. (*a*) An electromagnetic wave. (*b*) A sound wave. (*c*) A water wave. All these waves can be represented by the same kind of graphs as used for springs and strings.

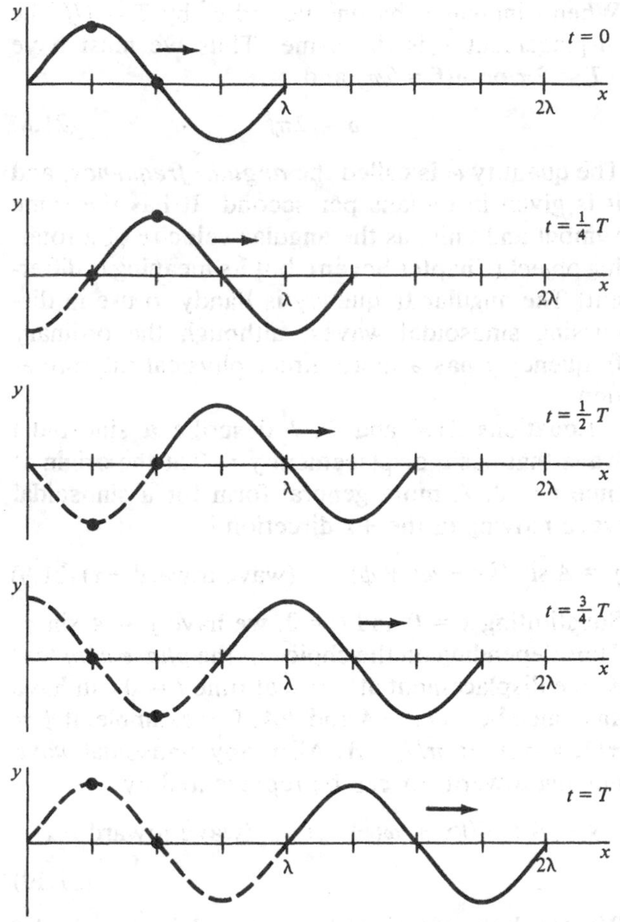

Figure 21.4. Graphs of the displacement at time intervals of one-quarter period. In one period T, the wave moves a distance equal to the wavelength λ, and the displacement at any point makes one full oscillation. For example, at $x = \frac{1}{4}\lambda$, the displacement is a maximum at $t = 0$ and again at $t = T$ (black dots). The displacement at $x = \frac{1}{2}\lambda$ has the same values but at times later by $\frac{1}{4}T$ (colored dots).

(b) The periodic wave has the same velocity, 200 m s^{-1}. Using $f\lambda = c$, the frequency of a 0.8-m wave is

$$f = \frac{c}{\lambda} = \frac{200 \text{ m s}^{-1}}{0.8 \text{ m}} = 250 \text{ s}^{-1} = 250 \text{ Hz}$$

Example 21.2

A typical sound wave associated with human speech has a frequency of 500 Hz, whereas the frequency of yellow light is about 5×10^{14} Hz. In air, sound travels at 344 m s^{-1} and light at 3×10^8 m s^{-1}. Find the wavelengths of the two waves.

For both waves, $f\lambda = c$, so for the sound wave,

$$\lambda = \frac{c}{f} = \frac{344 \text{ m s}^{-1}}{500 \text{ Hz}} = 0.688 \text{ m}$$

For the light wave,

$$\lambda = \frac{c}{f} = \frac{3 \times 10^8 \text{ m s}^{-1}}{5 \times 10^{14} \text{ Hz}} = 6 \times 10^{-7} \text{ m}$$

The fact that these characteristic wavelengths are so different is responsible for some of the apparent differences between the two types of waves. Waves tend to bend around obstacles comparable in size to their wavelength. Such effects are often apparent with sound or water waves but are seldom noticed for light because the wavelength of visible light is so short. Light waves will bend around objects that are small enough.

21.2 | THE MATHEMATICAL DESCRIPTION OF TRAVELING WAVES

Waves can be described mathematically as well as graphically. A wave traveling in the $+x$ direction at a speed c has a displacement y that can be written as

$$y = f(x - ct) \tag{21.2}$$

Here f is any function of the variable $(x - ct)$. To see that this is correct, suppose that the time t increases by an amount Δt and x increases by $\Delta x = c\Delta t$. Then the difference $(x - ct)$ remains the same, and y is unchanged. That is, the point in the wave pattern with displacement y has moved a distance $\Delta x = c\Delta t$ in the positive x direction (Fig. 21.5). This is the definition of a *traveling wave*. Similarly, a wave moving in the $-x$ direction is described by

$$y = f(x + ct) \tag{21.3}$$

Sinusoidal waves are an important type of traveling wave. When we speak of a 500-Hz sound wave or a beam of yellow light, we are referring to sinusoidal waves with a specific frequency or wavelength. Sinusoidal waves are special cases of Eqs. 21.2 and 21.3 where the function f is a sine or cosine. If the amplitude of the wave is A, then an example of a sinusoidal wave moving in the $+x$

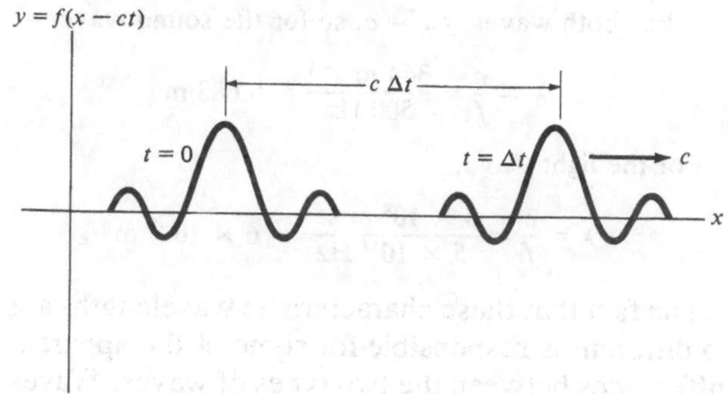

Figure 21.5. A wave pulse $y(x, t) = f(x - ct)$ is a traveling wave moving toward $+x$ at a velocity c. When t is increased by Δt and x by $c\,\Delta t$, the variable $(x - ct)$ stays the same. At $t = 0$ (black curve) and at $t = \Delta t$ (colored curve) the two waveforms are identical, but the wave at Δt has moved a distance $\Delta x = c\,\Delta t$ in the positive x direction. The variable $(x - ct)$ has the same value at the corresponding points on the two curves.

direction is

$$y = A \sin k(x - ct) \qquad (21.4)$$

Figure 21.4 illustrates a portion of such a wave. The sine function varies between -1 and $+1$, so y varies from $-A$ to $+A$.

The quantity k is called the *wave number*. We can relate it to the wavelength λ by noting that the sine repeats itself when the argument, or *phase*, increases by 2π radians, or 360°. (A graph illustrating this property is given in Fig. B.5 in Appendix B.) If x increases by λ, then the displacement y is also the same, and

$$y = A \sin k(x - ct) = A \sin k(x + \lambda - ct)$$

Since the sines are equal, their arguments differ by 2π. Thus $k\lambda = 2\pi$, or

$$k = \frac{2\pi}{\lambda} \qquad (21.5)$$

This is the desired relationship between the wave number and the wavelength. Since wavelengths are measured in length units, or metres, wave numbers are measured in inverse metres, m^{-1}.

With the definition

$$\omega = kc \qquad (21.6)$$

Eq. 21.4 can also be written in the form

$$y = A \sin (kx - \omega t) \qquad (21.7)$$

When t increases by one period or by $T = 1/f$, the displacement y is the same. Thus we must have $\omega T = 2\pi$ or $\omega/f = 2\pi$, and

$$\omega = 2\pi f \qquad (21.8)$$

The quantity ω is called the *angular frequency*, and it is given in radians per second. It has the same symbol and units as the angular velocity of a rotating object (Chapter Seven), but its meaning is different. The angular frequency is handy to use in discussing sinusoidal waves, although the ordinary frequency f has a more direct physical interpretation.

Equations 21.4 and 21.7 describe a sinusoidal wave that has a displacement $y = 0$ at the origin at time $t = 0$. A more general form for a sinusoidal wave moving in the $+x$ direction is

$$y = A \sin (kx - \omega t + \phi) \qquad \text{(wave toward } +x) \ (21.9)$$

Substituting $x = 0$ and $t = 0$, we have $y = A \sin \phi$. Thus depending on the choice of the *phase constant* ϕ, the displacement at $x = 0$ at time $t = 0$ can have any value between $-A$ and $+A$. For example, if $\phi = \pi/2$, $y = A \sin \pi/2 = A$. Also, any sinusoidal wave moving toward $-x$ can be represented by

$$y = A \sin (kx + \omega t + \phi) \qquad \text{(wave toward } -x) \qquad (21.10)$$

We use the expressions for sinusoidal waves in the following example.

Example 21.3

A sinusoidal wave on a string traveling in the $+x$ direction at 10 m s^{-1} has a wavelength of 2 m. (a) Find its wave number, frequency, and angular frequency. (b) If the amplitude is 0.1 m, and the point $x = 0$ on the string is at its equilibrium position ($y = 0$) at time $t = 0$, find the equation for the wave. (c) If instead the point at $x = 0$ is at its maximum displacement at $t = 0$, find the equation for the wave.

(a) The wave number is

$$k = \frac{2\pi}{\lambda} = \frac{2\pi}{2\text{ m}} = 3.14\text{ m}^{-1}$$

The frequency and angular frequency are

$$f = \frac{c}{\lambda} = \frac{10\text{ m s}^{-1}}{2\text{ m}} = 5\text{ Hz}$$

$$\omega = 2\pi f = 2\pi(5\text{ Hz}) = 31.4\text{ rad s}^{-1}$$

(b) Equation 21.7 is appropriate here, since it describes a wave in the $+x$ direction with a displacement $y = 0$ at the origin at $t = 0$. Thus with $A = 0.1$ m and the results of part (a), we have

$$y = A \sin (kx - \omega t)$$
$$= (0.1 \text{ m}) \sin [(3.14 \text{ m}^{-1})x - (31.4 \text{ s}^{-1})t]$$

This equation tells us the displacement y at any point x on the string for all times.

(c) Here we must use the form of the wave in Eq. 21.9, $y = A \sin (kx - \omega t + \phi)$. At $x = 0$, $t = 0$, the wave has a maximum, and $y = A$. Thus we must have

$$A = A \sin (0 - 0 + \phi)$$

or $\sin \phi = 1$. The sine function is 1 at 90° or $\pi/2$ radians. Thus $\phi = \pi/2$ and

$$y = (0.1 \text{ m}) \sin \left[(3.14 \text{ m}^{-1})x - (31.4 \text{ s}^{-1})t + \frac{\pi}{2}\right]$$

Example 21.4

A sinusoidal wave on a string is represented by $y = A \sin (kx - \omega t)$. Each point on the string moves along the y or transverse direction from $y = -A$ to $y = +A$ and back to $y = -A$ once in each cycle. This motion is at right angles to the direction of the wave, which is along the string. (a) At a given point x on the string, find the velocity v associated with this transverse motion as a function of time. (b) Find the corresponding transverse acceleration.

(a) The position of the string relative to its equilibrium position is given by a function $y(t)$ for a fixed value of x. To find the corresponding velocity, we must evaluate the derivative of the position,

$$v = \frac{dy}{dt} = \frac{d}{dt}[A \sin (kx - \omega t)] \qquad \text{(fixed } x\text{)}$$

(Technically, the derivative with respect to t for a fixed value of x is a *partial derivative*.) Now with $u = (kx - \omega t)$ and x held constant, using the chain rule (Appendix B.8), we find

$$\frac{d}{dt} \sin u = \left[\frac{d}{du} \sin u\right] \frac{du}{dt} = (\cos u)(-\omega)$$

Thus

$$v = -\omega A \cos(kx - \omega t)$$

We see that the velocity also varies sinusoidally with time. However, since it varies as $-\cos u$ instead of as $\sin u$, its maxima and minima occur a quarter-cycle before the maxima and minima in the displacement.

(b) The acceleration associated with the transverse motion is the derivative of the velocity,

$$a = \frac{dv}{dt} = \frac{d}{dt}[-\omega A \cos (kx - \omega t)] \qquad \text{(fixed } x\text{)}$$

With

$$\frac{d}{dt} \cos u = \left[\frac{d}{du} \cos u\right] \frac{du}{dt} = -(\sin u)(-\omega)$$

we have

$$a = -\omega^2 A \sin (kx - \omega t)$$

Note that the transverse acceleration a and the displacement y are related by $a = -\omega^2 y = -(2\pi f)^2 y$. As discussed in Chapter Nine, this is the defining equation for simple harmonic motion. This is the type of oscillatory motion frequently encountered when an object undergoes small oscillations about equilibrium. *Thus each point on the string is undergoing simple harmonic motion transverse to the wave direction.*

21.3 | THE VELOCITY OF WAVES

Although waves are common phenomena, each type of wave disturbance has its own specific physical origin. Accordingly, each type of wave has a characteristic velocity.

Electromagnetic waves are unique in that they require no medium in which to propagate. As we discussed in Chapter Twenty, these waves are due to mutually induced time-varying electric and magnetic fields. In a vacuum, they have a velocity of 3×10^8 m s^{-1}; in matter, their velocity is always smaller.

Sound is a coordinated mechanical disturbance involving large numbers of molecules. These molecules move and collide as a wave disturbance passes, but on the average they suffer no net change in position. As we show in the next chapter, the velocity of sound in a substance depends on how the pressure changes when the density changes. The velocity of sound in air at 30° C is 344 m s^{-1}, but it is much higher in solids; in aluminum, for example, $c = 5000$ m s^{-1}. In solids there may also be transverse as well as longitudinal sound waves. The two types of sound waves have different velocities.

The velocity of a wave can be predicted from the

physical laws that describe the specific wave phenomenon. For example, we saw in Chapter Twenty that Maxwell was able to derive an expression for the speed of an electromagnetic wave using the fundamental properties of electric and magnetic fields. Similarly, the velocities of the various kinds of mechanical waves, such as sound waves and waves in strings, springs, and water, can be predicted using Newton's laws of motion. Such calculations are mathematically complex and will not be carried out here. However, it is important to remember that the velocity of a wave depends on the type of wave, on the properties of the system in which the wave travels, and sometimes on the frequency. As an example, we describe the result for a wave on a string.

When a string is displaced, the restoring force is proportional to the tension in the string. Also, a thick string will respond more slowly to this restoring force than will a thin string. Hence we expect that the wave velocity on a string will depend on the tension $\mathcal{T}$ and the mass per unit length μ of the string. This is the case, and the detailed analysis for the wave velocity c on a string gives

$$c = \sqrt{\frac{\mathcal{T}}{\mu}} \tag{21.11}$$

This result has the features described above. The following example leads to a typical value for the wave velocity on a string.

Example 21.5

The tension on the longest string of a grand piano is 1098 N, and the mass per unit length is 0.065 kg m^{-1}. What is the velocity of a wave on this string?

Using the above result,

$$c = \sqrt{\frac{\mathcal{T}}{\mu}} = \sqrt{\frac{1098\ \text{N}}{0.065\ \text{kg m}^{-1}}} = 130\ \text{m s}^{-1}$$

21.4 | WAVE INTERFERENCE AND STANDING WAVES

When two or more waves travel in a medium, the resulting wave is the sum of the displacements associated with the individual waves. This property is referred to either as *linearity* or as the *principle of superposition* and is applicable to all the waves we consider here. As we have noted, the resulting wave may have a very complex shape when the waves overlap, but each individual wave is unchanged and displays its original form when the waves separate. Since waves add algebraically, the resultant of overlapping waves can be larger or smaller than the individual waves, depending on their relative sign. This characteristic interaction of waves is termed *interference* and leads to many interesting and curious effects. In this section, we see that waves traveling in opposite directions can combine to form a wave disturbance that does not appear to travel at all and is therefore called a *standing wave*. Many other examples of interference are considered later.

To illustrate these ideas, suppose first that a string is held at each end by individuals who simultaneously produce wave pulses. The only difference between the pulses is that they are inverted mirror images of each other (Fig. 21.6). As the waves pass by the same points on the string, the resulting wave

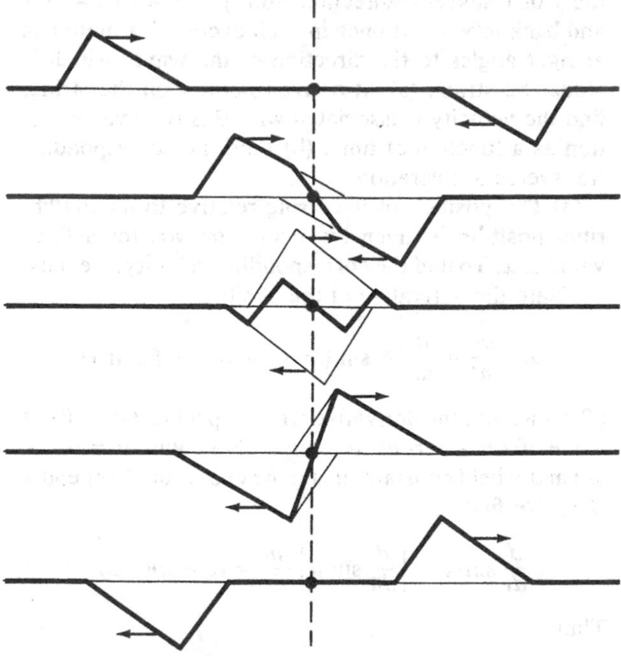

Figure 21.6. Two wave pulses that are inverted mirror images of each other are produced at the ends of a string. As the waves pass each other, the string has a complex shape but the one point on the dashed line is always at rest. The string shape is found by adding the displacements of the two pulses at every point.

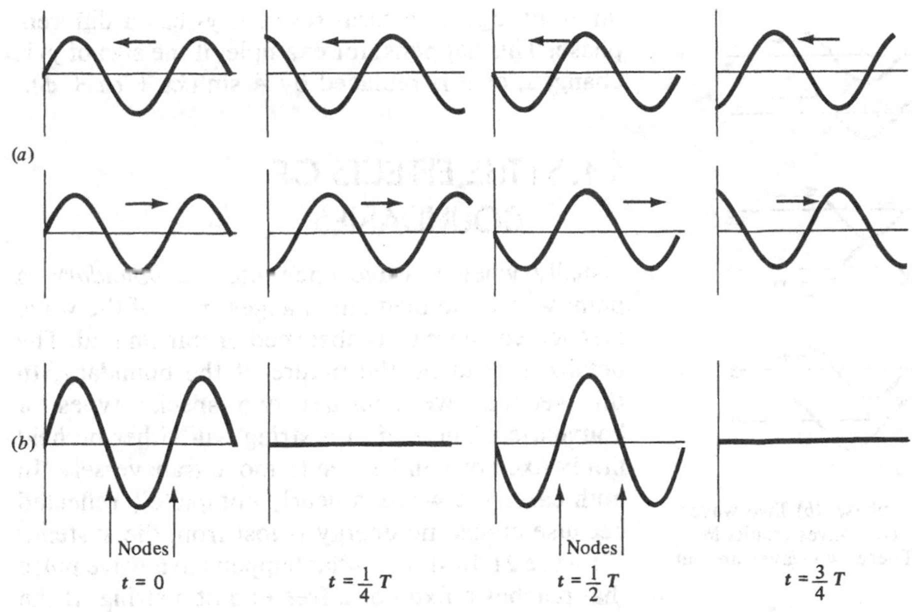

Figure 21.7. (*a*) Waves on a string at time intervals of $\frac{1}{4}T$. Top, a wave to the left; below, a wave to the right. (*b*) The appearance of the string if both waves are on the same string. The shape of the string changes with time, but its displacement is always zero at the nodes. A photograph taken with an exposure of several periods shows a blur corresponding to the maximum displacement at each point (Fig. 21.8).

is found by adding the displacements of the individual waves.

An important feature of this particular experiment is that despite the fact that the wave shape becomes quite complex, there is one point on the string that is never displaced. This point is called a *node*. The string could actually be held fixed at this point without affecting the results. The pulses are said to be interfering with each other *destructively* at this point.

The same experiment can be performed with two periodic waves traveling in opposite directions but having the same amplitude and wavelength (Fig. 21.7). Now there are a number of nodes spaced one half wavelength apart. Midway between two successive nodes are points called *antinodes* where the string can experience a maximum displacement. At an antinode the waves add *constructively*.

Figure 21.8 shows a multiple exposure series of pictures of a string vibrating in this way. Note that the traveling waves are no longer observed. What is seen is a pattern described as a *standing wave*: a wave with nodes and antinodes at fixed points.

The interference effects produced by waves depend on their *phases*. If two waves reaching a point have their maxima at the same time, they are *in phase* and add constructively. If a maximum of one wave coincides with a minimum of the other, they are a half wavelength out of phase and interfere destructively. Under these conditions the waves are said to be exactly out of phase. In general, there may be an arbitrary phase difference between two waves (Fig. 21.9).

Mathematical Description of Standing Waves

The mathematical description of sinusoidal traveling waves leads directly to formulas for standing waves. Suppose that, as in Fig. 21.7, we have waves with the same frequency and equal amplitudes traveling in both the $+x$ and $-x$ directions:

$$y_1 = A \sin(kx - \omega t), \quad y_2 = A \sin(kx + \omega t) \qquad (21.12)$$

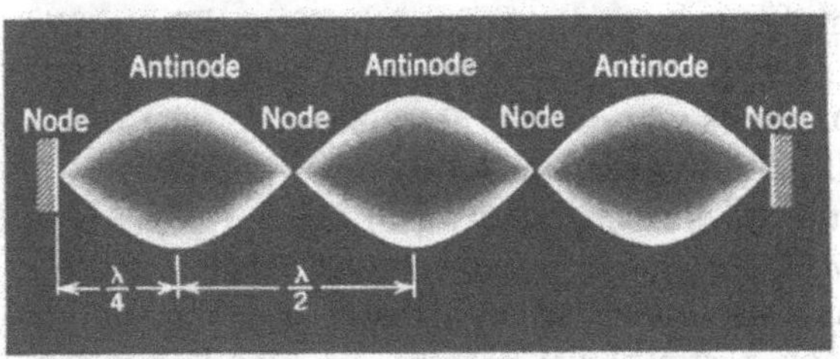

Figure 21.8. The pattern formed by the string of Fig. 21.7 if viewed at many different times.

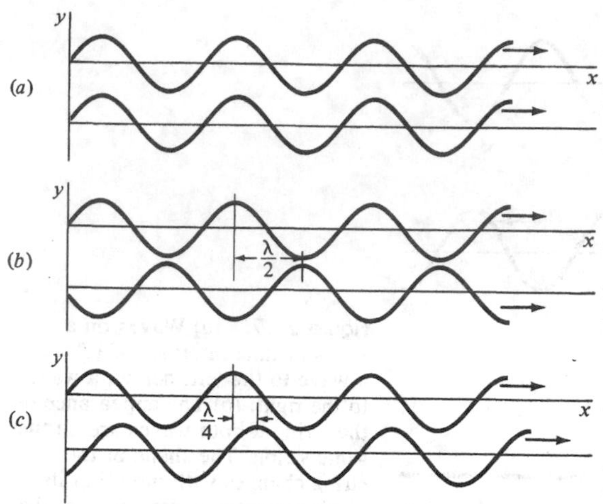

Figure 21.9. (a) Two waves exactly in phase. (b) Two waves exactly out of phase. Addition of these two waves results in complete destructive interference. (c) These two waves are out of phase by $\lambda/4$.

Then the superposition principle states that the net displacement is their sum

$$y = A \sin (kx - \omega t) + A \sin (kx + \omega t)$$

Now we can expand the sines using Eq. B.34 from Appendix B.11:

$$\sin (a + b) = \sin a \cos b + \cos a \sin b$$

$$\sin (a - b) = \sin a \cos b - \cos a \sin b$$

With $kx = a$ and $\omega t = b$, we find the formula for a standing wave,

$$y = 2A \sin kx \cos \omega t \qquad (21.13)$$

The shape of a string described by this equation is a sinusoidal wave. Its displacement depends on the time through the factor $\cos \omega t$. However, the locations of the nodes and antinodes are determined by the $\sin kx$ term and are fixed in time. The nodes occur in Fig. 21.7 at the places where $\sin kx = 0$. This happens where $kx = 0, \pi, 2\pi, \ldots$. Since $k = 2\pi/\lambda$, this corresponds to $x = 0, \lambda/2, \lambda, \ldots$. The antinodes occur where $|\sin kx| = 1$. This is at $kx = \pi/2, 3\pi/2, \ldots$, or $x = \lambda/4, 3\lambda/4, \ldots$.

Thus the superposition of two traveling waves produces a stationary pattern, or standing wave, much like the string in Fig. 21.8. Standing waves with nodes at other locations and with a slightly different algebraic form result if y_2 has a different phase. This happens, for example, if the sign of y_2 is changed, or it is replaced by $A \sin (kx + \omega t + \phi)$.

21.5 | THE EFFECTS OF BOUNDARIES

Usually when a wave encounters a *boundary*, a point where the medium changes, part of the wave is reflected and part is absorbed or transmitted. The details depend on the nature of the boundary. In this section, we consider two special types of boundaries. The end of a string will either be held firmly fixed or will be free to move transversely. In both cases the wave is nearly completely reflected because almost no energy is lost from the system.

Figure 21.10 shows what happens to a wave pulse that reaches a fixed or a free end of a string. If the string end is fixed, the reflected wave is the *inverted* mirror image of the incident pulse; the wavelength and shape are unchanged. If the string end is free, the reflected wave is the mirror image of the incident wave but is *not inverted*.

The results can be understood from the principles of mechanics. When a pulse arrives at a fixed end of a string, it exerts an upward force on the support. The support will exert an *equal and opposite* force on the string, producing a reflected pulse opposite to the incident pulse or reversed in phase. If a pulse reaches the free end of a string, the particles of the string there acquire momentum in the upward direction. When the end of the string reaches the maximum height of the wave pulse, this momentum is not zero, and the string overshoots or continues upward. Now the free end of the string exerts a force on the remainder of the string and produces a reflected wave of exactly the same shape as the incident wave. No inversion takes place, and the phase is unchanged.

Once we know how a pulse behaves at a boundary, we can consider the effects of a boundary on a periodic wave. When a sinusoidal wave $y_1 = A \sin (kx - \omega t)$ reaches the fixed end of a string at $x = 0$, a reflected wave $y_2 = A \sin (kx + \omega t)$ is produced. We may verify that the reflected way is inverted or reversed in phase by noting that at $x = 0$, $y_1 = A \sin (-\omega t)$, and $y_2 = A \sin (\omega t)$. The

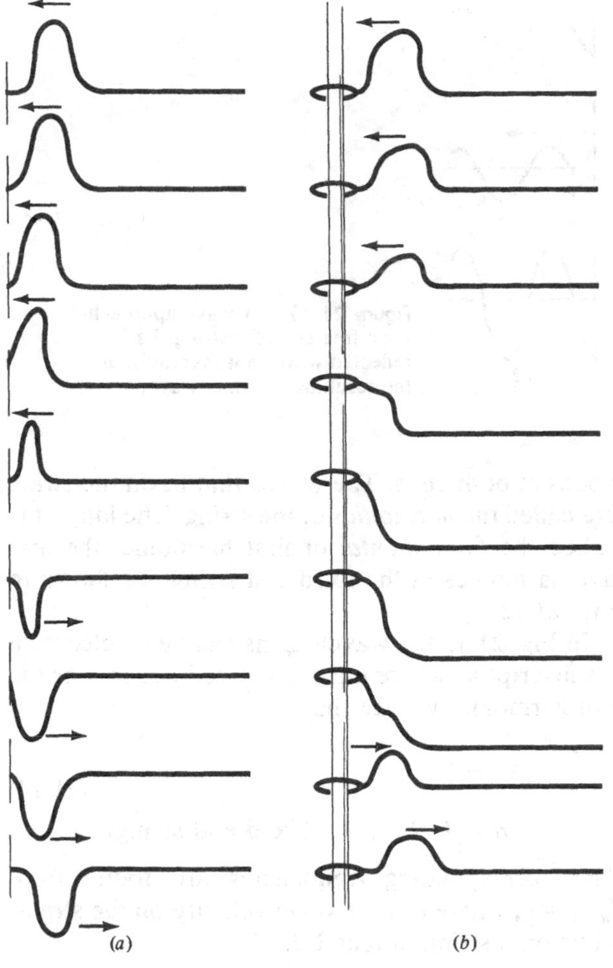

Figure 21.10. The reflection of a wave pulse on a string at (a) a fixed end boundary and (b) a free end boundary.

sine function is odd, so that $\sin(-\omega t) = -\sin(\omega t)$, and $y_2 = -y_1$ as required.

This means that two waves are present, traveling in opposite directions (Fig. 21.11). This is precisely the situation described in the preceding section by Eq. 21.12. Thus we know immediately that the incident and reflected waves interfere to produce a standing wave with a node at $x = 0$, the fixed end. There are additional nodes at $x = \lambda/2, \lambda, \ldots$.

The reflection of sinusoidal waves at a free end is shown in Fig. 21.12. Here the reflected wave is not inverted. Adding the incident and reflected waves algebraically leads to the result for this situation that the string has an antinode at the free end.

In summary, the reflection of sinusoidal waves at a boundary results in standing waves. On a string, a node appears at a fixed end and an antinode at a free end. Analogous standing waves are formed for all kinds of waves when reflections occur.

21.6 | RESONANT STANDING WAVES

In Chapter Nine, on harmonic motion, we found that many structures have specific resonant frequencies at which large-amplitude vibrations are readily produced. Musical instruments and the voice involve systems that combine vibrating strings or air columns with structures that have certain resonant frequencies.

The fact that strings have specific resonant frequencies can be seen by tying one end of a rope to a post and shaking the other end. After a few tries,

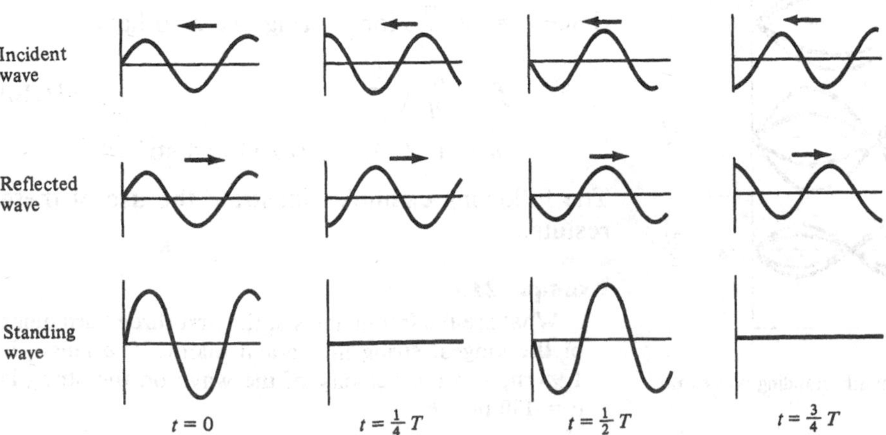

Figure 21.11. The top pictures show, at time intervals of $\frac{1}{4}T$, a wave approaching the fixed end of a string. The middle pictures show the reflected wave, which is inverted. The fact that it is inverted becomes apparent if we compare the leftmost quarter wavelength in the incident wave at $t = 0$ and in the reflected wave at $t = T/4$, the corresponding half wavelengths at $t = 0$ and $t = T/2$, and so on. In the actual string, both waves are present, and the result is the standing wave with a node at the fixed end (bottom).

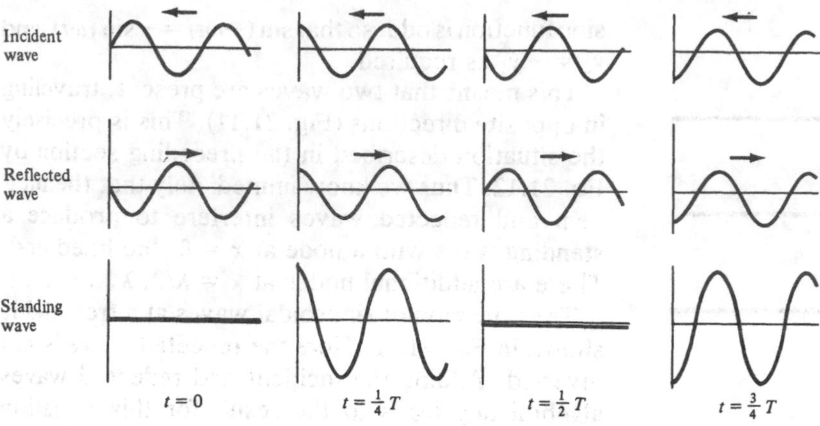

Figure 21.12. A wave approaching a free end of a string, its reflected wave (not inverted), and the resulting standing wave.

one finds standing waves are produced only at specific frequencies. At other frequencies the rope vibrates erratically and with a small amplitude.

To understand why only certain frequencies result in standing waves, consider a string of length l. With both ends rigidly fixed, only standing waves with nodes at each end can be produced. Figure 21.13 shows the five longest-standing waves for a fixed end string, that is, the longest waves with nodes at both ends. The waves that fit on the string are called the *harmonics* of the string. The longest is called the *fundamental* or first harmonic; the first five harmonics of the fixed end string are shown in Fig. 21.13.

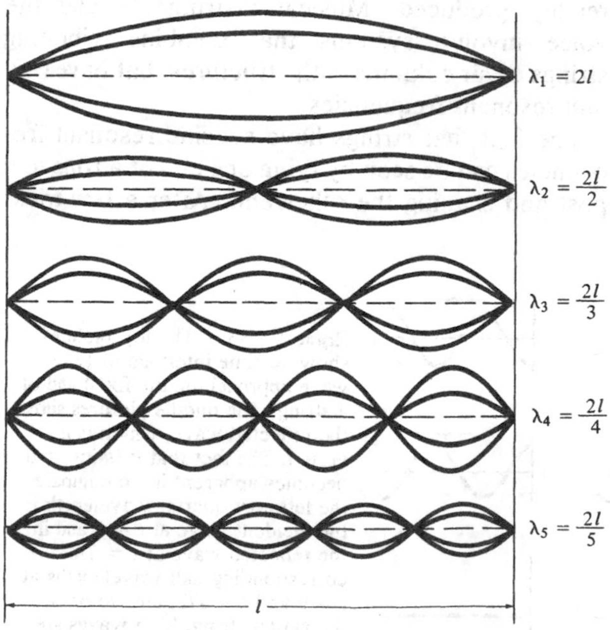

Figure 21.13. The five longest-wavelength standing waves on a string of length l with fixed ends.

In Fig. 21.13 the wavelengths can be labeled with a subscript n, where n is a positive integer. For the nth harmonic, we see that

$$\lambda_n = \frac{2l}{n}, \qquad n = 1, 2, 3, \ldots \text{ (fixed end string)} \tag{21.14}$$

The corresponding frequencies are found from $f_n \lambda_n = c$, where c is the wave velocity on the string. Thus on a string of length l,

$$f_n = \frac{n}{2l} c, \qquad n = 1, 2, 3, \ldots \text{ (fixed end string)} \tag{21.15}$$

Since $c = \sqrt{\mathcal{T}/\mu}$ for a string, we also have

$$f_n = \frac{n}{2l}\sqrt{\frac{\mathcal{T}}{\mu}}, \qquad n = 1, 2, 3, \ldots \text{ (fixed end string)} \tag{21.16}$$

The following examples illustrate the use of these results.

Example 21.6

What are the frequencies of the first three harmonics of the longest string in a grand piano? The length is 1.98 m, and the velocity of the wave on the string is $c = 130 \text{ m s}^{-1}$.

Using the result for the fixed end string with $n = 1$,

$$f_1 = \frac{c}{2l} = \frac{130 \text{ m s}^{-1}}{2(1.98 \text{ m})} = 32.8 \text{ Hz}$$

The second harmonic is at twice this frequency, or 2(32.8 Hz) = 65.6 Hz, and the third harmonic is at 3(32.8 Hz) = 98.4 Hz.

Example 21.7

The wave velocity on the highest-frequency violin string is 435 m s^{-1}, and its length l is 0.33 m. If a violin player lightly touches the string at a point a distance $l/3$ from an end, a node is produced there. What is the lowest frequency that can now be produced by the string?

Referring to Fig. 21.13, the third harmonic is the longest-wavelength and lowest-frequency standing wave with a node one-third of the distance from one end. Hence with $\lambda_3 = 2l/3$,

$$f_3 = \frac{c}{\lambda_3} = \frac{c}{2l/3} = \frac{3c}{2l} = \frac{3(435 \text{ m s}^{-1})}{2(0.33 \text{ m})} = 1977 \text{ Hz}$$

A violinist can, by lightly touching a string at some point along its length, produce a node on the string at that point so that only harmonics with nodes at that point are excited. However, if the string is pushed firmly against the finger board, its effective length is reduced, and all the harmonic frequencies are shifted upward.

The relationship between the frequency and mass per unit length of a string is discussed in the following example.

Example 21.8

The highest- and lowest-frequency strings of a piano are tuned to fundamentals of $f_H = 4186$ Hz and $f_L = 32.8$ Hz. Their lengths are 0.051 m and 1.98 m, respectively. If the tension in these two strings is the same, what is the ratio of the masses per unit length of the two strings?

Using Eq. 21.16 and solving for μ, we find for the fundamental, $n = 1$,

$$\mu = \frac{\mathcal{T}}{(2lf_1)^2}$$

The ratio of μ_L for the low-frequency string to μ_H for the high-frequency string is

$$\frac{\mu_L}{\mu_H} = \frac{\mathcal{T}/(2l_L f_L)^2}{\mathcal{T}/(2l_H f_H)^2} = \frac{(l_H f_H)^2}{(l_L f_L)^2}$$

$$= \left[\frac{(0.051 \text{ m})(4186 \text{ Hz})}{(1.98 \text{ m})(32.8 \text{ Hz})}\right]^2 = 10.8$$

This is a large difference. It was found empirically by piano makers that a thick solid string does not produce a pleasing tone. This is apparently due to the great stiffness of such strings. The solution developed was to wind a wire in a tight coil about a straight wire (here of length 1.98 m). This increases the mass per unit length without changing the stiffness of the wire very much.

21.7 | COMPLEX WAVES AND BEATS

Often when a string is disturbed or standing waves are set up in air columns, not only is the fundamental frequency present but so also are some of the higher harmonics. The higher harmonics that are actually present are called *overtones*. If all the harmonics are present, the second harmonic is the first overtone, the third harmonic is the second overtone, and so on. In the next chapter, we discuss situations where every other harmonic is present. In this case, the third and fifth harmonics are the first and second overtones, respectively. The higher overtones are numbered similarly.

The higher harmonics are not all excited with the same amplitude; instead, the higher harmonics usually have progressively smaller amplitudes. If several harmonics are simultaneously present, the actual shape of the string at any instant may be quite complex (Fig. 21.14). Any complex wave can be regarded as a sum of many sinusoidal waves.

In Fig. 21.15, we show two traveling waves with slightly different wavelengths and frequencies. At points B and D, the two waves add constructively. At the intermediate point C, the waves interfere destructively. The resultant wave is a rapid oscillation that changes amplitude with time. At points A, C, and E, the amplitude of the total wave is zero; and at points B and D, the amplitude is a maximum. This phenomena is called *beating*. The frequency with which the nodes pass a given point on the x axis is called the *beat frequency*.

We can add the equations for the two waves to find the beat frequency. We are interested in the net wave at a single point as a function of the time, so at that point we write

$$y_1 = A \cos 2\pi f_1 t \qquad y_2 = A \cos 2\pi f_2 t \quad (21.17)$$

Here we write $2\pi f$ instead of ω and represent the sinusoidal waves by cosines instead of sines to ob-

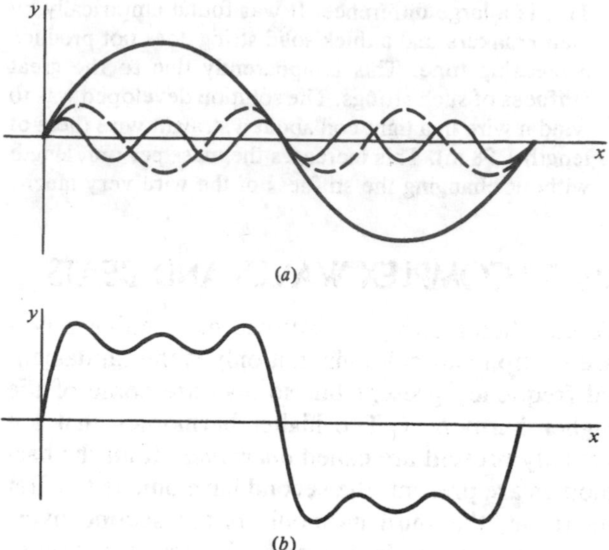

Figure 21.14. (*a*) The first, third, and fifth harmonics for a string fixed at both ends. (*b*) The addition of these harmonics produces the complex shape shown.

tain results that have a neater form. (This is permissible because the cosine and sine functions are the same except for a shift of 90°.) According to Eq. B.37 in Appendix B.11,

$$\cos a + \cos b = 2 \cos \frac{(a+b)}{2} \cos \frac{(a-b)}{2}$$

Thus the sum $y = y_1 + y_2$ can be written as

$$y = \left[2A \cos \frac{2\pi(f_1 - f_2)t}{2}\right] \cos \frac{2\pi(f_1 + f_2)t}{2} \qquad (21.18)$$

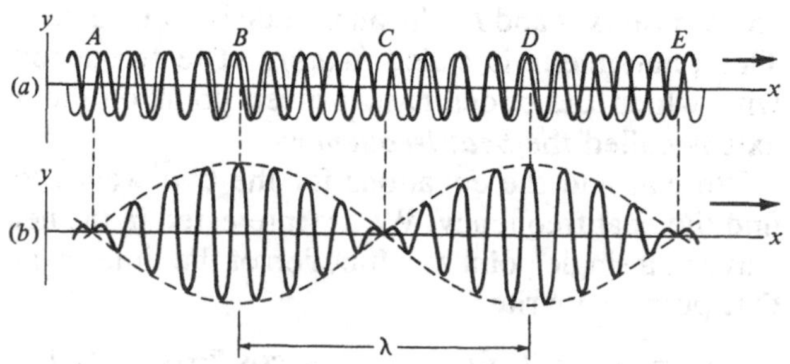

Figure 21.15. (*a*) Two waves of slightly different frequencies, f_1 (shown colored) and f_2 add to form the resultant wave in (*b*). The dashed lines show how the amplitude changes.

The second cosine represents a wave with the average of the two frequencies, $\bar{f} = (f_1 + f_2)/2$. The first cosine varies with a frequency $(f_1 - f_2)/2$, which is very small if the two frequencies are nearly equal. Thus Eq. 21.18 describes a wave with the average frequency $\bar{f}$ and an amplitude given by the factor in brackets that slowly varies in magnitude between 0 and $2A$. The amplitude has a maximum whenever $\cos 2\pi(f_1 - f_2)t/2$ is $+1$ or -1. Each of these values occurs once in each cycle, so the beat frequency f_b is twice $(f_1 - f_2)/2$, or

$$f_b = f_1 - f_2 \qquad (21.19)$$

The beat frequency is equal to the difference in the frequencies of the two waves.

Example 21.9

A tuning fork with a known frequency of 520 Hz is sounded at the same time that a violin string is plucked. Beats are heard with a frequency of 5 Hz. What is the frequency of the violin string?

From our discussion, we note that the difference between the frequencies of the tuning fork and violin string is 5 Hz. However, we cannot tell immediately which frequency is higher and which is lower. Since the fork has a frequency of 520 Hz, the violin string vibrates at either 525 Hz or 515 Hz.

We could determine which is the case by adjusting the tension in the violin string. From Eq. 21.16, the string frequency is proportional to the square root of the tension. If reducing the tension reduces the beat frequency, we know the violin was at 525 Hz. If the string were at 515 Hz, the tension would have to be increased to reduce the beat frequency.

Use is made of beats in tuning a piano. Most piano keys strike three strings that are supposed to produce identical notes. A modern piano tuner stops two of the three strings from vibrating and adjusts the tension of the third until it is synchronized with an electronic oscillator set at the desired frequency. Then the other two strings are released one at a time and adjusted until no beats are heard. A single note played on a poorly tuned piano has beats that are too rapid to be heard separately, but the sound is discordant and may be unpleasant. This is the sound produced by a honky-tonk piano.

Modern methods for studying large molecules with light use beats in a sophisticated way. A laser beam is split into two parts. One portion passes through a sample chamber, and its frequency is modified by the interaction with the molecules. Since the two portions of the beam now have different frequencies, they produce beats when recombined. Information about the molecules is obtained from the frequency changes.

21.8 | ENERGY AND MOMENTUM IN WAVES

Although it is not always apparent, waves of every kind carry energy and momentum obtained originally from their sources. This may be illustrated by some familiar examples. Light from the sun provides the energy that makes life possible on our planet. Ocean waves gradually transform the coastlines, and they can exert large forces on someone standing in shallow water. Intense sound waves can crack windows and cause other kinds of damage to mechanical structures including the human ear.

The specific expressions for the energy and momentum of a wave depend on the nature of the particular wave. However, it is always true that the energy and momentum stored in a sinusoidal wave are proportional to the square of its amplitude.

This fact can be understood if we make an analogy with the simple harmonic oscillator (Chapter Nine). If we observe a sinusoidal wave passing a given point, the displacement at that point varies with time as a sine or cosine. A simple harmonic oscillator, such as a mass on a spring, also has a displacement that varies sinusoidally with time. Hence each point in a sinusoidal wave is undergoing simple harmonic motion. This was also shown in detail in Example 21.4. In an oscillator, the potential energy $\frac{1}{2}kx^2$ is proportional to the displacement squared and hence to the amplitude squared. The kinetic energy $\frac{1}{2}mv^2$ and the total energy are also proportional to the amplitude squared. Accordingly, at any point in a sinusoidal wave, the energy stored is proportional to the amplitude squared. If the wave is a standing wave, no energy will be transported; the stored energy will be transformed from potential energy to kinetic energy and back again repeatedly, but it will remain in the same location. However, if the wave is moving in some direction, it will transport energy in that direction.

Discussions of sound and light waves frequently use the *intensity* I of the wave. This is the power transported across a unit cross-sectional area. In S.I. units, the intensity is measured in watts per square metre. From the previous discussion it follows that *the intensity of a wave is proportional to its amplitude squared*, or

$$I \propto A^2 \qquad (21.20)$$

The momentum carried by the wave also varies as the amplitude squared.

21.9 | THE POLARIZATION OF TRANSVERSE WAVES

Transverse waves have a property called *polarization* that is not shared by longitudinal waves. For example, in Fig. 21.16, a wave on a string is traveling along the x direction. The transverse wave disturbance can be along any line perpendicular to this direction of motion. If the disturbance is always along the same line, the wave is said to be *polarized* along that line. A wave whose direction of oscillation changes randomly from time to time or which is composed of many waves of random polarization is said to be *unpolarized*.

An unpolarized wave can be polarized by a *polarizer*. For the string shown in Fig. 21.16*a*, the polarizer is a slot. Beyond the slot the string can only vibrate in the y direction. In Fig. 21.16*b*, there is also a second slot. When the two slots are perpendicular the wave is totally suppressed.

The amplitude of the wave after passing through a polarizing structure is reduced, since only the *component* of the original wave parallel to the polarizer passes through. In Fig. 21.16*a* the amplitude of the wave on the left side of the slot is A_L and the intensity is $I_L \propto A_L^2$. The angle between the planes of polarization on the left side and right side of the slot is θ. The amplitude of the wave on the right side of the slot is $A_R = A_L \cos\theta$. The intensity is then

$$I_R = I_L \cos^2\theta$$

In Fig. 21.16*b* the angle between the two slots is 90°, and since $\cos 90° = 0$, the amplitude becomes zero.

Electromagnetic waves are transverse waves. We refer to the direction of the electric vector as the

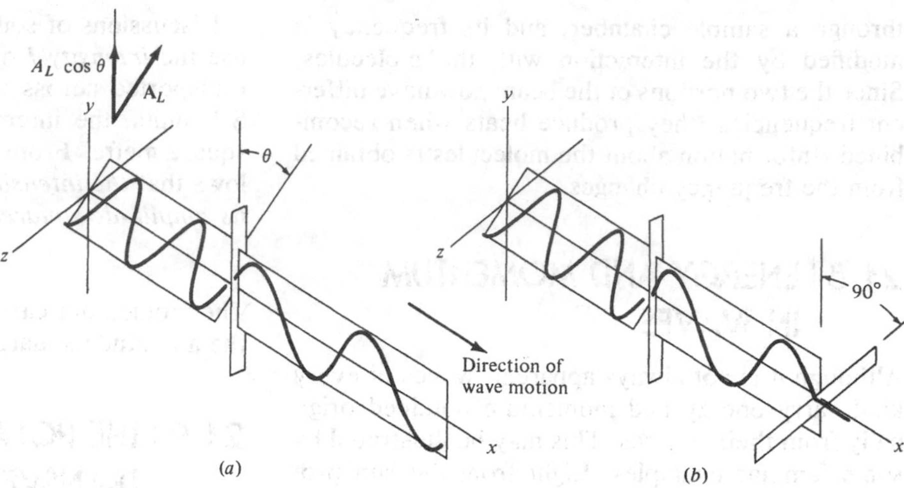

Figure 21.16. (*a*) A wave on a string is vibrating in some arbitrary direction. After passing through the slot, the wave is polarized in the *y* direction and has a smaller amplitude. (*b*) With the second slot at right angles to the first, the wave is completely suppressed. If the two slots were not perpendicular, the final wave would be polarized in the direction of the second slot.

direction of polarization. Polarized sunglasses use the transverse property of light to reduce glare. Light that is reflected from smooth horizontal surfaces tends to be polarized in the horizontal direction. Polaroid sunglass lenses almost totally suppress the component of light along one direction and are oriented so that only the vertically polarized component is transmitted. If one rotates a Polaroid lens relative to a second, the transmitted light is seen to decrease nearly to zero when the polarizing axes are perpendicular. A more extensive discussion of light polarization is given in Chapter Twenty-three.

SUMMARY

Waves of all kinds share many common features. Periodic waves are characterized by their frequency f, wavelength λ, and velocity c, which are related by $f\lambda = c$. The velocity depends on the properties of the medium and in some cases on the frequency. The amplitude of a wave is the maximum magnitude of its displacement.

Waves can interfere with one another. When two waves are present at a point, the resulting wave is found by algebraically adding the displacements of the individual waves. Two waves in phase add constructively, while two waves a half wavelength out of phase interfere destructively. The property of combining waves by the addition of displacements is called the principle of superposition or linearity.

Waves incident on a boundary can be transmitted, absorbed, or reflected. Waves that reach a fixed end of a string are reflected as inverted mirror images. At a free end the reflected wave is not inverted.

Standing waves are formed when two waves of equal amplitude but opposite direction interfere. Standing waves on a string can persist only at certain special frequencies, called harmonics, which are determined by the length of the string and the velocity of the wave.

When two waves arrive at a point at slightly different frequencies, the intensity varies at the beat frequency, which is equal to the difference in frequencies of the two waves. Beats can be heard in sound waves at frequencies up to about 20 Hz.

The energy and momentum in a sinusoidal wave are proportional to the square of its amplitude. The intensity of a wave is the power transported per unit area and also varies as the amplitude squared.

If the disturbance is always along some particular axis perpendicular to the direction of propagation of a transverse wave, it is said to be polarized along that direction. If the direction of oscillation changes randomly over time, the wave is unpolarized.

Checklist

Define or explain:

wave pulse	longitudinal waves
periodic wave	wavelength

amplitude	phase
sinusoidal waves	boundary
wave velocity	fundamental frequency
wave number	harmonics
angular frequency	overtones
superposition	beat frequency
destructive interference	intensity
node	polarized wave
standing waves	

REVIEW QUESTIONS

Q21-1 For a given type of wave, periodic waves with a higher frequency will have _____ wavelengths than those with lower frequencies.

Q21-2 True or false: The velocities of all waves on all strings are the same.

Q21-3 True or false: A standing wave on a string occurs when all points on the string stand still.

Q21-4 Standing waves can be regarded as a _____ of two or more traveling waves.

Q21-5 True or false: If one end of a string is fixed, the possible resonant standing waves that can occur are the same whether the other end is fixed or free.

Q21-6 True or false: The wavelengths of the possible resonant standing waves on a string depend only on the length of the string and on the boundary conditions.

Q21-7 Beats occur because waves _____ with one another.

Q21-8 Two waves of the same type but with different frequencies f_1 and f_2 will produce beats at a frequency _____.

Q21-9 The energy carried by a wave is proportional to the _____ of the wave.

Q21-10 Only _____ waves may be polarized.

EXERCISES

Section 21.1 | The Representation of Waves

21-1 What is the wavelength of a sound wave with a frequency of 1000 Hz and a velocity 344 m s^{-1}?

21-2 What is the frequency of a wave of velocity 200 m s^{-1} and wavelength 0.5 m?

21-3 A radar antenna emits electromagnetic radiation ($c = 3 \times 10^8$ m s^{-1}) with a wavelength of 0.03 m for 0.5 s. (a) What is the frequency of radiation? (b) How many complete waves are emitted in this time interval? (c) After 0.5 s, how far is the front of the wave from the antenna?

21-4 A TV station broadcasts using 2-m waves. What is the frequency of the broadcast wave if the speed of the wave is 3×10^8 m s^{-1}?

21-5 A radio telescope is built to observe microwaves from interstellar hydrogen atoms at frequencies near 1.4×10^9 Hz. Since the ability of a telescope to distinguish fine details is determined by the ratio of its diameter to the wavelength of the radiation, its diameter is chosen to be 1000 times the wavelength. How large is the diameter?

21-6 A light wave has a frequency of 6×10^{14} Hz. (a) What is its period? (b) What is its wavelength in vacuum? (c) When the light wave enters water, its velocity decreases to 0.75 times its velocity in vacuum. What happens to the frequency and wavelength?

Section 21.2 | The Mathematical Description of Traveling Waves

21-7 Green light has a wavelength of 5×10^{-7} m. Find the (a) frequency; (b) angular frequency; (c) wave number.

21-8 Two waves are represented by $y_1 = A \sin(kx - \omega t)$ and by $y_2 = A \sin(kx - \omega t + \pi/4)$. At time $t = 0$, draw rough graphs of each wave for $x = 0$ to 3λ, where $\lambda = 2\pi/k$. Explain the relationship between the graphs for the two waves.

21-9 A wave is represented by $y = A \sin(kx + \omega t)$. Draw two cycles of the wave from $x = 0$ to $x = 2\lambda$ at (a) $t = 0$; (b) $t = T/4$, where $T = 1/f = 2\pi/\omega$.

21-10 Sinusoidal waves can be represented equally well by sines or by cosines. For example, $y = A \sin(kx - \omega t)$ can be rewritten as $y = A \cos(kx - \omega t + \phi)$. What is the phase angle ϕ?

21-11 A sinusoidal wave with a wavelength of 2 m and a velocity of 5 m s^{-1}. At $t = 0$ s, the left end is at its equilibrium position, $y = 0$, and the displacement is decreasing. The maximum displacement is 0.1 m. Taking $x = 0$ at the left end and $+x$ toward the right, find an equation of the form of Eq. 21.7 for the wave.

c21-12 A wave on a string is represented by $y = (0.05\text{ m}) \sin[(10\text{ m}^{-1})x - (50\text{ s}^{-1})t]$. (a) Find the period T of the wave. (b) Find the transverse velocity at the point $x = 0$ at times $t = 0$ and at $T/4$. (c) Find the transverse acceleration at the same times.

Section 21.3 | The Velocity of Waves

21-13 A string on a steel guitar has a mass per unit length of 3×10^{-3} kg m^{-1}. If the tension in the string is 90 N, what is the velocity of a wave on the string?

21-14 The tension in a string is four times that in a second identical string. What is the ratio of the wave velocities of the strings?

21-15 The speed of a wave on a string is 160 m s^{-1} when the tension in the string is 100 N. To increase the speed to 200 m s^{-1}, to what value must the tension be increased?

21-16 When light enters heavy flint glass, its velocity is reduced from that in the vacuum by a factor of 1.647. What is its velocity in this kind of glass?

Section 21.4 | Wave Interference and Standing Waves

21-17 Two wave pulses on a string (Fig. 21.17) travel toward each other with speeds of 1 m s^{-1}. Sketch the shape of the string at t = 1, 1.25, and 1.5 s after the instant shown.

21-18 Two wave pulses travel toward each other on a string (Fig. 21.18). If the wave velocity is 2 m s^{-1}, sketch the string 1, 1.25, and 1.5 s after the instant shown.

21-19 Sketch the string of Fig. 21.19, 1, 1.25, and 1.5 seconds after the instant shown. The wave velocity is 1 m s^{-1}.

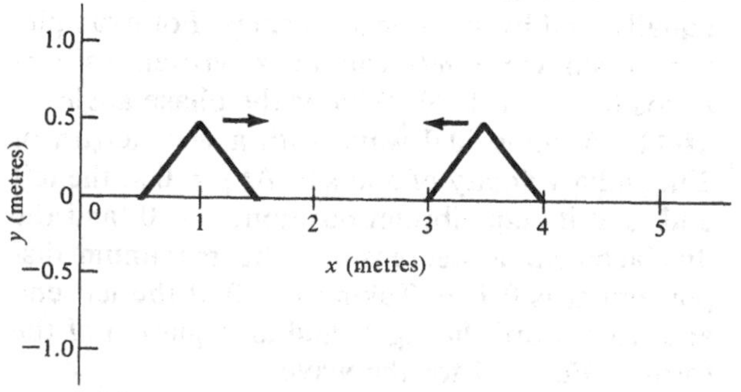

Figure 21.17. Exercise 21-17.

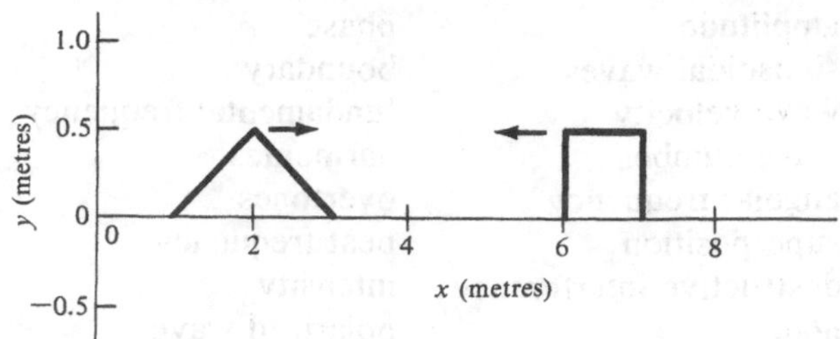

Figure 21.18. Exercise 21-18.

21-20 (a) Show that if $y_1 = A \sin (kx - \omega t)$ and $y_2 = -A \sin (kx + \omega t)$, the resulting wave $y = y_1 + y_2$ is a standing wave. (b) Where are its nodes and antinodes relative to those of the standing wave described by Eq. 21.13?

21-21 If $y_1 = A \sin (kx - \omega t)$ and $y_2 = 3A \sin (kx + \omega t)$, then the superposition $y = y_1 + y_2$ is a pure standing wave plus a traveling wave in the $-x$ direction. Find the amplitude of (a) the traveling wave; (b) the standing wave.

21-22 Sketch the standing wave represented by Eq. 21.13 from $x = 0$ to $x = 2\lambda$ at (a) $t = 0$; (b) $t = T/8$; (c) $t = T/4$.

21-23 For the standing wave represented by Eq. 21.13, at what values of x are (a) the nodes; (b) the antinodes?

Section 21.5 | The Effects of Boundaries

21-24 Sketch the shape of a square-wave pulse on a string (Fig. 21.20) if it is totally reflected from a fixed boundary.

21-25 Sketch the shape of the square-wave pulse on a string of Fig. 21.20 if it is totally reflected from a free end boundary.

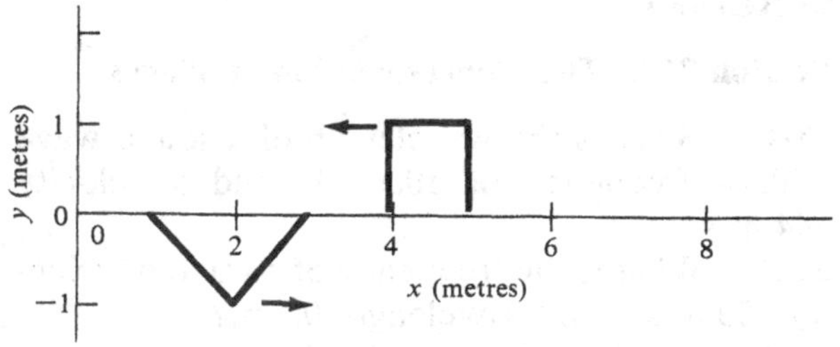

Figure 21.19. Exercise 21-19.

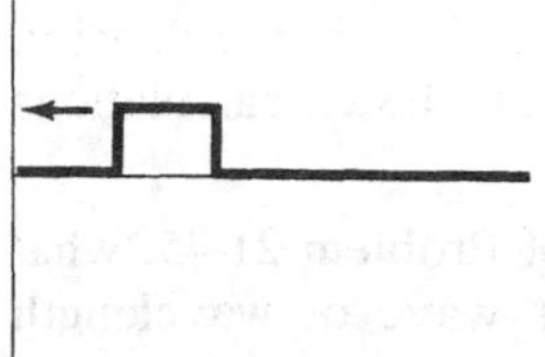

Figure 21.20. Exercises 21-24 and 21-25.

Section 21.6 | Resonant Standing Waves

21-26 The lowest-frequency string of a violin is 0.33 m long and is under a tension of 55 N. The fundamental frequency is 196 Hz. What is the mass per unit length of the string?

21-27 The E string of a violin has a length of 0.33 m and a fundamental frequency of 659 Hz. The tension of the string is 55 N. (a) What is the wave velocity of the string? (b) What is the mass per unit length of the string?

21-28 If the heaviest and lightest strings of a violin have masses per unit length of 3×10^{-3} kg m^{-1} and 2.9×10^{-4} kg m^{-1}, respectively, what is the ratio of the radii of these strings?

21-29 The fundamental frequency of a string with fixed ends is 100 Hz and the wave velocity is 350 m s^{-1}. (a) What is the wavelength of the fundamental? (b) What is the length of the string?

21-30 If the wave velocity of a 0.5-m-long guitar string is 170 m s^{-1}, what is its fundamental frequency?

21-31 The highest C string of a piano has a frequency of 4186 Hz and a length of 0.051 m. The lowest C string has a frequency of 32.8 Hz. If these strings had the same tension and mass per unit length, what would be the length of the lowest C string?

21-32 The A string on a violin is 0.33 m long and tuned to a fundamental frequency of 440 Hz. How far from the end of the string should one press it against the finger board to obtain the same fundamental frequency, 659 Hz, as the E string?

21-33 A harp string of length 0.5 m is tuned to a fundamental frequency of 650 Hz. (a) What is the wavelength of the fourth harmonic of the string? (b) What is the wavelength of the sound produced in the air if the fourth harmonic is excited? (Use $c = 344$ m s^{-1} in air.)

21-34 If a string of an instrument is touched lightly at a point one third of its length from one end, a node is formed there. Which harmonics of the string can be excited?

Section 21.7 | Complex Waves and Beats

21-35 The first and second harmonics of a string are shown at a certain instant in Fig. 21.21. Sketch the actual shape of the string at this instant.

21-36 The fundamental frequency of the heaviest string on a cello is 65.4 Hz. What is the beat frequency of the third harmonic of this string with the 196-Hz fundamental of the heaviest string on a violin?

21-37 What beat frequency is heard if two tuning forks vibrate with frequencies $f_1 = 200$ Hz and $f_2 = 205$ Hz?

21-38 What are the possible frequencies of a tuning fork that produces a beat frequency of $f = 4$ Hz with a standardized tuning fork that has a frequency of 300 Hz?

Section 21.8 | Energy and Momentum in Waves
Section 21.9 | The Polarization of Transverse Waves

21-39 A traveling wave on a rope has a vertical amplitude of 0.1 m. It passes through a slot that is

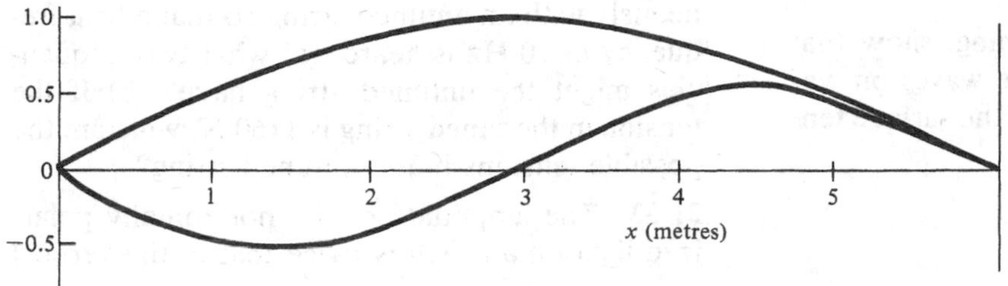

Figure 21.21. Exercise 21-35.

tilted at 30° with the vertical. What is the amplitude of the wave after passing through the slot?

21-40 A traveling wave on a rope has a vertical amplitude of 0.2 m. It passes through two successive slots; the first is tilted at 45° with the vertical and the second is vertical. (a) What is the amplitude of the wave after it has passed through the first slot? (b) What is the amplitude of the wave after it has passed through both slots?

21-41 What is the ratio of the intensity of the wave of Exercise 21-40 after it has passed through both slots to its original intensity?

21-42 In Fig. 21.7*b*, the second and fourth pictures of the superposition of two waves, there is no displacement. What has happened to the energy of the wave?

21-43 A symmetrical wave pulse travels to the right on a string, and an identical pulse of opposite sign travels to the left. When they meet, the waves cancel exactly, so the displacement is zero. What has happened to the energy, and why do the waves reappear shortly?

PROBLEMS

21-44 Using dimensional arguments, show that the velocity of a wave on a string with tension $\mathcal{T}$ and mass per unit length μ is proportional to $\sqrt{\mathcal{T}/\mu}$.

***21-45** The restoring force on long wavelength surface water waves is due to gravity as long as the water is deep and the bottom does not affect the wave. Using dimensional arguments and explaining your reasoning, show that the velocity of long water waves of wavelength λ is of the form

$$c = A\sqrt{g\lambda}$$

where g is the gravitational acceleration and A is a numerical constant. (Exact calculation shows that $A = \sqrt{1/8\pi}$.)

***21-46** Using dimensional reasoning, show that for very-short-wavelength surface waves on water, the wave velocity depends on the surface tension and has the form

$$c = B\sqrt{\frac{\gamma}{\rho\lambda}}$$

where γ is the surface tension, ρ is the density, and B is a numerical constant. (Exact calculations yield $B = \sqrt{9\pi/2}$.)

21-47 Using the results of Problem 21-45, what is the velocity of a water wave of wavelength 30 m?

21-48 The general expression for the velocity of surface water waves of wavelength λ is

$$c = \frac{1}{2}\sqrt{\frac{g\lambda}{2\pi} + \frac{18\pi\gamma}{\rho\lambda}}$$

where ρ is the density, g is the acceleration of gravity, and γ is the surface tension. At what wavelength λ does the transition from long to short waves take place? (This result is only valid if the water is very deep compared to the wavelength and crest height.)

21-49 How long will it take a 1-m bow wave from a boat to reach the shore of a river 25 m away? (See Problem 21-45.)

21-50 The 0.33-m-long A string of a violin is tuned to a fundamental frequency of 440 Hz. The 0.69-m-long A string of a cello is tuned to a fundamental frequency of 220 Hz. If both strings have the same tension, what is the ratio of the masses per unit length of these strings?

21-51 The E string of a violin is 0.33 m long, and the wave velocity of the string is 435 m s^{-1}. (a) What is the time required for the wave produced by plucking the string to make one complete circuit along the string and return to its original position? (b) Does this result have any bearing on the proper frequency of plucking or bowing the string?

21-52 If one of the three strings corresponding to middle C on a piano is adjusted to the proper frequency of 261.6 Hz and is struck simultaneously with an untuned string so that a beat frequency of 10 Hz is heard, (a) what two frequencies might the untuned string have? (b) If the tension in the tuned string is 1160 N, what are the possible tensions in the untuned string?

21-53 The amplitude of the horizontally polarized light on a beach is twice that of the vertical component. If a woman standing erect puts on Polaroid sunglasses, only a negligible portion of the horizontally polarized light reaches her eyes. (a) What is the percentage reduction of the light energy that reaches her eyes when she puts on the sunglasses? (b) If the woman is lying on her side, what is the percentage reduction in energy that reaches her eyes when she puts on the sunglasses? (*Hint:* The total amplitude of a wave is the vector sum of its horizontal and vertical components.)

21-54 A rope of length l has a wave velocity c. Find the characteristic standing wave frequencies if the rope is (a) tied at one end and free at the other; (b) free at both ends.

°21-55 A sinusoidal wave of amplitude A and angular frequency ω is traveling on a string. (a) What is the maximum transverse velocity of a point on the string? (b) What is the maximum kinetic energy of a small segment of the string of mass Δm? (c) Given the fact shown in Example 21.4 that the segment is undergoing simple harmonic motion, what is its maximum potential energy?

°21-56 A standing wave on a string is represented by Eq. 21.13. Show that each point on the string is undergoing simple harmonic motion transverse to the string.

21-57 The superposition of two sinusoidal waves traveling in the same direction with different phases, $y = A \sin (kx - \omega t) + A \sin (kx - \omega t + \phi)$, is a sinusoidal wave with an amplitude different from A. Find that amplitude. (*Hint:* Use Eq. B.36 from Appendix B.11.)

21-58 Show that beat frequency (Eq. 21.19) can also be derived by adding two waves at a point represented by $y_1 = A \sin 2\pi f_1 t$ and $y_2 = A \sin 2\pi f_2 t$. (*Hint:* Use Eq. B.36 from Appendix B.11.)

ANSWERS TO REVIEW QUESTIONS

Q21-1, shorter; **Q21-2**, false; **Q21-3**, false; **Q21-4**, superposition; **Q21-5**, false; **Q21-6**, true; **Q21-7**, interfere; **Q21-8**, $f_1 - f_2$; **Q21-9**, square of the amplitude; **Q21-10**, transverse.

SUPPLEMENTARY TOPICS

21.10 | THE DOPPLER EFFECT

When a train passes by, the frequency at which its whistle is heard drops suddenly. This *Doppler effect* arises because as the source approaches a listener, more waves arrive each second than are emitted; conversely, as the source recedes, fewer waves arrive each second than are emitted. A similar effect is heard when the listener moves and the source is fixed.

All types of waves exhibit a Doppler effect, although the results for light waves are somewhat different from those for other types of waves. In this section, we describe the Doppler effect for sound and other mechanical waves in detail and merely state the results for light waves.

Consider first a sound source stationary relative to the air with frequency f and wavelength $\lambda = c/f$, and a listener moving away from the source at a velocity v_l (Fig. 21.22). The speed of the sound waves will appear to the listener to be $c' = c - v_l$. The distance between two successive wave maxima in the listener's moving frame of reference is the same as for the stationary frame of the source, λ.

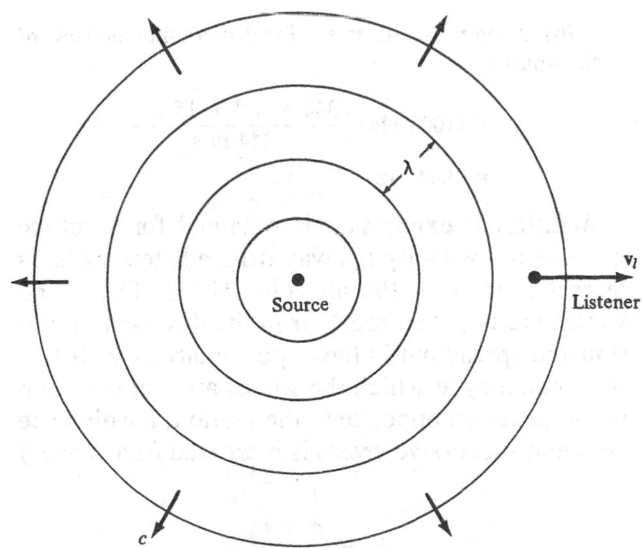

Figure 21.22. Waves leave the stationary source with a speed c but appear to the moving listener to have a speed of $c - v_l$.

The apparent frequency f' heard by the listener then satisfies $f'\lambda = c'$, or $f' = c'/\lambda$. With $\lambda = c/f$ and $c' = c - v_l$, this becomes for a *listener moving away from a source at a velocity* v_l

$$f' = f_0\left(\frac{c - v_l}{c}\right) \qquad (21.21)$$

When the listener is approaching the source, v_l *must be regarded as negative.* Notice that the frequency heard is lower than the source frequency when the listener is moving away from the source. The perceived frequency is greater than the source frequency when the listener approaches the source.

The following example illustrates this type of Doppler effect.

Example 21.10

A stationary civil defense siren has a frequency of 1000 Hz. What frequency will be heard by drivers of cars moving at 15 m s^{-1} (a) away from the siren; (b) toward the siren? The velocity of sound in air is 344 m s^{-1}.

(a) With v_l = 15 m s^{-1}, drivers moving away from the siren hear a frequency

$$f' = f\left(\frac{c - v_l}{c}\right) = (1000\text{ Hz})\left(\frac{344\text{ m s}^{-1} - 15\text{ m s}^{-1}}{344\text{ m s}^{-1}}\right)$$

$$= 956\text{ Hz}$$

(b) Using $v_l = -15$ m s^{-1} for drivers moving toward the source,

$$f' = (1000\text{ Hz})\left(\frac{344\text{ m s}^{-1} + 15\text{ m s}^{-1}}{344\text{ m s}^{-1}}\right)$$

$$= 1044\text{ Hz}$$

A different expression is obtained for a source moving at a velocity v_s away from a listener who is at rest relative to the air (Fig. 21.23). The sound waves are bunched together in the direction of motion and spread out in the opposite direction. If f_0 is the frequency at which the waves are emitted, then in the direction opposite to the motion, the distance between successive crests is increased from $\lambda = c/f$ to

$$\lambda' = \frac{c + v_s}{f}$$

The frequency heard by the stationary listener is determined by $f'\lambda' = c$, *so when the source is moving away from the listener at a velocity* v_s,

$$f' = \frac{c}{\lambda'} = f\left(\frac{c}{c + v_s}\right) \qquad (21.22)$$

If the source is approaching the listener, v_s *is negative.*

The frequency heard is lower than the source frequency when the source moves away, and higher

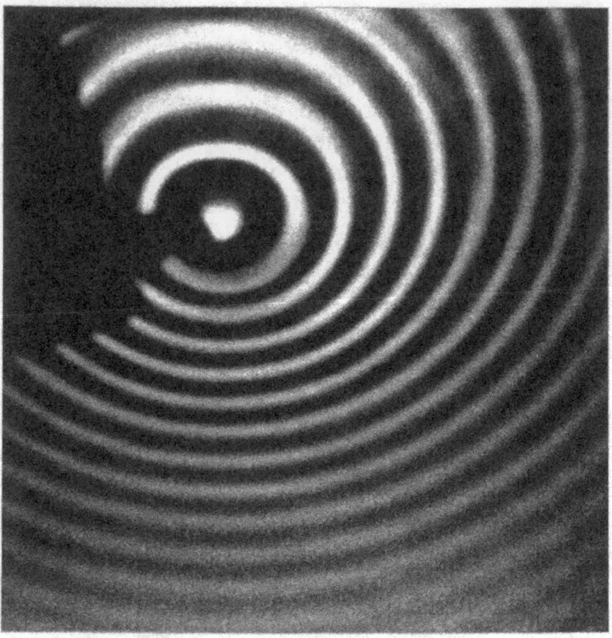

(a)

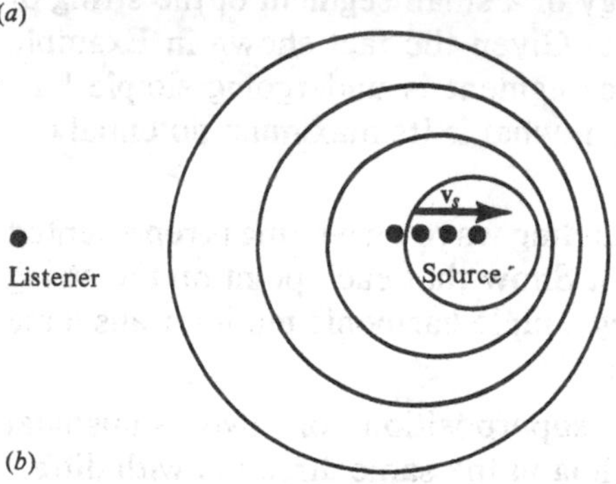

(b)

Figure 21.23. (*a*) A moving source of waves in a water-filled ripple tank produces waves that are bunched together in the direction of motion and spread out in the direction opposite the motion. (*b*) With a sound source moving with velocity v_s, a listener hears sound waves that have a longer wavelength than those from a source at rest. [(a)Courtesy Pasco Scientific]

when it approaches the stationary listener. Both of these effects are seen in the next example.

Example 21.11

A police car with a 1000-Hz siren is moving at 15 m s^{-1}. What frequency is heard by a stationary listener when the police car is (a) receding from and (b) approaching the listener?

(a) With c = 344 m s^{-1} and v_s = 15 m s^{-1} for the receding source,

$$f' = f\left(\frac{c}{c + v_s}\right)$$

$$= (1000 \text{ Hz})\left(\frac{344 \text{ m s}^{-1}}{344 \text{ m s}^{-1} + 15 \text{ m s}^{-1}}\right)$$

$$= 958 \text{ Hz}$$

Note this is a slightly higher frequency than our earlier result of 956 Hz for a listener receding from a stationary siren with the same frequency and speed.

(b) When the source is approaching the listener, $v_s = -15$ m s^{-1}, and

$$f' = f\left(\frac{c}{c + v_s}\right)$$

$$= (1000 \text{ Hz})\left(\frac{344 \text{ m s}^{-1}}{344 \text{ m s}^{-1} - 15 \text{ m s}^{-1}}\right)$$

$$= 1046 \text{ Hz}$$

Again this frequency is slightly greater than the frequency of 1044 Hz heard by a listener approaching a stationary siren.

Doppler Flow Meter | The Doppler frequency shift can be used to measure blood flow rates by using a high-frequency sound source on one side of a vessel and a detector on the other side (Fig. 21.24). The sound from the transmitter is reflected from red cells moving away from the source with a velocity v_c and detected at the receiver. If θ is small, the frequency of the sound incident on the red cells moving away from the source is given by Eq. 21.21,

$$f_1 = f\left(\frac{c - v_c}{c}\right)$$

where c is the speed of sound in the bloodstream. The cells then act as a moving source with a frequency f_1. From Eq. 21.22, the frequency f_r at the stationary receiver is then

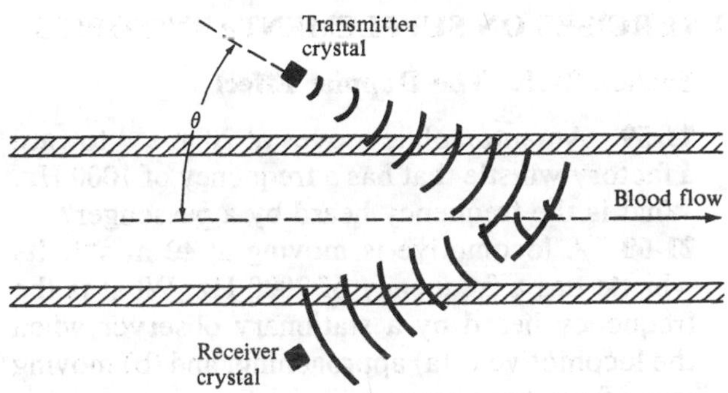

Figure 21.24. A schematic view of the use of the Doppler flow meter.

$$f_r = f_1\left(\frac{c}{c + v_c}\right) = f\left(\frac{c - v_c}{c}\right)\left(\frac{c}{c + v_c}\right)$$

$$f_r = f\left(\frac{c - v_c}{c + v_c}\right) \qquad (21.23)$$

Doppler Shift for Light | A Doppler shift is also observed with light waves, but it differs somewhat from that for sound waves. This arises from the fact that no medium is necessary for light wave propagation. Therefore, there is no way to distinguish between motion of an observer relative to a stationary source or motion of a source relative to a stationary observer. One can only say that they are moving with respect to each other. This is called the *principle of relativity* and is discussed further in Chapter Twenty-five.

When the analysis is carried out, it is found that if a light source of frequency f and an observer move away from each other with a relative velocity u, then the observed frequency is

$$f' = f\frac{c - u}{\sqrt{c^2 - u^2}} \qquad (21.24)$$

The velocity u should be interpreted as negative when the observer and source approach each other. This result is equivalent to our earlier result, Eq. 21.21, when u^2/c^2 is very small.

EXERCISES ON SUPPLEMENTARY TOPICS

Section 21.10 | The Doppler Effect

21-59 An automobile moves at 20 m s^{-1} toward a factory whistle that has a frequency of 1000 Hz. What is the frequency heard by a passenger?

21-60 A locomotive is moving at 40 m s^{-1}. Its whistle has a frequency of 2000 Hz. What is the frequency heard by a stationary observer when the locomotive is (a) approaching, and (b) moving away from the observer?

21-61 A source moves away from a stationary listener. If the frequency heard is 8 percent lower than the source frequency, what is the speed of the source?

21-62 The average velocity of blood flow in the aorta during systole is 1.5×10^{-2} m s^{-1}. What is the frequency shift in a Doppler flow meter with a source frequency of 10^5 Hz? (The speed of sound in blood is 1570 m s^{-1}.)

21-63 One of two identical 500-Hz tuning forks is at rest and the other is moving. These produce a beat frequency of 5 Hz. (a) What are the possible velocities of the moving fork? (b) Do you have enough information to determine whether the moving fork moves toward or away from the stationary fork? What additional information, if any, might be useful in this determination?

21-64 A galaxy is moving away from us with a speed of 3×10^7 m s^{-1}. What is the frequency of the light we would observe if it is emitted at 6×10^{14} Hz?

21-65 Light from distant galaxies that are moving away from us is said to be red-shifted; the wavelength observed is at longer wavelengths than that emitted by the galaxy. What is the observed wavelength shift for the galaxy of the preceding exercise?

PROBLEMS ON SUPPLEMENTARY TOPICS

21-66 A typical red blood cell has a radius of 5×10^{-6} m. Doppler shift flow meters depend on reflection from red cells and utilize ultrasonic frequencies. (a) If the source frequency is 10^7 Hz, how many red cells will "fit" into one wavelength of the sound? (b) Why are high frequencies necessary?

21-67 A tuning fork of frequency 500 Hz moves away from a stationary listener and toward a stationary wall at a speed of 2 m s^{-1}. (a) What is the frequency of the direct sound heard by the listener? (b) What is the detected frequency of the reflected wave? (c) How many beats per second are heard by the listener?

***21-68** The frequency of sound reflected from an object moving away from a detector was found in the text to be (Eq. 21.23)

$$f_r = f_0 \left(\frac{c - v_c}{c + v_c}\right)$$

(a) Show that if $v_c \ll c$, then

$$\Delta f = f_r - f_0 \simeq -\frac{2f_0 v_c}{c}$$

(b) If the object moves toward the detector, show that

$$\Delta f = f_r - f_0 \simeq \frac{2f_0 v_c}{c}$$

21-69 A bat emits squeaks of short duration at a frequency of 80,000 Hz. If the bat flies toward an obstacle at a speed of 20 m s^{-1}, what is the frequency of the reflected wave detected by the bat?

21-70 A bat travels toward a stationary obstacle. It emits sounds at a frequency of 50,000 Hz and detects a reflected sound of 51,000 Hz. How fast is the bat flying?

21-71 Show that the beat frequency detected when the reflected wave from an object moving toward or away from the source is combined with the unshifted wave of frequency f_0 is

$$f_B = \frac{2f_0 v}{c}$$

(Assume that v, the speed of the reflecting object, is small compared to c.)

21-72 The average velocity of blood flow in a dog's artery with an inner radius of 4.0×10^{-3} m is 2.3×10^{-2} m s^{-1}. (a) What is the average frequency of the sound detected in a Doppler shift flow meter if the source frequency is 10^5 Hz? (b) What is the blood flow rate? (The speed of sound in blood is 1570 m s^{-1}.)

21-73 An average frequency shift of 100 Hz is detected in a Doppler shift flow meter with a source frequency of 5×10^6 Hz. What is the average blood flow velocity in the vessel being studied? (The speed of sound in blood is 1570 m s^{-1}.)

21-74 If one approaches a red light of wavelength 6.5×10^{-7} m, at a speed of 10^8 m s^{-1}, what is the observed wavelength?

21-75 Show that if $u^2/c^2 \ll 1$, the formula for the Doppler effect for light, Eq. 21.24, is the same as Eq. 21.21.

21-76 Two tuning forks produce beats at 5 Hz when at rest next to each other. The higher-frequency fork has a frequency of 1000 Hz. (a) If the higher-frequency fork is set into motion, in what direction and at what speed is it moving if no beats are heard by a stationary listener? (b) In what direction and at what speed should the lower-frequency fork be moved, with the other at rest, so that beats are not heard by a stationary listener?

21-77 Two police cars with identical 1500-Hz sirens move south on a road, one at 80 km h^{-1} and the other at 70 km h^{-1}. At what frequency will a stationary observer farther south hear beats?

21-78 A source of sound waves moves away from a listener at a speed v_s relative to the air, while the listener moves away from the source at a speed v_l relative to the air. If the source frequency is f_0, show that the listener hears a frequency

$$f = f_0 \left(\frac{c - v_l}{c + v_s}\right)$$

21-79 Using the results of the preceding problem, find the frequency of the sound heard by a bat when its squeaks are reflected by an insect approaching it at a speed relative to the air of 3 m s^{-1}. Assume that the bat is flying toward the insect at 8 m s^{-1}, and that the squeaks are emitted at 50,000 Hz.

***21-80** A certain species of bat uses a pure sound wave of 83 kHz for detecting moving targets. When a Doppler-shifted wave is detected, the bat lowers its own emitted frequency until the returning wave is at 83 kHz. What is the lowered emission frequency for a bat moving at 10 m s^{-1} toward a target that is moving toward the bat at 2 m s^{-1}?

Additional Reading

Sources marked with asterisks (*) are appropriate references for this and the next chapter.

R. A. Waldron, *Waves and Oscillations*, Momentum Series, D. Van Nostrand and Co., Princeton, N.J., 1964.

Willard Boscom, *Waves and Beaches: The Dynamics of the Ocean Surface*, Science Study Series, Doubleday and Co., Garden City, N.Y., 1964.

* Arthur H. Benade, *Horns, Strings and Harmony*, Anchor Books, Doubleday and Company, Inc., Garden City, N.Y., 1960.

* Alexander Wood, *The Physics of Music*, University Paperbacks, Chapman and Hall, London, 1975.

* Charles A. Culver, *Musical Acoustics*, McGraw-Hill Book Co., New York, 1957.

* C. A. Taylor, *The Physics of Musical Sounds*, American Elsevier Publishing Co., New York, 1965.

* John Backus, *The Acoustical Foundations of Music*, W. W. Norton and Co., Inc., New York, 1969.

Kenneth M. Baird, Frequency Measurements of Optical Radiation, *Physics Today*, January 1983, p. 52.

Scientific American articles:

J. Bernstein, Tsunamis, August 1954, p. 60.

Frank Press, Resonant Vibrations of the Earth, November 1965, p. 28.

John R. Percy, Pulsating Stars, June 1975, p. 66.

Eugene Helm, The Vibrating String of the Pythagoreans, December 1967, p. 92.

* Carleen Maley Hutchings, The Physics of Violins, November 1962, p. 79.

* Arthur H. Benade, The Physics of Brasses, July 1973, p. 24.

J. T. Gosling and A. J. Hundhausen, Waves in the Solar Wind, March 1977, p. 36.

* Carleen Maley Hutchins, The Acoustics of Violin Plates, October 1981, p. 170.

David K. Lynch, Tidal Bores, October 1982, p. 146. The effects of water waves.

Jearl Walker, Walking on the Shore, Watching the Waves and Thinking on How They Shape the Beach, *The Amateur Scientist*, August 1982, p. 144.

CHAPTER 22
SOUND

When a gas, liquid, or solid is mechanically disturbed, sound waves are often produced. In these waves, the molecules of the substance vibrate and collide with one another but maintain the same average position. However, since their motions are coordinated, a wave results and energy is transmitted, even though no net particle displacement occurs.

The speed of sound depends on the physical properties of the substance in which it travels. When sound encounters a boundary between substances in which the sound speeds differ, some energy is transmitted and some is reflected. Thus a study of the characteristics of the production, propagation, detection, and uses of sound is necessarily a study of the transfer of mechanical energy.

Animals use sound for information exchange and for the detection and location of objects. Some bats and porpoises use sound for navigation and to locate food where inadequate light is present for vision. Humans also use sound as a substitute for light and even for X rays. *Sonar* is used for underwater navigation and observation, and *ultrasonic* or high-frequency, sound is now commonly used for medical diagnosis and therapy. Very-low-frequency sound is also used in geophysical studies.

The first part of this chapter deals with some basic properties of sound, including the speed of sound and the energy carried by sound waves. This is followed by a description of sound sources and detectors, including the human voice and ear. These are examples of *transducers*, devices that convert energy from one form to another. The remainder of the chapter is devoted to some special examples of our use of sound.

22.1 | THE NATURE AND SPEED OF SOUND

In our discussion of the physics of fluids, we found that it is impractical to apply Newton's laws of motion directly to small segments of fluid or individual molecules. Instead, we introduced the density and pressure and explored their relationships. These same variables are useful in characterizing a sound wave, which has millions of molecules in a single wavelength.

Figure 22.1 illustrates the production of a sound wave in a medium by a piston that oscillates back and forth at a frequency f. When it moves forward, it compresses the medium, and a compressional wave moves outward. When the piston moves

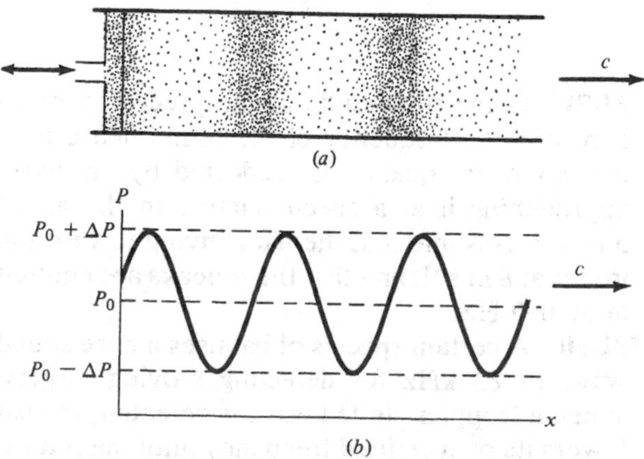

Figure 22.1. (*a*) The moving piston produces density and pressure changes that move to the right with a velocity c. (*b*) The graph of pressure versus position. P_0 is the equilibrium pressure.

backward, there is a region of reduced pressure, a *rarefaction*. This disturbance also travels outward. Note that the individual molecules do not travel any appreciable distance but only oscillate about their average positions.

The speed c with which a sound wave travels in a medium is determined by the strength of the forces among the molecules. At the macroscopic level, these forces are characterized by the *bulk modulus* K. This quantity is a measure of how hard it is to compress a substance. When the pressure on an object is increased, its volume decreases; its density, which is the mass-to-volume ratio, increases. The bulk modulus relates the fractional density change $d\rho/\rho$ to the pressure change dP as follows:

$$dP = K\frac{d\rho}{\rho} \qquad (22.1)$$

A fluid such as air that is easy to compress has a small bulk modulus. Water, which is hard to compress, has a large bulk modulus. In solids, the elastic moduli discussed in Chapter Eight characterize the molecular forces and determine the velocity of sound.

The velocity of sound in a fluid depends only on its bulk modulus K and density ρ. In Section 22.9 in the Supplementary Topics, we show that applying Newton's laws of motion to a fluid subjected to a sudden compression leads to the result

$$c = \sqrt{\frac{K}{\rho}} \quad \text{(fluid)} \qquad (22.2)$$

Note that the sound velocity is large for materials with large bulk moduli, which are stiff or hard to compress. This is reasonable if we consider the behavior of a simple harmonic oscillator (Chapter Nine). The period $T = (m/k)^{1/2}/2\pi$ decreases as the spring becomes stronger and the spring constant k increases. Thus the spring responds faster to a disturbance.

In Eq. 22.2, K is the *adiabatic bulk modulus*, not the isothermal bulk modulus sometimes tabulated. This is because, although temperature changes do accompany the compressions and rarefactions in a sound wave, they are so rapid that little heat flow occurs and the motion is effectively adiabatic. Representative values of the density ρ and the longitudinal sound velocity c are given in Table 22.1.

The following example uses the difference in sound velocities in air and in iron.

Example 22.1

Two children are at opposite ends of an iron pipe. One strikes an end of the pipe with a stone. What is the ratio of times it takes the sound waves in air and in iron to reach the second child?

TABLE 22.1

Representative densities and sound velocities. For solids, the velocity given is the velocity for longitudinal waves in thin rods. The temperature is 20°C unless otherwise noted.

Material	Density ($kg\ m^{-3}$)	Sound Velocity ($m\ s^{-1}$)
Air	1.20	344
Carbon dioxide (0°C)	1.98	259
Hydrogen (H_2) (0°C)	0.0899	1284
Alcohol (ethyl)	790	1207
Benzine	870	1295
Water (pure)	998	1498
Aluminum	2700	5000
Copper	8930	3750
Glass (Pyrex)	2320	5170
Iron	7900	5120
Blood (37°C)	1056	1570
Body tissue (37°C)	1047	1570

The time necessary for a sound wave of velocity c to travel the length of the pipe d is found from $d = ct$ or $t = d/c$. Using Table 22.1, the ratio of the times for air and iron is

$$\frac{t_{air}}{t_{iron}} = \frac{d/c_{air}}{d/c_{iron}} = \frac{c_{iron}}{c_{air}} = \frac{5120 \text{ m s}^{-1}}{344 \text{ m s}^{-1}} = 14.9$$

Note that the sound travels faster in the denser material. Sound velocities are generally larger in solids and liquids than in gases.

As in all other waves, the velocity of sound, the frequency, and the wavelength are related by $f\lambda = c$. Typical wavelengths for sound waves in air are calculated in the next two examples.

Example 22.2

A typical young adult has a hearing range from 20 Hz to 20,000 Hz. What are the wavelengths of sound waves in air corresponding to these two frequencies?

For air, $c = 344 \text{ m s}^{-1}$, so with $f\lambda = c$ and $f = 20$ Hz,

$$\lambda = \frac{c}{f} = \frac{344 \text{ m s}^{-1}}{20 \text{ s}^{-1}} = 17.2 \text{ m}$$

At 20,000 Hz,

$$\lambda = \frac{344 \text{ m s}^{-1}}{20{,}000 \text{ s}^{-1}} = 0.0172 \text{ m} = 1.72 \text{ cm}$$

Example 22.3

A bat can hear sound at frequencies up to 120,000 Hz. What is the wavelength of sound in air at this frequency?

Again we use

$$\lambda = \frac{c}{f} = \frac{344 \text{ m s}^{-1}}{120{,}000 \text{ s}^{-1}} = 2.87 \times 10^{-3} \text{ m}$$
$$= 0.287 \text{ cm}$$

One may ask why a bat utilizes sound waves of such high frequencies and short wavelengths. This is because a wave will be disturbed only by objects comparable to or larger than a wavelength; it will pass by smaller objects with little effect. A bat is nearly blind and avoids obstacles and finds food by using sound waves. The bat emits a series of high-frequency squeaks and senses the time it takes for the waves to return after being reflected by an object. The wavelength must be short enough so that reflections can occur from small objects.

Porpoises are sensitive to frequencies up to 2×10^5 Hz and use a similar system for underwater navigation and location.

Sound Waves in Solids | In solids, transverse as well as longitudinal sound waves occur. These transverse waves appear in solids because the forces among the ordered molecules not only act along the direction of the wave but also transverse to the wave. Thus a given molecule or atom can move, as it does in a gas, back and forth along the wave direction. It can also move at right angles to the wave direction, as does a molecule on a string when a wave passes by. Because the restoring forces are weaker for this transverse motion, the velocity of the transverse wave is generally lower than for the longitudinal wave. This velocity difference makes it possible to determine the distance from the center of an earthquake to a seismograph by noting the time of arrival of the different kinds of seismic waves. In this chapter, we will limit our attention to longitudinal sound waves.

22.2 | STANDING SOUND WAVES

In the preceding chapter, we discussed standing waves on strings. However, standing waves can occur for any type of wave. In particular, standing waves are an important feature of sound-producing instruments.

We can discuss sound waves either in terms of the longitudinal displacements of the molecules or of the pressure variations. A detailed analysis shows that the displacement and pressure variations are a quarter wavelength out of phase, so that when one wave is at its maximum, the other is passing through a zero! Similarly, a standing wave node for one is located at an antinode for the other. Here it is convenient to think in terms of the displacement wave, but we use the amplitude of the pressure wave in the next section to discuss intensity.

We consider sound waves in long narrow tubes or air columns. The standing waves for sound are set up exactly as are those on a string; periodic waves are reflected at a boundary, and the incident and reflected waves combine to form a standing wave.

Sound waves can be reflected at either open or closed ends of air columns. At the closed end of an air column, the molecules cannot oscillate normally; those adjacent to the end do not move at all, and a displacement node appears at a closed end. At an open end, part of the wave is transmitted and part reflected. Since molecules at the open end can move freely, the open end is a displacement antinode of the standing wave. The longest-wavelength standing waves for two types of air columns are shown in Fig. 22.2.

For a column with two open ends, there is a displacement antinode at each end. The wavelengths λ_n are related to the length of the column by $\lambda_n = 2l/n$, where n is an integer (Fig. 22.2*a*). From $f_n\lambda_n = c$, we find that the standing waves have frequencies

$$f_n = \frac{c}{\lambda_n} = \frac{nc}{2l} \quad (22.3)$$

$$n = 1, 2, 3, \ldots \quad \text{(two open ends)}$$

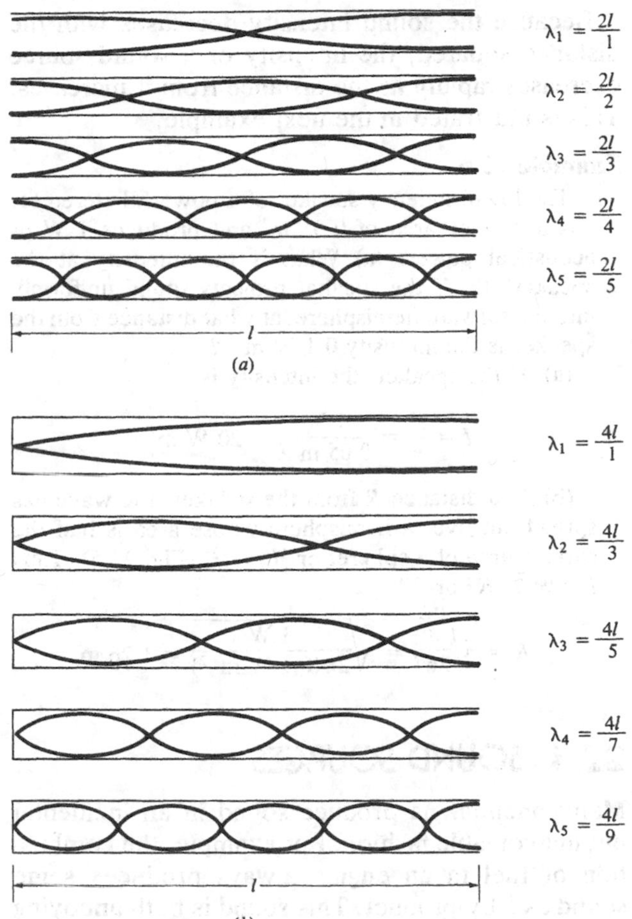

Figure 22.2. The first five resonant frequencies of an air column (*a*) with both ends open: (*b*) one end open.

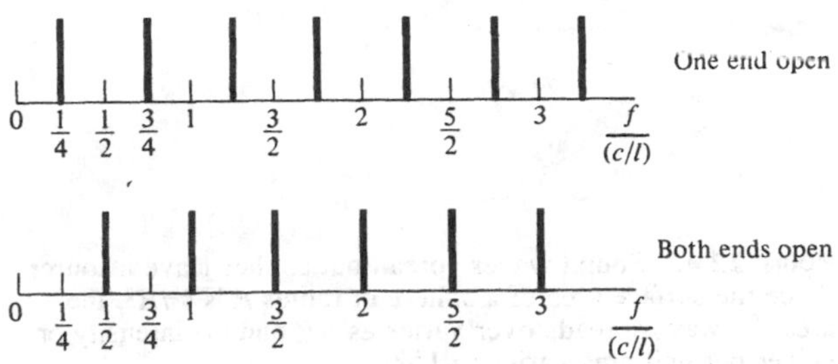

Figure 22.3. The lowest possible frequencies for air columns with one or both ends open.

These are the same as the standing wave frequencies on a string fixed at both ends. For the string, however, the ends are nodes rather than antinodes.

For a column with one end closed and one end open, $\lambda_n = 4l/(2n - 1)$, where n is an integer. (Note that $2n - 1$ is always an odd integer.) The frequencies for this column are

$$f_n = \frac{c}{\lambda_n} = \frac{(2n - 1)c}{4l} \quad (22.4)$$

$$n = 1, 2, 3, \ldots \quad \text{(one open end)}$$

Only odd harmonics, odd multiples of the fundamental $f_1 = c/4l$, are possible for this type of column. The lowest frequencies for the two types of air column are illustrated in Fig. 22.3. These are the fundamentals and overtones for these columns.

The clarinet is an example of a standing wave instrument.

Example 22.4

Instruments such as the clarinet employ air columns with one open end. What is the effective length of a clarinet that has a fundamental frequency of 147 Hz?

The fundamental frequency is found from Eq. 22.4 with $n = 1$. Solving for l,

$$l = \frac{c}{4f_1} = \frac{344 \text{ m s}^{-1}}{4(147 \text{ Hz})} = 0.585 \text{ m}$$

Because the end of a clarinet is flared, its actual length is closer to 0.67 m. Similar differences occur in many instruments.

22.3 | THE INTENSITY OF SOUND WAVES

For most purposes, the power per unit area, or intensity, of a sound wave is more important than the

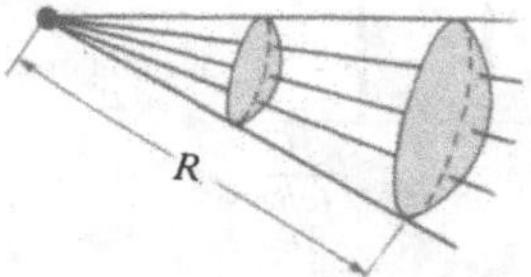

Figure 22.4. Sound waves spread out as they leave a source. Since the surface area of a sphere of radius R is $4\pi R^2$, the area the wave spreads over varies as R^2, and the intensity or power per unit area varies as $1/R^2$.

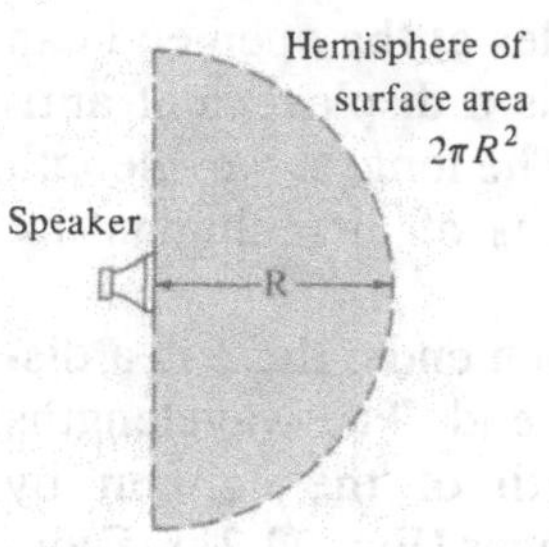

Figure 22.5. Example 22.6.

total energy carried over a period of time. For example, the noise of a jet engine will have very different effects on people and objects nearby than will the sound of a violin played for a much longer interval, even though the total sound energy produced might be the same in the two cases. However, a jet engine far away may be no louder than a nearby violin, since a sound wave spreads out as it travels (Fig. 22.4). Also, some sound energy is dissipated by the internal friction or viscosity of the medium in which it is moving. Since this energy loss is usually small, we neglect it.

As noted in the preceding chapter, the intensity of any wave is proportional to its amplitude squared. The intensity of a sound wave with pressure amplitude ΔP is proportional to $(\Delta P)^2$ and is given exactly by

$$I = \frac{(\Delta P)^2}{2\rho c} \tag{22.5}$$

The following example involves typical values of the pressure and intensity of audible sound waves.

Example 22.5

The maximum amplitude ΔP of a sound wave that is tolerable to a human ear is about 28 Pa. (a) What fraction is ΔP of normal atmospheric pressure? (b) What intensity of sound does ΔP correspond to in air at room temperature?

(a) Since normal atmospheric pressure is 1.013×10^5 Pa,

$$\frac{\Delta P}{P} = \frac{28 \text{ Pa}}{1.013 \times 10^5 \text{ Pa}} = 2.77 \times 10^{-4}$$

Thus even very loud sounds correspond to pressure fluctuations that are only a small fraction of a percent of atmospheric pressure.

(b) From Table 22.1, $\rho = 1.20$ kg m^{-3} and $c = 344$ m s^{-1}, so

$$I = \frac{(\Delta P)^2}{2\rho c} = \frac{(28 \text{ Pa})^2}{2(1.20 \text{ kg m}^{-3})(344 \text{ m s}^{-1})}$$
$$= 0.950 \text{ W m}^{-2}$$

Because the sound intensity decreases with the distance squared, the intensity of a sound source decreases rapidly as the distance from it increases. This is illustrated in the next example.

Example 22.6

The low-frequency speaker of a powerful stereo set has a surface area of 0.05 m^2 and produces 1 W of acoustical power. (a) What is the intensity at the speaker? (b) If the speaker projects sound uniformly into the forward hemisphere, at what distance from the speaker is the intensity 0.1 W m^{-2}?

(a) At the speaker, the intensity is

$$I = \frac{\mathcal{P}}{A} = \frac{1 \text{ W}}{0.05 \text{ m}^{-2}} = 20 \text{ W m}^{-2}$$

(b) At a distance R from the speaker, the wave has spread out over a hemisphere whose area is half the surface area of a sphere, or $\frac{1}{2}(4\pi R^2)$ (Fig. 22.5). Thus $I = \mathcal{P}/2\pi R^2$ or

$$R = \sqrt{\frac{\mathcal{P}}{2\pi I}} = \sqrt{\frac{1 \text{ W}}{2\pi(0.1 \text{ W m}^{-2})}} = 1.26 \text{ m}$$

22.4 | SOUND SOURCES

Many phenomena produce sound in an incidental but unavoidable fashion. For example, the combustion of fuel in an engine always produces some sound as a by-product. This sound is both annoying and wasteful of energy. However, there are many man-made and natural sources for which sound is the desired output. These usually have two primary components: a mechanism for producing a vibration and a *resonant structure*.

Musical instruments present a variety of arrangements for the production of sound. In a violin the strings vibrate, and their vibrations are efficiently transmitted to the air by the resonant hollow body of the instrument. In woodwinds and brasses, the vibrations are produced by causing the air in the mouthpiece to puff, swirl, and eddy. This causes the reeds in woodwinds to vibrate. In brasses, the lips themselves vibrate as air is blown into the mouthpiece. In both cases, the oscillatory flow of air results in standing waves in the extended hollow body of the instrument, and the energy is then efficiently transmitted to the air outside. Similarly, the oral and nasal cavities in humans serve as resonant structures for vibrations produced by the vocal cords.

Some insight into these somewhat complicated systems can be obtained by considering the experiment illustrated in Fig. 22.6. We know that a cylindrical tube of length l that is open at each end will sustain resonant standing waves of frequency $f_n = nc/2l$, where n is an integer. The experiment is performed by using a number of tuning forks with different but closely spaced frequencies and monitoring the sound with a microphone on the opposite side of the tube. When tuning forks with frequencies equal to the resonant frequencies of the tube produce sound, standing waves are produced in the tube, and sound is transmitted efficiently to the microphone. Forks with other frequencies produce sound that does not result in standing waves. Much less sound reaches the microphone; the actual amount depends on how close one is to a resonant frequency (Fig. 22.7).

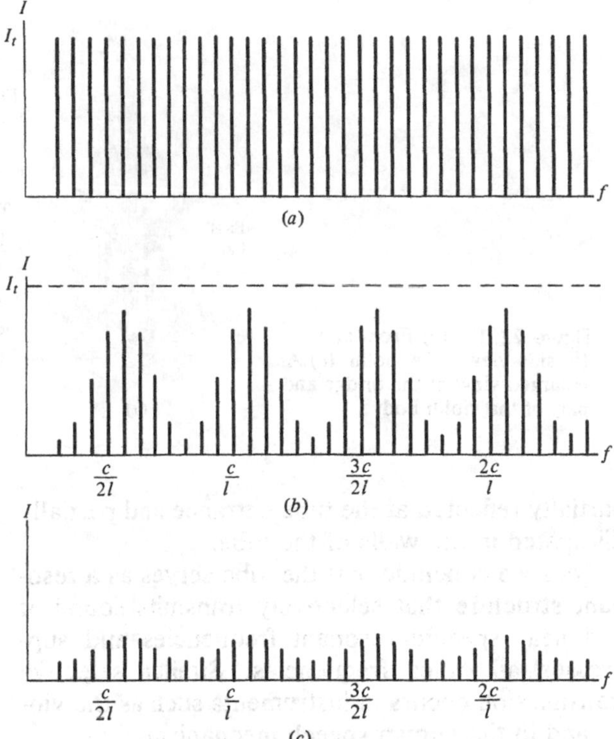

Figure 22.7. (*a*) A series of tuning forks used in the experiment of Fig. 22.6 produces sound of intensity I_t at the tube entrance at closely spaced frequencies. (*b*) The intensity reaching the microphone is greatest at the resonant frequencies of the tube. (*c*) The intensity received by the microphone through a narrower tube than that used in (*b*) is less sharply peaked about the resonant frequencies.

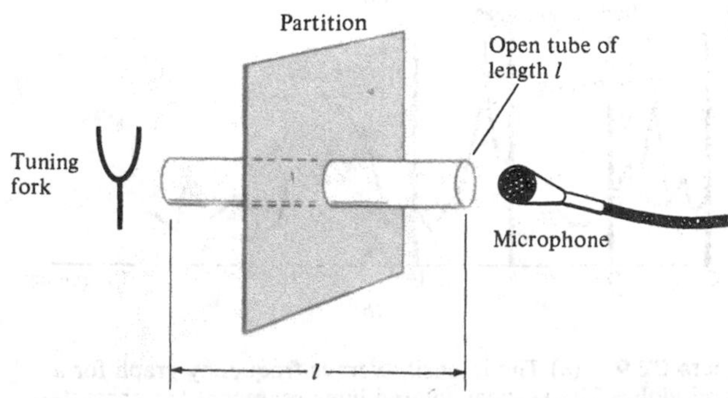

Figure 22.6. A tuning fork on the left of the partition produces sound at a single frequency. Sound can only reach the microphone by passing through the tube.

When sound enters the tube, the air inside vibrates, and the air near the tube wall loses some energy because of viscous forces. As we have seen with the harmonic oscillator and the *LRC* circuit, whenever the energy dissipation in a resonant system is increased, the intensity-versus-frequency curve, or *spectrum*, is lowered and proportionately broadened. If a narrower tube of the same length is used, the broadening is more pronounced because the relative amount of air near the walls is larger, and the viscous effects are proportionately greater (Fig. 22.7*c*). The sound energy not transmitted is

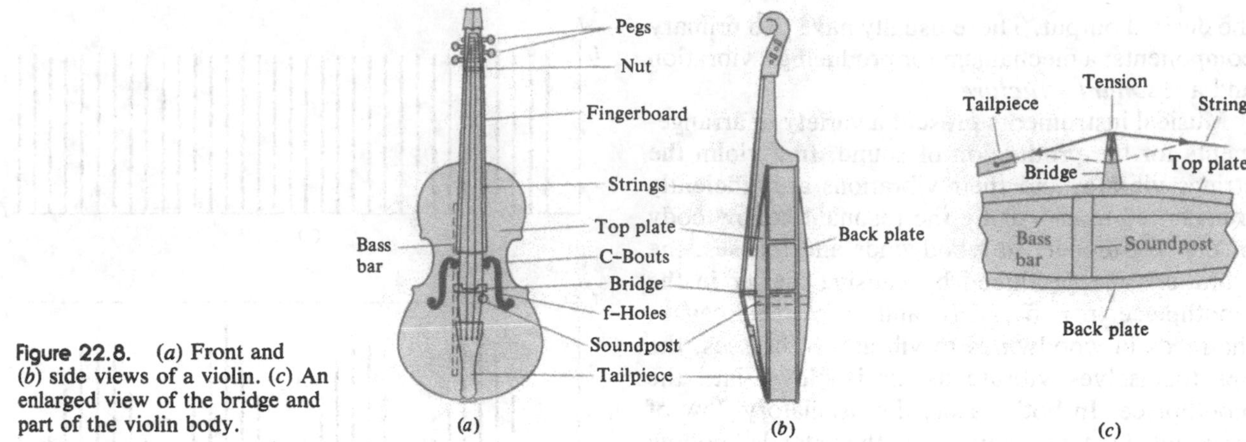

Figure 22.8. (*a*) Front and (*b*) side views of a violin. (*c*) An enlarged view of the bridge and part of the violin body.

partially reflected at the tube entrance and partially dissipated in the walls of the tube.

Thus we conclude that the tube serves as a resonant structure that selectively transmits sound at and near specific resonant frequencies and suppresses all other frequencies. Similar selective transmission occurs in instruments such as the violin and in the human speech mechanism.

The Violin | The body of a violin is a more complex resonant structure than the tube. When the strings of a violin are plucked or bowed, their vibrations are transferred to the body through the bridge (Fig. 22.8). Although the strings may vibrate with many different frequency components, the body resonates at and amplifies only certain frequencies.

The violin body vibrates so that its volume varies, and air is forced in and out through the f-holes. This is called the air resonance. The front and back plates of the body can also vibrate at characteristic frequencies called body resonances. Just as a string can vibrate at more than one frequency, so also can the violin plates, and several body resonances exist (Fig. 22.9). The frequencies of the air and body resonances should be at or near the fundamental string frequencies. If this is not achieved some notes will be muted or distorted.

The Human Voice | In human speech, the vocal cords initiate vibrations of the air; the throat and the nasal and oral cavities serve as resonant structures (Fig. 22.10). The remarkable ability of humans to produce so many different sounds stems from two facts. First, the vocal cord tension can be varied; hence the frequencies produced and the proportions of the harmonics present can be changed. Second, the resonant structures, particularly the oral cavity, can be changed in shape and dimensions to modify the frequency content of the amplified sounds. (These considerations apply to voiced sounds as opposed to nonvoiced sounds such as

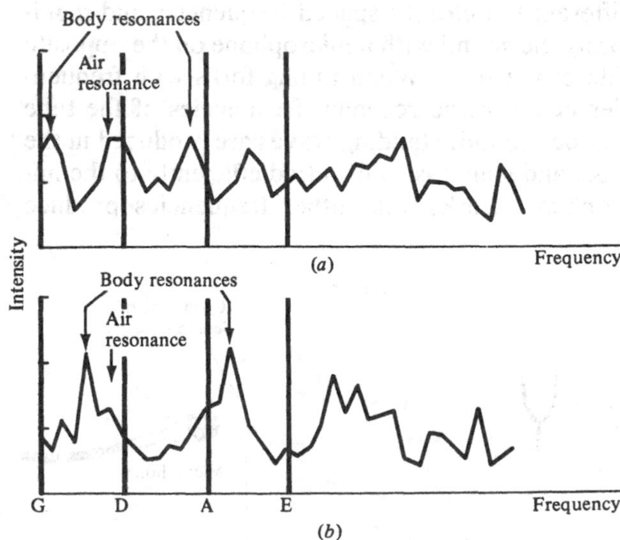

Figure 22.9. (*a*) The intensity-versus-frequency graph for a good violin. The vertical colored lines represent the characteristic frequencies of the four violin strings. Note that the resonances occur at nearly the same frequencies as those characteristic of the strings. (*b*) The spectrum of a poor violin.

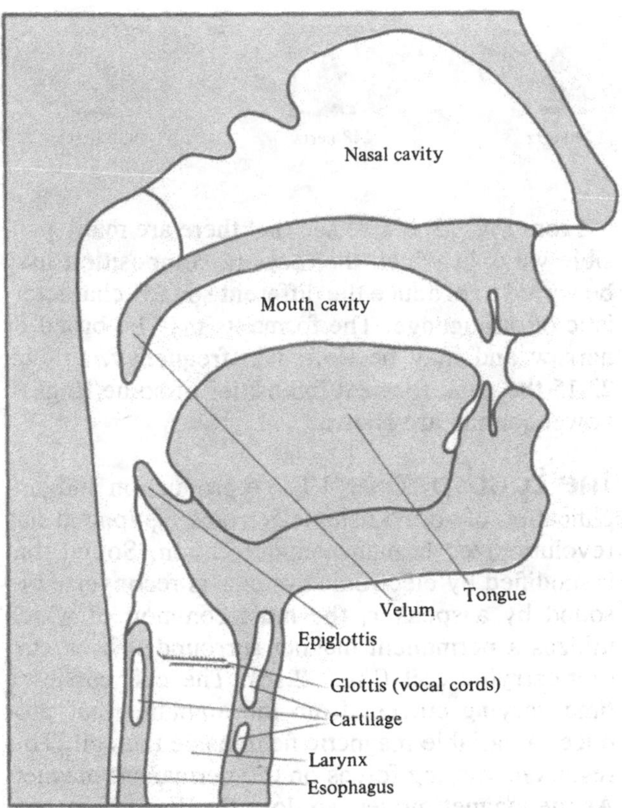

Figure 22.10. Essential components of the human speech mechanism.

"sh" in "shut" and "f" in "feet," which do not require the use of the vocal cords.) Normally the vocal cords are relaxed and present no obstruction to air passing through the larynx. During preparation for speech the tension in the vocal cords increases and the larynx is closed (Fig. 22.11). The air pressure below the vocal cords increases until the cords are forced open. The air then rushes through the opening, causing the vocal cords to vibrate.

The vibrations of the vocal cords can be understood from Bernoulli's equation (Chapter Thirteen). As air rushes through the opening, its velocity is large, and hence the pressure is lowered, allowing the vocal cords to start to close. Once the opening becomes sufficiently small, the pressure below the vocal cords increases and forces the cords to spread apart again. This process is continuous as long as exhalation persists and the fundamental as well as many harmonics of the vocal cords are excited (Figs. 22.12 and 22.13).

As illustrated in Fig. 22.13, the spectrum of sound produced by the vocal cords is quite uniform up to about 3000 Hz, the range of frequencies used in speech. Without modification this would result simply in noise. The modification takes place in the resonant structures.

The human oral cavity is a complex structure, but its properties are surprisingly close to those of a simple model. This model is a pipe 0.17 m long with one end open at the mouth and nose and the other end nearly closed at the vocal cords. The resonant frequencies of a pipe open at one end were found to be

$$f_n = \frac{(2n - 1)c}{4l} \qquad n = 1, 2, 3 \ldots \tag{22.4}$$

In speech, the frequencies of importance are between 300 and 3000 Hz. Using $c = 344$ m s^{-1} and $l = 0.17$ m, we find that the fundamental and first two overtones of the pipe, which are near 500, 1500, and 2500 Hz, respectively, are within this range. If one analyzes a typical voiced sound, one finds that there usually are three resonant peaks that are close to the resonant frequencies of the model. These resonant peaks are referred to as *formants*. For example, the sound "ae" in "at" has formants at about 600, 1700, and 2300 Hz.

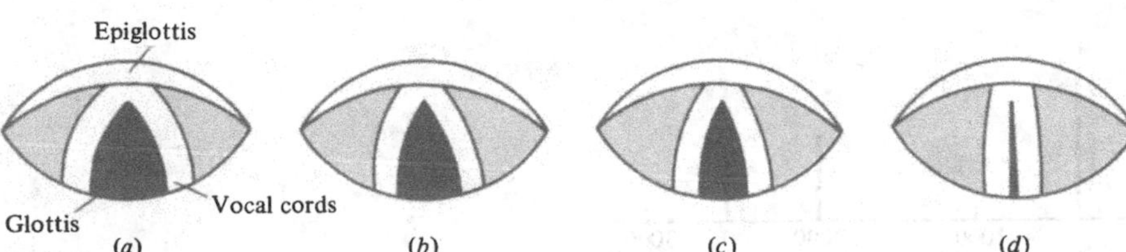

Figure 22.11. (*a*) The vocal cords are relaxed during normal breathing (*a*). When speech is begun, the vocal cord tension increases (*b*), (*c*), and the larynx is closed (*d*).

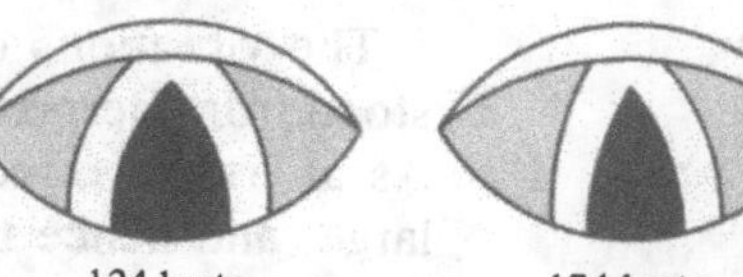

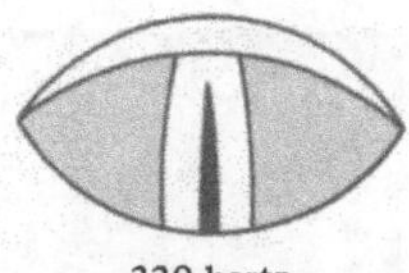

Figure 22.12. The vocal cords are shown for several fundamental frequencies during singing. Higher frequencies occur when the tension increases. Note the stretching of the cords just as in a string.

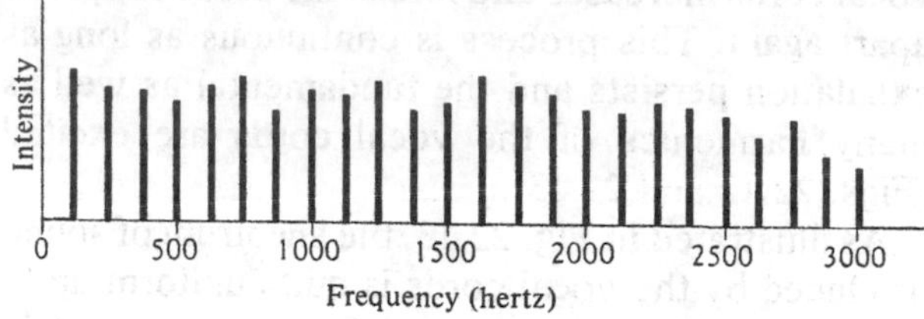

Figure 22.13. An example of the fundamental and harmonics produced by the vocal cords during speech. This spectrum will change with the tension in the vocal cords.

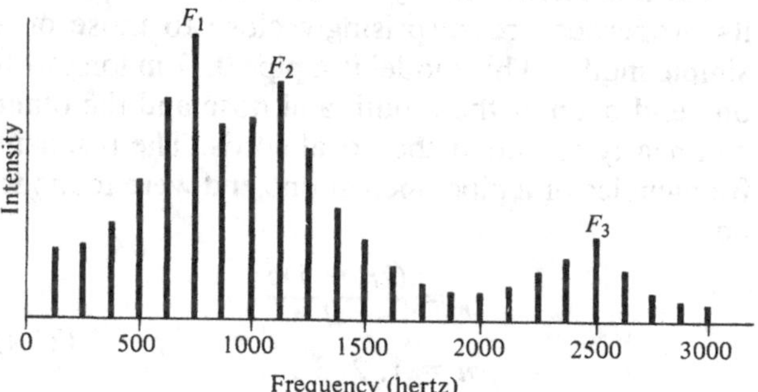

Figure 22.14. The intensity-versus-frequency spectrum of the sound "a" in "father." The formants are wide resonances labeled F_1, F_2, and F_3. The vertical lines show how the vocal cord frequencies shown in Figure 22.13 are selectively transmitted by the resonance structure.

From Fig. 22.14, we see that there are many possible ways in which the formant composition may be varied to produce the different sounds characteristic of a language. The formants may be broad or narrow and may be shifted in frequency. In Fig. 22.15 the peak formant intensities of some English vowel sounds are shown.

The Loudspeaker | The reproduction and amplification of sound using electronic equipment has revolutionized human communication. Sound that is modified by electronic systems is reconverted to sound by a speaker, the most common of which utilizes a permanent magnet surrounded by a current-carrying coil (Fig. 22.16). The coil carries a time varying current from the amplifier that produces a variable magnetic field inside the coil. This results in varying forces on the permanent magnet. As the magnet moves, so does the diaphragm, and its motion produces sound waves in the air.

22.5 | SOUND DETECTORS

Sound detection requires the conversion of the mechanical vibrations of sound waves into a form that

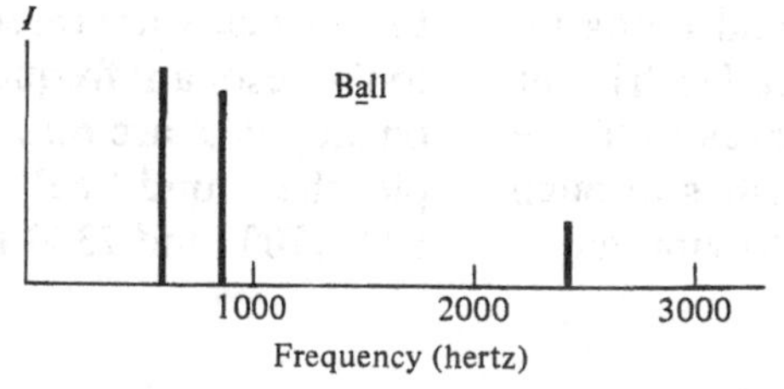

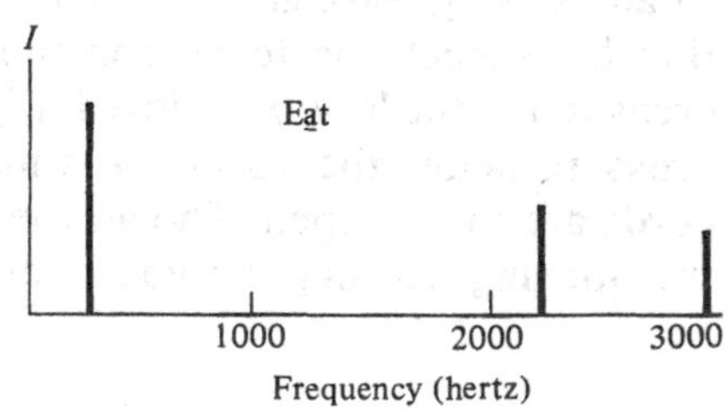

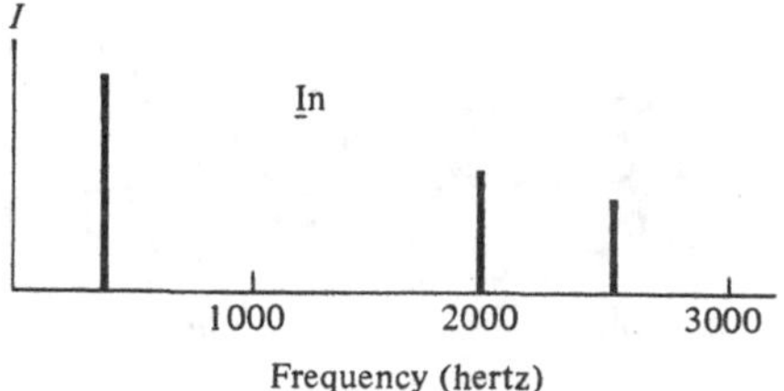

Figure 22.15. The position and relative intensity of the formants for some English vowel sounds as voiced by males.

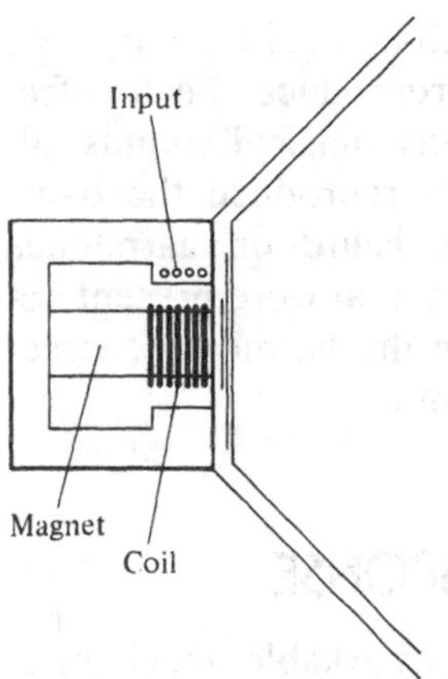

Figure 22.16. A speaker has a permanent magnet that is free to move along its length. One end of the magnet is attached to the speaker diaphragm and the magnet is surrounded by a current-carrying coil.

permits the analysis of their frequency and intensity. Here we discuss how this is done by the condenser microphone and the human ear.

The condenser microphone contains a flexible membrane that includes an electrically conducting layer. This membrane is close to a second rigid conductor, so together they form a capacitance that varies as the membrane vibrates in response to a sound wave. In a circuit, this variation of the capacitance causes a time variation in the current. Once this varying component of the current has been amplified electronically, it can drive a speaker or record information on magnetic tape.

Any useful sound detector must respond accurately to variations in the sound frequency and intensity. The human ear is remarkable, since it can do this well and is nevertheless virtually unaffected by motion and vibration of the body or by the sounds produced by the blood flow and in the internal organs. It also permits the listener to locate sound sources and to concentrate on specific sounds in a confused sound environment.

Sound waves are mostly reflected at a boundary between two media of very different density, such as air and body fluids. (This is discussed in detail in Section 22.8). Nevertheless, sound energy is transferred efficienty from the air to the fluid medium of the inner ear by means of a complex mechanical system. The outer ear collects sound waves and transmits them to the *eardrum* (Fig. 22.17*a*). The vibrations of the eardrum are transmitted by three bones called *ossicles* through the air-filled middle ear to the *oval window* and to the *perilymph* fluid to the inner ear canals. Since the area of the eardrum is about 30 times that of the oval window, the pres-

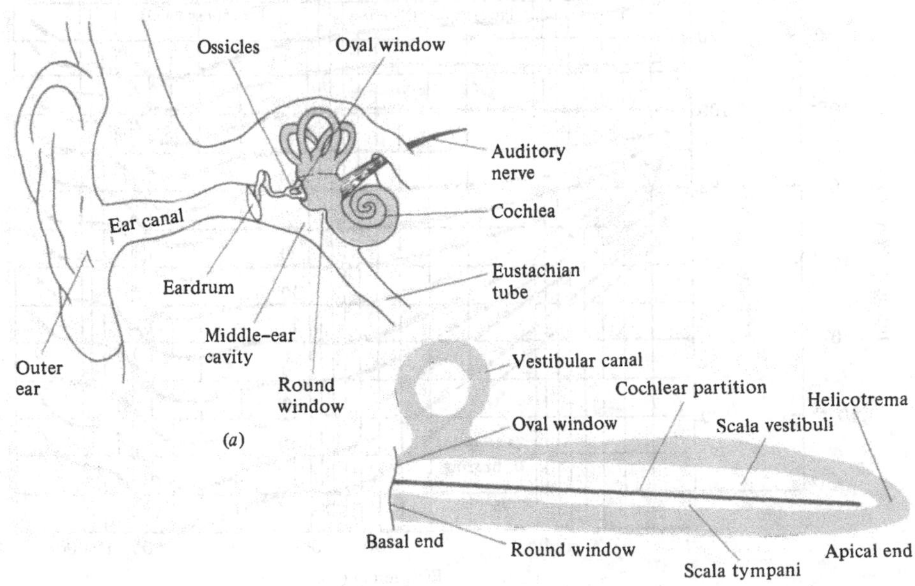

Figure 22.17. (*a*) Schematic diagram of the human ear. (*b*) The uncoiled inner ear.

sure exerted on the window is larger by that factor. The ossicles also function as a lever with a mechanical advantage of about 2, again doubling the pressure on the window. In addition, muscles connected to the ossicles control the amplitude of their motion, so that loud sounds will not damage the sensitive inner ear.

The inner ear (Fig. 22.17*b*) has two canals filled with fluid. The *cochlear duct*, containing nerve endings in the *organ of Corti*, divides the two chambers except at the end farthest from the windows. The *oval window* is driven by one of the ossicles. A flexible *round window* in the other chamber flexes as the perilymph moves, so the volume of the inner ear stays constant. Because the cochlear duct is thicker near the narrow end of the cochlea, different frequencies of vibration of the perilymph cause the partition to flex at different points along its length. The flexing is sensed by the nerve hairs in the region of excitation, and nerve impulses travel toward the brain.

The mechanical operation of the ear is well understood; however, the perception of sound involves complex neurological processing of information that is not yet fully explained. An example is the use of earphones. Any sound with a wavelength much larger than the diameter of a speaker cannot be efficiently produced by that speaker. Earphone speakers are too small to reproduce the low-frequency fundamentals of many musical sounds, although they may accurately reproduce the overtones. Nevertheless, music heard on earphones sounds as though the fundamental were present because the brain, recognizing the harmonics, effectively supplies the fundamental.

22.6 | AUDITORY RESPONSE

The ears of animals are remarkable mechanical structures. For example, the human ear can comfortably respond to intensities from as low as 10^{-12} W m^{-2} up to 1 W m^{-2}, 12 orders of magnitude. Without this range, many sounds in our natural environment would either be inaudible or unbearable.

Measurements of auditory response are somewhat subjective, but two objective characteristics have been fairly well established. One is the *threshold of hearing*; the minimum intensity that is just audible at a given frequency. This is represented by the lower curve of Fig. 22.18. The second is the *threshold of feeling*. At this high intensity, a tickling sensation is experienced when the ossicles vibrate so strongly that they strike the middle ear wall. The

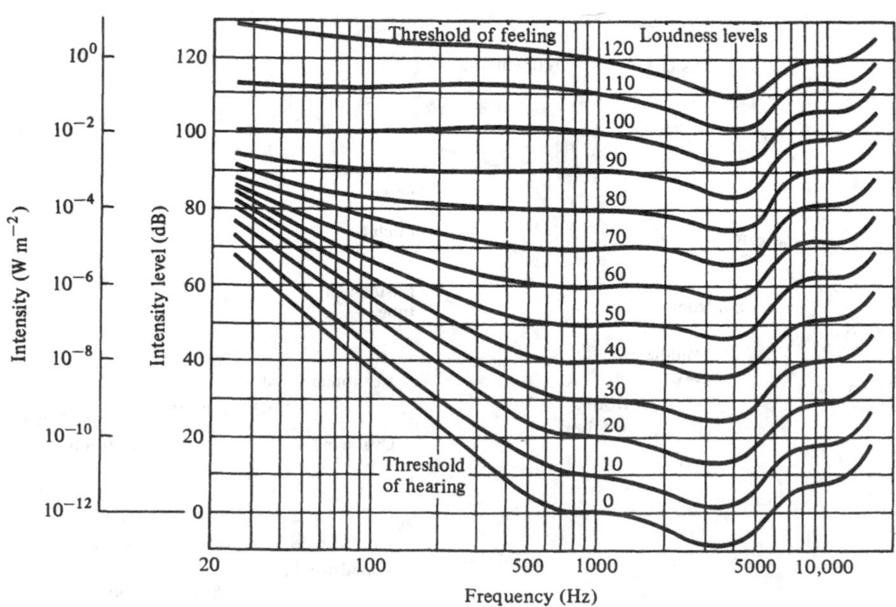

Figure 22.18. A logarithmic graph showing the range of audible intensities versus frequency. The human ear is most sensitive to frequencies near 3000 Hz; the audible range extends from about 20 to 20,000 Hz. The contours show the intensities required to produce the same subjective loudness levels for pure tones at various frequencies.

normal hearing range lies between these two curves.

The ear is sensitive to such an enormous intensity range in part because muscles around the eardrum and the ossicles respond to neural feedback and modify the tension in these parts. Thus the eardrum is somewhat like a flexible drum head with an adjustable tension.

Because of the enormous intensity range of the ear, it is common to measure intensities in logarithmic units, called *decibels* (dB). The *intensity level* is related to the intensity by

$$\beta = 10 \log \frac{I}{I_0} \qquad (22.6)$$

where β is measured in decibels, I is the sound intensity, $I_0 = 10^{-12}$ W m^{-2} is in an arbitrary reference level roughly equal to the lowest intensity normally audible, and log denotes the base 10, or common, logarithm. (See Appendix B.10 for a review of logarithms.) The decibel range of hearing at 1000 Hz is from near 0 dB up to about 120 dB (Fig. 22.18). Table 22.2 lists the intensity levels of common sound sources.

The following is an example of the relationship between intensity level and perception.

Example 22.7

If a 30-dB sound varies in frequency from 20 to 30,000 Hz, which frequencies will the normal ear hear?

From Fig. 22.18, we note that the horizontal line at 30 dB intersects the threshold of hearing curve at about 150 and 10,000 Hz. Thus, only frequencies within this range will be audible.

TABLE 22.2

The intensity level in decibels of common sound sources

Source	Intensity Level (in decibels)
Large orchestra (maximum)	98
Riveter	95
Bass drum (maximum)	94
Trumpet (maximum)	75
Busy street traffic	70
Clarinet (maximum)	67
Ordinary conversation	65
Quiet radio	40
Whisper	20

When more than one sound source is present, the intensity level does not usually increase markedly. This is shown in the next example.

Example 22.8

If the average intensity level of each of two radios is 45 dB, what is the average intensity level when both radios are on and tuned to different stations?

The intensity of one radio is I_r, where the corresponding intensity level is

$$\beta_1 = 45 \text{ dB} = 10 \log \frac{I_r}{I_0}$$

With both radios on, the intensity is $I_r + I_r = 2I_r$, so the intensity level is

$$\beta_2 = 10 \log \frac{2I_r}{I_0} = 10 \log 2 + 10 \log \frac{I_r}{I_0}$$
$$= 10 \log 2 + \beta_1$$

Since $10 \log 2 = 3$,

$$\beta_2 = 3 \text{ dB} + 45 \text{ dB} = 48 \text{ dB}$$

Note that although the intensity I_1 doubles, β increases by only 3 dB.

Subjective Factors

Properties such as *loudness*, *pitch*, and *quality* are often used to describe sound. These concepts are difficult to deal with because they are subjective. For example, a 20-dB sound at 1000 Hz will sound louder than a 20-dB sound at 400 Hz (Fig. 22.18). Thus loudness depends both on intensity and frequency. The pitch of a sound is closely related to the frequency. However, above about 3000 Hz, the pitch increases with intensity even if the frequency is constant. Below 2000 Hz, the pitch decreases with increasing intensity.

The quality of a sound is even more ambiguous. We know that some types of sounds that have certain harmonics present with specific intensities sound pleasing. However, again we cannot characterize quality with a precise statement about measurable physical parameters.

The combination of a mechanical ear structure, neurological processing, and the psychological aspects of perception has so far allowed us to classify but not to understand the subjective qualities of sound. These aspects are under intensive study by those concerned with hearing defects and the science of musical sounds.

22.7 | AUDITORY LOCALIZATION

We can sometimes locate a sound source by turning our heads, since the ear nearest the source will often hear the loudest sound. However, people can often accurately locate sound sources without turning their heads, unless the source is directly in front of or behind them. There are different explanations for this at low and high frequencies.

The human head is approximately a sphere of diameter 0.2 m, which is the wavelength of a 1700-Hz sound wave in air. Sound waves of longer wavelengths or lower frequencies will pass around the head largely unaffected. This is because, as we noted earlier in this chapter, a wave will be disturbed only by objects comparable to or larger than its wavelength. If at some time a peak in the wave is at one ear, the wave has a different pressure at the other ear. The nerve impulses from the two ears then contain information about the relative pressures at the two ears that the brain uses to locate the source. This mechanism is most effective below 1000 Hz, because the wavelength is then appreciably larger than the diameter of the head.

Sound waves with wavelengths much shorter than 0.2 m tend to be reflected when they strike the head, leaving a sound shadow with little or no sound on the far side. Thus above 5000 Hz, the source is usually located because the sound is distinctly louder in the ear nearest it. Between 1000 and 5000 Hz, both mechanisms are used, but the localization is less accurate.

An interesting correlation between auditory localization and the upper and lower frequency limits to hearing has been found for mammals of many different sizes. As we noted, the crossover frequency dividing two mechanisms of auditory localization is determined by the distance between the ears. More exactly, to take into account marine mammals, this frequency should be computed as $f = c/d$, the speed of sound in the surrounding medium, air or water, divided by the distance between the ears.

When this is done, it is found that mammals with a large ear separation (and hence a low crossover frequency) also have lower frequency limits to their hearing range. For example, the graph analogous to Fig. 22.18 for an elephant has very much the same shape but extends to lower frequencies on the left and only up to 10,000 Hz on the right. The reverse is found for small mammals; that is, they do not hear low frequencies as well but can hear up to higher frequencies. The average upper limits for several mammals reflect this; humans, 19,000 Hz; dogs, 44,000 Hz; rats, 72,000 Hz.

Thus there is a very strong correlation between how well a mammal can localize sounds at various frequencies and what frequencies the mammals can even hear. It appears that a mammal with a given ear separation only hears a wide enough range of frequencies to localize the sound source efficiently. This empirically uniform trend even includes mammals making special use of sound, such as bats and porpoises.

Barn Owls | The barn owl is an example of a predator having very special anatomical features that allow it to locate prey from its sounds when it is too dark to do this visually. These features help it to localize sounds both horizontally and vertically in relation to itself.

Like humans, the owl uses low-frequency pressure differences to locate sound sources in the horizontal plane. Its ears are about 5 cm apart, so this mechanism is effective up to about 7000 Hz. The owl uses higher-frequency sound for both horizontal and vertical plane localization. Here there are two interesting adaptations that enhance its abilities. First, the owl's facial feathers form a rather shallow round collector with two tapered, vertical troughs (Fig. 22.19). The round collector helps to collect faint sounds, and the troughs provide an additional collecting mechanism for each ear. The size of the troughs make these collectors effective only at high frequencies.

However, the troughs are not symmetric. The collecting area for the trough leading to the right ear favors collecting sound from above the owl, and the left ear trough collects more efficiently from below. So, in addition to the difference in high-frequency intensities due to shielding by the head, which

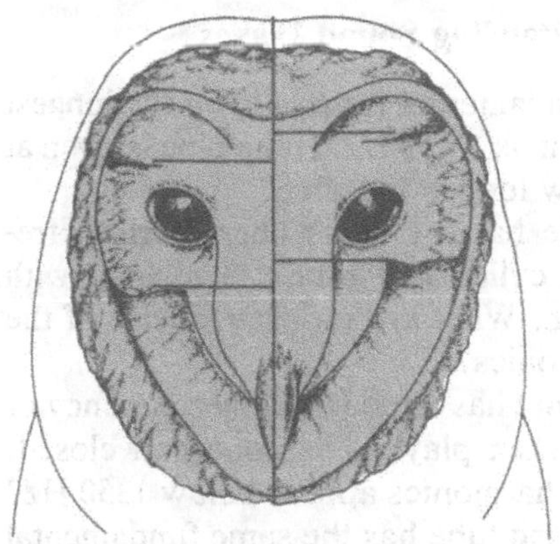

Figure 22.19. The face of the barn owl has asymmetrically positioned troughs which improve its vertical localization capabilities.

would provide horizontal and some vertical localization, the selective collection of high-frequency sounds from below in one ear and above in the other considerably improves vertical localization capabilities.

SUMMARY

Sound waves are the result of mechanical disturbances in materials. The speed of sound depends on how much of a pressure change is necessary to produce a given density change. This relationship depends on the molecular properties of the material.

Standing sound waves are often produced in certain geometries and play an important role in the production and detection of sound. In sound sources, a resonant structure determines which standing waves are produced, amplifying certain frequencies and suppressing others. A sound receiver has similar characteristics.

The intensity of sound, the transported power per unit area, is proportional to the square of the amplitude of the pressure change in the wave. As a sound wave spreads out from a source, its intensity at any point on the wave decreases with the square of the distance from the source.

The intensity level of sound in decibels is often used when one is dealing with auditory response. This decibel scale is a logarithmic scale and is used because of the enormous range of ear sensitivities of humans and other animals.

Checklist

Define or explain:

pressure variations	middle ear
bulk modulus	inner ear
standing waves	threshold of hearing
sound intensity	threshold of feeling
source of vibration	intensity level
resonant structure	loudness
sound spectrum	pitch
formant	quality
loudspeaker	auditory localization

REVIEW QUESTIONS

Q22-1 Why doesn't sound travel in a vacuum?

Q22-2 If a material is hard to compress, its velocity of sound is ______.

Q22-3 High-frequency sound waves have ______ wavelengths.

Q22-4 Standing sound waves occur because of the presence of ______ in the region in which the wave travels.

Q22-5 Displacement nodes in standing sound waves occur at ______ ends of a tube and antinodes at ______ ends.

Q22-6 The intensity of a sound wave depends on the ______ of the ______ amplitude.

Q22-7 Instruments designed to produce sound usually contain a mechanism to produce vibrations and ______.

Q22-8 The output of a sound source is often represented by a spectrum, a graph of ______ versus ______.

Q22-9 Typically the spectrum of a voiced sound is composed of three ______.

Q22-10 What plays the role of the resonant structure in the human ear?

Q22-11 In discussions of hearing, intensities are usually described in terms of ______ because the intensity range is so large.

EXERCISES

Section 22.1 | The Nature and Speed of Sound

22-1 Find the adiabatic bulk modulus of iron.

22-2 Find the adiabatic bulk modulus of water.

22-3 A sound wave has a wavelength of 2 m in air. What is its wavelength in water?

22-4 An underwater explosion is detected by a pair of microphones, one just below the surface of the water and one just above. The explosion is heard 10 s earlier by the underwater microphone. How far away did it occur?

22-5 A hi-fi speaker has a diameter of 0.3 m. What is the frequency of the sound produced if the wavelength is equal to the circumference of the speaker? (This is comparable to the resonant frequency of the speaker, and special enclosures must be designed so that most of the power is not emitted by the speaker at this frequency.)

22-6 A lightning bolt is seen by an observer. The accompanying thunder is heard 5 s later. What is the approximate distance of the observer from the storm cloud?

22-7 A stone is dropped into a well. The sound of the splash is heard 3 s after the stone is dropped. What is the depth of the well?

22-8 When one end of a copper pipe is struck, the time difference between the sounds heard in the copper and in air at the other end is 1 s. How long is the pipe?

22-9 The depth of a body of water can be found by emitting sound pulses at the surface and detecting the pulses reflected from the bottom. If the time interval from emission to detection is 2 s, what is the depth of the water?

22-10 A marching band takes a step each 0.8 s. At what distance will a marching band appear to be one half-step out of time with the music being played?

22-11 When approaching an object, a bat decreases the duration of its chirps and also the time interval between chirps. When the chirps last 3×10^{-4} s, what is the minimum distance at which the first part of the echo overlaps with the end of the chirp?

22-12 The telephone is designed to transmit efficiently frequencies from about 50 to 3000 Hz. What are the wavelengths of sound in air corresponding to these two frequencies?

22-13 Bats utilize sound up to frequencies of about 1.2×10^5 Hz, while porpoises are sensitive to frequencies up to 2×10^5 Hz. Why might porpoises be expected to have a greater frequency range?

Section 22.2 | Standing Sound Waves

22-14 The fundamental frequency of the longest pipe on an organ is 16.35 Hz. If the pipe is open at both ends, how long is the pipe?

22-15 A bugle has the same characteristic frequencies as a cylindrical tube 1.3 m long with both ends open. What are the frequencies of the first four harmonics?

22-16 A clarinet has a fundamental frequency of 147 Hz and, when played, has one end closed. (a) How many harmonics appear below 1350 Hz? (b) If an open-end tube has the same fundamental frequency, how many harmonics appear below 1350 Hz?

22-17 A pipe organ has open-end pipes and spans a frequency range from 65 to 2090 Hz. What are the lengths of the longest and shortest pipes of this organ?

22-18 The outer ear can be thought of as a pipe 2.7×10^{-2} m long with one closed end. (a) Using this model, predict what frequency sound would be most effectively detected by the ear. (b) How does this compare to the frequency of the minimum of the threshold of hearing curve (Fig. 22.18)?

Section 22.3 | The Intensity of Sound Waves

22-19 What is the pressure amplitude of thunder with an intensity of 0.1 W m^{-2}?

22-20 What is the total power output of a loudspeaker for which the intensity over the surface of a hemisphere 10 m away is 10^{-4} W m^{-2}?

22-21 Two sound waves of the same intensity travel in air and water. What is the ratio of the pressure amplitudes of the sounds in the two materials?

22-22 If the pressure amplitudes of sound in air and water are the same, what is the ratio of the two intensities?

22-23 If one sound wave has twice the pressure amplitude of another in the same medium, what is the ratio of the intensities of the two waves?

22-24 The ratio of the maximum intensities of a piano and a flute is 8. What is the ratio of the pressure amplitude produced by a piano to that of the flute?

22-25 The intensity of a large orchestra is equal to that of 216 trumpets. What is the ratio of the pressure amplitude of the orchestra to that of 1 trumpet?

22-26 What is the intensity of a sound wave in air with a pressure amplitude of 1 Pa?

22-27 What is the pressure amplitude of a sound wave in water of intensity $I = 10^{-12}$ W m^{-2}?

22-28 What is the pressure amplitude in air of a sound at the threshold of feeling, $I = 1$ W m^{-2}?

22-29 Find the intensity of a sound wave in water with a pressure amplitude of 1 Pa.

22-30 The surface area of the eardrum is about 8×10^{-5} m^2. If the pressure difference across the eardrum is 28 Pa, how large is the force on it?

Section 22.4 | Sound Sources

Section 22.5 | Sound Detectors

22-31 A bat needs two ears for direction finding, just as humans do. If the distance between the ears is 0.01 m, what is the minimum frequency for which the ears are separated by at least one half wavelength? (Assume that the sound approaches directly from one side of the head.)

22-32 In hearing tests, a tone of a given frequency is gradually reduced in intensity until it becomes inaudible. Why are tones of different frequencies used during the test?

22-33 Sound can be heard by humans when the vibrations are transmitted to the inner ear via bone. The outer and middle ear play no role in such hearing. (a) Suggest a method of testing hearing such that conclusions may be drawn about whether damage is present in the inner ear only or if middle ear damage is also present. (b) For what types of hearing losses would hearing aids that transmit sounds to the skull bones be useful?

22-34 Bone is a better conductor of low-frequency vibrations than is air. Why does a person feel that his or her voice is richer and lower pitched than do listeners?

22-35 Why do sinus infections in which the eustachian tubes are infected often impair hearing?

Section 22.6 | Auditory Response

22-36 Two sound waves have intensities of 10^{-9} W m^{-2} and 5×10^{-8} W m^{-2}. What is the difference in the intensity levels of the two sounds?

22-37 Find the ratio of intensities of two sounds, one of which is 10 dB louder than the other.

22-38 What is the intensity level of ultrasound of intensity 25×10^4 W m^{-2}?

22-39 If the intensity level of one person speaking is 50 dB, what is the intensity level when 10 such people are speaking?

22-40 What is the intensity of a sound that is 5 dB louder than that of a sound of intensity 10^{-9} W m^{-2}?

22-41 The surface area of the eardrum is about 8×10^{-5} m^2. What is the power transmitted to the eardrum by a sound wave of 40 dB if no sound is reflected?

Section 22.7 | Auditory Localization

22-42 A whale's ears are 1.5 m apart. What is the maximum frequency at which we might expect it to localize sounds from the pressure difference at the two ears?

22-43 When your head is in the usual vertical position, you can normally localize sounds horizontally better than you can vertically. Explain why.

PROBLEMS

22-44 Bats, which use echo location for navigation, are observed to emit chirps lasting 2×10^{-3} s with 7×10^{-2} s of silence between. How close to an object can a bat be so that the reflected sound from the first part of the chirp is not masked by the emission of the first part of the next chirp?

22-45 Equation 22.2 for the sound velocity, $c = \sqrt{K/\rho}$, hides an understanding of the physics involved in sound propagation. In fact, c is larger for dense substances than for less dense materials (see Table 22.1). If dominoes are placed on end beside one another and the end one is toppled, the entire row falls. By noting that the dominoes fall fastest when they are close together, discuss the dependence of the sound velocity on density.

22-46 During cruising flight, the interval between chirps of a bat is 7×10^{-2} s. What is the maximum distance a bat can be from an object so that the complete reflected wave returns before the next chirp begins?

22-47 For an ideal gas, the adiabatic bulk modulus is $K = \gamma P$, where P is the pressure and γ is the ratio of the specific heat capacities at constant pressure and volume, $\gamma = c_P/c_V$. (a) Show that the ideal gas law can be written as $P/\rho = RT/M$, where ρ is the mass density, and M is the molecular weight of the gas. (b) Show that the sound velocity in an ideal gas is $c = \sqrt{\gamma RT/M}$.

22-48 In Problem 22-47 the velocity of sound in an ideal gas is found to be $c = \sqrt{\gamma RT/M}$. Using this expression, can one account for the difference in sound velocities in air and hydrogen, H_2?

22-49 A bat using echo location emits chirps at intervals of 5×10^{-3} s, each having a duration of 0.3×10^{-3} s. (a) How far from an object will the bat be so that the first part of the chirp is being reflected at the time the chirp ends? (b) How much time is there between the return of the complete reflected wave of part (a) and the beginning of the succeeding chirp?

22-50 A sonar source used for underwater detection emits pulses of duration 0.1 s once every T seconds. What is the minimum value for T if the echo and the next pulse are not to overlap from objects (a) 50 m away; (b) 1 km away?

22-51 A vertical tube of length 2 m can be filled to any level with water. Sound entering the open end of the tube is reflected at the water surface and this is the position of a node. (a) If the tube is filled with water to a depth of 1 m, what is the lowest frequency at which resonance will occur? (b) What is the depth of the water if the lowest-frequency resonance occurs at 500 Hz?

22-52 The maximum tolerable pressure amplitude for the human ear in air is $\Delta P = 28$ Pa. What is the ratio of the corresponding density change to the mean density for sound waves in (a) air; (b) water.

22-53 The acoustic intensity of an antiaircraft shell exploding at an altitude of 1000 m is 10^{-3} W m^{-2} at ground level. (a) What is the total acoustic power released? (b) What total acoustic energy is released during the explosion if it lasts 0.1 s?

22-54 If the air and body resonances of a violin had a very narrow frequency width or range, the instrument might not be effective. Explain why.

22-55 A jet plane flying at an altitude of 3000 m produces a sound of 40 dB at ground level. What would the intensity level be if the altitude were 1000 m? (Assume that the total sound energy produced does not change.)

22-56 An outdoor public address system is adjusted to a level of 70 dB for listeners 10 m distant. What intensity level is heard at 50 m?

22-57 The average intensity level of a radio is adjusted to 40 dB at a distance of 10 m. (a) What is the intensity in watts per square metre at this distance? (b) What is the intensity level in decibels 3 m from the radio? (c) What is the output power of the radio in watts if the sound is spread uniformly over the forward hemisphere?

22-58 The normal human ear can distinguish a difference in intensities of about 0.6 dB at a given frequency. What percentage of power increase is required to raise the intensity level 0.6 dB?

22-59 The tropical oilbird is often found flying in totally darkened caves. It uses sounds for obstacle avoidance; but the highest frequency it can emit and recognize is 8000 Hz. (a) Estimate the minimum-size object that the bird can detect. (b) It is observed that the actual minimum diameter of round objects that are easily avoided is 0.2 m. What does this suggest about the actual frequency used by the bird?

22-60 The expected upper hearing limit of mammals may be compared if one assumes that it is determined by the separation of the ears. (a) Making this assumption and using the scaling model of Chapter Eight, $r \propto m^{3/8}$, what upper limit of hearing would one expect to find in elephants and rats whose body masses are typically 3×10^3 kg and 2×10^{-1} kg, respectively? Use the fact that a 70-kg human has an upper hearing limit of 19,000 Hz. (b) In fact, the upper limits of hearing for elephants and rats are 11,000 Hz and 72,000 Hz, respectively. Using the data for elephants and rats, find the experimental scaling exponent for the upper limit frequency-versus-body mass.

22-61 In Fig. 22.2*a*, assume that the two traveling waves are represented by $y_1 = A \cos(kx - \omega t)$ and $y_2 = A \cos(kx + \omega t)$, where $x = 0$ is at the left end of the tube and $x = l$ is at the right end. (a) Using an identity from Appendix B.11, show that $y = y_1 + y_2$ is a standing wave that satisfies the appropriate boundary condition at $x = 0$. (b) Derive Eq. 22.3.

22-62 In Fig. 22.2*b*, assume that the two traveling waves are represented by $y_1 = A \sin(kx - \omega t)$ and $y_2 = A \sin(kx + \omega t)$, where $x = 0$ is at the left end of the tube and $x = l$ is at the right end. (a) Using an identity from Appendix B.11, show that $y = y_1 + y_2$ is a standing wave that satisfies the appropriate boundary condition at $x = 0$. (b) Derive Eq. 22.4.

ANSWERS TO REVIEW QUESTIONS

Q22-1, sound is a mechanical disturbance with an actual movement of molecules and atoms; **Q22-2**, large; **Q22-3**, short; **Q22-4**, boundaries; **Q22-5**, closed, open; **Q22-6**, square pressure; **Q22-7**, a resonant structure; **Q22-8**, intensity, frequency; **Q22-9**, formants; **Q22-10**, the outer ear canal; **Q22-11**, decibels.

SUPPLEMENTARY TOPICS

22.8 | ULTRASOUND

In this section, we describe some of the properties and medical applications of ultrasound, which is sound with frequencies above 20,000 Hz. Ultrasound can currently be produced at frequencies as high as somewhat more than 10^9 Hz. It is widely used as a diagnostic, therapeutic, and surgical tool in medicine, as well as in a widening variety of industrial applications.

Physical Principles and Limitations | In most applications, ultrasound is sent out in pulses that are partially reflected. Between pulses, the transmitter acts as a receiver, detecting the reflected wave or echo. Accurately locating small objects at substantial distances requires narrow, short wavelength beams with sufficient range. These criteria tend to conflict, since short wavelengths (high frequencies) are strongly absorbed. For example, at a frequency of 1 megahertz (1 megahertz = 1 MHz = 10^6 Hz), the intensity drops 50 percent in 7 cm of soft animal tissue. Although in some situations the intensity is limited by the capacity of the apparatus, in medical applications the intensity limit is determined mainly by the destructive effects of intense ultrasound on animal tissues.

Ultrasound is useful because it is reflected from the boundaries between materials of nearly the same density and can be used without apparent harmful effects where X rays cannot. For example, ultrasonic scanning of the uterus during pregnancy is considered safe, while X rays must be avoided.

The fraction of the sound intensity reflected at a boundary can be found from a formula derived using advanced mathematical methods. Consider a sound wave passing from one medium of density ρ_1 and sound velocity c_1 to a second medium of density ρ_2 and sound velocity c_2. The ratio of the reflected to incident intensities when the wave travels perpendicular to the interface is

$$\frac{I_r}{I_i} = \left(\frac{\rho_1 c_1 - \rho_2 c_2}{\rho_1 c_1 + \rho_2 c_2}\right)^2 \qquad (22.7)$$

Since the sound velocity does not vary much, the amplitude of the reflected wave depends primarily on the density difference. It is this dependence that causes detectable reflections from boundaries even if the density change is small. This is illustrated by the next example.

Example 22.9

The densities of two types of muscle tissue are 1026 and 1068 kg m^{-3}. What is the ratio of the intensities of the reflected and incident waves if the wave passes from the more dense to the less dense medium? (Assume that the sound velocities are the same.)

Using the densities given and Eq. 22.7, the sound velocities factor out, and we have

$$\frac{I_r}{I_i} = \left(\frac{1068 \text{ kg m}^{-3} - 1026 \text{ kg m}^{-3}}{1068 \text{ kg m}^{-3} + 1026 \text{ kg m}^{-3}}\right)^2 = 0.00040$$

Although this ratio is small, the reflected sound is still measurable. The unreflected part of the wave continues on, and further reflections at other boundaries can occur.

Equation 22.7 becomes simpler if we assume that the sound velocities c_1 and c_2 are equal, so we have

$$\frac{I_r}{I_i} = \frac{(\rho_1 - \rho_2)^2}{(\rho_1 + \rho_2)^2}$$

We see that the reflection is minimal when ρ_1 and ρ_2 are nearly equal. Conversely, if one of the densities is much larger than the other, the reflection is comparatively large.

This result may be partially understood with the aid of a mechanical analog discussed in detail in Section 7.4. There we studied an elastic head-on collision of a moving object of mass m_1 with an object of mass m_2 that is initially at rest. We applied momentum and energy conservation to the case where they move away parallel to the original direction. In the present context, we can regard the energy acquired by the struck object as transmitted energy. We found that if the objects have equal mass—the billiards or pool situation—m_1 stops and m_2 has all the energy that m_1 originally had. Thus all the energy is transmitted, and none is reflected. We also saw that when the masses are not equal, m_2 still acquires some energy, but the percentage becomes steadily smaller as the mismatch between the masses increases. Whether m_1 is much larger than m_2 or the other way around, most of the energy is retained by m_1 or reflected, and little is transmitted.

A situation comparable to the case of very unequal masses occurs for ultrasonic waves at an air–tissue boundary, where virtually all the sound is reflected because the density change is large. In most medical work this necessitates using a liquid to provide good transmission between the ultrasound source and the tissue. Nearly total reflection occurs at air-tissue boundaries in the body.

Destructive Effects | Intense ultrasound produces large density and pressure changes within each small wavelength. This results in large stresses, and molecules are forced to move rapidly. It also produces heat in most materials and *cavitation* in liquids and perhaps in tissue. Cavitation is the formation of bubbles of vapor caused by the mechanical fracture of the liquid in a region where the pressure is decreasing. These bubbles may then collapse violently. This catastrophic collapse can be used for cleaning, since the implosion scatters the liquid along with impurities. Cavitation is also used to produce minute droplets of liquid. Medication used in inhalation therapy is broken with ultrasound into droplets fine enough to enter the alveoli of the lungs.

Another violent result of ultrasound treatment is the mechanical rupture of cell membranes and breakage of cell constituents, such as chromosomes (Fig. 22.20). A major fraction of the energy lost in tissue is absorbed by proteins.

All these effects limit the therapeutic use of ultrasound to intensities below 3×10^4 W m^{-2}. This may be compared with surgical intensities of 25×10^4 W m^{-2}.

Instrumentation and Display | Ultrasound sources are usually crystals that are either *piezoelectric* or *magnetostrictive*. A piezoelectric crystal is one in which an applied electric field alters the molecular positions, producing stresses in the crystal. If the applied field is periodic, the crystal vibrates, producing sound. Magnetostrictive materials exhibit similar behavior in an applied magnetic field. Both types of transducers also act as receivers, since the mechanical vibrations produce electric and magnetic fields that can be detected and used to monitor incoming sound waves.

In diagnostic medical work, two techniques of scanning and display are common. In an A-scan, the vertical deflection plates of an oscilloscope display voltages associated with the emission or reception of sound pulses. The horizontal motion of the beam is adjusted so that the sweep time is long enough to display the original pulse and its echo (Figs. 22.21 and 22.22).

A second technique, the B-scan, uses a movable transducer. In this case, the voltage due to the pulse or echo is added to the accelerating voltage in the electron gun of the cathode-ray tube. The oscilloscope is adjusted so that only when a pulse or echo voltage is present are the electrons fast enough to produce a bright spot on the screen (Fig. 22.23).

The echos then appear on the screen as bright spots whose brightness depends on the strength of the echo. Thus if the transducer were not moved,

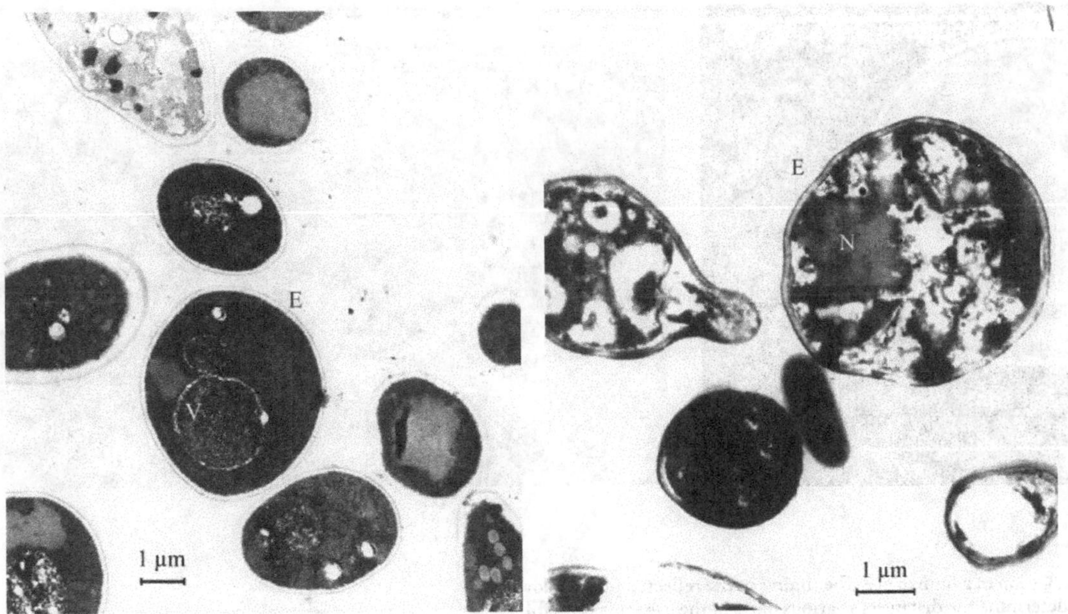

Figure 22.20. Electron photomicrographs of Baker's yeast cells (*a*) before and (*b*) after exposure to ultrasound. (From S. Radel, Ultrasonics 38:633-637, 2000. Reproduced with permission from Elsevier.)

the peaks would appear only as bright spots along a line. When the transducer is moved parallel to the body surface, the vertical deflection plates are adjusted so that the traces are displaced along horizontal lines one above another (Figs. 22.24 and 22.25). Newer instruments do not require movement of the transducer. The beam leaving the transducer can be swept across the region of interest. However, the principle of the display is the same.

Ultrasound is very useful for detection motion. For example, the motion of the heart wall or even of the mitral valve can be detected (Fig. 22.26). Special source probes can even be used to do ultrasonic scanning from inside the heart. The Doppler effect

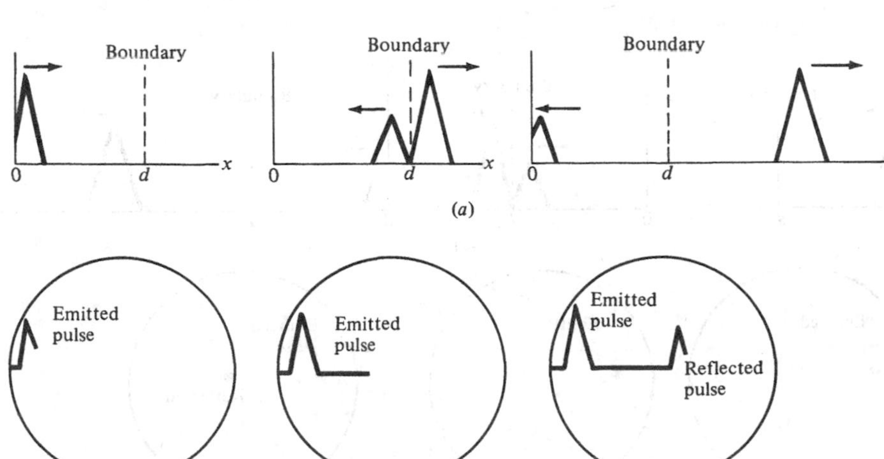

Figure 22.21. (*a*) A pulse is emitted and travels toward a tissue boundary a distance d away. Part of the pulse (shown colored) is reflected at the interface and returns to the transducer. (*b*) The oscilloscope trace monitors the emitted pulse and the reflected pulse a time $t = 2d/c$ later. Because these events are so rapid the eye only sees the completed trace.

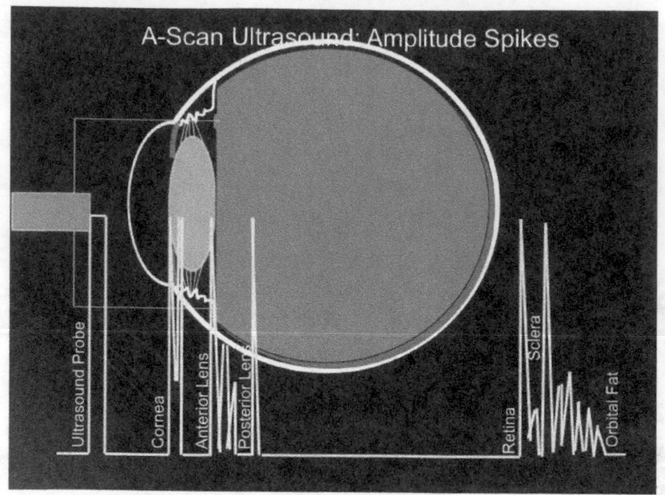

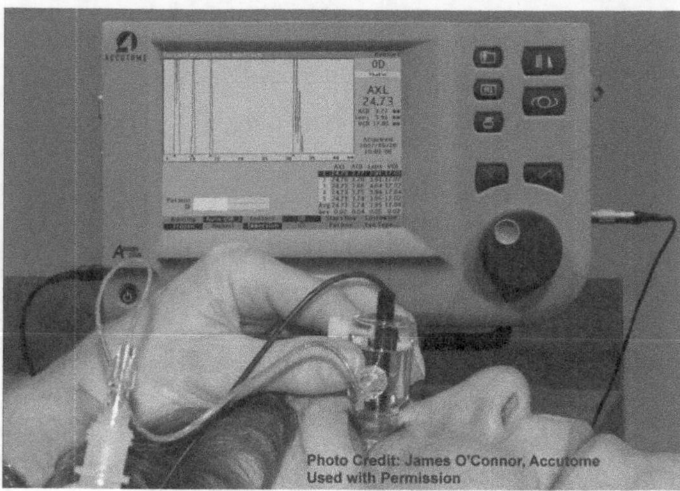

Figure 22.22. (a) An A-scan of a human eye. The timing of the reflected pulses allows the ophthalmologist to determine the distance to various parts of the eye. This is useful in planning cataract surgery, which implants a plastic lens to replace the patient's natural lens which has gradually become opaque. The human eye and cataracts are discussed later in Sec. 24.7. (b) A patient undergoing a scan of her eye. (Courtesy J. O'Connor, Accutome, Inc.)

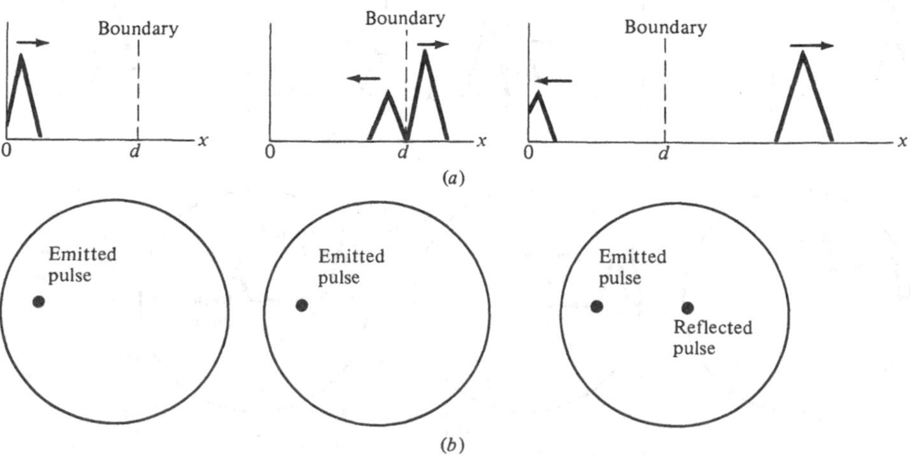

Figure 22.23. The sequence of events in (*a*) appears on a single scan of the oscilloscope trace (*b*) as bright spots.

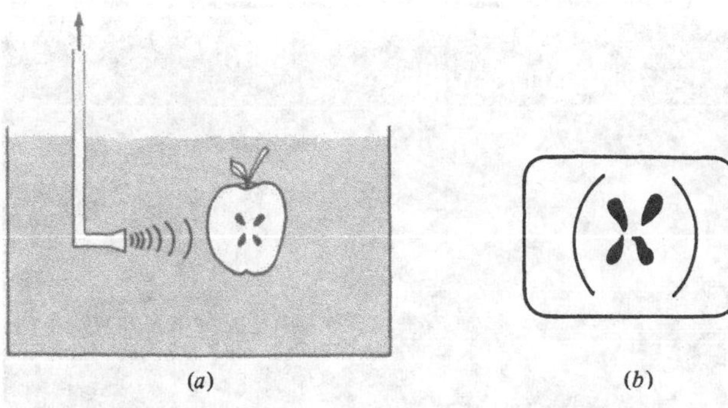

Figure 22.24. A B-scan performed on an apple (shown in cross section). (*a*) The apple and transmitter–receiver are immersed in water to improve transmission. The ultrasonic beam is directed to the right, and partial reflection occurs at the apple surface and from the seeds. The receiver is moved upward during the scan producing the oscilloscope trace shown in (*b*).

with ultrasound can be used to detect fetal heart beats and the pulsation of arterial walls.

22.9 | THE SPEED OF SOUND

We now derive the speed of sound in a medium by applying Newton's second law of motion as stated in Section 7.1: The impulse imparted to an object equals its momentum change. We consider a sound wave in fluid in a cylindrical tube as in Fig. 22.26, although the result is more general. Here the object in the second law is a segment of the fluid, and the impulse is imparted by the piston.

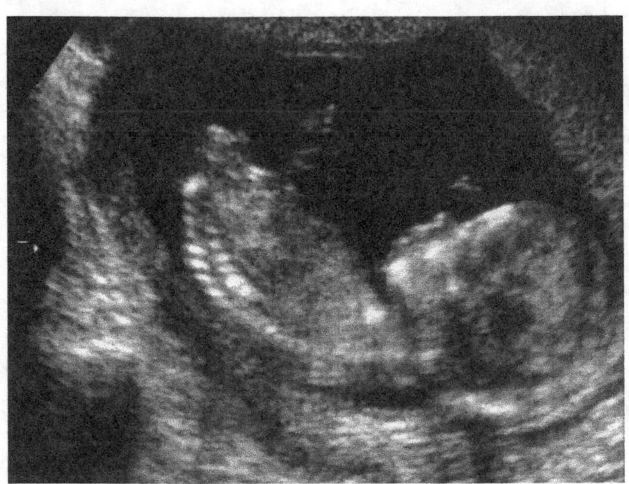

Figure 22.25. B-scan of a fetus at 13 weeks. The transducer is directed downward and is moved back and forth mechanically to obtain this result. (Zephyr / Photo Researchers, Inc.)

In Fig. 22.27, the fluid has an initial density ρ and a pressure P. The piston is suddenly pushed to the right, compressing the adjacent fluid and increasing the pressure by ΔP. The piston moves at a velocity v and the collisions with the molecules in the fluid nearby give them an average velocity v also. The disturbance in the fluid propagates forward at the sound velocity c. Note that the piston and sound velocities are different, just as the velocity of an individual falling domino differs from the rate at which a disturbance travels along a line of dominos. Normally the sound velocity c is much larger than v, the average velocity of the particles in the medium.

In a time Δt the piston moves a distance $v\ \Delta t$, while the front of the disturbed section of the fluid moves $c\ \Delta t$. The cross-sectional area of the piston and the fluid segment is A. Thus this segment has a volume $A(c\ \Delta t)$, and its mass is the density ρ times the volume, or $\rho(Ac\ \Delta t)$. The fluid within that segment is moving at a velocity v. Since the fluid is initially at rest, the magnitude of its momentum change $\Delta \mathbf{p} = \Delta(m\mathbf{v})$ is the product of its mass and its velocity, $(\rho Ac\ \Delta t)v$. The impulse is the product of the net force $A\ \Delta P$ on the fluid and the time it acts, $(A\ \Delta P)\Delta t$. Thus we have

$$A\ \Delta P\ \Delta t = \rho Ac\ \Delta t\ v$$

and the pressure change must satisfy

$$\Delta P = \rho c v \tag{22.8}$$

Now from the definition of the bulk modulus (Eq. 22.1) the pressure change satisfies $\Delta P = K(\Delta\rho/\rho)$. The density of the fluid is its mass-to-volume ratio, $\rho = m/V$. If the density increases slightly, there is a corresponding decrease in the volume of a given mass. (More formally, we note that if m is constant, $d\rho = d(m/V) = -m\ dV/V^2 = -\rho\ dV/V$.) Hence the fractional density change $\Delta\rho/\rho$ is equal in magnitude to the fractional volume change $\Delta V/V$ for small changes. The segment has an overall initial length $c\ \Delta t$ and is shortened by $v\ \Delta t$, so equating the magnitudes yields

$$\frac{\Delta\rho}{\rho} = \frac{\Delta V}{V} = \frac{Av\ \Delta t}{Ac\ \Delta t} = \frac{v}{c}$$

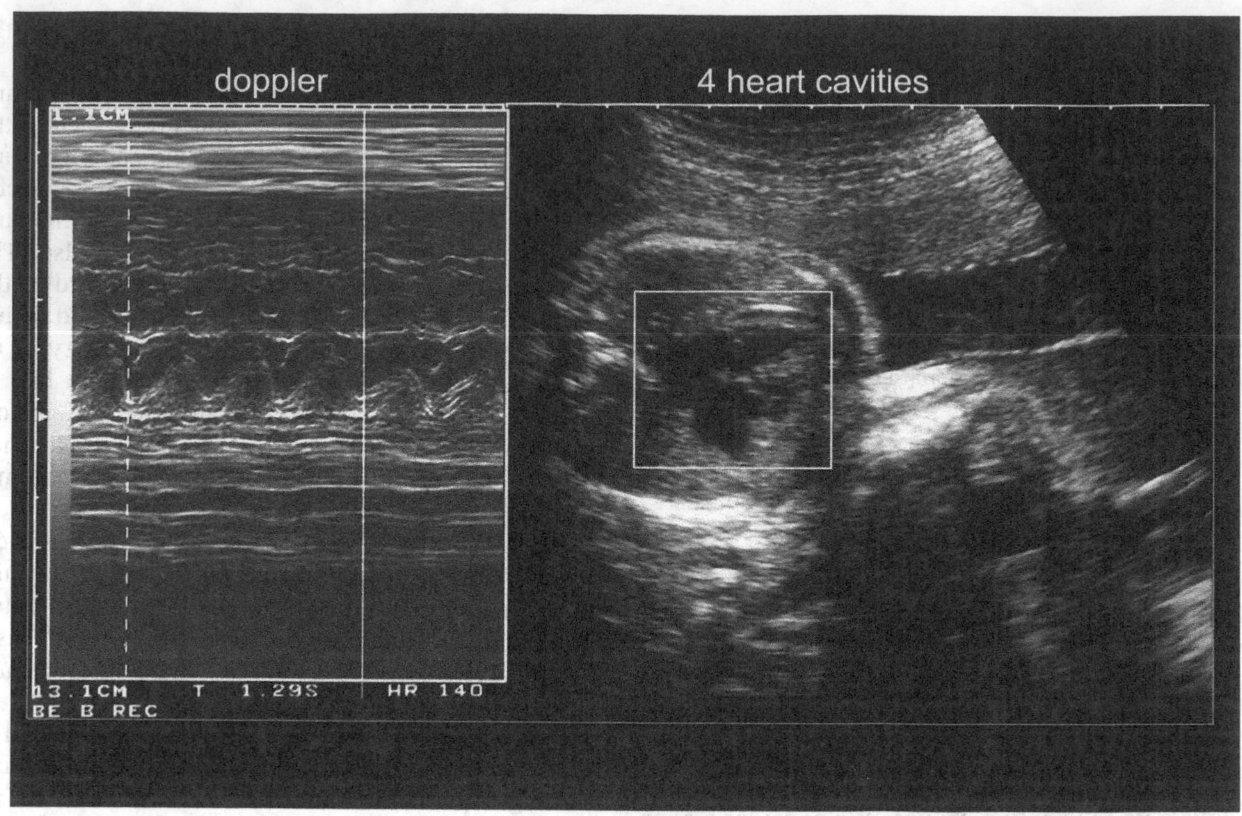

Figure 22.26. Doppler ultrasound. Examination of cardiac cavity of a 5-month-old fetus. (James Cavallini / Photo Researcher)

Thus $\Delta P = K\, \Delta\rho/\rho = Kv/c$. With Eq. 22.8, we have then

$$\frac{Kv}{c} = \rho c v$$

or

$$c = \left[\frac{K}{\rho}\right]^{1/2}$$

This is Eq. 22.2.

When a thin rod is struck, a similar compressional pulse travels along the rod. However, the rod also expands transverely when this occurs. A detailed analysis shows that Young's modulus (Chapter Eight) then replaces the bulk modulus in Eq. 22.2 for the velocity of the longitudinal sound wave. In an extended solid medium, the sound velocity also depends on the shear modulus.

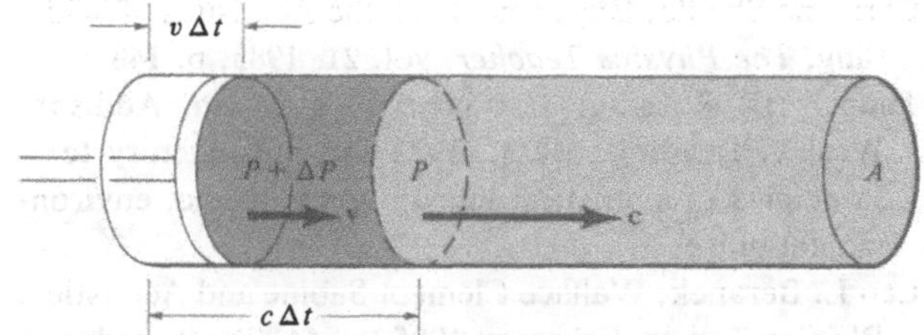

Figure 22.27. The fluid is initially at a uniform pressure P and density ρ. The piston is moved toward the right at a velocity v, and the disturbance it produces travels at the speed of sound c.

EXERCISES ON SUPPLEMENTARY TOPICS

Section 22.8 | Ultrasound

22-63 (a) If sound travels from air to water perpendicular to the interface, what percentage of the intensity is reflected? (b) If sound travels from water to air, what percentage of the intensity is transmitted?

22-64 A new ultrasound microscope uses frequencies of 3×10^9 Hz. What wavelength does this sound have in water at 20° C?

22-65 The energy loss of an ultrasonic wave is proportional to the square of the frequency. Find the ratio of the energy losses for waves at 1 MHz to those for waves at 3000 MHz.

PROBLEMS ON SUPPLEMENTARY TOPICS

22-66 The echo from the midline of the brain is detected on an oscilloscope 10^{-4} s after the source pulse. How far from the source is the midline? (Assume that the velocity of sound in brain tissue is 1540 m s^{-1}. Neglect corrections due to the skull bone.)

22-67 What would you expect the approximate limit of accuracy of distance measurements in human tissue to be when using sound of frequency 10^6 Hz?

22-68 In a brain scan, the echos from the right side of the skull, the midline of the brain, and the left side of the skull are observed after times of 0.10×10^{-4}, 1.26×10^{-4}, and 2.40×10^{-4} s, respectively. If the sound velocity is 1540 m s^{-1}, (a) how far is the midline of the brain displaced? (b) Which hemisphere of the brain is enlarged?

22-69 An object of mass m_1 and velocity v collides elastically and head on with one of mass m_2 that is initially at rest. We define the fractional transmitted energy as the ratio of the final kinetic energy of m_2 to that of m_1 before the collision. The fractional reflected energy is the ratio of the energies of mass m_1 after and before the collision. (a) Show that the fractional transmitted energy is given by

$$\frac{4m_1m_2}{(m_1 + m_2)^2}$$

(b) Show that the fractional reflected energy is given by

$$\left(\frac{m_1 - m_2}{m_1 + m_2}\right)^2$$

(c) What fractions of the energy are transmitted and reflected if $m_1 = m_2$, $m_1 = 10m_2$, and $m_2 = 100m_1$?

Additional Reading

See also the references marked with an asterisk (*) at the end of Chapter Twenty-one.

Winston E. Kock, *Sound Waves and Light Waves*, Science Study Series, Doubleday and Co., Garden City, N.Y., 1965.

William A. Van Bergeigk, John R. Pierce, and Edward B. David, Jr., *Waves and the Ear*, Science Study Series, Doubleday and Co., Garden City, N.Y., 1960.

Jess J. Josephs, *The Physics of Musical Sound*, D. Van Nostrand and Co., Princeton, N.J., 1967.

D. R. Griffin, How Bats Guide Their Flight by Supersonic Echoes, *American Journal of Physics*, vol. 12, 1944, p. 343.

F. S. Crawford, Singing Corrugated Pipes, *American Journal of Physics*, vol. 42, 1974, p. 278.

T. D. Rossing, Musical Acoustics (Resource Letter MA-1), *American Journal of Physics*, vol. 43, 1975, p. 944.

Arthur H. Benade, *Fundamentals of Musical Acoustics*, Oxford University Press, New York, 1976.

J. W. Coltman, Acoustics of the Flute, *Physics Today*, vol. 21, November 1968, p. 25.

H. Fletcher, The Pitch, Loudness, and Quality of Musical

Tones, *American Journal of Physics*, vol. 14, 1946, p. 215.

J. L. Flanagan, *Speech Analysis: Synthesis and Perception*, 2nd ed., Springer-Verlag, Berlin, 1972.

Peter B. Denes and Elliot N. Pruson, *The Speech Chain*, Bell Telephone Laboratories, Murray Hill, N.J., 1963.

Dale Esnminger, *Ultrasonics; The Low and High Energy Applications*, Marcel Dekker, Inc., New York, 1973. Chapter 14 is a summary of the medical applications of ultrasound.

Julian R. Frederick, *Ultrasonic Engineering*, John Wiley & Sons, Inc., New York, 1965, Chapters 7, 8, and 9.

P. N. T. Wells, *Physical Principles of Ultrasonic Diagnosis*, Academic Press, London and New York, 1969.

Thomas H. Maugh II, Acoustic Microscopy: A New Window to the World of the Small, *Science*, vol. 201, 1978, p. 1110.

Thomas H. Maugh II, Eavesdropping on Bones, *Science*, vol. 214, 1981, p. 172. Sounds from bones under stress diagnose bone fractures and monitor their healing.

James C. Smith, James T. Marsh, Steven Greenberg, and Warren S. Brown, Human Auditory Frequency-Following Responses to a Missing Fundamental, *Science*, vol. 201, 1978, p. 639.

Richard L. Popp and Albert Macovski, Ultrasonic Diagnostic Instruments, *Science*, vol. 210, 1980, p. 268.

Irwin Hersey, The Dangerous Decibels, *Engineering Opportunities*, August 1969, p. 9.

Beverly Karplus Hartline, Snow Physics and Avalanche Prediction, *Science*, vol. 203, 1979, p. 346.

Edgar A. G. Shaw, Noise Pollution—What Can Be Done? *Physics Today*, January 1975, p. 46.

Rickye Heffner and Henry Heffner, Hearing in the Elephant, *Science*, vol. 208, 1980, p. 518.

Gerhard Neuweiler, How Bats Detect Flying Insects, *Physics Today*, August 1980, p. 34.

James A. Simmons, M. Brock Fenton, and Michael J. O'Farrell, Echolocation and Pursuit of Prey by Bats, *Science*, vol. 203, 1979, p. 16.

Masakazu Konishi, How the Owl Tracks its Prey, *American Scientist*, vol. 61, 1973, p. 414.

Masakazu Konishi and Eric I. Knudsen, The Oilbird: Hearing and Echolocation, *Science*, vol. 204, 1979, p. 425.

Thomas D. Rossing, Physics and Psychophysics of High-Fidelity Sound, Part V, *The Physics Teacher*, vol. 22, 1984, p. 84. Earlier articles in the series are referenced.

Christine Shadle, Experiments on the Acoustics of Whistling, *The Physics Teacher*, vol. 21, 1983, p. 148.

Thomas D. Rossing, *The Science of Sound*, Addison-Wesley, Reading, Mass., 1982. An introductory text. Principles of acoustics, human voice, music, environmental noise.

Leo L. Beranek, Wallace Clement Sabine and Acoustics, *Physics Today*, February 1985, p. 44. The founder of the science of architectural acoustics.

Calvin F. Quate, Acoustic Microscopy, *Physics Today*, August 1985, p. 34.

Scientific American articles:

Maurice Ewing and Leonard Engel, Seismic Shooting at Sea, May 1962, p. 116.

Herbert A. Wilson, Jr., Sonic boom, January 1962, p. 36.

Mark R. Rosenzweig, Auditory Localization, October 1961, p. 132.

Richard M. Warren and Roslyn P. Warren, Auditory Illusions and Confusions, December 1970, p. 30.

Robert C. Chanard, Aerodynamic Whistles, January 1970, p. 40.

Edward E. David, Jr., The Reproduction of Sound, August 1961, p. 72.

Victor E. Ragosine, Magnetic Recording, November 1969, p. 70.

Leo L. Beranck, Noise, December 1966, p. 66.

Arthur A. Few, Thunder, July 1975, p. 80.

Veru O. Knudsen, Architectural Acoustics, November 1963, p. 78.

Gordon S. Kiuo and John Shaw, Acoustic Surface Waves, October 1972, p. 50.

Gerald E. Loeb, The Functional Replacement of the Ear, February, 1985, p. 104.

Georg von Békésy, The Ear, August 1957, p. 66.

Erik Borg and S. Allen Counter, The Middle-Ear Muscles, August 1989, p. 74.

James L. Flanagan, The Synthesis of Speech, February 1972, p. 48.

Adrian M. Wenner, Sound Communication in Honeybees, April 1964, p. 116.

Crawford Greenewalt, How Birds Sing, November 1969, p. 126.

Peter F. Ostwald, Acoustic Methods in Psychiatry, March 1965, p. 82.

Gerald Oster, Auditory Beats in the Brain, October 1973, p. 94.

Peter F. Ostwald and Phillip Peltzman, The Cry of the Human Infant, March 1974, p. 84.

F. A. Saunders, Physics and Music, July 1948, p. 33.

Arthur H. Benade, The Physics of Woodwinds, October 1960, p. 144.

E. Donnell Blackham, The Physics of the Piano, December 1965, p. 88.

Sinyan Shen, Acoustics of Ancient Chinese Bells, April 1987, p. 104.

Max V. Mathews and John R. Pierce, The Computer as a Musical Instrument, February 1987, p. 126.

John C. Schelleng, The Physics of the Bowed String, January 1974, p. 87.

B. Patterson, Musical Dynamics, November 1974, p. 78.

Diana Deutsch, Musical Illusions, October 1975, p. 92.

Johan Sundberg, The Acoustics of the Singing Voice, March 1977, p. 82.

G. E. Henry, Ultrasonics, May 1954, p. 54.

Klaus Dransfeld, Kilomegacycle Ultrasonics, June 1963, p. 60.

Kenneth D. Roeder, Moths and Ultrasound, April 1965, p. 94.

Calvin F. Quate, The Acoustic Microscope, October 1979, p. 62.

Gilbert B. Devey and Peter N. T. Wells, Ultrasound in Medical Diagnosis, May 1978, p. 98.

Kenneth S. Suslick, The Chemical Effects of Ultrasound, February 1989, p. 80.

Eric I. Knudsen, The Hearing of the Barn Owl, December 1981, p. 112.

Jearl Walker, Some Whispering Galleries Are Simply Sound Reflectors, But Others Are More Mysterious, *The Amateur Scientist*, October 1978, p. 179.

A. J. Hudspeth, The Hair Cells of the Inner Ear, January 1983, p. 54. Mechanical forces are converted into electrical signals to the brain.

Neville H. Fletcher and Suzanne Thwaites, The Physics of Organ Pipes, January 1983, p. 94.

Jearl Walker, What Makes You Sound So Good When You Sing in the Shower? *The Amateur Scientist*, May 1982, p. 170.

Thomas D. Rossing, The Physics of Kettledrums, *The Amateur Scientist*, November 1982, p. 172.

CHAPTER 23 WAVE PROPERTIES OF LIGHT

Historically, the wave theory of light was not readily accepted because many observations seemed easier to explain with a model that treated a light beam as a stream of particles. Both particle and wave theories could adequately describe the *reflection* of light, as well as *refraction*, the bending of light as it crosses a boundary between two media. Waves tend to bend around obstacles, as is readily observed with water or sound waves. Since we cannot see around obstacles, this was taken as evidence against wave theories until experiments in the early part of the nineteenth century demonstrated interference effects. These experiments also showed that the bending of light around ordinary objects is difficult to observe because the wavelength of visible light is very short. Later in the century, Maxwell's work on electromagnetic radiation gave the wave model of light a firm theoretical foundation.

Despite the great success of Maxwell's electromagnetic wave theory in predicting many phenomena involving light, it failed to describe correctly some processes in which light is absorbed or emitted by matter. The modern *quantum theory*, developed early in the twentieth century, states that light is composed of *quanta*, or *photons*. These are little packets or bundles of light waves, each with an energy proportional to the frequency. Photons have a particlelike aspect associated with the discreteness of their energy in addition to their wave attributes. The quantum theory of light will be discussed in Chapter Twenty-six, but for the situations considered in this unit, the classical electromagnetic wave theory is adequate.

In the first part of this chapter, we discuss the speed of light, reflection, and refraction. The next few sections cover some of the interference properties of light waves. The chapter concludes with a brief discussion of the polarization of light. Applications to optical instruments will be treated in the next chapter.

Although we concentrate mainly on visible light in this chapter, it should be noted that much of what we discuss applies also to other electromagnetic waves and to other wave phenomena, such as sound and water waves.

23.1 | THE INDEX OF REFRACTION

Electromagnetic waves of any frequency travel in a vacuum with the same velocity, $c = 3.00 \times 10^8$ m s^{-1}. In a material medium, the velocity v depends on the frequency of the wave, but it is never greater than the velocity c in a vacuum. The ratio of these velocities is the *index of refraction* of the medium,

$$n = \frac{c}{v} \tag{23.1}$$

Since v is never greater than c, n is never less than one. In comparing two media, the one with the larger refractive index is said to be *optically denser*. Representative indices of refraction are given in Table 23.1 for yellow light. The refractive index varies somewhat with the frequency. In a typical material the variation is 1 or 2 percent within the visible spectrum.

The frequency of a light wave is determined by its source and is unaffected by the medium. Since $f\lambda = v = c/n$, the wavelength changes when the index of refraction changes. If a beam of light goes from a

TABLE 23.1

Indices of refraction of representative materials for yellow sodium light (λ = 589 nanometres) We use the approximate values n = 1 for air and n = 4/3 for water.

Material	Index
Air	1.00029
Carbon dioxide	1.00045
Water	1.333
Ethyl alcohol	1.362
Benzene	1.501
Carbon disulfide	1.628
Glass, light crown	1.517
Glass, heavy flint	1.647
Fluorite	1.434
Diamond	2.417

medium with index n_1 to a medium with index n_2, then $f\lambda_1 = c/n_1$, and $f\lambda_2 = c/n_2$. Dividing these two equations,

$$\frac{\lambda_2}{\lambda_1} = \frac{1/n_2}{1/n_1} = \frac{n_1}{n_2} \quad (23.2)$$

This means that the wavelength is smaller in the optically denser medium, as is illustrated by the following example.

Example 23.1

Green light with a wavelength of 5×10^{-7} m in a vacuum enters a glass plate with refractive index 1.5. (a) What is the velocity of light in the glass? (b) What is the wavelength of the light in the glass?

(a) From the definition $n = c/v$, the velocity in the glass is

$$v = \frac{c}{n} = \frac{3.00 \times 10^8 \text{ m s}^{-1}}{1.5}$$
$$= 2.00 \times 10^8 \text{ m s}^{-1}$$

(b) In the vacuum, $v = c$ and $n = 1$. Thus

$$\lambda_2 = \lambda_1 \frac{n_1}{n_2} = (5 \times 10^{-7} \text{ m}) \left(\frac{1}{1.5}\right)$$
$$= 3.33 \times 10^{-7} \text{ m}$$

Several units of length are commonly employed in discussions of electromagnetic waves. Metres, centimetres, and millimetres are convenient for radio and microwaves. Discussions of optical instruments and biological applications of visible light often use the *nanometre* (nm), where

$$1 \text{ nanometre} = 1 \text{ nm} = 10^{-9} \text{ m}$$

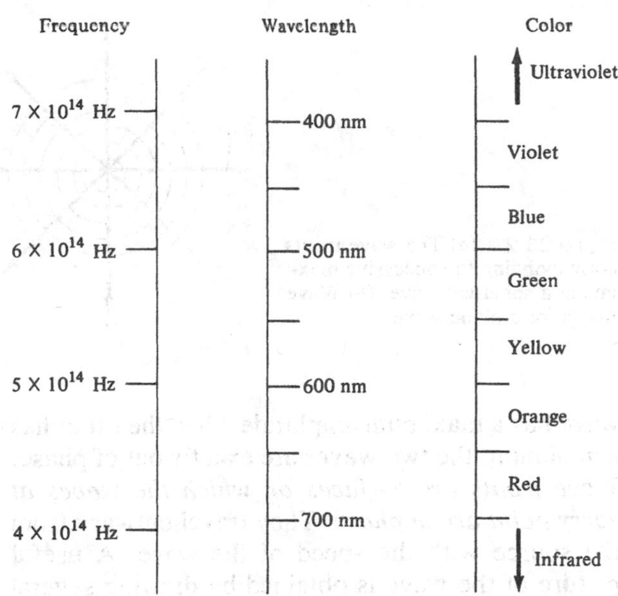

Figure 23.1. The spectrum of visible light. Color ranges are approximate.

The visible spectrum for humans extends approximately from 400 nm (violet) to 700 nm (red) (Fig. 23.1). *X rays* are very-high-frequency electromagnetic waves. They have many diagnostic and therapeutic uses in medicine and also serve as a powerful probe of the structure of complex molecules. A typical X-ray wavelength is about 0.1 nm = 10^{-10} m.

23.2 | HUYGENS' PRINCIPLE

In 1678, almost two centuries before Maxwell's work on electromagnetic waves, Christian Huygens (1629–1695) proposed a wave theory of light. It is still very useful for understanding many properties of light and other waves, since it makes no reference to the physical nature of the wave phenomenon.

To discuss Huygens' idea, now called *Huygens' principle*, it is useful to introduce the concept of a *wave front*. We recall from Chapter Twenty-one that two waves that have their maximum amplitude at the same time are said to be in phase. Also, if one

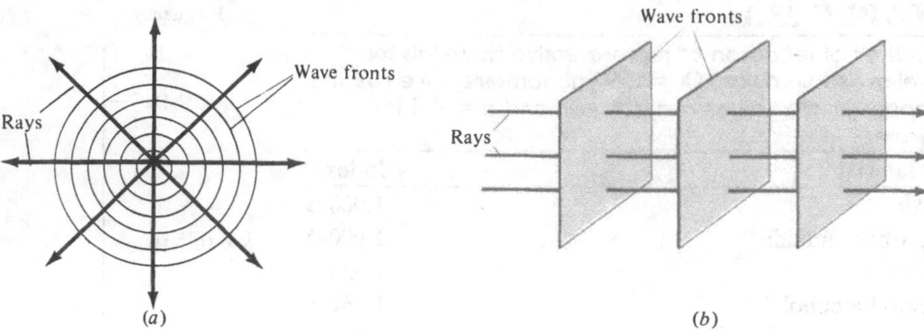

Figure 23.2. (*a*) The wave fronts corresponding to successive maxima in a spherical wave. (*b*) Wave fronts for a plane wave.

wave has a maximum amplitude when the other has a minimum, the two waves are exactly out of phase. *Wave fronts are surfaces on which the waves at every point are in phase.* They travel outward from the source with the speed of the wave. A useful picture of the wave is obtained by drawing several wave fronts (Fig. 23.2). A wave with spherical wave fronts is called a *spherical wave*. A wave that travels in a single direction has wave fronts that are planes, so it is called a *plane wave*. *A line perpendicular to the wave fronts is called a* ray *and indicates the direction of motion of the wave.* Often it is easier to draw only the rays and not the wave fronts.

Huygens' principle enables us to find the future shape and location of a wave front from its present shape and location. It states that *each point on a wave front can be considered as a source of small secondary spherical wavelets* (Fig. 23.3). The wave front at a later time is the surface tangent to the secondary wavelets, their *envelope*.

We can illustrate the use of Huygens' principle by considering a plane wave (Fig. 23.4). At several points on a wave front, we draw spheres of radius $r = ct$, representing the distance traveled by the secondary wavelets in time t. The tangent to these spheres is a plane displaced a distance ct from the original wave front. Thus the wave front has moved the expected distance in the time interval.

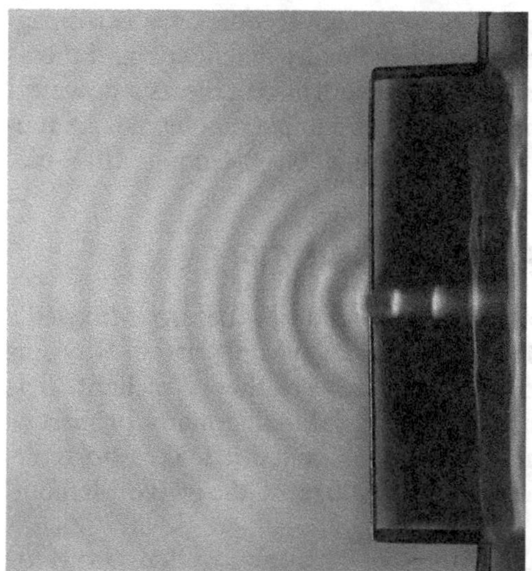

Figure 23.3. Water waves in a shallow ripple tank encounter a narrow slit in an obstacle. Circular wave fronts are produced to the left of the slit. (Andrew Lambert Photography / Photo Researchers, Inc.)

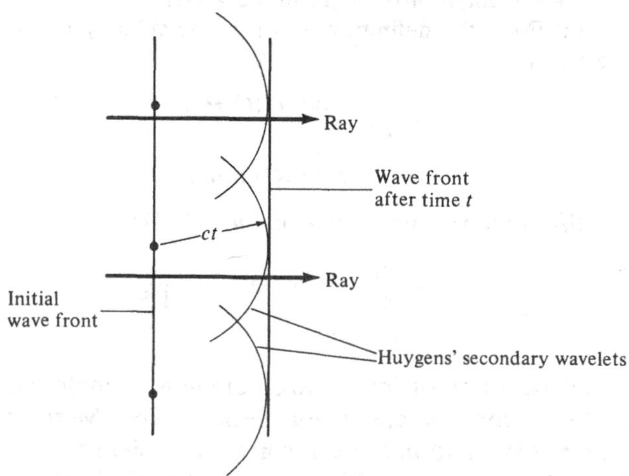

Figure 23.4. In a time t, the wave front moves a distance ct.

The original formulation of Huygens' principle stated that the wavelets radiate with equal intensity in all directions. This would imply that the waves travel backward as well as forward, contrary to what we see. In the nineteenth century, Fresnel and Kirchhoff put Huygens' ideas into a rigorous mathematical form and showed that the intensity of the wavelets is a maximum in the forward direction and gradually decreases to zero in the backward direction. Thus there is no wave going backward.

In the next two sections, we apply Huygens' principle to situations where light reaches a boundary between two media that extends over distances large compared to a wavelength. In such situations, the behavior of the light rays is simple to describe. Later in the chapter, we consider light beams encountering objects comparable in size to a wavelength. Interference effects then can be quite complex.

23.3 | REFLECTION OF LIGHT

When a beam of light reaches the boundary between two media, some light is transmitted, some is absorbed, and the remainder is reflected. The smooth surface of a piece of glass or polished metal reflects light in a particular direction. This is called *specular* reflection. Sometimes the reflection is *diffuse*, and the reflected light travels in all directions. This happens when light strikes a surface such as a sheet of paper or a painted wall with random irregularities that are large compared to a wavelength. Each smooth section of such a surface produces specular reflection, but because of the varying orientations of the sections, the total reflected beam has no unique direction.

In specular reflection (Fig. 23.5), the directions of the incident rays relative to the normal to the surface are related very simply:

The reflected light rays are in the same plane as the incident rays and the normal and make the same angle with the normal.

This equality of the angles of incidence and reflection is a general property of waves. It follows from Huygens' principle and applies equally well to sound waves or water waves (Fig. 23.6).

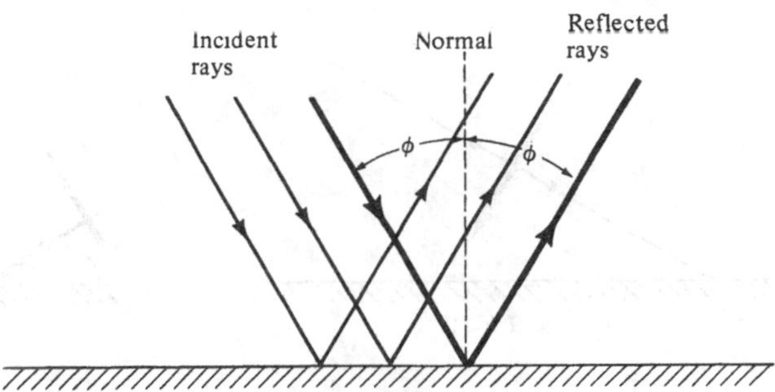

Figure 23.5. The reflected light rays are in the same plane as the incident rays and the normal and make the same angle with the normal.

Two additional properties of reflected light are important. First, we saw in Chapter Twenty-one that when waves on a string reach a fixed end, the reflected waves are *inverted* or *reversed in sign.* In this case, one says that the *phase is reversed.* This also happens to a light wave if it is incident on a boundary from an optically less dense medium moving toward a more dense medium. For example, a phase reversal occurs at an air-glass boundary when light is incident from the air. No phase reversal occurs when light is incident in the glass, which is the denser medium.

Second, the intensity I_r of the reflected wave is determined by the refractive indices n_1 and n_2 in the two media. The *reflectance R* is defined as the ratio of I_r and the incident intensity I_0. The *transmittance T* is the fraction transmitted, or $1 - R$. At normal incidence ($\phi = 0$) in either direction, the reflectance is

$$R = \frac{I_r}{I_0} = \left(\frac{n_2 - n_1}{n_2 + n_1}\right)^2 \quad \text{(normal incidence)} \quad (23.3)$$

This formula is also approximately correct if the angle of incidence is small but not zero. As the following example shows, significant amounts of light may be reflected at the air–glass surfaces of optical instruments.

Example 23.2

A lens is made of glass with $n = 1.5$. What fraction of the light is reflected at normal incidence?

With $n_1 = 1$ and $n_2 = 1.5$,

$$\frac{I_r}{I_0} = \left(\frac{n_2 - n_1}{n_2 + n_1}\right)^2 = \left(\frac{1.5 - 1}{1.5 + 1}\right)^2 = 0.040$$

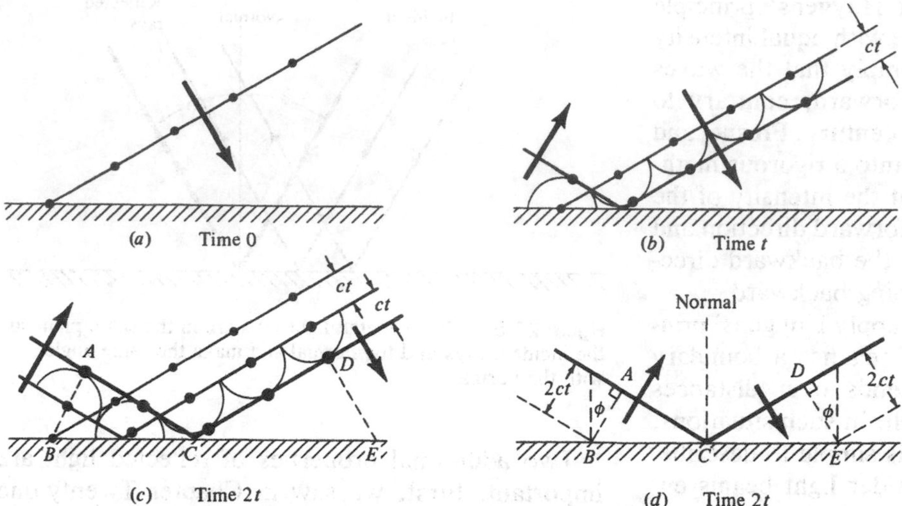

Figure 23.6. Huygens' principle applied to reflection. (*a*) A wave front reaches a reflecting surface. (*b*) After a short time *t*, the secondary wavelets from five equally spaced points on the original wave front have spread a distance *ct*. The new wave front is found by drawing lines tangent to the wavelets. (*c*) The wavelets from points on a wave front in part (*b*) have spread a distance *ct*. (*d*) Two right triangles redrawn from (*c*) for clarity. The reflected wave has traveled from *B* to *A* in time 2*t*, and the incident wave will travel from *D* to *E* in an equal time. Hence $AB = DE$. Also, since the points shown on the wave front are equally spaced, $AC = CD$. This means that the triangles *ABC* and *CDE* have two sides and an included angle equal, so they are congruent and all their corresponding sides and angles are equal. Consequently the two wave fronts are at the same angle with the surface. This means that the two rays also make the same angle with the normal.

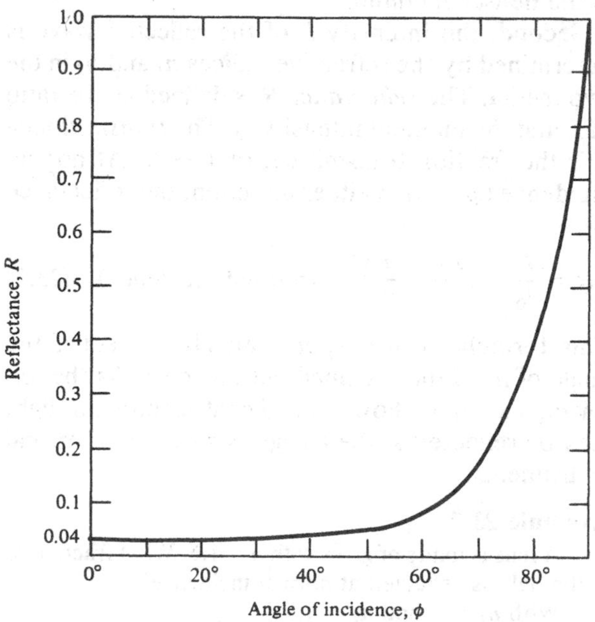

Figure 23.7. The reflectance $R = I_r/I_0$ versus the angle of incidence for unpolarized light incident in air on glass with a refractive index of 1.5. The fraction transmitted is $T = 1 - R$.

Thus 4 percent of the light is reflected. In a microscope or camera with several lenses, about 4 percent of the intensity is lost at each lens surface. Methods used to diminish these losses are discussed later in the chapter.

About 4 percent of the light is reflected when light is normally incident from air onto glass; 96 percent is transmitted. If the light is from an ordinary unpolarized source, the reflectance is small up to about 60°, but it increases rapidly beyond that angle. At grazing incidence, $\phi \approx 90°$, all the light is reflected; the fraction $T = 1 - R$ that is transmitted is zero (Fig. 23.7). A glass plate is nearly a perfect mirror when the light strikes it near 90°.

We further discuss the intensity of reflected and transmitted light waves in Section 23.10.

23.4 | REFRACTION OF LIGHT

When light rays go from one transparent medium to another with a different index of refraction, they are

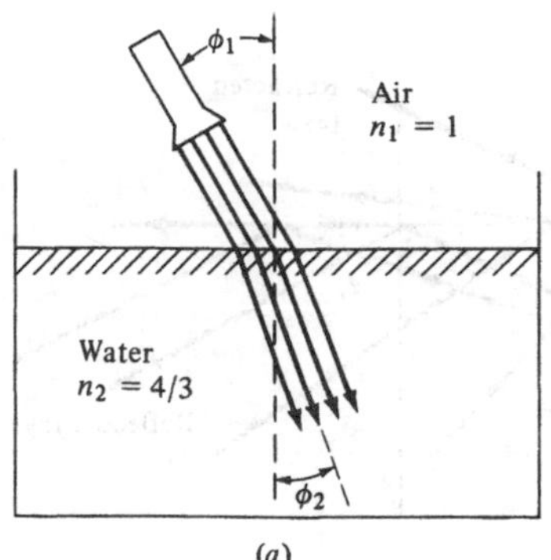

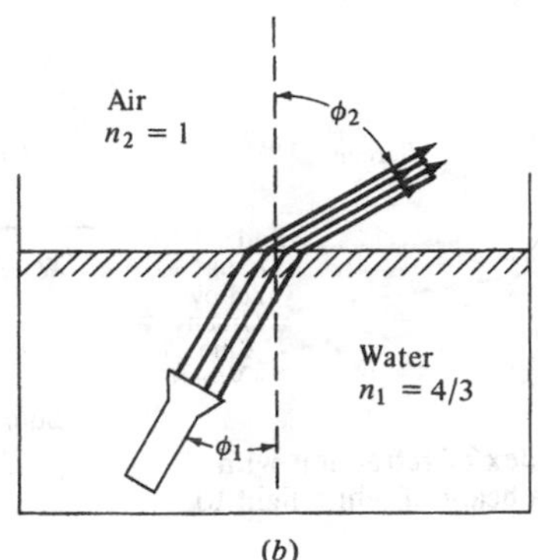

Figure 23.8. (*a*) Light bends toward the normal going from an optically rare to an optically dense medium. (*b*) Light bends away from the normal going from the denser to the rarer medium.

bent, or *refracted* (Fig. 23.8). As in the case of reflection, it is possible to find a relationship between the two directions with the aid of Huygens' principle. This relationship is called *Snell's law*, after Wilebrord Snell (1591–1626), who discovered it experimentally. If the indices of refraction of the media are n_1 and n_2, and the *angle of incidence* ϕ_1 and the *angle of refraction* ϕ_2 are measured relative to the normal direction, then Snell's law states that

$$n_1 \sin \phi_1 = n_2 \sin \phi_2 \tag{23.4}$$

As in the case of reflection, both rays and the normal are in the same plane.

Snell's law implies that if n increases, then $\sin \phi$ and consequently ϕ decrease. Thus a ray bends toward the normal when it enters an optically denser medium ($n_2 > n_1$) and away from the normal when it enters a rarer medium ($n_2 < n_1$). Illustrations of Snell's law are given in the following two examples.

Example 23.3

A beam of light is incident from air on water at an angle of 30°. Part of the light is reflected and part is refracted (Fig. 23.9). Find the angles of the two beams.

The incident and reflected rays form equal angles with the normal, so the angle of reflection is

$$\phi_1' = \phi_1 = 30°$$

By Snell's law, with $n_1 = 1$, $n_2 = 4/3$, and $\sin \phi_1 = \sin 30° = 0.5$, the angle of refraction is found from

$$\sin \phi_2 = \frac{n_1}{n_2} \sin \phi_1 = \frac{1}{4/3}(0.5) = 0.375$$

or $\phi_2 = 22°$.

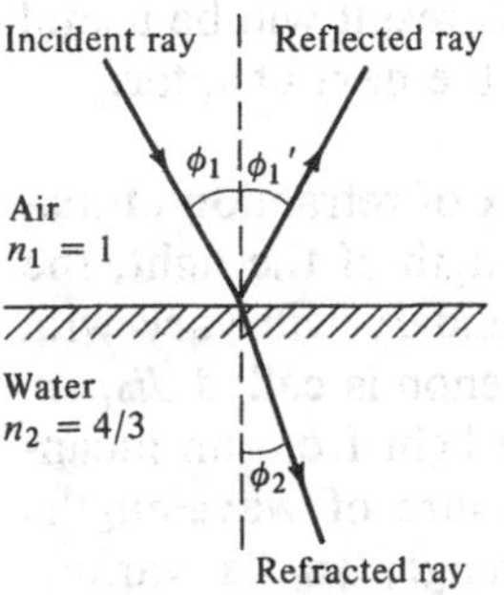

Figure 23.9. Example 23.3.

Example 23.4

Light is incident in air at an angle ϕ_1 on a flat glass plate with index n_2 (Fig. 23.10). At what angle does the transmitted beam emerge from the other side?

At the first surface, with $n_1 = 1$, Snell's law gives

$$n_2 \sin \phi_2 = n_1 \sin \phi_1 = \sin \phi_1$$

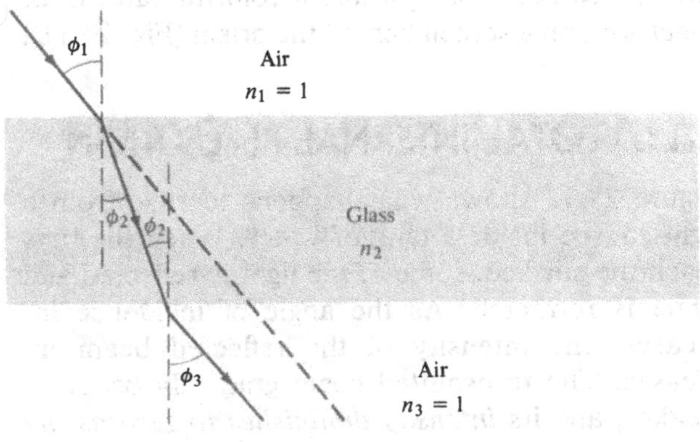

Figure 23.10. Example 23.4.

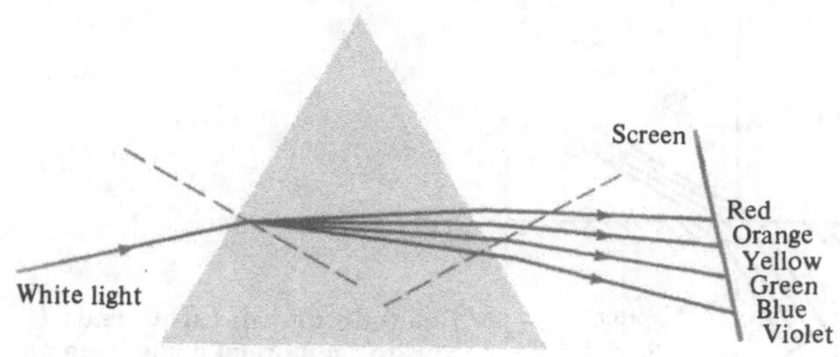

Figure 23.11. The variation of the index of refraction with wavelength causes different colors in a beam of white light to be separated by a glass prism.

Applying Snell's law at the second surface, with $n_3 = 1$,

$$n_2 \sin \phi_2 = n_3 \sin \phi_3 = \sin \phi_3$$

Comparing these equations, we have $\sin \phi_3 = \sin \phi_1$, or $\phi_3 = \phi_1$.

From this example, we see that a flat plate does not change the direction of a ray, although it does displace or shift the ray by a distance proportional to the thickness of the plate. This result will be useful in our discussion of lenses in the next chapter.

Dispersion | Since the index of refraction of materials varies with the wavelength of the light, the amount of bending at the boundary will vary with the wavelength. This phenomenon is called *dispersion. White light*, such as the light from an incandescent lamp, contains a mixture of wavelengths extending over the visible range, so its various wavelengths or colors are separated at an air–glass boundary, except at normal incidence. This effect occurs twice in a triangular glass *prism*, producing a fan-shaped beam of light and a colorful pattern, or *spectrum*, on a screen behind the prism (Fig. 23.11).

23.5 | TOTAL INTERNAL REFLECTION

Figure 23.12 shows what happens to rays from a light source inside a tank of water. When the rays reach the surface, some of the light is reflected and some is refracted. As the angle of incidence increases, the intensity of the reflected beam increases. The transmitted beam gradually becomes weaker, and its *intensity diminishes to zero as the angle of refraction reaches 90°*. The corresponding angle of incidence is called the *critical angle* ϕ_c. If the angle of incidence exceeds ϕ_c, no refracted beam is observed, and all the light is reflected. This is called *total internal reflection*.

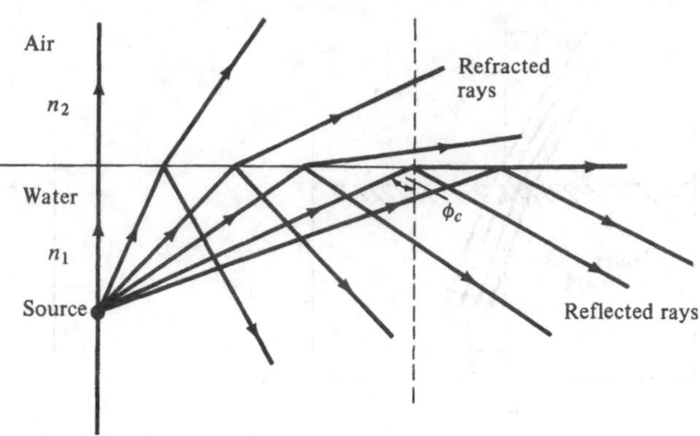

Figure 23.12. Total internal reflection occurs if the angle of incidence exceeds the critical angle ϕ_c.

The critical angle can be found from Snell's law by setting $\phi_2 = 90°$ or $\sin \phi_2 = 1$, corresponding to the maximum possible angle of refraction. This gives $n_1 \sin \phi_c = n_2$, or

$$\sin \phi_c = \frac{n_2}{n_1} \tag{23.5}$$

If a value of ϕ_1 larger than ϕ_c is substituted in Snell's law, $\sin \phi_2$ turns out to be greater than 1. Since no angle has a sine greater than 1, this implies that there is no refracted beam. This is in agreement with the observations that at any angle equal to or greater than ϕ_c, the beam is totally reflected.

Example 23.5

What is the critical angle for light going from glass with refractive index 1.5 into air?

Using $n_1 = 1.5$ and $n_2 = 1$,

$$\sin \phi_c = \frac{n_2}{n_1} = \frac{1}{1.5} = 0.667$$

and $\phi_c = 42°$. Thus light incident from the glass on a glass–air boundary will be completely reflected if the angle of incidence exceeds 42°. By contrast, light going from air into glass can enter at any angle of incidence.

In ordinary specular reflection, the reflected beam is always weaker than the incident beam,

THOMAS YOUNG (1773–1829)

Thomas Young was an unusually talented English physician and physicist. At the age of 2, he could read fluently; at 4, he had read the Bible twice; and at 14, he knew eight languages. Throughout his adult life he was active in both medicine and physics, and he also found the time to be the first person to make major progress on the problem of deciphering Egyptian hieroglyphics.

Young worked on various topics in the physics of fluids and made significant contributions relating to surface tension, capillarity, and the tides. He was the first to use the concept of energy as the ability of a system to do work, and he argued against the caloric theory of heat. He also studied the elastic properties of materials; as we have seen in Chapter Eight, his name is still associated with the parameter characterizing elastic deformations. However, Young's most important research related to the properties of light.

While he was still a medical student, Young discovered how the lens of the eye changes shape in order to focus on objects at different distances. He received his medical degree from Göttingen in Germany in 1796 and went into practice in London in 1799. In 1801, he discovered that irregularities in the cornea are responsible for astigmatism. Some years later, he proposed a theory of color vision based on the idea that the perception of three basic colors would, in combination, generate all the many shades we see. This theory was later refined by Helmholtz and is referred to as the Young–Helmholtz theory.

Turning his attention from the eye to the nature of light itself, Young performed some experiments that were crucial in demonstrating its wave properties. In 1803, he showed that when light went through a narrow slit, bright bands appeared in a region that would be totally dark if light did not bend. Even more striking was his double-slit experiment, which showed that two light beams can combine to produce alternating light and dark bands. The dark bands indicated a cancellation of the two beams, which was easily understood with waves but rather hard to explain with a particle model.

Young's demonstration of the wave nature of light was not well received in England, since Newton and his spiritual descendents had argued for a particle model. As a result, the work needed to extend his ideas was carried out by two French physicists, Fresnel and Arago. On the other hand, French physicists found it hard to abandon Lavoisier's "French" caloric theory. Several decades passed before this theory of heat was permanently put to rest.

---

even if the surface is highly polished. By contrast, *no loss of intensity occurs in total internal reflection*. For this reason, totally reflecting prisms are used rather than mirrors in binoculars, periscopes, and reflex cameras (Fig. 23.13). No loss of intensity is associated with the internal reflections in these prisms, although some light is reflected at the surfaces where the light enters or leaves.

The fact that no intensity loss occurs in total internal reflection is also the basis for *fiber optics*, a new and rapidly growing branch of optics. The basic principle of fiber optics is illustrated by a long transparent rod, or *light pipe* (Fig. 23.14*a*). A ray of light entering the pipe is totally reflected if the angle of incidence is large enough when the ray reaches the surface. Even if the pipe curves gradually, light will travel its entire length and arrive unattenuated after many reflections. Consequently, a single light pipe can transmit light energy quite efficiently. However, the rays from different parts of an object are completely scrambled by the multiple reflections, so a single pipe cannot transmit an image. Images can be transmitted using bundles of fine glass or plastic fibers, since each fiber transmits rays from a very small region of the object. The quality of the image is largely determined by the diameter of the fibers, which can be as small as 10^{-6} m (Fig. 23.14*b*).

Medical applications of fiber optics include instruments used in urinary bladder examinations and in studying the bronchi. Light pipes are also used to transmit intense light beams for surgery.

Glass fibers have been developed that have sufficiently low attenuation so that they can transmit light for many kilometres. This makes it feasible to construct optical communications systems (Fig. 23.15). In principle, the higher the frequency of a wave, the more data it can transmit per second. Fiber-optic cables carry more information than much larger copper cables, and have very low distortion. They offer significant cost advantages over copper cables or microwave links when there are enough data to transmit. One glass fiber can carry 8000 telephone conversations at one time, compared to only 48 for a copper wire.

Between 1980 and 1986, about 35,000 km of optical cable was installed in the United States for long-distance telecommunications. In addition, on a limited scale, fiber-optic links were built to connect local telephone offices and to provide communications channels on university campuses and in industrial settings. However, the amount of cable that was actually installed was less than had been predicted earlier. One reason was the rapid development of the equipment used to transmit data on the cable. This allowed data transmission rates to increase from 40 million bits per second to over a billion bits per second by 1987, reducing the amount of cable required.

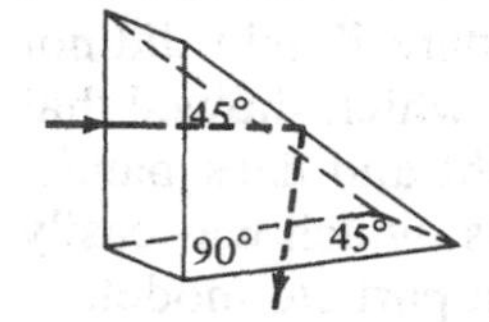

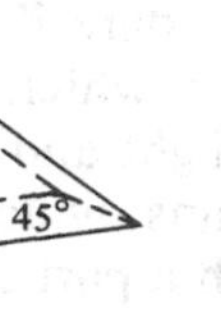

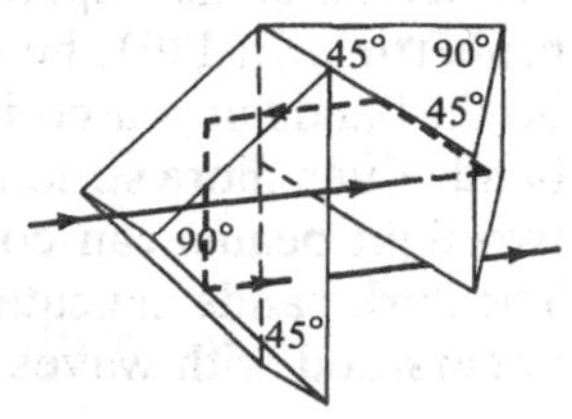

Figure 23.13. Totally reflecting prisms.

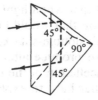

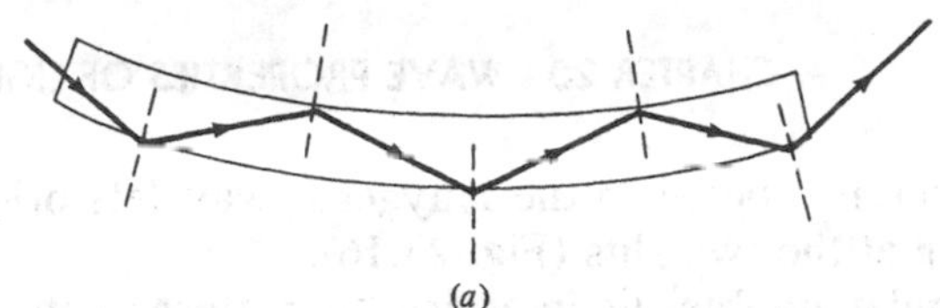

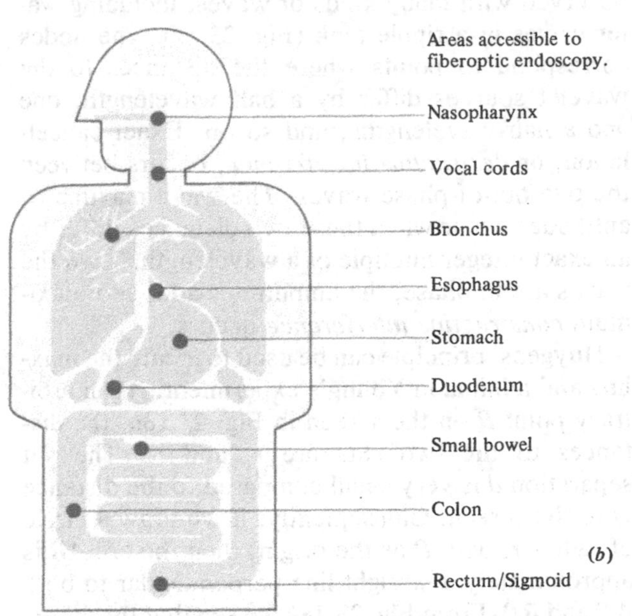

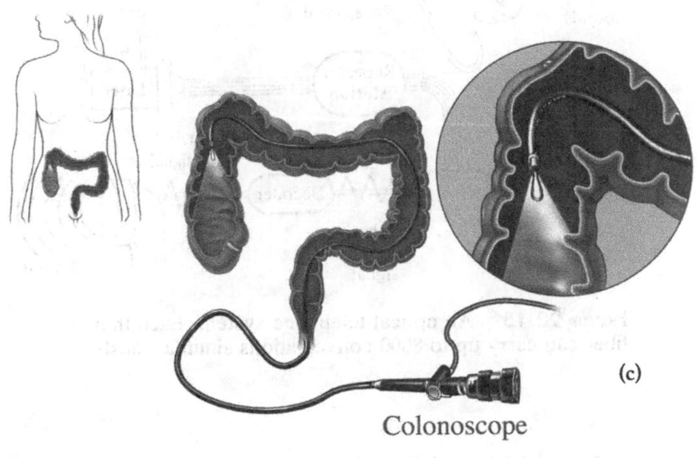

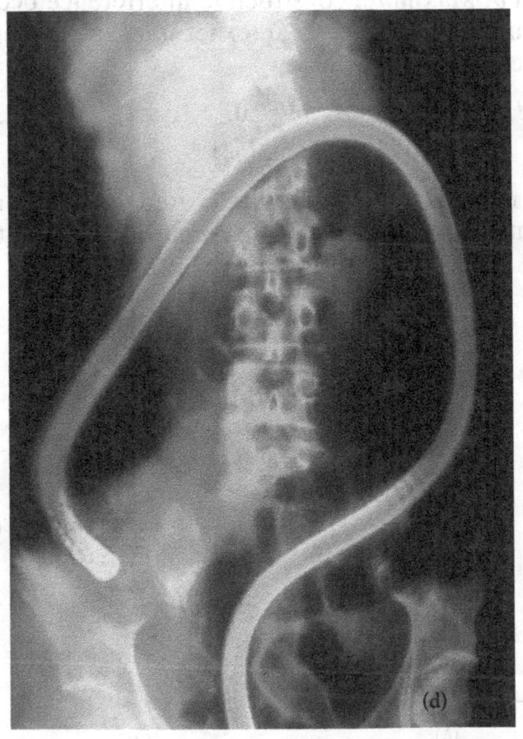

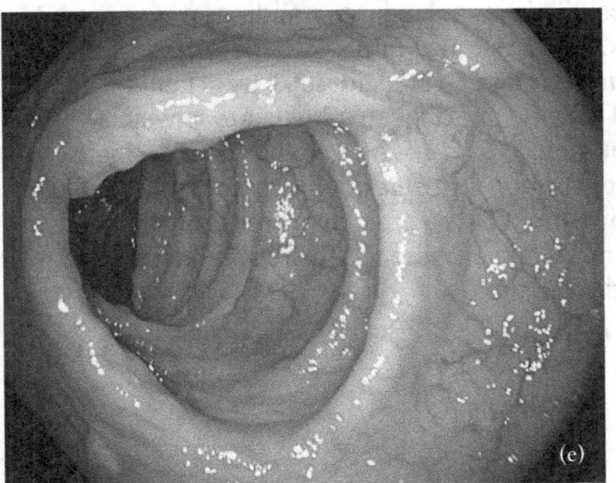

Figure 23.14. (*a*) In a light pipe, light suffers repeated total internal reflection, so it is transmitted without any loss of intensity. (*b*) Bundles of very fine glass fibers can transmit a sharp image even if the bundle is gradually bent. This permits a doctor to visually inspect a variety of internal organs without resorting to surgery. (*c*) A colonofiberscope. This instrument is fitted with a light source and can be used to remove abnormal growths. (*d*) An X-ray picture showing the colonofiberscope in use. (*e*) A photograph of a normal colon as seen with the colonofiberscope located as in (*d*). [(c) Nucleus Medical Art, Inc / Alamy Limited (d) VEM / Photo Researchers, Inc. (e) Gastrolab / Photo Researchers, Inc.]

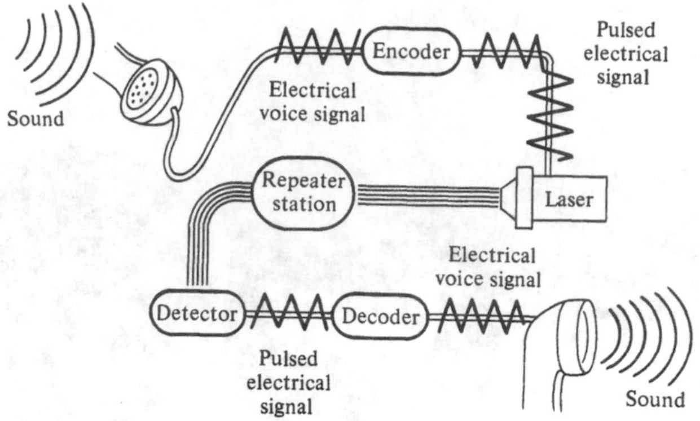

Figure 23.15. An optical telephone system. Each thin glass fiber can carry up to 8000 conversations simultaneously.

23.6 | YOUNG'S DOUBLE-SLIT INTERFERENCE EXPERIMENT

We have seen that when two waves are present in a string or in an acoustical medium, their interference results in a wave that is a superposition of the two waves. This can lead to standing waves and to beats. The existence of interference effects for light was first demonstrated in 1803 by Thomas Young (1773–1829), an English physician, physicist, and Egyptologist. In Young's experiment, single-frequency or *monochromatic,* light passes through two narrow slits spaced less than 1 mm apart. It then falls on a distant screen, forming a series of light and dark bands, or *fringes*. These arise from the interference between the Huygens' wavelets originating at the two slits (Fig. 23.16).

Similar double-slit interference patterns can be observed with many kinds of waves, including water waves in a ripple tank (Fig. 23.17). The nodes correspond to points where the distances to the wavelet sources differ by a half wavelength, one and a half wavelengths, and so on. Exact cancellation, or *destructive interference,* occurs between the two out-of-phase waves. The wave maxima or antinodes occur when these two distances differ by an exact integer multiple of a wavelength. Then the waves are in phase, the amplitudes add, and maximum *constructive interference* occurs.

Huygens' principle can be used to locate the maxima and minima in Young's experiment. At an arbitrary point P on the screen in Fig. 23.18*a*, the distances to the two slits are r_1 and r_2. The slit separation d is very small compared to the distance D to the screen. Consequently, if we draw a circle of radius r_1 with P as the origin, then the arc AB is approximately a straight line perpendicular to both AP and BP. From Fig. 23.18*b* we see that the difference in path lengths $x = r_2 - r_1$ is then equal to $d \sin \theta$. Maximum constructive interference occurs when this difference is an exact integer number of wavelengths, or when

$$d \sin \theta = m\lambda, \qquad m = 0, \pm 1, \pm 2, \ldots \quad \text{(maxima)} \tag{23.6}$$

The maxima, or fringes, are located symmetrically about the central $m = 0$ maximum. The negative

Figure 23.16. (*a*) Young's double-slit experiment. If the distances from a point on the screen to the two slits differ by an integer number of wavelengths, maximum constructive interference occurs there. (*b*) A photograph of the interference fringes produced on the screen. (*c*) A graph of the intensity I versus position y. [(b) sciencephotos / Alamy Limited]

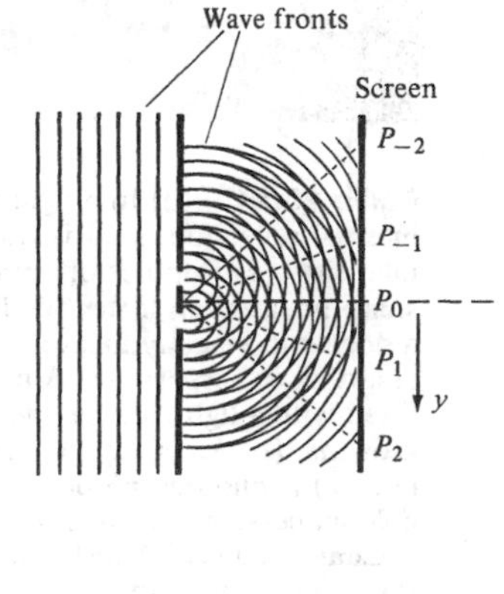

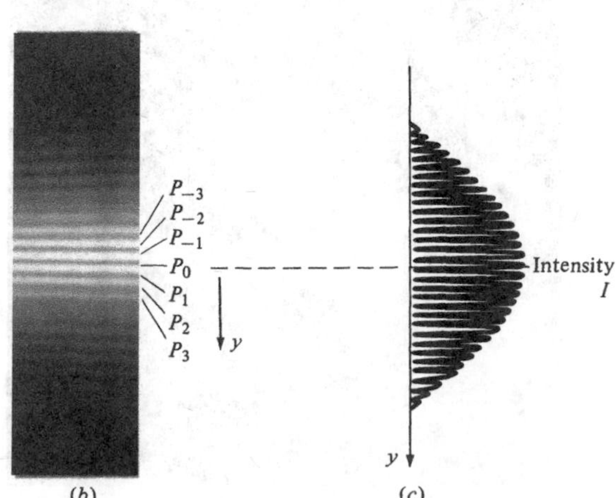

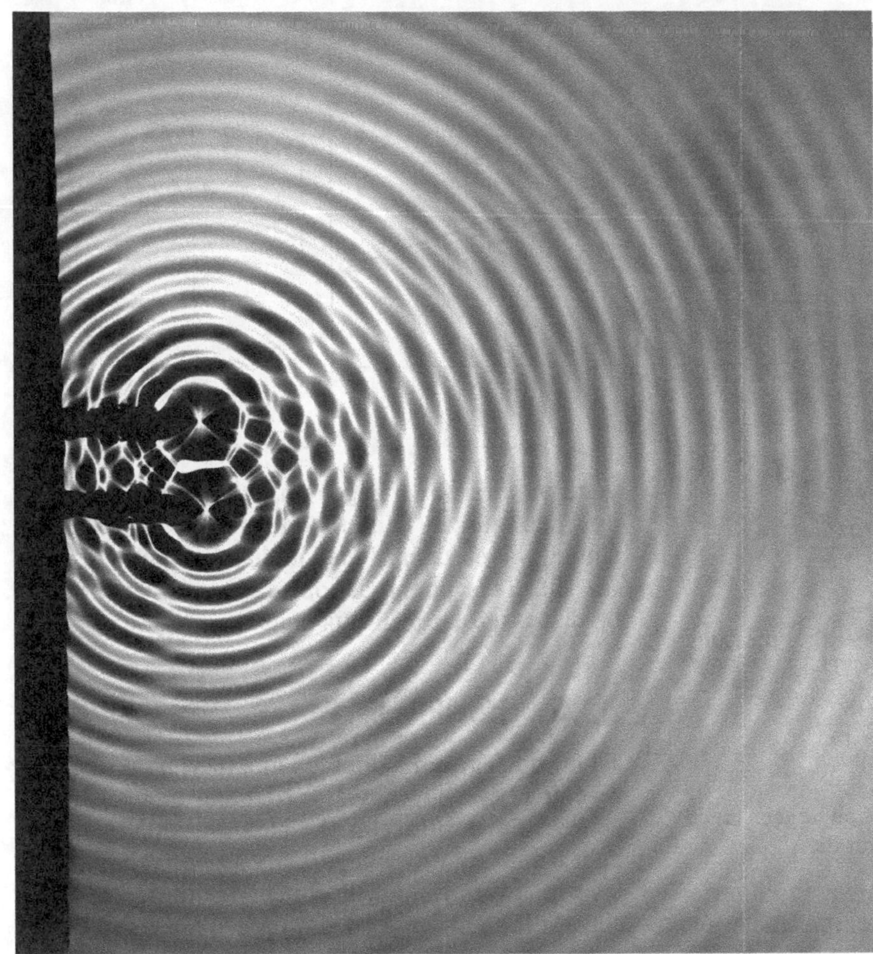

Figure 23.17. Interference of water waves in a ripple tank. The two waves are produced by identical synchronized vibrations. (Berenice Abbott / Photo Researchers, Inc.)

integers correspond to maxima above the axis, as indicated by the points $P_{-1}, P_{-2}, \ldots$ in Fig. 23.16.

The positions of the fringes on the screen can easily be found. In Fig. 23.18*a*, the distance r from the center of the screen to the fringe is approximately equal to the distance D to the screen, since θ is small. Thus $\sin\theta = y/r \simeq y/D$. Using this result in Eq. 23.6, we have $d(y/D) = m\lambda$, and

$$y = m\lambda\frac{D}{d}, \qquad m = 0, \pm 1, \pm 2, \ldots \qquad \text{(maxima)} \tag{23.7}$$

The intensity at the maxima is not simply the sum of the intensities of the waves from the two slits. The intensity of a wave is proportional to the square of its amplitude. If the amplitude of each wave is A, when the two waves are in phase the total amplitude of the combined wave is $2A$. The intensity at the maxima is then proportional to $(2A)^2 = 4A^2$, or four times the intensity from a single slit. When the double-slit interference pattern is averaged over both the maxima and the minima, it turns out that the resulting average intensity is twice that of a single slit. This is the result required by energy conservation, since the net energy reaching the screen is the sum of the energies from the two slits.

The position of a maximum is found in the next example.

Example 23.6

Find the angle of the $m = 3$ fringe if two slits 0.4 mm $= 4 \times 10^{-4}$ m apart are illuminated by yellow light of wavelength 600 nm.

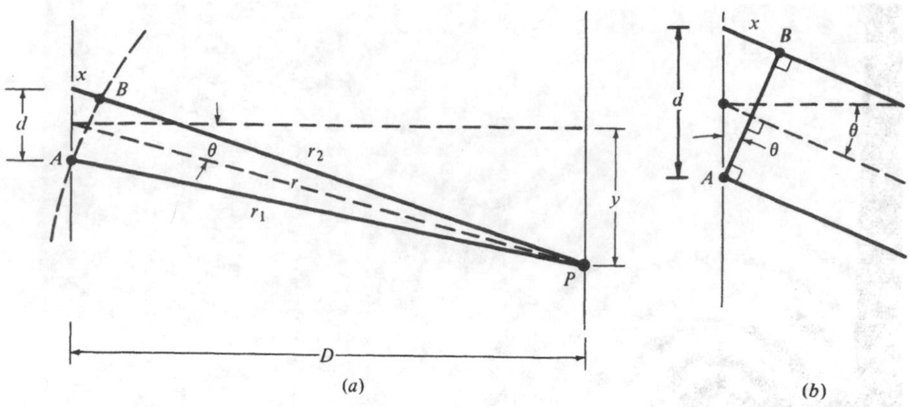

Figure 23.18. (*a*) The geometry of Young's double-slit apparatus. The scale is distorted for clarity; the screen distance D is actually very large compared to the slit spacing d. (*b*) Enlarged view of the region near the slits. Note that $x = d \sin \theta$.

Substituting $m = 3$ in $d \sin \theta = m\lambda$,

$$\sin \theta = \frac{m\lambda}{d} = \frac{3(600 \times 10^{-9}\text{ m})}{4 \times 10^{-4}\text{ m}} = 4.50 \times 10^{-3}$$

When the sine is very small, we can use the approximation $\sin \theta = \theta$, where θ is in radians. Thus

$$\theta = 4.50 \times 10^{-3}\text{ rad}\left(\frac{180°}{\pi\text{ rad}}\right) = 0.258°$$

This is a small angle, but the fringes can be seen readily if the screen is a metre or more from the slits.

When the slit separation is known, the interference pattern can be used to determine the wavelength of the light used.

Example 23.7

Two slits 4×10^{-4} m apart are 1 m from a screen. If the distance y between the central fringe and the $m = 1$ fringe is 1 mm $= 10^{-3}$ m, what is the wavelength of the light?

Solving $y = m\lambda D/d$ for λ, we have with $m = 1$

$$\lambda = \frac{yd}{mD} = \frac{(10^{-3}\text{ m})(4 \times 10^{-4}\text{ m})}{(1)(1\text{ m})} = 4 \times 10^{-7}\text{ m} = 400\text{ nm}$$

In practice, it is difficult to measure the positions of the maxima in the double-slit pattern with great accuracy. The diffraction grating discussed in Section 23.8 is a much better way to use interference methods to determine the wavelength of a light source.

The interference fringes in the double-slit pattern (Fig. 23.16) diminish appreciably in intensity beyond the first few fringes on either side of the central maximum. This is due to the interference among wavelets produced in different parts of a *single* slit. This phenomenon, called *diffraction*, will be discussed later in this chapter.

23.7 | COHERENCE

To form fringes in a double-slit experiment, the light reaching the slits must originate from a *single* source. By contrast, if the slits are illuminated by light from separate lamps, only a relatively uniform level of brightness will appear on the screen, because the light waves from an ordinary source are not emitted continuously but rather as short pulses at random intervals. Consequently, the phases of the waves from two lamps frequently change, as do the positions of the maxima and minima of the interference pattern; no single interference pattern persists long enough to be detectable. The two lamps are said to be *incoherent* light sources. Only *coherent* waves, those that have a stable phase relationship, can produce interference effects.

Coherent and incoherent sources can be illustrated by two vibrators in a ripple tank. If the vibrators oscillate in unison, they produce coherent waves, and the pattern in Fig. 23.17 results. But suppose that once every few seconds, one of the vibrators pauses for a brief but random period and then begins to vibrate again. The two sources will no longer be in phase. There will still be nodes and antinodes at the locations of maximum destructive and constructive wave interference. However, every time a vibrator pauses and restarts, these positions will shift. If these shifts occur frequently enough, no interference pattern will be discernible.

The electromagnetic waves produced by ordinary light sources such as heated wires or flames are emitted at random by single atoms or molecules. These act independently, much like the two vibrators in the ripple tank illustration of incoherent sources. Typically, the atoms or molecules produce wave pulses of about 10^{-8}-second duration, or a few metres in length. Such a light source can produce interference effects if a colored filter and a small hole are placed directly in front of it. The filtered light is nearly monochromatic and has originated in a small portion of the source. This light is at least approximately coherent, and it will produce fringes in a double-slit apparatus.

In recent years, intense, coherent light sources called *lasers* have become available. In a laser the atoms emit light in phase, instead of randomly or incoherently. The light produced from a laser has an extremely small range of frequencies, so it is almost exactly monochromatic, and it is highly coherent. As a result, light emerging from the laser at two different points or at two slightly different times can be used to produce interference patterns.

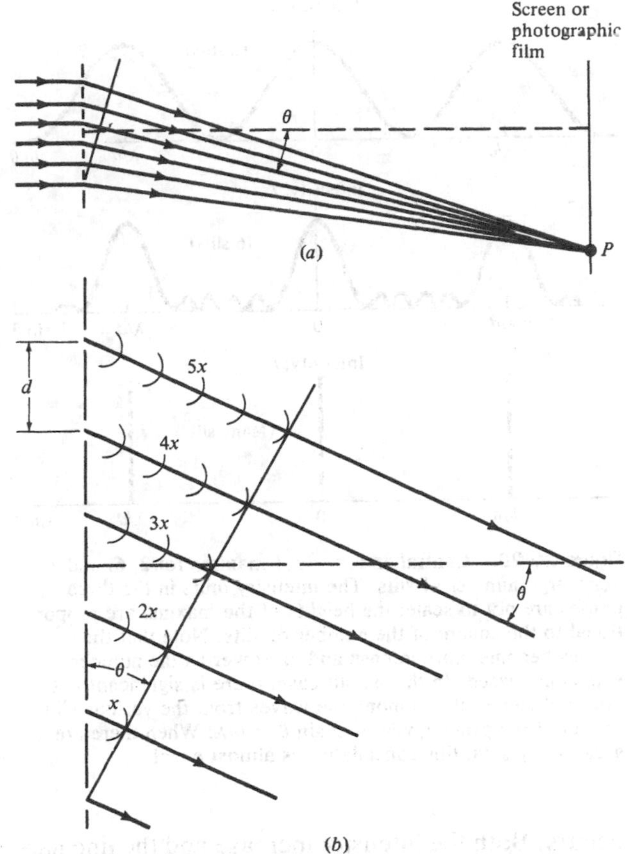

Figure 23.19. (*a*) Light rays reaching a point *P* on a screen from six closely spaced slits. (Light rays reaching other points are not shown.) (*b*) Enlarged view of the region near the slits.

23.8 | THE DIFFRACTION GRATING

The wavelength of a light beam can be found by measuring the spacing of the interference fringes in a double-slit arrangement. However, this is hard to do with accuracy, since the fringes are relatively wide and weak in intensity. A *diffraction grating*, which consists of many closely spaced slits, permits much more precise wavelength determinations. We will see that, as in the double slit, the *distance* between the slits in the grating determines the *locations* of the maxima; their *sharpness* depends on the *total number* of slits.

The principle of the diffraction grating is illustrated by considering the case of six slits (Fig. 23.19). If the difference $x = d \sin \theta$ of the distances from a point on the screen to any two adjacent slits is exactly an integral multiple of a wavelength, all the waves reaching the screen are in phase. Thus a maximum in the intensity occurs when

$$d \sin \theta = m\lambda, \qquad m = 0, \pm 1, \pm 2, \ldots \tag{23.8}$$

m is called the *order* of the maximum or spectrum produced by the grating.

This is the same formula as was found for the angular positions of the maxima in the two-slit apparatus. However, here the fringes are much more intense, since the amplitudes from each of the six slits add (Fig. 23.20). Equally important is the fact that the fringes are now much narrower. This happens because the waves from the six slits cancel almost completely as soon as the angle differs slightly from a value at which a maximum intensity

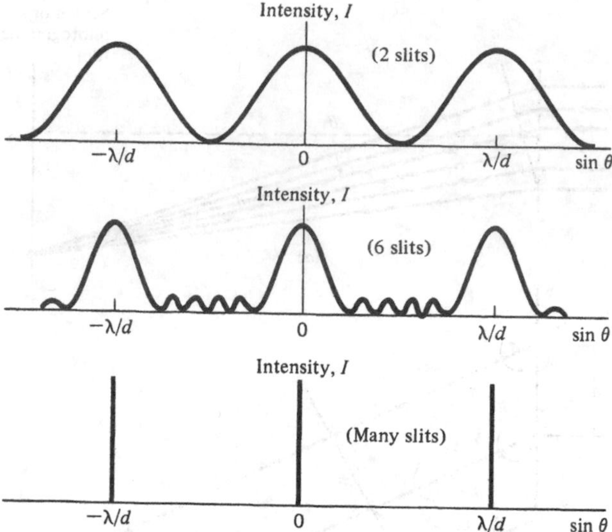

Figure 23.20. Central and $m = \pm 1$ maxima for 2, 6, and a very large number of slits. The intensity units in the three graphs are not to scale: the heights of the maxima are proportional to the square of the number of slits. Note that the fringes become more intense and narrower as the number of slits is increased. In the six-slit case, there is significant but not total cancellation among the waves from the various slits except at the peaks given by $d \sin \theta = m\lambda$. When there are a great many slits, this cancellation is almost exact.

occurs. Both the intensity increase and the line narrowing are accentuated as the number of slits is increased further.

Gratings are manufactured by cutting or ruling equally spaced parallel grooves or lines with an automatic ruling engine. Those used to measure wavelengths in the visible region usually have about 4000 to 12,000 lines per centimetre. Spacings not too much greater than a wavelength are employed so that the angular spacing of the maxima will be reasonably large. This makes it possible to measure the angles accurately. The large angles obtainable are illustrated by the next example.

Example 23.8

A grating has 4000 lines per centimetre. At what angles are maxima formed if it is illuminated with yellow light at 600 nm?

The slit spacing is

$$d = \frac{1}{4000} \text{ cm} = 2.5 \times 10^{-4} \text{ cm}$$
$$= 2.5 \times 10^3 \text{ nm}$$

Using $\lambda = 600$ nm, $d \sin \theta = m\lambda$ gives

$$\sin \theta = \frac{m\lambda}{d} = \frac{m(600 \text{ nm})}{2.5 \times 10^3 \text{ nm}}$$
$$= m(0.240)$$

Substituting $m = 1$ gives $\sin \theta = 0.24$, or $\theta = 14°$; maxima are formed at 14° to either side of the central $m = 0$ maximum. Similarly, $m = 2$, 3, and 4 give maxima at 29°, 46°, and 74°, respectively. There are no other maxima, since $m = 5$ requires $\sin \theta = 1.2$, and no angle has a sine greater than 1.

When a diffraction grating is used to measure wavelengths, a narrow slit is placed in front of the light source. If the source is monochromatic, the grating forms several bright lines on the screen, as in the previous example. If the light contains several specific frequencies, lines are formed for each frequency, and the pattern is called a *line spectrum* (Fig. 23.21). Such a spectrum results, for example, when atoms or molecules in a gas are disturbed by an electrical current. Measurements of the wavelengths of line spectra provide important atomic and molecular structure information. Other sources, such as incandescent lamps, produce white light, which is a continuous distribution of all frequencies in the visible region, and give rise with a grating to a *continuous spectrum*. The following example shows how rainbowlike patterns are formed when a grating is illuminated by white light.

Example 23.9

A grating with a slit spacing of 2.5×10^3 nm is illuminated with white light containing wavelengths from 400 to 700 nm. Describe the spectrum formed by the grating.

Using $m = 1$ and $\lambda = 400$ nm,

$$\sin \theta = \frac{m\lambda}{d} = \frac{(1)(400 \text{ nm})}{2.5 \times 10^3 \text{ nm}} = 0.16$$

Figure 23.21. The line spectrum of hydrogen produced by a diffraction grating. (Ted Kinsman / Photo Researchers, Inc.)

and $\theta = 9°$. For $m = 1$ and $\lambda = 700$ nm, $\theta = 16°$. Thus the first-order ($m = 1$) spectrum extends from 9° to 16° on each side of a central white maximum, with the shortest wavelength (violet) at the smallest angle. In the same way, one finds that the second-order ($m = 2$) spectrum extends from 19° to 34°, and the third-order spectrum, from 29° to 57°. Note that the second- and third-order spectra overlap. In general, the first-order visible spectrum of a grating is isolated, but all the higher orders overlap.

Angular Width of the Maxima; Resolution

We saw that as the number of lines is increased, the maxima formed by a grating become progressively narrower. The widths of the maxima determine how accurately a wavelength can be measured with the grating and set a limit on the ability of the grating to separate, or *resolve,* two closely spaced wavelengths present in a beam of light.

The amplitude at a maximum is proportional to N, the number of slits, and the intensity varies therefore as N^2. Since the total power reaching the screen varies as the number of slits N, the widths of the maxima must vary as $1/N$.

Suppose now that we wish to use a grating to separate two light waves of nearly equal wavelength, λ and $\lambda' = \lambda + \Delta\lambda$. Clearly, this is possible only if the two maxima do not overlap too much. A conventional criterion for setting a limit on this overlap was introduced by Lord Rayleigh (1842–1919). *Rayleigh's criterion* is that one can just resolve two adjacent maxima if their intensities are each half their respective peak values at the point where the overlap is greatest (Fig. 23.22). Since the width of each peak is proportional to $1/N$, it is found that the peaks of the mth-order spectrum can just be distinguished when

$$\frac{\Delta\lambda}{\lambda} = \frac{1}{Nm} \tag{23.9}$$

The resolution obtainable with typical gratings is quite impressive, as can be seen in the following example.

Example 23.10

Trace amounts of sodium in a flame result in a characteristic bright-yellow color due to a *doublet,* light at two nearby wavelengths, 589.59 and 589.00 nm. Can a grating with 10,000 lines resolve the two wavelengths in the first-order spectrum?

For the two wavelengths in the yellow sodium doublet,

$$\frac{\Delta\lambda}{\lambda} = \frac{(589.59 - 589.00)\ \text{nm}}{589\ \text{nm}} = 10^{-3}$$

The smallest wavelength difference that can be resolved by this grating in first order ($m = 1$) satisfies

$$\frac{\Delta\lambda}{\lambda} = \frac{1}{Nm} = \frac{1}{(10^4)(1)} = 10^{-4}$$

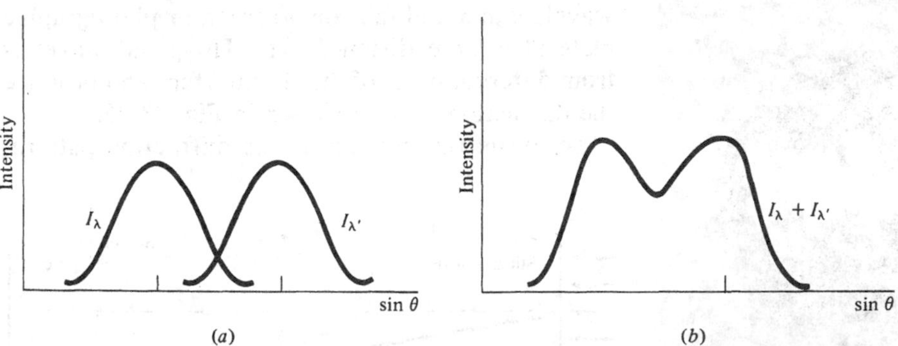

Figure 23.22. Intensity distributions in a very small angular region of a diffraction grating spectrum. (*a*) Light of wavelength λ produces the maximum shown by the black curve, while light with wavelength λ' produces the maximum shown by the colored curve. (*b*) When both waves are present, the intensity observed is the sum of the two curves in (*a*). In the case illustrated, the two peaks are just barely discernible. According to Rayleigh's criterion, when the wavelengths λ and λ' are significantly closer, the two peaks cannot be resolved.

Since this is only one tenth of the ratio $\Delta\lambda/\lambda$ for the sodium doublet, the grating readily resolves the two wavelengths.

Rayleigh's criterion for the minimum resolvable separation of two maxima is a good estimate of what can be achieved if a spectrum is examined visually. However, if an intensity pattern such as the one in Fig. 23.22*b* is carefully measured and analyzed, the minimum distinguishable wavelength separation can be greatly reduced.

23.9 | DIFFRACTION

Thus far, we have discussed examples of interference between waves from two discrete sources, as in a double-slit experiment, or from many discrete sources, as in the diffraction grating. However, parts of a wave from a single source will also interfere with each other. This causes effects such as the bending of waves around an obstacle. Single-source interference is referred to as *diffraction* and occurs for all kinds of waves.

Figure 23.23 shows the shadow of a razor blade placed between a point source of monochromatic light and a photographic plate. Some light is bent inside the *geometrical shadow*, the region that would be totally dark in the absence of any bending.

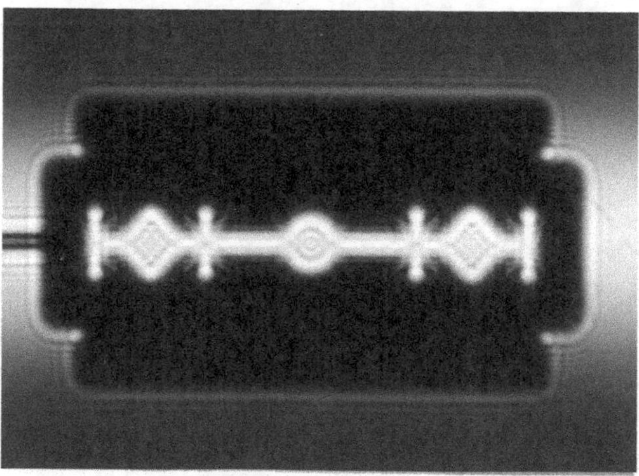

Figure 23.23. The shadow produced when a razor blade is illuminated by a monochromatic point source. (Ken Kay / Fundamental Photographs)

Near the edge of the shadow, a diffraction pattern of alternate light and dark bands appears. Thus even in this fairly simple situation, the diffraction pattern is quite complex.

Under ordinary conditions, we seldom notice the diffraction of light. Light sources such as incandescent lamps or the sun are not monochromatic point sources, and the diffraction patterns due to different parts of the source and to different wavelengths usually overlap and obscure each other. Nevertheless, diffraction patterns are visible when we look at a distant light source, such as a street lamp, through a crack between two fingers or through a cloth umbrella. By contrast, the diffraction of sound waves is hard to avoid. Sound readily bends around obstacles of ordinary size, such as furniture, and fills a room rather uniformly. This difference between the diffraction of visible light and of sound is due to their wavelengths, which are typically 5×10^{-7} m and 1 m, respectively. *Diffraction effects are large only when we deal with obstacles or apertures comparable in size to the wavelength.*

Diffraction by a Narrow Slit | Calculations of diffraction patterns are usually complex. However, for the case of light diffracted by a narrow slit, some of the main features can be obtained without elaborate mathematics. Qualitatively similar results are found for other situations.

In Fig. 23.24, monochromatic light passes through a slit whose width a is comparable to the wavelength λ and falls on a screen or photographic plate at a large distance. The Huygens' wavelets from different parts of the slit interfere and produce the diffraction pattern shown in Fig. 23.25.

To locate the minima in this diffraction pattern,

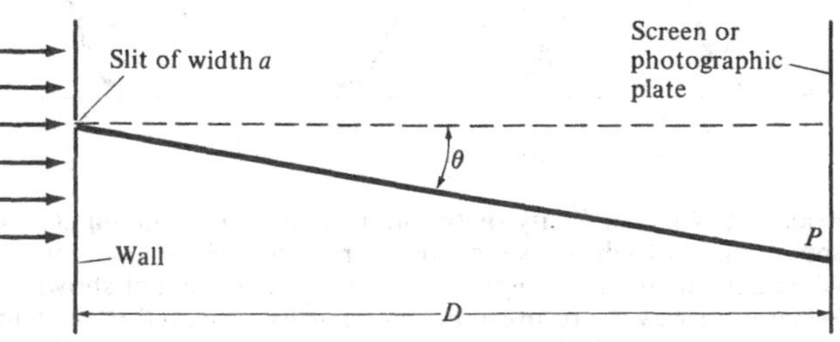

Figure 23.24. Geometry of the single-slit diffraction experiment. The pattern seen on the screen is shown in Fig. 23.25.

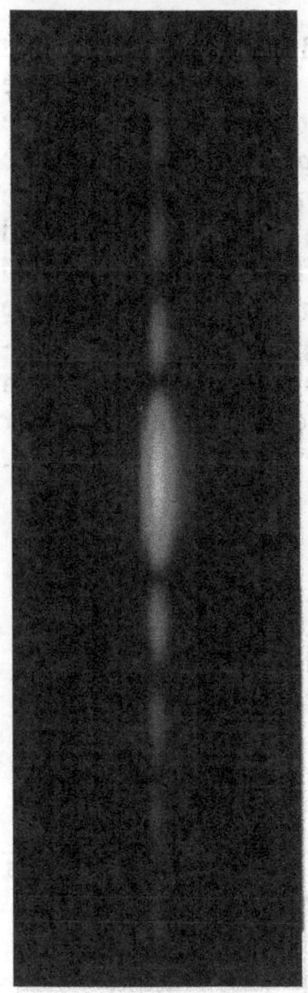

Figure 23.25. Photograph of the diffraction pattern produced by a single slit illuminated by monochromatic light as in Fig. 23.24. (Ted Kinsman / Photo Researchers, Inc.)

we start by dividing the slit into two halves (*AB* and *BC* in Fig. 23.26). The distance to the screen for the wavelet originating at *A* is greater than that for the wavelet from *B* by $x = \frac{1}{2}a \sin \theta$. Wavelets originating at any point on *AB* and at the corresponding point on *BC* will have the same path difference. Consequently, if x is exactly $\frac{1}{2}\lambda$, all the pairs of wavelets will be out of phase and cancel exactly, producing a minimum. Hence a minimum occurs when $x = \frac{1}{2}a \sin \theta = \frac{1}{2}\lambda$, or

$$a \sin \theta = \lambda$$

At this point, one might suppose that a maximum occurs when $x = \lambda$, since the wavelets from *A* and *B* will then be exactly in phase. However, this is not the case, as can be seen by dividing the slit into four equal parts (Fig. 23.26). Wavelets from *A* and *D* will have a path difference that is $\frac{1}{2}x = \frac{1}{2}\lambda$, so they will

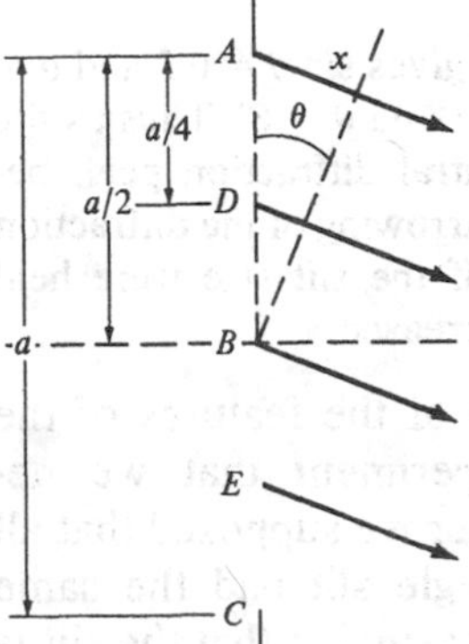

Figure 23.26. A diffraction minimum occurs when wavelets from different parts of the slit interfere destructively.

be exactly out of phase and cancel completely. The same is also true for wavelets from any two points $a/4$ apart, so $x = \lambda$ also implies a minimum. Similarly, we can divide the slit into 6, 8, . . . parts and find that total destructive interference occurs when $x = \frac{1}{2}a \sin\theta = \frac{1}{2}\lambda, \lambda, \frac{3}{2}\lambda, 2\lambda, \ldots$. Thus in general, diffraction minima occur at angles satisfying

$$a \sin\theta = m\lambda, \qquad m = \pm 1, \pm 2, \ldots \quad \text{(diffraction minima)} \quad (23.10)$$

The negative integers correspond to minima above the axis in Fig. 23.25.

The maxima are located approximately (but not exactly) midway between the minima, or at $m = 0, \pm\frac{3}{2}\lambda, \pm\frac{5}{2}\lambda, \ldots$. The central $m = 0$ maximum is very bright, since all the wavelets have nearly the same path length and are in phase. At the other maxima, the intensity is much smaller, and it diminishes rapidly as m increases (Fig. 23.25). This happens because, except at $\theta = 0$, the wavelets from some parts of the slit cancel even at the maxima. This partial cancellation becomes more and more complete as the angle increases.

The angular width of the diffraction pattern depends on the size of the slit relative to the wavelength of light, as is seen in the next example.

Example 23.11

A slit is illuminated by light of wavelength λ. Find the angular position of the first diffraction minimum as the slit width expands from λ to 5λ and finally to 10λ.

Substituting $m = 1$ and $a = \lambda$ in $a \sin\theta = m\lambda$, we find

$$\sin\theta = m\frac{\lambda}{a} = (1)\frac{\lambda}{\lambda} = 1$$

so $\theta = 90°$. Similarly, $a = 5\lambda$ gives $\sin\theta = 0.2$ and $\theta = 12°$; $a = 10\lambda$ gives $\sin\theta = 0.1$ and $\theta = 6°$. Thus as the slit becomes wider, the central diffraction peak becomes narrower. A similar narrowing of the diffraction pattern would be observed if the slit size were held fixed and the wavelength decreased.

Diffraction explains some of the features of the double-slit interference experiment that we neglected in Section 23.6. Earlier we supposed that all the light coming from a single slit had the same phase. This is equivalent to assuming that the slit is very narrow compared to a wavelength and that its diffraction pattern is very wide. However, if the slit widths are comparable to the wavelength, the waves reaching the screen from each slit will have an intensity that varies with position in accordance with the single-slit diffraction formulas. Thus the complete pattern for a double slit is actually formed from two superimposed diffraction patterns, and the double-slit interference maxima do not all have the same intensity. The single-slit diffraction pattern forms an *envelope* for the interference pattern so that the intensity of the peaks becomes smaller further away from the center of the pattern (Fig. 23.27).

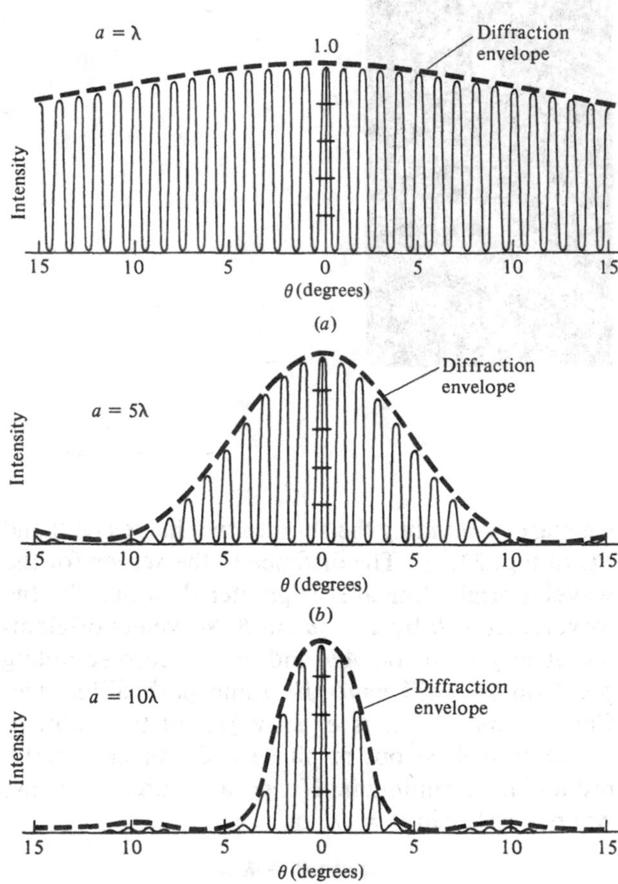

Figure 23.27. Interference patterns for two slits separated by $d = 50\lambda$. The fringes seen are centered at the peaks in the solid curve. Note how the pattern changes as the slit width a is increased and the single-slit diffraction envelope narrows. (From Halliday and Resnick, *Physics*, Part II, 3rd ed. Copyright © 1978, John Wiley & Sons, New York.)

Figure 23.28. Monochromatic light from a laser passes through a small circular aperture. On a screen, a bright central diffraction maximum forms with some weaker secondary maxima. (GIPhotoStock / Photo Researchers, Inc.)

Diffraction by a Circular Aperture | When a light wave enters an optical instrument with a circular opening, a diffraction pattern is produced by the interference of the wavelets originating at different points in the aperture. The diffraction pattern due to a distant point source of light has a bright central circular region, surrounded by concentric dark and light rings (Fig. 23.28). A detailed analysis shows that the first minimum for a circle with diameter d occurs when

$$\sin \theta = 1.22 \frac{\lambda}{d} \tag{23.11}$$

This is similar to the formula for the first minimum of a slit, $\sin \theta = \lambda/a$, but the circular geometry results in the factor of 1.22.

We see in the next chapter how diffraction limits the sharpness of images formed by optical instruments and the human eye.

23.10 | POLARIZATION OF LIGHT

In Chapter Twenty-one, we noted that light, like any other transverse wave, can be polarized. We now examine this idea in more detail.

Electromagnetic waves have electric and magnetic fields oscillating at right angles to the direction of motion of the waves. If the electric field vector is always along a certain direction, the wave is said to be *linearly polarized* along this direction. The radiation from a single atom or molecule is polarized, but because the many individual atoms or molecules usually act randomly, the resultant light beam from most sources is unpolarized. This means that at a particular instant, the electric field is equally likely to point in any direction perpendicular to the direction of motion of the light wave. If we resolve this field into components along two convenient perpendicular axes, on the average the components along each axis will be equally large.

Polarized light can be produced from an unpolarized beam in several ways, including *absorption*, *reflection*, and *scattering*. The most familiar way, mentioned in Chapter Twenty-one, is by *absorption* in Polaroid filters. These filters contain long molecules that are aligned. When light has its electric field vector along the molecules, electric currents are set up, and the light is absorbed. However, little happens to a light beam polarized at right angles to the molecules. A similar effect can be demonstrated nicely with microwaves, which are electromagnetic waves with wavelengths of the order of centimetres (Fig. 23.29). Microwaves with vertical electric fields pass readily through horizontal wires. However, when the wires are vertical, the electric field sets up currents in the wires, and the waves are absorbed.

Light can also be polarized by *reflection* off the surface of a nonconducting material. Except at normal incidence, the fraction of the light reflected by a surface depends on its polarization. It was discovered in 1812 by Sir David Brewster (1781–1868) that the reflected beam is completely polarized at an angle of incidence ϕ_p, which is determined by the indices of refraction n_1 and n_2 of the two media (Fig. 23.30). This angle is called *Brewster's angle* and satisfies

$$\tan \phi_p = \frac{n_2}{n_1} \tag{23.12}$$

If an unpolarized beam is incident at this angle, the relatively weak reflected beam will be fully polarized perpendicular to the *plane of incidence* defined by the incident ray and the normal. The stronger transmitted beam will be slightly polarized.

Brewster's angle can be derived using Maxwell's description of light as an electromagnetic wave.

Figure 23.29. Microwaves polarized so that the electric field is vertical are beamed toward a detector. (*a*) Horizontal metal wires permit the waves to pass unimpeded. (*b*) Vertical wires absorb the waves, as shown by the reduced detector reading. (Courtesy M. Sternheim)

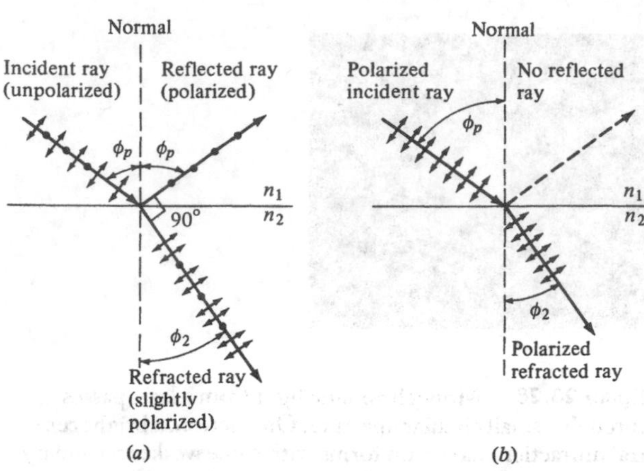

Figure 23.30. Polarization by reflection. (*a*) On the average the unpolarized incident beam has equally large electric fields perpendicular to the plane of incidence (dots) and in the plane (arrows). When the wave is incident at Brewster's angle, the reflected beam is fully polarized. The transmitted beam is only slightly polarized, since only a small fraction of the light is reflected. (*b*) A wave polarized with its electric field in the plane of incidence is fully transmitted at Brewster's angle.

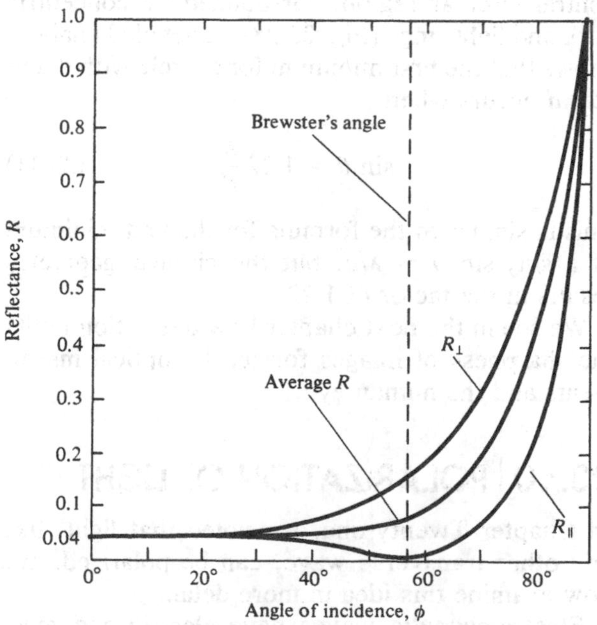

Figure 23.31. Light is incident from air on glass with an index of refraction of 1.5. The reflectance is plotted versus the angle of incidence for light polarized perpendicular and parallel to the plane of incidence. The average of $R_{\perp}$ and $R_{\parallel}$ is the reflectance for unpolarized light shown earlier in Fig. 23.7.

When unpolarized light is incident on a surface, half its intensity corresponds to electric fields perpendicular to the plane of incidence and half to fields in or parallel to the plane. Maxwell's theory shows that the reflectance for the two components varies with the angle of incidence ϕ in quite different ways (Fig. 23.31). At Brewster's angle, the reflected intensity for the parallel component is zero, and only the perpendicular component is reflected. Thus the reflected light is completely polarized. Note that $R_{\perp}$

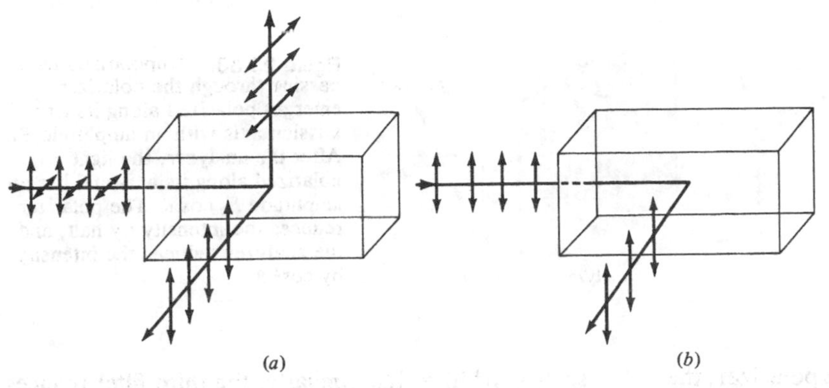

Figure 23.32. (*a*) Light incident on water containing powdered skim milk or soap is scattered in all directions. Light scattered at right angles is fully polarized. (*b*) If the incident light is vertically polarized, the vertically scattered beam disappears. (*c*) A vertically polarized incident beam causes charges to oscillate vertically. These oscillating charges produce radiation with an electric field component along the direction of oscillation.

is much larger than $R_\parallel$ for a large range of angles about the Brewster angle. Therefore, the reflected light is partially but not fully polarized at those angles.

The use of Brewster's angle is illustrated by the following common situation.

Example 23.12

(a) Sunlight reflected off a still lake is fully polarized. At what angle is it incident on the lake? (b) At what angle of incidence will light incident from the water on the air–water boundary be fully polarized upon reflection?

(a) Since $n_1 = 1$ for air and $n_2 = 4/3$ for water, the reflected light is polarized perpendicular to the plane of incidence when

$$\tan \phi_p = \frac{n_2}{n_1} = \frac{4/3}{1} = 1.333$$

or $\phi_p = 53°$.

(b) When light is incident on the surface from the water, the formula for Brewster's angle still applies, but n_1 and n_2 are interchanged; $n_1 = 4/3$ and $n_2 = 1$. Hence

$$\tan \phi_p = \frac{1}{4/3} = 0.75, \qquad \phi_p = 37°$$

Note that the sum of the two Brewster angles is $53° + 37° = 90°$. This is a general result: the sum of the Brewster angles for light incident from medium 1 and medium 2 is always 90° (Problem 23-66).

Polarized light is also produced by *scattering*, which is the absorption and reradiation of light. An interesting demonstration of the polarization of scattered light can be done using a tank of water containing some powdered skim milk or soap. Using a Polaroid filter, one finds that the light scattered at right angles to the incident beam is polarized perpendicular to the plane of the incident and scattered rays (Fig. 23.32). If a Polaroid filter is used to polarize the incident beam vertically, no change is observed in the light scattered at right angles in the horizontal plane. However, the vertical beam now disappears.

These observations are explained by the fact that the incident light sets charges in the atoms into oscillatory motion along the direction of the electric field. The oscillating charges then emit radiation with an electric field that has a component along the direction of oscillation. Since the waves are transverse, this means that no radiation is emitted along the direction of oscillation. Accordingly, the horizontal beam originates from vertical oscillators and is polarized vertically.

The daytime sky appears blue because short-wavelength light is most readily scattered. The sunlight scattered at right angles is fully polarized, and all the scattered sunlight is at least partially polarized. Bees are able to sense this polarization and can use the information to determine the direction of the sun from a view of only a small part of the sky.

Polarizers and Analyzers

Several simple but fascinating experiments can be done with a few Polaroid filters. In Fig. 23.33, an unpolarized beam passes through two filters referred to as a *polarizer* and *analyzer*, respectively. The fields along the transmission axis of the polarizer (x axis) and along the direction perpendicular to it (y axis) have the

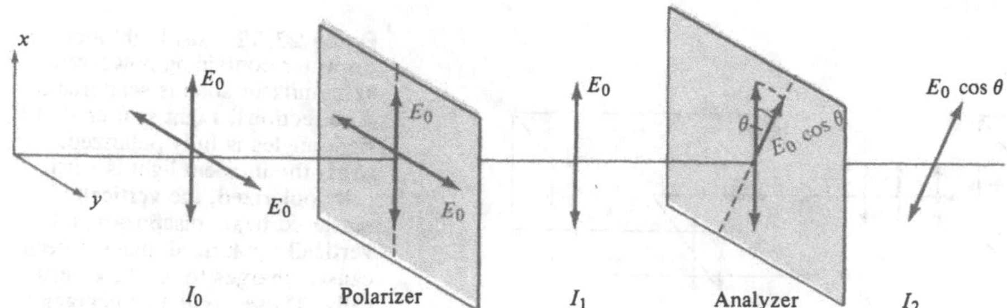

Figure 23.33. Unpolarized light passing through the polarizer emerges polarized along its transmission axis with an amplitude E_0. After the analyzer, the light is polarized along its axis and has an amplitude $E_0 \cos\theta$. The polarizer reduces the intensity by half, and the analyzer reduces the intensity by $\cos^2\theta$.

same average amplitude, E_0. After the polarizer, the beam is polarized along the transmission axis with an amplitude E_0. Since the intensity is proportional to $E^2 = E_x^2 + E_y^2$, the intensity I_0 before the polarizer is proportional to $E_0^2 + E_0^2 = 2E_0^2$, whereas the intensity after it is proportional to E_0^2. *Hence the intensity after the polarizer is half the original intensity of the unpolarized beam*:

$$I_1 = \tfrac{1}{2}I_0 \quad \text{(polarizer)} \tag{23.13}$$

The transmission axis of the analyzer is at an angle θ to that of the filter. The electric field amplitude reaching the analyzer has a component $E_0 \cos\theta$ along its transmission axis. This component is permitted to pass through the analyzer, whereas the component at right angles is absorbed. Hence the intensity I_2 after the analyzer is proportional to $E_0^2 \cos^2\theta$, and we have

$$I_2 = I_1 \cos^2\theta \quad \text{(analyzer)} \tag{23.14}$$

This relationship, which was obtained in Chapter Twenty-one for transverse waves on a string, was discovered experimentally by Etienne Louis Malus (1775–1812) in 1809 and is called *Malus' law*.

The following example shows how surprising results can be obtained.

Example 23.13

Unpolarized light of intensity I_0 is passed through three successive Polaroid filters. The second has its axis rotated 45° relative to the first, and the third has its axis rotated an additional 45°, so that it is at 90° to the first. (a) What is the final intensity after the last filter? (b) If the second filter is removed without disturbing the others, what is the final intensity?

(a) The first filter acts as a polarizer, so it reduces the intensity to $I_1 = \tfrac{1}{2}I_0$. The second acts as an analyzer, reducing the intensity by a factor of $\cos^2\theta = \cos^2 45° = \tfrac{1}{2}$, so $I_2 = \tfrac{1}{2}(\tfrac{1}{2}I_0) = \tfrac{1}{4}I_0$. Similarly, the third filter reduces the intensity by an additional factor of $\cos^2 45° = \tfrac{1}{2}$, bringing the final intensity to $I_3 = \tfrac{1}{8}I_0$.

(b) With the second filter gone, the two remaining filters are at 90°. The first again reduces the intensity to $\tfrac{1}{2}I_0$, but now the next filter reduces the intensity by a factor of $\cos^2 90° = 0$. Eliminating the middle filter reduces the intensity to zero!

23.11 | X-RAY DIFFRACTION AND THE STRUCTURE OF BIOLOGICAL MOLECULES

Because waves are unaffected by objects that are small compared to a wavelength, wavelengths comparable to the interatomic spacing are needed to "see" the arrangement of atoms in a molecule. This spacing is typically a few tenths of a nanometre, where 1 nanometre = 10^{-9} metre. Visible light has a wavelength of 400 to 700 nm, so it cannot be used to study molecular structure. However, X rays, which are electromagnetic waves with typically a 0.1-nm wavelength, are well suited to this task. A crystalline material, which consists of a regular array of atoms, serves for X rays as a three-dimensional analog to the diffraction grating. Information obtained from such X-ray diffraction studies has contributed greatly to unraveling the structure of complex biological molecules such as proteins and DNA, the carrier of the genetic code.

X rays were discovered accidentally by Wilhelm Konrad Roentgen in 1895 while he was studying the properties of cathode rays (electrons) in a gaseous discharge tube. He observed that even though the tube was inside a box, a barium platinocyanide screen emitted light whenever the tube was on. He named the invisible radiation X rays because of their unknown nature. Within a very short time, their ability to penetrate matter was put to use in medicine as an invaluable diagnostic tool. However, the hazards associated with X rays were discovered more gradually, as we see in Chapter Thirty-one.

When electrons from a heated filament are accelerated through a large potential difference and allowed to strike a metal target in an X-ray tube, X rays are produced with a continuous distribution of wavelengths (Fig. 23.34). If the X rays then strike a crystal, the reflected X rays form intense *Laue spots* on a screen or film (Fig. 23.35). These spots are due to the constructive interference of wavelets produced by many atoms.

To understand how one Laue spot is formed, consider a crystal made up of identical atoms in a cubic arrangement that is exposed to a beam of X rays containing many different wavelengths. We can imagine the atoms as forming a series of partially reflecting planes, so that some X rays are reflected by each plane (Fig. 23.36). If the distance between two successive planes is d, then the path lengths for waves reflected by two successive planes will differ by $2x = 2(d \sin \alpha)$, where α is the angle between the incident X-ray direction and the crystal plane. (Conventionally, α is used in X-ray diffraction discussions rather than the angle between the beam and the normal direction.) Constructive interference occurs among the reflected beams from all the parallel planes if the path length difference is an integer number of wavelengths, or if

$$2d \sin \alpha = m\lambda, \qquad m = 1, 2, 3, \ldots \tag{23.15}$$

This equation was first obtained by Sir William Henry Bragg (1862–1942), a pioneer in X-ray research, and is called the *Bragg condition*.

Although the incident beam contains many wavelengths, for a given angle of incidence α, spots will be produced only for those wavelengths satisfying Eq. 23.15. The remainder of the beam, containing all other wavelengths, is either absorbed or transmitted. (Because there are many parallel reflecting planes, nearly total cancellation occurs among reflected beams if the Bragg condition is not satisfied.) Note that spots, and not lines, are formed, because the incident beam is very narrow and would itself form a single spot if it were not deflected. The selective nature of the crystal diffraction is illustrated by the next example.

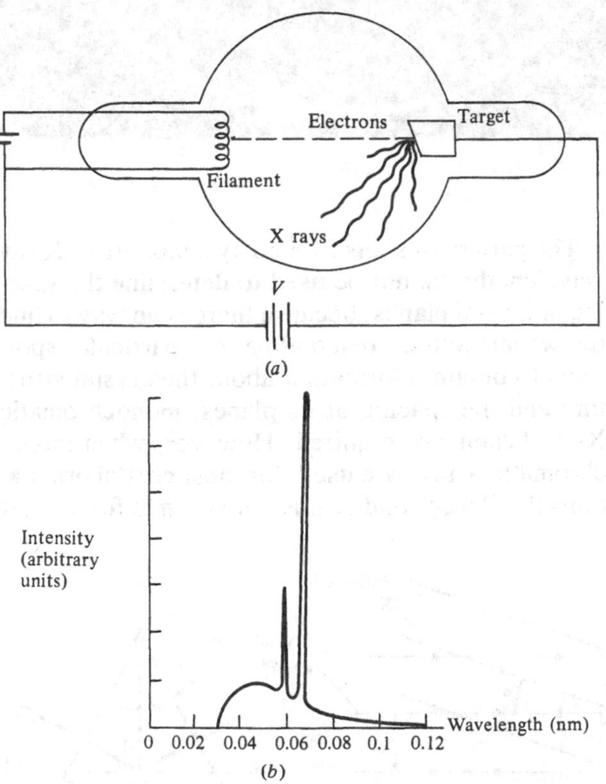

Figure 23.34. (*a*) An X-ray tube. Electrons from the heated filament are accelerated through the potential difference V and produce X rays when they strike the metal target at the anode. (*b*) The spectrum of X rays produced by a typical X-ray tube.

Example 23.14

The interatomic spacing d in Fig. 23.36 is 0.2 nm, and the angle α is 10°. If the shortest wavelength in the X-ray beam is 0.04 nm, which wavelengths will be reflected strongly from the planes shown?

The wavelengths strongly reflected satisfy $m\lambda = 2d \sin \alpha$. Using $m = 1$ and $\sin 10° = 0.174$,

$$\lambda = \frac{2d \sin \alpha}{m} = 2\,\frac{0.2 \text{ nm}}{1}\,(0.174) = 0.0696 \text{ nm}$$

Using $m = 2$, we get half this wavelength, or 0.0348 nm, which is less than the 0.04-nm minimum wavelength of the beam. Hence only the 0.0696-nm X rays will interfere constructively, and the reflected beam will be monochromatic. We see then that reflection

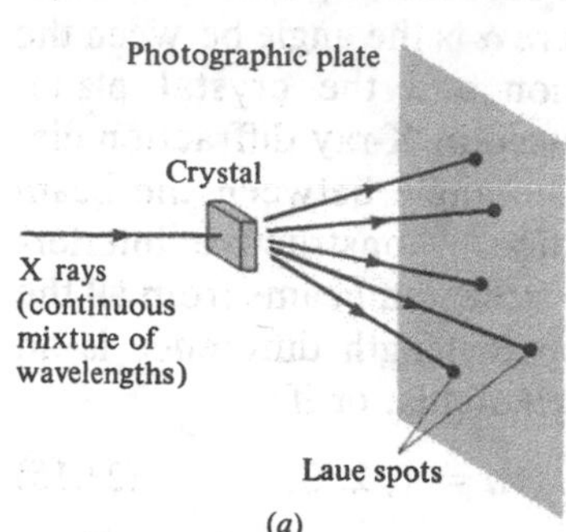

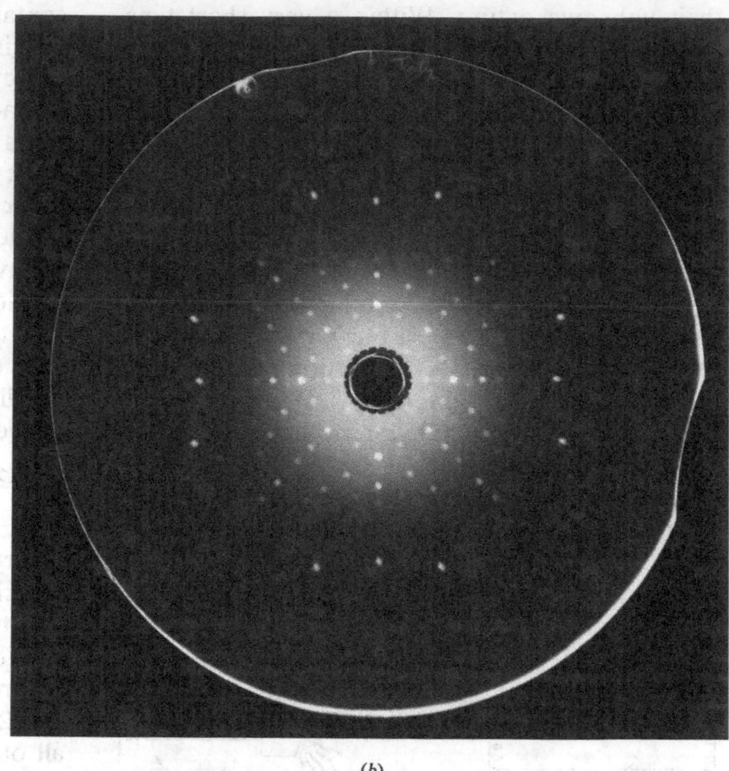

Figure 23.35. (*a*) A narrow beam of nonmonochromatic X rays strikes a crystal and forms a pattern of Laue spots on a photographic plate. (b) The Laue spots from a titanium dioxide ionic crystal. [(b)Science Source / Photo Researchers, Inc.]

from crystals provides a way of making monochromatic X-ray sources.

The Laue pattern in Fig. 23.35 contains a large number of spots. This is because there are many sets of parallel reflecting planes in a crystal, with various orientations (Fig. 23.37). Each set of planes produces one or more spots in accordance with the Bragg condition.

The pattern of spots formed by a mixture of X-ray wavelengths cannot be used to determine the spacing of crystal planes, because there is no way to find the wavelength corresponding to a particular spot. Thus to obtain information about the crystal structure and the spacing of its planes, monochromatic X-ray beams are required. However, when monochromatic X rays are used, for most crystal orientations the Bragg condition is not satisfied for *any* set

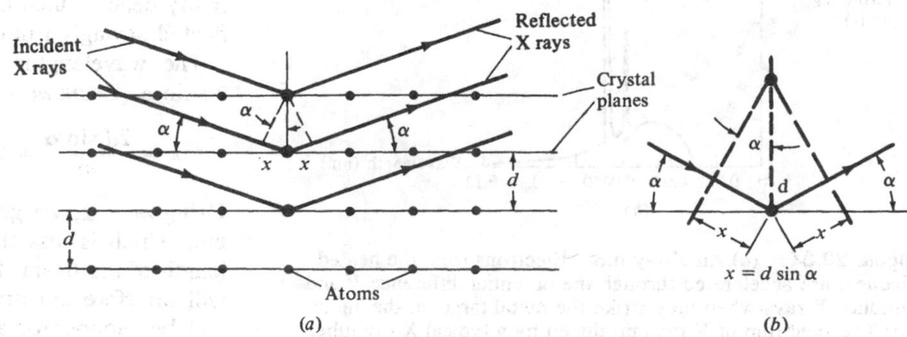

Figure 23.36. (*a*) X rays are reflected by parallel planes of atoms in a crystal. (*b*) An enlarged view of the geometric details.

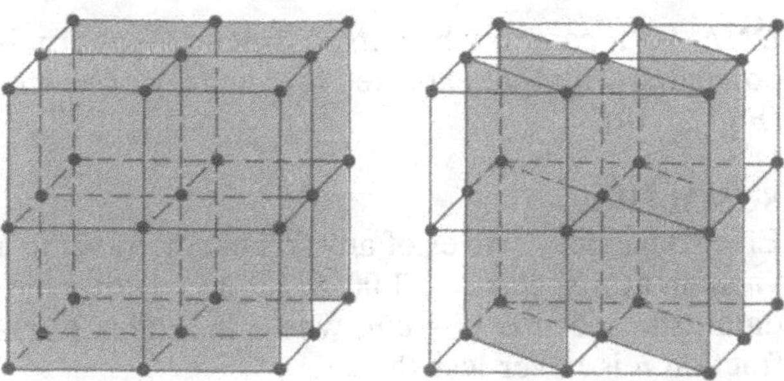

Figure 23.37. Two of the many sets of reflecting planes in a NaCl crystal.

of planes and *no* spots are formed. To overcome this, the crystal is gradually rotated (Fig. 23.38). Spots are formed on the plate as sets of planes are brought to the required angles.

The locations and intensities of these spots contain remarkably detailed information about the crystal. Since a spot is formed whenever the Bragg condition is satisfied for some set of planes, the spot *positions* depend only on the geometric structure of the crystal and the spacing of its planes. For example, sodium chloride (Fig. 23.39) and all other cubic crystals have the same characteristic X-ray diffraction pattern, with the overall scale of the pattern set by the atomic spacing. However, the *relative intensities* of the spots depend on the chemical composition of the crystal. This is because the X rays are actually reflected by the electronic clouds of the atoms, and heavy atoms, which have more electrons, are better reflectors. For example, in Fig. 23.39, different sets of planes contain different relative numbers of Na^+ and Cl^- ions, and this determines the intensity of the associated spots.

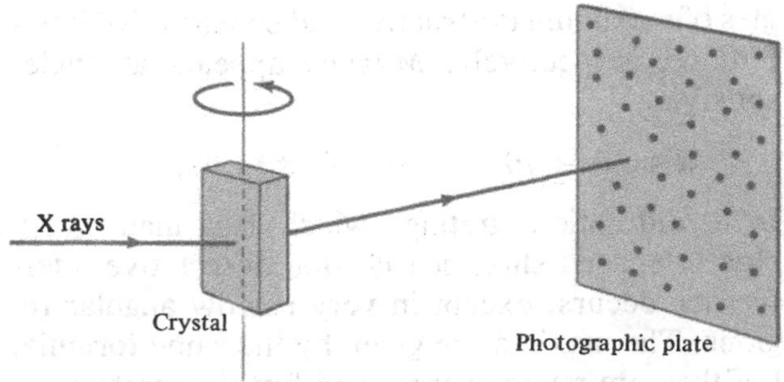

Figure 23.38. Monochromatic X rays are allowed to strike a crystal that is gradually rotated, forming a series of spots characteristic of the crystal structure.

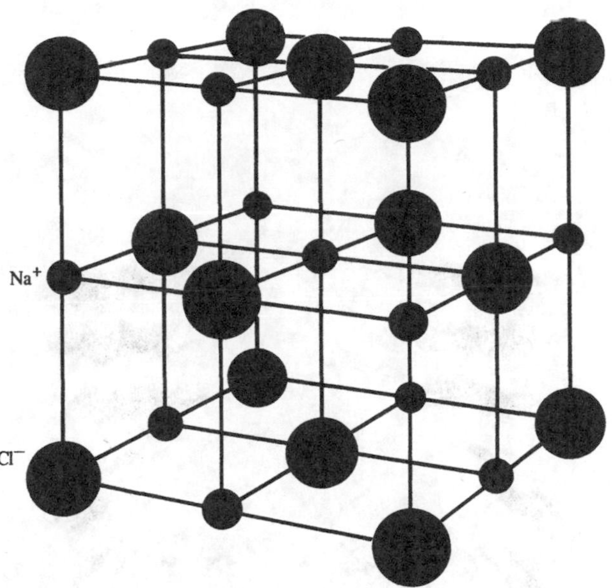

Figure 23.39. The crystal structure of sodium chloride. (From Halliday and Resnick, *Physics*, Part II, 3rd ed. Copyright © 1978, John Wiley & Sons, New York.)

Although X-ray diffraction was originally used with relatively simple inorganic crystals, it has also been applied with spectacular success to biological molecules, such as proteins and nucleic acids, that can be put into crystalline form. For example, in the 1950s, Perutz compared the positions and intensities of thousands of spots for hemoglobin with those expected from various models of the molecule. He found that this oxygen-carrying protein of the blood consists of about 10,000 atoms assembled into four chains, each with a helical form and several bends. Combining the X-ray data with chemical determinations of the sequence of the amino acid building blocks in the hemoglobin molecule, he was able to construct a detailed picture of the location and spacing of the atoms. Perutz also showed how the shape of hemoglobin changes when it gains or loses oxygen.

Another major advance in biology based in part on X-ray studies was the discovery of Crick and Watson in 1953 that the structure of the nucleic acid DNA is a double helix. The helical structure of

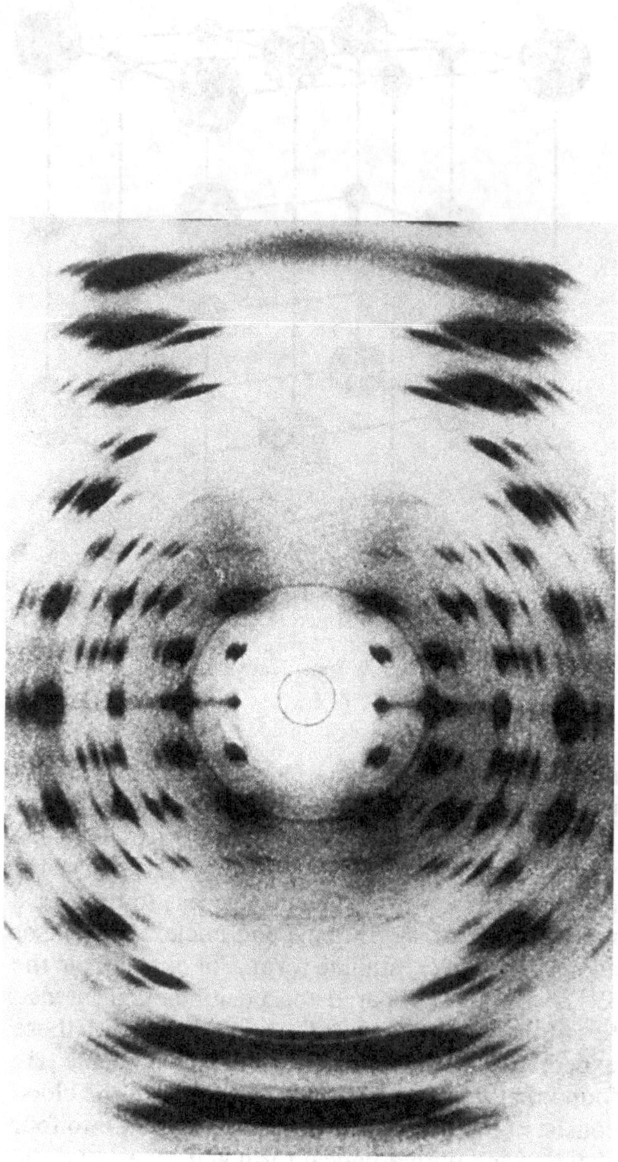

Figure 23.40. The X-ray diffraction pattern for DNA first obtained by Rosalind Franklin in 1953. Her work aided the discovery of the structure of DNA by Watson and Crick. (Science Source / Photo Researchers, Inc.)

DNA is apparent when its diffraction pattern is compared with that expected for an array of helices (Fig. 23.40).

SUMMARY

Electromagnetic waves of any frequency travel in a vacuum at a speed $c = 3.00 \times 10^8$ m s^{-1}. In a medium, the speed is $v = c/n$, where the index of refraction n is never less than 1.

The wave nature of light is demonstrated by many kinds of interference effects. For any wave, Huygens' principle states that each point on a wavefront can be considered as the source of small secondary wavelets. These wavelets can be used to predict many properties of light waves.

When light is reflected or refracted by objects large compared to its wavelength, the wave character of light plays a minor role and can usually be neglected. A light ray reflected from a smooth surface has its angle of reflection equal to the angle of incidence. When light enters a medium with a different index of refraction, it is bent or refracted; the angles of incidence and refraction are related by Snell's law,

$$n_1 \sin \phi_1 = n_2 \sin \phi_2$$

A ray bends toward the normal on entering an optically denser medium and away from the normal on entering a rarer medium. Total internal reflection will occur in the latter case if Snell's law gives $\sin \phi > 1$ for the refracted ray.

For a pair of narrow slits illuminated by a coherent beam of monochromatic light, Huygens' principle predicts a pattern of alternating dark and bright fringes on a distant screen. These appear at the angles of maximum destructive and constructive interference, respectively. *Maxima* appears at angles satisfying

$$d \sin \theta = m\lambda, \qquad m = 0, \pm 1, \pm 2, \ldots$$

In a diffraction grating, which has many very closely spaced slits, nearly total destructive interference occurs, except in very narrow angular regions. The maxima are given by the same formula, but they are much sharper and further apart.

Secondary Huygens' wavelets from different parts of a single wavefront also interfere with each other. This diffraction property gives rise to a small but detectable bending of light around objects of ordinary size and is a limiting factor in the resolution obtained with optical instruments. When light passes through a narrow slit, diffraction *minima* appear at

$$a \sin \theta = m\lambda, \qquad m = \pm 1, \pm 2, \ldots$$

The maxima are approximately halfway between the minima.

When the electric field vector of an electromagnetic wave is always directed along some line, the wave is said to be linearly polarized in that direction. Light can be polarized by various means, including absorption, reflection, and scattering. A polarizer reduces the intensity of an unpolarized beam by a half. If it is followed by an analyzer with its axis rotated by an angle θ, then the intensity is reduced further by a factor of $\cos^2 \theta$ (Malus' law).

A crystal serves as a diffraction grating for X rays. If α is the angle between the beam and the crystal planes, maxima occur when the Bragg condition is satisfied,

$$2d \sin \alpha = m\lambda, \qquad m = 1, 2, 3, \ldots$$

Checklist

Define or explain:

index of refraction	light pipe
nanometre	critical angle
Huygens' principle	coherence
wave front	diffraction grating
envelope	Rayleigh criterion
ray	resolution
secondary wavelets	line, continuous spectra
diffuse, specular reflection	diffraction
reflectance	Brewster's angle
Snell's law	scattering
angles of incidence, reflection, refraction	polarizer
white light	analyzer
dispersion	Malus' law
total internal reflection	Bragg condition
	Laue spots

REVIEW QUESTIONS

Q23-1 If the index of refraction is 2, the speed of light is ______ times the speed in the vacuum.

Q23-2 The wavelength of a beam of light ______ when it goes from air into water, and the frequency ______.

Q23-3 On a wave front, the waves at every point have ______.

Q23-4 When a light ray is reflected, the angle of reflection equals ______.

Q23-5 When a light goes from an optically denser medium to an optically rarer medium, the rays are bent ______.

Q23-6 Total internal reflection can occur when light goes from a ______ dense to a ______ dense region. It occurs when the sine of the angle of refraction would be ______.

Q23-7 In a double-slit interference pattern, the bright fringes occur where the waves from the two slits are ______.

Q23-8 In order for interference effects to be observed, the light sources must be ______.

Q23-9 As more slits are added to a grating, the lines formed become ______.

Q23-10 The diffraction pattern formed by light passing through a small opening arises from interference among ______.

Q23-11 Light can be polarized by ______, ______, and ______.

Q23-12 The spacing of atoms in a crystal is comparable to the wavelength of ______.

EXERCISES

Section 23.1 | The Index of Refraction

23-1 Find the speed of light in water.

23-2 What is the speed of light in diamond?

23-3 A lamp emits yellow light with wavelength 600 nm in air. (a) What is the wavelength of the light in water? (b) What color will the lamp appear to be to a diver who is not wearing a mask? Explain.

23-4 A beam of light has a wavelength of 640 nm in glass with a refractive index of 1.5. What is the frequency of the light?

23-5 Light with a wavelength of 500 nm in air enters water. What is its wavelength in the water?

23-6 A lamp emits light at a frequency of 5×10^{14} Hz. (a) Find the wavelength in air. (b) If the light enters glass with an index of refraction equal to 1.5, find the frequency and wavelength.

Section 23.3 | Reflection of Light

23-7 What fraction of the light intensity is reflected when light is normally incident in air on water?

23-8 In which direction must light initially travel to have a phase reversal at (a) an air–water surface; (b) a water–glass surface?

23-9 Light is incident in water along the normal to a glass plate with refractive index 1.5. What fraction of the light intensity is transmitted into the glass?

23-10 Light is normally incident in air on a glass lens with an index of refraction of 1.6. (a) What fraction of the light is reflected? (b) What fraction is transmitted? (c) If the light emerges from the second surface along the normal direction, what fraction of the original intensity leaves the lens on this side?

23-11 When light is normally incident in air on a surface, 6 percent of the intensity is reflected. What is the index of refraction of the material?

Section 23.4 | Refraction of Light

23-12 A ray of light is incident on a glass–water surface from the glass at an angle of 45°. Find the angle of refraction if the index of refraction of the glass is 1.5.

23-13 Light is incident in air on water at an angle of 15° to the normal. (a) At what angle is the reflected ray? (b) At what angle is the refracted ray?

23-14 Light is incident in water on an air–water boundary at an angle of 30° to the normal. What are the angles of reflection and refraction?

23-15 When light is incident in air at 30° to the normal of a surface of an unknown material, the angle of refraction is 25°. What is the refractive index of the material?

23-16 A student notes in his lab notebook that a light beam has an angle of incidence in air of 40° and an angle of refraction in a plastic slab of 50°. Is this reasonable? Explain.

23-17 The index of refraction of air depends on its density. How does this fact explain the shimmering or watery appearance of distant parts of black roads on hot, sunny days?

Section 23.5 | Total Internal Reflection

23-18 What is the critical angle for total internal reflection in diamond? (Assume the diamond is in air.)

23-19 A glass light pipe in air will totally internally reflect a light ray if its angle of incidence is at least 39°. What is the minimum angle for total internal reflection if the pipe is in water?

23-20 The critical angle for light going from glass to air is found to be 36°. What is the refractive index of the glass?

Section 23.6 | Young's Double-Slit Interference Experiment

23-21 Two narrow slits are illuminated with light of wavelength 500 nm. Adjacent maxima near the center of the interference pattern are separated by 1.5°. How far apart are the slits?

23-22 Two narrow slits 0.2 mm = 2×10^{-4} m apart are illuminated with red light of wavelength 700 nm. At what angles are the five maxima closest to the center of the pattern formed?

23-23 A double-slit apparatus is illuminated with yellow sodium light ($\lambda = 589$ nm). The maxima on a screen 1 m away are 1 cm apart. Find the slit separation.

23-24 Two slits separated by 10^{-4} m are illuminated with monochromatic light and form a pattern on a screen 2 m away. The fifth maximum, not counting the one at the center of the pattern, is 6 cm from the center of the screen. What is the wavelength of the light?

Section 23.7 | Coherence

23-25 A double-slit apparatus is illuminated with a narrow beam of white light from a small portion of a lamp. A filter that transmits only red light is placed just before one slit and a similar green filter before the other. Will a double-slit pattern be observed on the screen? Explain.

Section 23.8 | The Diffraction Grating

23-26 A diffraction grating with 5000 lines per centimetre is illuminated with yellow sodium light of wavelength 589 nm. (a) What is the angular position of the $m = 1$ line? (b) How many lines can be seen?

23-27 A grating has 4000 lines per centimetre. What is the longest wavelength for which the fourth-order line can be observed?

23-28 A source emits a red doublet near 656 nm with a separation of 0.2 nm. (a) At what angles will lines be seen if the diffraction grating has 8000 lines per centimetre? (b) If the two first-order lines are just resolved, how many lines does the grating have?

23-29 What is the minimum number of lines needed in a diffraction grating to resolve in second order the sodium doublet at 589.59 and 589.00 nm?

23-30 A diffraction grating with 8000 lines per centimetre is illuminated with light from a hydrogen lamp. In the first-order spectrum, what is the angular separation between the 656- and 410-nm lines emitted by atomic hydrogen in the lamp?

23-31 Explain why diffraction gratings have (a) closely spaced slits; (b) a large number of slits.

23-32 A grating has 8000 lines per centimetre, and it is 0.5 m from a screen. When it is illuminated with light of wavelength 550 nm, how far from the center of the screen will the first-order line be located?

23-33 A grating has 6000 lines per centimetre. It is located 0.7 m from a screen, and the first-order lines appears 0.32 m from the center of the screen. What is the wavelength of the light?

Section 23.9 | Diffraction

23-34 A narrow slit is illuminated with white light. What will be seen on a screen beyond the slit?

23-35 A narrow slit is illuminated with yellow light of wavelength 589 nm. If the central diffraction maximum extends from 0° to 40°, how wide is the slit?

23-36 A slit of width 1000 nm is illuminated by light of wavelength 600 nm. At what angle is the first diffraction minimum?

23-37 A slit of width 1600 nm is 0.5 m from a screen. It is illuminated by light with a wavelength of 400 nm. What is the distance between the first minima on either side of the bright central maximum?

23-38 A circular aperture of radius 10^{-5} m is illuminated with light of wavelength 500 nm. At what angle is the first diffraction minimum?

23-39 A circular aperture of radius 800 nm is illuminated by light of wavelength 600 nm. The first diffraction minimum appears as a circle on a screen 0.3 m away. What is the radius of that circle?

Section 23.10 | Polarization of Light

23-40 Light is incident from air on glass with an index of refraction 1.5. At what angle will the reflected light be fully polarized?

23-41 When light goes from air into a plastic, the reflected beam is completely polarized if the angle of incidence is 60°. If the light goes from the plastic into the air, at what angle of incidence will the reflected beam be completely polarized?

23-42 A light beam is initially unpolarized and is passed through a Polaroid filter. If the beam emerging from the filter has an intensity of 10 W m^{-2}, what is the intensity of the incident beam?

23-43 A light beam is partially polarized so that it has an average amplitude E_0 along one axis and an average amplitude $2E_0$ along the axis at right angles. If a Polaroid filter is rotated in front of the beam, find (a) the minimum fraction of the intensity transmitted; (b) the maximum fraction transmitted.

23-44 Unpolarized light passes through three filters. The first has its axis vertical, the second at 30° to the vertical, and the third at 60° to the vertical, or at 30° to the second. (a) What fraction of the intensity is transmitted through the three filters? (b) Suppose the second and third filters are interchanged, without altering the orientation of their axes. What fraction of the intensity is transmitted now?

23-45 When unpolarized light passes through two successive Polaroid filters, its intensity is reduced by 90 percent. What is the angle between the transmission axes of the filters?

Section 23.11 | X-ray Diffraction and the Structure of Biological Molecules

23-46 It is found that X rays are reflected strongly from crystal planes 0.2 nm apart when they are incident at 20° from the planes. What is their longest possible wavelength?

23-47 A set of planes in a crystal has a spacing of 0.3 nm. If a beam of monochromatic X rays of wavelength 0.1 nm is incident on the crystal, what is the smallest angle relative to the planes at which constructive interference occurs?

23-48 X rays are reflected from crystal planes separated by 0.3 nm. They are incident at an angle of 12° to the planes. If the beam contains wavelengths as short as 0.2 nm, what wavelengths will be strongly reflected?

PROBLEMS

23-49 A monochromatic light ray enters the prism shown in Fig. 23.41 at an angle of 30° to the normal. The refractive index is 1.5. At what angle θ does the ray leave the prism?

23-50 A beam of light enters the top of a glass cube at an angle greater than zero to the normal direction, and then hits a side of the cube. If the refractive index of the cube is 1.5, can the beam emerge from the side into the air? Explain your answer with the aid of a diagram.

23-51 A small lamp is 10 m below the surface of a lake. It emits light in all directions. A boat goes from directly over the lamp to the point where it can no longer be seen. How far does it go?

23-52 A glass plate with refractive index 1.5 is inserted into a beam so that the angle of incidence is 30°. (a) What is the direction of the refracted ray inside the plate? (b) What is the direction of the ray emerging from the far side of the plate? (c) How far is the ray shifted at right angles to its original path by the plate if it is 0.02 m thick?

***23-53** An object 1 m under water is observed from the air. (a) What is the angle of refraction of

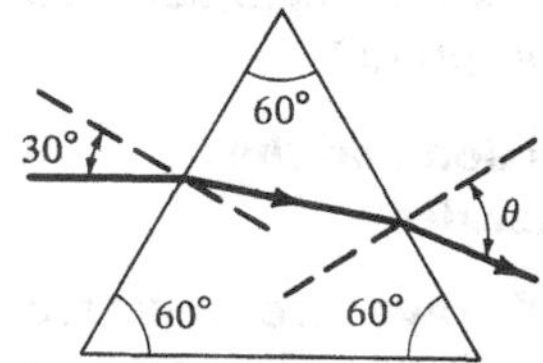

Figure 23.41. Problem 23-49.

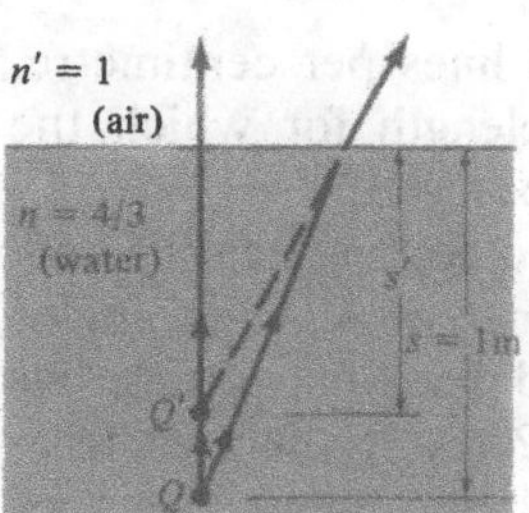

Figure 23.42. Problem 23-53.

a light ray from the object reaching the surface at an angle of 10° to the normal? (b) Where does the object appear to be? (*Hint*: Calculate where the refracted ray appears to intersect a ray normal to the surface as in Fig. 23.42. Q is the actual position and Q' is the apparent position.)

***23-54** Snell's law of refraction can be derived from Huygens' principle by using a procedure similar to that used in Fig. 23.6 to derive the law of reflection. (a) Draw a series of diagrams showing how a wave front changes as it travels from a medium with light velocity v_1 into a medium with velocity v_2. (b) Using similar triangles derive Snell's law.

23-55 Obtain a formula for the angular positions of the minima in a double-slit apparatus.

23-56 One does not normally detect interference effects between the sound coming from two loudspeakers of a stereo system. Explain why.

23-57 Show how one could devise a simple experiment to demonstrate the interference between sound waves from two sources.

23-58 What will be observed in a double-slit experiment if white light is used? Explain.

***23-59** A coherent light beam is produced by placing a filter and a slit of adjustable width in front of an incandescent lamp. The light then falls on a double-slit apparatus and forms an interference pattern on a screen. Describe what happens as the source slit is gradually increased in width. (Ignore the effects of source-slit diffraction.)

23-60 A grating with 6000 lines per centimetre is illuminated with white light. (a) What is the highest-order spectrum that includes the entire visible spectrum? (b) What is the highest-order spectrum that includes any portion of the visible spectrum?

23-61 A grating with 4000 lines per centimetre forms a line at 45°. (a) What are the possible wavelengths of the light illuminating the grating? (b) How could one determine the actual wavelength?

23-62 When a small opaque circular disk is illuminated by a coherent plane wave, a bright spot is seen at the center of the shadow formed on a distant screen. Explain why.

***23-63** Suppose that light is incident on a diffraction grating at an angle ϕ to the normal direction (Fig. 23.43). (In the discussion in this chapter, ϕ was always chosen to be zero.) Show that the maxima occur at angles θ such that $d(\sin\phi + \sin\theta) = m\lambda$, where $m = 0, 1, 2, \ldots$ and d is the slit separation.

23-64 A slit of width 10^{-5} m is illuminated with light of wavelength 500 nm. How wide is the central diffraction peak on a screen 0.5 m away?

23-65 A lens when properly focused on a distant-point light source of wavelength 550 nm forms a circular spot 0.1 mm = 10^{-4} m in diameter on a screen 0.2 m from the lens. If the spot size is entirely due to diffraction by the lens, what is the diameter of the lens?

***23-66** (a) Using a right triangle, show that $\tan\theta = 1/[\tan(90° - \theta)]$. (b) Use this identity to prove the statement made in Example 23.12 that the sum of the Brewster angles for light incident from medium 1 and from medium 2 is 90°.

23-67 Using Snell's law, show that when light is incident at Brewster's angle, the reflected and refracted beams are at right angles.

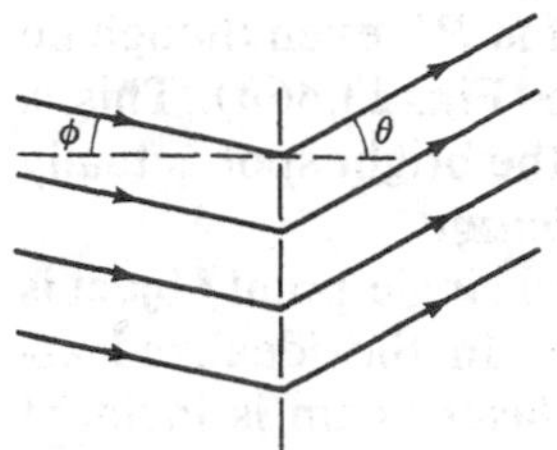

Figure 23.43. Problem 23-63.

23-68 Suppose a sodium chloride crystal is ground into a powder, so that it becomes a large number of randomly oriented small crystals. If monochromatic X rays are incident on the powder, what kind of interference pattern will be formed? (*Hint:* Consider what will happen to the spots in Fig. 23.35 if the axis of rotation is changed.)

ANSWERS TO REVIEW QUESTIONS

Q23-1, 0.5; **Q23-2**, decreases, stays the same; **Q23-3**, the same phase; **Q23-4**, the angle of incidence; **Q23-5**, away from the normal; **Q23-6**, more, less, greater than 1; **Q23-7**, in phase; **Q23-8**, coherent; **Q23-9**, sharper; **Q23-10**, different parts of the wave; **Q23-11**, absorption, reflection, scattering; **Q23-12**, X rays.

SUPPLEMENTARY TOPICS

23.12 | HOLOGRAPHY

One of the most intriguing and versatile advances of recent years is *holography*. A *hologram* is a photograph of the interference pattern produced when monochromatic light reflected or transmitted by an object interferes with a coherent *reference* light beam. When a hologram is illuminated by a coherent light source, an image of the original object is formed. Unlike an ordinary two-dimensional photograph, this *reconstructed* image is three-dimensional. Consequently, a moving viewer observes *parallax*: the relative displacement of nearer and more distant parts of the object (Fig. 23.44).

Holography was invented in 1947 by D. Gabor, who received the 1971 Nobel prize for his work. However, the lack of sufficiently strong coherent light sources limited the usefulness of holography until the advent of the laser in 1960. Since then, increasingly varied and ingenious applications of holography have been developed.

In order to understand how holography works, it is useful first to consider a circular arrangement of concentric transparent and opaque rings called a *zone plate* (Fig. 23.45) illuminated by coherent monochromatic light of wavelength λ. Going outward from the center of the plate, the average distance from a ring to a particular point P on the axis is one wavelength greater than from the preceding

Figure 23.44. (a) Photograph of the reconstructed image from a hologram of coins. (b) Same image at a slighly different angle. The parallax shows that holography reconstructs the images in three dimensions. (Paul Silverman / Fundamental Photographs)

ring. Accordingly the Huygens' wavelets from all the transparent rings arrive approximately in phase and interfere constructively. The opaque rings block out the wavelets that would interfere destructively with those from the transparent rings.

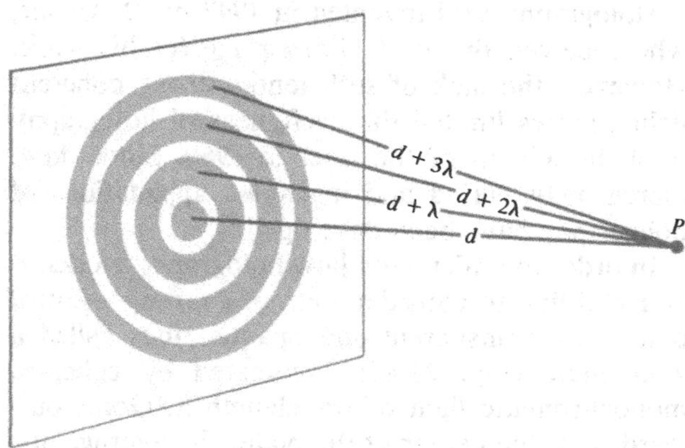

Figure 23.45. A zone plate has alternate opaque and transparent rings. All the wavelets reaching point P are in phase and interfere constructively.

Because of the opaque rings, about half of the incident light is blocked by the zone plate. Much of the remaining light travels straight ahead. However, the Huygens' wavelets from the transparent rings arrive at P approximately in phase, forming a bright spot due to the constructive interference (Fig. 23.46*a*). Wavelets spreading outward as though they had originated at point P', a distance d to the left of the zone plate, are also in phase. If they are eventually brought together by a lens, as in the eye or a camera, they interfere constructively. Hence, if one looks through a zone plate toward a light source, one sees a bright spot at P', even though no light actually originates there (Fig. 23.46*b*). This is called a *virtual image*, while the bright spot actually formed at P is called a *real image*.

The hologram produced by a single-point object is very similar to a zone plate. In the idealized arrangement of Fig. 23.47*a*, a laser beam is incident on a pointlike object, producing spherical Huygens' wavelets. At some places on the photographic plate, the spherical wave from the object and that

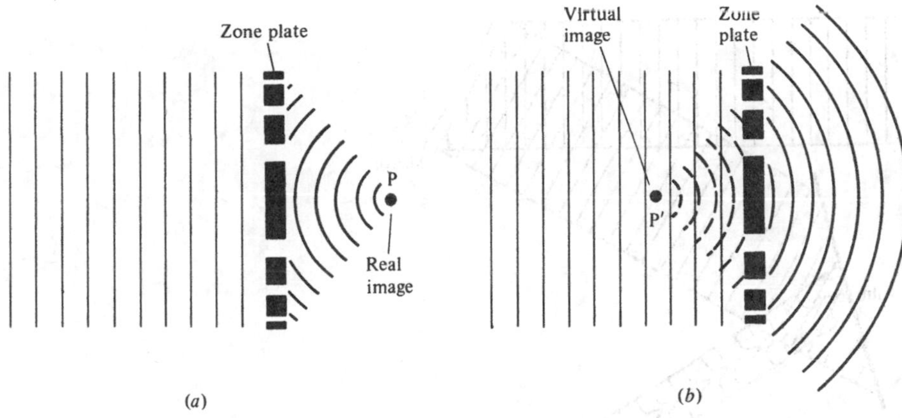

Figure 23.46. A coherent monochromatic wave incident on a zone plate has alternate zones blocked by the plate. Some transmitted light goes straight through, some forms a real image at P as shown in (*a*), and some forms a virtual image at P' as shown in (*b*).

from the undeflected reference wave are exactly in phase, and maximum constructive interference occurs. At other places, the waves are out of phase, and destructive interference occurs. This produces a pattern that looks like a zone plate, although the abrupt changes from opaque to transparent rings are replaced by a more gradual variation in intensity. If the developed photographic plate is later illuminated by a laser beam, virtual and real images are formed of the point object just as they were for the zone plate (Fig. 23.47*b*).

When a hologram is made of a complex object, each point on the object produces spherical waves that interfere with the reference wave and form a

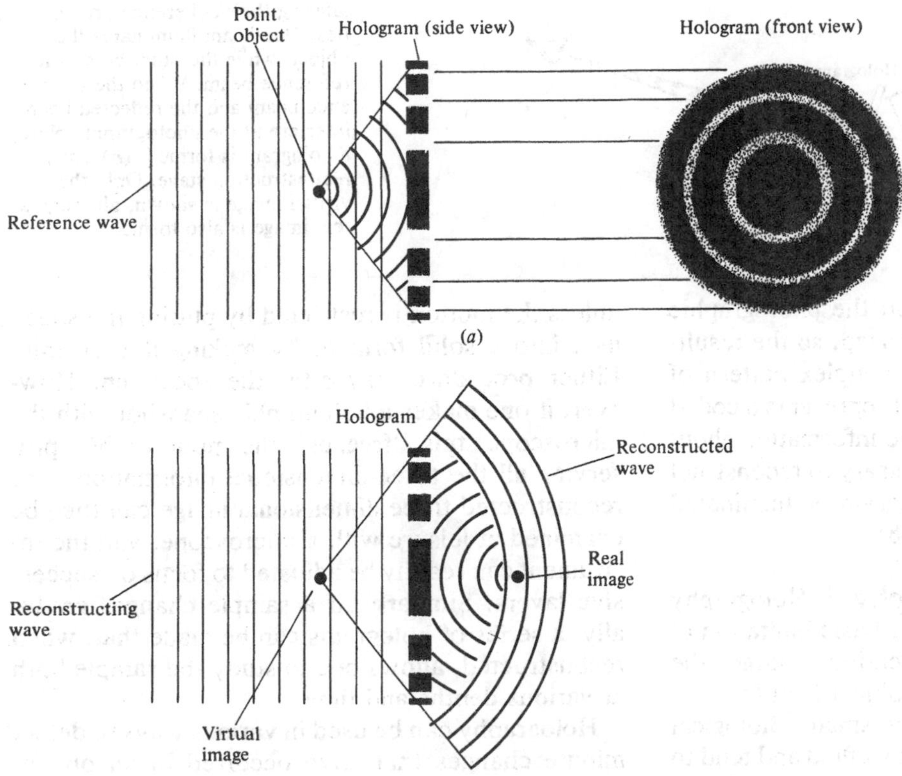

Figure 23.47. (*a*) An idealized arrangement for making a hologram of a point object. (*b*) The corresponding reconstruction of the virtual and real images.

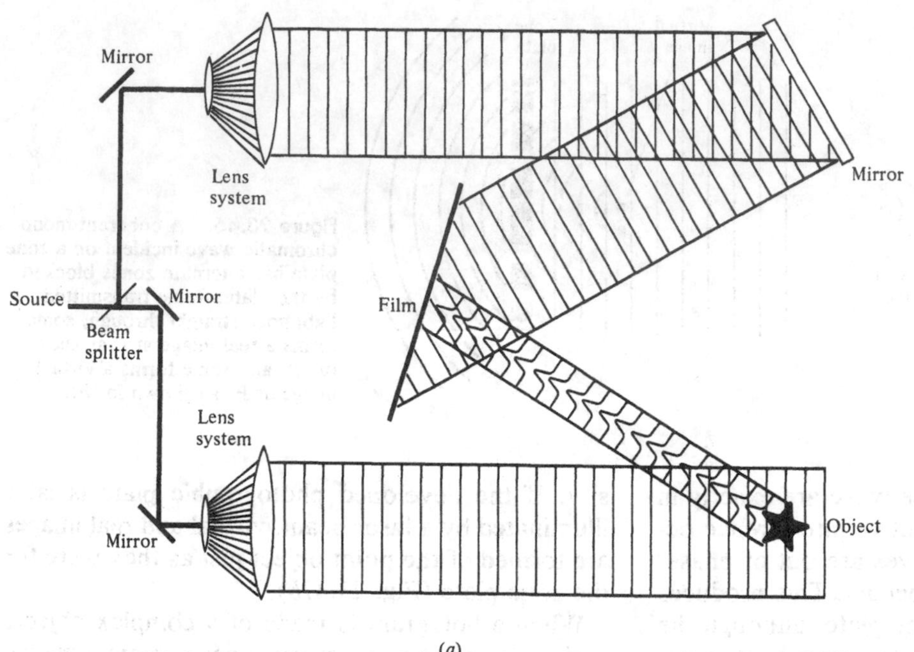

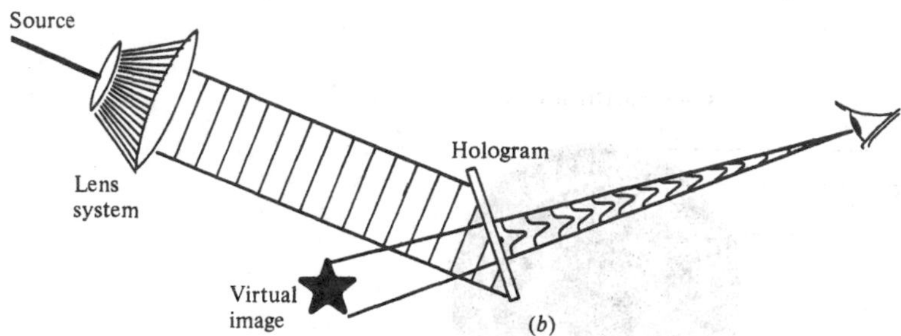

Figure 23.48. (*a*) Production of a hologram for a complex object. A single highly coherent laser beam is split into two by a partially silvered mirror. Lenses are used to broaden the beams without altering their coherence properties. One beam illuminates the object, while the other acts as a reference beam. When the reference beam and the reflected beam interfere at the photographic plate, a hologram is formed. (*b*) The reconstruction stage. Only the virtual image is shown, although a real image is also formed.

series of zone platelike rings on the photographic plate. These rings are superimposed, so the resulting hologram is an incredibly complex pattern of lines and swirls. Nevertheless, it represents a coded diffraction pattern containing the information about all the points on the object necessary to reconstruct the wave fronts when the hologram is illuminated by a coherent source (Fig. 23.48).

Applications of Holography | Holography makes it possible to overcome a basic limitation of the microscope. If the magnification is large, the range of depths over which an object is in focus at any microscope setting is very small. Biological specimens often are suspended in a fluid and tend to drift about. Hence they move in and out of focus, unless the motion is restricted by putting the specimen into a solid form or by making it very thin. Either procedure may alter the specimen. However, if one makes a holographic snapshot with the microscope, this "freezes" the motion while preserving all the three-dimensional information. The reconstructed three-dimensional image can then be examined at leisure with a microscope, and the instrument can readily be adjusted to focus on successive layers. Similarly, if a sample changes gradually, a series of holograms can be made that, when reconstructed, allows one to study the sample both at various depths and times.

Holography can be used in various ways to detect minute changes that have occurred in an object. Suppose an object and its hologram made at an earlier time are returned to precisely the positions they had when the hologram was originally made. If the same laser again is used to illuminate them, then the wave from the object and the reconstructed wave from the hologram will interfere. Any changes that have occurred in the appearance of the object will produce light and dark interference fringes, which directly pinpoint changes not readily found by visual inspection. Differences between two carefully machined parts can be determined in a similar way.

A closely related procedure is to make two successive holograms on a single photographic plate by a double exposure. When the image is reconstructed, interference effects will occur if the object has changed in any way. A remarkable photograph made from a double-exposed hologram is shown in Fig. 23.49.

Figure 23.49. Two holograms were made of a soda can on a single photographic plate. A rubber band was stretched around the can's center to compress it before the first exposure. The second exposure was made after the rubber band was cut, so that the can had expanded and reduced the distance the laser beam had to travel. The photograph shows the reconstructed image. For each half wavelength change in the distance to the can, the photo shows a dark fringe where the two reconstructed waves are out of phase. By counting these fringes the compression of the can can be determined. Similar photos can be used in a variety of medical and industrial applications. (Courtesy of Thomas Gilliss, Physics Department, The College of Wooster.)

So far, we have discussed cases in which the original light source and the reconstructing beam have the same wavelength. However, this is not necessary. If a shorter wavelength is used in the reconstruction, this will have the effect of increasing the apparent depth of the object. Also, it is not necessary that the original and reconstructing waves have the same physical nature. Using special photographic techniques, holograms have been made from the interference between reference and reflected or transmitted beams of ultrasonic waves. Holograms are also made with X rays. In both cases visible light is used for reconstructing the image. The ability of ultrasound and X rays to penetrate where light may not is thereby combined with the great flexibility of image manipulation afforded by lenses for visible light.

23.13 | INTERFERENCE EFFECTS IN THIN FILMS

The colors produced by light reflected from soap bubbles and oil films, the irridescent eye of a peacock's tail feather, and the purple or amber color of coated camera lenses all are due to the interference of light reflected by the opposite surfaces of thin films. When the two reflected beams are in phase, there is constructive interference, and a maximum reflected intensity results. Conversely, when the two beams are exactly out of phase, destructive interference reduces the intensity of the reflected light. Since the interference conditions depend on the wavelength, the intensity of the light reflected by a given film varies considerably with the wavelength. This causes the colored effects mentioned previously when the film is illuminated with white light.

We now investigate reflection by films quantitatively. Figure 23.50 shows monochromatic light incident in air on a thin film of refractive index n and thickness d. At normal incidence, light reflected by the second surface travels a distance $2d$ farther than light reflected by the first surface. If the wavelength in vacuum or air is λ, then the wavelength in the film is $\lambda' = \lambda/n$. The light reflected at the first surface is reversed in phase. However, the light reflected at the second surface is not, because the phase reversal occurs only when the light is incident from the less dense medium. Thus if $2d$ is exactly one wavelength, the waves are exactly out of phase and inter-

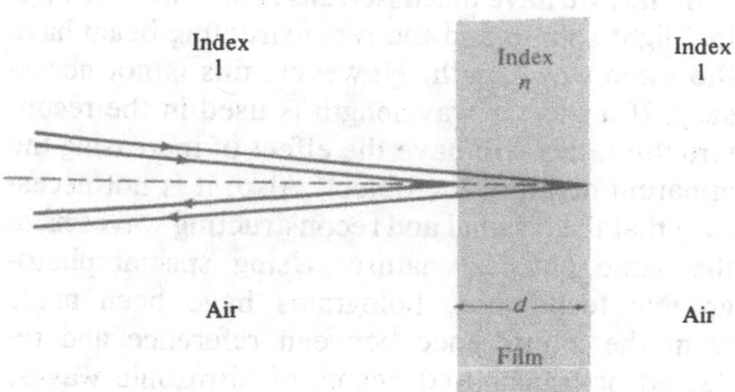

Figure 23.50. When light is incident on a thin film, some of the light is reflected at each surface, although most of it is transmitted (not shown). At normal incidence the light reflected by the second surface travels a distance $2d$ farther than the light reflected by the first surface. A phase reversal occurs at the first surface, where the light is incident from the less dense medium, the air. No reversal occurs at the second, because the light is incident from the denser medium.

fere destructively. In general, destructive interference occurs if $2d$ is any integer multiple of λ', or if $2d = m\lambda' = m\lambda/n$. Thus the reflected intensity is a minimum if

$$2nd = m\lambda, \qquad m = 0, 1, 2, \ldots \qquad (23.16)$$

Similarly, the constructive interference and the reflected intensity are a maximum when

$$2nd = (m + \tfrac{1}{2})\lambda, \qquad m = 0, 1, 2, \ldots \qquad (23.17)$$

These two equations also hold true if the film is less dense than the media on either side. However, the conditions for the maxima and minima are reversed when the film is intermediate in density between the media on either side, since then either both reflected beams or neither is reversed in sign. The following example illustrates the reflecting properties of a typical film.

Example 23.15

A film of soap solution ($n = 1.33$) is just thick enough to cause the maximum reflection of red light of wavelength 700 nm at normal incidence. (a) How thick is the film? (b) The film is illuminated with white light at close to normal incidence. If an observer sees the reflected light, what color does the film appear to be?

(a) Using $m = 0$ in Eq. 23.17 for the maximum reflected intensity,

$$d = \frac{(m + \frac{1}{2})\lambda}{2n} = \frac{(\frac{1}{2})(700\text{ nm})}{2(1.33)} = 132\text{ nm}$$

(b) The distance across the film and back is a half wavelength at 700 nm, so it is a full wavelength at 350 nm. This is the longest wavelength at which the reflected intensity is a minimum, and it is just beyond the limit of visible light, 400 nm. This means that partial destructive interference also occurs at wavelengths in the visible near 400 nm, so relatively little light is reflected at the shorter wavelengths. Conversely, the reflection at wavelengths close to the long wavelength or red end of the spectrum will be enhanced. Thus if the observer sees light reflected at or near normal incidence, the film will appear red. However, if the film is part of a curved surface or a bubble, the angle of incidence and path length will vary over the film, and various colors will be seen in different parts of the film.

Nonreflective Coatings | We saw in Section 23.3 that about 4 percent of the light is reflected at each of the several air–glass surfaces in an optical instrument such as a camera or a microscope. Hence the reduction of these intensity losses made possible by nonreflective coatings is of considerable practical value.

A nonreflective coating is illustrated in Fig. 23.51. A thin film of a material with index n_c is evaporated onto glass with index n_g. Since n_c is chosen to be less than n_g, the waves reflected from *both* sides of the film are reversed in sign. Hence maximum destructive interference and minimal reflection occurs when the path lengths differ by a half wavelength. For normal incidence, this happens if the film thickness d is a quarter-wavelength. For light with wavelength λ in air, the wavelength in the coating is λ/n_c,

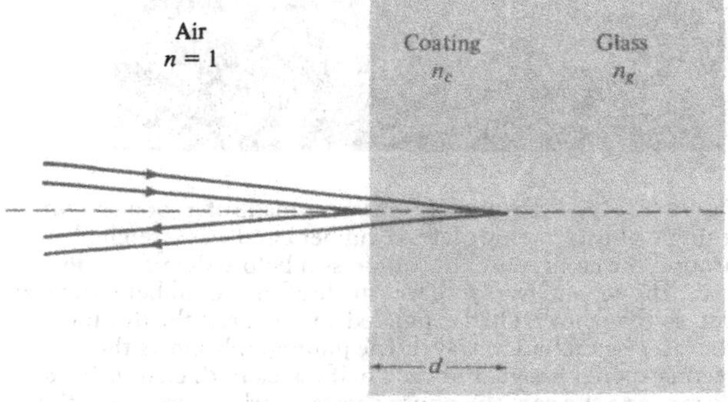

Figure 23.51. A nonreflecting coating on glass. The refractive index of the coating is less than that of the glass.

and $d = \lambda/4n_c$. This result is illustrated by the following example.

Example 23.16

A camera lens has a coating of magnesium fluoride, which has a refractive index $n_c = 1.38$. If the reflected intensity at normal incidence of blue light of wavelength 500 nm is a minimum, how thick is the coating?

From the previous discussion, the thickness of the coating is

$$d = \frac{\lambda}{4n_c} = \frac{500 \text{ nm}}{4(1.38)} = 90.6 \text{ nm}$$

Total cancellation, or zero reflected light intensity can occur only if the two reflected beams have the same intensity. It follows from Eq. 23.3 that the intensities are equal if $n_c = \sqrt{n_g}$. For glass with index 1.5, this means that the coating should have an index of $\sqrt{1.5} = 1.22$. However, suitable materials with the necessary hardness are not available with this index, and magnesium fluoride, which has an index equal to 1.38, is used as a compromise.

A single coating on a lens reduces the reflected light intensity to varying degrees throughout the visible range. Camera lenses designed for color film are least reflective in the blue, and they appear amber because the reflection is greater at longer wavelengths. Lenses designed primarily for black and white film are least reflective for green light. They reflect more red and violet light, which gives them a purple appearance. In recent years, techniques have been developed to place two or even three layers on lenses. Although difficult and expensive, this process further reduces the reflective intensity (Fig. 23.52).

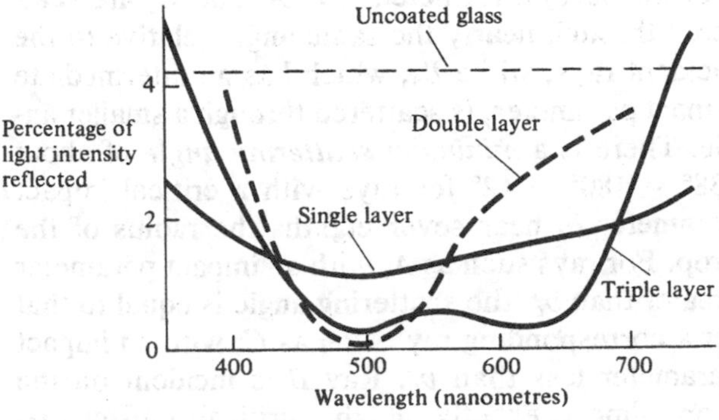

Figure 23.52. Percentage of light intensity reflected by glass with one, two, or three coating layers.

23.14 | THE ORIGIN OF RAINBOWS

Rainbows are often seen during or after a rain shower when the sun is behind the observer, or under similar conditions in the fine spray from a fountain or waterfall. The familiar colorful display can be largely understood using what we have just learned about reflection, refraction, and dispersion.

A rainbow is often thought of as a single colored ring or part of a ring, with the red portion at the outermost edge and the blue and violet light at the innermost edge. In fact favorable conditions allow observation of a fainter secondary rainbow outside the primary in which the color ordering is reversed, with the red inside. Also, one can see that the region within the primary ring is fairly bright, as is the region outside the secondary ring. However, the region between the rings is noticeably darker. This dark area is called Alexander's dark band (Fig. 23.53).

The rainbow arcs are formed by the reflection and refraction of light by water droplets. Figures 23.54*a* and 23.54*b* show two rays incident on a raindrop located in the air, above the ground. They enter at the same distance from the centerline of the drop or *impact parameter b*, but one is above the centerline and the other below. At point *A*, some of the light is reflected, and some is refracted into the drop. The ray is partially reflected and partially transmitted out of the drop at each subsequent encounter with the drop surface. The directions of the second refracted ray in (*a*) and that of the third in (*b*) are toward the ground. These rays are responsible for the primary and secondary rainbows, respectively.

The paths of the rays in Fig. 23.54 are found using the laws of reflection and refraction. At each encounter with the air–water boundary, the reflected ray leaves the surface at an angle equal to the incident angle. The refracted ray bends toward the normal to the surface when passing from air to water and away from the normal when leaving the drop.

The colors of the rainbow are caused by the differences in the refracted angles for the various wavelengths in the incident light. The separation and ordering of the colors in the primary and secondary rainbows are due to the different paths taken by the different wavelength components in the ray (Fig. 23.54*c*). In the primary rainbow, the red light is deflected or scattered through the small-

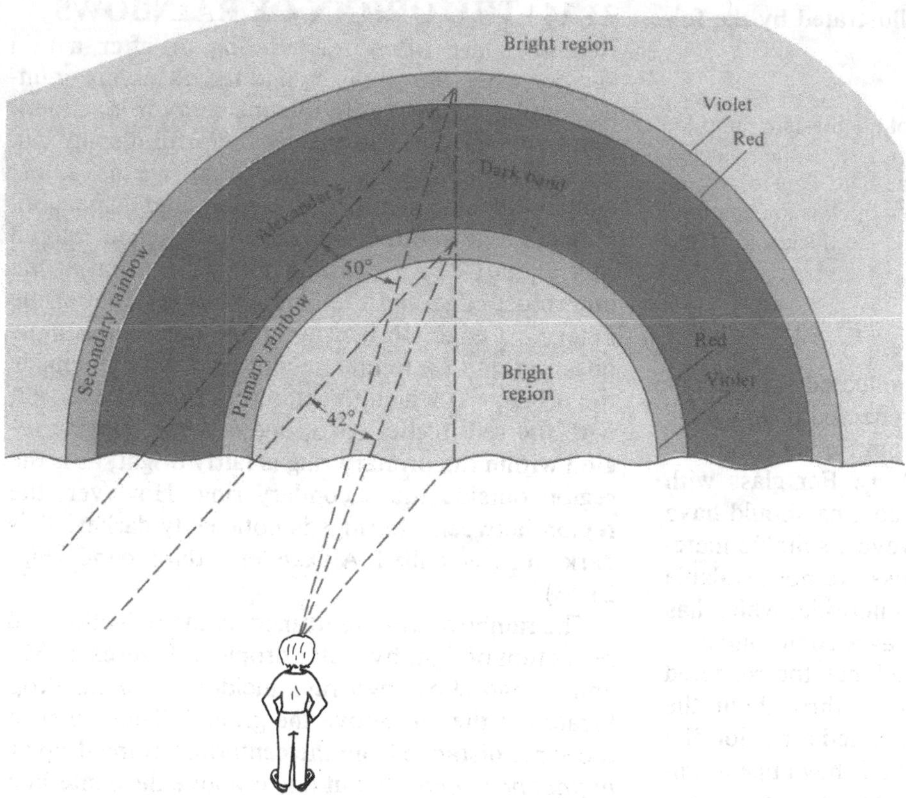

Figure 23.53. A schematic view of an observer and a rainbow showing the angles between the direction of the incident sunlight and the lines to the midpoints of the primary and secondary rainbow bands. Note the reversal in the color order between the primary and secondary rainbows.

est angle from the incident direction. We see red light coming from droplets relatively high in the sky and violet light from lower droplets. Thus the red appears on the outside of the arc. In the secondary rainbow, red is deflected the most, so it appears on the inside.

So far we have stated but not really explained why the two rainbow arcs are formed by the second and third refracted rays. In fact, without any additional investigation, it seems surprising that any particular features show up in the light returned by the raindrops. Instead, it might be expected that the drops cause light to be returned toward the observer but that, if all rays are considered, the net effect is a sort of brightening. In fact, the appearance of the rainbow and dark band are a result of an interesting quirk of the geometry.

In Fig. 23.55*a*, we show several rays (A through D) incident on a drop with smaller and smaller impact parameters. Note the curious circumstance that the second refracted rays A_3 and C_3 are scattered through nearly the same angle relative to the incident rays, while B_3, which has an intermediate impact parameter, is scattered through a smaller angle. There is a *minimum scattering angle* of about $138° = 180° - 42°$ for rays with a critical impact parameter b_c near seven-eighths the radius of the drop. For rays such as A, with an impact parameter greater than b_c, the scattering angle is equal to that for a corresponding ray, such as C, with an impact parameter less than b_c. Ray B is incident on the drop almost exactly at the critical impact parameter.

The existence of a minimum scattering angle ac-

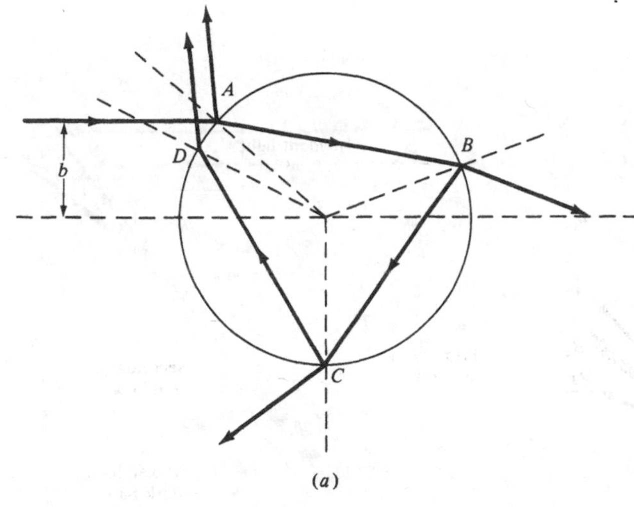

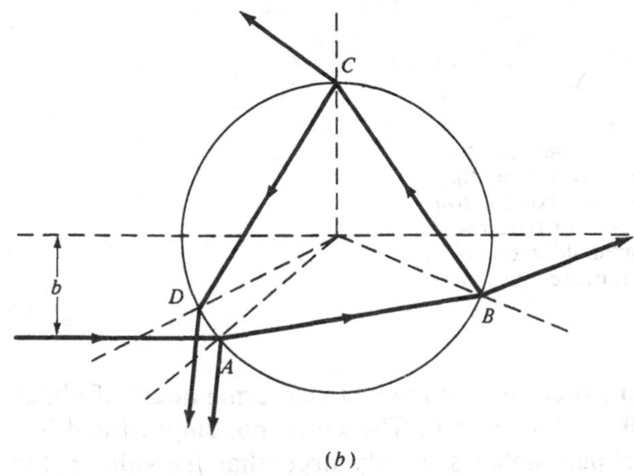

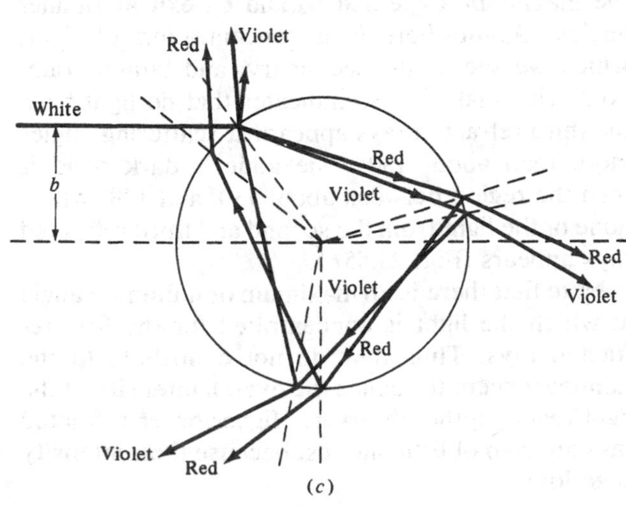

Figure 23.54. (*a*) A ray of light incident with an impact parameter b on a spherical raindrop. At point A, it is partially reflected and partially transmitted (refracted). The refracted ray continues through the drop and at B is again partially reflected (now internally) and partially transmitted. At points C and D, the same thing happens. The intensity inside the drop decreases each time a reflection occurs because some of the light escapes the drop. (*b*) A ray incident with the same impact parameter but below the center line of the drop. If one imagines this drop in the air, the second refracted ray in (*a*) and the third refracted ray in (*b*) both travel down toward the earth. (*a*) and (*b*) show an "average" ray. Dispersion causes red light to bend less than violet light when entering or leaving the drop. (*c*) is (*a*) redrawn to show the paths of the red and violet components of the incident ray.

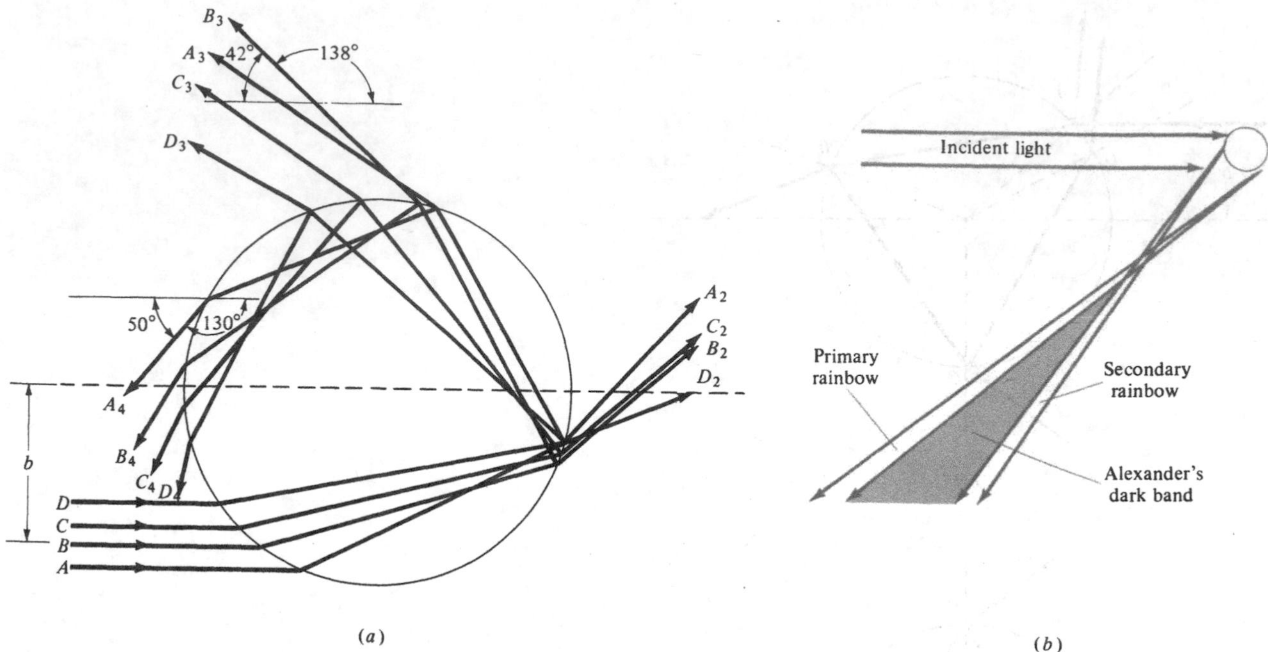

Figure 23.55. (*a*) Rays incident on a spherical water drop at a variety of impact parameters. The second refracted rays are responsible for the primary rainbow. Ray B_3 exits the drop at the minimum scattering angle of 138°. All other second refracted rays exit the drop at larger deflections. Ray A_4 exits at the maximum scattering angle possible for third refracted rays. (*b*) Alexander's dark band is the region between the minimum deflection of the second refracted rays (primary rainbow) and the maximum of the third refracted rays (secondary rainbow).

counts for several features of the primary rainbow. There is a concentration of light leaving the drop near this angle. Rays such as *A*, *B*, and *C* that enter with a considerable range of impact parameters emerge at nearly the same angle. Because of the dispersion, this concentration appears as the primary rainbow. Note also that the full primary rainbow is a ring, not an arc. The second refracted rays from rays incident below the centerline also form a rainbow arc. Observers in an airplane can look at drops both above and below themselves and can see the full ring. Secondary rays that exit at larger scattering angles do not contribute to the rainbow but do produce the brightening inside of it. Also, none of the incident light in the second refracted ray exits at scattering angles less than the minimum. This is part of the explanation of why there is a dark region at scattering angles less than 138°.

If we continue the ray tracing, we discover a similar geometric anomaly in the third refracted rays. Here there is a *maximum* scattering angle of about $130° = 180° - 50°$. The corresponding critical impact parameter is slightly larger than the value b_c for the second refracted rays. In this case, A_4 exits near the maximum angle and B_4 and C_4 exit at smaller angles. Again there is a concentration of light, which we see as the secondary, and fainter, rainbow. The analysis also indicates that no light from the third refracted rays appears at scattering angles more than about 130°. Alexander's dark band is then the region between about 130° and 138° where none of the light from the second and third refracted rays appears (Fig. 23.55*b*).

Note that there is no maximum or minimum angle at which the light is concentrated for the first refracted rays. Thus they do not contribute to the rainbow except to reduce the overall intensity of the light reaching the observer. Higher-order refracted rays are also of little interest because their intensity is so low.

An interesting feature of the primary rainbow is that it is very strongly polarized. To understand why this occurs requires a careful calculation of the angles of reflection and refraction of rays that leave the drop at nearly the same angle as does ray B in Fig. 23.55a. These are the rays that form the primary rainbow.

The results of the analysis of ray B itself are as follows. Every time the ray strikes the drop surface, the ray outside the drop in the air is at about 65° to the normal to the drop surface. The ray inside the drop is at 43° to the normal. At each encounter with the drop wall, the amplitudes of the reflected and refracted rays depend on the polarization (see Section 23.10). The incident light is unpolarized, with equal components E_0 parallel and perpendicular to the plane of incidence. The angles 65° for the air–water side and 43° for the water–air side are close enough to Brewster's angle, 53° for air–water and 37° for water–air, so that the perpendicular components are reflected much more strongly.

The ray that forms the primary rainbow is reflected once and refracted twice. The strongly reflected perpendicular component has an amplitude $0.14E_0$ when it emerges. By contrast, the amplitude of the parallel component is much smaller, $0.056E_0$. Since the intensities of the polarization components are proportional to the square of the amplitudes, the ratio of the intensity in the primary rainbow ray to the incident intensity is

$$\frac{I}{I_0} = \frac{(0.14E_0)^2 + (0.056E_0)^2}{E_0^2 + E_0^2} = 0.11$$

The primary rainbow has only about 11 percent of the incident light; most of the light is not in the primary rainbow.

More noteworthy is the ratio of the intensities of the two polarization components,

$$\frac{I_{\|}}{I_{\perp}} = \frac{(0.056E_0)^2}{(0.14E_0)^2} = 0.16$$

The parallel polarized light is only 16 percent as intense as the perpendicularly polarized light in the primary rainbow. Since the transmission through the surface depends only slightly on the polarization, it is the single reflection of the ray within the drop that primarily selects the perpendicular polarization component. You may observe this strong polarization by looking at a rainbow through polaroid sun glasses as you rotate them.

EXERCISES ON SUPPLEMENTARY TOPICS

Section 23.12 | Holography

23-69 An object is located so that the light diffracted from any one point on the object interferes with the reference beam at every point on a photographic plate. (a) If the resulting hologram is cut in half and one half is illuminated in the usual way with a laser beam, what portion of the original object will be seen? (b) Compare what happens here to the case where a diffraction grating is cut in half, parallel to the lines.

Section 23.13 | Interference Effects in Thin Films

23-70 A lens with refractive index 1.6 is coated with magnesium fluoride with index 1.38. (a) If it is designed to be nonreflecting for green light of wavelength 550 nm, how thick is the film? (b) If this lens is used in water, will it be nonreflecting for green light? Explain.

23-71 A soap film with refractive index 1.33 is just thick enough to produce destructive interference of the shortest wavelength visible light (400 nm) at normal incidence. How thick is the film?

23-72 Room acoustics can be modified by placing slots in the walls. (a) How deep should the slots be to minimize sound reflections at 500 Hz? (Use 344 m s^{-1} as the speed of sound.) (b) What effect will such slots have at 1000 Hz?

PROBLEMS ON SUPPLEMENTARY TOPICS

23-73 The zone plate in Fig. 23.45 is constructed so that the center of the mth dark ring is at a distance $d_m = d + m\lambda$ from pont P. (a) Show that the distance r_m from the center of the plate to the center of the mth ring satisfies $r_m^2 = d_m^2 - d^2$. (b) Show that when d is large compared to λ, $r_m^2 = 2md\lambda$ is a good approximation.

***23-74** If a hologram is made with ultrasonic waves and reconstructed with visible light, the depth of the image is highly distorted. (a) Use the result of the preceding problem to explain this observation. (b) Make a numerical estimate of the effect.

***23-75** A zone plate is constructed to produce a bright spot 0.1 m from the plate when illuminated with red light of wavelength 700 nm. Using the result of Problem 23-73, determine what will happen when the plate is illuminated with yellow light of wavelength 600 nm.

***23-76** Using the result of Problem 23-73, describe what will happen when a zone plate is illuminated with white light.

23-77 Explain why a soap film appears black when illuminated with white light if it is much thinner than the average wavelength of visible light.

***23-78** Show that if a lens with refractive index n_g is coated with a film of index n_c, the intensity ratio I_r/I_0 is the same for the light reflected from the two sides of the film when $n_c^2 = n_g$. (Assume that the lens is used in a vacuum and that the light is incident normally.)

23-79 Explain why the reflections from thin oil layers are brightly colored but those from thick ones are not.

***23-80** Two glass plates are placed in contact, and a sheet of paper is inserted at one end so that an angle of 0.0005 rad is made by the plates. If the plates are illuminated normally from above with light of wavelength 600 nm, what is the spacing of the observed bright and dark fringes?

Additional Reading

Gerald S. Birth, Diffuse Reflection, *The Physics Teacher*, vol. 24, 1986, p. 138.

Edward W. Stark, Diffuse Reflection: Uses That Affect Our Lives, *The Physics Teacher*, vol. 24, 1986, p. 144.

J. B. Cohen, The First Explanation of Interference, *American Journal of Physics*, vol. 8, 1940, p. 99.

Horace W. Babcock, Diffraction Gratings at the Mount Wilson Observatory, *Physics Today*, July 1986, p. 34.

R. W. Pohl, Discovery of Interference by Thomas Young, *American Journal of Physics*, vol. 28, 1960, p. 530.

R. B. Setlow and E. C. Pollard, *Molecular Biophysics*, Addison-Wesley Publishing Co., Reading, Mass., 1962. Chapter 5 is on X-ray diffraction.

Eugene Ackerman, *Biophysical Science*, Prentice-Hall, Inc., Englewood Cliffs, N.J., 1962. Chapter 15 is on X-ray diffraction.

J. F. Mulligan and D. F. McDonald, Recent Determinations of the Speed of Light, *American Journal of Physics*, vol. 20, 1952, p. 165; vol. 25, 1957, p. 180.

Winston E. Kock, *Radar, Sonar, and Holography*, Academic Press, New York, 1973.

B. G. Ponseggi and B. J. Thompson (eds.), Holography, *Proceedings of the Society of Photo-Optical Instrumentation Engineers*, vol. 15, 1968.

Winston E. Kock, Sound Visualization and Holography, *The Physics Teacher*, January 1975, p. 14.

A. G. Porter and S. George, An Elementary Introduction to Holography, *American Journal of Physics*, vol. 43, 1975, p. 954.

R. A. R. Tricker, *Introduction to Meteorological Optics*, American Elsevier Publishing Co., New York, 1970.

Lightwave Communications, a special issue of *Physics Today*, vol. 29, number 5, May 1976.

The Light Fantastic, *Science 84*, May 1984, p. 26. Photo essay on interference effects in thin films in nature.

James H. Underwood and David T. Attwood, The Renaissance of X-ray Optics, *Physics Today*, April 1984, p. 44.

Phillip H. Abelson, Glass Fiber Communication, *Science*, vol. 220, 1983, p. 463.

Scientific American articles:

J. H. Rush, The Speed of Light, August 1955, p. 62.

The entire issue of September 1968 is devoted to the subject of light.

J. A. Giordmaine, The Interaction of Light with Light, April 1964, p. 38.

A. G. Ingalls, Ruling Engines, June 1952, p. 45.

Karl H. Drexhage, Monomolecular Layers and Light, March 1970, p. 108.

Phillip Baumeister and Gerald Pincus, Optical Interference Coatings, December 1970, p. 59.

Eric Deuton, Reflectors in Fish, January 1971, p. 64.

H. Moyses Nussensvieg, The Theory of the Rainbow, April 1977, p. 116.

Richard J. Wurtman, The Effects of Light on the Human Body, July 1975, p. 69.

N. S. Kapany, Fiber Optics, November 1960, p. 72.

J. S. Cook, Communication by Optical Fibers, November 1978, p. 28.

Henri Birsigonies, Communication Channels, September 1972, p. 99.

W. S. Boyle, Light-Wave Communications, August 1977, p. 40.

Arthur Ashkin, The Pressure of Laser Light, February 1972, p. 62.

Victor Vali, Measuring Earth Stresses by Laser, December 1969, p. 88.

Stewart E. Miller, Communication of Laser, January 1966, p. 19.

Glenn L. Berge and George A. Seilestad, The Magnetic Field of the Galaxy, June 1965, p. 46.

Rüdiger Wehner, Polarized Light Navigation by Insects, July 1976, p. 106.

Don R. Sullenger and C. H. Keunard, Boron Crystals, July 1966, p. 96.

M. F. Perutz, The Hemoglobin Molecule, November 1964, p. 64.

J. C. Kendrew, The Three-Dimensional Structure of a Protein Molecule, December 1961, p. 96.

D. C. Phillips, The Three-Dimensional Structure of an Enzyme Molecule, November 1966, p. 78.

Sir Laurence Bragg, X-ray Crystallography, July 1968, p. 58.

Edward A. Stern, The Analysis of Materials by X-ray Absorption, April 1976, p. 96.

Herman Winick, Synchroton Radiation, November 1987, p. 88. New sources and uses for ultraviolet light and X-rays.

Emmett N. Leith and Juris Upatnieks, Photography by Laser, June 1965, p. 24.

S. Henman, How to Make Holograms, *The Amateur Scientist*, February 1967, p. 122.

Keith S. Pennington, Advances in Holography, February 1968, p. 40.

Alexander F. Metherell, Acoustical Holography, October 1969, p. 36.

Emmett N. Leith, White Light Holograms, October 1976, p. 80.

David K. Lynch, Atmospheric Halos, April 1978, p. 144.

A. D. Moore, Henry Rowland, February 1982, p. 159. The scientist who developed techniques for ruling high-precision diffraction gratings.

Anthony C. S. Readhead, Radio Astronomy by Very-Long-Baseline Interferometry, June 1982, p. 52.

Jearl Walker, The Bright Colors in a Soap Film Are a Lesson in Wave Interference, *The Amateur Scientist*, August 1978, p. 232.

Jearl Walker, Studying Polarized Light with Quarter-Wave and Half-Wave Plates of One's Own Making, *The Amateur Scientist*, December 1977, p. 172; More About Polarizers and How to Use Them, Particularly for Studying Polarized Sky Light, *The Amateur Scientist*, January 1978, p. 132; The Physics of the Patterns of Frost on a Window, Plus an Easy-to-Read Sundial, *The Amateur Scientist*, December 1980, p. 230.

Jearl Walker, Mysteries of Rainbows, Notably Their Rare Supernumerary Arcs, *The Amateur Scientist*, June 1980, p. 174.

Jearl Walker, Dazzling Laser Displays That Shed Light on Light, *The Amateur Scientist*, August 1980, p. 158; More About Edifying Visual Spectacles Produced by Laser, January 1981, p. 164.

Jearl Walker, The "Speckle" on a Surface Hit by Laser Light Can Be Seen with Other Kinds of Illumination, *The Amateur Scientist*, February 1982, p. 82.

Richard E. Dickerson, The DNA Helix and How It Is Read, December 1983, p. 94. X-ray analysis.

Jearl Walker, Simple Optical Experiments in Which Spatial Filtering Removes the "Noise" from Pictures, *The Amateur Scientist*, November 1982, p. 194.

Jearl Walker, What Causes the Color in Plastic Objects Stressed Between Two Polarizing Filters? *The Amateur Scientist*, June 1983, p. 146.

Jearl Walker, In Which a Lifesaver Lights Up in the Mouth and Light Takes Funny Bounces Through a Lens, *The Amateur Scientist*, July 1982, p. 146.

Jearl Walker, What Is a Fish's View of a Fisherman and the Fly He Has Cast on the Water? *The Amateur Scientist*, March 1984, p. 138.

Dina F. Mandoli and Winslow R. Briggs, Fiber Optics in Plants, August 1984, p. 90.

William E. Carter and Douglas S. Robertson, Studying the Earth by Very-Long-Baseline Interferometry, November 1986, p. 46.

Walter Tape, The Topology of Mirages, June 1985, p. 120.

Jearl Walker, How the Sun's Reflection from Water Offers a Means of Calculating the Slopes of Waves, *The Amateur Scientist*, June 1985, p. 130.

Jearl Walker, Reflections from a Water Surface Display Some Curious Properties, *The Amateur Scientist*, January 1987, p. 120.

Jearl Walker, Mirrors Make a Maze So Bewildering That the Explorer Must Rely on a Map, *The Amateur Scientist*, June 1986, p. 120.

Jearl Walker, The Kaleidoscope Now Comes Equipped with Flashing Diodes and Focusing Lenses, *The Amateur Scientist*, December 1985, p. 134.

Jearl Walker, An Inexpensive Homemade Polarimeter

Can Analyze Optically Active Compounds, *The Amateur Scientist*, January 1986, p. 120.

Jearl Walker, A Ball Bearing Aids in the Study of Light and Also Serves as a Lens, *The Amateur Scientist*, November 1986, p. 186.

John S. Mayo, Materials for Information and Communication, October 1986, p. 59. Optical fibers.

Martin G. Drexhage and Cornelius T. Moynihan, Infrared Optical Fibers, November 1988, p. 110.

Abraham Katzir, Optical Fibers in Medicine, May 1989, p. 120.

Jearl Walker, Rainbow Holograms, Unlike Conventional Ones, Can Be Observed in Ordinary Light, *The Amateur Scientist*, September 1986, p. 114.

Vladimir V. Shkunov and Boris Ya. Zel'dovich, Optical Phase Conjugation, December 1985, p. 54. Light can be reflected back along its path to produce an undistorted image.

David M. Pepper, Applications of Optical Phase Conjugation, January 1986, p. 74.

CHAPTER 24 MIRRORS, LENSES, AND IMAGING SYSTEMS

Cameras, microscopes, telescopes, and the human eye are examples of optical instruments that employ lenses and, in some cases, mirrors. Ordinarily lenses and mirrors are large compared to the wavelengths of visible light, so their principal effects on beams of light can be discussed without reference to interference or diffraction phenomena. However, as expected from the preceding chapter, these wave phenomena do play a role in limiting the resolution and sharpness of the images formed by optical instruments.

The properties of mirrors and lenses are discussed in the first part of this chapter. The later sections cover applications to specific optical instruments.

24.1 | MIRRORS

When we stand a metre away from a plane mirror and look into it, we see someone apparently standing a metre behind the mirror who looks much like us but whose hair is parted on the wrong side. The light reaching our eyes seems to originate at a place behind the mirror called the *image*. The image is *virtual* rather than *real*, since the light never actually passes through that location. It is called an *erect* image, since we do not seem to be standing upside down, or *inverted*.

It is useful to infer these observed properties of the image formed by a mirror from the equality of the angles of incidence and reflection for a light ray, because similar reasoning can be applied to the more complex problem of image formation by a lens. Figure 24.1*a* shows two of the many light rays produced by a point source of light or a point *object* at O, a distance d from the mirror. The ray incident along the normal to the mirror is reflected directly back along the normal, so it appears to have originated behind the mirror on the normal. The light ray that strikes the mirror at an angle ϕ to the normal is reflected at an equal angle and appears to come

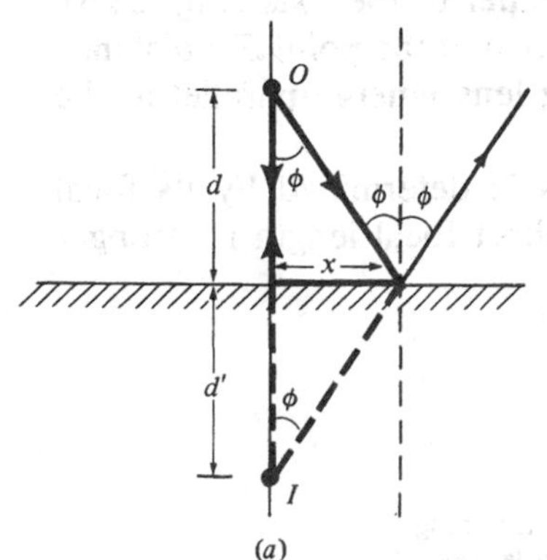

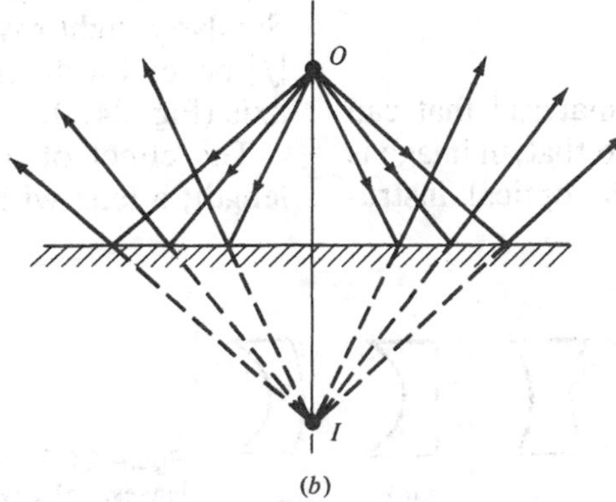

Figure 24.1. (*a*) The two colored triangles are congruent, so $d = d'$. (O is the object and I is its image.) (*b*) All the light reflected by the mirror appears to originate at the image I.

Figure 24.2. In a plane mirror, the image of each point on an object is directly in front of it. (K. Bendo / John Wiley & Sons Photo)

from somewhere behind the mirror along the dashed projection of the outgoing ray. The two projected paths cross behind the mirror at point I, the image position. In Fig. 24.1*a*, the two colored right triangles have a common side x and an equal angle ϕ. Hence the triangles are congruent, and all their angles and sides are equal. *This means that the object distance* d *and the image distance* d' *are the same.*

When we have a complex illuminated object instead of a point, the image of each point on the object is directly in front of it (Fig. 24.2). This image is sometimes said to be reversed side to side, but not vertically; that is, the image is erect rather than inverted. This remark is not quite correct, as can be seen if we lie on our sides in front of a mirror. Then we perceive our images as reversed vertically but not horizontally!

24.2 | LENSES

A lens is a piece of transparent material that can focus a transmitted beam of light so that an image is formed. The lenses in man-made optical instruments are usually manufactured from glass or plastic, while the lens in the human eye is formed by a transparent membrane filled with layers of crystalline tissues. For our purposes, it is sufficient to consider *thin, spherical lenses*. These have two spherical surfaces or a spherical and a plane surface and a thickness that is small compared to the radii of the surfaces.

We can categorize all lenses as either *converging* or *diverging*. In the usual situation where a lens is placed in a medium of lower refractive index, a converging lens is thicker at its center than at the edge, while the opposite is true for a diverging lens (Fig. 24.3). A converging lens bends light rays toward its *axis*, the line through its centers of curvature, so that a beam of parallel rays converges at a point (Fig. 24.4). For example, in bright sunlight, a converging lens may produce a spot of light intense enough to ignite paper. A diverging lens bends rays outward from its axis.

Suppose a very distant object is on the axis of a lens, so that the light rays are nearly parallel to the axis when they reach the lens. A converging lens will refract these parallel rays so that they meet or form an *image* at a *focal point* F' beyond the lens, whereas a diverging lens will bend the rays outward so that they *appear to have come from* a focal point F' before the lens (Figs. 24.4 and 24.5). The distance from the center of the lens to the focal point is called the *focal length* f. Conventionally f is taken to be positive for converging lenses and negative for diverging lenses.

Lenses also have a second focal point. If an object is placed at the point F, which is a distance f in front of a converging lens, then light rays from the object will emerge parallel to the axis (Fig. 24.4). Similarly, light rays aimed at the point F a distance $|f|$ beyond a diverging lens emerge parallel to the axis (Fig. 24.5).

The effect of a lens is determined by its focal length; a lens with a short focal length is stronger

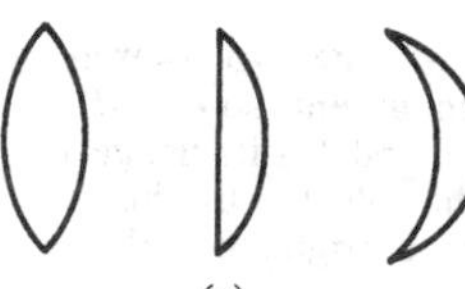

Figure 24.3. (*a*) Converging lenses. (*b*) Diverging lenses.

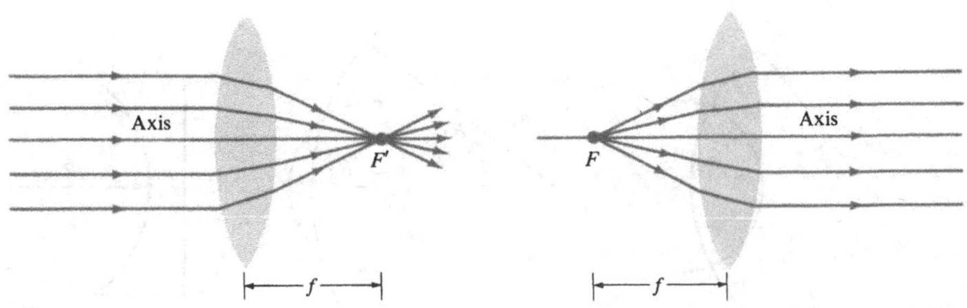

Figure 24.4. Focal points of a converging lens. The focal length f is positive for a converging lens.

and bends light rays more than one with a long focal length. The focal length depends on the index of refraction of the lens and on its shape, that is, on the *radii of curvature* of its surfaces. Lens surfaces may be *convex*, *concave*, or *plane*. (A convex surface bulges outward, like the outside of a spoon; a concave surface bulges inward, like the inside of a spoon.) We use the following conventions in characterizing lens surfaces:

1 A convex surface has a positive radius of curvature.
2 A concave surface has a negative radius of curvature.
3 A plane surface has an infinite radius of curvature.

These conventions are illustrated by Fig. 24.6.

The focal length of a lens is related to its index of refraction n and the radii of curvature R_1 and R_2 of its surfaces by a formula that can be derived using Snell's law and the approximation that the angles of incidence are small. Since the derivation is lengthy, we only present the result here. The focal length of a lens with index n in a medium of index 1 is

$$\frac{1}{f} = (n - 1)\left(\frac{1}{R_1} + \frac{1}{R_2}\right) \qquad (24.1)$$

This is called the *lensmaker's equation*. Its use is illustrated by the following example.

Example 24.1

Lenses similar to those in Fig. 24.6*a* and 24.6*c* are made from glass with a refractive index of 1.5. Find the focal length if there are (a) two convex surfaces with radii of curvature 0.1 m and 0.2 m; (b) one plane surface and one concave surface of radius 4 m.

(a) According to our conventions, convex surfaces have positive radii of curvature, so $R_1 = 0.1$ m and $R_2 = 0.2$ m. Thus, the lensmaker's equation gives

$$\begin{aligned}\frac{1}{f} &= (n - 1)\left(\frac{1}{R_1} + \frac{1}{R_2}\right) \\ &= (1.5 - 1)\left(\frac{1}{0.1\text{ m}} + \frac{1}{0.2\text{ m}}\right) \\ &= (0.5)(10 + 5)\text{ m}^{-1} = 7.5\text{ m}^{-1}\end{aligned}$$

or $f = 0.133$ m.

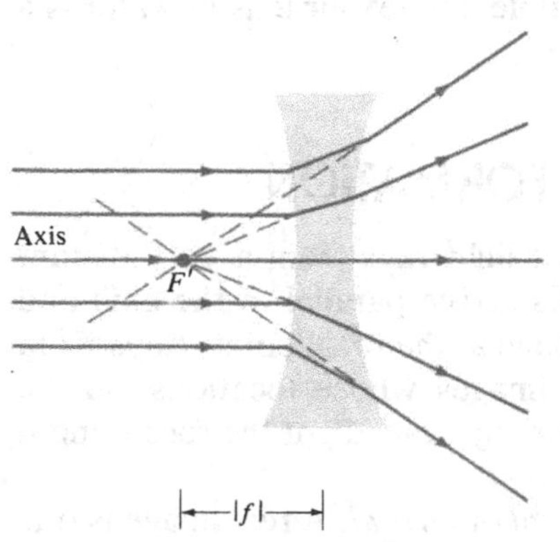

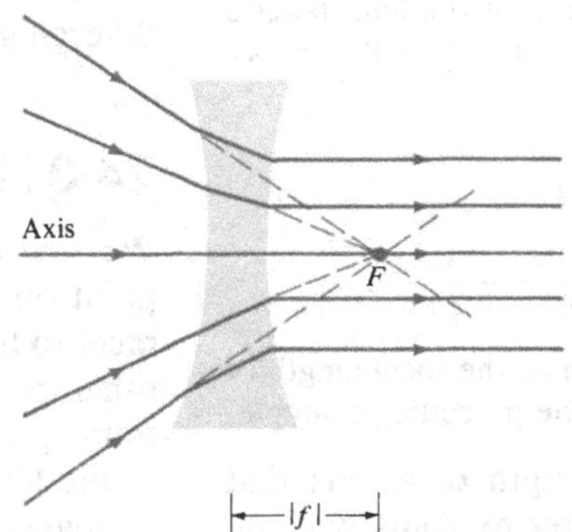

Figure 24.5. Focal points of a diverging lens. The focal length f is negative for diverging lenses.

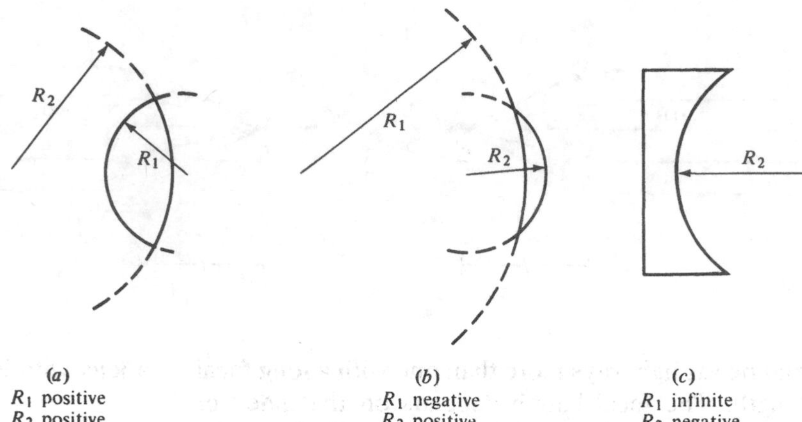

Figure 24.6. Conventions for radii of curvature. From left to right, the surfaces are (*a*) convex, convex; (*b*) concave, convex; (*c*) plane, concave.

(b) A plane surface has an infinite radius of curvature, so $1/R_1 = 1/\infty = 0$. A concave surface has a negative radius of curvature. Thus with $R_2 = -4$ m,

$$\frac{1}{f} = (1.5 - 1)\left(0 + \frac{1}{-4 \text{ m}}\right)$$
$$= -0.125 \text{ m}^{-1}$$

and $f = -8$ m. The minus sign indicates that this is a diverging lens.

The lensmaker's equation in the form given in Eq. 24.1 assumes that the lens is in a medium with index of refraction one. If the lens is not used in air or vacuum, then the symbol n in the equation must be interpreted as the *relative* index of refraction, $n(\text{lens})/n(\text{medium})$. Lenses have longer focal lengths in water than in air, as seen in this example.

Example 24.2

What is the focal length of the lens in Example 24.1*a* if it is placed in water?

Since the index of refraction of water is 1.333, we should use $n = 1.5/1.333 = 1.125$ in the lensmaker's equation. Then with $R_1 = 0.1$ m and $R_2 = 0.2$ m, we find

$$\frac{1}{f} = (n - 1)\left(\frac{1}{R_1} + \frac{1}{R_2}\right)$$
$$= (1.125 - 1)\left(\frac{1}{0.1 \text{ m}} + \frac{1}{0.2 \text{ m}}\right)$$

and $f = 0.533$ m. This is four times the focal length of the lens in air as determined in the preceding example.

The increase in the focal length of a lens that occurs when it is placed in water explains why we see so poorly under water. Our eyes contain fluids whose indices of refraction are close to that of water. Light bends appreciably when it enters the eye through the curved transparent *cornea*, but it bends very little when it enters from water. Consequently, the eye forms a badly focused image when it is in contact with water. When a person wears goggles or a face mask, light passes through the glass into an air layer at or near normal incidence without appreciable deflection. The light is then refracted in the usual fashion as it enters the eye from the air, so that vision is improved.

Since n is the relative index of refraction in the lensmaker's equation, it is less than 1 when the lens is less dense optically than the medium. This will happen, for example, if we construct an air-filled lens using curved plastic sheets and place it in water. Then the factor $n - 1$ is negative, and the sign of the focal length is the opposite of what we would get for a glass less in air with the same curvatures. For example, a double-convex air lens in water is a diverging lens.

24.3 | IMAGE FORMATION

We saw earlier that light rays from a very distant point on a lens axis arrive parallel to the axis and meet to form an image at the focal point. Rays from other points form images whose locations can be found graphically or algebraically if the focal length of the lens is known.

Images may be *real* or *virtual*. A real image is one

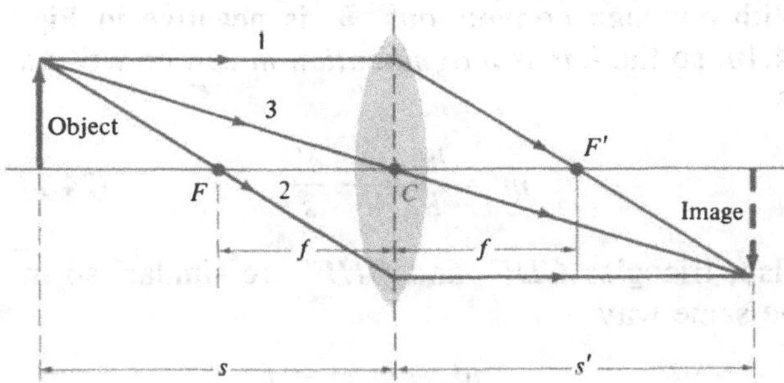

Figure 24.7. Three rays are used to locate an image graphically.

that is actually formed; if a screen is placed at that location, the image appears on the screen (Fig. 24.7). When there is a virtual image, the outgoing light seems to be coming from a place before the lens. However, if a screen is put there, no image is seen (Fig. 24.8*a*). Most objects are real; the light rays actually diverge from points at the object location. Virtual objects sometimes occur in multilens systems when the converging rays from one lens pass through a second lens (Fig. 24.8*b*).

We use the following conventions in the graphical or *ray-tracing* approach to locating an image:

1. Light always goes from left to right.
2. Real objects are to the left of the lens, and real images to the right.
3. Virtual images are to the left of the lens, and virtual objects to the right.

Three of the many rays emanating from a point on an object not on the axis have readily predicted paths. Their intersection determines the location of the image. Two rays are actually sufficient to find the image location; the third serves as a check. This ray-tracing procedure is illustrated in Fig. 24.7, where an illuminated arrow serves as a real object located at an *object distance s* from the lens. The lens forms a real image at an *image distance s'*. The three numbered rays in the diagram are drawn from the arrowhead as follows:

1. The ray leaving the arrowhead parallel to the axis is deflected by the lens so that it passes through the focal point F', in accordance with the definition of the focal point.
2. The ray going through the focal point F emerges from the lens parallel to the axis.
3. The ray directed at the center of the lens is undeflected. This happens because at that point the two sides of the lens are almost parallel, so a ray is effectively going through a flat plate (Fig. 24.9). Since the lens is thin, the ray is displaced from its original path by an amount that is negligibly small.

Points below the top of the arrow at the same object distance s will have images at the same image distance s'. Thus, once we have located the image of the top, we can sketch in the entire image of the arrow.

Ray tracing is illustrated again in Fig. 24.8 for situations involving virtual images and virtual objects. In each case, the rays through F', F, and the center are followed and their intersection located. We use ray tracing in several applications later in this chapter.

Although ray tracing provides good qualitative insight into the formation of an image by a lens or system of lenses, numerical work is best done with algebraic formulas. In order to develop and apply

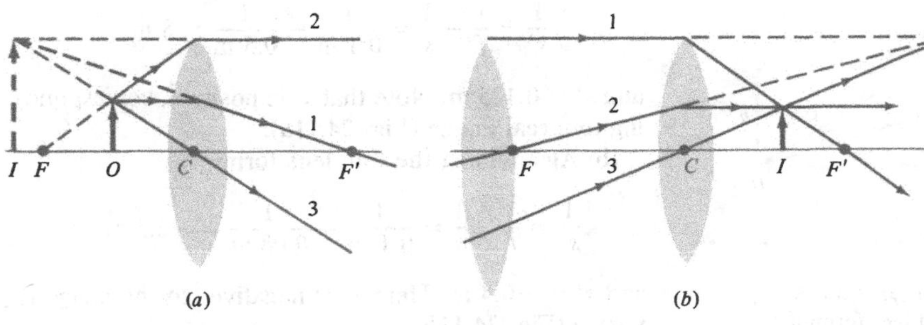

Figure 24.8. (*a*) Real object, virtual image. (*b*) Virtual object, real image. The virtual object is formed by the lens shown in color.

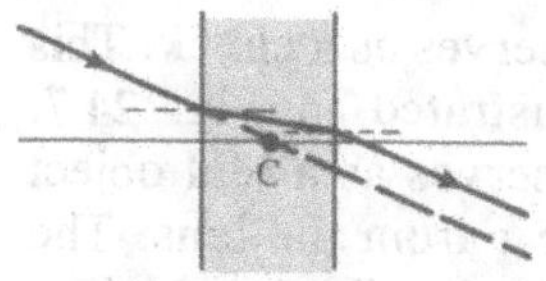

Figure 24.9. A ray passing through a flat plate is displaced but not deflected. Accordingly, a ray passing through or near the center of a thin lens is displaced very slightly.

these formulas, we adopt the following sign conventions for the quantities shown in Fig. 24.10:

1. s is positive for a real object, negative for a virtual object.
2. s' is positive for a real image, negative for a virtual image.
3. The *object height h* is positive if it points above the axis and negative it if points below the axis.
4. The *image height h'* is positive if it points above the axis and negative if it points below the axis.

The *linear magnification m* is the ratio of the image and object heights h'/h. The linear magnification is negative when the image is inverted as in Fig. 24.7; it is positive when the image is erect, as in Fig. 24.8*a*.

We can derive formulas relating s, s', f, and m using similar triangles. Two triangles are similar, and their corresponding sides are therefore proportional, if two of their angles are equal. In Fig. 24.10, the triangles ACB and GCH each have a right angle and the same angle α, and so they are similar. Thus

$$\left|\frac{h'}{h}\right| = \left|\frac{s'}{s}\right|$$

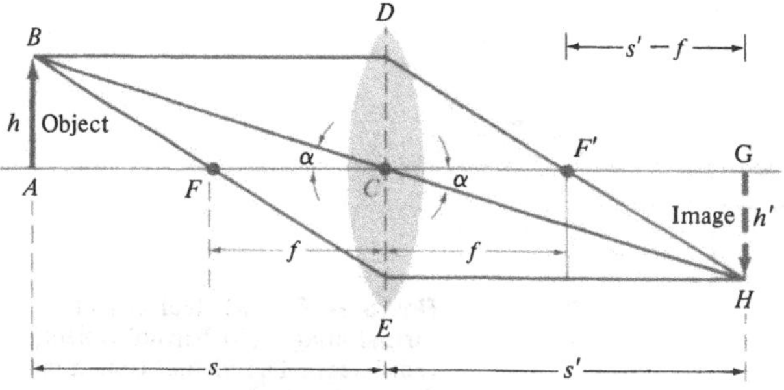

Figure 24.10. The object distance s, the image distance s', and the focal length f are related by the thin lens formula.

With our sign conventions, h' is negative in Fig. 24.10, so the *linear magnification m* can be written as

$$m = \frac{h'}{h} = -\frac{s'}{s} \tag{24.2}$$

Also, triangles CDF' and GHF' are similar, so in the same way

$$m = \frac{h'}{h} = -\frac{s' - f}{f} \tag{24.3}$$

Comparing these equations, we find

$$\frac{s'}{s} = \frac{s' - f}{f}$$

Dividing by s' and rearranging, we find the *thin lens formula*,

$$\frac{1}{s} + \frac{1}{s'} = \frac{1}{f} \tag{24.4}$$

We can check to see that this equation agrees with our earlier discussion. For a very distant object, s is infinite and $1/s$ is zero, so the thin lens formula gives $1/s' = 1/f$, or $s' = f$, as expected from our definition of the focal point. Similarly, for a very distant image, s' is infinite and $s = f$. Note that for a given focal length, the image distance s' depends only on the object distance s and not on the height h of the object. *This means that all object points at a distance* s *from the lens have their images on the same plane*. The following examples further illustrate the thin lens formula.

Example 24.3

A lens has a focal length of +0.1 m. Find the image distance when the object distance is (a) 0.5 m; (b) 0.08 m.

(a) Using the thin lens formula,

$$\frac{1}{s'} = \frac{1}{f} - \frac{1}{s} = \frac{1}{0.1\text{ m}} - \frac{1}{0.5\text{ m}} = 8\text{ m}^{-1}$$

and $s' = 0.125$ m. Note that s' is positive, corresponding to a real image (Fig. 24.11*a*).

(b) Again using the thin lens formula,

$$\frac{1}{s'} = \frac{1}{f} - \frac{1}{s} = \frac{1}{0.1\text{ m}} - \frac{1}{0.08\text{ m}} = -2.5\text{ m}^{-1}$$

and $s' = -0.4$ m. Here s' is negative, so the image is virtual (Fig. 24.11*b*).

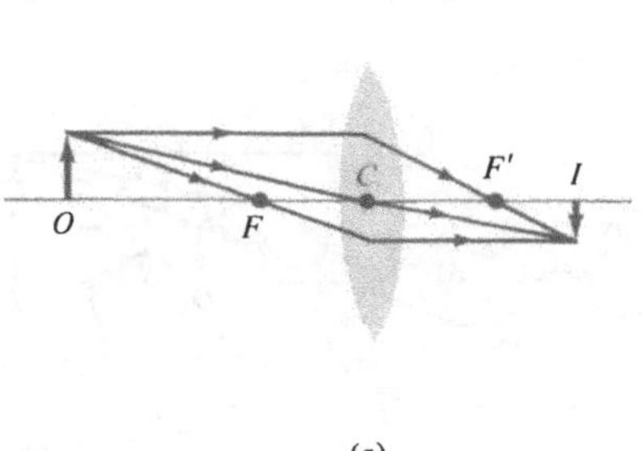

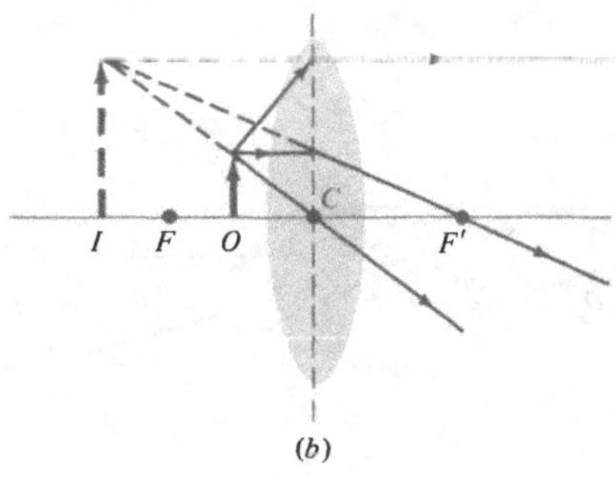

Figure 24.11. (a) When the distance from a real object to a converging lens is greater than the focal length, a real image is formed. (b) When the object is between the focal point and the converging lens, the image is virtual.

Example 24.4

A camera lens has a focal length of +0.1 m. (a) If the camera is focused on a child 2 m from the lens, what is the distance from the lens to the film (Fig. 24.12)? (b) If the child has a height of 1 m, how tall is the image on the film?

(a) If a sharp image is to be formed, the distance from the lens to the film must equal the image distance s'. Using the thin lens formula

$$\frac{1}{s'} = \frac{1}{f} - \frac{1}{s} = \frac{1}{0.1\ \text{m}} - \frac{1}{2\ \text{m}} = 9.5\ \text{m}^{-1}$$

and $s' = 0.105$ m. Thus the film should be at a distance from the lens slightly greater than the focal length, 0.1 m. Except when extreme closeups are taken, the object distance is always large compared to f, so the image and the correct film location are just beyond the focal point.

(b) The image height can be found from the object height, $h = 1$ m, and the linear magnification, $m = h'/h = -s'/s$. Approximating s' by f in accordance with our discussion above,

$$m = -\frac{s'}{s} \simeq -\frac{f}{s} = \frac{-0.1\ \text{m}}{2\ \text{m}} = -0.05$$

Hence

$$h' = mh = (-0.05)(1\ \text{m}) = -0.05\ \text{m}$$

The height of the image is 0.05 m. The minus sign indicates that the image is inverted.

Since the magnification is approximately proportional to the focal length, cameras are often equipped with interchangeable lenses of varying focal lengths. The film size remains constant, so the field of view decreases as the focal length and magnification increase.

Example 24.5

A diverging lens has a focal length of −0.4 m. (a) Find the image location for an object placed 2 m from the lens. (b) If there is a real image 1 m from the lens, where is the object?

(a) Since the object is real, $s = +2$ m. Thus

$$\frac{1}{s'} = \frac{1}{f} - \frac{1}{s} = \frac{1}{-0.4\ \text{m}} - \frac{1}{2\ \text{m}} = -3\ \text{m}^{-1}$$

and $s' = -0.333$ m. The image is virtual, and it is located between the focal point F' and the lens (Fig. 24.13a).

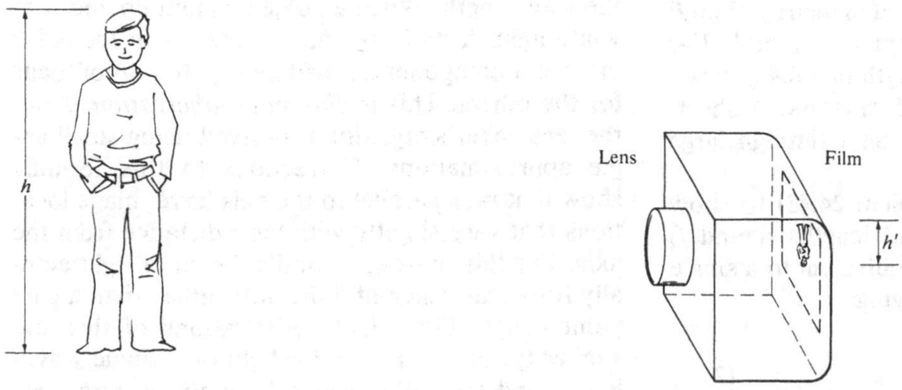

Figure 24.12. Principle of the camera.

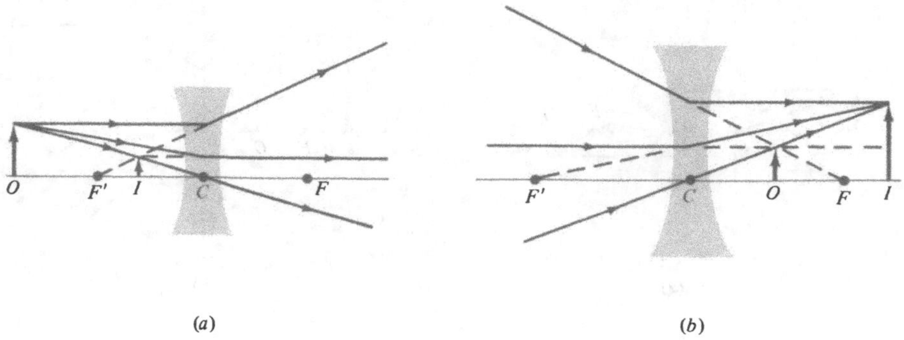

Figure 24.13. (*a*) A diverging lens always forms a virtual image of a real object. (*b*) When there is a virtual object between the lens and *F* formed by another lens (not shown), a diverging lens forms a real image.

(b) With $s' = +1$ m,

$$\frac{1}{s} = \frac{1}{f} - \frac{1}{s'} = \frac{1}{-0.4 \text{ m}} - \frac{1}{1 \text{ m}} = -3.5 \text{ m}^{-1}$$

so $s = -0.286$ m. The object is virtual and therefore must be due to another lens. The object is located between the lens and the focal point *F* (Fig. 24.13*b*).

24.4 | THE POWER OF A LENS; ABERRATIONS

In discussing lenses, it is often more convenient to deal with the reciprocal of the focal length, which is called the *power* of the lens:

$$P = \frac{1}{f} \tag{24.5}$$

It is clear from this definition that the meaning of the word power in optics is unrelated to its meaning in mechanics, work per unit time.

If the focal length f is measured in metres, then P is measured in *diopters*; 1 diopter = 1 m^{-1}. For example, a lens with a focal length of -0.4 m has a power $P = 1/(-0.4 \text{ m}) = -2.5$ diopters. A short-focal-length lens, which bends light through large angles, has a large power.

It is left as a problem (Problem 24.43) to show that two thin lenses with focal lengths f_1 and f_2 placed next to each other are equivalent to a single lens with a focal length f satisfying

$$\frac{1}{f} = \frac{1}{f_1} + \frac{1}{f_2} \tag{24.6}$$

Alternatively, with $P_1 = 1/f_1$ and $P_2 = 1/f_2$, the power of the pair of lenses is

$$P = P_1 + P_2 \tag{24.7}$$

The powers of lenses in contact are simply added to find the net power. Thus using powers instead of focal lengths avoids a good deal of arithmetic involving fractions. For example, an ophthalmologist placing 3-diopter and 0.25-diopter lenses in front of a patient's eye immediately knows that the combination is equivalent to a single 3.25-diopter lens.

We see in the following subsection how the additivity of the powers can be used to treat a lens configuration designed to minimize aberrations.

Aberrations | No matter how perfectly spherical its surfaces, any lens suffers from various kinds of *aberrations*, which limit the sharpness of its images independently of diffraction effects. Since the index of refraction of glass varies with the wavelength of the light, the focal length of a lens also varies with the wavelength. When an object is illuminated with white light, if its image on a screen is in focus for one color component, it will be slightly out of focus for the others. This is *chromatic aberration*. Also, the lensmaker's equation is derived using small angle approximations. Corrections to this formula show that rays parallel to the axis have image locations that vary slightly with their distance from the axis. For this reason, a parallel beam of light actually forms an image of finite size rather than a true point image (Fig. 24.14). Aberrations of this and similar types occur even for light of a single wavelength and are called *monochromatic aberrations*.

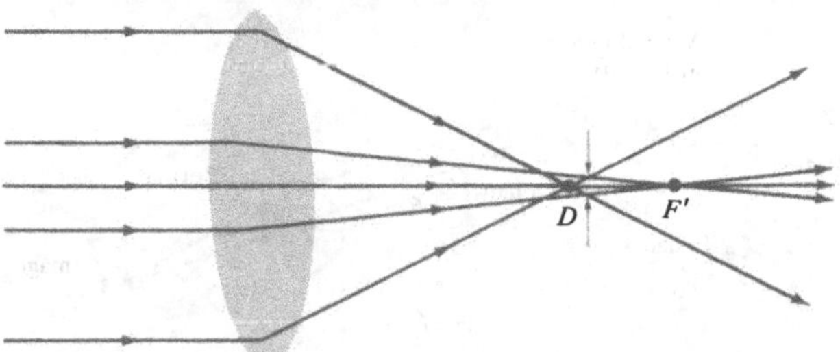

Figure 24.14. Monochromatic light rays near the axis are focused at F', whereas those near the edge of the lens meet at D. The arrows show where the bundle of rays has the smallest diameter.

Complex lens systems with several elements are designed so that their separate aberrations tend to cancel (Fig. 24.15).

We can illustrate these cancellations by considering a doublet, two lenses in contact (Fig. 24.16). Lens 1 has two convex sides and is made from crown glass. Lens 2 has one flat side and one concave side and is made from flint glass. All the curved surfaces have radii of curvature of 10 cm. In both types of glass, the refractive index varies about 1 percent over the visible spectrum. The powers P_1 and P_2 can be calculated using the lensmaker's equation,

$$P = \frac{1}{f} = (n - 1)\left(\frac{1}{R_1} + \frac{1}{R_2}\right)$$

As is seen in Fig. 24.16, P_1 varies by 2 percent over the spectrum, and P_2 by 3 percent. However, when

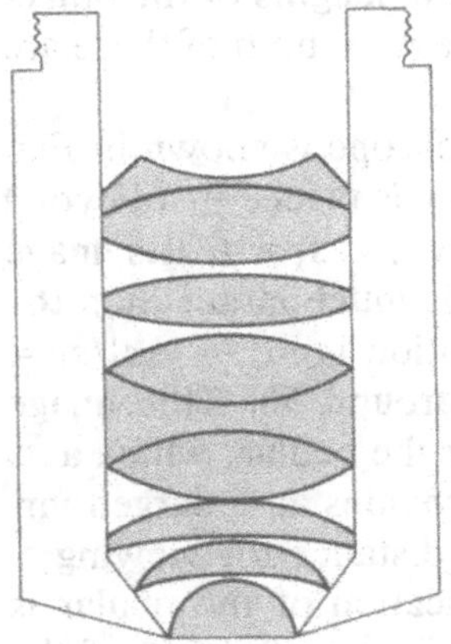

Figure 24.15. A modern multielement microscope lens.

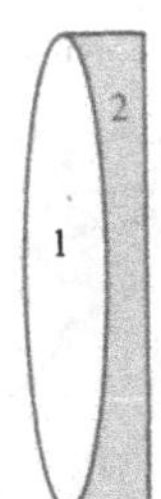

	656 nm (red)	589 nm (yellow)	486 nm (blue)
Refractive indices:			
Crown glass	1.517	1.520	1.527
Flint glass	1.644	1.650	1.664
Powers:			
P_1 (crown)	10.34	10.40	10.54
P_2 (flint)	−6.44	−6.50	−6.64
$P = P_1 + P_2$	3.90	3.90	3.90

Figure 24.16. A doublet made up of two different kinds of glass and designed to minimize chromatic aberration. The curved surfaces all have 10-cm radii of curvature. Note that the combined power is independent of the wavelength.

the lenses are in contact, the effective power $P = P_1 + P_2$ is constant! Thus the doublet is free of chromatic aberration.

24.5 | THE SIMPLE MAGNIFIER

The normal human eye can just barely distinguish two well-illuminated point objects with an angular separation $\theta_0 \simeq 5 \times 10^{-4}$ rad $\simeq 0.03°$. This minimum angular separation is called the *visual acuity* and can, in effect, be reduced with a *simple magnifier* or *magnifying glass*.

To see fine details, a person holds an object as close to the eye as possible, or at the *near point*: the closest point at which one can focus comfortably. For a normal young adult the distance x_n to the near point is about 0.25 m (Fig. 24.17*a*). At the near point, two points a small distance y apart have an angular separation small enough so that $\theta \simeq \tan\theta = y/x_n$ is a good approximation. If θ is $\theta_0 = 5 \times 10^{-4}$ rad, then

$$\begin{aligned} y = x_n\theta &= (0.25\text{ m})(5 \times 10^{-4}) \\ &= 1.25 \times 10^{-4}\text{ m} \\ &= 0.125\text{ mm} \end{aligned}$$

Thus the finest details discernible to the naked eye have a size of about 0.1 mm.

The simple magnifier is a converging lens that allows the object to be brought closer to the eye so that it subtends a larger angle and permits one to see finer details. Usually the object under study is

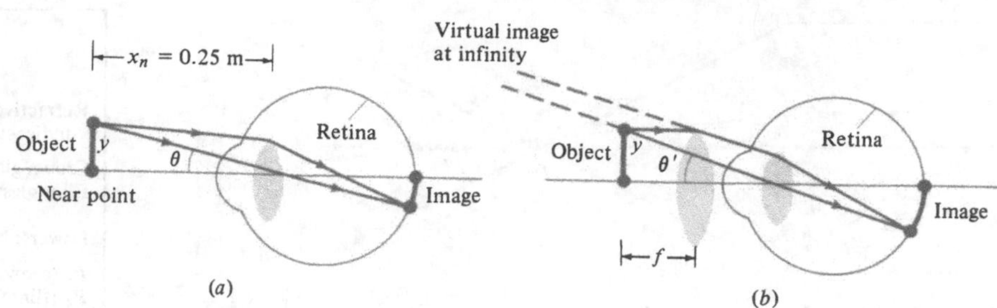

Figure 24.17. The simple magnifier. The lens permits the object to be brought closer to the eye, thereby subtending a larger angle.

placed just inside the focal point of the lens, which is held close to the eye (Fig. 24.17*b*). The resulting virtual image is far from the eye and thus can be viewed comfortably. The angle subtended by the image is

$$\theta' \simeq \tan \theta' = \frac{y}{f}$$

The *angular magnification M* is the ratio (Fig. 24.17*b*)

$$M = \frac{\theta'}{\theta} = \frac{y/f}{y/x_n} = \frac{x_n}{f}$$

or with $x_n = 0.25$ m,

$$M = \frac{0.25 \text{ m}}{f} \tag{24.8}$$

The following example illustrates the use of a typical magnifier.

Example 24.6

A collector uses a lens with a focal length of 0.1 m to examine a stamp. What angular magnification is provided by the lens?

The angular magnification is

$$M = \frac{0.25 \text{ m}}{f} = \frac{0.25 \text{ m}}{0.1 \text{ m}} = 2.5$$

Details will appear 2.5 times larger with this magnifier.

Lenses with focal lengths much shorter than the 0.1 m of the previous example would give much larger magnifications, but they would require that the object under study be held very close to the lens. Also, they will have large aberrations. Thus simple magnifiers usually have an angular magnification of only two or three. Magnifiers containing two or more lenses can have considerably greater useful magnification, since the aberrations can be partially corrected.

24.6 | THE BRIGHT-FIELD LIGHT MICROSCOPE

Although the microscope is one of the oldest and most widely used physical instruments in biology and medicine, new types of microscopes have been developed in recent decades. These make possible more detailed study of cellular structures and sometimes avoid the need for destructive methods in observing living cells.

Figure 24.18 shows a bright-field light microscope, the ordinary microscope found in every biological laboratory. The lenses in the *condenser* focus the incident light on the specimen, and the *diaphragm* regulates the intensity. The magnification is determined by the focal lengths of the *objective* and *ocular* lenses. In practice, both of these are multielement lenses.

The principle of the microscope is shown in Fig. 24.19. The object under study is placed just beyond the focal point of the objective, so $s_1 \simeq f_1$. Its image is real and inverted, and it is much larger than the object. The linear magnification is $m_1 = -s_1'/s_1 \simeq -s_1'/f_1$, and it is typically around 50. This image then serves as the object for the ocular, which acts as a simple magnifier and provides an enlarged virtual image at a comfortable distance for viewing.

Since the angular magnification of the ocular is $M_2 = (0.25 \text{ m})/f_2$, the overall magnification of the

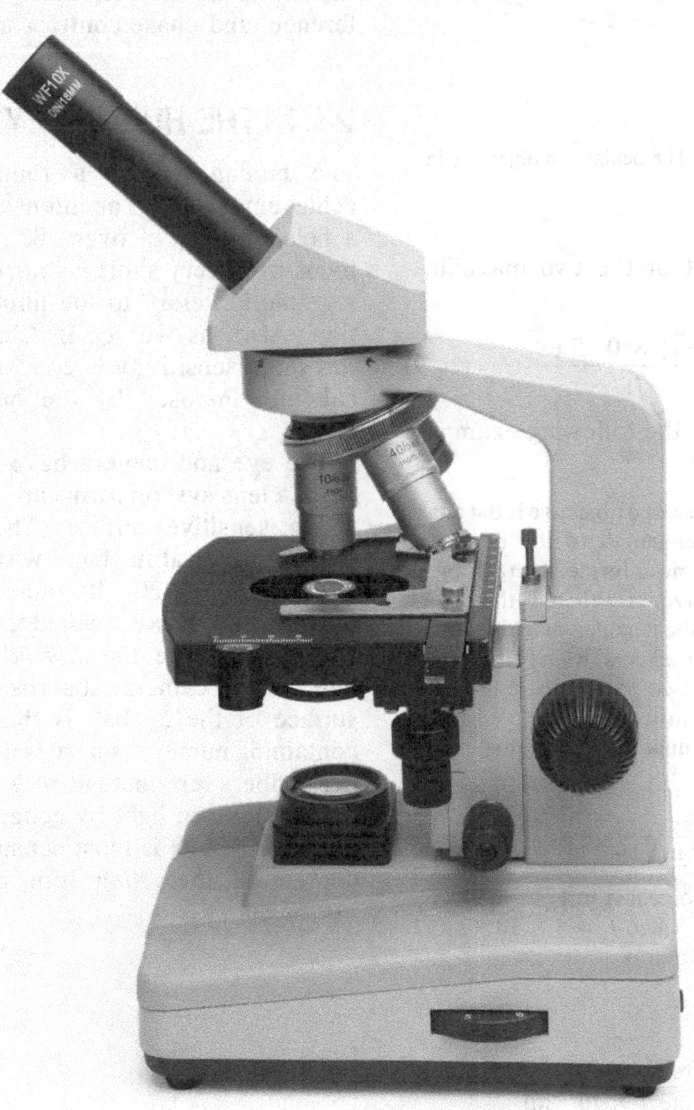

Figure 24.18. A compound microscope. (Martin Shields / Photo Researchers, Inc.)

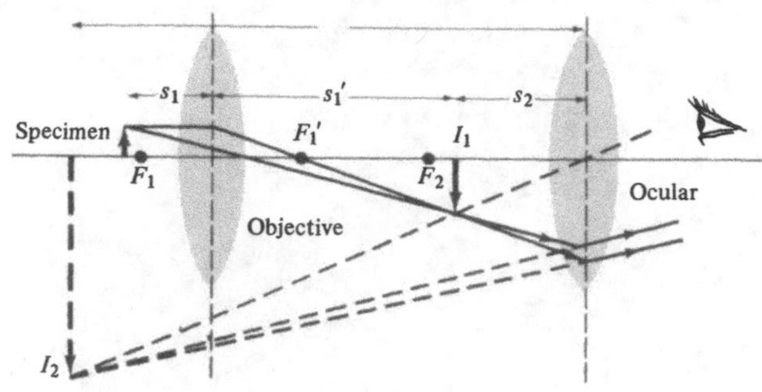

Figure 24.19. The microscope. The ocular and objective in practice are multielement lenses.

microscope is the product of the two magnifications:

$$M = m_1 M_2 = \frac{-s_1' \times 0.25 \text{ m}}{f_1 f_2} \tag{24.9}$$

This result is illustrated by the following example.

Example 24.7

The focal length of a microscope objective is 0.4 cm = 4×10^{-3} m, and the focal length of the ocular is 3.2 cm = 3.2×10^{2} m. The image formed by the objective is 0.2 m from the objective. (a) Where is the object under study? (b) What is the angular magnification? (c) Neglecting any diffraction effects, what is the smallest separation between the two points that can be resolved by the eye with this instrument?

(a) From the thin lens formula, the object distance s_1 satisfies

$$\frac{1}{s_1} = \frac{1}{f_1} - \frac{1}{s_1'} = \frac{1}{4 \times 10^{-3} \text{ m}} - \frac{1}{0.2 \text{ m}} = 245 \text{ m}^{-1}$$

so $s_1 = 4.08 \times 10^{-3}$ m. The object is just outside of the focal point of the objective, since $f_1 = 4 \times 10^{-3}$ m.

(b) The angular magnification is

$$\begin{aligned} M &= \frac{-s_1' \times 0.25 \text{ m}}{f_1 f_2} \\ &= \frac{-(0.2 \text{ m})(0.25 \text{ m})}{(4 \times 10^{-3} \text{ m})(3.2 \times 10^{-2} \text{ m})} \\ &= -391 \end{aligned}$$

The minus sign means that the image is inverted.

(c) The smallest resolvable separation of two points for an unaided eye is about 0.1 mm = 10^{-4} m. If the angular size is increased by a factor of $391 \simeq 400$, then the minimum resolvable separation becomes 10^{-4} m/400 = 2.5×10^{-7} m = 250 nm, or about half the average wavelength of visible light. This separation is comparable to the resolution limit of the microscope arising from the diffraction of light by the specimen.

Resolution and contrast in the bright-field microscope are discussed in the supplementary topics at the end of this chapter, along with polarizing, interference, and phase contrast microscopes.

24.7 | THE HUMAN EYE

The human eye is a remarkable evolutionary achievement. It has an intensity range of 10^9, covers a field of view of over 180°, can rapidly shift its focus from very short distances to infinity, and has a resolution close to the limit imposed by diffraction. Also, as we see in Chapter Twenty-six, its threshold sensitivity is comparable to the theoretical limit imposed by the quantum properties of light.

The eye and camera have many similarities. In both, a lens system forms an inverted real image on a light-sensitive surface. The eyeball is approximately spherical in shape with a diameter of about 2.3 cm (Fig. 24.20). Its outer covering is a nearly opaque, fibrous layer called the *sclera*. Inside this is a dark membrane, the *choroid*, which, like the black interior of a camera, absorbs stray light. The inner surface of the eyeball is the *retina*, a membrane containing numerous nerves and blood vessels. The nerve fibers terminate at *rods* or *cones* in the retina that respond to light by generating electrical nerve pulses. The eye is most sensitive at a small retinal depression, the *yellow spot*, or *macula*; its central

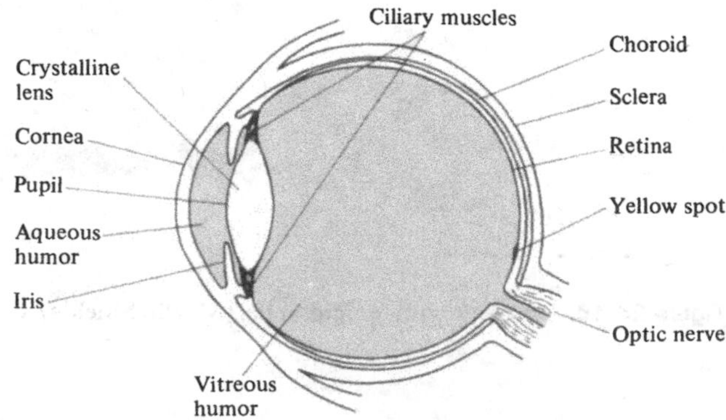

Figure 24.20. The human eye.

portion, the *fovea centralis*, is about $\frac{1}{4}$ mm in diameter and contains only densely packed cones. The eye tends to rotate so that the object under examination is imaged on the fovea centralis.

Light enters the eye through a thin membrane called the *cornea*, which covers a transparent bulge on the surface of the eyeball. The *iris* is a colored ring behind the cornea; like a camera diaphragm, it adjusts in size and aids in regulating the amount of light entering the eye through the *pupil*. The *crystalline* lens is composed of fibrous layers of material. Its shape and therefore its focal length are controlled by the *ciliary muscles*. The space between the cornea and the lens contains a watery fluid called the *aqueous humor*; behind the lens is a thin jelly, the *vitreous humor*. Both humors have an index of refraction equal to 1.336, very close to that of water, which is 1.333. The crystalline lens has a slightly larger index, 1.437.

Somewhat surprisingly, most of the bending of light occurs at the cornea. This is because the cornea has a small radius of curvature (0.8 cm), and the change in the refractive index is large when the light goes from the air ($n = 1$) into the aqueous humor ($n = 1.336$). The function of the lens is to provide the fine adjustments needed to focus on objects at different distances.

If the ciliary muscles are relaxed, the front surface of the lens is kept relatively flat and light from distant objects is focused on the retina. When the ciliary muscles contract, the lens assumes a more rounded shape, and its focal length decreases, bringing light from nearby objects into focus on the retina. The ability of the lens to adjust its focal length is called *accommodation*.

Because their presence would interfere with its transparency, there are no blood vessels in the lens, and all the nutrients reaching its cells diffuse in from the surrounding humors. As a person ages, some cells in the poorly nourished center die and turn white. The lens also becomes less flexible, reducing the accommodation. Eventually the lens may become so opaque that it must be removed. People who have had such a *cataract* operation have no accommodation, and unless they have had a lens implanted, they need strong corrective eyeglasses or contact lenses.

The *power of accommodation* of the eye is the maximum variation of its power for focusing on near and distant objects. Suppose, with the eye relaxed, a person sees objects at a distance x_f clearly. This is the person's far point, and it is at infinity for someone with normal vision. The image distance s' to the retina is somewhat less than the diameter of the eye. We will use an image distance $D = 2$ cm $= 0.02$ m for simplicity in the arithmetic, although the correct value is slightly smaller; the value used is not important for our considerations. At the far point, the power P_f of the eye is

$$P_f = \frac{1}{f} = \frac{1}{s} + \frac{1}{s'} = \frac{1}{x_f} + \frac{1}{D} \qquad (24.10)$$

For a person with normal vision, $x_f = \infty$, and this gives $P_f = 1/0.02\text{ m} = 50$ diopters. When the eye adjusts its focal length so that it focuses on an object at the near point, the object distance is $s = x_n$. Since again $s' = D$, the power of the eye is now

$$P_n = \frac{1}{f} = \frac{1}{s} + \frac{1}{s'} = \frac{1}{x_n} + \frac{1}{D} \qquad (24.11)$$

For a young adult with normal vision, $x_n = 0.25$ m, and $P_n = (1/0.25\text{ m}) + (1/0.02\text{ m}) = 54$ diopters. The power of accommodation is the difference,

$$A = P_n - P_f \qquad (24.12)$$

For a young adult with normal vision, $A = (54 - 50)$ diopters $= 4$ diopters. Young children have a much greater power of accommodation, and often can read books held quite close to their eyes. The accommodation decreases with aging, and most people find their near point gradually recedes until they cannot read comfortably without corrective glasses. Corrective glasses are discussed in the supplementary topics.

Acuity | We noted in our discussion of the magnifier that the visual acuity of a typical person is about 5×10^{-4} rad; objects with a smaller angular separation cannot be distinguished. It is reasonable to inquire whether this limit is due to diffraction effects. According to Chapter Twenty-three, when light from a distant source passes through a small circular aperture of diameter d, the first diffraction minimum is at $\sin\theta = 1.22\ \lambda/d$. To estimate what this implies for the eye, let us take the iris diameter to be

5 mm = 5×10^{-3} m, and the wavelength to be 500 nm = 5×10^{-7} m. Using the fact that θ is small, and keeping only one significant figure, we find

$$\theta \simeq \sin\theta = 1.22\frac{\lambda}{d}$$
$$= 1.22\left(\frac{5 \times 10^{-7}\text{ m}}{5 \times 10^{-3}\text{ m}}\right)$$
$$= 10^{-4}\text{ rad}$$

According to the Rayleigh criterion, two objects will just barely be resolvable if they are separated by this angle (Fig. 24.21). Experiments show that while a few people under optimum conditions have an acuity of twice the diffraction limit, or 2×10^{-4} rad, nobody can reach the limit of 10^{-4} rad.

An explanation for this failure of the eye to quite match the diffraction limit is provided by the structure of the retina. From Fig. 24.21*a*, the radius of the image circle due to diffraction is

$$r = D\tan\theta \simeq D\theta$$
$$= (2.3 \times 10^{-2}\text{ m})(10^{-4})$$
$$= 2.3 \times 10^{-6}\text{ m}$$

This is about equal to the separation of the cones in the fovea, which is the most sensitive region of the retina and contains only cones and not rods. Now the best resolution observed is about 2×10^{-4} rad, corresponding to diffraction centers separated by about 4.6×10^{-6} m, or by two cones. *Thus it appears that to distinguish two small objects, at least one unexcited cone must intervene between the excited cones.*

The interpretation of the images detected on the retina as meaningful patterns involves complex neurological processing and is a fascinating problem inviting computer simulations and theories of pattern recognition. Given a complex scene, the brain suddenly locks into an interpretation that looks "correct" (Fig. 24.22).

Sensitivity The *minimum*, or *threshold, intensity* needed to see a flash of light depends on the wavelength. The cornea is opaque to wavelengths shorter than 300 nm, and the crystalline lens to wavelengths below 380 nm, so ultraviolet light does not normally contribute to vision. However, people who have had their lenses removed surgically can see objects illuminated with ultraviolet light alone; they appear violet.

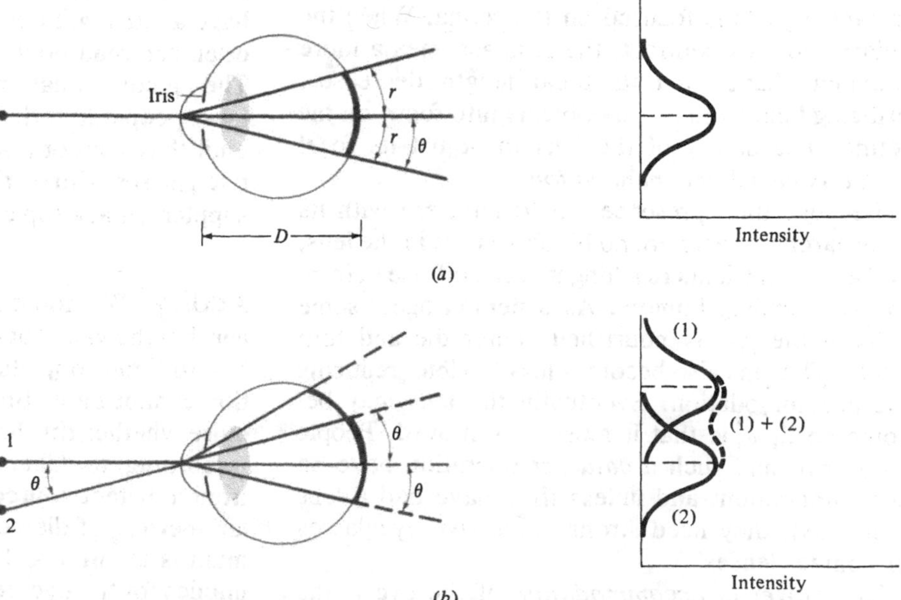

Figure 24.21. (*a*) The minimum image size for a point object due to diffraction at the iris. (*b*) If two point objects are separated by θ, their images will be barely distinguishable.

Figure 24.22. When our neurological decoding of a visual image contradicts our experience, we find it disturbing. (M. C. Escher's "Waterfall" ©2012 The M.C. Escher Company-Holland. All rights reserved. www.mcescher.com

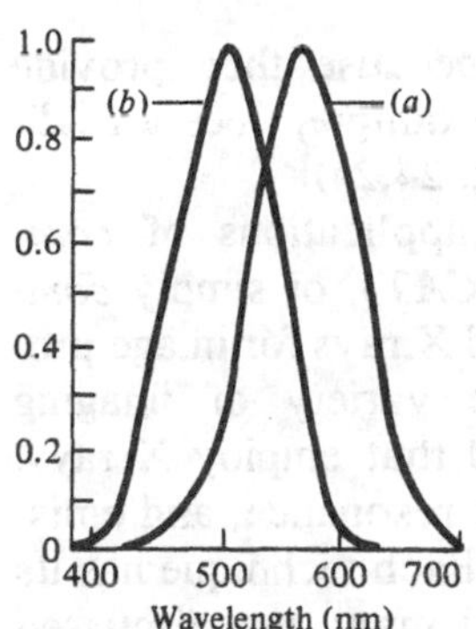

Figure 24.23. Relative sensitivity curves for the (*a*) light-adapted and (*b*) dark-adapted eye. Although the dark-adapted eye is more sensitive, both curves are drawn with the same maximum values. (Adapted from Eugene Ackerman. *Biophysical Science*, Prentice-Hall, Inc., Englewood Cliffs, N.J., 1962.)

One long wavelength limit on the sensitivity of the eye is set by the strong absorption of light by water in the cornea and the aqueous humor at wavelengths above 1200 nm. However, the sensitivity of the eye goes to zero rapidly above 700 nm. It is thought that the photosensitive molecules in the rods and cones do not respond to the longer wavelengths.

Figure 24.23 shows the variation with wavelength of the sensitivity, which is the inverse of the threshold intensity, for *dark-adapted* and *light-adapted* eyes. When we go from daylight into a dimly lit room, our eyes gradually adapt and reveal initially invisible details. This adaptation takes over half an hour to be complete. Since the dark-adapted eye is much more sensitive, the two curves have been adjusted to have the same maximum value.

The cones are active only in light-adapted vision, while the rods are always active. Accordingly, the fovea, which lacks rods but has the greatest concentration of cones, is the most sensitive part of the retina of the light-adapted eye, while the edges of the retina, which have more rods, are more sensitive in the dark-adapted eye. The visual acuity of the dark-adapted eye is much poorer than that of the light-adapted eye.

From Fig. 24.23 it can be seen that the sensitivity is greatest near (500 and 550) nm for dark- and light-adapted eyes, respectively. Both wavelengths correspond to green light. Often, green glass is used in sunglasses and in tinted windows. Since green glass absorbs green light less than other wavelengths, it provides the most useful illumination while reducing the total transmitted intensity.

The dark-adapted eye responds to a large range of wavelengths, but the sensation of color is perceived only in the light-adapted eye. Color perception will be discussed in the supplementary topics.

24.8 | TOMOGRAPHY, IMAGING A SLICE

Tomography is a procedure that produces an image of a slice of an object. The production of such images has been made commonplace, though not inexpensive, by the development of a number of scanning tools in combination with the use of digital computers. Such images are extremely useful tools in research and medicine because they provide more information than, for example, does a traditional X-ray photograph (Fig. 24.24).

The earliest widespread applications of *computer-assisted tomography (CAT)*, or simply *computer tomography* (*CT*), used X rays for image production. However, a wide variety of imaging systems are now being used that employ X rays, ultrasound, nuclear magnetic resonance, and emission-computed tomography. Each technique has its own special advantages, and many are discussed elsewhere in this text. Here we discuss the basic method by which the tomographic image is constructed.

In a conventional X-ray exposure, a beam of radiation from a single source passes through an object all at once. Each narrow portion of the beam is reduced in intensity by absorption occurring along its path through the object. Since this absorption can occur anywhere along the path, the resulting image cannot distinguish between absorbing areas that mask one another. For example, nothing can be seen that is totally "behind" a bone in a chest X ray.

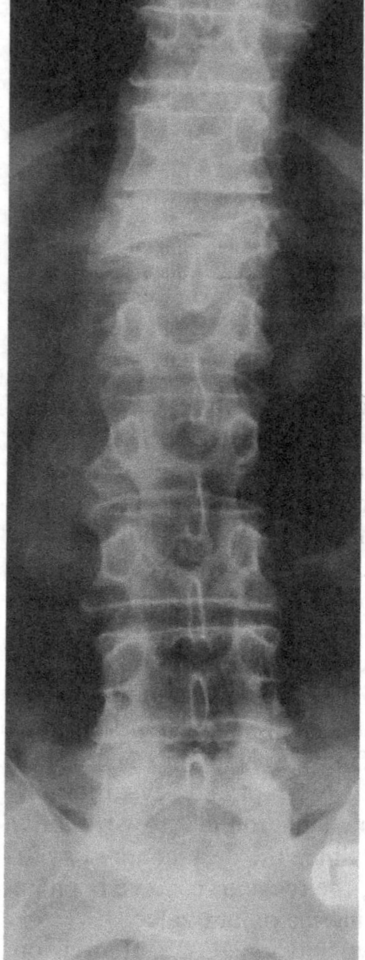

(*a*)

Figure 24.24. (a) A conventional X-ray of the spine. (b) A CAT scan of the spine shows much more detail. [(a) Biophoto Associates / Photo Researchers, Inc. (b) Living Art Enterprices, LLC. / Photo Researchers, Inc.]

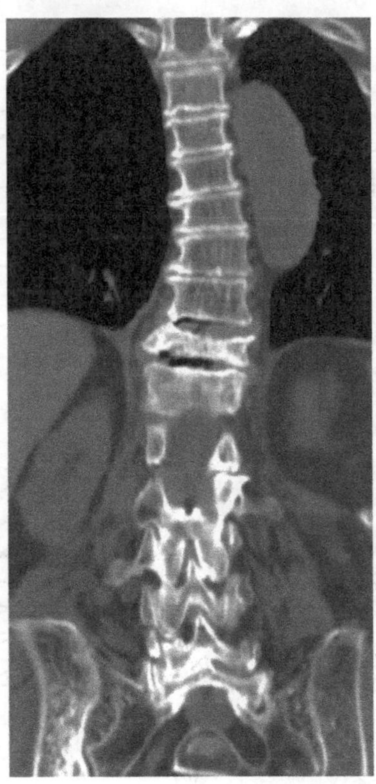

(b)

Figure 24.24. (*Continued*)

In a tomogram, a picture of a selected cross section of the object is obtained and nothing in that cross section is shielded or hidden. A series of scans of a slice or section of an object is made. Each scan of the series is made from a different angle about the edge of the slice. The image is then formed by unraveling all the information from all the scans to produce a picture of the slice. While this unraveling can become rather sophisticated, we can describe the underlying principle fairly easily.

Consider a narrow beam of X rays passing through an object and impinging on a detector (Fig. 24.25*a*). For a given orientation of the object, the source is moved up and down to expose a narrow slice of the object, through the slice edge. After a complete scan, the object is rotated 30° and another scan is done. The detector records the intensity of the emerging beam from each scan for analysis with the results of the other scans. The object used for illustration is assumed to absorb X rays very little except for the dark spot.

The analysis can be graphically illustrated by considering a circle of paper on which lines are drawn indicating the absorption for each position of the X-ray source. Thus the lines in Fig. 24.25*a* are all rather light, indicating little absorption except for the line representing the ray that passes through the dark spot; it is shown much darker. If the data were analyzed from just one position, one would obtain a conventional picture of a thin slice of the object in which the only feature would be a single dark spot.

If the object and the paper are now rotated 30° clockwise and another scan is done, the lines on the paper would now appear as shown in Fig. 24.25*b*. After a number of such rotations and scans, the paper has many lines drawn on it (Fig. 24.25*c*). Note that the lines representing the ray influenced by the dark spot at each orientation pass through a common point. Now we put dots on the paper at points where any lines cross and make the darkness of the dots proportional both to the number of lines crossing and to the darkness of the lines and then

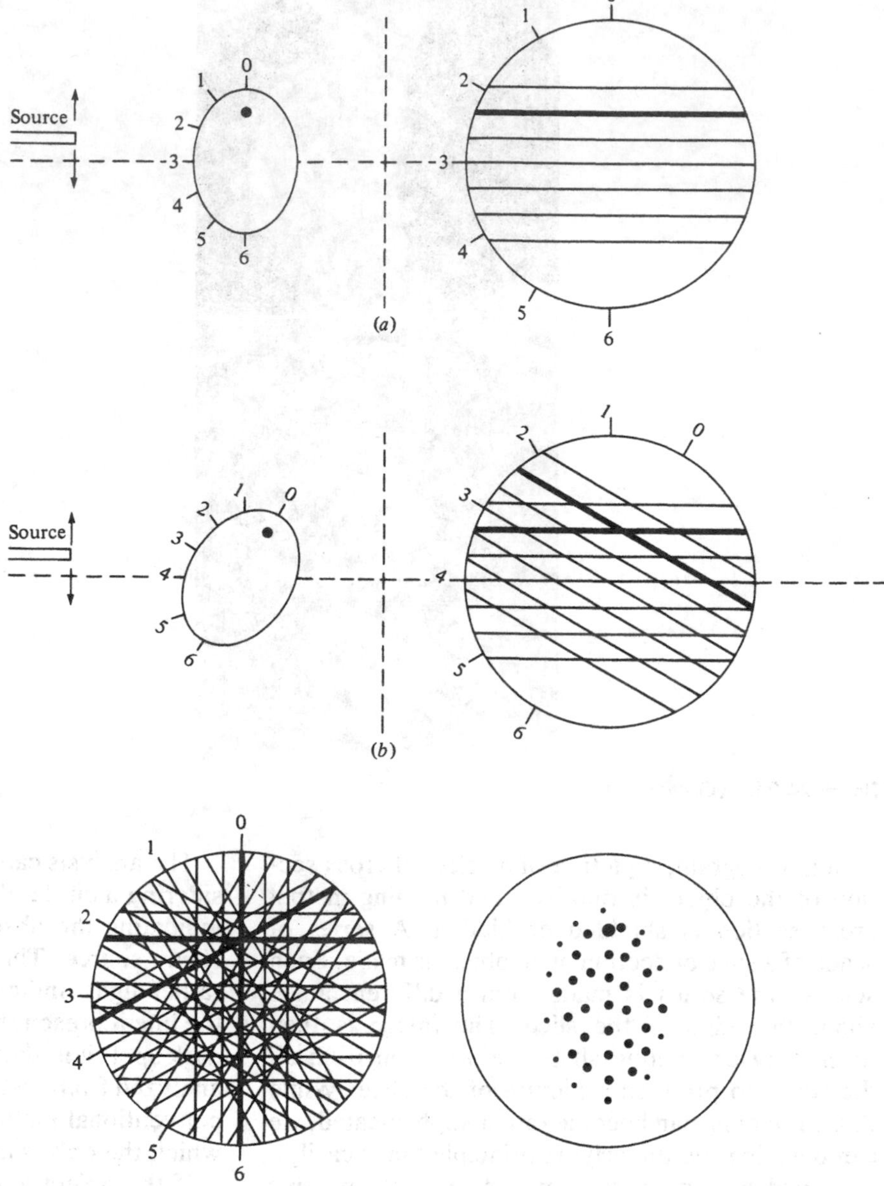

Figure 24.25. (*a*) A narrow beam of X rays is incident from the left on an oval (in cross section) object. The X-ray source can be moved up and down, producing narrow beams through the object a fixed distance apart. The vertical dashed line represents a detector. We imagine that the intensity of each emerging beam is represented by a line across a round piece of paper. The intensity of the line is inversely proportional to the emerging beam intensity. The lines shown represent the results of one complete set of scans through the object in the position shown. In (*b*) the same procedure is followed after the object and paper are both rotated through 30°. (*c*) shows the paper after scans through the object from six different directions 30° apart. In (*d*) the lines are removed from the paper and dots show where the lines crossed. The darkness of each dot is proportional to the number and intensity of the lines that crossed there.

erase the lines. The paper now appears as in Fig. 24.25*d*. The very dark dot represents the dark spot in the object. Lighter dots appear inside the boundaries of the area imaging the whole object and very light dots appear outside the boundaries.

Two things should be clear from this. First, increasing the number of lines and scanning positions would more precisely locate borders of the object as well as additional details in the interior were they present. Second, the reconstructed image is an accurate representation of the cross section of the object itself.

We have used the device of drawing lines on paper to represent the data recorded and the drawing of dots at the line intersections to indicate how the image is reconstructed. In practice, elaborate computer programs are used to sort out the large amounts of data that are collected. An image of considerable detail is extracted from an accumulation of averaged absorption data.

In this discussion, we have stated that the object being imaged is rotated while the source and detector remain fixed. One may instead hold the object fixed and rotate the source and detector. The analysis is the same and the choice is made on the basis of convenience.

SUMMARY

A plane mirror forms a virtual image whose distance from the mirror is equal to the object distance. The image of each point on a complex object appears directly in front of that point.

A converging lens will bend rays parallel to its axis so that they meet at the focal point, whereas a diverging lens will bend such rays outward so that they appear to have come from a focal point before the lens. The focal length is determined by the index of refraction of the lens and the radii of curvature of its surfaces with the aid of the lensmaker's equation,

$$\frac{1}{f} = (n - 1)\left(\frac{1}{R_1} + \frac{1}{R_2}\right)$$

The radius of curvature is positive for a convex surface and negative for a concave surface.

The intersection of three special rays determines the location of the image of a point on an object. The ray parallel to the axis is deflected so it passes through the focal point F', the ray going through the focal point F emerges parallel to the axis, and the ray through the center is undeflected. Alternatively, the image and object distances are related by the thin lens formula,

$$\frac{1}{s} + \frac{1}{s'} = \frac{1}{f}$$

The linear magnification of a thin lens is

$$m = \frac{h'}{h} = \frac{-s'}{s}$$

A simple magnifier produces an angular magnification that is approximately

$$M = \frac{0.25 \text{ m}}{f}$$

Multiple lens systems such as microscopes are analyzed by considering the image of one lens as the object of the next. The common bright-field light microscope consists of an objective and an ocular. The objective forms a real image just inside the focal point of the ocular. The ocular then forms an enlarged virtual image, which is seen by the viewer. For a microscope, the overall angular magnification is

$$M = \frac{-s_1' \times 0.25 \text{ m}}{f_1 f_2}$$

In the human eye, most of the bending of light occurs at the cornea. The lens of the eye provides the additional adjustments needed to focus on objects at varying distances. The limit of resolution of the eye corresponds to the requirement that the diffraction circles corresponding to the images of two object points must fall on cones in the retina separated by at least one unexcited cone.

Checklist

Define or explain:

object, image
virtual, real
erect, inverted
converging, diverging lenses
focal length
lens axis
lensmaker's equation
radius of curvature
linear magnification
thin lens formula
aberration
angular magnification
visual acuity
accommodation
power
tomography

REVIEW QUESTIONS

Q24-1 The image distance for a plane mirror equals the _____.

Q24-2 Converging lenses have _____ focal lengths; diverging lenses have _____ focal lengths.

Q24-3 The focal point F' is the place where rays _____ meet after passing through a converging lens.

Q24-4 A plane lens surface has a radius of curvature equal to ______.
Q24-5 When a lens is moved from air to water, the light rays bend ______, and the focal length is ______.
Q24-6 A ray through the center of the lens emerges ______.
Q24-7 A ray passing through the focal point F emerges from the lens ______.
Q24-8 If the image distance is twice the object distance and of the same sign, the image is ______ and has a linear magnification of ______.
Q24-9 The variation of the refractive index of glass with wavelength is responsible for ______ aberration.
Q24-10 When you use a lens as a simple magnifier, the object under study is placed ______.
Q24-11 If a lens has a focal length of -2 m, its power is ______.
Q24-12 For the eye to distinguish two small objects, at least ______ must intervene between two excited cones.
Q24-13 The eye is most sensitive to wavelengths corresponding to ______ light.

EXERCISES

Section 24.1 | Mirrors

24-1 A man stands 2 m from a vertical plane mirror. What is the distance from the man to his image?
24-2 A cat sees its image in a plane mirror. The cat is 1 m from the mirror. (a) Where is the image? (b) The cat lunges at the mirror at 2 m s^{-1}. How fast does the cat approach its image?
24-3 A nearsighted man cannot see objects clearly beyond 40 cm from his eyes. How close must he stand to a mirror in order to see what he is doing when he shaves?

Section 24.2 | Lenses

24-4 An eyeglass lens has one concave surface with a radius of 0.5 m and a convex surface with a radius of 0.7 m. If the index of refraction of the lens is 1.6, find the focal length.
24-5 A lens is made from a plastic with a refractive index of 1.4. One side is flat and the other is concave with a radius of 0.2 m. Find the focal length of the lens.
24-6 A lens is made of glass with $n = 1.5$. One side is convex and has a radius of curvature equal to 0.1 m. Find the radius of curvature of the other surface and draw a sketch of the lens if (a) $f = 0.15$ m; (b) $f = 0.1$ m; (c) $f = -0.15$ m.
24-7 A lens made of glass with refractive index 1.6 has a focal length of 0.5 m in air. What is the focal length in water?
24-8 Crown glass has a refractive index of 1.523 for blue light and an index of 1.517 for red light. If a crown glass lens has a focal length of 1 m for red light, what is its focal length for blue light?
24-9 Flint glass has a refractive index of 1.645 for blue light and an index of 1.629 for red light. A lens made of flint glass has two convex surfaces of radius of curvature 0.1 m. Find its focal lengths for blue and red light.

Section 24.3 | Image Formation

24-10 A lens has a focal length of 0.2 m. A real object is placed 0.08 m from the lens. (a) Locate the image approximately using graphical methods. (b) Locate the image algebraically. (c) What is the magnification?
24-11 An object is placed 1 m from a lens with a focal length of -0.5 m. Locate the image position (a) graphically; (b) algebraically.
24-12 A lens 0.1 m from a lamp forms a real image of this lamp that is 10 times larger. What is the focal length of the lens?
24-13 A lens of focal length 0.1 m is held 0.08 m from an insect. (a) Where is the image of the insect? (b) What is the magnification of the image? Is it erect or inverted?
24-14 An eyeglass lens has a focal length of -2 m. If it is 4 m from a book, where is the image of the book?
24-15 A camera is focused on a group of people 3 m from the lens, which has a focal length of 50 mm $= 0.05$ m. (a) What is the lens-to-film distance? (b) What is the linear magnification? (c) If the film height is 24 mm $= 0.024$ m, what is the maximum height of a person whose image can completely fit on the film?

24-16 Accessories are available for some cameras which permit the lens-to-film distance to be increased when extreme close-ups are taken of very small objects. Why are these accessories needed?

24-17 A photographer replaces a lens with a focal length of 50 mm by a lens with a focal length of 200 mm. What happens to the image size for distant objects?

Section 24.4 | The Power of a Lens; Aberrations

24-18 A doctor finds that a nearsighted person needs one lens with a power of −8 diopters and one with a power of −6 diopters. Find the focal lengths of the lenses.

24-19 Find the focal length of a lens with a power of 4 diopters.

24-20 A person wears reading glasses with a focal length of 2 m. What is their power?

24-21 An optometrist fitting a person for eyeglasses places a 0.25-diopter lens directly in front of a 4.5-diopter lens. (a) What is the power of the combination? (b) What is the effective focal length of the combination?

24-22 A lens has a focal length of 2 m. When a second lens is placed in contact the pair has a focal length of 1.5 m. What is the focal length of the second lens?

24-23 A 50-year-old woman who is nearsighted wears eyeglasses with a power of −5.5 diopters for distance viewing. Her doctor prescribes a correction of +2 diopters in the close-vision section of her bifocals. This is measured relative to the main part of the lens. (a) What is the focal length of her distance-viewing part of the lens? (b) What is the focal length of the close-vision section of the lens?

Section 24.5 | The Simple Magnifier

24-24 A lens of focal length 0.1 m is used as a simple magnifier. What is its magnification?

24-25 A farsighted woman has a near point 1 m from her eyes. If her visual acuity is 10^{-3} rad, what is the smallest separation between two objects that she can distinguish?

24-26 A lens used as a simple magnifier gives an angular magnification of 6. What is its focal length?

Section 24.6 | The Bright-Field Light Microscope

24-27 An insect of length 2 mm = 2×10^{-3} m is observed through a microscope that has an angular magnification of 100. How large an "insect" would one have to find to see its details as well with the unaided eye?

24-28 A microscope objective of focal length 5 mm forms an image 150 mm from the objective. If the ocular has a focal length of 28 mm, find the magnification of the microscope.

24-29 A microscope has an objective with a 4-mm focal length and an ocular with a 30-mm focal length. The two lenses are separated by 0.16 m, and the final image is formed 0.25 m from the ocular. (a) Where is the image formed by the objective? (b) Where is the specimen relative to the objective? (c) What is the magnification of the microscope?

24-30 A microscope provides an angular magnification of 150. What is the smallest separation that can be distinguished with this instrument?

Section 24.7 | The Human Eye

24-31 Explain why faint stars are best seen by looking "out of the corner of the eye" rather than directly at the stars.

24-32 Why is it believed that color perception is due only to cones and not to the rods?

24-33 (a) At approximately what wavelengths is the sensitivity of the light-adapted eye half its maximum value? (b) What are the corresponding wavelengths for the dark-adapted eye?

24-34 A bright star can have a sufficiently intense diffraction pattern on the retina so that the second ring will be above the threshold intensity. What effect will this have on its apparent size?

24-35 (a) Under optimum conditions, the smallest black dot that can be seen subtends an angle of 2.3×10^{-6} rad. If a dot is viewed at a distance of 0.25 m, the near point of a normal adult, what is the smallest diameter it can have and still be seen? (b) The maximum resolution is obtained when the image falls on the fovea centralis. At 10° away from this region, the acuity is 10 times poorer. What is the minimum size spot that can be seen at that angle under these conditions?

24-36 It is possible for a trained person to align two straight lines on a slide rule or a vernier scale to within 9×10^{-6} rad, much less than the minimum separation needed to resolve two points. How large is the alignment error if the instrument is held at the near point, 0.25 m from the eye?

24-37 Images on the retina are inverted. Explain why this must be true and suggest how we see things properly.

PROBLEMS

24-38 A girl 1.5 m tall stands in front of a vertical mirror that is just large enough so that she can see her entire body. How tall is the mirror?

24-39 A man holds a plane mirror of height 0.1 m vertically at a distance of 0.25 m from his eyes and observes that the image of a building just fills the height of the mirror. If the building is 200 m from the mirror, what is its height?

24-40 Prove that a ray of light travels the shortest possible distance in going from a light source at point P to point Q after reflection at the mirror (Fig. 24.26). (*Hint*: Draw a straight line from Q to the image of P.)

24-41 For a lens with a positive focal length f, (a) calculate the image position for $s = 0, f/2, f, 3f/2$, and $3f$. (b) Sketch a graph of the image position as s varies from 0 to $+\infty$.

24-42 A lens has a focal length of -1 m. (a) Calculate the image position when the object is placed at $s = 0$, 0.5, 1, 1.5, and 3 m from the lens. (b) Sketch a graph of the image position as s varies from 0 to $+\infty$.

24-43 Show that if two thin lenses with focal lengths f_1 and f_2 are in contact, they are equivalent to a single lens with focal length f satisfying

$$\frac{1}{f} = \frac{1}{f_1} + \frac{1}{f_2}$$

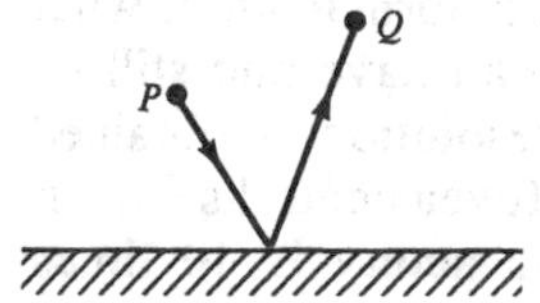

Figure 24.26. Problem 24-40.

(*Hint*: The image formed by the first lens is the object for the second, so $s_2 = -s_1'$.)

24-44 An object is 1 m from a screen. At what points may a 0.05-m focal length lens be placed so as to produce a sharp image on the screen? What are the corresponding magnifications?

24-45 A lens of index 1.5 has one plane side and one concave side of radius 0.2 m. The lens is placed horizontally with the concave side up and is filled with water. What is the focal length of the water–glass system? (*Hint*: Treat the system as a pair of thin lenses in contact.)

24-46 A slide projector lens is 3 m from the screen and has a focal length of 0.08 m. (a) Where is the slide located when the projector is in focus? (b) A child has a height on the screen of 10 cm. What is her height on the slide? (c) If we want to double the size of images on the screen, where should we put the projector? (d) If we wish to double the image size without moving the projector, what focal length lens must we use?

24-47 A converging lens has a focal length f. At what object location is the magnification equal to -1?

24-48 The radius of curvature of the cornea is typically 7.7 mm. If we construct a lens with this radius of curvature on one side, a plane surface on the other, and a refractive index of 1.37 (the index of the cornea), what power lens do we obtain? (This calculation shows that most of the focusing power of the eye comes from the cornea.)

24-49 The focal length of a converging lens can easily be found by seeing where a distant object is imaged. Explain how this can be done for a diverging lens with the aid of an additional converging lens of known power.

24-50 An ocular consists of two identical thin lenses of focal length 5 cm separated by a distance of 2.5 cm. Where is light from a distant point source focused?

ANSWERS TO REVIEW QUESTIONS

Q24-1, object distance; **Q24-2**, positive, negative; **Q24-3**, initially parallel to the axis; **Q24-4**, infinity; **Q24-5**, less, longer; **Q24-6**, undeflected; **Q24-7**, parallel to the axis; **Q24-8**, inverted, 2; **Q24-9**, chromatic; **Q24-10**, just inside the focal point; **Q24-11**, −0.5 diopters; **Q24-12**, one unexcited cone; **Q24-13**, green.

SUPPLEMENTARY TOPICS

24.9 | SPHERICAL MIRRORS

Spherical mirrors are encountered in applications as varied as medical instruments and truck rearview mirrors. Although their effects are quite different, spherical mirrors can be analyzed using concepts and equations very similar to those we developed for spherical lenses.

If light rays are incident on a concave mirror parallel to its axis, they are reflected and meet at a common point F (Fig. 24.27*a*). Thus a concave mirror is converging, and it can form a real image. Since light rays from a very distant source are parallel when they reach the mirror, F is the focal point. Similarly, parallel rays incident on a convex mirror are reflected so that they diverge as though they had come from a focal point behind the mirror (Fig. 24.27*b*).

As for lenses, we draw our diagrams with the light incident from the left and real objects to the left of the mirror. Real objects are at positive object distances s, and real images are at positive image distances s'. However, since mirrors reverse the ray directions, real images are also to the left of a mirror, and virtual objects and images are to the right. The distances s and s' are measured from the *vertex* of the mirror, point V in Fig. 24.27.

The focal length f is related to the radius of curvature R of the mirror by

$$f = \frac{R}{2} \qquad (24.13)$$

This equation assumes these sign conventions for R:

1 R is positive for a concave (converging) mirror.
2 R is negative for a convex (diverging) mirror.

Like the lensmaker's formula, $f = R/2$ holds exactly only in the small angle limit, that is, when all the rays are almost normally incident on the mirror. However, it is easier to derive. In Fig. 24.28, C is the center of curvature. The radius CA is perpendicular to the mirror, so by the law of reflection, the incident and reflected rays each make the same angle ϕ with CA. Since the incident ray is parallel to the axis, θ is also equal to ϕ. Thus the triangle CFA is isosceles, and the sides CF and FA are equal. In the small angle limit, CF and FA are each half of CA, so $R - f = R/2$, or $f = R/2$.

As in the case of a lens, three special rays from a point on the object (Fig. 24.29) can be used to find the position of an image:

1 The ray parallel to the axis is reflected through the focal point F of a concave mirror and ap-

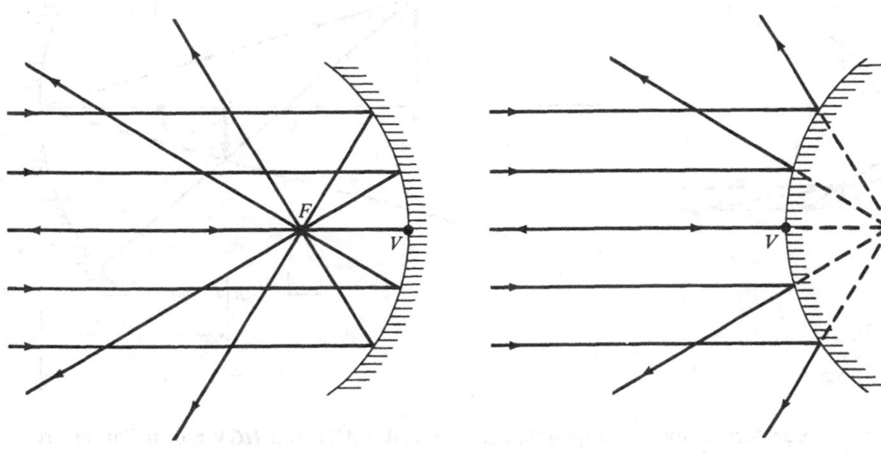

Figure 24.27. Focal points of (*a*) a converging mirror; (*b*) a diverging mirror. V is the vertex.

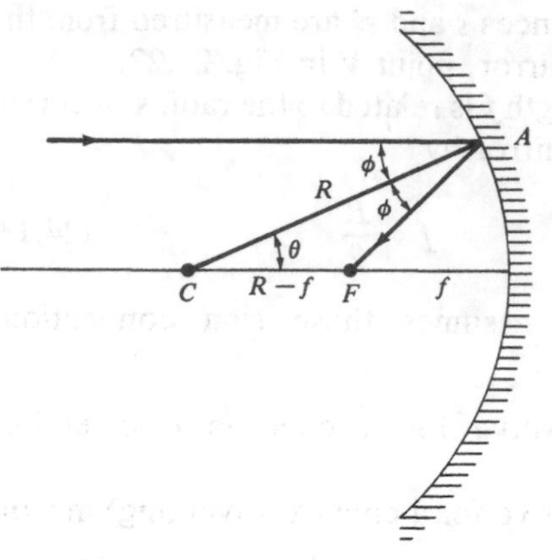

Figure 24.28. Since the angle of incidence equals the angle of reflection, both rays make the same angle ϕ with the radius CA. θ is also equal to ϕ, so the triangle CFA is isosceles. If ϕ is small, the sides CF and FA are each approximately half of CA.

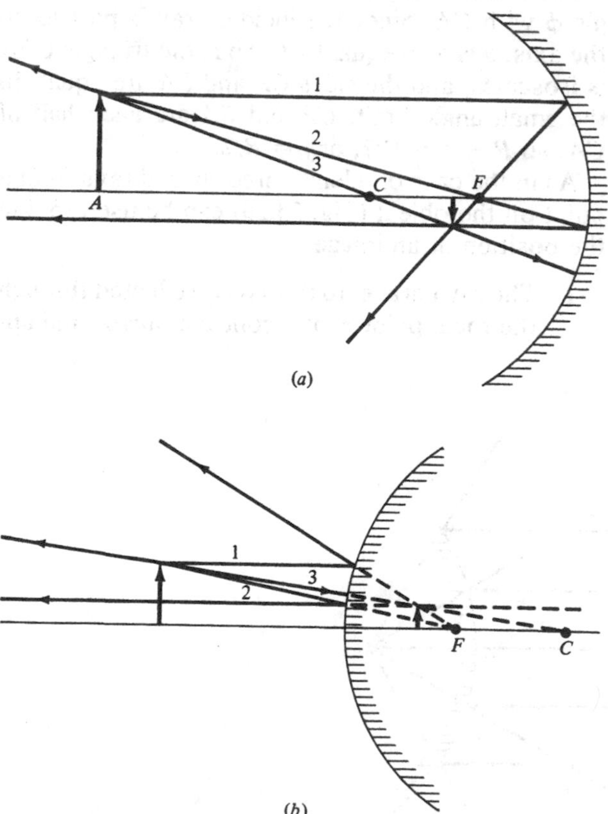

Figure 24.29. Three rays used to locate an image formed by a spherical mirror. (*a*) A concave mirror. (*b*) A convex mirror.

pears to come from the focal point of a convex mirror.

2 The ray passing through the focal point is reflected parallel to the axis.

3 The ray passing through the center of curvature is normally incident and is reflected directly backward.

Neglecting aberrations, all three rays meet at a common image point. Two rays are sufficient to locate the image; the third serves as a check. Note that for the case shown the concave mirror forms a real, inverted image. This happens whenever there is a real object at an object distance greater than the focal length. A convex mirror forms an erect, virtual image for any real object.

We can again derive formulas relating s, s', and f and the linear magnification m with the aid of similar triangles. In Fig. 24.30, the ray striking the vertex V reflects at the angle of incidence ϕ and passes through the image. Thus the right triangles ABV and HGV are similar. Since the image is inverted, its height h' is negative, and the linear magnification is

$$m = \frac{h'}{h} = \frac{-s'}{s} \qquad \text{(linear magnification)} \qquad (24.14)$$

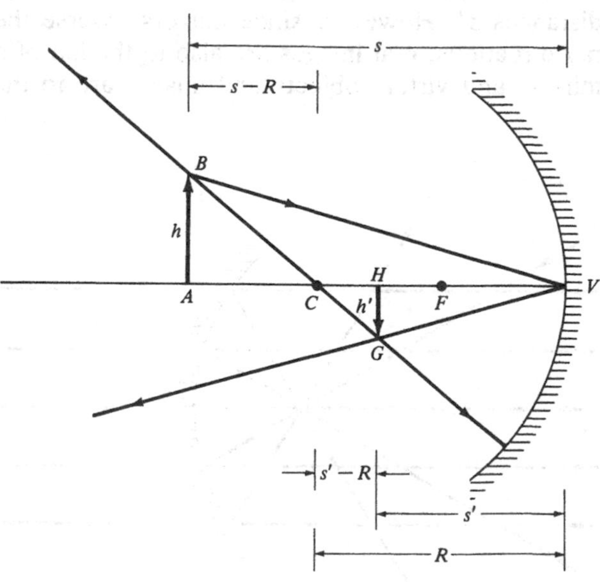

Figure 24.30. Triangles ABV and HGV are similar, as are triangles ABC and HGC.

A second expression for m follows from the similar triangles ABC and HGC:

$$m = \frac{h'}{h} = \frac{-(R - s')}{s - R} \qquad (24.15)$$

We can equate the right sides of these expressions for m. With the relation $f = R/2$, we find after a few lines of algebra that

$$\frac{1}{s} + \frac{1}{s'} = \frac{1}{f} \quad \text{(spherical mirrors)} \qquad (24.16)$$

Equations 24.14 and 24.16 are identical to the corresponding formulas for thin lenses.

Another useful quantity is the *longitudinal magnification* m'. This is the ratio of the change in the image distance ds' to the corresponding object distance change ds. If we regard s as the independent variable in Eq. 24.16 and differentiate, we find

$$\frac{-1}{s^2} - \frac{1}{s'^2}\frac{ds'}{ds} = 0$$

Solving for $m' = ds'/ds$, we obtain

$$m' = -\frac{s'^2}{s^2} = -m^2 \qquad (24.17)$$

This equation states that the longitudinal magnification is minus the square of the linear magnification. Since m^2 is always positive, m' is always negative. Suppose, for example, that the object approaches the mirror, so that ds is negative. Then ds' is positive, and the image moves toward the object.

In many applications, such as the convex rearview mirrors used on vehicles to give a large field of view, the linear magnification m is small compared to 1. The longitudinal magnification $m' = -m^2$ is then very small. This makes it difficult to judge the distances to other vehicles.

The following examples illustrate the use of these equations.

Example 24.8

A convex truck rearview mirror has a radius of curvature of 0.4 m. A car is 30 m from the mirror, and its height is 1.2 m. (a) Where is the image of the car? (b) How large is this image? (c) If the car decreases its distance by 5 m, how far does the image move?

(a) The mirror is convex, so its radius of curvature is negative. The focal length of the mirror is $f = R/2 = -(0.4\text{ m})/2 = -0.2$ m. With $s = 30$ m, $1/s + 1/s' = 1/f$ becomes

$$\frac{1}{30\text{ m}} + \frac{1}{s'} = \frac{1}{-0.2\text{ m}}$$

Solving for s', we find $s' = -0.1987$ m. The image is virtual, and it is very close to the focal point, since the object is very far away compared to the focal length.

(b) The image size is found from the linear magnification,

$$m = h'/h = -s'/s = -(-0.1987\text{ m})/30\text{ m} = 0.00662$$
$$h' = 0.00662\,h = (0.00662)(1.2\text{ m})$$
$$= 0.00785\text{ m} = 0.785\text{ cm}$$

The image is less than 1 cm tall, so it is not easy to see.

(c) The longitudinal magnification is

$$m' = -m^2 = -(0.00662)^2 = -4.38 \times 10^{-5}$$

Thus if the object distance changes by $\Delta s = -5$ m, the image distance changes by

$$\Delta s' = m'\,\Delta s = (-4.38 \times 10^{-5})(-5\text{ m})$$
$$= 0.000219\text{ m} = 0.219\text{ mm}$$

Since $\Delta s'$ is positive, s' has become less negative. That is, the image has moved toward the mirror. However, the position of the image has changed by a mere two-tenths of a millimetre. Thus it is extremely hard to judge the location of the car from the position of its image. A better clue is provided by the size of the image, since this changes to a good approximation in proportion to the object distance.

Example 24.9

A concave makeup mirror has a radius of 0.5 m. (a) If it is held 0.2 m from a woman's face, where is her image and how large is it? (b) Where is the image of a light bulb 3 m from the mirror? What will it look like?

(a) Using $1/s + 1/s' = 1/f$, with $f = R/2 = (0.5\text{ m})/2 = 0.25$ m,

$$\frac{1}{0.2\text{ m}} + \frac{1}{s'} = \frac{1}{0.25\text{ m}}$$
$$s' = -1\text{ m}$$

The image of her face is 1 m behind the mirror. The linear magnification is $m = -s'/s = -(-1\text{ m})/0.2\text{ m}) = 5$, so her face is enlarged by a factor of 5.

(b) Again applying $1/s + 1/s' = 1/f$,

$$\frac{1}{3\text{ m}} + \frac{1}{s'} = \frac{1}{0.25\text{ m}}$$
$$s' = 0.273\text{ m}$$

s' is positive, so the image of the light bulb is real; it is located just beyond the focal point. The linear magnification is

$$m = \frac{-s'}{s} = \frac{-0.273 \text{ m}}{3 \text{ m}} = -0.091$$

Thus a bright spot with a radius less than one tenth that of the bulb will be seen if a hand or sheet of paper is placed at the image location.

24.10 | THE CAMERA

The essential elements of any camera are a light-tight box, a converging lens, a shutter that can open briefly, and a film that records the image. In order to admit enough light to permit short exposures, a lens with a large opening or aperture must be used. This, in turn, requires that in a high-quality camera, complex multielement lens designs be used in order to reduce aberrations.

Camera lenses are specified by two quantities. One of these is the focal length f. As we saw in Example 24.4, the image size is approximately proportional to the focal length. The other quantity is the diameter d of the lens. Usually this is expressed in terms of the f-number. For example, an $f/8$ lens has a diameter $d = f/8$, which is one eighth its focal length. The light-gathering power of a lens is proportional to its area or to its diameter squared. All but the simplest camera lenses have a diaphragm that can be adjusted to vary the aperture or effective diameter of the lens. For example, changing from f/8 to $f/16$ means halving the diameter and reducing the area by a factor of $2^2 = 4$. The shutter time must be increased by a factor of 4 to admit the same total light energy.

Because of lens aberrations, a point on the object being photographed will always have an image of finite size no matter how well the lens is positioned or focused. This image size will be reduced if the effective lens diameter or aperture is reduced with a diaphragm. Reducing the aperture also increases the *depth of field*, the range of distances over which object points are imaged with satisfactorily small circles (Fig. 24.31). Thus a photographer must compromise between the need for short exposure times to stop the motion of a scene and the need for small apertures to reduce aberrations and increase the depth of field.

When the lens aperture is small, diffraction effects may be more important than lens aberrations in limiting the sharpness of photographs. We saw in Chapter Twenty-three that when light passes

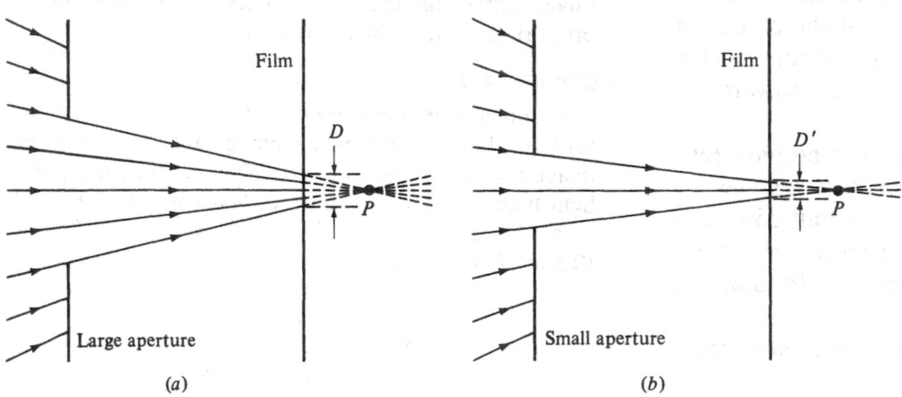

Figure 24.31. The effect of aperture size on the depth of focus. The lens (not shown) of a camera is positioned so that distant objects are imaged sharply on the film. (*a*) Light rays from a point object closer to the lens converge toward a point P behind the film. An image circle of diameter D is formed on the film. (Diffraction and aberration effects would make the actual diameter larger.) (*b*) When the aperture is made smaller, the beam of light rays is narrower and the diameter D' of the image circle of the film is smaller. Consequently, the blurring is reduced, and objects located over a larger range of distances appear adequately focused. However, the light intensity reaching the film is reduced, and a longer exposure time is required.

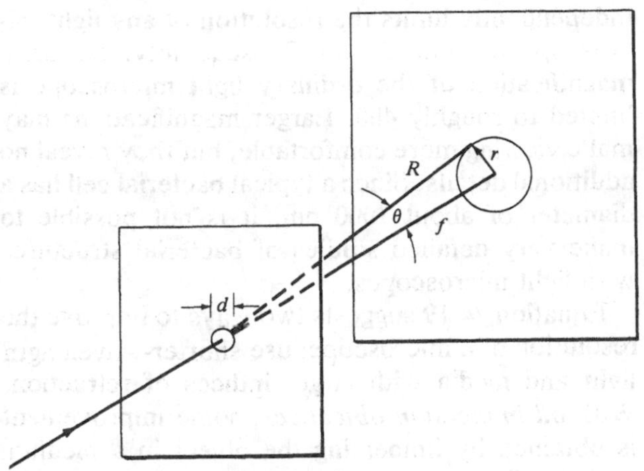

Figure 24.32. The central diffraction circle for light passing through a smaller circular lens aperture of diameter d.

through a small circular aperture, a diffraction pattern is formed consisting of a bright central circle and weak concentric rings. If the diameter of the aperture is d, the bright central region extends to the first diffraction minimum at $\sin\theta = r/R \simeq r/f$ (Fig. 24.32). With $\sin\theta = 1.22\lambda/d$, we have

$$r = 1.22\lambda \frac{f}{d} \tag{24.18}$$

This result indicates that when a camera is properly focused on a point object, the image formed on the film will be a circle of radius r even in the absence of aberrations. (The weak concentric rings are not normally noticeable.) Since this radius is proportional to f/d, the effects of diffraction grow as the diaphragm is closed (Fig. 24.33). This sets an upper limit on the useful aperture, as can be seen from thé following example.

Example 24.10

If the lens of a 35-mm camera is stopped down to $f/22$ and a photograph is taken, what are the effects due to diffraction? (The film size in a 35-mm camera is 35 × 24 mm.)

In accordance with our discussion, each point in the scene being photographed will have an image that, at best, is a circle whose radius r is determined by diffraction. If the scene is illuminated with white light, the wavelengths range from 400 to 700 nm, averaging about 550 nm. Using this wavelength and $f/d = 22$,

$$\begin{aligned} r &= 1.22\lambda \frac{f}{d} = 1.22(550 \times 10^{-9}\ \text{m})(22) \\ &= 1.5 \times 10^{-5}\ \text{m} \\ &= 0.015\ \text{mm} \end{aligned}$$

This result means that all details on the film smaller than about 0.015 mm are hopelessly blurred by the overlapping diffraction patterns. Enlarging the photo 10 times produces a picture 35 by 24 cm. It also increases the diffraction circles to 0.15 mm in radius, making them large enough to be discernible to someone looking carefully at the photograph. For this reason, apertures smaller than $f/22$ are not normally provided on 35-mm cameras. Instead, filters are used if the light intensity must be reduced further.

(a)

(b)

(c)

Figure 24.33. In these enlargements, aberrations affect image quality somewhat in the smallest aperture (a). An intermediate aperture (b) provides the sharpest image, and diffraction is seen in the largest aperture (c). [(a-c) Courtesy M. Sternheim]

24.11 | RESOLUTION AND CONTRAST IN MICROSCOPES

When the separation between two points in a microscopic specimen is comparable to the wavelength λ of the light, we would expect diffraction effects to be important. A detailed analysis shows that the minimum separation d that can be resolved by a microscope is

$$d = \frac{\lambda}{2n \sin \theta} \qquad (24.19)$$

Where, λ is the wavelength in air, n is the refractive index of the medium between the objective lens and the object under study, and θ is the angle subtended by the objective lens (Fig. 24.34). The product $n \sin \theta$ is called the *numerical aperture* and is sometimes marked on the instrument. If two points in a specimen are separated by less than d, their diffraction patterns overlap so much that their images cannot be distinguished.

A typical value of this minimum separation is found in the next example.

Example 24.11

What is the minimum resolvable separation for objects in air illuminated by green light (λ = 500 nm) if the angle subtended by the objective is 90°?

With $n = 1$ and $\sin 90° = 1$,

$$d = \frac{\lambda}{2n \sin \theta} = \frac{500 \text{ nm}}{2(1)(1)} = 250 \text{ nm}$$

We saw in Example 24.7 that a magnification of 400 leads to a minimum resolvable separation of about 250 nm if diffraction is ignored. However, we see now that diffraction cannot be ignored, since it independently limits the resolution of any light microscope to about 250 nm. Consequently, the useful magnification of the ordinary light microscope is limited to roughly 400. Larger magnifications may make viewing more comfortable, but they reveal no additional details. Since a typical bacterial cell has a diameter of about 1000 nm, it is not possible to make very detailed studies of bacterial structures with light microscopes.

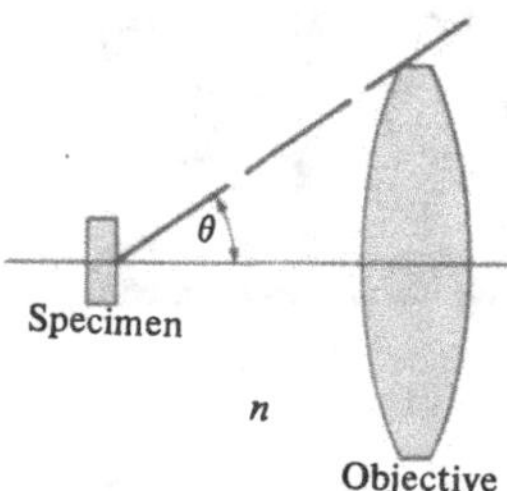

Figure 24.34. The numerical aperture of this lens is $n \sin \theta$, where n is the refractive index of the medium between the lens and the specimen.

Equation 24.19 suggests two ways to improve the resolution of a microscope: use shorter-wavelength light and media with larger indices of refraction. With *oil immersion objectives*, some improvement is obtained by immersing the object in a medium such as oil of cedar, which has $n = 1.4$. *Ultraviolet microscopes* use light with wavelengths somewhat shorter than visible light. In addition to having a smaller minimum resolvable separation, ultraviolet microscopes are useful because substances such as nucleic acids and proteins strongly absorb ultraviolet light. This leads to very good contrast, which is also necessary to obtain good resolution.

Much greater resolution can be achieved with *electron microscopes*, in which electrons are accelerated by a potential difference and focused by magnetic fields. Although electrons behave in many ways as particles, they also have wave attributes that are discussed in Chapter Twenty-seven. The wavelength associated with electrons accelerated through 50,000 V is 5×10^{-3} nm, or about $1/10^5$ times that of visible light. In practice, the resolution is limited to about 0.2 nm, which is about 1000 times better than can be achieved with light microscopes.

Contrast | To distinguish an object from its surroundings, there must be sufficient contrast or variation in light intensity. Without good contrast, the actual resolution achieved will be much less than that implied by the design of the microscope. *Staining* with dyes that are absorbed differently in various parts of an object is sometimes used to improve contrast. Other dyes are used to make a sample *fluoresce*. In this case the sample is illuminated with intense ultraviolet light, and the fluorescent constituents emit light at a longer wavelength. This light is detected after the ultraviolet light is removed from the beam by a filter.

24.12 | POLARIZING, INTERFERENCE, AND PHASE CONTRAST MICROSCOPES

We now briefly describe *polarizing*, *interference*, and *phase contrast* microscopes. These instruments ingeniously exploit the wave properties of light in improving the contrast of transparent structures.

A *polarizing microscope* uses polarized light to illuminate an object. When the object has a random or uniform character, the polarization of the light passing through it is unaffected. If this light then passes through an analyzer set at 90° to the original polarization direction, no light is transmitted. However, if the sample contains *birefringent* materials, whose indices of refraction depend on the direction of the light beam and on the electric field direction, then the polarization vector of the light is rotated and some light passes through the analyzer (Fig. 24.35). Proteins and nucleic acids are birefringent and can be seen in a polarizing microscope.

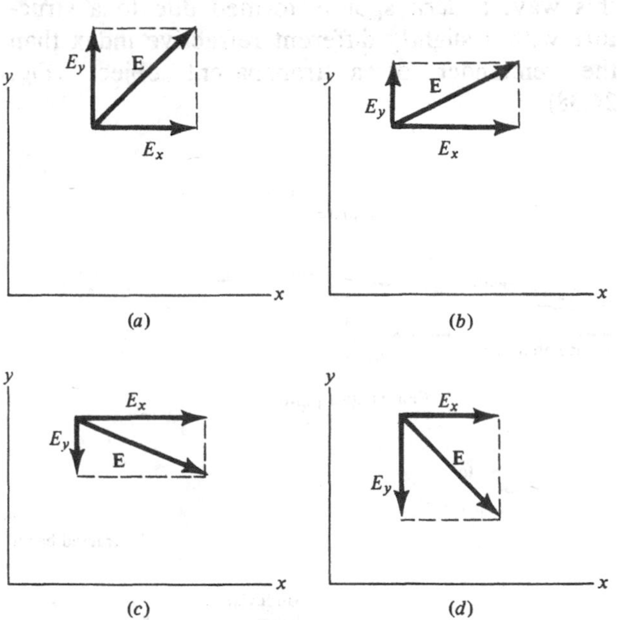

Figure 24.35. The polarization of an electromagnetic wave is parallel to the electric field vector **E**. In a birefringent medium, waves with electric fields along different crystal axes travel with different velocities. (*a*) Traveling into the page, the wave enters the birefringent medium. The initial electric field has *x* and *y* components that now travel at different velocities. (*b*) At a point inside the medium, E_x has a maximum at some instant. The wave with an electric field in the *y* direction travels slower, so E_y is not yet a maximum. Hence the **E** vector is rotated somewhat from its original direction. (*c*) Further into the medium, E_y is still negative when E_x is a maximum. (*d*) After an additional distance, E_y has a maximum negative value when E_x is a maximum. The polarization has now been rotated 90° from its original direction by the birefringent material.

In an *interference microscope*, the illuminating light is split into two beams (Fig. 24.36). One beam passes through a sample whose refractive index varies with the position. The phases of the different parts of this beam have corresponding variations after it leaves the sample. The second beam travels through an identical optical path, except that it does not go through the sample. When the two beams are recombined, interference between them produces intensity variations. Thus, many kinds of structures can be made visible, even though the sample is completely transparent.

The *phase contrast microscope*, invented in 1932 by Fritz Zernike, is an ingenious instrument that employs interference to enhance contrast but involves only a single beam of light. Consequently, it is less costly and complicated than the interference microscope.

Since the operation of this microscope depends on diffraction effects, we first consider some aspects of diffraction. We have seen in Chapter Twenty-three that when a parallel beam of monochromatic light passes through a narrow slit, an undeviated bright central line is formed on a screen, with progressively weaker lines on either side. (Similarly, when light goes through a circular aperture, a bright central circular spot and weak concentric rings are seen.) The central line and the lines

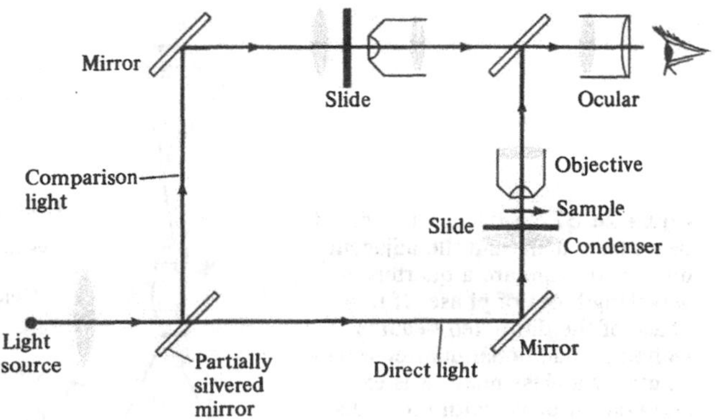

Figure 24.36. Interference microscope. The elements are described in the text.

immediately adjacent on either side can be shown to be exactly a quarter wavelength out of phase. Now suppose the screen is removed, and the bright central beam passes through a partially absorbing coated glass plate so that its amplitude becomes equal to that of an adjacent diffracted beam (Fig. 24.37*a*). The latter passes through a thicker transparent glass plate. The beam travels slower in the glass than in air, so it emerges an *additional* quarter wavelength out of phase with the central beam. These two beams are now a half wavelength out of phase, or exactly opposite in sign, and equal in amplitude. Hence they interfere destructively when they are recombined with a lens.

Essentially, this idea is applied to a rather different geometry in the phase contrast microscope (Fig. 24.37*b*). A transparent ring is placed in front of the light source, producing a hollow cone of light with its point at the specimen. If there is no specimen, this light forms a bright circular image just beyond the focal point of the objective. The same thing happens if there is a completely uniform transparent specimen. However, suppose the specimen contains a small transparent structure. This structure will have a diffraction pattern consisting of an undeviated bright circle and weak diffracted concentric circles (Fig. 24.37*c*). The adjacent diffracted circles are again a quarter wavelength out of phase with the undeviated beam. A *phase plate* placed at the location of this image has a circular groove corresponding to the bright circle. The groove is coated so that it absorbs much of the light passing through this part of the plate, reducing its amplitude to that of the adjacent diffracted light. The latter passes through a thicker portion of the phase plate, emerging exactly out of phase with the light passing through the groove, so that destructive interference occurs when the two beams are later recombined. In this way, a dark spot is formed due to a structure with a slightly different refractive index than the remainder of a transparent object (Fig. 24.38).

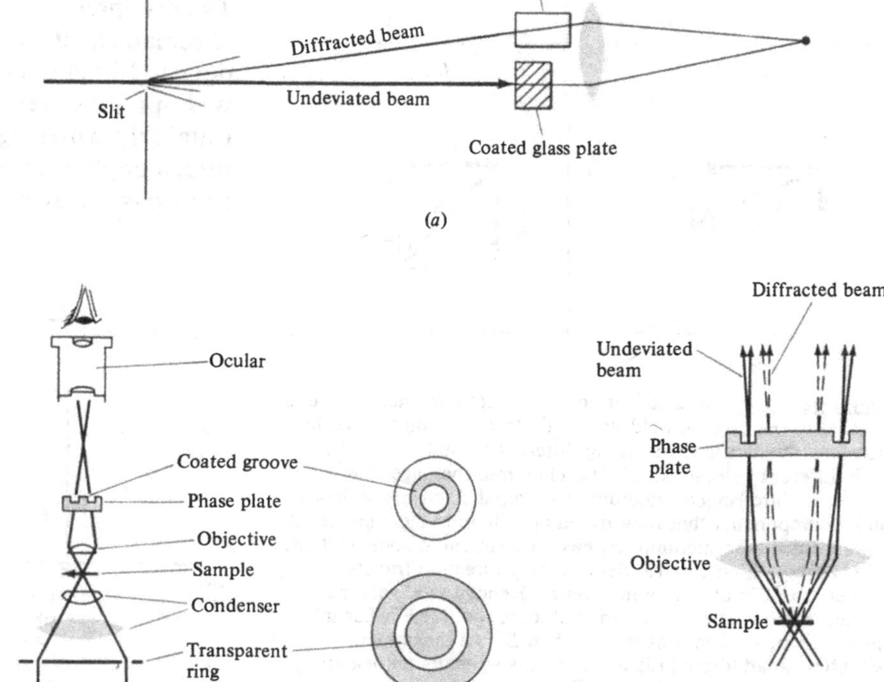

Figure 24.37. (*a*) The undeviated beam from a slit and the adjacent diffracted beam are a quarter wavelength out of phase. If the phase of the diffracted beam is shifted an additional quarter wavelength by a glass plate, it is exactly out of phase with the undeviated beam. (*b*) A phase contrast microscope. (*c*) An expanded view near the objective.

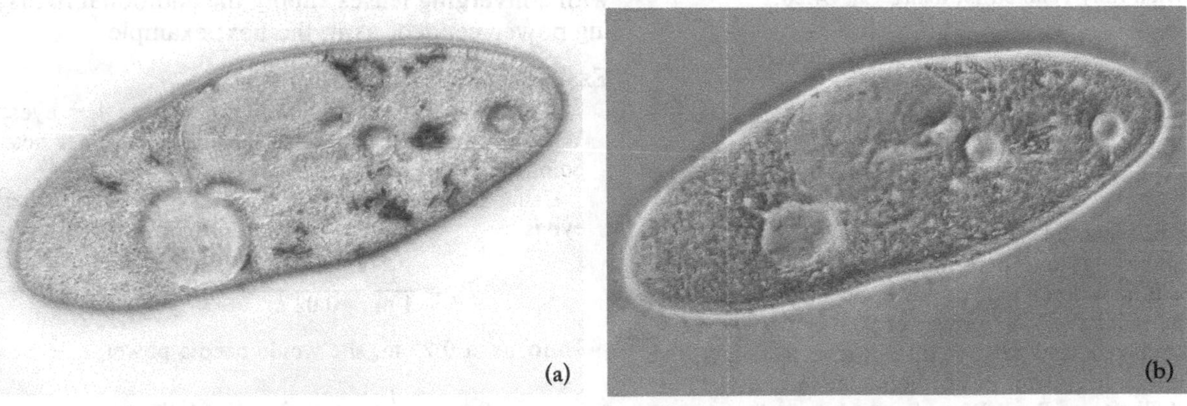

Figure 24.38. (a) Paramecium caudatum as seen with a bright-field microscope. P. Caudatum is a single-celled organism or ciliate protozoa covered with hair-like projections, which it uses to move and feed. Their natural habitat is fresh water in which it feeds on bacteria. (b) The same organism as seen with a phase contrast microscope. (Kent Wood / Photo Researchers, Inc.)

24.13 | OPTICAL DEFECTS OF THE EYE

Four common optical defects of the eye can be corrected by the use of eyeglasses. In three of these defects, the glasses are used to shift the apparent position of an object, so that the defective eye is able to focus properly. In the last, *astigmatism*, the glasses correct for a distortion produced by the eye.

In *myopia*, or nearsightedness, parallel light from a distant object is focused by the relaxed eye at a point in front of the retina (Fig. 24.39). Consequently, a nearsighted person cannot focus clearly on objects farther away than the far point located at a distance x_f. This problem arises because the power of the eye is too great; either the cornea has an excessive curvature or the eye is longer than normal. Diverging lenses with negative powers will compensate for this defect.

To calculate the required correction, we find the power of the eye at its far point, and then select a lens of the correct power to move the far point to infinity. We use the thin lens formula, $1/f = 1/s + 1/s'$, rewritten in terms of the power $P = 1/f$:

$$P = \frac{1}{s} + \frac{1}{D} \qquad (24.20)$$

Here D is the image distance in the eye, approximately 0.02 m. The procedure is illustrated by the following example.

Example 24.12

A nearsighted man has a far point at a distance of 0.2 m. His power of accommodation is 4 diopters. (a) What power lenses does he need to see distant objects? (b) What is his near point without the glasses? (c) What is his near point with the glasses?

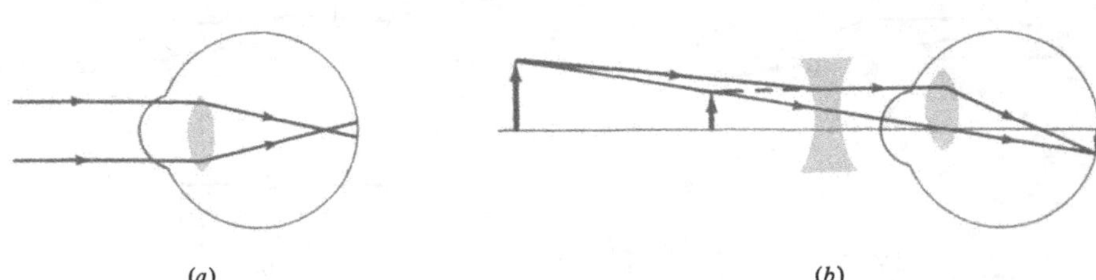

Figure 24.39. (*a*) Parallel light rays from a distant object are focused at a point before the retina of a nearsighted or myopic eye. (*b*) A divergent lens bends the rays so that they appear to come from a closer location and enables the eye to image the rays on the retina.

(a) At the far point, $s = 0.2$ m. Thus the power of his eye when fully relaxed is, using Eq. 24.20,

$$P_f = \frac{1}{0.2\text{ m}} + \frac{1}{0.02\text{ m}} = 55 \text{ diopters}$$

To have his far point at infinity, he needs a power of

$$P_f' = \frac{1}{\infty} + \frac{1}{0.02\text{ m}} = 50 \text{ diopters}$$

When he wears glasses, the sum of the powers of the lens and of his eye determines the effective power. Hence if he wears a lens of power $50 - 55 = -5$ diopters, he will have a net power of 50 diopters when his eye is relaxed, and will see distant objects clearly.

(b) Since his power of accommodation is $A = P_n - P_f = 4$ diopters, $P_n = P_f + A = (55 + 4)$ diopters $=$ 59 diopters. He will focus at a point $s = x_n$ satisfying

$$P_n = \frac{1}{x_n} + \frac{1}{D}$$

$$59 \text{ diopters} = \frac{1}{x_n} + \frac{1}{0.02\text{ m}} = \frac{1}{x_n} + 50 \text{ diopters}$$

$$x_n = 0.11 \text{ m}$$

(c) With the glasses, $P_n' = P_f' + A = (50 + 4)$ diopters $= 54$ diopters. Then

$$P_n = \frac{1}{x_n'} + \frac{1}{D}$$

$$54 \text{ diopters} = \frac{1}{x_n'} + \frac{1}{0.02\text{ m}} = \frac{1}{x_n'} + 50 \text{ diopters}$$

$$x_n' = 0.25 \text{ m}$$

This is the near-point distance for a person with normal vision and average accommodation. The lenses have fully corrected his vision.

Hypermetropia, or farsightedness, is the opposite of myopia. Light from an object close to the eye is focused toward a point behind the retina, even when the lens is adjusted by the ciliary muscles to have its maximum power (Fig. 24.40). Eyeglasses with converging lenses supply the additional focusing power needed, as in the next example.

Example 24.13

A woman has her near point 1 m from her eyes. What power glasses does she require to bring her near point to 0.25 m from her eyes?

Using Eq. 24.20, at her near point the power of her eye is

$$P_n = \frac{1}{1\text{ m}} + \frac{1}{0.02\text{ m}} = 51 \text{ diopters}$$

To focus at 0.25 m, she would need a power

$$P_n' = \frac{1}{0.25\text{ m}} + \frac{1}{0.02\text{ m}} = 54 \text{ diopters}$$

A lens with a power of +3 diopters will give her the required power to bring her near point to the normal location.

Presbyopia, the reduction in accommodation that occurs with age, is the result of a gradual weakening of the ciliary muscles and diminishing flexibility of the lens. The far point of a person who has normal vision as a young adult eventually recedes far enough so that converging lenses are needed for close work or reading, much like the person with hypermetropia. Many people eventually require bifocal lenses. In the most common type of bifocals, the upper portion of the lens is used for distant vision, and the lower part is used for close work. For example, an elderly myopic person will wear bifocals with a diverging lens in the upper part and a weaker diverging lens below.

A person with *astigmatism* cannot simultaneously focus on both horizontal and vertical lines. Usually this is due to a cornea that is not perfectly spherical, so that it has different curvatures in different directions. Occasionally, astigmatism is

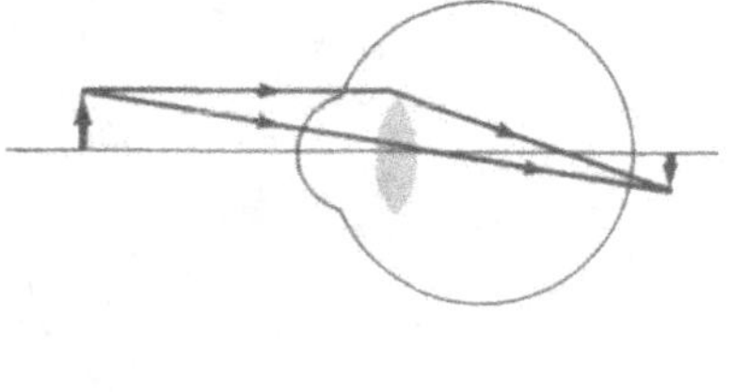
(a)

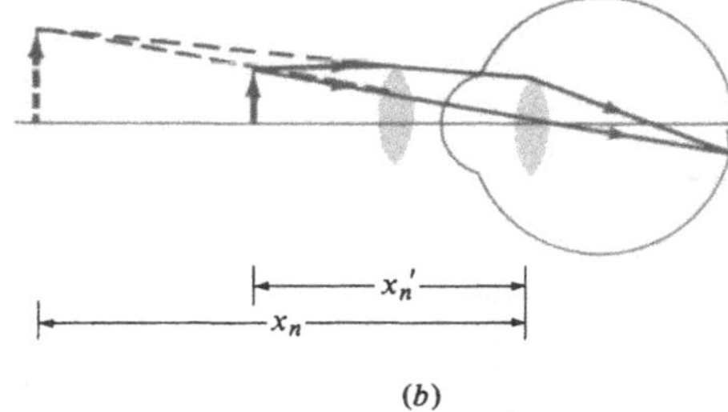

(b)

Figure 24.40. (*a*) Rays from a nearby object are bent so they would focus at a point beyond the retina of a farsighted or hypermetropic eye. (*b*) A converging lens bends the rays so they appear to come from a more distant location. The distance x_n' to the near point with the glasses is less than the distance x_n without the glasses.

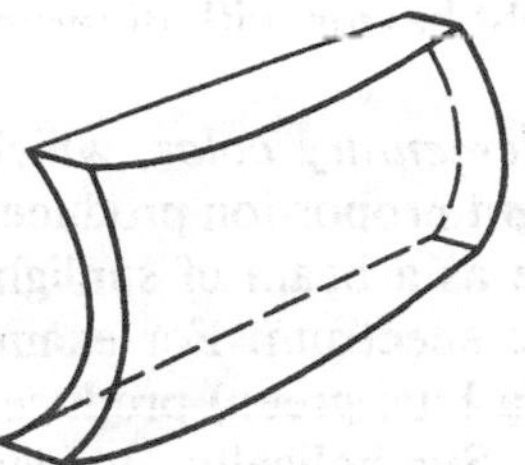

Figure 24.41. A cylindrical lens is used in eyeglasses to correct for astigmatism.

caused by irregularities elsewhere in the eye. Astigmatism can be corrected by cylindrical lenses oriented to compensate for the distortion (Fig. 24.41). If a correction for myopia or hypermetropia is also needed, then lenses shaped like the outer surface of a doughnut are used. The maximum and minimum radii of curvature are chosen to correct both defects.

Contact lenses are an alternative to ordinary eyeglasses and have many advantages (Fig. 24.42). Hard contact lenses are made of rigid plastic and are about 1 mm thick and 1 cm in diameter. Placed directly on the eye, they are separated from the cornea by a layer of tears, *effectively replacing the cornea as the front of the eye*. Since the light now enters the eye through a spherical lens surface, astigmatism due to corneal irregularities is automatically corrected. Also, the lenses move with the eyes, avoiding the aberrations that distort the view near the edges of strong eyeglass lenses. Soft contact lenses are somewhat larger than hard contact lenses. They conform to the shape of the cornea and are often more comfortable. Since most soft contacts do not maintain a spherical surface when placed on an irregular cornea, they do not correct for astigmatism. Toric soft contacts, which are relatively expensive and sometimes less comfortable, are shaped to compensate for corneal irregularity, so they do correct for astigmatism.

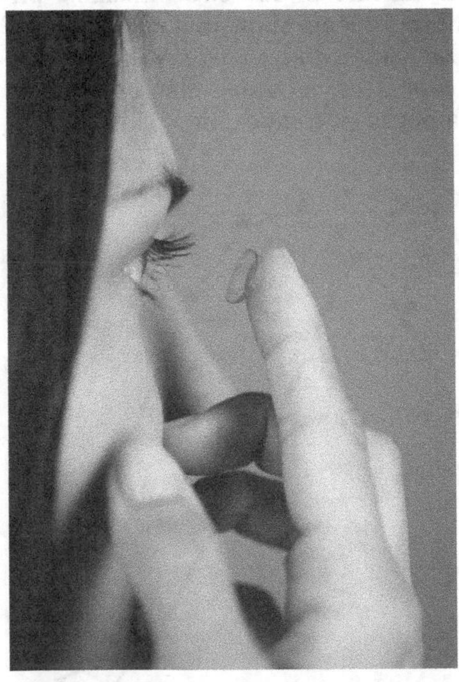

Figure 24.42. A soft contact lens being inserted. (I love images / Alamy Limited)

Surgeons in Colombia, the Soviet Union, and more recently the United States have corrected the vision of nearsighted and farsighted patients by reshaping the cornea. In one procedure in use since the 1960s, the front of the cornea is removed and reshaped on the inside by a computer-controlled lathe. For a farsighted patient, tissue is removed from the edges, increasing the curvature and power. Alternatively, tissue from a donor's cornea is properly shaped and placed under the center of the cornea before it is replaced to increase the curvature. Similarly, for a nearsighted person, tissue is removed from the center to flatten the cornea and decrease the power. In a newer operation for nearsightedness, 16 or so shallow radial cuts are made from the outer edge of the cornea toward the center, rather like the spokes of a wheel. This stretches and flattens the nicked regions. Both procedures are still considered experimental, and there are limited data on long-term benefits and problems.

24.14 | COLOR PERCEPTION AND MEASUREMENT

Scientists, artists, and paint manufacturers have long been intrigued by our perception of color, and by the complex relationship between the physical properties of light and its perceived attributes of *hue*, *brightness*, and *saturation*. *Hue* is what we colloquially call color; it includes the basic spectral colors corresponding to single wavelengths—red, yellow, blue, and so forth—as well as some *extraspectral* hues, such as crimson and purple, formed by mixing violet and red lights from the opposite ends of the visible spectrum. *Brightness* is the subjective impression of intensity, but differs from it because of the wavelength variation of the intensity discussed in Section 24.7. *Saturation* is the purity of depth of a color; when mixed with a neutral color (white, gray, black), a color becomes less saturated. For example, white light added to saturated red results in pink. The hue, brightness, and saturation can all be changed somewhat by variations in any one of the physical parameters, the wavelength, intensity, and spectral composition, as well as by changes in the surroundings. Clearly, color perception is a very complex phenomenon.

Color perception is made possible by the existence of three kinds of cones in the retina, each with its own photosensitive pigment. Each pigment can absorb light over a large range of wavelengths, but the peak sensitivities occur at different wavelengths: 445 nm, 535 nm, and 575 nm (Fig. 24.43). Light at a particular wavelength will excite all three kinds of cones to some extent, depending on how close it is to the corresponding peaks. Although the existence of three different kinds of detectors was confirmed in recent years by direct experiments, it had been suggested in the last century by Young, Helmholtz, and Maxwell because of the observed properties of mixtures of light beams with different wavelengths.

Every color has a *complementary color*, which when mixed with it in the right proportion produces the same sensation of white as a beam of sunlight containing the whole visible spectrum. For example, red (R) plus cyan (C) (a blue green) produces the sensation of white (W). Symbolically, we can write $W = R + C$, or $C = W - R$. That is, the complementary color is obtained if we subtract the original color from white by absorbing it with a suitable pigment.

Any color that is not too saturated can be matched in appearance by a suitable mixture of *primaries*, a set of three saturated colors well spread across the spectrum but otherwise arbitrary, such as red, green, and blue. This is why color television screens use three kinds of colored dots, and color photography employs three emulsions. Mixing colors always results in some desaturation, so a saturated color that is not selected as a primary cannot be exactly matched by such a mixture. However, if enough of one of the primaries is added to this color as a *desaturant*, the resulting mixture can be matched by a mixture of the two remaining primaries. Thus experiments show that *any perceived color can be represented mathematically by a mixture of three primaries*, provided that a desaturant is treated as a negative component.

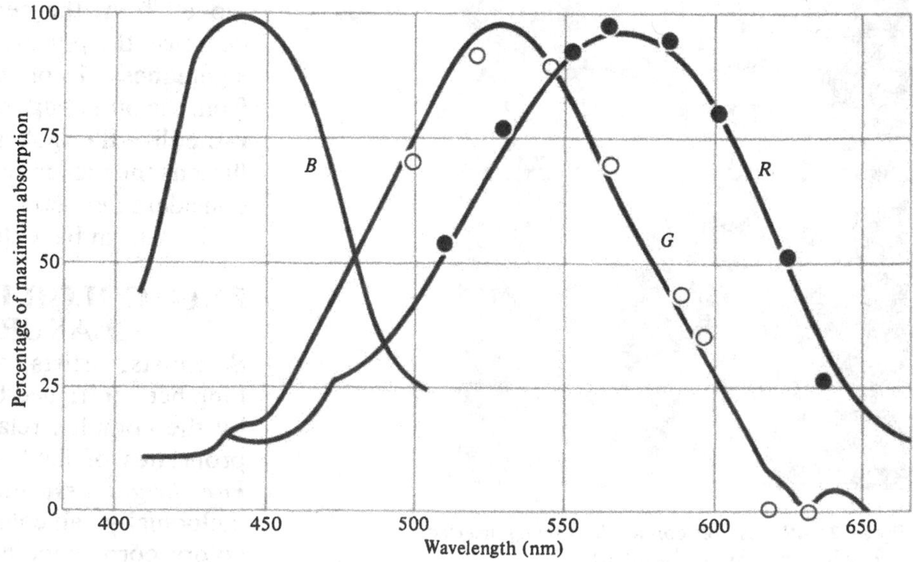

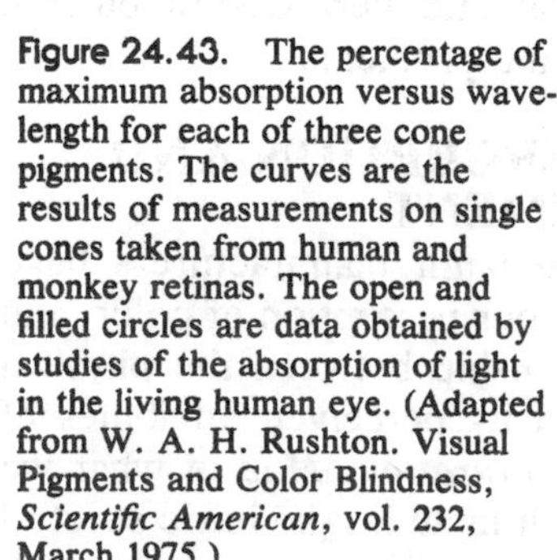
Figure 24.43. The percentage of maximum absorption versus wavelength for each of three cone pigments. The curves are the results of measurements on single cones taken from human and monkey retinas. The open and filled circles are data obtained by studies of the absorption of light in the living human eye. (Adapted from W. A. H. Rushton. Visual Pigments and Color Blindness, *Scientific American*, vol. 232, March 1975.)

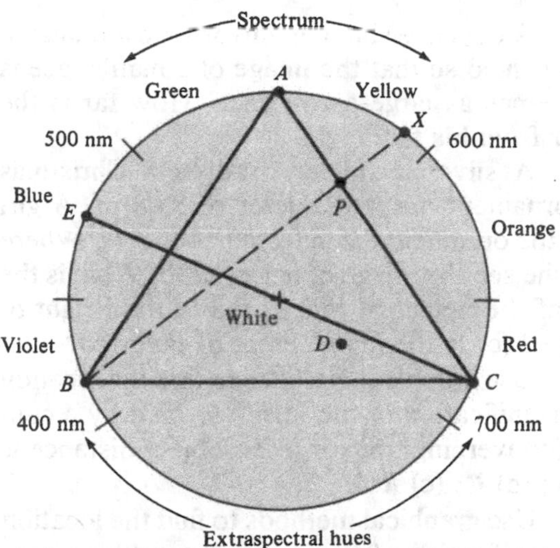

Figure 24.44. A simplified model of color mixing that displays many of the observed properties. Points on the perimeter are fully saturated; the center is pure white, and saturation decreases as one approaches the center. Mixing the three primaries *A*, *B*, and *C* in varying proportions leads to colors matching any color such as *D* within the triangle they define. The saturated color *X* is outside this triangle and cannot be matched. However, if enough *B* is admixed to *X*, they produce a mixture which falls at point *P*, and this color can also be produced by mixing *A* and *C*. The complement to *C* is *D*; when these colors are combined, they produce the sensation of white.

A crude circular model that displays all these general features of color mixing is shown in Fig. 24.44. Three primaries *A*, *B*, and *C* define a triangle that represents in an approximate way the colors that can be obtained by mixing the primaries. It also allows the identification of complementary colors. Saturated colors, such as *C* and *E*, which are at the ends of a line through *W*, are complementary.

The representation of colors in terms of three primaries can be cast into a compact, symbolic form. The chosen primaries are designated as *X*, *Y*, and *Z*. The fractional amount of each primary is given by the *chromaticity coordinates x*, *y*, and *z*; since they are fractional parameters, their sum is 1:

$$x + y + z = 1 \qquad (24.21)$$

If x and y are known, z is equal to $(1 - x - y)$ and is also known. Thus a color represented by the chromaticity coordinates (x, y, z) can be located on an x–y plane, or *chromaticity diagram*.

A standard chromaticity diagram was adopted in 1931 for the specification of colors (Fig. 24.45). It uses imaginary primaries to avoid negative values of the chromaticity coordinates corresponding to desaturants. The heavy colored line shows the saturated colors. Moving inward from this line, the saturation decreases, reaching pure white at the point indicated; the intensity units for the primaries have been adjusted so that $x = \frac{1}{3}$, $y = \frac{1}{3}$, $z = \frac{1}{3}$ produces the sensation of white. Effects of color matching are readily found with this diagram. For example, mixing the saturated colors *A* and *B* in varying proportions yields matches to unsaturated colors along the line *AB*. At point *P*, $x = 0.2$, $y = 0.4$, and $z = 1 - 0.2 - 0.4 = 0.4$. The same perceived color is produced equally well by this mixture of primaries or by a mixture of *A* and *B* with relative proportions 5:3, which is the inverse of the ratio of the distances found with a ruler from *P* to *A* and from *P* to *B*. The matches predicted by this diagram hold over a large range of brightness levels, even though in

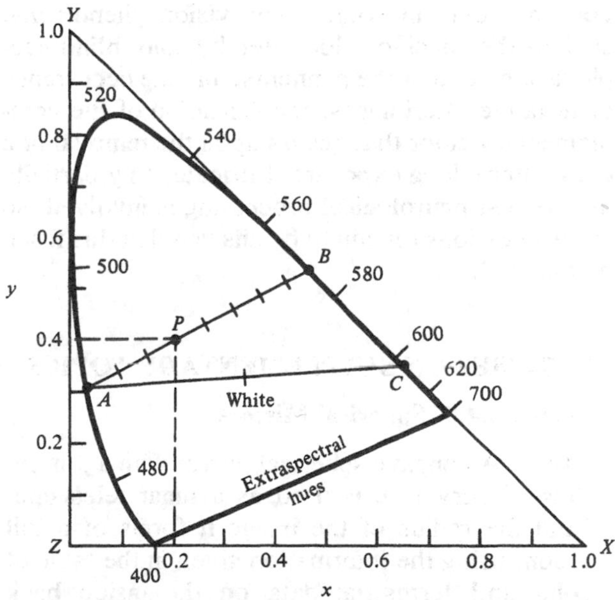

Figure 24.45. The standard chromaticity diagram adopted in 1931 by the International Commission on Illumination. A point on the diagram corresponds to a color with chromaticity coordinates x, y, and $z = 1 - x - y$. These coordinates specify the relative amounts of the imaginary primaries *X*, *Y*, and *Z*. The points on the colored curve are labeled with wavelengths in nanometres and correspond to the saturated spectral hues; *C* is the complement of *A*.

some cases the perceived colors will vary as the brightness changes.

The standard chromaticity diagram (Fig. 24-45) defines a *standard observer* and is based on the average of what was seen under specified illumination conditions by a few dozen people with "normal color vision." These subjects examined small color samples whose images fell on the most sensitive part of the retina, the fovea centralis. Larger objects form images spread over a greater retinal area, producing slightly different apparent colors. For this reason, a second chromaticity diagram was adopted in 1964 which is more accurate for objects subtending an angle of 4° or more at the eye. This diagram is not very different from the original 1931 plot, and it is seldom used. In any case, the character of the ambient lighting plays a major role in determining the colors we see, and variations in the responses of individual observers are substantial. These variations are due only in part to a gradual yellowing of the lens that occurs as a person ages.

By itself, the existence of three kinds of detectors does not explain some color vision phenomena, such as the specific colors seen by color-blind people lacking one of the pigments, and the occurrence of negative afterimages, the sensation of the complementary color that occurs upon the removal of a color after a long exposure. Intricate, only partially understood neurological processing is involved, so many questions remain to be answered in this fascinating field.

EXERCISES ON SUPPLEMENTARY TOPICS

Section 24.9 | Spherical Mirrors

24-51 A concave spherical mirror with a 3-m radius of curvature is used as a lunar telescope. Find the radius of the image it forms of a full moon, using the information given in the table of solar and terrestrial data on the inside back cover.

24-52 A peacock standing 2 m from the highly polished curved metal of a car sees "another bird" (its own image) 0.5 m behind the metal. (a) What is the radius of curvature of this part of the car? (b) If the peacock moves 0.01 m closer to the car, where does the other bird move?

24-53 A concave shaving mirror with a radius of 0.3 m is held so that the image of a man's face is three times as large as his face. How far is the mirror from his face?

24-54 A silvered sphere used as a Christmas tree ornament has a diameter of 0.08 m. A girl holds the ornament 0.2 m from her eye. (a) Where does she see the image of her eye? (b) What is the ratio of the height of this image to the height of her eye? (c) Is the image erect or inverted?

24-55 Use graphical methods to find the location and magnification of the image formed by a concave (converging) mirror if the object distance is (a) $2R$; (b) R; (c) $R/4$.

24-56 Use graphical methods to find the location and magnification of the image formed by a convex (diverging) mirror if the object distance is (a) $2|R|$; (b) $|R|$; (c) $|R/4$.

Section 24.10 | The Camera

24-57 An $f/1.4$ camera lens has a focal length of 50 mm = 0.05 m. What is the lens diameter?

24-58 With a certain set of lighting conditions, a photographer finds that an exposure of 1/25 s is needed at $f/16$. What exposure is needed at $f/8$?

24-59 The diaphragm of a lens is stopped down from $f/2$ to $f/16$. By what factor is the light intensity reduced?

24-60 Why do telephoto (long focal length) lenses usually have larger f-numbers than normal camera lenses of similar cost and quality?

24-61 A camera lens is focused on a distant scene illuminated with white light. Find the radii of the diffraction circles on the film at f-numbers of (a) $f/2$; (b) $f/32$.

Section 24.11 | Resolution and Contrast in Microscopes

24-62 An oil immersion objective is immersed in oil of cedar with a refractive index 1.4. If the objective subtends an angle of 80°, find the (a) numerical aperture; (b) minimum resolvable separation at a wavelength of 400 m.

Section 24.13 | Optical Defects of the Eye

24-63 An elderly man has his near point 2 m from his eyes. What power lenses does he need to read comfortably at 0.25 m?

24-64 A woman has a far point 0.5 m from her eyes. (a) If she is to see distant objects clearly, what focal length lenses does she require? (b) If her power of accommodation is 4 diopters, where is her near point without the glasses? (c) Where is her near point with the glasses?
24-65 A farsighted person with an accommodation of 3 diopters has a near point 2 m from the eyes. (a) What power eyeglasses are needed to move the near point to 0.25 m from the eyes? (b) Where is the far point with these eyeglasses?
24-66 A very nearsighted man has his near point at 0.1 m. His power of accommodation is 4 diopters. (a) Where is his far point? (b) What power lens does he require? (c) What is his near point when wearing the glasses?
24-67 A nearsighted man wears glasses with a correction of −6 diopters to see distant objects clearly. Where is his far point without the glasses?
24-68 A farsighted woman wears glasses with a power of +3 diopters to read books at a distance of 0.25 m. Where is her near point without glasses?

Section 24.14 | Color Perception and Measurement

24-69 (a) In Fig. 24.43, at what wavelength will the pigments labeled B and G have equal percentages of their maximum absorption? (b) What is the corresponding percentage for the pigment labeled R at that wavelength?
24-70 In Fig. 24.43, what are the percentages of maximum absorption for the pigments labeled G and R if light with a wavelength of 600 nm is incident on the retina?
24-71 What are the chromaticity components and wavelength of the complementary color of (a) spectral 480 (blue); (b) spectral 520 (green)? (Use Fig. 24.45).
24-72 (a) What are the chromaticity coordinates of a mixture of equal parts of spectral 500 (green) and spectral 580 (yellowish orange)? (b) What spectral color should be mixed with white and in what proportions to give the same result? (Use Fig. 24.43.)

PROBLEMS ON SUPPLEMENTARY TOPICS
24-73 Show in detail that equating the expressions for m in Eqs. 24.14 and 24.15 leads to $1/s + 1/s' = 1/f$.
24-74 A boy walks toward a convex spherical mirror at 2 m s^{-1} and sees his image walk toward him at 0.5 m s^{-1}. If the radius of curvature of the mirror is 2 m, how far is he from the mirror?
24-75 A nearsighted middle-aged man has a near point of 0.1 m and a power of accommodation of 2 diopters. Find his far point (a) without glasses; (b) with the correct glasses to move his near point to 0.25 m.
***24-76** A refracting telescope (Fig. 24.46) focused on an astronomical object forms an image at infinity. (a) If the focal lengths of the objective and ocular are f_1 and f_2, respectively, show that the separation between the lenses is $f_1 + f_2$. (b) Using small-angle approximations, show that the angular magnification $M = \theta_2/\theta_1$ satisfies $M = -f_1/f_2$.
24-77 A telescope is constructed using lenses of focal lengths 2 m and 0.1 m. Using the result of the preceding problem, find its angular magnification.
24-78 The ocular of a refracting telescope has a focal length of 0.1 m. If the length of the telescope is 3 m, what is its angular magnification? (Use the results of Problem 24-76.)
24-79 The discussion of color mixing in the text is based on mixing lights of different wavelengths and perceived colors. The colors of surfaces follow quite different rules, because surfaces absorb particular parts of the visible spectrum, and transmit or reflect the remainder. Thus a pigment

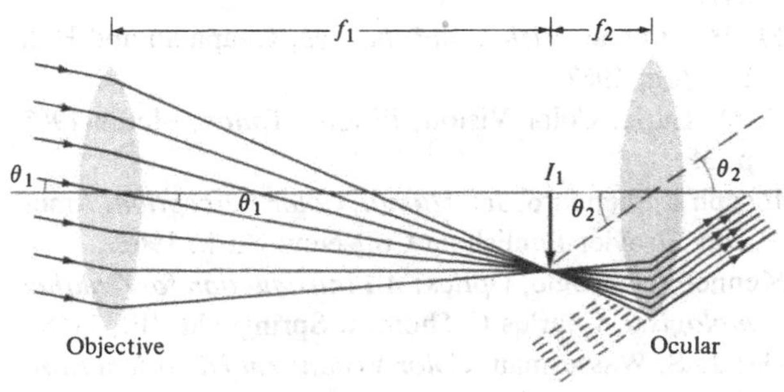

Figure 24.46. Problem 24-76. A refracting telescope.

or dye that absorbs one color strongly will make the surface appear to have the complementary color. Suppose we take our primaries to be red (R), green (G), and blue (B). The complementary colors are cyan (C) (a blue green), magenta (M), and yellow (Y), respectively. (a) What primaries are reflected by magenta paints? (b) What primaries are reflected by yellow paints? (c) What primary will be reflected if the paints are mixed? (*Hint*: White (W) = $R + G + B$.)

Additional Reading

The following books have chapters on microscopes and the eye:

R. B. Setlow and E. C. Pollard, *Molecular Biophysics*, Addison-Wesley Publishing Co., Reading, Mass., 1962, Chapters 12 and 14.

Simon G. G. MacDonald and Desmond M. Burns, *Physics for the Life and Health Sciences*, Addison-Wesley Publishing Co., Reading, Mass., 1975, Chapters 20, 21, and 23.

D. Ackerman, *Biophysical Science*, Prentice-Hall, Inc., Englewood Cliffs, N.J., 1962, Chapters 2, 7, 19, and 29.

John R. Cameron and James G. Skofronick, *Medical Physics*, John Wiley & Sons, Inc., New York, 1978, Chapters 14 and 15.

William Hughes, *Aspects of Biophysics*, John Wiley & Sons, Inc., New York, 1979, Chapter 15.

Other references on the material of this chapter:

Michael J. Ruiz, Camera Optics, *The Physics Teacher*, vol. 20, 1982, p. 372.

S. F. Jacobs and A. B. Stewart, Chromatic Aberration in the Eye, *American Journal of Physics*, vol. 20, 1952, p. 247.

M. H. Pirenne, *Vision and the Eye*, Chapman and Hall, London, 1967.

S. M. Luria, Color Vision, *Physics Today*, March 1968, p. 35.

Joseph J. Sheppard, Jr., *Human Color Perception*, American Elsevier Publishing Co., New York, 1968.

Kenneth Neil Ogle, *Optics: An Introduction for Ophthalmologists*, Charles C Thomas, Springfield, Ill., 1968.

Gerald S. Wasserman, *Color Vision: An Historical Introduction*, John Wiley & Sons, Inc., New York, 1978.

Fred W. Billmeyer, Jr., and Max Saltzman, *Principles of Color Technology*, 2nd ed., John Wiley & Sons, Inc., New York, 1981.

Timothy H. Goldsmith, Hummingbirds See Near Ultraviolet Light, *Science*, vol. 207, 1980, p. 786.

Micheal J. Ruiz, The Physics of Visual Acuity, *The Physics Teacher*, vol. 18, 1980, p. 457.

Thomas H. Maugh III, A New Microscopic Tool for Biology, *Science*, vol. 206, 1979, p. 918. Near-infrared microscopy.

Michael L. Brines and James L. Gould, Bees Have Rules, *Science*, vol. 206, 1979, p. 573. Honey bee dances correlate with patterns of polarized skylight.

Karl Von Frisch, *The Dance Language and Orientation of Bees*, Belknap Press of Harvard University Press, Cambridge, Mass., 1967.

David Falk, Dieter Brill, and David Stork, *Seeing the Light: Optics in Nature, Photography, Color, Vision, and Holography*, Harper & Row, Publishers, Inc., New York, 1986.

Malcolm Howells, Janos Kirz, David Sayre, and Gunter Schmahl, Soft X-ray Microscopes, *Physics Today*, August 1985, p. 34.

Tingye Li, Lightwave Telecommunication, *Physics Today*, May 1985, p. 24.

Special Issue: The Physics of Imaging, *Physics Today*, September 1989.

Lucian V. Del Priore, The Biophysics of Visual Photoreception, *Physics Today*, January 1988.

Scientific American articles:

F. Dow Smith, How Images Are Formed, September 1968, p. 97.

R. Clark Jones, How Images Are Detected, September 1968, p. 111.

P. K. Tien, Integrated Optics, April 1974, p. 28.

Ivo Kohler, Experiments with Goggles, May 1962, p. 62.

P. Connes, How Light Is Analyzed, September 1968, p. 72.

W. R. A. Muntz, Vision in Frogs, March 1964, p. 110.

Talbot H. Waterman, Polarized Light and Animal Navigation, July 1955, p. 88.

John F. Harris and Igor Gamow, The Infrared Receptors of Snakes, May 1973, p. 94.

Eric A. Newman and Peter H. Hartline, The Infrared "Vision" of Snakes, March 1982, p. 106.

George Wald, Eye and Camera, August 1950, p. 32.

Charles R. Michael, Retinal Processing of Visual Images, May 1969, p. 105.

Derek H. Fender, Control Mechanisms of the Eye, July 1964, p. 24.

Ulric Neisser, The Processes of Vision, September 1968, p. 204.

G. Adrian Horridge, The Compound Eye of Insects, July 1977, p. 108.

Edwin H. Land, Experiments in Color Vision, May 1959, p. 84.

Edwin H. Land, The Retinex Theory of Color Vision, December 1977, p. 108.

George Wald, Life and Light, October 1959, p. 92.

W. A. H. Rushton, Visual Pigments and Color Blindness, March 1975, p. 64.

W. A. Rushton, Visual Pigments in Man, November 1962, p. 120.

Jacob Bech, The Perception of Surface Color, August 1975, p. 62.

Bela Julesz, Experiments in the Visual Perception of Textures, April 1975, p. 34.

Robert Sekular and Eugene Levinson, The Perception of Moving Targets, January 1977, p. 60.

Gunnar Johannson, Visual Motion Perception, June 1975, p. 76.

Robert H. Wurtz, Michael E. Goldberg, and David Lee Robinson, Brain Mechanisms of Visual Attention, June 1982, p. 124.

Olga Eizner Favreau and Michael E. Corballis, Negative Aftereffects in Visual Perception, December 1976, p. 42.

Edward F. MacNichol, Jr., Three-Pigment Color Vision, December 1964, p. 48.

Joseph S. Levine and Edward F. MacNichol, Jr., Color Vision in Fishes, February 1982, p. 140.

John I. Yellott, Jr., Binocular Depth Inversion, July 1981, p. 148.

Michael Menaker, Nonvisual Light Reception, March 1972, p. 22.

Alistair B. Fraser and William H. Mack, Mirages, January 1976, p. 102.

Leonard A. Herzenberg, Richard G. Sweet, and Leonore A. Herzenberg, Fluorescence-Activated Cell Sorting, March 1976, p. 108.

William H. Price, The Photographic Lens, August 1976, p. 72.

David Emil Thomas, Mirror Images, December 1980, p. 206.

Eberhard Spiller and Ralph Feder, The Optics of Long-Wavelength X Rays, November 1978, p. 70.

Jearl Walker, Experiments with Edwin Land's Method of Getting Color Out of Black and White, *The Amateur Scientist*, June 1979, p. 189.

Jearl Walker, Anamorphic Pictures: Distorted Views from Which Distortion Can Be Removed, *The Amateur Scientist*, July 1981, p. 176.

Jearl Walker, Interference Patterns Made by Motes on Dusty Mirrors, *The Amateur Scientist*, August 1981, p. 146.

Jeremy M. Wolfe, Hidden Visual Processes, February 1983, p. 94.

Donald D. Hoffman, The Interpretation of Visual Illusions, December 1983, p. 154.

Robert H. Wurtz, Michael E. Goldberg, and David Lee Robinson, Brain Mechanisms of Visual Attention, June 1982, p. 124.

Tomaso Poggio, Vision by Man and Machine, April 1984, p. 106.

John N. Bahcall and Lyman Spitzer, Jr., The Space Telescope, July 1982, p. 40.

Eitan Abraham, Colin T. Seaton, and S. Desmond Smith, The Optical Computer, February 1983, p. 85.

Don L. Anderson and Adam M. Dziewonski, Seismic Tomography, October 1984, p. 60.

Jearl Walker, The Hyperscope and the Pseudoscope Aid Experiments on Three-Dimensional Vision, *The Amateur Scientist*, November 1986, p. 134.

Jearl Walker, Wonders with the Retroreflector, a Mirror That Removes Distortion from a Light Beam, *The Amateur Scientist*, April 1986, p. 118.

Philippe Brou, Thomas R. Sciascia, Lynette Linden, and Jerome Y. Lettvin, The Colors of Things, September 1986. Color perception.

Dana Z. Anderson, Optical Gyroscopes, April 1986, p. 94.

Lubert Stryer, The Molecules of Visual Excitation, August 1987, p. 42.

Julie L. Schnapf and Denis A. Baylor, How Photoreceptor Cells Respond to Light, 1987, p. 40.

Jane F. Koretz and George H. Handelmain, How the Human Eye Focuses, July 1988, p. 92.

Vladimir V. Vasyutin and Artur A. Tischenko, Space Coloristics, July 1989, p. 84.

UNIT SEVEN

MODERN PHYSICS

In the latter part of the nineteenth century, physics was considered by many to be a completed science. The fundamental laws of motion and electromagnetism, including light waves, were well understood, and it seemed that only calculational and experimental difficulties would hinder further progress. However, after only 20 years of the twentieth century, this description of the physical world was severely shaken. The very few unsolved problems that existed in 1900 proved to be explainable only by drastic assumptions that had no historical precedents. The illusion of a complete science proved to be a result of a lack of experience with atomic-sized particles and with objects that move at nearly the speed of light.

By 1912, the work of Max Planck, Niels Bohr, and Albert Einstein had given us a new picture of the world. These three set forth the tentative but crucial ingredients of what is now known as quantum mechanics. During the same period, Einstein also developed the special theory of relativity. Quantum mechanics and relativity are our present basis for understanding nature. Since their predictions agree with many kinds of experiments, they must be considered not as speculative but as a largely correct description of nature.

The three chapters of this unit set forth our fundamental concepts of special relativity, the particle nature of light, and the wave nature of matter. These concepts are the foundations of the remaining chapters in this book, which cover atoms, molecules, and atomic nuclei.

It should be recognized at the outset that while modern physics has forced us to change our philosophy of natural processes, the procedures of the old or classical physics are still essentially correct under certain conditions. Those conditions are that the objects under consideration are large compared to atomic sizes and that their velocities are much less than the speed of light. In nearly all the situations that we have considered up to now, these conditions are well satisfied.

CHAPTER 25 SPECIAL RELATIVITY

At the end of the nineteenth century, several fundamental problems existed in physics. One set of problems eventually led to the development of the revolutionary concepts of quantum mechanics, although it took several decades and many people to develop them. A second set of problems was solved in a single stroke by Einstein when his theory of special relativity was published in 1905.

The problem solved by Einstein was almost obscure enough to be largely ignored, but his solution has had a profound effect on our conception of the physical world. The *special theory of relativity* relates time and length measurements made by inertial observers moving at constant velocities with respect to one another. The *general theory of relativity*, which Einstein began to develop in 1911, deals with accelerated systems and gravitational forces. However, in this book, we only discuss the special theory of relativity.

The problem that Einstein originally addressed was an apparent violation of a fundamental rule of physics. This rule is called the principle of relativity and was developed first by Galileo. It states that the laws of physics should be the same for all observers moving at constant velocities with respect to each other. We describe this idea further in the next section. Here we need only remark that Newton's laws of mechanics seemed in agreement with this rule, but the laws of electricity and magnetism did not. It appeared that the effects of moving charges on each other depended on which ones were moving. If this were the case, there would be different results measured by different moving observers.

Einstein found that electromagnetism would be a consistent theory if one insisted that the speed of light in the vacuum is the same for all observers and is independent of the motion of the source and the detector. In this way, light waves are different from sound or water waves, whose velocities are determined by their media. Einstein's view, which is now well supported by experiment, is that there is no medium required for the propagation of electromagnetic waves.

If one accepts Einstein's principles that the laws of physics and the speed of light are the same for all inertial observers, one is led directly to some remarkable conclusions. Moving clocks run slow, and moving objects are shortened. Thus according to an earth observer, a fast-moving astronaut will live longer, and his rocket ship is shorter than before blastoff. Also, events that appear simultaneous according to the astronaut are not simultaneous as viewed by the earth observer.

Because our ideas of space and time are altered for rapidly moving objects, the laws of mechanics are also affected. The definitions of energy and momentum must be changed if these quantities are to obey the usual conservation laws. If an object has a mass m and a velocity v, its relativistic energy turns out to be

$$E = \frac{mc^2}{\sqrt{1 - (v^2/c^2)}}$$

When the velocity is zero, the energy becomes the *rest energy*

$$E_0 = mc^2$$

This is the most famous equation of twentieth-century physics. It asserts that mass (or matter) and energy are equivalent. Mass is converted into energy in the nuclear reactions that provide the energy of the sun and in nuclear explosives and reactors. If just 1 kg of matter is converted into energy, the energy released is $mc^2 = (1 \text{ kg})(3 \times 10^8 \text{ m s}^{-1})^2 = 9 \times 10^{16}$ J. This is comparable to the total energy used per day to generate electricity in the United States.

25.1 | THE FUNDAMENTAL PRINCIPLES OF SPECIAL RELATIVITY

We saw in Chapter Three that Newton's laws of motion apply only to measurements made with respect to inertial reference frames. These are frames in which Newton's first law holds true: an object with no net force on it remains at rest or in motion with a constant velocity. For example, observers in accelerating vehicles or on rotating merry-go-rounds cannot apply Newton's laws directly to their observations. Special relativity also deals only with measurements made by observers in inertial reference frames.

The theory of special relativity is based on two fundamental principles:

(1) *All the laws of physics (and nature) have exactly the same form in all inertial reference frames.* This is the *principle of relativity.*

(2) *The speed of light in free space is the same for all observers in inertial reference frames.*

The full implications of these ideas will become gradually clearer in this chapter, but we can immediately see some of the consequences. For example, the first principle implies that two people moving at a constant velocity with respect to each other can never decide which is moving and which is at rest. This is because all physical laws are the same in both systems, and they do not depend on any absolute velocity. Thus the observers can only determine their relative motion. For example, a woman on a train moving with constant velocity relative to the ground might say that she is stationary and the earth is moving. No experiment will decide whether this is true or false. The assumption that the earth is at rest and the train is moving is no more and no less valid.*

* Actually, the earth is not exactly an inertial frame; as it rotates about the sun and spins on its axis, objects on the earth experience a centripetal acceleration. In most situations the effects of this acceleration are small, so we assume in this chapter that the earth is an inertial frame.

Turning to the second principle, it is apparent that if the speed of light is the same for all inertial observers, light must be different from all other waves we have studied. For example, a listener moving toward a sound source will observe a higher speed of sound than someone at rest relative to the air. Nothing like this happens for light.

It was long thought that there was some medium, the *ether*, in which light moved at a speed c. This ether was the counterpart of the medium in which sound moves. Thus if one were moving relative to the ether, the speed of light would appear different from c. However, no experiment ever detected the ether or measured changes in the speed of light due to motion relative to the ether, and as far as we know now, there is no ether. In fact, the strongest evidence we have that there is no ether is the success of the theory of relativity. The theory of relativity could not be correct if the ether existed.

Einstein's motivation for the theory of relativity was to remove the contradictions then present in the laws of mechanics and electromagnetism. To the objection that the results were disturbing to our commonsense view of things, he answered, "Common sense is that layer of prejudices laid down in the mind prior to the age of eighteen."

25.2 | MOVING CLOCKS AND TIME DILATION

Einstein's theory predicts that if a clock is moving with respect to an observer in an inertial reference frame, he will observe it to be running slower than a clock at rest relative to the observer. The latter clock is said to be in the observer's *rest frame*. In order to show how this follows directly from the principles of special relativity, we first consider a particular type of clock called a *light clock*.

This clock is a stick of length l with a mirror R and a photodetector P at opposite ends (Fig. 25.1). A flash of light emitted at one end will be reflected by the mirror at the other end and return to the photodetector next to the light source. Each time a light flash is detected, the clock "ticks" and emits another flash.

We can easily relate the time t between ticks of the clock to the length l when the clock is at rest in a laboratory. From Fig. 25.1a, the total distance trav-

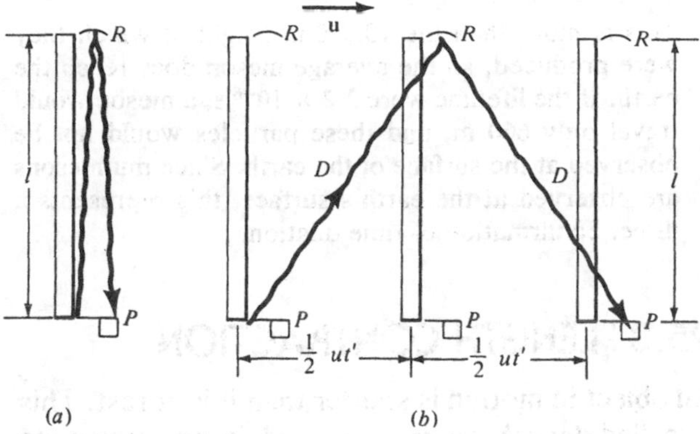

Figure 25.1. (*a*) Each time a flash of light is reflected from the mirror *R* and returns to the photodetector *P* beside the source, the light clock "ticks" and emits a new pulse. (*b*) The same clock moving to the right at a constant velocity **u**. The light pulse must travel the distance 2*D* to return to the photodetector *P*.

eled by a light pulse is $x = 2l$, and the speed of the light is c. Thus $x = vt$ becomes $2l = ct$, or $l = ct/2$, where t is the time between ticks.

When the clock is moving with a speed u relative to the laboratory, the speed of light is again c (principle 2), but the distance it must travel between ticks is $2D$ (Fig. 25.1*b*). With the Pythagorean theorem, we have

$$D^2 = l^2 + \left(\frac{1}{2}ut'\right)^2$$

where t' is the time for the light to return to the photodetector of the moving clock. But we also know that $2D = ct'$ or $D = ct'/2$ and that $l = ct/2$. Substituting these for D and l, we find

$$\left(\frac{ct'}{2}\right)^2 = \left(\frac{ct}{2}\right)^2 + \left(\frac{ut'}{2}\right)^2$$

Solving for t',

$$t' = \frac{t}{\sqrt{1-(u^2/c^2)}} \tag{25.1}$$

The time t' is greater than t because the factor $\sqrt{1-(u^2/c^2)}$ is less than 1. (We see later that u must be less than c.) This result is referred to as *time dilation*. It states that as measured by the observer at rest in the laboratory, time does not pass as rapidly in the moving frame. Note that we have *not* concluded that an observer moving with the clock would see any difference in the interval between ticks of his clock. He would, however, observe that a clock at rest in the laboratory has slowed down by exactly the same time dilation factor. *Each observer observes that the other's clocks are slowed down.*

To illustrate the remarkable implications of time dilation, consider an imaginary world in which the effects of special relativity are very pronounced. We do this by pretending that the speed of light is not 3×10^8 ms^{-1} but is instead comparable to everyday speeds.

Example 25.1

Assume for this example that the speed of light is 100 km h^{-1}. A woman relates the story of the delivery of her baby. She says that she drove herself at 80 km h^{-1} to the hospital, which was 100 km away according to the highway signs. She also says that according to her watch the baby was born 1 hour after she left. Was the baby born in the hospital?

If we use our usual reasoning, we would say no, since it would take $t = x/u = 100$ km/80 km h^{-1} = 1.25 hours to get to the hospital. However, because of time dilation, once she is traveling at 80 km h^{-1}, we see that her watch slows down. Thus when her watch indicates 1 hour, our watches indicate that the elapsed time is

$$t' = \frac{t}{\sqrt{1-\dfrac{u^2}{c^2}}} = \frac{1\text{ h}}{\sqrt{1-\left(\dfrac{80\text{ km h}^{-1}}{100\text{ km h}^{-1}}\right)^2}}$$

$$= \frac{1\text{ h}}{0.6} = 1.67\text{ h}$$

Since all clocks, *including biological ones*, must behave in the same way, in 1 hour of her time she can drive (80 km h^{-1})(1.67 h) = 133.6 km. The hospital is only 100 km away, so she must have arrived with time to spare.

In this example, one might object to the idea that the woman's wristwatch and her biological processes obey the same law that we derived for a light clock. However, *all* clocks and processes must obey this law; otherwise, the principle of relativity would be violated. For example, we can synchronize a light clock and several other types of clocks when they are all at rest. Now when they are set in motion with a common velocity, all the clocks must behave the same way. If some but not all apparently slow down, those that do not could be said to operate correctly in only one reference frame.

There is one more point to clarify about this example. The woman can consider herself to be at rest and the other people in motion. *Accordingly, their clocks will appear to be ticking slowly to her*. Nevertheless, when she arrives, her watch reads an earlier time than the hospital clocks. Since her watch agreed with the clocks where she started, she concludes that the hospital clocks have not been properly synchronized with those at her starting point. We can interpret this to mean that *clocks synchronized in one inertial frame are not synchronized in another*. Note, however, the difference between her experience and that of someone who did not make the trip. Since she accelerated and decelerated, she was not always in the same inertial frame. We explore these questions more fully in Section 25.5 in the Supplementary Topics.

The violent disagreement between the conclusions of this example and our expectations derives from the fact that in our world speeds are normally very small compared to that of light. Our intuition leads us astray when speeds approach c. An experiment that represents one of many direct confirmations of special relativity is described in the next example.

Example 25.2

Short-lived subatomic particles called mu mesons are created by cosmic rays in the upper atmosphere, approximately 10,000 m above us. They travel at $0.999c$ ($c = 3 \times 10^8$ m s^{-1}). In laboratory experiments with mu mesons at rest, they have an average lifetime of 2.2×10^{-6} s. (a) How long will the moving particles appear to live to an observer on the earth? (b) Will the average meson reach the earth?

(a) The average lifetime of the moving meson will appear increased to the earth observer. The average lifetime will appear to be

$$t' = \frac{t}{\sqrt{1 - u^2/c^2}} = \frac{2.2 \times 10^{-6} \text{ s}}{\sqrt{1 - (0.999c/c)^2}}$$
$$= 4.92 \times 10^{-5} \text{ s}$$

This lifetime is more than 20 times the lifetime of a stationary mu meson.

(b) Using this as the average lifetime, the earth observer sees the average meson travel a distance of

$$D = vt'$$
$$= (0.999)(3 \times 10^8 \text{ m s}^{-1})(4.92 \times 10^{-5} \text{ s})$$
$$= 14{,}700 \text{ m}$$

This is more than the 10,000-m height at which they were produced, so the average meson does reach the earth. If the lifetime were 2.2×10^{-6} s, a meson would travel only 660 m, and these particles would not be observed at the surface of the earth. Since mu mesons are observed at the earth's surface, this represents a direct confirmation of time dilation.

25.3 | LENGTH CONTRACTION

An object in motion is shorter than it is at rest. This is called *length contraction* and is an immediate consequence of the time dilation effect. To take a concrete situation, consider the woman in Example 25.1. She and an observer stationary with respect to the road must agree on their relative velocity, in accordance with the principle of relativity. As far as she can tell, her clocks are working normally. Therefore, she will reason that she was able to reach the hospital safely because the distance she had to travel was less than the posted distance of 100 km. In other words, as measured by this moving observer, the length of the road was reduced.

According to a stationary observer, the woman's velocity was $u = l/t'$, where t' is the time as measured by *a clock at rest relative to the road*, and l is the length of the road. The woman measures the same velocity. As we saw in the preceding section, according to *her clock* the time elapsed t is less than t' by the time dilation factor, so

$$t = t'\sqrt{1 - \frac{u^2}{c^2}}$$

Hence the length l' of the road as observed by the woman is $l' = ut = (l/t')[t'\sqrt{1 - (u^2/c^2)}]$, or

$$l' = l\sqrt{1 - \frac{u^2}{c^2}} \qquad (25.2)$$

This means that the road is measured to be shorter by the factor $\sqrt{1 - (u^2/c^2)}$ by an observer moving relative to the road. *An object is shortened or contracted according to an observer moving along its length*. Let us again examine the mu meson example from this point of view.

Example 25.3

A mu meson approaches the earth from a height of 10,000 m at a speed of $0.999c$. According to an observer moving with the velocity of the meson, what is the height of the atmosphere?

Using the length contraction formula, the height as measured by this observer is

$$l' = l\sqrt{1 - \frac{u^2}{c^2}}$$

$$= (10^4 \text{ m})\sqrt{1 - (0.999)^2}$$

$$= 447 \text{ m}$$

Since the atmosphere rushes by at $0.999c$, the meson reaches the ground in $(447 \text{ m})/(0.999 \times 3 \times 10^8 \text{ m s}^{-1}) = 1.49 \times 10^{-6}$ s, which is less than its average lifetime of 2.2×10^{-6} s. Thus the average meson reaches the earth's surface, in agreement with our earlier conclusion.

Contemporary spaceships travel at speeds that are small compared to the speed of light. However, exploration beyond our solar system involves distances so large that it would be practical only at speeds comparable to c. Relativistic effects such as length contraction would then be important. Note that distances in astronomy are usually not measured in metres but in *light-years*, the distance a light pulse travels in one year:

$$D = vt = c(1 \text{ year}) = 1 \text{ light-year}$$

The following example illustrates these remarks.

Example 25.4

Suppose that on January 1, 2000 a spaceship leaves the earth at $0.6c$ and heads toward planet X orbiting a star 12 light-years distant according to earth observers. (a) How far away from the earth is this planet according to the astronauts? (b) When does the spaceship reach planet X according to the earth observers and to the astronauts?

(a) Using the length contraction formula, in the rest frame of the spaceship the distance to be traveled is

$$l' = l\sqrt{1 - \frac{u^2}{c^2}}$$

$$= (12 \text{ light-years})\sqrt{1 - \frac{(0.6c)^2}{c^2}}$$

$$= (12 \text{ light-years})(0.8) = 9.6 \text{ light-years}$$

(b) According to earth observers, the time required is

$$t_E = \frac{l}{v} = \frac{12 \text{ light-years}}{0.6c} = 20 \text{ years}$$

The ship arrives on January 1, 2020, according to earth observers. The astronauts observe the time required is

$$t_S = \frac{l'}{v} = \frac{9.6 \text{ light-years}}{0.6\, c} = 16 \text{ years}$$

and arrive on January 1, 2016, according to their clocks. This is 4 years before the date indicated by the earth clocks.

As in the case of the woman traveling to the hospital, earth observers find that the moving spaceship clocks tick slowly, while the astronauts moving relative to the earth and planet X see a shortened separation between them. Both sets of observers agree that the spaceship clocks indicate an elapsed time of 16 years, 4 years less than on earth clocks, although they differ as to why this has happened.

No change in length is seen by an observer moving at right angles to the length of an object. It is left as a problem (Prob. 25-30) to show that this is a direct consequence of the principle of relativity.

25.4 | MOMENTUM AND ENERGY

In Chapter Seven, we saw that the momentum $p = mv$ is a useful quantity in ordinary nonrelativistic mechanics because the momentum of a system remains constant in a collision. When collisions occur between objects moving at speeds approaching that of light, it is found that momentum is not conserved if the nonrelativistic definition is used. However, the momentum can be redefined so that momentum conservation does hold true in collisions. Specifically, it is found by considering collisions that the correct definition of the relativistic momentum of an object of mass m and velocity v is

$$p = \frac{mv}{\sqrt{1 - (v^2/c^2)}} \tag{25.3}$$

Note that the square root factor becomes 1 at low velocities, so we recover the nonrelativistic expression for the momentum.

In this equation, as well as everywhere else in this chapter, m is the ordinary mass of the object as measured by an observer in its rest frame. (Some books refer to this quantity as the rest mass and also define a velocity-dependent mass. We do not do this.)

ALBERT EINSTEIN (1879–1955)

By the end of 1905, at the age of 26, Albert Einstein had developed the special theory of relativity and explained the photoelectric effect. He was also well on his way to formulating the general theory of relativity. This precocious activity was not preceded by exhibitions of genius. On the contrary, Einstein had dropped out of secondary school in his native Germany and later returned to school only because he could not pass the university entrance examinations without further preparation. He was graduated from the University of Zurich in 1900 and settled for a position in the Swiss Patent Office in Bern, since his mediocre performance at Zurich precluded his obtaining an academic position.

The Patent Office was quiet and afforded him the time to do research in theoretical physics. Because of his isolation from others working on contemporary problems, some of his work was a duplication of that already done. However, by 1905, Einstein was working on unsolved problems and was having immense success in developing new ideas and concepts. The work on the photoelectric effect was later cited in his Nobel prize award. The special theory of relativity not only explained a number of fundamental problems in physics but also changed the way in which we regard space and time. In this same year, Einstein finished his doctoral dissertation, and in 1907, he joined the faculty at the University of Zurich. By 1913, his work had brought great professional praise, an important position at the University of Berlin, and increasing fame among nonphysicists. Popular descriptions of the theory of relativity captured the imagination of his time.

The general theory of relativity was published in 1916. It predicted the deflection of light in a gravitational field, which was confirmed in England in 1919. The emotions of World War I affected these scientific achievements of a German-born physicist. In Einstein's words, "Today in Germany I am called a German man of science and in England I am represented as a Swiss Jew. If [my theory is overthrown] the description will be reversed, and I shall become a Swiss Jew for the Germans and a German for the English."

While the theory never was overthrown, the situation did change. As the Nazis gained power, his Jewish heritage and his advocacy of world government and disarmament led to vitriolic personal attacks on him. Consequently, he emigrated to the United States in 1933 and never returned to his homeland.

Although we shall see that he also helped to initiate the development of quantum mechanics, it evolved in a way that he found unsatisfying. Modern quantum mechanics holds that only the relative likelihood of various outcomes from an experiment may be predicted and not the result of a specific measurement. Einstein did not like this notion of "God playing dice with the Universe." While he played an important role as a consultant and sympathetic protagonist in the development of quantum mechanics, in his later years Einstein's research concentrated on attempts at a unified theory of gravitation and electromagnetism. His philosophy and work took him out of the mainstream of physics, although his early contributions continued to play an important role in the theory of modern physics.

Einstein's reputation was greater and more lasting than that of any other scientist of this century. His name was and is still used as a synonym for the revolutionary developments of modern natural science.

We illustrate the relativistic momentum formula in this next example.

Example 25.5

An object has a speed of 0.9*c*. Find the ratio of the relativistic and nonrelativistic momenta for this object.

The relativistic momentum is

$$p = \frac{mv}{\sqrt{1 - v^2/c^2}} = \frac{m(0.9c)}{\sqrt{1 - (0.9)^2}} = 2.29(0.9mc)$$

Since the nonrelativistic momentum is $mv = 0.9mc$, the relativistic expression is larger by a factor of 2.29. Since momentum is conserved in the absence of external forces, this larger momentum will be evident in collisions.

In nonrelativistic mechanics. Newton's second law is $\mathbf{F} = m\mathbf{a} = m\,d\mathbf{v}/dt$, or with $\mathbf{p} = m\mathbf{v}$

$$\mathbf{F} = \frac{d\mathbf{p}}{dt} \qquad (25.4)$$

The force is the rate of change of the momentum. In this form, Newton's second law applies in relativistic mechanics as well.

If an object is initially at rest, the work done on it as it accelerates is equal to its final kinetic energy. The work done in an infinitesimal displacement dx parallel to the force is the product $dW = F\,dx = (dp/dt)dx$. By definition, the velocity of the object is $v = dx/dt$, so $dx = v\,dt$. Thus $dW = (dp/dt)v\,dt = v\,dp$, and the final kinetic energy is found by evaluating

$$K = \int_0^v v\,dp$$

If we differentiate Eq. 25.3, we find after some algebra that

$$dp = \frac{dp}{dv}\,dv = \frac{m\,dv}{[1 - (v^2/c^2)]^{3/2}}$$

Then we obtain an expression which integrates readily:

$$K = \int_0^v \frac{mv\,dv}{[1 - (v^2/c^2)]^{3/2}} = mc^2\left[\frac{1}{[1 - (v^2/c^2)]^{1/2}}\right]_0^v$$

Thus we find that the kinetic enery of an object with mass m and velocity v is

$$K = mc^2\left(\frac{1}{\sqrt{1 - (v^2/c^2)}} - 1\right) \qquad (25.5)$$

If the denominator is expanded in powers of v^2/c^2, this reduces at low velocities to the nonrelativistic kinetic energy $\frac{1}{2}mv^2$. However, the kinetic energy of a rapidly moving object is much larger than $\frac{1}{2}mv^2$.

The following example shows that it takes much more work to accelerate an object to high velocities than predicted by nonrelativistic mechanics.

Example 25.6

An object of mass m has a speed $v = 0.9c$. What is the ratio of the relativistic kinetic energy of this object to its nonrelativistic kinetic energy?

The nonrelativistic kinetic energy is

$$K_n = \tfrac{1}{2}mv^2 = \tfrac{1}{2}m(0.9c)^2 = 0.405mc^2$$

The relativistic kinetic energy is

$$\begin{aligned} K_r &= mc^2\left(\frac{1}{\sqrt{1-(v^2/c^2)}} - 1\right) \\ &= mc^2\left(\frac{1}{\sqrt{1-(0.9)^2}} - 1\right) \\ &= 1.29mc^2 \end{aligned}$$

Thus $K_r/K_n = 1.29/0.405 = 3.19$. This means that the work necessary to accelerate an object from rest to a velocity $v = 0.9c$ is more than three times greater than we would have predicted nonrelativistically. As the velocity approaches the velocity of light, the kinetic energy of the object increases very rapidly. Hence it takes proportionately more work to achieve these speeds. In fact, it would require an infinite amount of work to have an object achieve a speed of c. This is one way of showing that *the velocity of light cannot be attained by objects with a nonzero mass.*

The *rest energy* of an object of mass m is defined to be

$$E_0 = mc^2 \tag{25.6}$$

This says that the mass m of an object is equivalent to an amount of energy mc^2. The *total energy* of the object is then the sum of the rest energy and the kinetic energy, $E = E_0 + K$, or

$$E = \frac{mc^2}{\sqrt{1-(v^2/c^2)}} \tag{25.7}$$

This is a statement that mass and energy are two forms of the same thing, and that one can be converted into the other. This was a revolutionary idea when Einstein introduced it, but it is now very well supported by experiment.

Before we examine some of the experimental evidence for the equivalence of mass and energy, let us consider an imaginary experiment in which two identical masses m collide and stick together (Fig. 25.2). They form a single object of mass M moving with a velocity v_y, which does not change, since by symmetry neither object can exert a vertical force on the other. We can determine the mass of this object using momentum conservation.

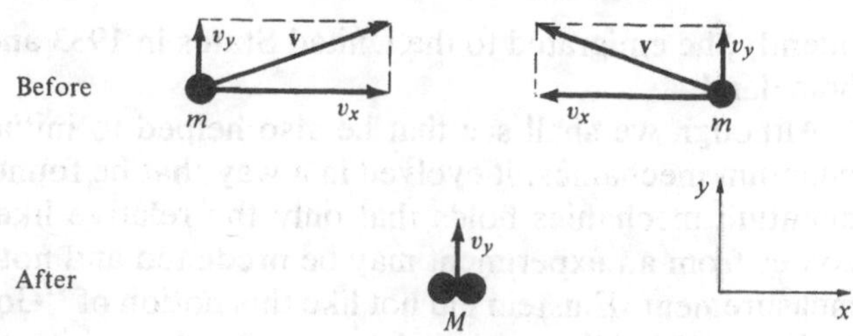

Figure 25.2. Two objects each with mass m collide and stick together.

The x component of the total momentum of the system is zero after and before the collision. Equating the y components after and before, we have

$$\frac{Mv_y}{\sqrt{1-(v_y^2/c^2)}} = \frac{2mv_y}{\sqrt{1-(v^2/c^2)}}$$

Dividing out the factor of v_y and multiplying by c^2,

$$\frac{Mc^2}{\sqrt{1-(v_y^2/c^2)}} = \frac{2mc^2}{\sqrt{1-(v^2/c^2)}}$$

This equation must hold for *any* value of v_y. In particular, if v_y is very small, then this becomes

$$Mc^2 = \frac{2mc^2}{\sqrt{1-(v^2/c^2)}}$$

This is a remarkable result. It states that the rest energy of the combined object is equal to the total energy—rest plus kinetic—of the original two objects; *kinetic energy has been converted into mass.* Note that this result has followed directly from the conservation of the relativistic momentum. Thus the equivalence of mass and energy is an automatic consequence of momentum conservation.

There are many interesting situations in which the opposite of this experiment occurs, and mass is converted into energy. Every *particle* in nature has its *antiparticle*, which is identical in mass but opposite in charge. Our world is made up of particles, but a few particle–antiparticle pairs may be created by very energetic cosmic rays entering the atmosphere or by an accelerator beam striking a target. If, for example, an *antiproton* with a charge $-e$ encounters a proton with a charge $+e$, their entire mass may be converted into gamma rays, very-high-frequency electromagnetic waves. Both the proton and antiproton cease to exist.

Other examples of the conversion of matter into energy are provided by *nuclear fission* and *fusion.* In nuclear fission, a uranium nucleus splits into two smaller nuclei whose total mass is less than that of the uranium nucleus by about 0.25 u. This is approximately 0.1 percent of the original mass and is equivalent to an amount of energy

$$\begin{aligned} E_0 = mc^2 &= (0.25 \text{ u})(1.66 \times 10^{-27} \text{ kg u}^{-1}) \\ &\quad \times (3 \times 10^8 \text{ m s}^{-1})^2 \\ &= 3.7 \times 10^{-11} \text{ J} = 2.3 \times 10^8 \text{ eV} \end{aligned}$$

This is about 10^8 times the energy released in a typical chemical reaction, which is a few electron volts. We can see that nuclear fission reactors and explosives employ huge energy sources.

Nuclear fusion, in which two light nuclei fuse to form a larger nucleus, releases even more energy in proportion to the mass of the constituents. This is the source of energy in the stars and may eventually provide us with almost unlimited amounts of energy. Both fission and fusion are discussed further in Chapter Thirty.

Mass is also converted into energy in chemical reactions. However, because the energies released are very small compared to the rest energies of the atoms, the mass changes are too small to be directly measured.

Relation Between Energy and Momentum

If one squares the defining equations for the relativistic energy E and momentum p, one finds that

$$E = \sqrt{p^2c^2 + m^2c^4} \tag{25.8}$$

When v/c is small, pc is small compared to mc^2, and this equation can be expanded to give $E = mc^2 + p^2/2m$. The first term is the rest energy. The second term can be rewritten as $(mv)^2/2m = mv^2/2$, which is the usual nonrelativistic kinetic energy.

If the mass m is zero, which is the case for light, Eq. 25.8 becomes

$$E = pc \qquad (m = 0) \tag{25.9}$$

The energy equals the momentum times the speed of light. Exactly this result had been obtained decades earlier by Maxwell, when he calculated the energy and momentum carried by an electromagnetic wave. This is another indication that Einstein's theory of relativity is in full agreement with Maxwell's theory of electromagnetism.

SUMMARY

The special theory of relativity is based on two fundamental facts about our natural world. First, there is no way for inertial observers moving with a constant relative velocity to determine which is at rest and which is in motion, since all the laws of nature are the same for both. Second, the speed of a light beam in a vacuum is $c = 3 \times 10^8 \text{ m s}^{-1}$, no matter which observer makes the measurement. These two facts are our clues to the nature of space and time and lead to a number of interesting results.

If two observers are moving with a constant relative velocity, each will observe that objects used by the other are foreshortened in the direction of motion. An observer in motion relative to an object sees it foreshortened according to

$$l' = l\sqrt{1 - \frac{u^2}{c^2}}$$

Each of the two observers will also say that the time t between ticks of the other's clocks is longer and is

$$t' = \frac{t}{\sqrt{1 - \frac{u^2}{c^2}}}$$

The total energy of an object is the rest energy

$$E_0 = mc^2$$

plus the kinetic energy, $E = E_0 + K$. For an object with velocity v,

$$E = \frac{mc^2}{\sqrt{1 - \frac{v^2}{c^2}}}$$

The modifications of our ideas of space and time require corresponding changes in our identification of momentum and energy. The work necessary to increase the energy of an object by a given amount increases with the speed of the object. This increase is such that an infinite amount of energy is necessary to cause an object with nonzero mass to travel with the speed of light.

Checklist

Define or explain:

inertial reference frames
principle of relativity
constancy of the speed of light
time dilation
length contraction
relativistic momentum
relativistic kinetic energy
rest energy
energy-momentum relationship

REVIEW QUESTIONS

Q25-1 An inertial reference frame is one that moves with ______ velocity.

Q25-2 One postulate of special relativity states that the speed of light is the same for all observers in ______.

Q25-3 An observer *A*, moving at a constant, nonzero velocity with respect to another observer *B*, observes that *B*'s clocks are running slow compared to *A*'s. *B*, in turn, observes that *A*'s clocks are running ______ with respect to *B*'s.

Q25-4 True or false? All clocks, no matter how constructed, should keep the same time if in the same inertial reference frame.

Q25-5 True or false? An observer at rest observes that the dimensions of a moving object are lengthened along the direction of motion.

Q25-6 True or false? The work required to increase the kinetic energy of an object of mass m from zero to the speed of light is $mc^2/2$.

Q25-7 The idea that mass and energy are different forms of the same entity is embodied in the equation $E_0 =$ ______.

Q25-8 Why can't an object of mass m travel faster than the speed of light?

Q25-9 Why is $E_0 = mc^2$ called the rest energy of an object?

EXERCISES

Use $c = 3 \times 10^8$ m s^{-1} unless the problem specifies otherwise.

Section 25.1 | The Fundamental Principles of Special Relativity

25-1 An observer at rest on the ground sees a jet plane fly overhead at a constant speed of 2000 km h^{-1}. At what speed does the pilot see the ground moving?

25-2 A spaceship is traveling away from the earth at a constant speed of $c/2$. A light pulse is emitted by a lamp on the earth and travels toward the rocket. Find the speed of the light pulse according to observers on (a) the earth; (b) the rocket.

25-3 A spaceship traveling away from the earth at a speed of $c/4$ emits a light pulse when it is a distance of 3×10^{10} m from the earth as measured by earth observers. How long will it take for the light pulse to reach the earth according to earth clocks?

Section 25.2 | Moving Clocks and Time Dilation

25-4 A person on a spaceship travels for 1 year (earth time) at a speed of $0.95c$. (a) How much time will have elapsed for the traveler? (b) How far will the traveler observe he has traveled?

25-5 A beam of pi mesons has a velocity of $0.6c$ relative to the earth. Their average lifetime when at rest is 3×10^{-8} s. (a) On the average, how long will the moving pi mesons appear to live to an observer at rest on the earth? (b) How far will they travel in this time?

25-6 Two identical twins *A* and *B* are each 20 years old when *B* starts on a round trip that lasts 20 years according to *A*. If *B* travels at a speed of $u = 0.99c$ except during brief acceleration periods, what are the ages of the twins when *B* returns?

Section 25.3 | Length Contraction

25-7 A pi meson is moving at $0.9c$ relative to a magnet. If the magnet has a length of 2 m in its rest frame, how long is it in the frame of the meson?

25-8 (Assume that the speed of light is $c = 100$ m s^{-1} for this exercise.) Suppose you are driving a racing car at Indianapolis. The homestretch is 1300 m long according to the spectators, and you are driving at 90 m s^{-1}. (a) How long does the homestretch appear to you? (b) How long do you think it takes you to drive this far? (c) How long do the spectators think it took you to drive that far?

25-9 At what speed would a moving metrestick appear to be 0.5 m long to an observer at rest?

25-10 Suppose we see a pole passing us, moving parallel to its length at $0.6c$. What length would we measure it to be if its length in its rest frame is 20 m?

25-11 A star is 10 light-years from the earth according to earth observers. If a spaceship travels toward it from the earth at $0.6c$, how far from the earth is the star according to its occupants?

25-12 How many metres are there in a light-year?

25-13 Pi mesons produced in an accelerator experiment are found to travel 10 times as far on the average before they decay as would be expected based on their lifetime and nonrelativistic mechanics. How fast are the mesons moving?

25-14 Particles moving at $0.95c$ are found to travel 3 m on the average before decaying. (a) In their rest frame, how far does the earth move? (b) How long do they live according to clocks in their rest frame?

Section 25.4 | Momentum and Energy

25-15 The kinetic energy and rest energy of a particle are equal. What is the speed of the particle?

25-16 The energy obtained by burning 1 g of coal is about 3×10^4 J. What is the ratio of this energy to the rest energy of the 1 g of coal?

25-17 The energy released in chemical reactions is on the order of 5 eV per molecule. (a) Estimate the mass change in atomic mass units (1 u = 1.66×10^{-27} kg). (b) If the mass of the constituent atoms is 30 u, what is the fractional mass change?

25-18 A nuclear power plant produces 10^9 W of electrical power and simultaneously releases 2×10^9 W to the environment as waste heat. (a) At what rate is mass converted to energy? (b) How much mass is used up in 1 year? (1 year = 3.16×10^7 s.) (c) What fraction is this of the 10^5 kg of uranium oxide in the reactor core?

25-19 In the decay of a neutron at rest into a proton, an electron e^-, and an antineutrino $\bar{\nu}$, one observes a total kinetic energy release of 1.25×10^{-13} J. What is the difference between the mass of a proton plus electron and the mass of a neutron? (The antineutrino has zero mass.)

25-20 Although our world is made up of matter, it has been conjectured that some galaxies may be composed of antimatter. If a 10-kg meteor of antimatter struck the earth, (a) how much mass would be converted into energy? (b) How much energy would be released?

25-21 A proton has a rest energy of 938 MeV. (1 MeV = 10^6 eV.) When its velocity is $0.9c$, what is its (a) total energy; (b) kinetic energy?

25-22 An electron has a rest energy of 0.51×10^6 eV. (a) What is its total energy if it is accelerated from rest through a potential difference of 12×10^6 V? (b) What is its velocity?

25-23 The total energy of a particle is 10 times its rest energy. Find (a) its speed; (b) its momentum.

25-24 In nuclear physics, energies are often measured in megaelectron volts (1 MeV = 10^6 eV). Momenta are then quoted in MeV/c, so that the quantity pc has the units MeV. A nucleus is found to have a total energy of 10,000 MeV and a momentum of 9280 MeV/c. Find its rest energy in MeV.

25-25 (a) What is the rest energy in MeV of a particle with a mass of 1 u? (b) In a nuclear reaction, the mass of the final products is less than that of the initial particles by 1 u. How much kinetic energy has been released?

25-26 Suppose one uses the nonrelativistic approximation for the kinetic energy. The fractional error resulting from the use of this approximation is $|K_{\text{exact}} - K_{\text{approx}}|/K_{\text{exact}}$. Find the fractional error when v/c is (a) 0.1; (b) 0.5.

PROBLEMS

25-27 A person on a rocket notes that she is traveling toward a star 1 light year away from the earth with a speed u. A person on earth sees the rocket traveling with speed u but says the star is 10 light years away. (a) How long will the traveler say the trip takes? (b) How long does the earth observer say the trip takes? (c) Discuss who is correct.

25-28 If the speed of light were $c = 100 \text{ m s}^{-1}$, what would a sprinter say about his time needed to run the 100-m dash? (The officials say the time is 10 s.)

25-29 Consider two islands 10 km apart on a straight river flowing at 3 km h^{-1}. Using a boat that moves at 5 km h^{-1} with respect to the water, (a) how long does the upstream trip from island to island take? (b) How long does the downstream trip take? (c) How long does the total round trip take? (d) Compare the duration of the trip with the time it would take in still water. (e) Describe the analogy between the results of this problem and the derivation leading to Eq. 25.1.

25-30 Two identical sticks both have pins at their ends and will leave scratch marks on each other if they come into contact. Suppose they are set into relative motion perpendicular to their length as in Fig. 25.3. Show that it follows from the principle of relativity that they cannot change in length.

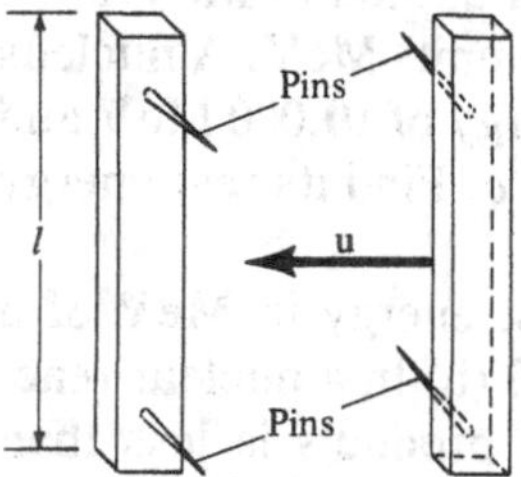

Figure 25.3. Two identical sticks with length l in their rest frames are in relative motion perpendicular to their length (Problem 25.30).

25-31 The energy flux from the sun on the earth averages about 1 kW m^{-2} (24 hours per day). How much of the sun's mass reaches each square metre of the earth each year in the form of energy? (1 year = 3.16×10^7 s).

25-32 (a) Using the relativistic expressions for the energy and momentum, show that the velocity of a particle satisfies $v = pc^2/E$. (b) Show how this goes over into a correct nonrelativistic formula when v/c is small.

25-33 An electron is accelerated from rest through a potential difference of 60,000 V. (a) What is the ratio of the total energy of the moving electron to its rest energy? (b) What is the final speed of the electron? (c) What is the final speed of the electron according to nonrelativistic mechanics?

25-34 Verify that $E = \sqrt{p^2c^2 + m^2c^4}$ follows from the definitions of E and p.

25-35 From the binomial theorem,

$$(1 - x)^{-1/2} = 1 + \tfrac{1}{2}x + \tfrac{3}{8}x^2 + \cdots$$

Use this to show that the relativistic expression for the kinetic energy reduces to the nonrelativistic formula when v/c is small.

25-36 Tom flies on an airplane at 1000 km h^{-1}. How many hours must he fly to be 1 s younger than his twin Harry who stays on the ground? [*Hint*: Because u/c is very small, you cannot simply plug the velocities into a calculator; instead, use the binomial expansion $(1 - u^2/c^2)^{1/2} = 1 - \frac{1}{2}u^2/c^2 + \cdots$.]

25-37 An airplane is 50 m long in its rest frame and has a speed relative to the ground of 900 m s^{-1}. By how much is it shorter according to the measurements of observers on the earth? (See the hint in the preceding problem.)

c25-38 Using Eq. 25.3, show that $dp/dv = m/[1 - (v^2/c^2)]^{3/2}$.

c25-39 Verify the integration in the equation preceding Eq. 25.5.

ANSWERS TO REVIEW QUESTIONS

Q25-1, constant; **Q25-2**, inertial reference frames; **Q25-3**, slow; **Q25-4**, true; **Q25-5**, false; **Q25-6**, false; **Q25-7**, mc^2; **Q25-8**, it would require an infinite amount of energy to reach the speed of light; even this is impossible; **Q25-9**, the total energy is $E = mc^2/\sqrt{1 - (v^2/c^2)}$, which is mc^2 when $v = 0$, and the object is at rest.

SUPPLEMENTARY TOPICS

25.5 | THE PROBLEM OF SIMULTANEOUS EVENTS; TWIN PARADOX

We have seen that Einstein's postulates led to the conclusion that the time elapsed between events is not an absolute quantity; rather, it depends on the motion of an observer. The mu meson observations described in Example 25.2 represent just one of many experimental verifications of this prediction.

A further consequence of Einstein's postulates is that observers may disagree on the question of whether two spatially separated events occur simultaneously. To see this qualitatively, suppose that an observer S standing at the center of a room sends two light pulses simultaneously toward the front and back of the room. Since the distances to the two walls are the same, the pulses strike the walls simultaneously according to this observer. If an observer M passes S at a velocity u just as the pulses are emitted, he too sees the two pulses traveling at a speed c (principle 2) toward the walls. However, he sees one wall approaching at a speed u and the other wall receding at the same rate. Consequently, M sees the pulse arrive at the approaching wall first, and he disagrees with S's observation that the two pulses arrive simultaneously at the walls.

To consider this question of simultaneity quantitatively, we consider what happens when an observer S synchronizes two clocks at different locations. Suppose S is stationary relative to a stick of length l with a clock at each end. To synchronize the clocks so that they both read $t = 0$ at the same time, S has a light pulse emitted at one clock at $t = 0$. This pulse will travel the distance l to the second clock in a time $t = l/c$. If the second clock reads $t = l/c$ at the instant the pulse arrives, S will conclude that both his clocks read $t = 0$ when the pulse was emitted and that they are synchronized (Fig. 25.4).

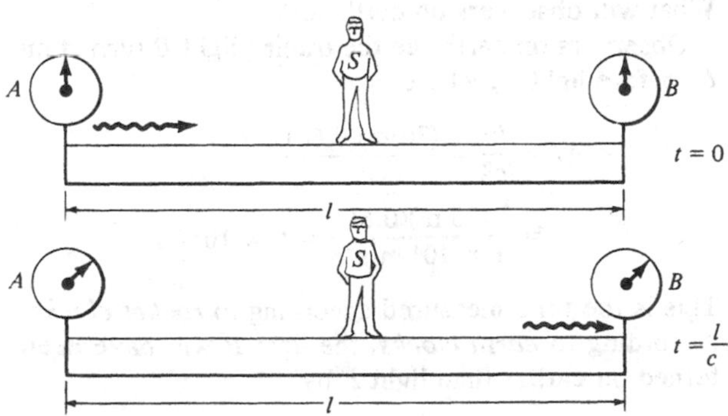

Figure 25.4. An observer S is stationary with respect to the stick and clocks shown. He wil say that the clocks are synchronized if clock A reads $t = 0$ when a light pulse is emitted and clock B reads $t = l/c$ when the pulse arrives.

We now ask how an observer M moving at a speed u relative to the stick observes these events (Fig. 25.5). He agrees with S that a light pulse is emitted when S's clock at A reads $t = 0$ and that the pulse reaches clock B when that clock reads $t = l/c$. According to S, the time it takes for the light pulse to travel from clock A to clock B is $t = l/c$. M disagrees, since he observes the stick to have a foreshortened length $l' = l\sqrt{1 - (u^2/c^2)}$ and also sees clock B moving toward the pulse. According to M, the pulse must travel a distance $ct' = l' - ut'$. Thus

$$t' = \frac{l'}{c + u} = \frac{l\sqrt{1 - (u^2/c^2)}}{c[1 + (u/c)]}$$

This is the transit time t' for the pulse as observed by M *using his own clocks*. It is less than the time interval l/c measured by S. Now suppose M looks at the *clocks belonging to S*. According to M, these clocks run slower by the time dilation factor. Hence, when a time interval t' has elapsed on M's clocks, M will observe that S's clocks indicate an interval t given by $t = t'\sqrt{1 - (u^2/c^2)}$. Using our result for t', this becomes

$$t = \frac{l}{c}\frac{1 - (u^2/c^2)}{1 + (u/c)} = \frac{l}{c}\left(1 - \frac{u}{c}\right)$$

This is the transit time for the pulse as observed by M using S's clocks. Thus M concludes that even according to S's clocks, the light pulse does not take as long in transit as the time l/c measured by S. In fact, M reasons that since the pulse arrives at clock B when it reads $t = l/c$, then when the pulse was emitted, clock B read $t = lu/c^2$, not $t = 0$ as S concluded! While S says the clocks read $t = 0$ simultaneously, M says that when clock A read $t = 0$, clock B read $t = lu/c^2$. This is a real difference; neither M nor S is wrong.

This result can be restated in more general terms. Suppose two clocks a distance l apart in their rest frame are synchronized according to an observer in that frame. An observer who sees them in motion with a speed u sees the *trailing clock set ahead* by

$$\Delta t = l\frac{u}{c^2} \qquad \text{(trailing clock leads)} \qquad (25.10)$$

This is the time difference he sees on the *moving clocks*. Because of time dilation, his own clocks

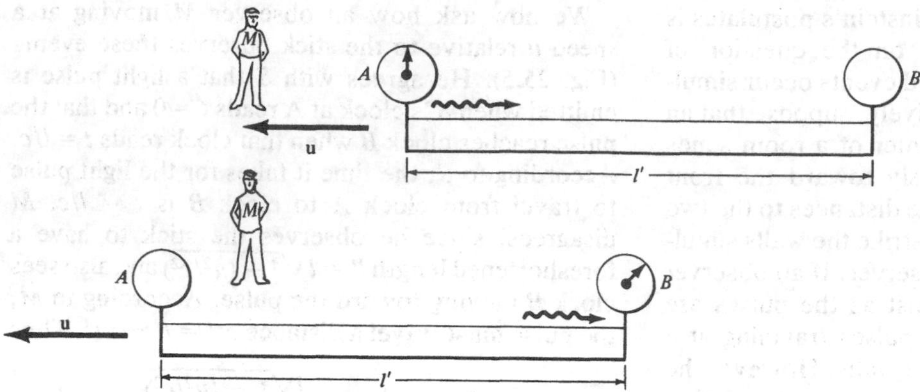

Figure 25.5. An observed M in motion relative to the stick sees the stick and clocks of Fig. 25.4 moving past him with a speed u. M sees the pulse emitted when clock A reads $t = 0$ and sees the pulse arrive when clock B reads $t = l/c$. When M measures the length of the moving stick, he finds it has a contracted length $l' = l\sqrt{1 - (u^2/c^2)}$.

indicate a larger difference in t' when the two clocks read $t = 0$:

$$\Delta t' = \frac{\Delta t}{[1 - (u^2/c^2)]^{1/2}} \quad \text{(trailing clock leads)} \quad (25.11)$$

We now apply this result to the spaceship clock problem of Example 25.4.

Example 25.7

Astronauts travel at $0.6c$ from the earth to planet X located 12 light years away, as measured by earth observers. X clocks have been synchronized with earth clocks by light pulses. The trip starts on January 1, 2000; it lasts 20 years according to earth clocks and 16 according to spaceship clocks. (a) What date do the astronauts expect to see on X clocks upon arrival? (Assume they do not correct for the relativistic effects.) (b) Explain why they do not see what they expected.

(a) The astronauts find X clocks read January 1, 2020, upon their arrival. But the astronauts see the earth and X clocks in motion and, therefore, ticking slowly. Thus they had expected to arrive after (16 years) $(1 - 0.6^2)^{1/2} = 12.8$ years or in October 2012 according to these clocks. The astronauts therefore infer that the clocks on planet X were not correctly synchronized with earth clocks. Instead, they conclude that these clocks were set ahead by $20 - 12.8 = 7.2$ years in their own inertial frame.

(b) The astronauts see the earth and planet X moving past their ship at $0.6c$. If their clocks have been synchronized in their rest frame, the astronauts will see the X clocks (trailing clocks) set ahead of the earth clocks by

$$\Delta t = \frac{lu}{c^2} = \frac{(12 \text{ light-years})(0.6c)}{c^2} = 7.2 \text{ years}$$

This is precisely the difference in clock settings according to *earth clocks*, as seen by the astronauts.

Another rocket problem illustrates the relationship between time differences as seen in two inertial frames.

Example 25.8

People in a rocket of length $l = 30$ m traveling toward the earth at a speed of $u = 0.6c$ turn on lights in the front and back of the rocket simultaneously (Fig. 25.6). What will observers on earth see?

Observers on earth see the trailing light B turned on Δt before light F, where

$$\Delta t = \frac{lu}{c^2} = \frac{(30 \text{ m})(0.6c)}{c^2}$$

$$= \frac{(30 \text{ m})(0.6)}{3 \times 10^8 \text{ m s}^{-1}} = 6 \times 10^{-8} \text{ s}$$

This is the time measured according to *rocket clocks*. According to *earth clocks*, the light B will have been turned on earlier than light F by

$$\Delta t' = \frac{\Delta t}{\sqrt{1 - (u^2/c^2)}} = \frac{6 \times 10^{-8} \text{ s}}{\sqrt{1 - (0.6c/c)^2}}$$

$$= \frac{6 \times 10^{-8} \text{ s}}{0.8}$$

$$= 7.5 \times 10^{-8} \text{ s}$$

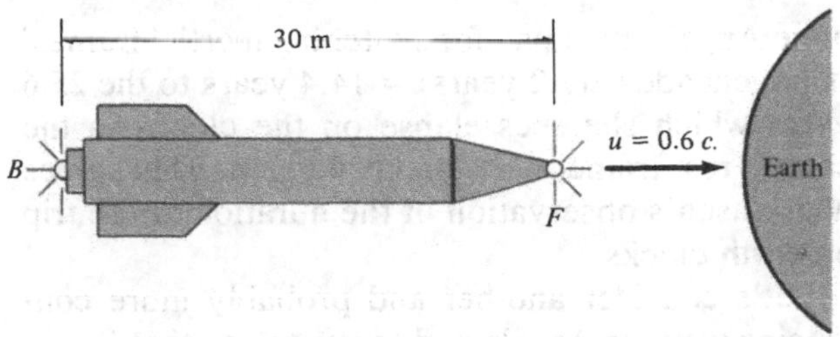

Figure 25.6. Observers on a rocket turn on lights at F and B simultaneously.

The results we have obtained in this section can sometimes lead to very intriguing apparent paradoxes. The following example that takes place in an imaginary world where c is comparable to everyday speeds illustrates one of these.

Example 25.9

(For the purpose of this example, assume that the speed of light is $c = 5\ \text{m s}^{-1}$.) Three people own some boards 5 m long and a barn 4 m wide. They know that a moving object is contracted in length. Hence they decide to move the boards at a speed $u = 3\ \text{m s}^{-1}$, so that the length of the boards will be contracted to

$$l' = l\sqrt{1 - \frac{u^2}{c^2}} = 5\ \text{m}\sqrt{1 - \left(\frac{3}{5}\right)^2}$$
$$= (5\ \text{m})(0.8) = 4\ \text{m}$$

Thus the boards will fit into the barn. They station one person (B) at the back door of the barn and another (F) at the front door. The third (M) will run with the board (Fig. 25.7). F and B are to close the doors simultaneously when the board is exactly inside the barn.

The apparent paradox is that M, moving with the board, sees the board as 5 m long and the barn as having a contracted width of only (4 m)(0.8) = 3.2 m.

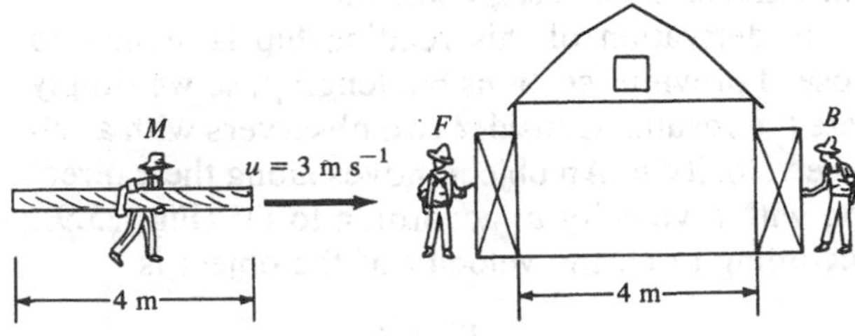

Figure 25.7. The barn and board *as measured by the observers F and B who are at rest relative to the barn.* F and B plan to close the doors of the barn simultaneously when the board is inside. When the board is at rest it has a length of 5 m.

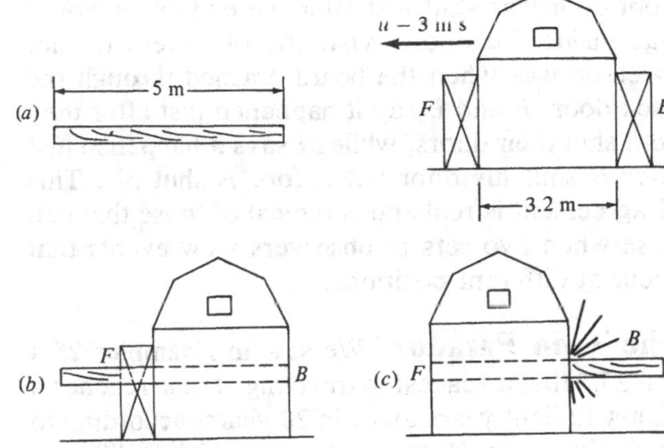

Figure 25.8. (*a*) The board and bard as viewed by M, the person moving with the board. (*b*) The back door is shut as the board reaches it. The board crashes through this door and instant later. (*c*) The front door is shut later, when the trailing end of the board is just inside the barn.

How can the two sets of observations be compatible?

We first consider the situation as measured by F and B who are at rest with respect to the barn. F and B observe:

1 The barn and board are the same length.
2 When the board is just inside the barn they both close the doors.
3 They both observe the board crashing into the closed back door just after both doors are closed.

However, M's measurements indicate that (Fig. 25.8)

1 The barn is 3.2 m long and the board is 5 m long.
2 B does shut his door just as the front of the board reaches him, but the back of the board is still 5 m − 3.2 m = 1.8 m outside the barn.
3 F does *not* shut his door when B does. According to F and B's clocks, M sees F shut his door

$$\Delta t = \frac{lu}{c^2} = \frac{(4\ \text{m})(3\ \text{m s}^{-1})}{(5\ \text{m s}^{-1})^2} = 0.48\ \text{s}$$

later than B. In M's frame, this is

$$\Delta t' = \frac{0.48\ \text{s}}{\sqrt{1 - (3/5)^2}} = 0.6\ \text{s}$$

Now, in 0.6 s, M sees the barn move toward him a distance of $u\,\Delta t' = (3\ \text{m s}^{-1})(0.6\ \text{s}) = 1.8$ m. This is just the distance that places the back of the board inside the barn when F shuts his door.

We see that all observers agree that the back door was shut just before the board reached it and the front door was shut just after the end of the board was inside the door. What the observers do not agree on was when the board crashed through the back door. F and B say it happened just after they both shut their doors, while M says it happened just after B shut his door but before F shut his. This disagreement is real and is typical of those that can arise when two sets of observers view events that occur at different positions.

The Twin Paradox | We saw in Examples 25.4 and 25.7 that a spaceship traveling at $0.6c$ reaches a planet 12 light years away in 20 years, according to earth observers. However, because of time dilation, the elapsed time according to the astronauts is only 16 years. The return trip takes equally long. Thus, on her return, astronaut Angela has aged 32 years, while her stay-at-home identical twin Susan has aged 40 years. However, from Angela's point of view, she has been at rest. Susan and the earth were in motion, and *their* clocks therefore ticked slowly, with only $32(1 - 0.6^2)^{1/2} = 25.6$ years passing; hence Susan must be younger! They can't both be right, so which twin has actually aged less? This is the *twin* or *clock paradox*. It is resolved by looking critically at the statements we have just made.

The twin who has aged less is astronaut Angela: she has lived 32 years, while Susan has lived 40. The basic point is that Angela cannot consider herself to be at rest throughout her trip, because she was not in an inertial frame during the periods of acceleration and deceleration at the trip's beginning, midpoint, and ends. The lack of uniformity in her motion removes the symmetry between her experience and Susan's. Furthermore, we can account for the difference in their ages using the clock synchronization results above.

To see this in detail, suppose Angela starts her voyage with a very brief (and uncomfortable) acceleration from rest to $0.6c$. She then travels at a constant velocity toward planet X, so she is in an inertial frame. Upon arrival she sees the trailing clock on X set ahead by 7.2 years (Example 25.6). After a rapid deceleration and acceleration, she is heading back toward the earth in a *different* inertial frame. According to observers in this frame, the trailing clock is set ahead by 7.2 years, but now this is the clock on the *earth*. These two adjustments are the price Angela must pay for switching inertial frames! If Angela adds 2(7.2 years) = 14.4 years to the 25.6 years which she sees elapse on the clocks in the earth's rest frame, her sum is 40 years. This agrees with Susan's observation of the duration of the trip on earth clocks.

Let's consider another and probably more convincing way for Angela and for us to see that Susan has lived 40 years while Angela was away. Suppose that on each birthday Susan sets off a fireworks display. During the outward trip, the earth is moving away at $0.6c$, and explosions occur every $1/(1 - 0.6^2)^{1/2} = 1.25$ years according to Angela's clocks. Furthermore, to reach the spaceship, successive flashes must travel an additional distance (0.6 light year)$/(1 - 0.6^2)^{1/2} = 0.75$ light year. (The distance is *longer* in the rest frame of the spaceship than in the moving frame of the earth.) Adding the time between flashes to the extra travel time gives $1.25 + 0.75 = 2$ years. Angela sees flashes once every 2 years, or 8 flashes during the 16 outbound years. On the return trip, successive flashes travel distances shorter by 0.75 light years, so they arrive every $1.25 - 0.75 = 0.5$ years. During the 16 years of the return trip, Angela sees 32 flashes. All together she sees $8 + 32 = 40$ flashes, and she knows that Susan has celebrated 40 birthdays!

25.6 | THE ADDITION OF VELOCITIES

According to special relativity, two observers in relative motion disagree about the properties of their metresticks and clocks. Accordingly, when they measure the velocity of an object moving relative to both of them, their observations are related in a way that reflects these disagreements.

The derivation of this relationship is similar to those of previous sections but lengthy, so we simply state the results. Consider two observers with a relative velocity u. An object moves along the x direction with a velocity v' according to O' (Fig. 25.9). According to O, the velocity of the object is

$$v = \frac{v' + u}{1 + (v'u/c^2)} \qquad (25.12)$$

This is called the *velocity addition formula*.

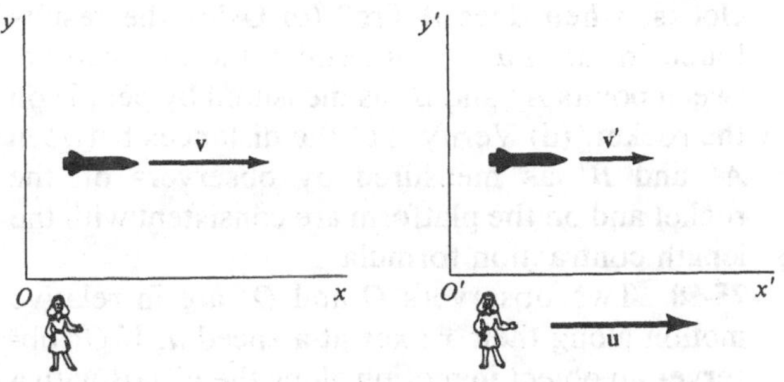

Figure 25.9. Observer O' moves relative to O at a velocity $\mathbf{u}$. An object has a velocity $\mathbf{v}'$ according to O' and $\mathbf{v}$ according to O.

When the velocities are small, we can neglect u/c and v'/c. This gives the usual nonrelativistic result, $v = v' + u$. However, when v' is comparable to or equal to c, the results are quite different. In particular, it turns out that if v' and u are less than c, but $v' + u$ is greater than c, then v is still less than c. This means that nothing can be observed to move faster than the speed of light. The case $v' = c$ is considered in the next example.

Example 25.10

An observer moving away from the earth at $0.5c$ sends a light pulse along his direction of motion and measures its speed to be c. How fast does the pulse travel according to the earth observer?

Here $v' = c$ and $u = 0.5c$. Using the velocity addition formula, the velocity according to an earth observer is

$$v = \frac{v' + u}{1 + \dfrac{v'u}{c^2}} = \frac{c + 0.5c}{1 + \dfrac{(c)(0.5c)}{c^2}} = c$$

Thus both observers measure the same speed of light, in agreement with Einstein's second principle.

When the motion of the object is not along the x axis, the addition of velocities involves more complicated expressions. However, these expressions again ensure that no object can be observed to travel faster than the speed of light.

EXERCISES ON SUPPLEMENTARY TOPICS

Section 25.5 | The Problem of Simultaneous Events; Twin Paradox

25-40 An observer on an earth satellite traveling at 8×10^3 m s^{-1} relative to the earth sees rocket launchings occurring in New York and in Los Angeles, which he judges to be simultaneous. (a) The distance between the two cities is 4.5×10^6 m. What will the time interval between these launchings be according to observers on earth? (The satellite is moving directly from Los Angeles toward New York.) (b) In which city does the rocket launching occur first according to earth observers?

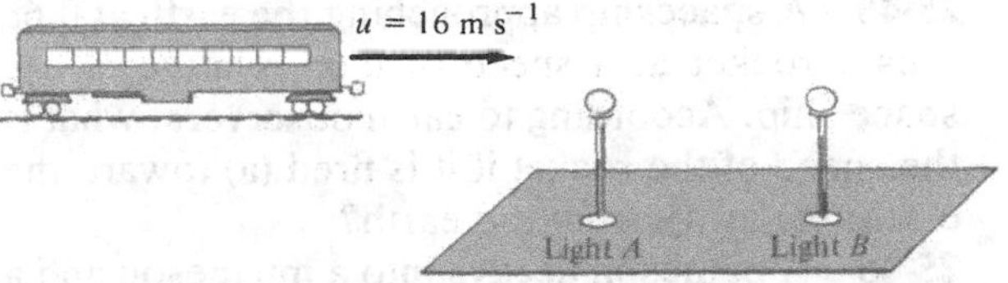

Figure 25.10. Exercise 25.41.

25-41 An observer on a train sees two lights flash on the station platform. Light A is seen to flash 0.8 second after light B (Fig. 25.10), and this observer measures the lights as being 100 m apart. If the train is moving at 16 m s^{-1} and the speed of light is c = 20 m s^{-1}, (a) what is the distance between the lights as measured by an observer at rest on the platform? (b) Which light flashes first according to an observer at rest on the platform?

25-42 According to Susan, the stay-at-home twin in the twin paradox discussion, how many flashes will reach astronaut Angela on (a) the outward part of the trip; (b) the inward leg?

25-43 Assume for this exercise that c = 100 km h^{-1}. A woman drives to a hospital at 80 km h^{-1}. According to the highway signs, the distance is 100 km. When she arrives, she finds the hospital clocks are set ahead of the clocks she saw on the road at her starting point. By how much does she say they are ahead according to (a) clocks in the hospital; (b) her watch?

Section 25.6 | The Addition of Velocities

25-44 In a large-particle accelerator facility, two beams of protons are directed toward each other, each with a velocity of $0.8c$ as measured in the laboratory. What is the speed of one beam as measured by an observer at rest with respect to the other beam?

25-45 A spaceship approaching the earth at $0.6c$ fires a rocket at a speed of $0.6c$ relative to the space ship. According to earth observers, what is the speed of the rocket if it is fired (a) toward the earth; (b) away from the earth?

25-46 A pi meson decays into a mu meson and a neutrino. In the rest frame of the pi meson, the velocity of the mu meson is always found to be $0.507c$. Suppose now the pi meson is moving relative to the laboratory at $0.6c$ when it decays, emitting the mu meson along its direction of motion. What will be the speed of the mu meson relative to the laboratory?

25-47 Particle A decays into particles B and C. When the A particle is at rest, B is always found to have a speed $0.6c$. If the A particle is moving at $0.4c$ relative to the laboratory when it decays, find the velocity of the B particle as measured in the laboratory frame if the B particle moves (a) parallel to the direction of the A particle; (b) opposite to the direction of the A particle.

PROBLEMS ON SUPPLEMENTARY TOPICS

25-48 An observer on earth sees a rocket P traveling away from the earth at 2×10^8 m s^{-1}. P is overtaking a second rocket Q, which is traveling away from the earth at 1.5×10^8 m s^{-1}. Find the velocity of (a) P measured by observers in Q; (b) Q measured by observers in P.

25-49 A rocket ship moves at $0.6c$ past two observers, A and B, at rest on a platform. They arrange to fire guns simultaneously, striking the rocket at points A' and B' (Fig. 25.11). (a) How far apart are A and B as measured by those on the rocket? (b) Observers on the platform and on the rocket agree that B fires at $t = 0$. According to observers on the rocket looking at their own clocks, when does A fire? (c) Using the results found in (a) and (b), determine the distance between points A' and B' as measured by people on the rocket. (d) Verify that the distances between A' and B' as measured by observers on the rocket and on the platform are consistent with the length contraction formula.

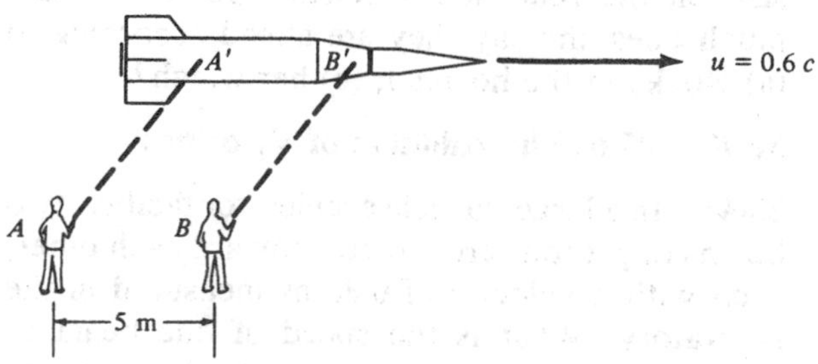

Figure 25.11. Exercise 25.42.

25-50 Two observers O and O' are in relative motion along their x axes at a speed u. If O' observes an object in motion along the y' axis with a speed v', then O will observe it to have both x and y velocity components, where

$$v_x = u, \qquad v_y = v'\sqrt{1 - (u^2/c^2)}$$

If $v' = c$, find $v = \sqrt{v_x^2 + v_y^2}$.

25-51 Observer O' observes a rocket ship traveling along the y direction at a speed $0.9c$. O' is moving at $0.8c$ along the x direction relative to observer O. Using the formulas in the preceding problem, find the components of the rocket ship velocity as observed by O and show that v is less than c.

Additional Reading

N. David Mermin, *Space, Time, and Relativity*, McGraw-Hill Book Co., New York, 1965.

Hermann Bondi, *Relativity and Common Sense*, Science Study Series, Doubleday and Co., Garden City, N.Y., 1964.

Lev B. Okun, The Concept of Mass, *Physics Today,* June 1989, p. 42. Mass in special relativity.

Special Issue: Michelson-Morley Centennial, *Physics Today,* May 1987. Michelson and Morley showed there was no evidence for the existence of the ether.

Scientific American articles:

R. S. Shankland, The Michelson-Morley Experiment, November 1964, p. 107.

J. Bronowski, The Clock Paradox, February 1963, p. 134.

Milton A. Rothman, Things That Go Faster than Light, July 1960, p. 142.

V. L. Ginzburg, Artificial Satellites and Relativity, May 1959, p. 149.

Gerard K. O'Neill, Particle Storage Rings, November 1966, p. 107.

Albert B. Stewart, The Discovery of Stellar Aberration, March 1964, p. 100.

CHAPTER 26 PARTICLE PROPERTIES OF LIGHT: THE PHOTON

As physics moved into the twentieth century, just a very few physical phenomena appeared unexplained. However, these few observations proved to be the tip of the iceberg of results that led to quantum mechanics. At that time, the wave theory of light and electromagnetic radiation was on a particularly firm basis due to the work of Maxwell and others. It was only when certain experiments involving the interaction of light with matter were performed that the theory appeared incomplete. In these experiments light interacted with single atoms, molecules, or electrons. Such experiments became possible only toward the end of the last century and hence were initially few in number.

While the experiments were few, they proved to be explainable only by the development of the idea that light sometimes behaves like a wave and sometimes like a collection of particlelike objects called *photons*. These photons are small bundles of light with discrete energies. Although this idea was radical, it was soon accepted because it explained the new observations so completely. Furthermore, as a complete quantum theory developed in the first decades of the new century, photons became a natural part of that theory.

In retrospect, it is easy to understand why electromagnetic radiation or light was considered to consist of continuous waves. Any particlelike behavior was masked by the enormous number of light quanta usually present. The situation is analogous to that encountered in electrostatics where the amount of charge present is usually very large. The fact that charge comes in discrete amounts is irrelevant under these conditions.

In this chapter, we describe the particlelike properties of light and see how these ideas explain several crucial experiments.

26.1 | THE PHOTOELECTRIC EFFECT

An early experiment that most clearly illustrates the particle properties of light is also the one that prompted Einstein to develop the concept of the photon. A description of the experiment follows.

The photoelectric effect apparatus is shown in Fig. 26.1. Monochromatic light incident on the metal plate yields sufficient energy to allow electrons to escape from the metal. Some of these emitted electrons reach a collection plate, and the ammeter measures the resulting *photoelectric current*. The intensity and frequency of the incident light can be varied, as can the potential difference V between the metal plate and the collector.

The conduction electrons in a metal move in the attractive electric field of the stationary positive ions of the lattice. While electrons move relatively freely inside, it requires a minimum energy actually to pull them from inside to outside the metal. This minimum energy is called the *work function* W and depends on the properties of the metal and of the surface. If an electron is given an energy E larger than W, it can escape the metal and will have a maximum kinetic energy

$$\tfrac{1}{2}mv_{\max}^2 = E - W$$

The results of the photoelectric experiment can be summarized as follows:

1 When $V = 0$, photoelectrons are detected whenever the metal is illuminated by light at a

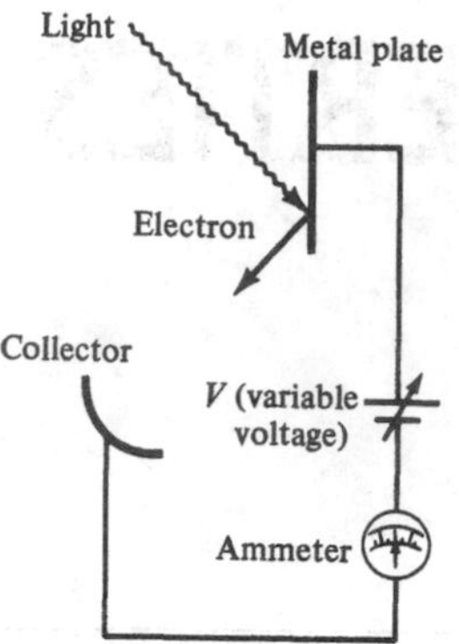

Figure 26.1. The photoelectric effect apparatus. Light incident on the metal plate causes electrons to be emitted. These can travel to the collector producing a current.

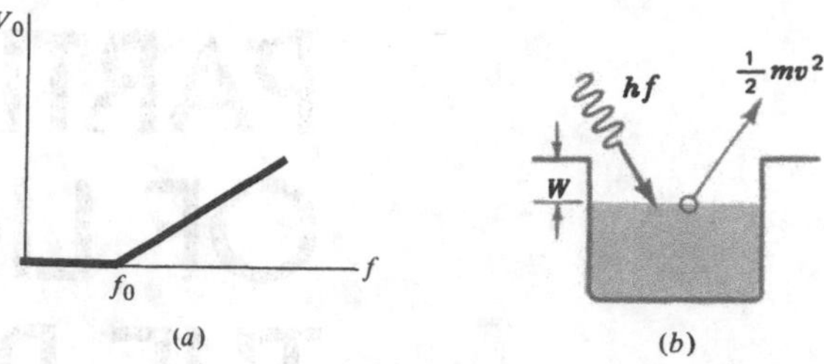

Figure 26.2. (*a*) The stopping voltage V_0 versus incident light frequency. If f is less than f_0, no current is observed, even with zero stopping potential. Above f_0, the stopping potential increases linearly with f. This graph is valid for *all* nonzero light intensities. (*b*) Electrons in a metal have energies that vary over the colored region. The minimum energy required to remove an electron is the work function W. Thus if an electron at the highest energy (top of the colored region) absorbs a photon of energy hf, it acquires a kinetic energy $\frac{1}{2}mv^2_{max} = eV_0 = hf - W$. Other electrons acquire smaller kinetic energies when they absorb photons.

frequency f, which is greater than a critical or threshold frequency f_0. However, no matter what the intensity of the light, no current is observed if the frequency is below f_0.

2 At each light frequency above the threshold, the potential V can be increased until, at some value V_0, the current becomes zero. If the emitter and collector are made of the same material, this occurs when the potential energy difference eV_0 of an electron with charge $-e$ is just equal to the *maximum* kinetic energy of the emitted electrons

$$eV_0 = \frac{1}{2}mv^2_{max}$$

A graph of V_0, the stopping potential, versus the frequency of the incident light appears in Fig. 26.2*a*.

3 Above the threshold frequency, an increase in intensity results in an increase in the number of photoelectrons, but the maximum kinetic energy of the electrons does not change.

These observations are in direct conflict with predictions based on the wave picture of light. If light is a classical wave, the electrons should absorb energy continuously, and at any intensity it should be merely a matter of time until an electron has sufficient energy to escape. Hence there would be no threshold frequency, although there would be a delay in production of photoelectrons at low intensities until enough light energy had been absorbed by the material. Furthermore, at high intensities the electrons should receive more energy, so the stopping potential should be greater. No such effects are observed.

Einstein's Explanation | In 1905, Einstein discovered that the photoelectric effect experiments could be explained in a straightforward way if one assumed that the energy carried by the incoming light came in discrete amounts rather than continuously. Furthermore, he suggested that the amount of energy in each *light quantum* or photon depends only on the frequency of the light, and not on its intensity. The intensity of a beam of light is determined by the number of photons present; the energy of each photon is determined by the frequency.

The light quanta behave like particles that travel at the speed of light. If the light has a frequency f and wavelength $\lambda = c/f$, the photons each have an energy

$$E = hf \quad \text{(photon energy)} \qquad (26.1)$$

The intensity of monochromatic light is proportional to the number of photons present. A beam of white light contains photons of many different energies. The quantity h is a proportionality constant and is fit to experiment. In fact, h was first introduced in 1900 by Max Planck (1858–1947) in a less fully developed theory of discrete radiation; for this reason, h is known as *Planck's constant*. Its value is

$$h = 6.625 \times 10^{-34} \text{ J s} = 4.135 \times 10^{-15} \text{ eV s}$$

The small size of this constant is our first hint that classical physics may fail when extremely small energies are important.

The photon theory of light offers a complete explanation of the photoelectric effect. An electron will leave the metal only if it absorbs a photon of energy equal to or greater than the work function W (Fig. 26.2*b*). The threshold corresponds to the frequency at which the photon energy hf_0 equals W, or

$$f_0 = \frac{W}{h} \quad (26.2)$$

If the photon frequency is above threshold, the excess energy appears as kinetic energy of the photoelectrons. Since W is the minimum energy necessary to remove an electron, the maximum kinetic energy is

$$\tfrac{1}{2}mv_{\max}^2 = hf - hf_0 = hf - W \quad (26.3)$$

Increasing the intensity with f constant will result in more electrons being emitted, but with the same maximum kinetic energy.

Since the stopping voltage V_0 is adjusted so that $eV_0 = \tfrac{1}{2}mv_{\max}^2$, we see that $eV_0 = hf - W$, or

$$V_0 = \frac{h}{e}f - \frac{W}{e} \quad (26.4)$$

This is an important result, because it predicts that the slope of the V_0-versus-f curve is h/e. Planck's constant h and the electronic charge e were known, and the slope in Fig. 26.2 turned out just as predicted. This convincing demonstration was one of the first in a series of discoveries that led to the acceptance of a particle or photon description of electromagnetic radiation.

The following example illustrates the ideas we have discussed.

Example 26.1

Light is incident on the surface of a metal for which the work function is 2 eV. (a) What is the minimum frequency the light can have and cause the emission of electrons? (b) If the frequency of the incident light is 6×10^{14} Hz, what is the maximum kinetic energy of the electrons?

(a) At the threshold frequency, the energy of the photon equals the work function, so $hf = W$ or

$$f = \frac{W}{h} = \frac{2 \text{ eV}}{4.135 \times 10^{-15} \text{ eV s}} = 4.84 \times 10^{14} \text{ Hz}$$

(b) The energy of a photon of frequency 6×10^{14} Hz is

$$E = hf = (4.135 \times 10^{-15} \text{ eV s})(6 \times 10^{14} \text{ Hz}) = 2.48 \text{ eV}$$

Hence the maximum kinetic energy is the difference

$$\tfrac{1}{2}mv_{\max}^2 = 2.48 \text{ eV} - 2 \text{ eV} = 0.48 \text{ eV}$$

26.2 | THE PHOTON; BLACKBODY RADIATION

As we saw in the previous section, Einstein's explanation of the photoelectric effect showed that a light beam is composed of quanta. In this section, we first explore this idea a bit further and then discuss blackbody radiation.

For monochromatic light of frequency f, each quantum of light, or photon, has an energy hf. The number of photons present determines the intensity. The following example shows that under usual conditions the number of photons present is so large that their quantum nature may be overlooked.

Example 26.2

Monochromatic green light of frequency 6×10^{14} Hz is produced by a laser. The power emitted is 2×10^{-3} W. (a) What is the energy of a photon in the beam? (b) How many photons per second pass a point in the beam?

(a) Each photon has an energy

$$E = hf = (6.63 \times 10^{-34} \text{ J s})(6 \times 10^{14} \text{ s}^{-1}) = 3.98 \times 10^{-19} \text{ J}$$

(b) Let N be the number of photons passing a point in the beam each second. The power $\mathcal{P}$ transmitted in the beam must be equal to N times the energy per photon, $\mathcal{P} = NE$. Thus

$$N = \frac{\mathcal{P}}{E} = \frac{2 \times 10^{-3} \text{ W}}{3.98 \times 10^{-19} \text{ J}} = 5.03 \times 10^{15} \text{ photons per second}$$

Blackbody Radiation | As we mentioned earlier, Max Planck was the first to suggest that light has discrete energies proportional to the frequency. Planck was trying to explain the observed relation between the power radiated by a hot object versus the wavelength (and frequency) at which the radiation appears.

In Chapter Twelve, we found that the power radiated from a heated object depends on the wavelength of the radiation. The details of how this power varies with wavelength and temperature usually depend on the characteristics of the object. However, the radiation emitted through a small opening from a cavity does not depend either on the material of its walls or on the shape of the cavity and the hole. The cavity radiation obeys a universal law of nature and acts as a perfect blackbody: a perfect absorber and emitter with emissivity equal to 1.

Many attempts were made to derive the blackbody radiation curve (Fig. 26.3) using classical electromagnetic theory, but all of them failed. The most famous of these, called the Rayleigh–Jeans law, was correct at long wavelengths, but at short wavelengths the theoretical power emitted became infinite. This failure was referred to as the ultraviolet (short wavelength) catastrophe.

The electromagnetic radiation in a cavity can be thought of as coming from atomic oscillators in the walls. These oscillators absorb and emit radiation at many frequencies. The rate at which radiation at a given frequency f leaves the cavity turns out to be proportional to f^2 times the average energy of an oscillator of that frequency. Thus the calculation boils down to finding the average energy of an oscillator.

To understand the classical result for the average energy of oscillator, we recall the discussion of the average kinetic energy of Chapter Ten. We found that in an ideal gas at a temperature T, the average translational kinetic energy of a molecule is $3k_B T/2$. This is equivalent to a contribution of $k_B T/2$ for each of the three directions. Similarly, for a harmonic oscillator, the average kinetic and potential energies each turn out to be $k_B T/2$. The average total energy of an oscillator is then $k_B T$, independent of the frequency.

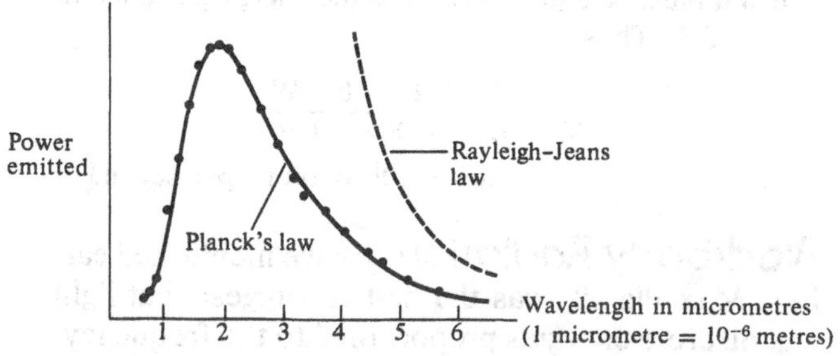

Figure 26.3. Blackbody radiation at 1600 K. The curve predicted by Planck's law passes through the data points. The Rayleigh–Jeans prediction becomes very large at short wavelengths.

Since the energy radiated is proportional to f^2 and since every oscillator has the same average energy, it is clear that at high frequencies or short wavelengths the radiation will be very intense. This is the "catastrophe" mentioned above. On the other hand, the result is experimentally correct at low frequencies or long wavelengths. Thus the classical formula for the average energy of an oscillator is apparently correct at low frequencies.

The derivation of the Rayleigh–Jeans formula involved many steps, and Planck suspected that it might have mathematical inconsistencies. To study this possibility, he tried restricting the oscillator energies to only discrete values proportional to a constant, h. His idea was to calculate the average energy of an oscillator and then make the energy steps arbitrarily small by letting h approach zero. He found that with $h = 0$, he again obtained the Rayleigh–Jeans formula. However, much to his surprise, he discovered that when h was given a nonzero value, he could reproduce the experimental data!

Planck actually made two assumptions about the oscillators that are equivalent to the photons which Einstein introduced a few years later in explaining the photoelectric effect:

1 The oscillators could only have energies given by

$$E = nhf, \qquad n = 0, 1, 2, 3, 4, \ldots \qquad (26.5)$$

where f is the oscillator frequency and the proportionality factor h is Planck's constant.

2 The oscillators could emit energy only in discrete or quantized amounts corresponding to a change in n of one unit:

$$E_{n+1} - E_n = (n + 1)hf - nhf = hf$$

This is equivalent to saying the oscillator can change its energy by emitting or absorbing a photon of energy hf.

As we noted, a central prediction of the classical theory, and its downfall, is that the average energy of an oscillator in an environment at a temperature T does not depend on the oscillator's frequency. With Planck's assumptions, one must compute, for a collection of oscillators at a given temperature, the average energy when only certain energies are allowed. The result for the average energy is quite different.

Consider one of Planck's oscillators with a characteristic frequency f. The energies it may have are 0, hf, $2hf$, $3hf$, and so on. The calculation of the average energy becomes one of finding the probability of an oscillator having a given energy and then multiplying the probability by that energy. If $k_B T \ll hf$, then the probability that the oscillator will have an energy of hf or more is very small. This means that the only likely energy value is zero, and the average energy is close to zero. The high-frequency oscillations are "frozen out" at low temperatures, and the oscillator will not radiate at all. At any temperature T, the oscillators with frequencies such that $k_B T \ll hf$ are not thermally excited, and they do not contribute in the calculation of the average energy. Thus Planck's assumption of a set of discrete energies builds in the high-frequency radiation cutoff that is needed to describe the blackbody radiation.

At low frequencies, Planck's result is essentially the same as the classical Rayleigh–Jeans prediction. When $hf \ll k_B T$, many different oscillator energies are thermally excited and contribute to the average energy. The average energy then turns out to be $k_B T$, and the classical radiation intensity is found again.

Planck's calculation resulted in a formula for the blackbody radiation that was in excellent agreement with experiment at all frequencies. Its underlying assumptions were revolutionary and hard to accept initially. However, the discreteness of the energy levels of the oscillator and the associated concept of a photon have been verified in many ways.

Typical light beams contain so many photons that the discrete nature of the light is not ordinarily apparent. Similarly, the discreteness of the possible energies of an oscillator is important for atomic-sized objects but is not discernible for macroscopic objects, as we see in the next example.

Example 26.3

(a) A 1-kg mass is suspended from a spring with a constant of 16 N m^{-1}. Its amplitude of oscillation is 0.01 m. (a) What is the quantum number n associated with its energy? (b) If n changes by 1, what is the fractional change in the energy of the spring? (c) If the spring constant for an atom in a molecule is the same but the mass is 10^{-26} kg and the amplitude is 3.25×10^{-11} m, what is the fractional energy change when n changes by 1?

(a) We found in Chapter Nine that the energy of an oscillator with an amplitude A is $E = \frac{1}{2}kA^2$. Thus

$$E = \tfrac{1}{2}(16 \text{ N m})(0.01 \text{ m})^2 = 8 \times 10^{-4} \text{ J}$$

Also, we found that the characteristic frequency is $f = [k/m]^{1/2}/2\pi$, so

$$f = \frac{[(16 \text{ N m})/(1 \text{ kg})]^{1/2}}{2\pi} = 0.637 \text{ Hz}$$

Hence with $E = nhf$,

$$n = \frac{E}{hf} = \frac{8 \times 10^{-4} \text{ J}}{(6.63 \times 10^{-34} \text{ J s})(0.637 \text{ Hz})} = 1.895 \times 10^{30}$$

(b) The fractional change in the energy is

$$\frac{\Delta E}{E} = \frac{1}{n} = \frac{1}{1.895 \times 10^{30}} = 5.28 \times 10^{-31}$$

Such a small energy change would not be measurable.

(c) Repeating the calculation,

$$E = \tfrac{1}{2}kA^2 = \tfrac{1}{2}(16 \text{ N m})(3.25 \times 10^{-11} \text{ m})^2$$
$$= 8.45 \times 10^{-21} \text{ J}$$

$$f = \frac{[k/m]^{1/2}}{2\pi} = \frac{[(16 \text{ N m})/(10^{-26} \text{ kg})]^{1/2}}{2\pi} = 6.37 \times 10^{12} \text{ Hz}$$

$$n = \frac{E}{hf} = \frac{8.45 \times 10^{-21} \text{ J}}{(6.63 \times 10^{-34} \text{ J s})(6.37 \times 10^{12} \text{ Hz})} = 2$$

Thus we have a very large fractional energy change,

$$\frac{\Delta E}{E} = \frac{1}{n} = \frac{1}{2} = 0.5$$

26.3 | X RAYS

Experiments involving the scattering and production of X rays provided additional convincing evidence that the photon picture of light is correct.

An experiment performed in 1923 by A. H. Compton (1892–1962) showed that when monochromatic X rays are scattered by graphite, their frequency decreases. This is called the *Compton effect*. Although this effect is hard to understand classically, Compton demonstrated that it has a simple explanation in terms of photons.

Classically, the scattering of electromagnetic radiation by matter occurs because the electric field of waves incident at a frequency f causes charges to oscillate at that frequency. These oscillating charges reradiate electromagnetic waves in various directions at the same frequency f.

Compton's solution was to treat the scattering as an elastic collision of a photon and an electron, much like the collision of two billiard balls (Fig. 26.4). The energy of an X-ray photon is large compared to the kinetic and potential energies of the electrons in a carbon atom. The energy that will be transferred to the electron by the photon is also very large compared to these energies. Thus we can make the approximation that initially the electrons are free and at rest. When a photon collides with one and is deflected, the electron recoils with an energy E_{el}. The scattered photon has an energy hf', where f' must be less than f since energy conservation requires that

$$hf' = hf - E_{el}$$

The analogy of a billiard ball collision implies that the total momentum of the photons and the electron is conserved. Using classical electromagnetic theory, Maxwell showed that the energy E carried by a light wave is related to the momentum of the wave by $E = pc$, where c is the velocity of light. (This is also the result we obtained from relativity for a particle with zero mass.) Thus the photon momentum is given by

$$p = \frac{E}{c} = \frac{hf}{c} \qquad (26.6)$$

Qualitatively, we expect that the photons that scatter through the largest angles—nearly straight back toward the source—will transfer the most momentum and energy to the electrons and therefore experience the greatest decrease in energy and frequency. This is in agreement with Compton's measurements. Furthermore, if the equations of energy and momentum conservation are written down, it takes only a few lines of algebra to find a specific variation of the frequency change with θ. This prediction is in good agreement with experiment. Thus Compton's work provided further clear evidence for the particle nature of light.

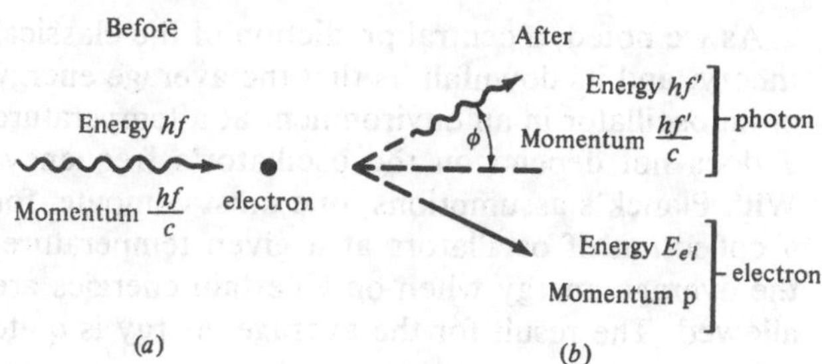

Figure 26.4. (*a*) A photon incident on a stationary electron is scattered (*b*) through an angle ϕ. The energy and momentum lost by the photon are taken up by the electron.

The energy transferred to the electron can be found from the change in photon frequency, as in the next example.

Example 26.4

In a Compton scattering experiment, the incident X rays have a frequency of 10^{20} Hz. At a certain angle, the outgoing X rays have a frequency of 8×10^{19} Hz. Find the energy of the recoiling electrons in electron volts.

Since energy is conserved in the photon–electron collision and the electron was originally at rest, its recoil energy is

$$\begin{aligned} E_{el} &= hf - hf' = h(f - f') \\ &= (4.135 \times 10^{-15} \text{ eV s})(10^{20} \text{ Hz} - 8 \times 10^{19} \text{ Hz}) \\ &= 82{,}700 \text{ eV} \end{aligned}$$

X-Ray Spectrum | X-ray production provided another significant verification of the photon theory. We saw in Chapter Twenty-three that when an electron beam is accelerated in a vacuum and allowed to strike a target, X rays are emitted with various frequencies up to some maximum frequency f_{max} (Fig. 26.5). It was found that f_{max} depends only on the accelerating potential difference V and is independent of the number of electrons in the beam. Classically, these observations are difficult to comprehend, but the photon theory gives a ready explanation. If the electrons are accelerated from rest through a potential difference V, their kinetic energy is eV. The electrons lose part or all of their kinetic energy when they interact with an atom in the target. The highest-frequency photon will be

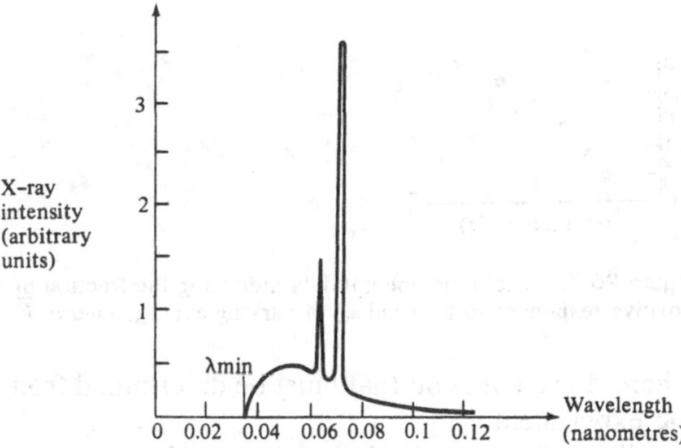

Figure 26.5. X rays produced by the electron bombardment of a target result in X-ray photons of a maximum frequency $f_{max} = eV/h$ and a minimum wavelength $\lambda_{min} = c/f_{max}$. The sharp peaks appear at different wavelengths for different target materials. They are due to the rearrangement of electrons disturbed from their normal atomic orbits.

produced when all the kinetic energy of one electron is converted into a single photon, or when

$$hf_{max} = eV \tag{26.7}$$

This equation is in excellent agreement with the observed frequency maxima.

Example 26.5

What are (a) maximum frequency and (b) minimum wavelength of X rays produced by 40,000 V electrons?

(a) Using Eq. 26.7 for the photon frequency,

$$f_{max} = \frac{eV}{h} = \frac{(1.60 \times 10^{-19}\ \text{C})(4 \times 10^4\ \text{V})}{6.63 \times 10^{-34}\ \text{J s}}$$
$$= 9.65 \times 10^{18}\ \text{Hz}$$

(b) The corresponding minimum wavelength is

$$\lambda_{min} = \frac{c}{f_{max}} = \frac{3 \times 10^8\ \text{m s}^{-1}}{9.65 \times 10^{18}\ \text{Hz}}$$
$$= 3.11 \times 10^{-11}\ \text{m} = 0.0311\ \text{nm}$$

26.4 | WAVE–PARTICLE DUALITY

Having discussed a number of situations where the particle, or quantum, nature of light is important, we recall the wide variety of phenomena that were described by a wave theory of light. The two pictures seem very contradictory.

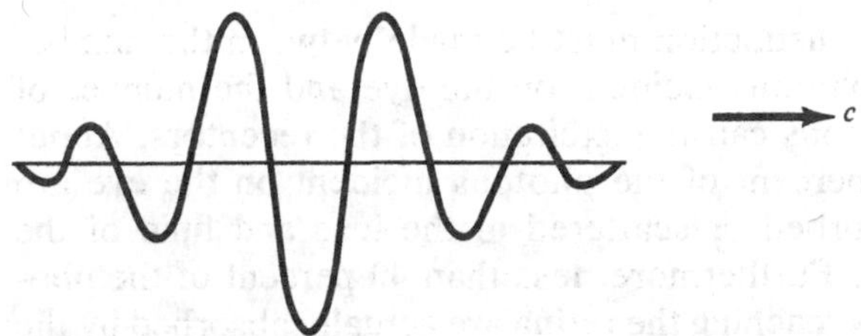

Figure 26.6. The photon pictured as a wave packet traveling at the speed of light. It is a bundle of electromagnetic energy with energy *hf*.

Some reconciliation of these two ideas can be achieved if we view the photon as a small *wave packet* (Fig. 26.6). This illustration is a representation of the mathematical formulation of quantum mechanics. It shows a bundle of waves traveling at the speed of light. The total energy of the bundle or packet is *hf*. If the frequency *f* is increased, so is the energy of the packet; the energy contained in a packet is determined by the frequency. The packet is a wave disturbance, but it is localized in a small region of space, much like a particle. Large numbers of photons at a single frequency behave in a way similar to a continuous wave when they pass through slits, reflect off objects, and so on.

The dual wave–particle nature of light is now a basic part of our theory of light and matter. The theory as formulated mathematically contains both aspects of light, and the outcome of any experiment can in principle be predicted. On the other hand, a verbal description of the behavior of light is not so unambiguous. As a tentative rule, we may say that light behaves as a wave as long as no absorption or emission of light occurs. Whenever light is absorbed, its quantum, or particle, nature may be expected to be evident.

26.5 | PHOTONS AND VISION

Light energy is received by the visual receptors of the eye, that is, the rods and cones, in discrete amounts as photons are absorbed. Hence there is necessarily a minimum number of photons needed for vision. This minimum number is called the *absolute threshold of vision*.

A distinction must be made between the number of photons incident on the eye and the number of photons causing excitation of the receptors. About 90 percent of the photons incident on the eye are absorbed or scattered in the lens and fluid of the eye. Furthermore, less than 40 percent of the photons reaching the retina are actually absorbed by the receptors. Thus the number of photons incident on the eye is far larger than the number of photons used by the receptors for visual perception. Our discussion will involve only photons absorbed by the receptors.

We might guess that a single photon is sufficient for vision. However, theoretical and experimental evidence seems to rule this out. Theoretically we know that molecules in the eye have an average thermal energy that is quite small. However, there is a small probability that an occasional atom or molecule will have an energy large enough to emit a photon that could cause excitation of the receptor. Multiplying this small probability by the large number of molecules present and the large number of receptors available indicates that about one photon per second might be detected. These photons have nothing to do with the external visual scene, and hence their perception would be a constant source of annoyance and confusion. This *background* would be eliminated by the requirement that *coincident* or nearly simultaneous absorption of more than one photon must occur to stimulate the visual process.

Experimentally, coincident absorption of photons apparently must take place in a region where the neutrons are interconnected. This region includes about 100 rods in the dark-adapted eye. In this region, if the coincidence does not occur during the eye's "storage time" of 0.2 s, the coincidence is not counted. Thus the visual memory of the absorption of one photon lasts about 0.2 s.

The actual experiment is performed with pulses that illuminate about 100 rods and last 0.2 s. Subjects are asked to say when they see a pulse. The fraction of positive responses is then plotted versus the average pulse energy $\overline{E}$ (Fig. 26.7). The average number of photons $\bar{n}$ absorbed by the rods is proportional to $\overline{E}$,

$$\bar{n} = A\overline{E} \tag{26.8}$$

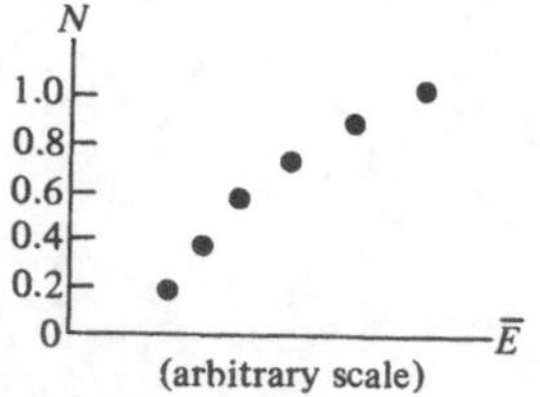

Figure 26.7. The experimental data indicating the fraction of positive responses to light pulses of varying average energy $\overline{E}$.

where A is a constant that must be determined from the experiment.

A light source emits photons randomly in time, so not every pulse in a group with average energy $\overline{E}$ will result in exactly $\bar{n}$ absorbed photons. For each pulse of the group with an average of $\bar{n}$ absorbed photons, there is some probability, denoted by $P(k, \bar{n})$, that at least k photons are actually absorbed.

This is analogous to the following situation. When rain falls on a sidewalk divided into squares, the average number $\bar{n}$ of drops per square equals the total number of drops divided by the number of squares. However, examination will show that some squares have fewer and some have more than the average number of drops. The number of squares receiving k or more drops divided by the total number of squares is $P(k, \bar{n})$.

The visual threshold experiment effectively measures $P(k, \bar{n})$, where k is the minimum number of photons necessary for vision. That is, there should be a correspondence between the graph of Fig. 26.7 and a graph of the theoretical value of $P(k, \bar{n})$ versus $\bar{n}$ (Fig. 26.8).

The problem is that neither k nor the quantity A in Eq. 26.8 is known. By plotting the number of positive responses versus $\bar{n}$, using A as an adjustable parameter, N of Fig. 26.7 can be compared with $P(k, \bar{n})$. Typical results are shown in Fig. 26.9. It is found that an approximate fit to the data can be obtained for k between 2 and 6. Hence at least 2 but fewer than 7 photons are apparently necessary for vision.

SUMMARY

The wave nature of light was well established by the end of the nineteenth century. However, several experiments, including blackbody radiation and the

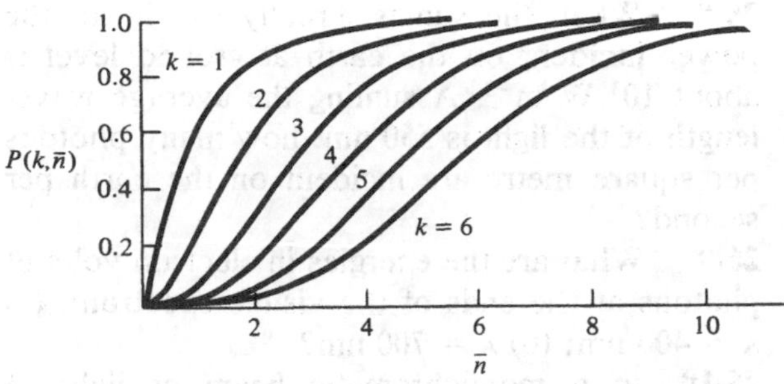

Figure 26.8. Graphs of the predicted value of $P(k, \bar{n})$ versus $\bar{n}$ for $k = 1, \ldots, 6$. One of the curves of this type should correspond to the results shown in Fig. 26.7. (Adapted from R. K. Clayton, *Light and Living Matter*, Volume II: *The Biological Part*, McGraw-Hill Book Co., New York, 1971. Used with permission.)

photoelectric effect, could not be explained in terms of such a picture. Max Planck made the first tentative assertion that vibrating atoms emitted light energy in specific amounts, and Einstein extended this idea to say that light itself is composed of quanta called photons. These carry a specific amount of energy equal to Planck's constant times the light frequency,

$$E = hf$$

Compton's studies of photon-electron collisions provided further evidence that light has a particle-like nature and that photons have a definite energy and momentum. X-ray production was also understood using the photon concept.

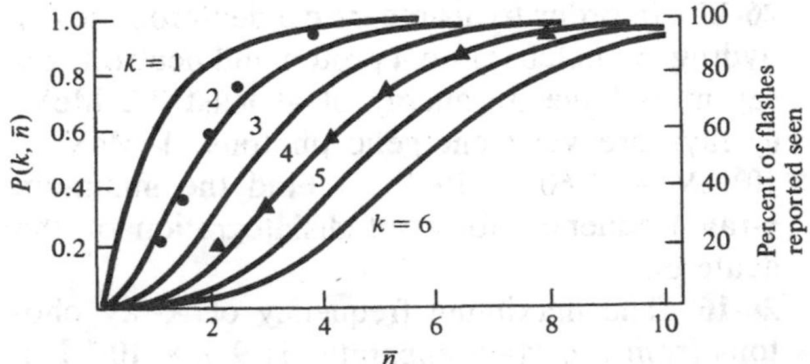

Figure 26.9. The curves showing the fractional probability of absorption of at least k photons versus the average number of photons $\bar{n}$. The symbols ● and ▲ represent two attempts to fit a single set of data to the curves for $k = 2$ and $k = 4$. The fits are achieved by adjusting the constant A in Eq. 26.8. (Adapted from Clayton. See Fig. 26.8.)

Present-day theories describe the wave–particle nature of light correctly as far as we know. When experimental results of the interaction of light with matter are discussed in other than a formal mathematical way, the nature of the experiment will determine whether a wave or particle description is best suited for understanding the results. The eye is an excellent example of this. The gathering and focusing of light is well described in terms of waves, but the ultimate absorption of light in rods and cones involves the absorption of photons.

Checklist

Define or explain:

photon	Planck's law
Planck's constant	Compton effect
photoelectric effect	X-ray spectrum
work function	absolute threshold of vision
blackbody radiation	

REVIEW QUESTIONS

Q26-1 True or false? If light behaved only as a wave, electrons would be emitted from a metal for any frequency.

Q26-2 The maximum energy of an electron emitted in the photoelectric effect is determined by the ______ of the absorbed photon.

Q26-3 The intensity of a beam of light is determined by the ______ of photons in the beam.

Q26-4 The frequency of the light with photons of energy E is ______.

Q26-5 When a blackbody emits radiation, the oscillators in the material lower their energy by emitting ______.

Q26-6 The collision of an electron and a photon can be analyzed by requiring that the total ______ and ______ are conserved.

Q26-7 When photons are produced by electrons colliding with atoms, a ______ frequency photon is produced when all of the electron kinetic energy is converted into a single photon.

EXERCISES

Section 26.1 | The Photoelectric Effect

26-1 When light of frequency 7×10^{14} Hz shines on a metal surface, electrons with a maximum speed of 6×10^5 m s^{-1} are emitted. What is the photoelectric threshold frequency of the sample?

26-2 The work function of metallic sodium is 2.3 eV. What is the maximum wavelength of the incident light for which photoemission of electrons will occur?

26-3 The work function of a metal is 6.4×10^{-19} J. What is the minimum (threshold) frequency for photoemission of electrons?

26-4 The maximum energy for photoelectrons emitted from a metal with work function 3 eV is 20 eV. What are the (a) maximum energy; (b) maximum frequency of the incoming photons?

26-5 An electroscope has two metal foil leaves that normally hang side by side. They are both connected to a metal plate (Fig. 26.10). If light of a sufficiently high frequency is shone on the plate, the leaves are observed to spread apart. Describe what causes this.

Section 26.2 | The Photon; Blackbody Radiation

26-6 A radio antenna radiates 10^4 W of power at 9.2×10^5 Hz. How many photons per second are emitted?

26-7 A sodium vapor lamp emits 10 W of light at $\lambda = 590$ nm uniformly in all directions. How far from the lamp will the number of photons per square metre per second be equal to 10^{15}?

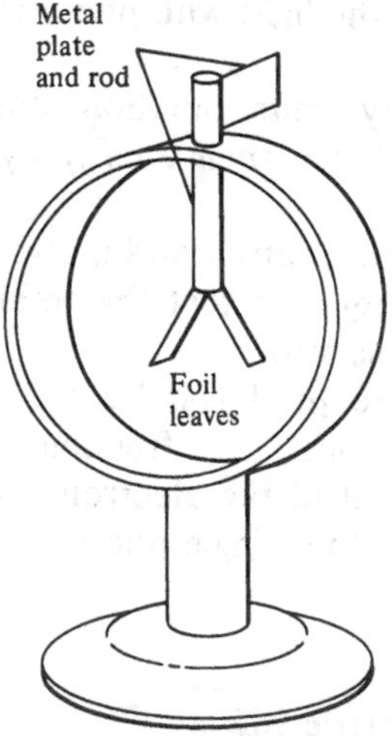

Figure 26.10. When light strikes the plate, the leaves of an electroscope spread apart at the bottom.

26-8 When the sun is directly overhead, the power incident on the earth at ground level is about 10^3 W m^{-2}. Assuming the average wavelength of the light is 550 nm, how many photons per square metre are incident on the earth per second?

26-9 What are the energies in electron volts of photons at the ends of the visible spectrum, (a) $\lambda = 400$ nm; (b) $\lambda = 700$ nm?

26-10 In a monochromatic beam of light of wavelength 500 nm, what is the photon (a) energy; (b) momentum?

26-11 Find the frequency corresponding to $hf = k_BT$ if (a) $T = 300$ K; (b) $T = 6000$ K. (c) To what portions of the electromagnetic spectrum do these frequencies correspond?

26-12 According to the Wien displacement law, the radiation is most intense at a wavelength $\lambda = B/T$, where $B = 2.898 \times 10^{-3}$ m K. (a) At 1000 K, what is this wavelength? (b) Find the corresponding frequency. (c) Find the frequency corresponding to $hf = k_BT$.

26-13 In a molecule, a chlorine atom with a mass of 5.85×10^{-26} kg has a spring constant of 50 N m^{-1}. If $n = 10$, find (a) the energy; (b) the amplitude of oscillation.

Section 26.3 | X rays

26-14 In a Compton scattering experiment, the initial and final photon frequencies are 2.4×10^{20} Hz and 1.6×10^{20} Hz, respectively. What is the recoil energy of the scattering electron in electron volts?

26-15 In order to disintegrate a deuteron (heavy hydrogen nucleus) into a proton and neutron, a γ ray must have an energy of at least 2.2 MeV. (γ rays are very energetic photons; 1 MeV = 10^6 eV = 1.60×10^{-13} J.) Find the minimum γ-ray frequency for photodisintegration of the deuteron.

26-16 The maximum frequency of X-ray photons from a certain apparatus is 9.5×10^{18} Hz. What is the accelerating voltage of the X-ray tube?

26-17 The electrons in an X-ray tube are accelerated from rest through a potential difference of 50,000 V. (a) What is the maximum frequency

X-ray photon that is produced? (b) What is the wavelength of this photon?

26-18 Find the momentum of (a) a photon of wavelength 600 nm; (b) a photon of wavelength 1 nm.

26-19 A photon has an energy of 10^6 eV. Find its (a) frequency; (b) wavelength; (c) momentum.

Section 26-5 | Photons and Vision

26-20 The center-to-center distance between rods is 5×10^{-6} m in one portion of the eye. Estimate the area on the retina taken up by 100 rods.

26-21 A minimum of 100 photons incident on 2.5×10^{-9} m^2 of the pupil of the eye is necessary for vision. These must be incident during the eye's storage time of 0.2 s. (a) What is the minimum intensity of the light if $\lambda = 500$ nm? (b) If the source is 2 m from the eye and radiates uniformly in all directions, what is the power of the source?

26-22 A candle emits energy at a rate of 1 W at an average wavelength of 550 nm. (a) How many photons are emitted per second? (b) How far from the eye can the candle be seen if the threshold intensity is 10^{-7} W m^{-2}? (c) How many photons per square metre per second is this?

26-23 How far from a lamp emitting 5 W of power at a wavelength of 590 nm can one be and still see it with the naked eye? (The threshold intensity is 10^{-7} W m^{-2}.)

PROBLEMS

26-24 The vibrational motions of the atoms of a diatomic molecule are like Planck's oscillators. If we assume that the two atoms are connected by a spring with constant k, the vibrational energy of the molecule is $E = nhf$, where $f = \sqrt{k/\mu}$. μ is called the *reduced mass*, and for two atoms of masses m_1 and m_2,

$$\mu = \frac{m_1 m_2}{m_1 + m_2}$$

For the diatomic molecule H_2, $m_1 = m_2 = 1.67 \times 10^{-27}$ kg, and the measured energy-level spacing is 0.55 eV $= 8.74 \times 10^{-20}$ J. (a) What is the reduced mass of the molecule? (b) What is the spring constant k for the molecule?

26-25 The minimum frequency of photons emitted in vibrational transitions of the HCl molecule is 8.97×10^{13} Hz. The masses of the two atoms are 1.67×10^{-27} kg and 5.85×10^{-26} kg for hydrogen and chlorine, respectively. (a) What is the reduced mass of the molecule? (b) What is the spring constant of the molecule? (See Problem 26-24.)

26-26 The masses of O and H in the OH group are 2.67×10^{-26} kg and 1.67×10^{-27} kg, respectively. The effective spring constant is 50.5 N m^{-1}. (a) What is the reduced mass of the group? (b) What is the characteristic vibrational frequency of the group? (See Problem 26-24.)

26-27 The work function of tungsten is 4.49 eV. (a) Find the threshold wavelength for photoemission. (b) Ultraviolet light of wavelength 250 nm falls on the surface. What is the maximum kinetic energy of the emitted electrons? (c) What is the stopping potential?

***26-28** Light of intensity 10^{-2} W m^{-2} falls on a metallic surface. The energy required to emit a photoelectron is 3 eV (1 eV $= 1.60 \times 10^{-19}$ J). If a single electron absorbs light from a surrounding area 10 atoms in radius (10^{-9} m), how long will it take the electron to absorb enough energy to be emitted if light is assumed to be a classical wave?

26-29 In a Compton effect experiment, the incident X-ray photons have an energy of 10^5 eV $= 1.6 \times 10^{-14}$ J. (a) What is the frequency of the incident photons? (b) An electron gains 4000 eV of kinetic energy when a photon scatters through a certain angle. What is the frequency of the scattered photons?

26-30 Nuclear reactions can produce γ rays, which are very energetic photons. When a π° meson decays at rest, 135 MeV is shared equally by two γ rays. Find the wavelength of the γ rays. (1 MeV $= 10^6$ eV $= 1.60 \times 10^{-13}$ J.)

26-31 An X-ray photon has an energy of 100,000 eV. (a) What is its momentum? (b) If 5 percent of its momentum is transferred to an electron as it scatters, what is the recoil kinetic energy of the electron? (c) What is the energy of the recoiling photon? (d) Find the decrease in frequency of the scattered photon.

26-32 When a photon undergoes Compton scattering, energy and momentum conservation require that the change in its wavelength is

$$\Delta\lambda = \left(\frac{h}{mc}\right)(1 - \cos\theta)$$

Where m is the electron mass and θ is the angle through which the photon is scattered. Suppose a beam of X rays has a wavelength of 0.5 nm. For photons scattered 90°, find (a) the change in wavelength; (b) the change in frequency. (c) How much energy does the recoiling electron acquire?

26-33 Using the equation in the preceding problem, explain why Compton scattering from atomic nuclei is harder to observe than the scattering by electrons.

26-34 Using the equation in Problem 26-32, find the fractional change in the wavelength when a photon incident at 400 nm is scattered 90° by an electron. Comment on how easily this frequency change can be observed.

ANSWERS TO REVIEW QUESTIONS

Q26-1, true; **Q26-2**, frequency; **Q26-3**, number; **Q26-4**, *E*/*h*; **Q26-5**, photons; **Q26-6**, energy, momentum; **Q26-7**, maximum.

Additional Reading

J. Andrade, E. Silva, and G. Lochak, *Quanta*, World University Library, McGraw-Hill Book Co., New York, 1969. Paperback.

A. H. Compton. The Scattering of X rays as Particles, *American Journal of Physics*, December 1961, p. 817.

Roderick K. Clayton, *Light and Living Matter*, Volume I: *The Physical Part*; Volume II: *The Biological Part*, McGraw-Hill Book Co., New York, 1971.

Albert Rose, Quantum Effects in Human Vision, in *Advances in Biological and Medical Physics*, vol. V., Academic Press, New York, 1957, p. 211.

Giorgio Margaritondo, 100 Years of Photoemission, *Physics Today,* April 1988, p. 66.

Scientific American articles:

Karl K. Darrow, The Quantum Theory, March 1952, p. 47.

Richard Gordon, Image Reconstruction from Projections, October 1975, p. 56.

CHAPTER 27
WAVE PROPERTIES OF MATTER

The photon theory of radiation did not resolve all the difficulties facing physicists in the early part of the twentieth century. In many experiments, it was noted that matter absorbed and emitted radiation only at certain frequencies. For example, it had long been known that if hydrogen gas is placed in an electric discharge tube, only a specific set of wavelengths is observed when the light emitted is analyzed with a diffraction grating. Furthermore, every pure gas had its own characteristic frequencies of absorption and emission. By contrast, all classical models of atoms predicted a continuous range of light frequencies.

By 1911, experiments had also shown conclusively that atoms have a positively charged but very small nucleus. The nucleus accounts for most of the mass of the atom, and the negatively charged electrons occupy a region outside the nucleus. This immediately suggests a "planetary" model of atoms with electrons orbiting about the nucleus and the charges held together by the electric forces among them. The electrons must move, or they will be pulled into the nucleus, just as the earth would fall into the sun if it stopped moving. However, according to classical physics, accelerating charges produce electromagnetic radiation and hence lose energy. For example, if electrons are in circular orbits in atoms, they have a centripetal acceleration. Consequently, they must radiate energy and very soon fall into the nucleus. Thus the experimental structure of the atom and classical physics led to the unacceptable result that all atoms are unstable.

In discussing the resolution of these and other difficulties, we focus our attention on the work of two physicists. In 1912, Niels Bohr proposed a model of the one-electron atom that was successful in accounting for many observations. In a more refined form, many of the ideas of Bohr's model are contained in our present-day theories. Also, in 1924, Louis de Broglie hypothesized that electrons and all other "particles" possess wave attributes. This was strikingly confirmed when it was found that electrons reflected from a crystal form a pattern similar to that produced when X rays are diffracted by a crystal.

By about 1930, most of the fundamental puzzles involving the wave–particle behavior of light and matter had been resolved. Although the sequence of events that occurred in the unraveling of these problems is extremely interesting, we do not present them in chronological order here. Rather, we take a retrospective view of how the ideas and experiments were made compatible and how a solid foundation for our modern picture of nature was established. Specifically, we are concerned in this chapter with the wave properties of matter that, along with the photon theory of light, give us a consistent view of nature.

27.1 | FAILURES OF CLASSICAL PHYSICS

In the 1880s, experiments showed that when electrodes of opposite polarity are immersed in a gas, a current may be produced in the gas. In 1897, J. J. Thomson (1856–1940) showed that this current is composed of negatively charged particles now called electrons. These particles can be deflected by a magnetic field and the charge-to-mass ratio e/m measured. The same particles appear no matter what gas or electrode material is used. Hence

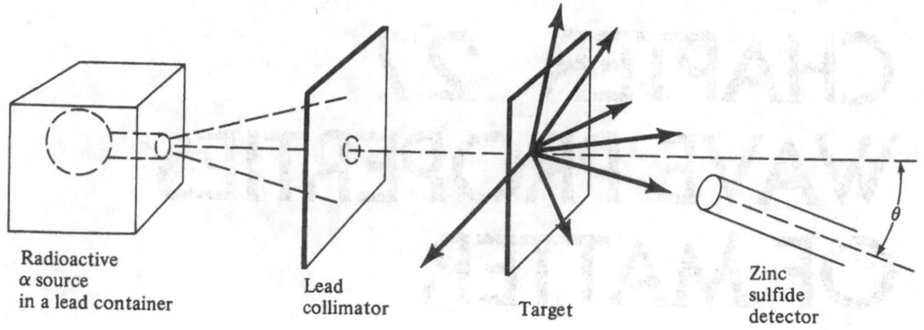

Figure 27.1. In Rutherford's experiments, α particles are emitted by a radioactive source. The lead collimator absorbs all the α particles except those that pass through a tiny hole and form a beam. The α particles scatter in all directions after striking the target and are detected at different angles by a movable zinc sulfide detector.

Thomson concluded that these electrons are a fundamental constituent of matter.

In 1906, Thomson proposed that atoms consist of electrons imbedded in a positively charged background. The total charge added up to zero because atoms are normally electrically neutral. This model could be tested by bombarding materials with charged particles and observing the way in which they are deflected.

Radioactivity was receiving a great deal of attention at this time, and one of those most prominent in that work was Ernest Rutherford (1871–1937). One of his most important early discoveries was the spontaneous emission by some heavy radioactive elements of *alpha* (α) *particles*. These particles have a positive charge that is twice the magnitude of the electronic charge; they are about 7000 times as massive as an electron. Starting in 1907, Rutherford began an intensive study of scattering α particles by various targets. The scattered α particles were detected by observing the flashes of light they produced upon reaching a zinc sulfide screen (Fig. 27.1).

According to Thomson's atomic model, the α particles should not be disturbed much by the diffuse positive charge, and the light electrons should also deflect them only slightly. Thus most of the α particles should pass almost straight through the very thin gold foil target (Fig. 27.2*a*).

When the experiment was performed, it was found that most of the α particles were scattered through small angles, but a significant fraction were scattered through much larger angles. And occasionally an α particle was stopped and sent back out toward the source! This remarkable fact was described by Rutherford: "It was almost as incredible as if you had fired a 15-inch shell at a piece of tissue paper and it came back and hit you."

The only explanation consistent with Rutherford's data is that of a small positively charged nucleus (of radius on the order of 10^{-14} m) with the electrons occupying the remainder of the atom. (Atoms were known to be on the order of 10^{-10} m in radius, a factor of 10,000 times larger than the nucleus.) The α particles experience a repulsive force from the heavy, positively charged nuclei. Occasionally, in a head-on collision, an α particle is stopped close to a nucleus and scattered directly back toward the source (Fig. 27.2*b*).

Rutherford's nuclear atom was an important step forward, but it presented serious problems. It now appeared that the electrons must be in some sort of orbit in the attractive electric field of the nucleus. The energy of an electron was the sum of its kinetic energy in its orbit plus the potential energy due to the positive nucleus. If the energy were to decrease,

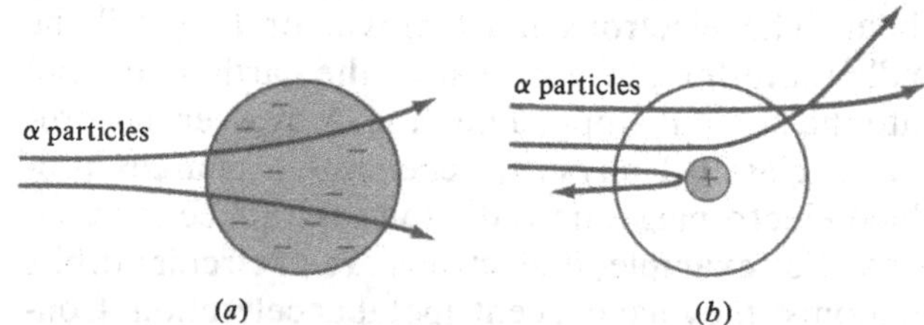

Figure 27.2. (*a*) In Thomson's model of the atom, all the α particles would travel through the foil, deflected slightly by the diffuse positive charge (shown colored) and by the light electrons. (*b*) Rutherford explained the relatively frequent large angle scatterings as due to the repulsive electric force of a small positively charged nucleus. The light electrons occupying the remainder of the atom would not scatter the α particles significantly.

the electron would move closer to the nucleus. The problem was that accelerated charges were known to radiate energy as electromagnetic waves. For example, an electron in a circular orbit has a centripetal acceleration and should radiate energy. As its energy decreases, it should move to smaller radii. A detailed calculation shows that within 10^{-10} s, the electron would spiral into the nucleus! We are still here, so this prediction cannot be correct. All classical descriptions of the nuclear atom led to essentially the same result. It remained for Bohr and those who followed him to resolve these problems through the development of quantum mechanics.

Discrete Spectra | A second important body of data existed during the same period that showed that atoms emitted and absorbed light only at specific frequencies. For illustrative purposes, we describe the data for hydrogen.

In examining a flame or an electric discharge tube containing hydrogen through a diffraction grating, only certain characteristic frequencies and wavelengths of emitted light were observed (Fig. 27.3). Johann Balmer (1825–1898) discovered in 1884 that

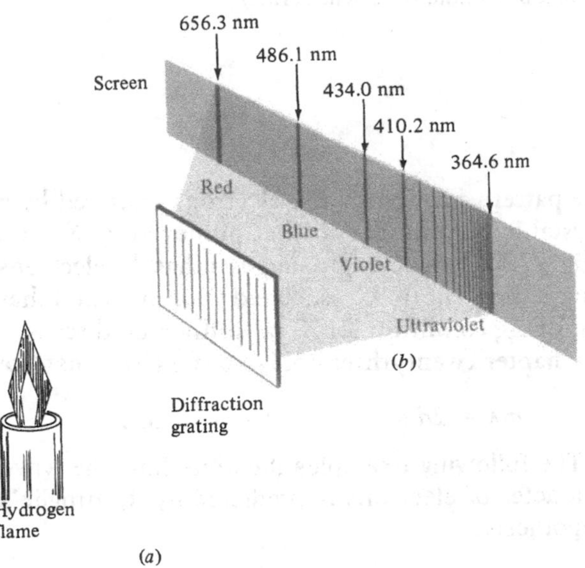

Figure 27.3. (*a*) When the light from a flame containing hydrogen passes through a diffraction grating and is projected on a screen, discrete lines are seen corresponding to the emission of monochromatic light at several different wavelengths. (*b*) The visible and near ultraviolet lines of hydrogen.

the wavelengths of the visible and near ultraviolet lines of hydrogen obey a remarkably simple formula almost exactly:

$$\frac{1}{\lambda} = R_H \left(\frac{1}{2^2} - \frac{1}{n^2}\right), \qquad n = 3, 4, 5, \ldots \qquad (27.1)$$

Here $R_H = 1.097 \times 10^7 \text{ m}^{-1}$ is called the *Rydberg constant*.

The longest visible wavelength in the hydrogen spectrum is found in the next example.

Example 27.1

What is the longest wavelength light predicted by the Balmer formula?

The longest wavelength is found using Balmer's formula for $n = 3$,

$$\frac{1}{\lambda} = R_H\left(\frac{1}{2^2} - \frac{1}{3^2}\right) = \frac{5}{36} R_H$$

Then

$$\lambda = \frac{36}{5R_H} = \frac{36}{5(1.097 \times 10^7 \text{ m}^{-1})}$$

$$= 6.56 \times 10^{-7} \text{ m} = 656 \text{ nm}$$

which is the longest visible wavelength observed (Fig. 27.3).

Other spectral lines were also observed including some not in the visible spectrum. The wavelengths of *all* the observed lines could be predicted using

$$\frac{1}{\lambda} = R_H\left(\frac{1}{n_f^2} - \frac{1}{n_i^2}\right) \qquad (27.2)$$

$$n_i = n_f + 1,\ n_f + 2, \ldots$$

The visible lines correspond to $n_f = 2$, the ultraviolet spectrum has $n_f = 1$, and the infrared spectrum corresponds to $n_f \geq 3$.

Using energy conservation, when a photon of energy hf is emitted by an atom the internal energy of the atom must decrease. Because the observed photons only appear at certain frequencies, the atoms must only change their energies by fixed amounts. This too contradicts a classical picture of electrons orbiting a nucleus at an arbitrary radius and a corresponding arbitrary energy.

From the point of view of classical physics, it seemed impossible for Rutherford's nuclear atom to be able to change its energy in discrete jumps. In the remainder of this chapter we describe the new ideas needed to explain the observations we have discussed.

27.2 | THE de BROGLIE WAVE HYPOTHESIS

In 1924, Louis de Broglie suggested that matter as well as light might have wave properties. This would give both light and matter a dual wave–particle nature and put them both on the same footing. De Broglie also suggested a formula relating the wavelength of any object to its momentum. This formula was rapidly verified by experimental measurements.

De Broglie noted that photons are zero-mass particles and their energy and momentum are related by $E = hf = pc$, where h is Planck's constant and c is the speed of light (Chapter Twenty-six). Using $f\lambda = c$, the relation between the photon momentum and wavelength is $hc/\lambda = pc$, or

$$\lambda = \frac{h}{p} \tag{27.3}$$

Using this as a guide to the possible dual nature of particles, de Broglie suggested that particles of momentum p should also have a wavelength λ associated with them, given by exactly the same relation.

This idea was tested beautifully in 1926 in an experiment performed by C. Davisson (1881–1958) and L. H. Germer (1896–1971). They directed a beam of electrons at a crystal and observed that the electrons scattered in various directions for a given crystal orientation (Fig. 27.4). In this experiment

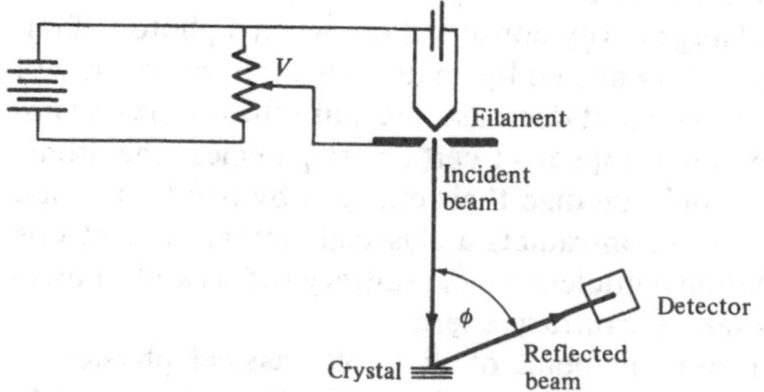

Figure 27.4. The apparatus of Davisson and Germer. Electrons emitted from a hot filament are accelerated through a potential difference V. They strike a crystal, and the scattered electrons are detected at an angle ϕ with the incident beam.

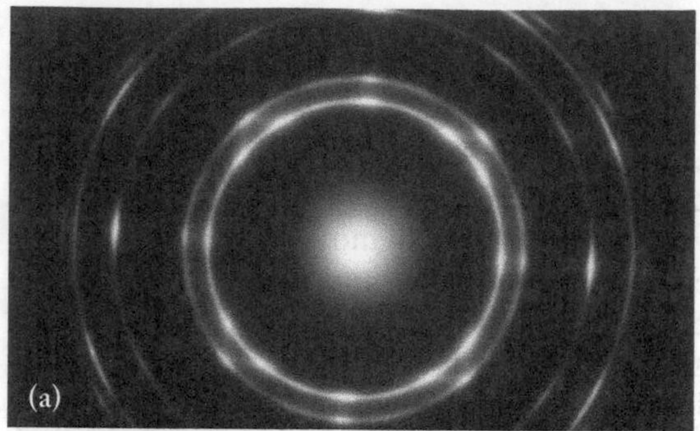

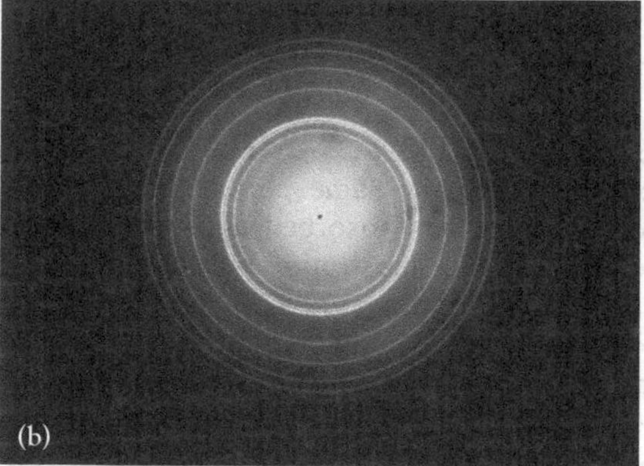

Figure 27.5. Diffration patterns (a) with X-rays on chromium and (b) electrons on beryllium. The targets are randomly oriented crystal powders so the Bragg spots become circles. (Omikron / Photo Researchers, Inc.)

the pattern formed by the electrons scattered by a crystal is very similar to that produced by X rays. (Fig. 27.5). This strongly suggests that the electrons have a wavelength λ associated with them and that the Bragg condition for X-ray diffraction discussed in Chapter Twentythree holds true for electrons also:

$$m\lambda = 2d \sin\theta, \qquad m = 1, 2, 3, \ldots$$

The following examples illustrate how the wave character of electrons is predicted by de Broglie's hypothesis.

Example 27.2

What is the wavelength associated with the electrons that scatter as shown in Fig. 27.6?

From the figure $\theta = 90° - \frac{1}{2}(52°) = 64°$, and $\sin 64° = 0.899$. With $d = 0.09$ nm $= 9 \times 10^{-11}$ m, the Bragg condition with $m = 1$ gives

$$\lambda = 2d \sin\theta = 2(9 \times 10^{-11}\ \text{m})(0.899)$$
$$= 1.62 \times 10^{-10}\ \text{m}$$
$$= 0.162\ \text{nm}$$

Example 27.3

What is the momentum and corresponding de Broglie wavelength of the electrons scattered in Fig. 27.6?

The momentum of electrons accelerated through a 56-V potential difference can be found by noting that their kinetic energy is

$$\tfrac{1}{2}mv^2 = eV$$

where m is the electron mass and e is the magnitude of the electronic charge. Using $p = mv$, $\frac{1}{2}mv^2 = p^2/2m = eV$, so

$$p = \sqrt{2emV}$$
$$= \sqrt{2(1.6 \times 10^{-19}\ \text{C})(9.1 \times 10^{-31}\ \text{kg})(56\ \text{V})}$$
$$= 4.04 \times 10^{-24}\ \text{kg m s}^{-1}$$

Using de Broglie's hypothesis,

$$\lambda = \frac{h}{p} = \frac{6.63 \times 10^{-34}\ \text{J s}}{4.04 \times 10^{-24}\ \text{kg m s}^{-1}}$$
$$= 1.64 \times 10^{-10}\ \text{m} = 0.164\ \text{nm}$$

This value agrees with that found from experiment (Example 27.2).

As a result of this and other experiments, we now accept de Broglie's idea as one of the cornerstones of modern physics. The diffraction effects of electrons and neutrons are now important tools to the scientist.

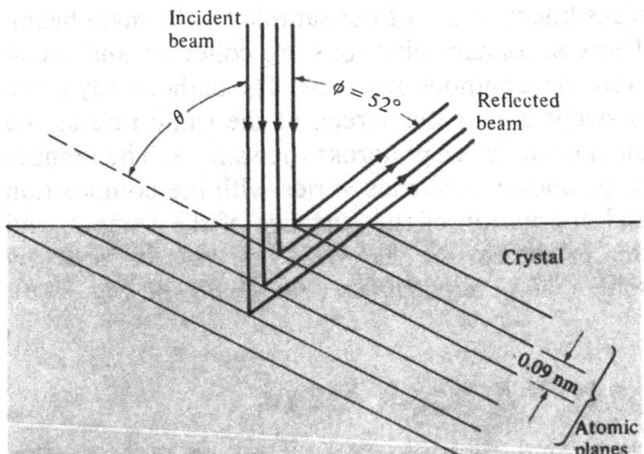

Figure 27.6. When the electron accelerating voltage is 56 V, electrons scattered from atomic planes 0.09 nm apart in the crystal appear mostly at $\phi = 52°$.

Neutron Diffraction | The wave properties of matter provide us with ways to study microscopic objects on a much smaller scale than is possible with the ordinary microscope. Both neutrons and electrons have been used extensively for this purpose.

No analog to the lens is available for neutrons, so it is not possible to construct a neutron microscope. However, a crystal serves as a three-dimensional diffraction grating for neutrons, just as it does for electrons and X rays. In many situations, neutron diffraction provides molecular structure information that cannot be obtained in other ways.

The reactions occurring in a nuclear reactor produce many neutrons with a wide range of energies. If neutrons collide with several atoms before or after leaving the reactor, their average kinetic energy is comparable to the average thermal energy of the atoms. When the temperature is T, this energy is $\frac{3}{2}k_BT$. Thus the average energy and de Broglie wavelength of such *thermal neutrons* can be controlled by varying the temperature of the materials.

The wavelength of a thermal neutron is approximately the size of an atom, as is shown in the next example.

Example 27.4

What is the wavelength of a neutron with kinetic energy $\frac{3}{2}k_BT$ when $T = 300$ K?

The neutron kinetic energy is $\frac{1}{2}mv^2 = \frac{3}{2}k_BT$ so the momentum $p = mv$ is found from $p^2 = (mv)^2 = 3k_BTm$, or

$$p = \sqrt{3mk_BT}$$

Using $m = 1.67 \times 10^{-27}$ kg and $T = 300$ K,

$$\lambda = \frac{h}{p} = \frac{h}{\sqrt{3mk_BT}}$$
$$= \frac{6.63 \times 10^{-34}\ \text{J s}}{\sqrt{3(1.67 \times 10^{-27}\ \text{kg})(1.38 \times 10^{-23}\ \text{J K}^{-1})(300\ \text{K})}}$$
$$= 1.46 \times 10^{-10}\ \text{m} = 0.146\ \text{nm}$$

This is a typical atomic or molecular distance.

Electron Microscope | The electron microscope is an astonishing improvement over the optical microscope. The shortest useful wavelength and resolution for optical work is about 200 nm, but

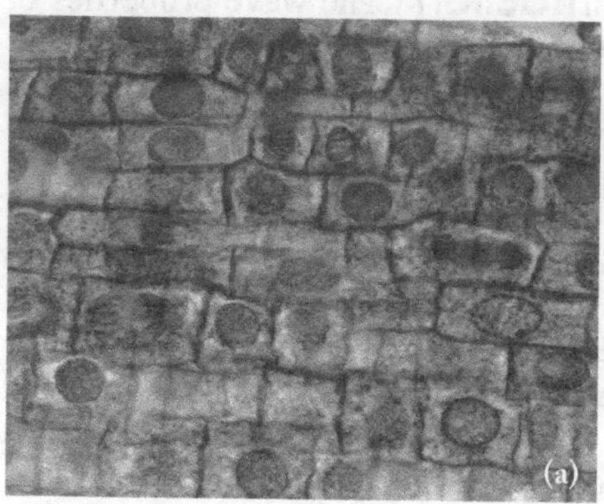

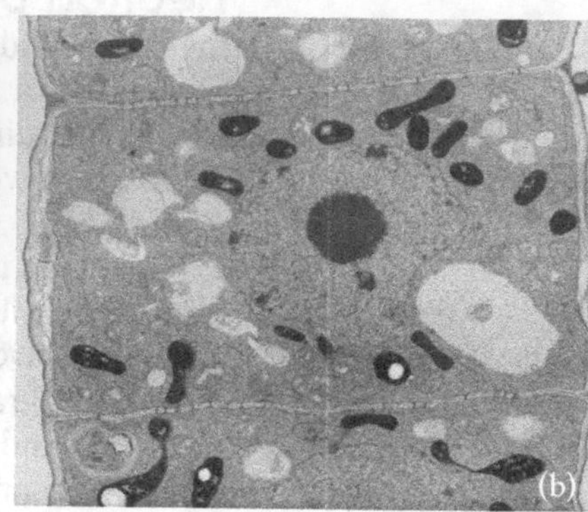

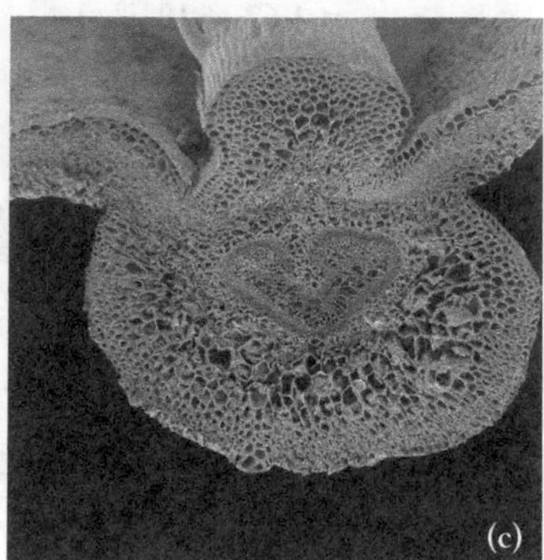

Figure 27.7. (a) Light microscope picture of an onion root tip. (b) Transmission electron microscope image of an onion root cell. (c) Scanning electron micrograph of a section through the midrib of a frond of a tree fern. [(a) Eye of Science / Photo Researchers, Inc.; (b) David M. Phillips / Science Source / Photo Researchers, Inc.; (c) Steve Gschmeissner / Photo Researchers, Inc.]

electrons produced by using accelerating voltages of 50 kV have a de Broglie wavelength of 0.0055 nm. Theoretically, this would be the resolution of an electron microscope. In practice, electrons must be focused using electric and magnetic fields as lenses, and these limit the resolution to about 0.2 nm. However, even this is 1000 times better than that obtained with optical instruments and allows the study of minute cellular constituents and molecules.

Two types of electron microscopes are in common use. The *transmission microscope* requires the use of samples less than 100 nm thick. If the sample is too thick, the energy lost by off-axis electrons is much greater than that lost by electrons going directly through the sample. The wavelengths are then sufficiently varied so that the electrons cannot all be focused simultaneously. Although the resolution of these microscopes is excellent, sample preparation limits their usage somewhat, and the depth of field is very small. Thus three-dimensional structures will not be properly focused. These disadvantages are overcome with a *scanning microscope*, but at the price of a reduction of the resolution to about 10 nm. Live samples can be used, and the results show three-dimensional structures clearly (Fig. 27.7).

The transmission microscope is schematically much like an optical microscope. Produced at a hot cathode, the electrons pass through the sample and are focused into a real image (Fig. 27.8*a*). In the scanning microscope the electrons are focused to a very small spot, which is swept across the sample. The image is formed by monitoring secondary electrons knocked out of the sample by the main beam. These secondary electrons are collected and accelerated in a cathode-ray tube. The cathode-ray beam is swept across the screen at the same rate as the main beam is swept across the sample. The number of secondary electrons varies with the composition and orientation of the surfaces of the sample, and the brightness of the trace on the cathode-ray screen varies accordingly (Fig. 27.8*b* and Fig. 27.9).

27.3 | THE BOHR ATOM

In the remaining sections of this chapter, we describe the resolution of the atomic spectra and nuclear atom problems discussed earlier. The wave–

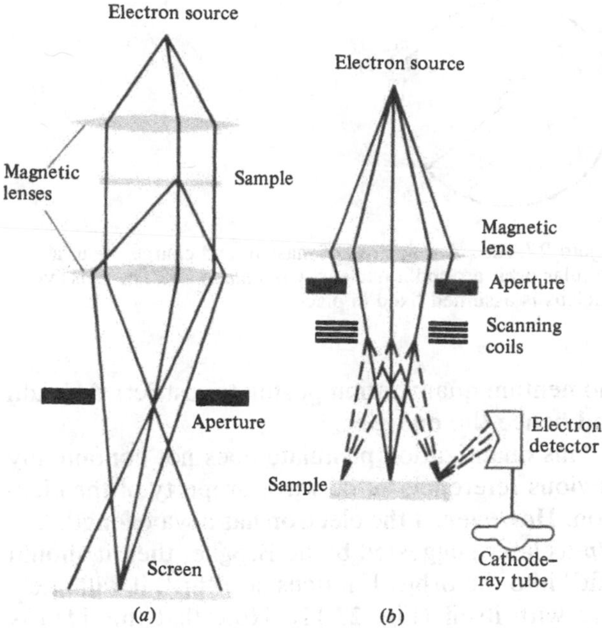

Figure 27.8. (*a*) Transmission and (*b*) scanning electron microscopes.

particle nature of matter provides the basis for these discussions.

In 1913, well before de Broglie postulated the wave nature of matter, Niels Bohr (1885–1962) proposed a model of one-electron atoms. The immediate purpose of the model was to explain the observed emission spectrum of hydrogen. Although the model was successful in this respect, it is now known to be quite incomplete and oversimplified. However, it does provide a very simple picture that we sometimes use to visualize complex atomic processes.

Bohr adopted Rutherford's nuclear atom model with electrons moving in the electric field of a small massive nucleus. He also suggested that certain orbits are stable; the accelerating electrons do not radiate energy when in these orbits. We can find these orbits by attributing a wavelength $\lambda = h/p$ to the electron, although Bohr used a different approach.

Bohr built his theory on four postulates. The first two assert the existence of *quantized energy levels* and of *quantum jumps* between them that are accompanied by photon emission or absorption. These concepts survive today in our modern quantum description of nature. The last two enabled

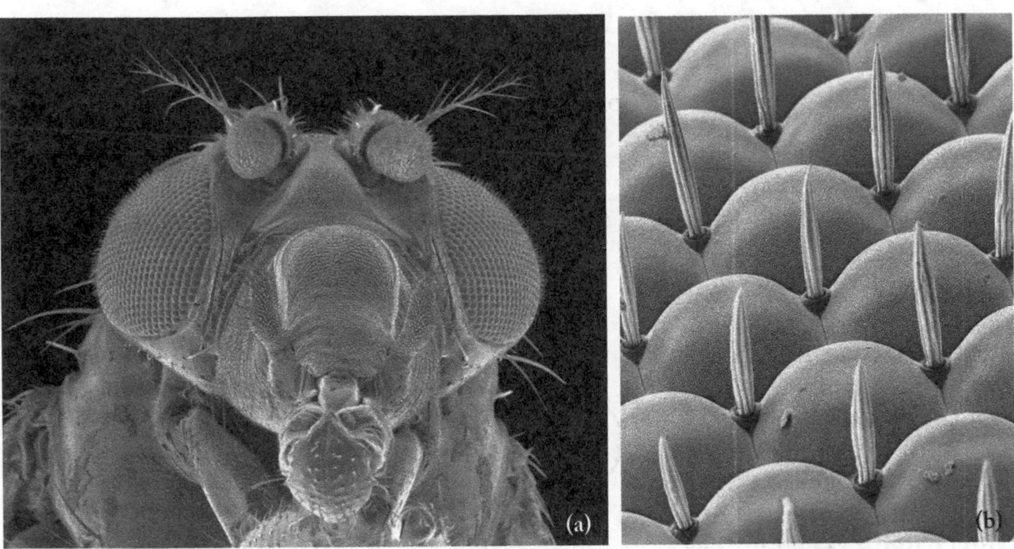

Figure 27.9. Scanning electron microscope pictures of (*a*) a fruit fly and (*b*) a portion of the eye alone. [(a) Thomas Deerinck, NCMIR / Photo Researchers, Inc.; (b) Martin Oeggerli / Photo Researchers, Inc.]

Bohr to calculate the allowed radii and energies for the hydrogen atom. They state that the motion of the electron is determined by Newton's laws and that the electron has a quantized angular momentum. In modern quantum mechanics, the motion satisfies Schrödinger's wave equation. This is discussed in the next chapter.

1. *The energies of electrons in the atom are quantized.* Electrons can only be in certain orbits with specific energies. Although they are accelerated, the electrons do not radiate when they are in these orbits.
2. *An electron can make a sudden quantum jump from one orbit to another by emitting or absorbing a photon.* The photon energy equals the change in the energy of the electron. The electron is never found at radii between those of the allowed orbits; it jumps from one to the other discontinuously.
3. *While it is in one of its allowed orbits, classical mechanics can be used to describe the motion of the electron.* Specifically, Newton's laws of motion and Coulomb's law for the electric force are applicable.
4. *The orbital angular momenta of the electrons are quantized.* The angular momentum of an allowed orbit is an integer multiple of a basic unit, $h/2\pi$, so

$$L = mvr = n\frac{h}{2\pi} = n\hbar, \qquad n = 1, 2, 3, \ldots \tag{27.4}$$

The combination $h/2\pi$ appears frequently, so the symbol $\hbar$ is used for conciseness. It is read as "h-bar" and has the value

$$\hbar = 1.055 \times 10^{-34}\ \text{J s} = 6.58 \times 10^{-16}\ \text{eV s}$$

To apply Bohr's postulates, we consider an atom composed of a heavy nucleus containing Z protons and a single electron in a circular orbit of radius r about the nucleus (Fig. 27.10). Since the nuclear mass is much greater than that of the electron, we assume that the nucleus is at rest. The electric force between the nucleus (with charge Ze) and the electron (with charge $-e$) holds the electron in orbit. Classically, the energy is determined by the radius, and all radii are possible. However, Bohr's angular momentum quantization postulate restricts the radii and hence the energies.

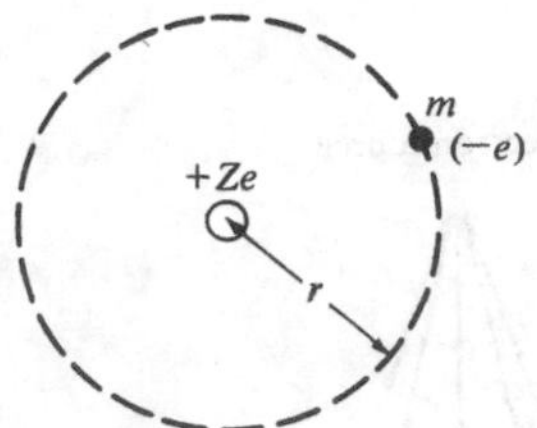

Figure 27.10. An electron of mass m and charge $-e$ in a circular orbit around a nucleus with charge Ze. The massive nucleus is assumed fixed in place.

This quantization postulate does not contain any obvious reference to the wave property of the electron. However, if the electron has a wavelength $\lambda = h/p$ as later suggested by de Broglie, then it should "fit" into the orbit. If it does not "fit," it will interfere with itself (Fig. 27.11). Note that this idea is similar to the one that we used for waves on strings. Resonant standing waves occur when the wavelength "fits" on a string. Here the wavelength must fit into the orbit.

With this assumption, we must fit an integer number of waves of wavelength $\lambda = h/p = h/mv$ into the orbital circumference $2\pi r$. Thus

$$2\pi r = n\lambda = n\frac{h}{mv}$$

or

$$rmv = n\frac{h}{2\pi} = n\hbar, \qquad n = 1,2,3, \ldots \tag{27.5}$$

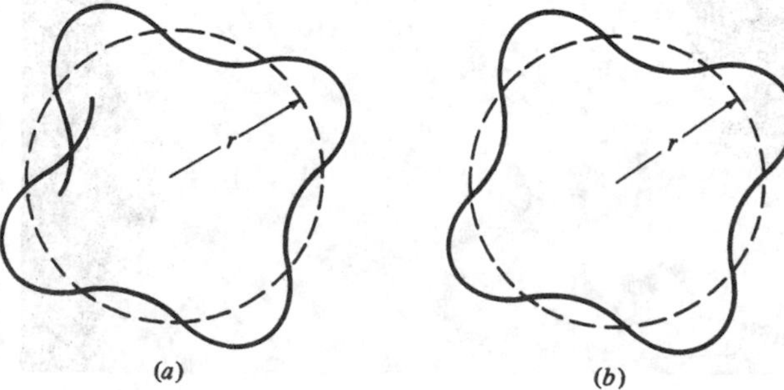

Figure 27.11. (*a*) The wavelength associated with the electron does not fit into the orbit. In (*b*), the wave "fits" correctly. The orbital circumference is $2\pi r$.

NIELS HENRIK DAVID BOHR

(1885–1962)

The years from 1910 to 1930 were among the most exciting in physics. A unique generation of physicists participated in the conception and development of the revolution called quantum physics. Most of this excitement centered on three places, Rutherford's laboratory in Manchester, England, the University of Göttingen in Germany, and the Institute for Theoretical Physics at the University of Copenhagen. The center of attraction in Copenhagen was Niels Bohr. In addition to his abilities as a physicist, Bohr was able to cultivate an atmosphere in which incredible progress and understanding was possible by physicists from all over the world. The flavor of this period is illustrated by the following story told by George Gamow*:

> The evening work in the Institute's library was often interrupted by Bohr, who would say that he was very tired and would like to go to the movies. The only movies he liked were wild Westerns (Hollywood style), and he always needed a couple of students to go with him and explain the complicated plots. . . . But his theoretical mind showed even in these movie expeditions. He developed a theory to explain why although the villain always draws first, the hero is faster and manages to kill him. This Bohr theory was based on psychology. Since the hero never shoots first, the villain has to decide when to draw, which impedes his action. The hero, on the other hand, acts according to a conditional reflex and grabs the gun automatically as soon as he sees the villain's hand move. We disagreed with this theory, and the next day I went to a toy store and bought two guns in Western holsters. We shot it out with Bohr, he played the hero, and he "killed" all his students.

Bohr was the son of a physiology professor. He received his doctorate in physics in Copenhagen in 1911 and then spent three years in England, two of them in Manchester with Rutherford. It was during this period that Bohr took the revolutionary steps described now as the Bohr model for the hydrogen atom.

Bohr's model combined elements of classical physics with ideas and pos-

* George Gamow, *Thirty Years That Shook Physics*, Anchor Books, New York, 1966.

tulates which, at the time, were not verifiable nor even readily believable. For example, Max Planck, whose work Bohr used as a point of departure, was very reluctant to accept Bohr's ideas. It was the task of physicists during the next two decades to fill in the missing pieces and put the entire picture together in a coherent way. In this process, Bohr represented the generation that had to cast off the old and press forward with the new. The generation he helped educate was not so tied to classical physics and felt less need to look back.

It is important to realize that during this period it was not simply new physics problems that were being solved; rather, an entirely new view of natural law was at issue. During this time, one needed not only new equations but also new philosophies and new pictures of a world that was beyond the direct reach of the senses but not beyond experimental reach. Bohr's role in forging the physics and philosophy of this age was immense.

By 1930, the quantum picture of atoms was fairly firm, and Bohr joined others in trying to understand the atomic nucleus. This led to Bohr's interest in fission. In 1939, in a paper with G. V. Wheeler, Bohr showed how many one may understand the role of neutrons in causing the ^{235}U nucleus to break apart. This work was fundamental in the process that ultimately led to nuclear chain reactions.

In 1943, Bohr's ever-present concern for others resulted in his having to flee Denmark to avoid arrest by the Nazis. He was flown to England from Sweden in a British fighter plane. Given an oxygen mask that was too small, he was saved when the pilot noticed that Bohr had lost consciousness, and he reduced the altitude.

From England, Bohr went to the United States and participated in the atomic bomb development program. After the war, he became an early and persistent voice in calling for international reason in the face of the tremendous power he had helped to release. He also played an important role in developing international and Danish facilities for atomic and nuclear research. Having given birth in 1913 to a model that was awesome in both its simplicity and its novel character, Bohr was an active participant of the scientific and political events that followed for another half-century.

This is exactly Bohr's criterion for the angular momentum! Thus our assumption is equivalent to Bohr's postulate.

We now use Bohr's postulates to obtain equations for the radii and energies of the electron orbits. If the electron is in a circular orbit of radius r, the acceleration is $a = v^2/r$. Using Newton's second law, $\mathbf{F} = m\mathbf{a}$, where $\mathbf{F}$ is the electric force with magnitude kZe^2/r^2,

$$k\frac{Ze^2}{r^2} = \frac{mv^2}{r} \qquad (27.6)$$

From this we see that the kinetic energy of the electron is

$$K = \frac{1}{2}mv^2 = k\frac{Ze^2}{2r} \qquad (27.7)$$

From Eq. 27.5, we have $v = n\hbar/mr$. If we substitute this expression for v in Eq. 27.7, we can solve for the radius r associated with n wavelengths. Labeling this radius with a subscript n, we find

$$r_n = \frac{n^2\hbar^2}{kZme^2} = \frac{n^2}{Z}a_0, \qquad n = 1, 2, 3, \ldots \qquad (27.8)$$

Here $a_0 = \hbar^2/kme^2 = 5.29 \times 10^{-11}$ m is called the *Bohr radius*. There are an infinite number of allowed values of r_n corresponding to all the integer values of n. The electrons can only be in these orbits. This is quite different from the classical idea that any value of r is possible.

The potential energy of the electron is $\mathcal{U} = -kZe^2/r$, so the total energy for an orbit of radius r is, with Eq. 27.7,

$$E = K + \mathcal{U} = -\frac{kZe^2}{2r}$$

Using our result for the possible radii r_n, this becomes

$$E_n = -\frac{kZ^2e^2}{2a_0n^2} = -\frac{Z^2}{n^2}E_0, \qquad n = 1, 2, 3, \ldots \tag{27.9}$$

where

$$E_0 = \frac{ke^2}{2a_0} = 13.6 \text{ eV} = 2.18 \times 10^{-18} \text{ J}$$

E_0 is the lowest possible energy of the electron. The corresponding orbit is called the *ground state.*

This is the fundamental result that Bohr obtained. The electrons can only occupy orbits with certain energies. The allowed values of the electron energy E_n are termed *energy levels*, and n is called a *quantum number*.

Bohr's result is in close agreement with experiment for *any* atom with one electron, such as hydrogen ($Z = 1$), singly ionized helium, He^+($Z = 2$), and doubly ionized lithium, Li^{++}($Z = 3$). The lowest levels for He^+ are found in the next example.

Example 27.5

(a) What are the lowest three energy levels of singly ionized helium? (b) What are the radii associated with these levels?

(a) Helium has two protons in the nucleus ($Z = 2$), and when it is singly ionized, it has one electron. Using $Z = 2$ and $n = 1$,

$$E_1 = -\frac{Z^2}{n^2}E_0 = -\frac{(2)^2}{(1)^2}(13.6 \text{ eV})$$
$$= -54.4 \text{ eV}$$

If instead we use $n = 2$, the result obtained is smaller by $1/2^2$, and is -13.6 eV; for $n = 3$, the energy is -6.04 eV.

(b) Using Eq. 27.8, the $n = 1$ radius is

$$r_1 = \frac{n^2}{Z}a_0 = \frac{(1)^2}{2}(5.29 \times 10^{-11} \text{ m})$$
$$= 2.65 \times 10^{-11} \text{ m}$$

Similarly, $r_2 = 10.6 \times 10^{-11}$ m, and $r_3 = 23.8 \times 10^{-11}$ m (Fig. 27.12).

The first of Bohr's postulates states that electrons in allowed orbits do not radiate energy, even though they are accelerated. Note, by contrast, that according to classical physics, the electrons in these small circular orbits would radiate energy at a very great rate. In Bohr's theory, electrons can only lower their energy by dropping into lower energy orbits and emitting a photon in the process. If the initial and final energies of the electron are $E_{n,i}$ and $E_{n,f}$, from energy conservation the photon energy hf must be

$$hf = E_{n,i} - E_{n,f}$$

Using our result for the energy levels, this gives for hydrogen

$$hf = \frac{hc}{\lambda} = hcR_H\left(\frac{1}{n_f^2} - \frac{1}{n_i^2}\right) \tag{27.10}$$
$$n_i = n_f + 1, n_f + 2, \ldots$$

where the theoretical value of the Rydberg constant R_H is

$$R_H = \frac{mk^2e^4}{2\hbar^2hc} = 1.097 \times 10^7 \text{ m}^{-1} \tag{27.11}$$

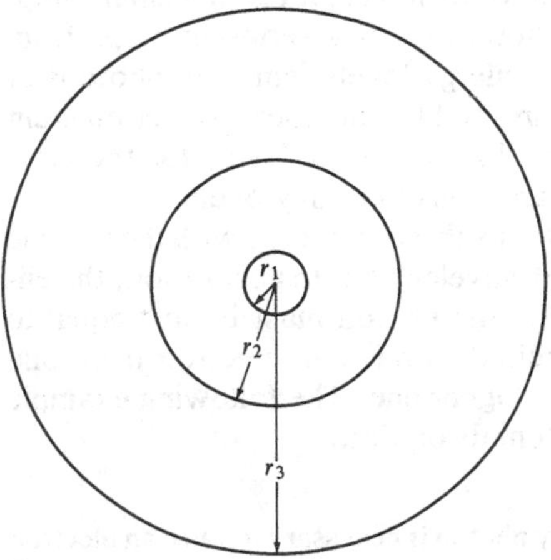

Figure 27.12. The radii predicted by the Bohr model for the three lowest energy orbits in a one-electron atom. Here $r_3 = 9r_1$ and $r_2 = 4r_1$.

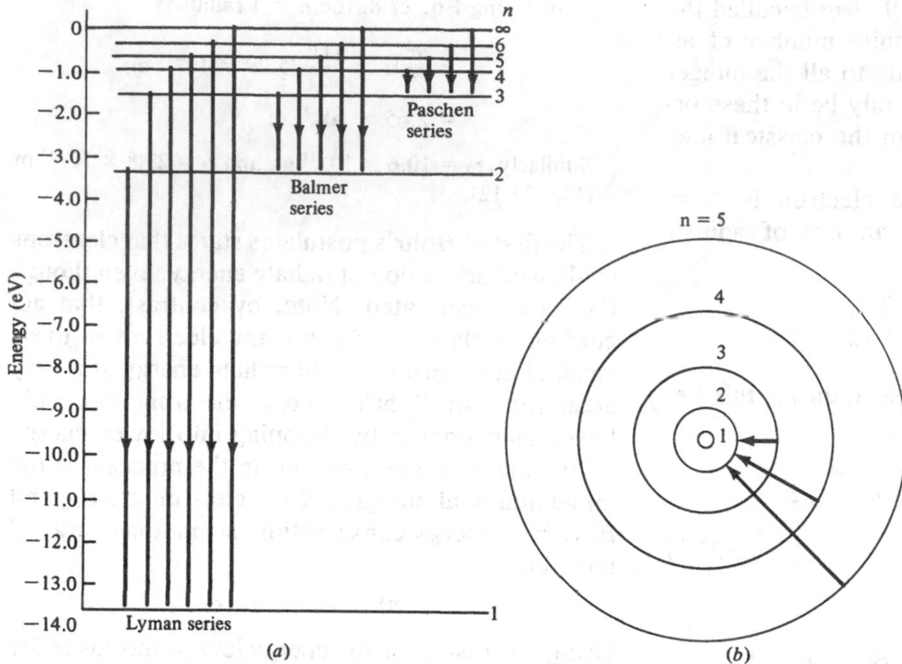

Figure 27.13. (*a*) The energy levels of hydrogen corresponding to the quantum numbers $n = 1$ through 6 and the highest level ($n = \infty$) that has zero energy. The vertical arrows show possible electron transitions that are accompanied by photon emission. For example, the longest wavelength line in the Balmer series corresponds to an electron dropping from the $n = 3$ to the $n = 2$ energy level in its hydrogen atom. The three series shown involve ultraviolet (Lyman), visible (Balmer), and infrared (Paschen) photons. (*b*) The transitions corresponding to the first three lines of the Balmer series.

This is exactly the empirical result found by Balmer and others and described in the preceding section.

Ordinarily, the electrons in hydrogen atoms are in the energy level with the lowest or most negative energy, the $n = 1$ level, or ground state. In a flame or an electric discharge tube, many of the atoms are in *excited states*, with the electrons in less tightly bound orbits that have larger values of n. An electron may return to the lowest level in a single step, emitting one photon, or in a series of steps from higher to lower energy levels, emitting photons at each step. Figure 27.13 is an energy-level diagram that shows the allowed energy levels for the electron and the transitions that may occur.

An atom will also absorb photons with these same frequencies and wavelengths. In absorption, the energy provided by the photon must be just equal to the energy required to raise an electron from one stable level to a higher one. The following example illustrates photon absorption.

Example 27.6

What energy photon is necessary to raise an electron in hydrogen from the $n = 1$ to the $n = 3$ energy level?

From Fig. 27.13, we see that this is the reverse of the process indicated by the second line in the Lyman series. The electron increases its energy from E_1 to E_3, and the photon energy must be

$$hf = E_3 - E_1 = -\frac{1}{3^2}E_0 - \left(-\frac{1}{1^2}E_0\right)$$
$$= \left(1 - \frac{1}{9}\right)E_0$$

With $E_0 = 13.6$ eV, the photon energy is

$$hf = \frac{8}{9}(13.6 \text{ eV}) = 12.1 \text{ eV}$$

Bohr's results are correct for any one-electron atom, despite the fact that the model on which they are based is now considered to be a great oversimplification. However, we do see how the two problems described earlier are explained. The fact that the electron is not a particle as we usually think of one classically leads to quantized energy levels. The discrete spectra observed are the result of electrons jumping from one orbit to another. The wavelike behavior of the electron also means that it is not an object that radiates energy when accelerated. The orbital radii we have calculated represent the average distances of electrons from the nucleus but are not actually the radii of electronic trajectories.

Despite the success of Bohr's model for one-electron atoms, most attempts to extend these ideas to multielectron atoms and molecules were unsuccessful. The requirement that the angular momentum is quantized is insufficient to determine the orbits in these complex systems.

In 1925, two detailed theories of *quantum mechanics* were proposed, one by Erwin Schrödinger (1887–1961) and the other by Werner Heisenberg (1901–1975). Although the two theories were very different in appearance, they were soon recognized to be equivalent in content. Unlike Bohr's theory, these are complete theories that, in principle, can be applied to all physical systems, including atoms, molecules, and macroscopic objects. We discuss Schrödinger's form of quantum mechanics in the next chapter.

We have seen that Bohr's model predicts that there is a lowest energy level. It is interesting to ask, why can't the electron go into a deeper energy level, one closer to or even inside the nucleus? In nature, systems tend to stay in the lowest energy state whenever possible, and the electron could reduce its energy enormously by moving much closer to the nucleus. This question can be partially answered using the *uncertainty principle*.

27.4 | THE UNCERTAINTY PRINCIPLE

Both Schrödinger's and Heisenberg's formulations of quantum mechanics implicitly contain the de Broglie hypothesis of the wave character of matter. They also contain the uncertainty principle, which was first discussed by Heisenberg in 1927.

The uncertainty principle describes limits imposed by nature on the precision of *simultaneous* measurements of the position and momentum of an object. Mathematically stated, if an object is said to be at a position x within an uncertainty of Δx, then any simultaneous measurement of the x component of momentum must have an uncertainty Δp_x consistent with

$$\Delta x \, \Delta p_x \geq \hbar \tag{27.12}$$

This means that an increase in the accuracy of a position measurement must be accompanied by a decrease in the accuracy of the momentum measurement. The best that can be done even with idealized experiments is to have the equality hold, $\Delta x \, \Delta p_x = \hbar$. The x direction here is chosen arbitrarily; the uncertainty relation could equally well be stated as

$$\Delta y \, \Delta p_y \geq \hbar \tag{27.13}$$

Before pursuing the ramifications of these statements, we may ask just how important these naturally occurring limitations are.

Example 27.7

Suppose the velocities of an electron and of a rifle bullet of mass 0.03 kg are each measured with an uncertainty of $\Delta v = 10^{-3}$ m s^{-1}. What are the minimum uncertainties in their positions according to the uncertainty principle?

Using $\Delta p_x = m \, \Delta v_x$ for each, the minimum position uncertainty satisfies $\Delta x \, m \, \Delta v_x = \hbar$. For the electron $m = 9.11 \times 10^{-31}$ kg, so

$$\Delta x = \frac{\hbar}{m \, \Delta v_x} = \frac{1.055 \times 10^{-34} \text{ J s}}{(9.11 \times 10^{-31} \text{ kg})(10^{-3} \text{ m s}^{-1})}$$

$$= 0.116 \text{ m}$$

For the bullet,

$$\Delta x = \frac{\hbar}{m \, \Delta v_x} = \frac{1.055 \times 10^{-34} \text{ J s}}{(0.03 \text{ kg})(10^{-3} \text{ m s}^{-1})}$$

$$= 3.5 \times 10^{-30} \text{ m}$$

We can see from the preceding example that for normal macroscopic objects such as the bullet, the uncertainty principle does not impose any effective limit on experimental measurements because errors in position measurements are always very much larger than 10^{-30} m. However, the opposite is true of objects as small as electrons. For example, since atoms in a solid are about 10^{-9} m apart, a position measurement with an uncertainty of about 0.1 m means that the electron could be anywhere among billions of atoms!

The uncertainty principle leads to the conclusion that, in any experiment, one cannot simultaneously observe the wave and particle properties of light or matter. This can be illustrated with a double-slit interference experiment performed with electrons. Consider a beam of monoenergetic electrons incident on two slits of width $d/4$ a distance d apart (Fig. 27.14). Since the electrons have a wavelength $\lambda = h/p$ associated with them, an interference pat-

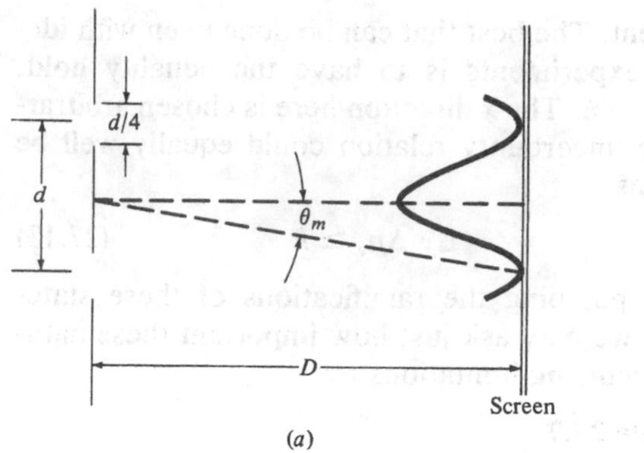

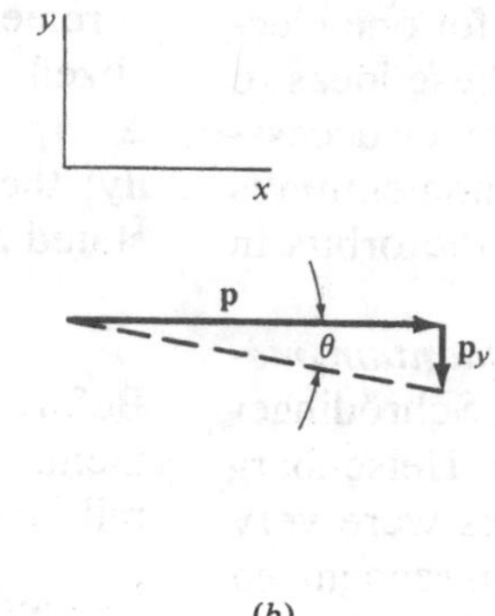

Figure 27.14. (*a*) Electrons of wavelength $\lambda = h/p$ are incident from the left. After passing through the slits, they form an interference pattern at the screen. (*b*) The slit area is shown much enlarged; in practice, $D \gg d$ and θ is very small.

tern will be detected at the screen. From Chapter Twenty-three, we know that there will be an intensity maximum at $\theta = 0$, and the first minimum occurs when $\sin\theta = \lambda/2d$. As long as $\lambda/2d$ is small, we can use $\sin\theta \simeq \theta$, so the first minimum occurs at

$$\theta_m = \frac{\lambda}{2d}$$

Thus a measurement of θ_m can be used to determine the wavelength λ. This value can be compared with de Broglie's prediction to test his hypothesis.

The interference pattern is a manifestation of the wave properties of electrons. However, electrons also have particle properties. If they are regarded as particles, we should be able to say which slit each electron passes through. This might be done by having a beam of photons passing to the right of the slits, so that each time an electron goes through a slit, it will collide with a photon. The electron proceeds toward the screen, but the scattered photon can be detected and the area of the collision located. For example, if the collision takes place above the centerline of Fig. 27.14, we would say the electron went through the upper slit, and its position uncertainty at the slits would be, at most, $\Delta y = d/4$, the slit width.

We must find out what our measurements mean in the light of the uncertainty principle. The uncertainty principle requires that $\Delta y\, \Delta p_y \geq \hbar$. Since $\hbar = h/2\pi$,

$$\Delta p_y \geq \frac{h}{2\pi\, \Delta y} = \frac{h}{2\pi d/4} = \frac{2h}{\pi d}$$

The angular deflection of the electron is then at least

$$\theta = \frac{\Delta p_y}{p} = \frac{2h/\pi d}{h/\lambda} = \frac{2\lambda}{\pi d}$$

But this deflection is larger than $\theta_m = \lambda/2d$, the angular position of the interference minimum. This means that the interference pattern will be hopelessly blurred if we determine which slit the electron passes through. The act of measurement that pinpoints the electron as a particle going through one slit also destroys the evidence of the wave property of the electron!

Viewed in this way, the uncertainty principle is nature's way of ensuring that the wave and particle properties of an object cannot be simultaneously observed. We also face the extraordinary fact that *the measurement process itself affects the results.* In the case illustrated, the measurement of the electron position deflects the particle enough to destroy the interference pattern.

It is important to realize that the interference pattern is caused by the matter wave of a single electron interfering with itself. For example, if the beam of electrons has a very low intensity, then usually at most one electron is in the apparatus; rarely are there two or more present at once. Nevertheless, the interference pattern is still formed. If we run the experiment long enough to get sufficient data, the distribution of electrons follows the characteristic double-slit pattern.

This wave character of electrons and of all matter is a truly amazing property of nature. It has been verified directly and indirectly in a wide range of experiments, and it forms the foundation of modern quantum physics. The concept that matter can sometimes behave much like a classical particle and at other times more like a wave is a necessary ingredient of any description of atomic and subatomic phenomena.

We conclude this section by considering the question raised in the previous section: Why doesn't an electron radiate energy and drop into the nucleus where its potential energy would be much lower than it is in the first Bohr orbit? Suppose an electron is within a distance r of the nucleus. Then we could say that we know its position within an uncertainty $\Delta x = r$. From the uncertainty principle, the electron momentum cannot be zero, and it must be at least $p = \Delta p_x = \hbar/r$. The total energy of the electron is then at least (for $Z = 1$)

$$E = \frac{1}{2}mv^2 - \frac{ke^2}{r} = \frac{p^2}{2m} - \frac{ke^2}{r} = \frac{\hbar^2}{2mr^2} - \frac{ke^2}{r}$$

If the electron approaches the nucleus, r becomes small; the potential energy $-ke^2/r$ becomes more negative, but the kinetic energy $\hbar^2/2mr^2$ increases (Fig. 27.15). We would expect the electron to stay at an average radius r such that its total energy is a minimum. This occurs when r equals the Bohr radius $a_0 = \hbar^2/kme^2$. Thus the lowest energy state of an atom is not one with the electron in the nucleus. The uncertainty principle requires that the kinetic energy becomes large as the position uncertainty decreases, more than offsetting the reduction in the potential energy.

We see from this discussion that the stability of atoms and of matter depends on the uncertainty principle.

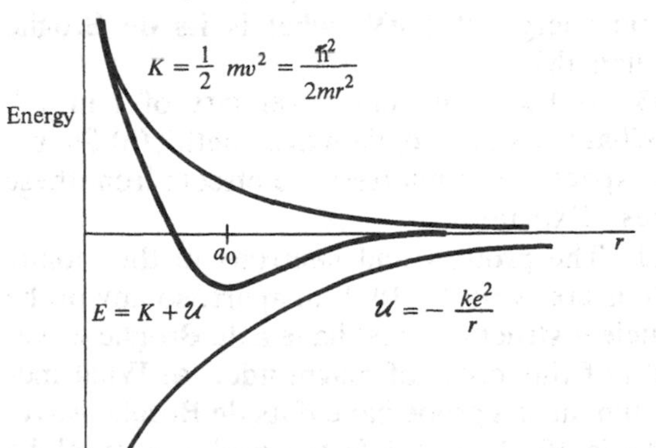

Figure 27.15. The kinetic and potential energy contributions to give the total energy $E = \lambda + \mathcal{U}$. The total energy is a minimum at $r = a_0$.

SUMMARY

Matter, as well as light, has both wave and particle characteristics. The wavelength is associated with the momentum of an object according to de Broglie's relationship,

$$\lambda = \frac{h}{p}$$

where h is Planck's constant. This concept is one of the fundamental ideas of quantum theory.

By combining the wave properties of electrons with the picture of an atom as a massive, positively charged nucleus with orbiting electrons, Bohr was able to find the energy levels for an atom with one electron. The allowed energy levels have energies

$$E_n = -\frac{Z^2}{n^2}E_0, \qquad n = 1, 2, 3 \ldots$$

where $E_0 = 13.6$ eV. Photons with specific energies are emitted or absorbed when an electron goes from one energy level to another.

The uncertainty principle describes a natural limit to the precision of simultaneous measurements of the position and momentum of particles,

$$\Delta x \, \Delta p_x \geq \hbar$$

It also implies that either wave or particle properties, but not both, may be observed in a given experiment.

Checklist

Define or explain:

nuclear atom	quantized angular momentum
discrete spectra	Bohr radius
Balmer formula	ground state
Rydberg constant	excited state
de Broglie wavelength	energy levels
electron diffraction	quantum number
neutron diffraction	uncertainty principle
electron microscope	wave–particle duality
Bohr atom	

REVIEW QUESTIONS

Q27-1 Rutherford's experiments led to the idea that an atom was composed of a massive _____ nucleus with _____ orbiting outside it.

Q27-2 True or false? When the light from a discharge in hydrogen gas is passed through a diffraction grating, a continuous spectrum of colors is seen.

Q27-3 De Broglie postulated that there is a relationship between the _____ of an object and the wavelength associated with it.

Q27-4 Electron diffraction is an example of the appearance of the _____ properties of what were originally considered "particles."

Q27-5 The de Broglie wavelength of large objects is irrelevant because it is so _____.

Q27-6 In Bohr's model, it is the _____ force that holds the atom together.

Q27-7 The incorporation by Bohr of angular momentum quantization in an otherwise classical theory is equivalent to the idea that the electron _____ "fits" into the allowed orbits.

Q27-8 The spectral lines discovered for hydrogen are explained by the _____ or _____ of photons as electrons move from one allowed energy level to another.

Q27-9 The uncertainty principle explains why an electron does not get arbitrarily _____ to the nucleus to lower its energy.

Q27-10 The uncertainty principle plays no significant role in classical phenomena because the predicted uncertainties are _____.

EXERCISES

Section 27.1 | Failures of Classical Physics

27-1 A 4.8-MeV (1 MeV = 10^6 eV) α particle makes a head-on collision with a gold nucleus ($Z = 79$ for gold). What is the distance of closest approach of the α particle and the gold nucleus at which the α particle has zero kinetic energy? (Neglect the kinetic energy transferred to the gold nucleus.)

27-2 A gold ($Z = 79$) nucleus has a radius of about 7×10^{-15} m. If an α particle gets within the nuclear radius, the scattering will differ from that produced by a point charge. At what incident energy, in MeV, will the α particle have zero kinetic energy at a distance of 7×10^{-15} m from the center of the nucleus?

27-3 In hydrogen, the proton radius is 0.8×10^{-15} m and the average distance of the electron from the proton center is 5.3×10^{-11} m. If the proton is represented by an orange 0.06 m in radius, how far away will the electron be?

27-4 Find the longest wavelength radiation corresponding to $n_f = 3$ for hydrogen.

27-5 What is the wavelength of the visible light of atomic hydrogen corresponding to $n = 4$?

27-6 What is the wavelength of the ultraviolet radiation from hydrogen corresponding to $n_i = 2$ and $n_f = 1$?

Section 27.2 | The de Broglie Wave Hypothesis

27-7 An electron has a de Broglie wavelength of 10^{-10} m. Find its kinetic energy in electron volts.

27-8 Find the de Broglie wavelength of a baseball of mass 0.15 kg moving at 30 m s^{-1}.

27-9 An electron and a photon each have a wavelength of 0.1 nm. What are their momenta?

27-10 Compare the de Broglie wavelengths of an electron and a neutron each having energy $\frac{3}{2}k_BT$, where $T = 300$ K.

27-11 What is the de Broglie wavelength associated with the earth in its motion about the sun? (The earth's mass is 6×10^{24} kg, and its orbital radius is 1.5×10^{11} m.)

27-12 An oxygen atom has a mass of 16 u, where 1 u = 1.66×10^{-27} kg. If the atom has a kinetic energy of 1 eV, what is its de Broglie wavelength?

27-13 A 1-kg mass has a velocity of 1 m s^{-1}. (a) What is its de Broglie wavelength? (b) Should one expect to see interference effects from these waves? Explain.

27-14 The protons and neutrons in the atomic nucleus are typically 10^{-15} m apart, so any probe of nuclear structure must have a de Broglie wavelength of this order of magnitude. (a) What momentum must a probe have if its de Broglie wavelength is 10^{-15} m? (b) If the probe is an alpha particle of mass 6.64×10^{-27} kg, what is its kinetic energy in electron volts?

27-15 Electrons incident on a set of crystal

planes at an angle of 20° to the planes interfere constructively and form a spot on a photographic plate. If the crystal planes are 0.12 nm apart, find (a) the wavelength of the electrons; (b) the energy of the electrons.

27-16 Neutrons with a de Broglie wavelength of 0.3 nm are needed to perform a molecular structure experiment. (a) What is the velocity of these neutrons? (b) A monoenergetic neutron pulse can be made by opening a nuclear reactor port and using only those neutrons that reach the target within a certain time interval. How long will it take the neutrons in part (a) to travel 10 m?

Section 27.3 | The Bohr Atom

27-17 Can a hydrogen atom absorb a photon of energy greater than 13.6 eV? Explain.

27-18 In an electric discharge tube, an electron in a hydrogen atom is excited from the $n = 1$ to the $n = 4$ level. (a) How much energy has the atom absorbed? (b) Sketch an energy level diagram showing all the transitions that the electron may make in returning to the $n = 1$ level. (c) What is the wavelength of the most energetic photon that may be emitted?

27-19 The binding energy of a one-electron atom is the energy necessary to completely remove the electron from the atom. What are the binding energies in electron volts of (a) hydrogen; (b) singly ionized helium; (c) doubly ionized lithium?

27-20 How many wavelengths of an electron "fit" into the orbit if it is in the $n = 3$ energy level in hydrogen?

27-21 If a photon of energy 2.55 eV is emitted when an electron drops out of the $n = 4$ level of hydrogen, into which level will it drop?

27-22 What frequency photon is absorbed when an electron in hydrogen jumps from the $n = 2$ to the $n = 4$ energy level?

27-23 The *Pfund* series in hydrogen corresponds to electrons dropping from higher orbits to the $n = 4$ level. What is the longest wavelength in this series?

27-24 An atomic physicist uses a laser beam to ionize hydrogen atoms. What is the maximum wavelength of this light source?

27-25 Two hydrogen atoms in the ground state collide inelastically, losing 20 eV of kinetic energy. One atom remains in the ground state, and an electron is ejected from the other atom. What is its kinetic energy?

27-26 Two hydrogen atoms in the ground state collide inelastically. What is the minimum amount in electron volts by which their combined kinetic energy can be reduced?

27-27 Carry out the algebraic steps to derive Eq. 27.8 from Eq. 27.7 and the angular momentum quantization postulate.

27-28 Compute the numerical value of the Bohr radius, $a_0 = \hbar^2/kme^2$, from the values of the fundamental constants listed on the inside rear cover.

27-29 Compute the numerical value of R_H from the formula in Eq. 27.11 and the values of the fundamental constants listed on the inside rear cover.

27-30 Compute the numerical value of $E_0 = ke^2/2a_0$ from the values of the fundamental constants listed on the inside rear cover.

Section 27.4 | The Uncertainty Principle

27-31 An electron is confined to a region of 0.1 m. What is the uncertainty in its velocity?

27-32 Find the uncertainty in the velocity of a 60-kg woman with a position uncertainty equal to the Bohr radius.

27-33 What is the position uncertainty of a 0.1-kg stone if its velocity is uncertain by 0.003 m s^{-1}?

27-34 What is the minimum kinetic energy of a particle of mass 10^{-29} kg if its position uncertainty is 10^{-10} m?

27-35 Suppose that an electron and a stone of mass 0.2 kg each have the same position uncertainty, 10^{-10} m. Find for each (a) the minimum momentum uncertainties; (b) the minimum velocity uncertainties.

PROBLEMS

27-36 If the angular momentum of the earth in its motion about the sun satisfies Bohr's angular momentum hypothesis, $L = rmv = n\hbar$, what is the quantum number associated with the earth's orbit? (The earth's mass is 5.98×10^{24} kg, and the orbital radius is 1.50×10^{11} m.)

***27-37** Bohr's theory can be used for positronium, a negative electron and a positron (positive electron) orbiting around one another. (*Note*: Since both particles have the same mass, they circle about the center of mass, halfway between them. The atom must be analyzed as if one particle with half the mass of an electron orbits around the stationary second particle.) (a) What is the binding energy of positronium in its ground state? (b) What is the radius of the lowest energy orbit?

***27-38** The dimensionless number $\alpha = ke^2/\hbar c$ is called the *fine structure constant* and is almost exactly 1/137 (c is the velocity of light). (a) What is the velocity of an electron in the lowest energy level of a one-electron atom with atomic number Z, expressed as a fraction of c, the velocity of light? (b) The model of a one-electron atom given in this chapter does not take relativistic effects into account. Thus we would expect that for atoms with v/c fairly large, the numerical predictions of the model will fail. For what value of Z would the model fail completely? Explain your reasoning.

27-39 A negative mu meson (μ^-) has a mass 207 times that of an electron and charge $-e$. It can orbit a nucleus much like an electron. If a μ^- orbits a sulfur nucleus ($Z = 16$), find (a) the lowest energy level; (b) the corresponding average radius. (c) Find the ratio of this orbital radius to that of the sulfur nucleus, 4×10^{-15} m.

***27-40** The conduction electrons in a metal may be considered as free particles in a box the size of the sample. As a start to such a model, consider an electron moving in one dimension with momentum p. The de Broglie wavelength must "fit" between walls a distance D apart with a node at each wall. (a) Draw the longest and next to longest waves that will "fit" between the walls. (b) What is the momentum associated with the longest wave that will "fit" between the walls? (c) What are all of the allowed values of the kinetic energy of an electron? (d) If $D = 0.01$ m, what is the spacing between the lowest two energy levels?

27-41 Hydrogen atoms initially in the ground state are exposed to photons of energies up to 13 eV. What energy photons will be produced as the atoms are excited and return to their ground states? (Neglect the recoil of the atoms during the absorption and emission processes.)

27-42 What are the average velocities of electrons in the lowest energy states of (a) hydrogen; (b) singly ionized helium? (c) Would you expect relativistic effects to be important in either case?

***27-43** Bohr's quantum condition states that the angular momentum L must be some integer times $\hbar$. This condition can also be applied to the rotation of a diatomic molecule. If we assume that a diatomic molecule is like a dumbbell (Fig. 27.16) with a moment of inertia I, its angular momentum is $L = I\omega$, where ω is the rotational angular velocity of the molecule. The kinetic energy is $K = \frac{1}{2}I\omega^2 = L^2/2I$. (a) Apply Bohr's quantum condition to the rotating molecule and find a general expression for the energy levels. (b) Sketch an energy level diagram for the four lowest levels. (The complete quantum theory gives the result that $L^2 = n(n + 1)\hbar^2$. The energy levels of the rotating diatomic molecule are then correctly given by $n(n + 1)\hbar^2/2I$.)

27-44 The moment of inertia of the O_2 molecule is 1.92×10^{-46} kg m^2. (a) What is the energy of the photon emitted during a rotational transition of the molecule from the $n = 2$ to the $n = 0$ level? (See Problem 27-43.) (b) What is the wavelength of this photon?

27-45 A hydrogen atom emits light of wavelength 486 nm. (a) What is the corresponding fre-

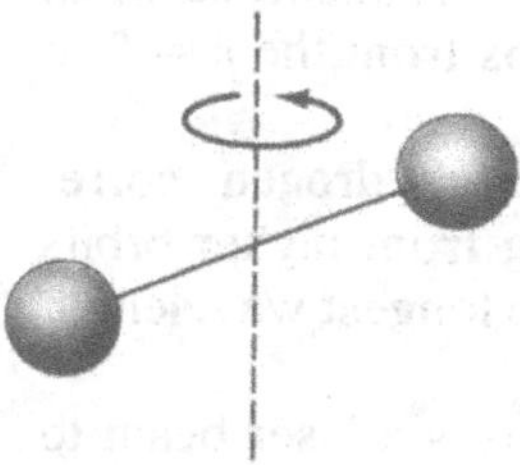

Figure 27.16. Problem 27-43. A dumbbell model of a diatomic molecule.

quency? (b) How much energy did the electron lose as it emitted the photon? (c) What were its initial and final values of n?

27-46 A double-slit interference experiment is performed with electrons. No attempt is made to determine which slit each electron passes through, so the position uncertainty of the electrons equals the slit separation d. Show that the uncertainty in the angle through which the electrons are deflected is less than $\theta_m = \lambda/2d$.

***27-47** Assume that the smallest average distance of an electron from the proton in hydrogen is $a_0 + \varepsilon$, where a_0 is the Bohr radius and ε is much smaller than a_0. Show, using the uncertainty principle argument of Section 27.4, that the energy of the electron is smallest for $\varepsilon = 0$.

27-48 Before Chadwick discovered the neutron in 1932, it was suggested that atomic nuclei were composed of protons and electrons. For example, a carbon nucleus has a mass of about 12 proton masses, but only 6 units of charge, so it was considered to have 12 positive protons and 6 negative electrons. (a) Show that, according to the uncertainty principle, the minimum kinetic energy for an electron confined to a box of size 10^{-14} m (a typical nuclear size) is much larger than the typical 1-MeV = 10^6-eV spacing of nuclear energy levels. (b) Is this true also for neutrons? (This problem should actually be solved using the theory of special relativity, but the qualitative conclusion is the same as found using $E = p^2/2m$.)

ANSWERS TO REVIEW QUESTIONS

Q27-1, positively charged, electrons; **Q27-2**, false; **Q27-3**, momentum; **Q27-4**, wave; **Q27-5**, small; **Q27-6**, electric; **Q27-7**, wave; **Q27-8**, absorption, emission; **Q27-9**, close; **Q27-10**, very small.

Additional Reading

Niels Bohr Centennial, *Physics Today*, October 1985, p. 23. Several articles on Bohr's contributions.

C. E. Behrens, Atomic Theory from 1904–1913, *American Journal of Physics*, vol. 11, 1943, p. 60; The Early Development of the Bohr Atom, p. 135; Further Developments of Bohr's Early Atomic Theory, p. 272.

T. H. Osgood and H. S. Hirst, Rutherford and His Alpha Particles, *American Journal of Physics*, vol. 32, 1964, p. 681.

G. P. Thomson, J. J. Thomson and the Discovery of the Electron, *Physics Today*, August 1956, p. 19.

M. A. Medicus, Fifty Years of Matter Waves, *Physics Today*, vol. 27, February 1974, p. 38.

Bruce R. Wheaton, Louis de Broglie and the Origins of Wave Mechanics, *The Physics Teacher*, vol. 22, 1984, p. 297.

C. Jönsson, Electron Diffraction at Multiple Slits, *American Journal of Physics*, vol. 42, 1974, p. 4.

George Gamow, *Mr. Tomkins in Wonderland: Stories of c, G, and h*. Macmillan Publishing Company, New York, 1940. A world in which h is so large that quantum mechanics is part of daily life.

George Gamow, *Thirty Years That Shook Physics*, Anchor Books, New York, 1966.

John L. Heilbron, J. J. Thomson and the Bohr Atom, *Physics Today*, vol. 30, April 1977, p. 23.

F. P. Ottensmeyer, Scattered Electrons in Microscopy and Microanalysis, *Science*, vol. 215, January 29, 1982, p. 461.

Ferdinand G. Brickwedde, Harold Urey and the Discovery of Deuterium, *Physics Today*, September 1982, p. 34.

Scientific American articles:

Karl K. Darrow, The Quantum Theory, March 1952, p. 47.

R. Furth, The Limits of Measurement, July 1950, p. 48.

George Gamow, The Principle of Uncertainty, January 1958, p. 51.

Yoseph Imry and Richard A. Webb, Quantum Interference and the Aharonov–Bohm Effect, April 1989, p. 56.

Karl K. Darrow, Davisson and Germer, May 1948, p. 50.

Erwin Schrödinger, What Is Matter? September 1953, p. 52.

E. N. DaCosta Andrade, The Birth of the Nuclear Atom, November 1956, p. 93.

Albert V. Crewe, A High Resolution Scanning Electron Microscope, April 1971, p. 26.

Thomas E. Eberhart and Thomas L. Hayes, The Scanning Electron Microscope, January 1972, p. 54.

Urve Essmann and Hermann Träuble, The Magnetic Structure of Superconductors, March 1971, p. 74.

F. Reif, Quantized Vortex Rings in Superfluid Helium, December 1964, p. 116.

Lester H. Germer, The Structure of Crystal Surfaces, March 1965, p. 32.

Donald M. Engelman and Peter B. Moore, Neutron Scattering Studies of the Ribosome, October 1976, p. 44.

S. W. Hawking, The Quantum Mechanics of Black Holes, January 1977, p. 34.

Phillip Ekstrom and David Wineland, The Isolated Electron, August 1980, p. 104.

Abner Shimony, The Reality of the Quantum World, January 1988, p. 46.

Allan H. Sørensen and Erik Uggerhøf, The Channeling of Electrons and Positrons, June 1989, p. 96.

UNIT EIGHT

ATOMS AND MOLECULES

We have seen that the failure of classical physics to explain several crucial experiments led to fundamental changes in scientists' view of the physical world. Specifically, physicists now believe that wave–particle duality, and in some cases special relativity, must be built into any theory of microscopic phenomena that can hope to be successful. The modern quantum mechanics developed by Schrödinger and others has extended the basic ideas of Planck, Einstein, de Broglie, and Bohr into a more general and complete theory of matter and energy. In this unit, we study the application of quantum mechanics to the structure of atoms and molecules, including such topics as lasers and methods of probing the structure of complex biological molecules.

CHAPTER 28 QUANTUM MECHANICS AND ATOMIC STRUCTURE

In 1925, Schrödinger proposed an equation whose solutions would represent the matter waves associated with electrons or other "particles." This *wave equation* and some related concepts introduced soon afterward comprise what has come to be called quantum mechanics. Quantum mechanics has been highly successful in predicting and correlating a vast amount of information about atoms. It is also able to deal successfully with aggregates of atoms and with atomic nuclei, as we shall see in later chapters.

Schrödinger noticed that starting from Newton's laws, it is possible to obtain an equation for the disturbance associated with a wave traveling along a string or in an acoustical medium. Similarly, from the laws of electricity and magnetism, one can find an equation for the electric and magnetic fields in an electromagnetic wave. Thus for any classical wave there is a wave equation whose solutions are formulas for the possible wave disturbances, or *wave functions*.

Schrödinger reasoned that de Broglie's matter wave hypothesis might explain why atoms have discrete energy levels. While waves generally can have any wavelength, boundary conditions can restrict the possible values. For example, sound waves in a pipe or waves on a string with fixed ends form resonant standing waves only when they "fit." If the matter waves in an atom could have only specific wavelengths, the corresponding momenta and energies would also be discrete.

Accordingly, Schrödinger developed a procedure for constructing the wave equation for a particle or system of particles if the force or forces acting among them are known. For example, in a hydrogen atom consisting of a proton and an electron, this force is the electrical attraction given by Coulomb's law. The equation relates derivatives of the wave function, and solving it in most situations involves mathematical complexities beyond the level of this book. However, we do summarize the results for the hydrogen atom in this chapter. We also develop and apply Schrödinger's equation for a few idealized situations in the Supplementary Topics.

Schrödinger's equation determines the quantum mechanical wave function $\psi(x)$ (Greek letter psi), the analog for a matter wave in an atom or molecule of the displacement $y(x)$ for a wave on a string. Its absolute value squared $|\psi(x)|^2$ is proportional to the probability of finding the particle at the point x.

In classical physics, the *state* of a system at any instant in time is defined by giving the positions and velocities of all the objects making up the system. The uncertainty principle tells us that such a detailed description is impossible at the microscopic level. Classically, we can predict with arbitrary accuracy the results of a measurement on a system whose state we know. However, in quantum mechanics the specification of the state of a physical system provided by the wave function only enables us to make probabilistic or statistical statements about the outcomes of many kinds of experiments.

The wave function itself cannot be directly measured or observed. However, if we know the wave function, we can compute measurable quantities such as the energy of an atom or a molecule. Also, from the appropriate wave functions, we can predict the outcome of experiments, such as the double-slit electron interference experiment discussed in the previous chapter. The results of all such analyses are consistent with the uncertainty principle and with de Broglie's wave hypothesis. Thus these two concepts are embedded firmly in quantum mechanics.

A remarkable example of the parallel development of major scientific ideas is the fact that Werner Heisenberg developed an entirely different form of quantum mechanics at almost the same time that Schrödinger did his initial work. Heisenberg represented observable quantities, such as the position or momentum of an electron, by mathematical quantities called matrices and proposed certain equations relating these matrices. Although no wave functions appeared in his theory, it was soon realized that its predictions are always identical to those of Schrödinger's wave theory. Hence the matrix and wave forms of quantum mechanics are completely equivalent. We restrict our discussions to Schrödinger's approach, although Heisenberg's methods are sometimes more convenient for detailed calculations.

28.1 | THE OUTLINE OF QUANTUM MECHANICS

In this chapter, we discuss those aspects of Shrödinger's theory that are important in understanding atomic structure. This will also set the foundation for our picture of how atoms combine to form molecules.

There are many major differences between Schrödinger's theory and Bohr's model of the hydrogen atom. The newer theory is fundamentally different in form. It is a wave theory in which boundary conditions determine the possible wave functions. Also, it is applicable to a much greater variety of physical systems, and it is much more successful in describing and predicting a wide range of phenomena. Nevertheless, Schrödinger's theory still preserves some of the central ideas of Bohr's model. The possible energies of electrons in an atom or molecule are quantized; electrons can only have certain specific energies. When the electron is in one of these allowed *quantum states,* it does not radiate, but an electron can make a quantum jump from one allowed state to another by emitting or absorbing a photon.

According to Bohr's model, the electron has certain allowed orbital radii labeled by a *quantum number*. Each value of the quantum number designates a unique configuration or quantum state of the system. There are as many quantum states as there are values of the quantum number, each with its own characteristic energy.

In Schrödinger's theory the full specification of an atomic state requires additional quantum numbers. Some of these are associated with the *orbital angular momentum* corresponding to the electronic motion about the nucleus. Others are associated with the *spin angular momentum* of the electrons or, more concisely, the electron *spin*. This spin can be pictured as due to a rotation somewhat like that of the earth about its axis. However, this classical analogy to the quantum mechanical concept of spin is of only limited applicability, since electrons have no discernible structure or size. Furthermore, all electrons have a spin angular momentum of exactly the same magnitude. Spin appears to be an intrinsic property of all the basic constituents of matter, the so-called *elementary particles*. These include not only the electron, proton, neutron, and photon but also some more recently discovered particles, such as neutrinos, mesons, and hyperons. The fact that all particles of a given type have the same spin cannot be explained classically.

In addition to lacking a classical analog, the spin angular momentum does not appear in the original form of Schrödinger's theory. Although spin can be inserted into this theory, it appears naturally in the theory only when special relativity is included at the outset. The existence of the electron spin was first found experimentally in studies of the properties of atoms and plays a crucial role in our understanding of the structure of matter.

In the next two sections, we describe the quantum numbers and wave functions found from Schrödinger's theory for the hydrogen atom. We will then be able to make the step to atoms with more than one electron.

28.2 | HYDROGEN ATOM QUANTUM NUMBERS

Schrödinger's theory requires the solution of an equation for a wave function ψ. It is found that each allowed configuration of any system has a unique wave function labeled by certain values of the quantum numbers. We describe the quantum numbers for atomic hydrogen in this section and the wave functions in the following section. The quantum numbers for hydrogen are n, l, m_l, and m_s. These are associated with the energy, the total orbital angular momentum, a component of the orbital angular momentum, and a component of the spin angular momentum, respectively.

The Principal Quantum Number n | In Schrödinger's original theory of hydrogen, the electronic energy levels are completely determined by a *principal quantum number n* and satisfy the Bohr formula

$$E_n = -\frac{Z^2}{n^2}E_0, \quad E_0 = \frac{ke^2}{2a_0} \quad \text{(Bohr formula)} \tag{28.1}$$

Using $Z = 1$ and $E_0 = 13.6$ eV,

$$E_n = -\frac{13.6}{n^2}\text{ eV}, \qquad n = 1, 2, 3, \ldots$$

This formula is only approximately correct. The more complete relativistic theory of hydrogen developed shortly after Schrödinger's original work includes the small magnetic forces associated with the motion of the charges in the atom. This relativistic theory leads to energy levels that have a slight dependence on other quantum numbers. The energy levels in multielectron atoms depend even more strongly on other quantum numbers because of the additional forces among the electrons.

The Angular Momentum Quantum Number l | In the Bohr model, one quantum number labeled both the angular momentum and the energy of each state. However, in solving Schrödinger's equation, it is found that the magnitude L of the total orbital angular momentum $\mathbf{L}$ is related to a separate quantum number l by

$$L = \sqrt{l(l+1)}\,\hbar, \qquad l = 0, 1, 2, \ldots, n-1 \tag{28.2}$$

Two important results should be noted. First, the angular momentum may be zero for any value of n. A classical picture of an electron with zero angular momentum would be one in which the electron moves back and forth directly through the nucleus! The second point is that for each value of n, l may be an integer up to an including $n - 1$.

TABLE 28.1

Spectroscopic notation for the first seven angular momentum states in atoms. The sequence is alphabetic for $l \geq 3$.

$l =$	0	1	2	3	4	5	6
Notation	s	p	d	f	g	h	i

A somewhat archaic nomenclature is still used to designate states with certain values of n and l. Table 28.1 shows the letters assigned to states with $l = 0$ through 6. With this notation, the state with $n = 1$, $l = 0$ is said to be the 1s state, while $n = 2$, $l = 0$ is the 2s state, and $n = 2$, $l = 1$ is the 2p state. Other states are denoted in a similar way.

The z Component of the Angular Momentum | The direction of the angular momentum of the one electron in hydrogen becomes important when a magnetic field is applied to the atom. An electron with an orbital angular momentum $\mathbf{L}$ is effectively a current loop or magnetic dipole. The energy of the loop depends on its orientation relative to the magnetic field $\mathbf{B}$ (Fig. 28.1).

In Section 19.5 on magnetic dipoles, we found that an electron of charge $-e$ and mass m moving in an orbit with angular momentum $\mathbf{L}$ has a magnetic dipole moment that is proportional to $\mathbf{L}$. In vector

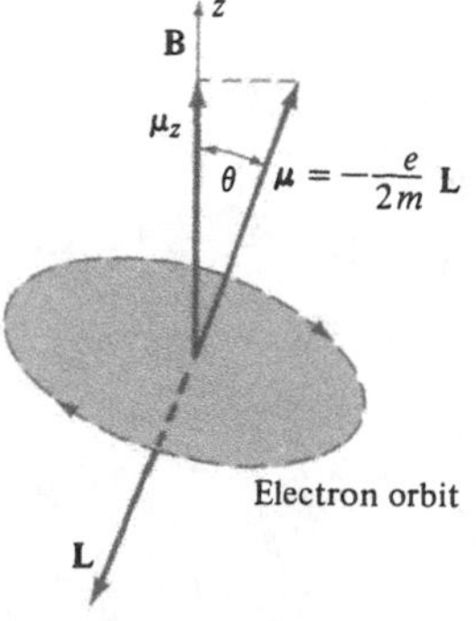

Figure 28.1. An electron with orbital angular momentum $\mathbf{L}$ has a magnetic dipole moment $\boldsymbol{\mu}$ opposite to $\mathbf{L}$ because the electron charge is negative. The energy of the dipole in the field $\mathbf{B}$ is $E = -\mu B$.

form, this relationship is

$$\boldsymbol{\mu} = \frac{e}{2m}\mathbf{L} \quad (28.3)$$

The minus sign is needed because the electronic charge is negative. The energy of the dipole in a magnetic field is $E = -\mu B \cos\theta$. If **B** is in the z direction, this can also be written in terms of the z component of $\boldsymbol{\mu}$ (Fig. 28.1),

$$E = -\mu_z B \quad (28.4)$$

Thus we expect that the energy of an electron due to a magnetic field can have any value between $-\mu B$ and $+\mu B$.

The electron can change its energy by emitting or absorbing a photon. Since its energy can vary between $-\mu B$ and $+\mu B$, the photons observed might be expected to have a spread of energies, but in experiments only certain photon energies are seen. The analysis of the experimens and Schrödinger's theory both show that L_z, the z component of **L**, can have only certain values:

$$L_z = m_l\hbar,$$

$$m_l = -l, -l+1, \ldots, 0, \ldots, l-1, l \quad (28.5)$$

Thus m_l, the quantum number denoting the z component of **L**, can have any of $2l + 1$ integer values for a given value of l (Fig. 28.2).

Since L_z can only have certain values, μ_z also has specific allowed values. The resulting energy levels

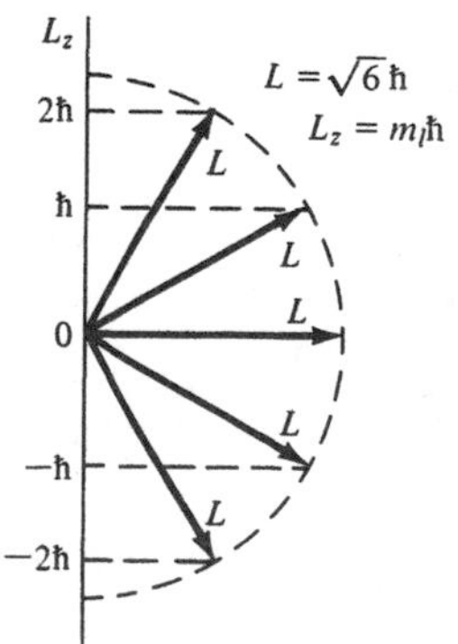

Figure 28.2. The allowed orientations of **L** for $l = 2$ correspond to five values of $L_z = m_l h$. Here m_l can have any of the values 0, ±1, ±2.

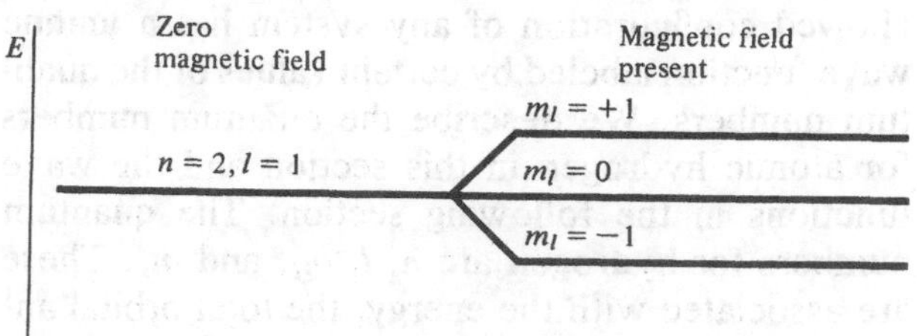

Figure 28.3. In the presence of a magnetic field, the $2p$ state is broken up into three energy levels corresponding to the three allowed values of m_l. In the $m_l = +1$ state, the magnetic dipole is parallel to the magnetic field: for $m_l = -1$, it is antiparallel, and for $m_l = 0$, it is perpendicular to the field.

are given (Fig. 28.3) by

$$E_{m_l} = -\mu_z B = -\left(-\frac{e}{2m}\right)m_l\hbar B = m_l\frac{e\hbar}{2m}B$$

The quantity $\mu_B = e\hbar/2m$ is a convenient unit for magnetic moments. It is called the *Bohr magneton* and has the numerical value

$$\mu_B = \frac{e\hbar}{2m} = 9.27 \times 10^{-24}\ \mathrm{J\ T^{-1}} \quad \text{(Bohr magneton)} \quad (28.6)$$

In terms of this unit, we rewrite the energy levels in the magnetic field as

$$E_{m_l} = m_l\mu_B B \quad (28.7)$$

The following examples illustrate the enumeration of the states and the calculation of their energy differences.

Example 28.1

What are the allowed values of l and m_l for states of the hydrogen atom with $n = 2$?

For $n = 2$, the orbital angular momentum number l can be either 0 or 1. For $l = 0$, we can only have $m_l = 0$; for $l = l$, m_l can be −1, 0, or +1. In tabular form,

State (n, l, m_l)	n	l	m_l
$2s$ state (2, 0, 0)	2	0	0
$2p$ states			
(2, 1, −1)	2	1	−1
(2, 1, 0)	2	1	0
(2, 1, 1)	2	1	1

We see that for $n = 2$, there are four possible combinations of the quantum numbers l and m_l. However, we see below that an additional quantum number is needed to specify fully all the $n = 2$ states.

Example 28.2

Hydrogen atoms in the $2p$ state are in a magnetic field of 2 T. What frequency radiation must be supplied to cause electrons to jump from the $m_l = 0$ state to the $m_l = 1$ state?

The energy of the atom in the magnetic field is $E_{m_l} = m_l \mu_B B$. If m_l increases by 1, then the energy increases by $\Delta E = (1)\mu_B B$. It does this by absorbing a photon with an energy hf that equals ΔE. Thus the frequency of the radiation must be

$$f = \frac{\Delta E}{h} = \frac{\mu_B B}{h}$$

$$= \frac{(9.27 \times 10^{-24}\ \mathrm{J\ T^{-1}})(2\ \mathrm{T})}{6.63 \times 10^{-34}\ \mathrm{J\ s}} = 2.80 \times 10^{10}\ \mathrm{Hz}$$

Spin Angular Momentum

When experiments were performed on atoms in a magnètic field, the energy levels were found to be split, but more levels were observed than anticipated. Furthermore, even when no external magnetic field was present, it was found that many of the observed spectral lines were, in fact, closely spaced pairs of lines or *doublets*. These energy-level splittings led to the conclusion that the electron has not only an orbital angular momentum but also an intrinsic spin angular momentum with an associated magnetic dipole moment. The observed effects were explained in terms of both the orbital and spin magnetic moments.

The magnitude of the spin angular momentum **S** of a particle is found to be (Fig. 28.4)

$$S = \sqrt{s(s+1)}\,\hbar \qquad (28.8)$$

where s is the *spin quantum number*. For electrons, $s = \frac{1}{2}$, as it is for protons and neutrons; for photons, $s = 1$. These particles are said to have spin one-half and spin one, respectively.

In atomic structure, it is the z component of the spin angular momentum S_z that is importnat. For a spin one-half particle, S_z is

$$S_z = m_s\hbar, \quad m_s = \tfrac{1}{2}, -\tfrac{1}{2} \qquad (28.9)$$

Despite the fact that **S** never points directly along the z axis, the two states $m_s = \pm\frac{1}{2}$ are often referred to as spin up ($m_s = \frac{1}{2}$) and spin down ($m_s = -\frac{1}{2}$).

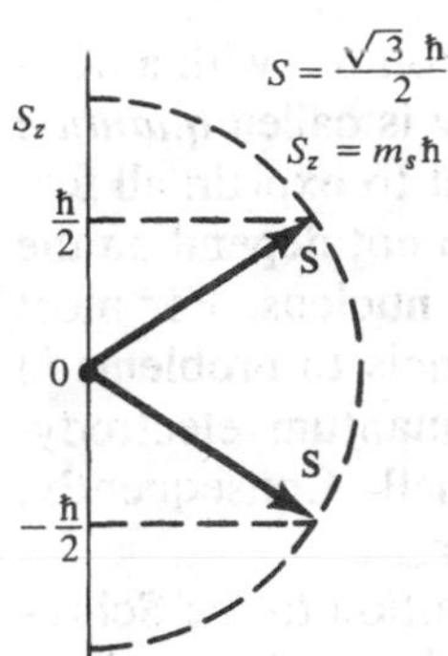

Figure 28.4. For electrons, with spin $\frac{1}{2}$, the z component of the spin angular momentum is either $+\hbar/2$ or $-\hbar/2$. **S** is always at an angle with the z axis.

Thus for every set of values for n, l, and m_l, there are two allowed values of m_s. This means that the results of Example 28.1 are incomplete. There are two $n = 1$ states and either, rather than four, $n = 2$ states.

The electron spin accounts for the extra observed spectral lines. The electron has an orbital and a spin magnetic moment, and these two dipoles may have two possible relative orientations corresponding to the two values of S_z. Hence all the energy levels are split into two, giving rise to the doublet spectral lines observed. This is called the *spin-orbit splitting*, or *fine structure*.

Later Developments

In the two decades following Schrödinger's work, theory and experiment were found to be in excellent agreement for hydrogen and for more complex atoms. However, after World War II, totally new tools were applied to the study of atomic structure. Most notable was the use of short-wavelength electromagnetic radiation (microwaves) employing technology developed in wartime radar research. It was found that the existing theory failed to predict small but significant details of the measurements.

Feynman, Schwinger, Tomonaga, and others showed that agreement with experiment could be restored if several new processes were taken into account. These processes included the emission and reabsorption of photons by electrons in atoms and the spontaneous production of short-lived pairs of electrons and *positrons*. The positron is a particle with the same mass as the electron but with a positive charge $+e$. This new theory is called *quantum electrodynamics* and is sufficient to explain all features of atomic structure that do not depend on the internal structure of the atomic nucleus. For most applications of quantum mechancis to problems in chemistry and biochemistry, quantum electrodynamic effects are negligibly small. Consequently, we do not consider them further.

In summary, the complete solution to the Schrödinger's equation for hydrogen shows that neglecting spin, the energy levels are given correctly by the Bohr model if no external fields are present. The multiplicity of the states for a given energy level can be found from the splitting in a magnetic field. In the next section, we examine the wave functions corresponding to different sets of quantum numbers.

28.3 | HYDROGEN ATOM WAVE FUNCTIONS

As we mentioned earlier, the wave functions used to describe the states available to electrons are not measurable quantities. However, these wave functions are used to calculate measurable quantities such as the energy and angular momentum of a state. The wave function, denoted by ψ, is the analog of the displacement in the standing waves on strings and in air columns. In quantum mechanics the wave function is most directly related to the probability of finding an electron at a certain position when it is in a given state.

The square of the absolute value of the wave function, $P = |\psi|^2$, is a measure of the probability of finding an electron at a given point in space. (Sometimes ψ contains $\sqrt{-1}$ and is therefore a complex quantity. However, $|\psi|^2$ is a positive, real number as we would expect for a probability. If ψ is real, then $|\psi|^2 = \psi^2$.) Graphs of the wave functions and of $|\psi|^2$ for the $n = 1$ and 2 states of hydrogen are shown in Fig. 28.5. Three-dimensional representations of $|\psi|^2$ (Fig. 28.6) can be thought of as superpositions of many photographs of the electron position. An electron is most likely to be found in the darker areas.

What is the probability of locating an electron at a given radius r? The probability of finding an electron in a given small volume ΔV is proportional to ΔV; the larger the detector, the greater the chance of finding the electron. Thus the probability of finding the electron in ΔV is determined by the product $|\psi|^2\Delta V$. A sphere of radius r has a surface area $A = 4\pi r^2$, and a thin spherical shell of thickness Δr has a volume $\Delta V = A\Delta r = 4\pi r^2\,\Delta r$, which varies as r^2. (For example, an orange peel of a given thickness has a volume that is proportional to the square of its radius.) Hence the probability of finding an electron within a spherical shell of radius r is proportional to the *radial probability*, $r^2P = r^2|\psi|^2$. These radial probabilities for the $n = 1$ and 2 states are shown in Fig. 28.7.

From the $n = 1$, $l = 0$ (1*s*) graph in Fig. 28.5, we see that ψ and $|\psi|^2$ are largest at $r = 0$, suggesting a relatively large probability of finding a 1*s* electron near the nucleus. However, because of the r^2 factor, the radial probability is zero at $r = 0$; its greatest value occurs at $r = a_0$ (Fig. 28.7). The nuclear radius is about 10,000 times smaller than the Bohr radius. On the graphs, the nuclear radius falls within the width of the line representing the vertical

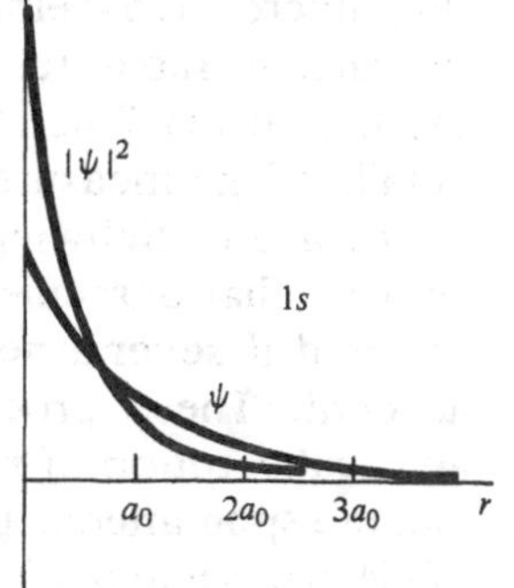

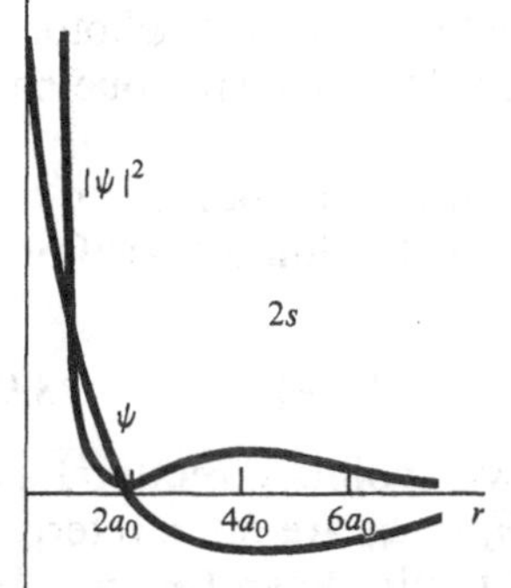

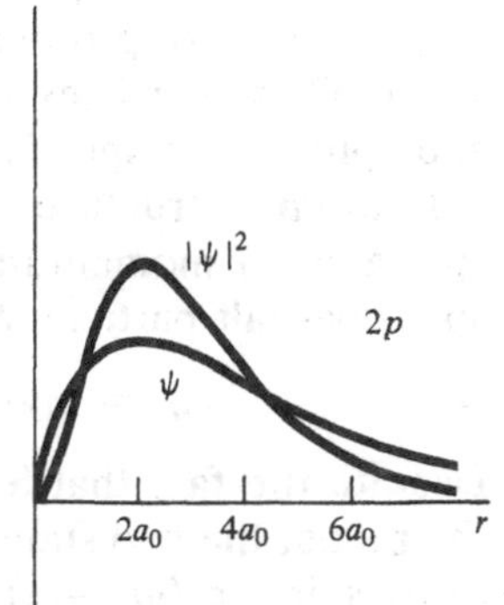

Figure 28.5. Graphs of the radial variation of ψ and $|\psi|^2$ for the $n = 1$ and $n = 2$ states of hydrogen. The *p* state wave functions vary with the direction as well. a_0 is the radius of the first Bohr orbit. The graphs are drawn with an arbitrary vertical scale for clarity.

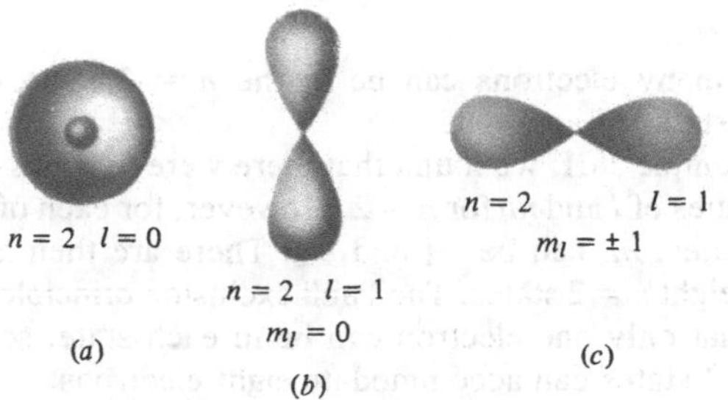

Figure 28.6. The representations of $|\psi|^2$ for the $n = 2$ states of hydrogen. (*a*) The $l = 0$ cloud is darkest at $r = 0$. (*b*) For $l = 1$ and $m_l = 0$ the representation of $|\psi|^2$ appears as two droplets above and below the origin. For this state, $|\psi|^2 = 0$ at $r = 0$. (*c*) For $l = 1$, $m_l = \pm 1$. $|\psi|^2$ is doughnut shaped. (Here it is viewed in cross section from the side.) Again $|\psi|^2 = 0$ at $r = 0$ for this state. While the pictures for $m_l = +1$ and $m_l = -1$ appear the same, the angular momentum is opposite. Thus one may think of the electron in the doughnut as circulating one way for $m_l = 1$ and oppositely for $m_l = -1$.

axis. Thus the probability is very small of finding a 1*s* electron actually within the tiny nuclear volume. The 2*s* and all the higher *s* states also have wave functions that are largest at $r = 0$. With the r^2 factors included, their radial probabilities for being found at small r values diminish rapidly as n increases. The *s* states are all spherically symmetric (Fig. 28.6).

Now consider the 2*p* wave functions. It is clear from Fig. 28.6 that these are dependent on the direction, unlike the *s* states. The wave functions are zero at $r = 0$ (Fig. 28.5), and the radial probabilities are small even at $r = a_0$ (Fig. 28.7); the peaks occur at $r = 4a_0$. Thus 2*p* electrons are less likely to be

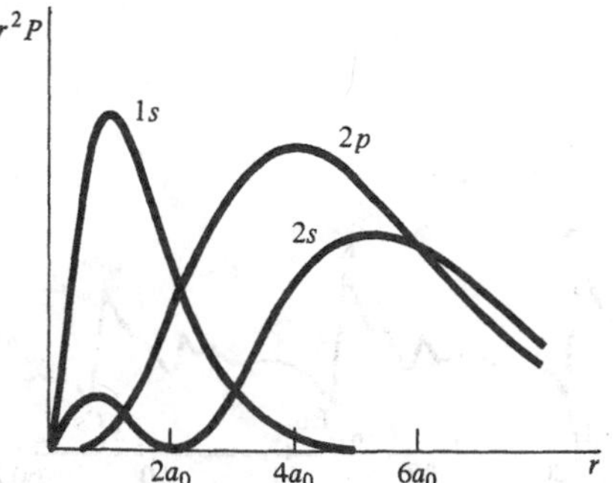

Figure 28.7. The radial probability distributions $r^2P = r^2|\psi|^2$ for the $n = 1$ and $n = 2$ states. The maximum in r^2P is at $r = a_0$ for the 1*s* state, at $4a_0$ for the 2p state, and at a slightly larger radius for the 2*s* state.

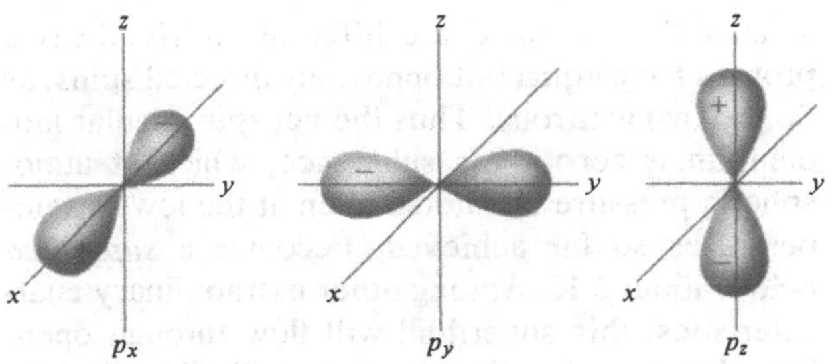

Figure 28.8. The three 2*p* wave functions of hydrogen most often used in chemistry. These wave functions are positive on one side of the origin and negative on the other side.

found near the nucleus than are 1*s* or even 2*s* electrons. This has important implications for multielectron atoms, which we explore in Section 28.5.

The wave functions we have described are those that are most useful for atomic physics, where the magnetic interactions between the spin and orbital magnetic moments play a role. However, when atoms bind to one another, it is more convenient to use a different set of wave functions. In Fig. 28.8, we show representations of the three 2*p* states for hydrogen that are used in discussions of molecular binding. The wave functions labeled p_x, p_y, and p_z are superpositions of the three 2*p* states of Fig. 28.6. Both sets of wave functions are solutions of Schrödinger's equation and the choice of which set to use depends on whether one is interested in magnetic effects or molecular structure. We use the states of Fig. 28.8 in discussing molecular binding in the next chapter.

Explicit formulas for the hydrogen atom wave functions and examples of their use are given in the Supplementary Topics in Section 28.14.

28.4 | THE PAULI EXCLUSION PRINCIPLE

We noted that all elementary particles have an intrinsic spin angular momentum. The spin plays a crucial role in atomic and molecular structure and in the behavior of collections of particles. For example, the two isotopes of helium, ^{3}He, with two protons and a neutron in the nucleus, and ^{4}He, with two protons and two neutrons, have very different properties at low temperatures because the net spins of the two nuclei are different. In ^{4}He, the two protons have equal but oppositely directed spins, as do the two neutrons. Thus the net spin angular momentum is zero. This substance, which at atmospheric pressure is a liquid even at the lowest temperatures so far achieved, becomes a *superfluid* below about 2 K. Among other extraordinary characteristics, this superfluid will flow through openings that no other liquid or gas will. ^{3}He displays equally remarkable but very different behavior below about 5×10^{-3} K. Here the net nuclear spin is one-half due to the single unpaired neutron.

Another example of the effects of spin is observed in metals. At low temperatures, the free electrons, each having a spin of one-half, match up to form pairs with a net spin of zero. When this happens, the metal becomes a superconductor; its electrical resistance becomes zero!

All these characteristics depend on two observations:

1 *The Pauli exclusion principle.* Two or more indistinguishable or identical particles with spin one-half cannot be in the same quantum state. This means, for example, that in atoms with many electrons, no more than one electron can be in a level denoted by a given set of quantum numbers, n, l, m_l, and m_s.
2 *Indistinguishable or identical particles with a spin of zero or one* can be put in any quantum state whether it is occupied or not.

The word "indistinguishable" in these rules is important because in classical physics, individual particles are usually considered as being identifiable and distinguishable. That is, if we know the position and momentum of a particle at a certain moment, then using Newton's laws we can, in principle, follow the motion of that particle as long as we wish. In quantum systems, the uncertainty principle precludes an accurate determination of the position and momentum, so at different times we cannot tell if we are seeing the original particle or another that looks just like it. In the latter case, the particles must be considered as indistinguishable. Atoms provide many illustrations of the effects of the Pauli exclusion principle.

Example 28.3

How many electrons can be in the $n = 2$ hydrogenlike states of an atom?

In Example 28.1, we found that there were four possible values of l and m_l for $n = 2$. However, for each of these states, m_s can be $+\frac{1}{2}$ and $-\frac{1}{2}$. There are then a total of eight $n = 2$ states. The Pauli exclusion principle states that only one electron can be in each state, so the $n = 2$ states can accommodate eight electrons.

28.5 | ATOMIC STRUCTURE AND THE PERIODIC TABLE

We now have sufficient information to gain some insight into atoms with more than one electron. We will see that many of the physical and chemical properties of atoms can be explained by the *atomic shell model,* which is based on the idea that the electrons in atoms are in hydrogenlike states.

In the ground state of an atom, the electrons occupy the lowest states allowed by the Pauli exclusion principle. When all the states corresponding to the same or nearly the same energy have been filled, an *electron shell* is said to be completed, or *closed.* Atoms with all their electrons in closed shells are similar to each other in their physical and chemical properties and are very stable. For example, the minimum energy needed to remove one electron from a neutral ground state atom, the *ionization energy,* is very large in these closed-shell atoms (Fig. 28.9). The regularities associated with successive shell closures are responsible for similarities among

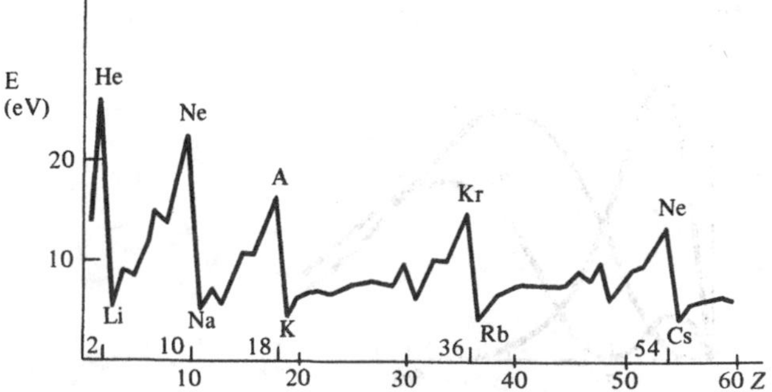

Figure 28.9. The ionization energy, the minimum energy required to remove one electron from a neutral atom in its ground state, versus Z for atoms up to $Z = 60$. Closed shell inert gases have $Z = 2$, 10, 18, 36, and 54.

the elements in the same column of the periodic table (Appendix A).

We now consider individual atoms in more detail, starting with $Z = 2$.

Helium ($Z = 2$) | Helium has two electrons and a nucleus with a charge $2e$. It is not currently possible to find exact solutions to the Schrödinger equation when there are three or more objects present, although very accurate approximate solutions to the helium atom problem can be obtained. These solutions show, as one might expect, that in the helium ground state the two electrons are both in $n = 1$, $l = 0$ states. In accordance with the Pauli principle, one electron has its spin directed up ($m_s = \frac{1}{2}$) and the other down ($m_s = -\frac{1}{2}$).

The fact that two electrons are present affects the energies of their states. Each electron has a probability distribution $|\psi|^2$ similar to that of Fig. 28.5*a*, so the electrons partially shield each other from the nucleus. Roughly half the time, each electron "sees" an attractive nuclear charge $Z = 2$, and half the time, it is shielded and sees a net charge $Z = 1$. Thus we might suppose that in the Bohr formula we should use an effective nuclear charge $Z_{eff} = \frac{1}{2}(2 + 1) = 1.5$. However, the mutual repulsion of the electrons pushes them apart and reduces the shielding effect, so that Z_{eff} increases to approximately 1.7. Hence when they are in $n = 1$ orbitals, using Eq. 28.1 with $Z = Z_{eff}$, the two electrons have a total energy

$$E_2 = -2\frac{Z_{eff}^2}{n^2}E_0 = -2\frac{(1.7)^2}{1^2}(13.6 \text{ eV})$$

$$= -79 \text{ eV}$$

If one electron is removed, then the remaining electron experiences the full nuclear charge $Z = 2$. The energy of this electron is then

$$E_1 = -\frac{2^2}{1^2}(13.6 \text{ eV}) = -54 \text{ eV}$$

The difference $E_1 - E_2 = -54 \text{ eV} - (-79 \text{ eV}) = 25$ eV is the energy needed to remove one electron from the helium atom. This ionization energy is greater than the 13.6 eV needed to ionize hydrogen. We see then that the two electrons in helium are in the two 1*s* states, and despite their mutual repulsion, they are each more tightly bound than is the one electron in hydrogen. Helium is the lightest closed-shell atom, since it has the $n = 1$ levels filled; chemically, it is the lightest inert or *noble gas*. In lithium, with $Z = 3$, the third electron will have to go into the higher-energy $n = 2$ orbital.

Lithium–Neon ($Z = 3$–10) | From our discussion of the hydrogen energy states, the $n = 2$ level contains a total of eight states with different values of l, m_l, and m_s. The $n = 2$ levels are significantly higher in energy than the $n = 1$ levels but are still well below the $n = 3$ levels (Fig. 28.10). In lithium ($Z = 3$), two electrons occupy the $n = 1$ states and one electron goes into a $n = 2$ level. Because this third electron is farther from the nucleus on the average, it is shielded from the nuclear charge by the two inner electrons. This shielding is less complete in the $n = 2$, $l = 0$ state than in the $n = 2$, $l = 1$ state, since in the $l = 0$ state the electron has a higher probability of being close to the nucleus. Accordingly, the energy is somewhat lower in the $l = 0$ state, and that level will be filled in the ground state of the atom. We find the effective

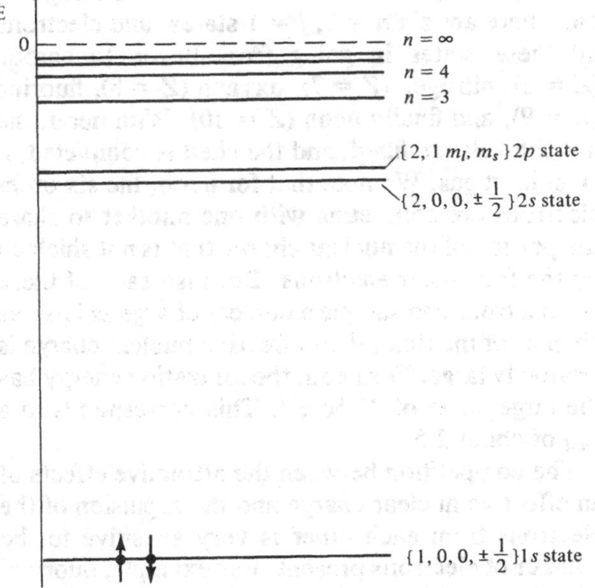

Figure 28.10. A schematic energy-level diagram for the neutral helium atom. The two electrons have opposite spins and are both in 1*s* states. The states are labeled by $\{n, l, m_l, m_s\}$.

nuclear charge for the $n = 2$, $l = 0$ electron in the next example.

Example 28.4

From the Bohr formula, an $n = 2$ electron in the presence of an effective nuclear charge $Z_{eff} = 1$ will have an energy of $E_2 = -13.6/(2)^2$ eV $= -3.4$ eV. In lithium, the energy of this electron is -5.39 eV. What is the effective nuclear charge for this state?

From the Bohr formula with $Z = Z_{eff}$,

$$E_2 = -5.39 \text{ eV} = -13.6 \frac{(Z_{eff})^2}{(2)^2}$$

Solving, we find $Z_{eff} = 1.26$. Thus because the electron can be close to the nucleus, it sees an effective nuclear charge that is 26 percent greater than that of a completely shielded electron.

For $Z = 4$, beryllium, the fourth electron can also be in an $n = 2$, $l = 0$ state with its spin opposite to that of the third electron. These two electrons shield each other somewhat. However, the nuclear charge is now 4 and the inner electrons only shield two of the protons. Thus the two outer electrons see an effective nuclear charge of between 1 and 2. The ionization energy is found to be 9.32 eV for beryllium.

With $Z = 5$, boron, the $n = 2$, $l = 1$ levels begin to fill. There are six $n = 2$, $l = 1$ states, and electrons fill these states in going from boron to carbon ($Z = 6$), nitrogen ($Z = 7$), oxygen ($Z = 8$), fluorine ($Z = 9$), and finally neon ($Z = 10$). With neon, the $n = 2$ levels are filled, and the shell is completed; it is an inert gas. We note that for neon, the six outer electrons are competing with one another to share the portion of the nuclear charge that is not shielded by the four inner electrons. Because each of these six electrons can sample a nuclear charge as large as six part of the time, their effective nuclear charge is relatively large. For neon, the ionization energy has the large value of 21.56 eV. This corresponds to a Z_{eff} of about 2.5.

The competition between the attractive effects of an effective nuclear charge and the repulsion of the electrons from each other is very sensitive to the number of electrons present. For example, fluorine, with five $n = 2$, $l = 1$ electrons, is one electron short of having a filled shell. The effect of adding an additional electron to fluorine to obtain the negative ion F^- is to cause six outer electrons to compete for five unshielded nuclear charges. The energy gained in this sharing is sufficient to offset the repulsive effects of the added electron, and F^- is quite stable. Its ionization energy is 4.2 eV. Fluorine is said to have a high *electron affinity*.

In a crude model of the molecule NaF, the fluorine atom takes one of the electrons from sodium. The molecule is then held together by the attractive electric force between Na^+ and F^-. This is called *ionic binding*. Fluorine is the lightest of the *halogens*, which include chlorine, bromine, iodine, and astatine, all of which are one electron short of having a closed shell. All are highly reactive as they try to gain an electron.

We can also see how carbon ($Z = 6$), a constituent of so many organic compounds, combines with other elements. The $n = 2$ level of carbon has two electrons in the $l = 0$ states and two in the $l = 1$ states. Four more are needed to completely fill the $n = 2$ shell. Since atoms are most stable when they have closed shells, carbon will usually try to "share" four electrons from other elements. This is called *covalent binding*.

$Z = 11-18$ | As Z increases from 11, the 3*s* and then the 3*p* levels fill just as the 2*s* and 2*p* states were filled. The chemical characteristics of these elements are very similar to the corresponding elements with Z between 3 and 10. At first glance, we would expect that the next closed shell inert gas would appear at $Z = 28$, when all the $n = 3$ levels are filled (Table 28.2). However, the electrons in the $l = 2$ states spend much less time near the nucleus than those in $l = 1$ or 0 states and are therefore

TABLE 28.2

Atomic states for $n = 3$.

State	l	m_l	m_s	
3*s*	0	0	$\pm\frac{1}{2}$	2 states
3*p*	1	−1	$\pm\frac{1}{2}$	6 states
		0	$\pm\frac{1}{2}$	
		+1	$\pm\frac{1}{2}$	
3*d*	2	−2	$\pm\frac{1}{2}$	10 states
		−1	$\pm\frac{1}{2}$	
		0	$\pm\frac{1}{2}$	
		+1	$\pm\frac{1}{2}$	
		+2	$\pm\frac{1}{2}$	

substantially higher in energy. In fact, the 4s levels ($n = 4$, $l = 0$) are also below the 3d levels ($n = 3$, $l = 2$). Accordingly, the 3s and 3p states form a complete shell by themselves. Argon ($Z = 18$) has filled 3s and 3p states and is therefore an inert gas. Similarly, chlorine ($Z = 17$) is a halogen like fluorine, and potassium ($Z = 19$) is an *alkali metal* similar to lithium and sodium, which also have one electron outside a closed shell.

$Z \geq 19$ | Above $Z = 18$, the order in which levels are filled becomes complicated. The zero angular momentum states in a shell are always filled first because electrons in these states penetrate closest to the nucleus. This effect is so strong that for $Z = 19$, the $n = 4$, $l = 0$ states begin to fill even though the $n = 3$, $l = 2$ states are empty. Thus in Fig. 28.11, we see that for intermediate values of Z, closed shells are not always associated with a single value of n. The one-to-one correspondence between shells and the quantum number n reappears for large values of Z.

Two general features of atomic structure are important. First, there is no obvious reason that elements with very large values of Z could not exist. However, naturally occurring or artificially produced elements have only been found for values of Z up to slightly over 100. Very heavy atoms do not exist because their nuclei tend to break up.

A second notable feature of atoms is the remarkable similarity in their radii. The alkali atoms, with a single, weakly bound s electron, have the largest radii. But the largest alkali atom, cesium, has a volume that is only about twice that of helium. This happens because, in heavy atoms, the innermost electrons see a very large Z_{eff} and consequently are much closer to the nucleus than in light atoms. This permits the outer electrons to be closer to the nucleus as well, so that the average atomic radius does not increase much with Z.

We conclude this introduction to atomic structure with one more example.

Example 28.5

Potassium ($Z = 19$) has one outer 4s electron and an ionization energy of 4.3 eV. (a) What is Z_{eff} for this outermost electron in potassium? (b) Calcium ($Z = 20$) has two outer 4s electrons. A rough estimate for the effective nuclear charge for the single electron of Ca^+

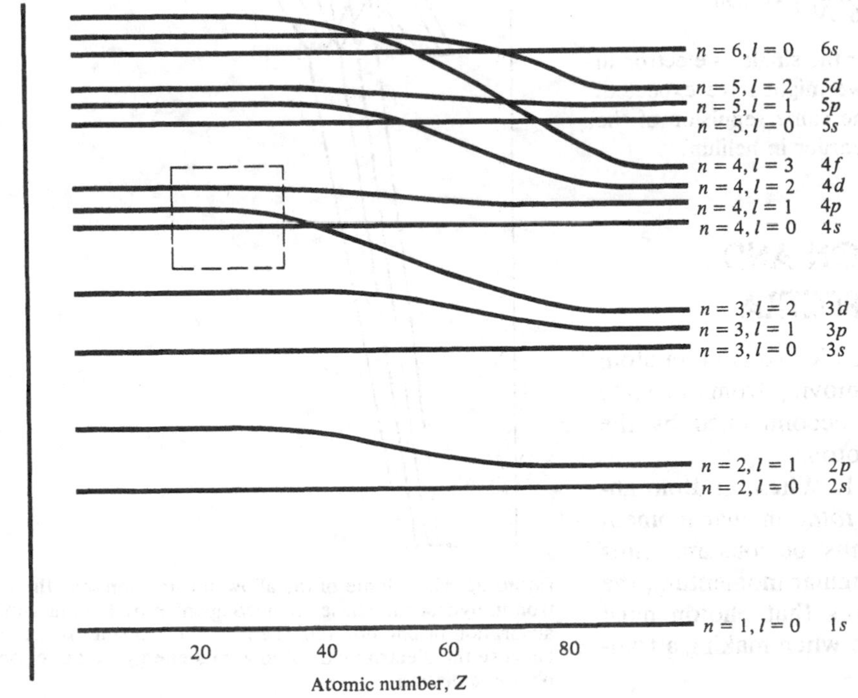

Figure 28.11. The positions of the energy levels of atoms versus the atomic number Z. The dashed square indicates the levels filled for $Z = 19$ through 36. The shells contain different levels in different parts of the periodic table. For example, for $Z = 30$, the 3s and 3p levels comprise a shell, but for $Z = 70$, the 3s, 3p, and 3d levels form a shell.

would be $Z_{eff} + 1$, where Z_{eff} is the result from (a). The measured ionization energy of calcium is 6.09 eV. Estimate Z_{eff} for the two 4*s* electrons of neutral calcium.

(a) Substituting $n = 4$ in the Bohr formula, we have for the outermost electron in potassium

$$E_4 = -4.3 \text{ eV} = \frac{-Z_{eff}^2}{4^2}(13.6 \text{ eV})$$

$$Z_{eff} = \sqrt{16\left(\frac{4.3 \text{ eV}}{13.6 \text{ eV}}\right)} = 2.25$$

As in the preceding example, the potassium 4*s* electron has Z_{eff} greater than 1 because it can be close to the nucleus.

(b) With $Z_{eff} = 2.25 + 1 = 3.25$ for a single 4*s* electron in Ca^+, the removal energy for the second 4*s* electron would be

$$E = Z_{eff}^2 \frac{E_0}{n^2} = (3.25)^2 \frac{13.6 \text{ eV}}{4^2} = 8.98 \text{ eV}$$

Since 6.09 eV is needed to remove one electron, the total energy of the two 4*s* electrons is $-(8.98 + 6.09)$ eV $= -15.07$ eV. Thus Z_{eff} for each of the two Ca 4*s* electrons is found from

$$-15.07 \text{ eV} = -2Z_{eff}^2 \frac{E_0}{n^2} = -2Z_{eff}^2 \frac{13.6 \text{ eV}}{4^2}$$

$$Z_{eff} = \sqrt{8\left(\frac{15.07 \text{ eV}}{13.6 \text{ eV}}\right)} = 2.98$$

This is less than $Z_{eff} = 3.25$ for the single 4*s* electron in Ca^+ by 0.27, not by 0.5 as we might have expected. This is presumably due to the same repulsion of the two *s* electrons that we saw earlier in helium.

28.6 | ATOMIC EMISSION AND ABSORPTION SPECTRA

We described earlier how the electrons in an atom can change their energies by moving from one state to another. This process is accompanied by the emission or absorption of photons.

The photon has a spin of 1. When an atom absorbs or emits a photon, the *total* angular momentum of the atom and photon must be constant. Thus because the photon carries angular momentum, the electron that emits or absorbs that photon must change its angular momentum when making a transition.

Usually the electrons change their orbital angular momentum quantum number l by 1 when making transitions. For example, suppose a hydrogen atom in its ground state, which is a $l = 0$ state, absorbs a photon. It can only do so if its final orbital angular momentum quantum number is $l = 1$. During a downward transition, the electron must also change its angular momentum by 1. Figure 28.12 shows these *allowed* transitions among the lowest five energy levels of hydrogen.

When atoms are excited, the electrons usually return to their ground states via allowed transitions. These excited states are very short-lived, lasting no more than about 10^{-8} s. However, when the electrons cannot return to their ground states via allowed transitions, they may do so by the emission of two photons. This is a relatively slow process,

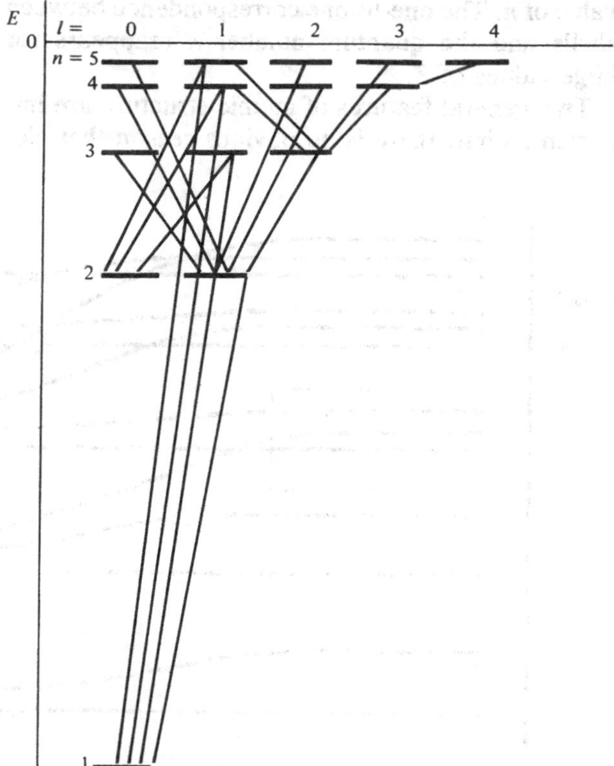

Figure 28.12. Some of the allowed transitions for the electron in hydrogen. These are accompanied by the emission or absorption of one photon. The $n = 2$, $l = 0$ state is metastable because the electron cannot lower its energy by direct one-photon emission.

and such *metastable* states may last for times of the order of a second.

Direct Observation of Quantum Jumps

In 1986, almost three fourths of a century after Bohr originally introduced the concept of a sudden quantum jump between two atomic states, physicists finally observed such jumps in isolated, individual atoms. Three similar experiments were performed independently by groups in the United States and in Germany. They confirmed that quantum mechanics does not merely describe the average behavior of large groups of particles. Rather, individual atoms do indeed behave in the probabilistic way implied by the wave function description.

In one of these experiments, a single positively charged barium ion is trapped for many minutes by a radio frequency electric field. A 493-nm (blue-light) laser beam causes an electron to jump from its ground state orbit to an excited energy level, from level 1 to level 3 in Fig. 28.13. The electron quickly drops back to the ground state, emitting a photon of the same frequency in some random direction. This "resonance fluorescence" occurs millions of times per second. The atom actually looks like a faint star in a specially designed microscope.

Now a weak lamp is turned on which supplies photons with the right energy to allow the electron to jump to level 4 in Fig. 28.13. Sometimes the electron then jumps down to level 2, which is a long-lived or metastable state. From this state it takes an average of 30 s before the electron jumps back again to the ground state. During that time, the ion does not jump back and forth between levels 1 and 3, emitting the blue fluorescence signal. Thus to an observer, the ion actually "blinks" off and on for intervals of many seconds (Fig. 28.14). Each blink represents a quantum jump!

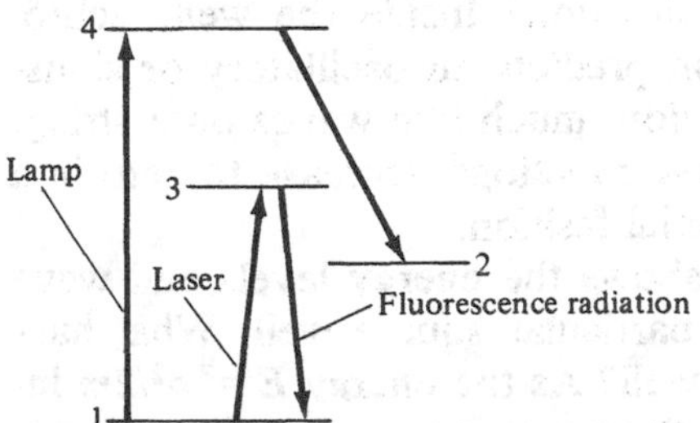

Figure 28.13. Simplified barium ion level structure. The laser causes a jump from level 1 to level 3; the electron returns to level 1 rapidly, emitting the fluorescence radiation. When the lamp excites an electron to level 4 and it drops into level 2, it stays there for an average of 30 s. To an observer, the ion has blinked off for this time interval.

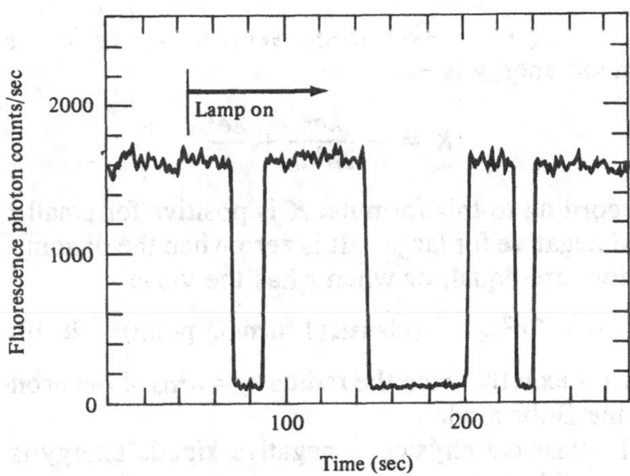

Figure 28.14. A typical record of the fluorescence photons detected. Once the lamp has been turned on, the quantum jumps to and from level 3 are signaled by the blinking of the fluorescence signal. (W. Nagourney, J. Sandberg, and H. Dehmelt, *Physical Review Letters*, vol. 56, 1986, p. 2797.)

28.7 | BARRIER PENETRATION AND TUNNELING

One of the most striking predictions of quantum mechanics is that particles can sometimes be found in or pass through regions that are forbidden by energy conservation. In classical physics, a ball or a car rolling up a hill can travel uphill only until its kinetic energy $K = \frac{1}{2}mv^2 = p^2/2m$ decreases to zero; it can never be negative. The fact that this restriction does not hold in quantum mechanics is responsible for many remarkable phenomena in atoms, molecules, and nuclei.

The hydrogen atom wave functions shown earlier in this chapter clearly display this *barrier penetration* property. We can see this by calculating the kinetic energy of the electron in a hydrogen atom. The total energy is $E = K + \mathcal{U}$, so the kinetic energy is $K = E - \mathcal{U}$. For $Z = 1$, the Bohr formula is

$E_n = -E_0/n^2 = -ke^2/2n^2a_0$. With $\mathcal{U} = -ke^2/r$, the kinetic energy is

$$K = -\frac{ke^2}{2n^2a_0} + \frac{ke^2}{r}$$

According to this formula, K is positive for small r and negative for large r. It is zero when the denominators are equal, or when r has the value

$$r_t = 2n^2a_0 \qquad \text{(classical turning point)} \quad (28.10)$$

This is exactly twice the radius $r_n = n^2a_0$ of the orbit in the Bohr model.

In classical physics, a negative kinetic energy is impossible, so the electron can never be at a radius greater than r_t. Hence the radius r_t is called the *classical turning point*. The electron must turn around and go back to smaller radii when it reaches this point. The situation is quite different in quantum mechanics. For example, in a hydrogen atom, the 1*s* state turning point is at $r_t = 2(1)^2a_0 = 2a_0$. However, Fig. 28.15 shows that the 1*s* wave function extends well beyond $2a_0$. The area under the radial probability (r^2P) curve indicates the probability of finding the electron in a given region. Here 24 percent, or about a fourth, of that area is at larger radii. For this state, there is a 24 percent probability of finding the electron at $r > r_t$, a region where classical physics says it can never be!

This penetration of the wave function into regions of negative kinetic energy is a quite general phenomenon in quantum mechanics. Let's consider another example: a particle that can move freely in one dimension between $x = 0$ and $x = a$, but experiences large forces opposing its motion when it reaches these points. A large amount of work must be done if it is to go farther, so the potential energy rises sharply. The resulting potential energy curve is a *square well* (Fig. 28.16). The potential energy $\mathcal{U}$ equals zero inside and $\mathcal{U}_0$ outside.

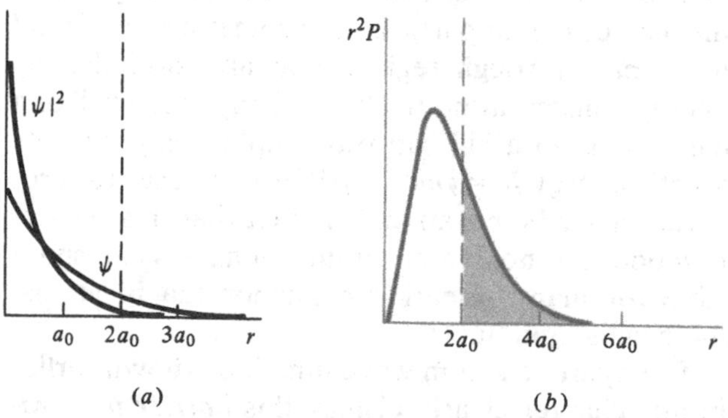

Figure 28.15. (*a*) The 1*s* hydrogen atom wave function and its square. The dashed line indicates the classical turning point $r_t = 2a_0$. (*b*) The radial probability $r^2P = r^2|\psi|^2$. About one fourth of the area under the r^2P curve is in the classically inaccessible region $r > r_t$.

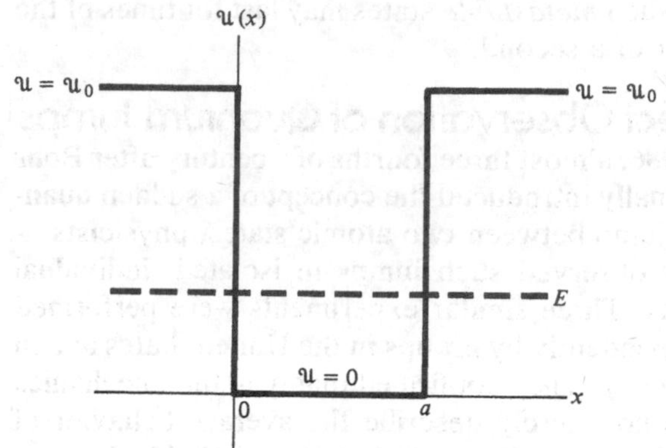

Figure 28.16. A one-dimensional square well. If the total energy E is less than $\mathcal{U}_0$ as shown here, the kinetic energy $K = E - \mathcal{U}_0$ is negative for $x < 0$ or $x > a$. According to classical physics, the particle cannot be found in these regions.

Now suppose we have a particle with a total energy $E = K + \mathcal{U}$. As it leaves the well, its potential energy increases by $\mathcal{U}_0$. Since E is constant, its kinetic energy decreases by an equal amount. Classically, the particle cannot leave the well if $E < \mathcal{U}_0$, since it would then have a negative kinetic energy, which is impossible. What does quantum mechanics say about this situation? Inside the well, Schrödinger's equation predicts an oscillatory or sinusoidal wave function, much like waves on a string. Outside, the wave functions decrease to zero in a gradual exponential fashion.

Figure 28.17 shows the energy levels and wave functions for a particular square well. What happens inside the well? As the energy $E = p^2/2m$ increases, so does the momentum p, and the de Broglie wavelength $\lambda = h/p$ decreases. Thus for each successive level there is a shorter wavelength and an additional oscillation. Outside the well, the exponential "tails" extend farther and farther as E increases and $K = E - \mathcal{U}_0$ becomes less negative.

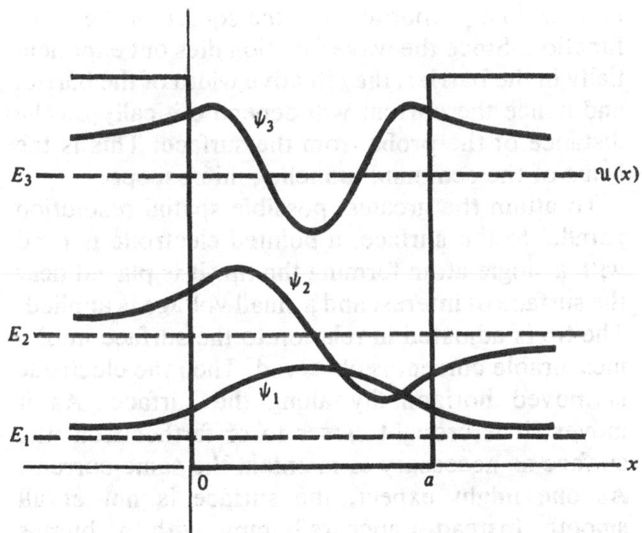

Figure 28.17. The first three square well energy levels. The corresponding wave functions are shown, using the energy levels as axes for convenience. Note that the wave functions are oscillatory inside the well and decrease exponentially outside.

Note, however, that in every state, the wave function penetrates beyond the well. Thus the particle has a nonzero probability of being found in a region where it cannot go according to classical physics. This is a real effect, with readily observable consequences.

Tunneling

The penetration of the wave function into classically inaccessible regions has remarkable effects. Suppose, for example, that a proton is directed at an atomic nucleus. Since both particles are positively charged, their electrical repulsion limits how close the proton can come to the nucleus. The nuclear force plays no role at large distances; the proton must be nearly at the nucleus before its effect is noticeable. Thus if the kinetic energy of the proton is small, it cannot get close enough to the nucleus for a nuclear interaction to occur. Nevertheless, because of this penetration of the wave function, the wave function of the proton can overlap with the nucleus at quite low energies. Hence nuclear fusion reactions can occur in stars at much lower energies and temperatures than would otherwise be required.

Tunneling through a barrier is an even more striking quantum effect. We can illustrate what it means by thinking about a ball on a hill. Objects tend to move toward the place where their potential energy is lowest, and if it is on the slope, the ball tends to roll downhill. This won't happen, however, if the ball is stuck inside a hole on the hillside without enough energy to get out.

Now consider an electron or an alpha particle instead of a macroscopic object. Then classical concepts do not apply, and we must turn to quantum mechanics. What we find is that there is a chance that the electron or alpha particle will be found outside the hole, "rolling" downhill! It is as though it had tunneled through the region between the bottom of the hole and the adjacent slope.

To see this in a little more detail, consider Fig. 28.18. It is a quantum mechanical analog of the ball in a hole on a hill. To the left of the barrier, the wave function is sinusoidal and within the barrier ψ is decreasing exponentially. To the right, ψ again is oscillatory, although it is not just a simple sine or cosine in this region where $\mathcal{U}$ is varying. The requirement of matching smoothly at each edge of the barrier leads to the wave function shown, with a small but nonzero wave function on the right. If a particle is initially in the region to the left, this means it has a finite probability of later being found on the right of the barrier where its potential energy

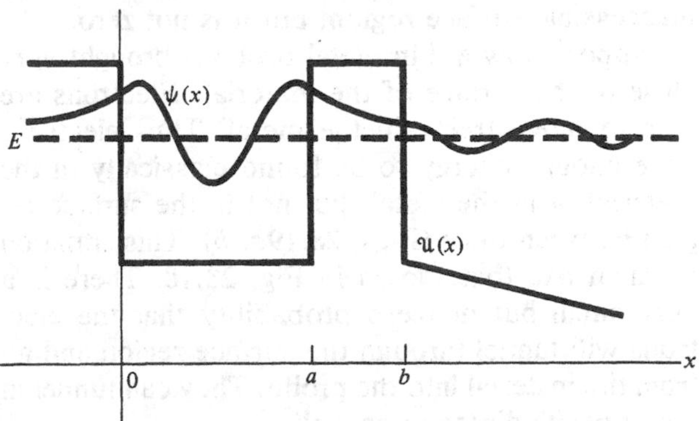

Figure 28.18. Inside the well, $\psi(x)$ is sinusoidal. In the classically inaccessible regions, it is exponentially decreasing. Beyond the barrier, $x > b$, $\psi(x)$ is again oscillatory rather than decreasing. Each time the particle hits the barrier, it has a small but nonzero chance of tunneling through.

is lower. Effectively, it is repeatedly striking the barrier as it moves back and forth, and eventually it will escape and go lower down the hill. This tunneling phenomenon is responsible for nuclear alpha decay (Chapter Thirty) and for many processes that occur in solid-state physics.

28.8 | SCANNING TUNNELING MICROSCOPE

The scanning tunneling microscope is a remarkable new application of tunneling. This instrument mechanically tracks the electronic wave functions outside the surface of a material, producing an extremely accurate representation of the atoms at the surface. These can, for example, be atoms on the surface of a silicon chip or of a virus. A great advantage is that this technique demands no special surface preparation. By contrast, electron microscopy requires that a metal film be deposited on the surface of interest.

Our discussion of barrier penetration and tunneling in the previous section allows us to understand how this device operates. Under ordinary conditions, an electron in a solid material cannot leave it, since there are forces acting at the surface that prevent its escape. This is similar to the square well problem (Fig. 28.16), although the potential energy is more complicated. The surface is a region where the kinetic energy $K = E - \mathcal{U}$ is negative. The wave function decreases exponentially in the classically inaccessible surface region, but it is not zero.

Suppose now a thin metal probe is brought very close to the surface of the material. Electrons are able to move freely in the metal. Thus electrons have enough energy to be found classically in the material or in the metal, but not in the surface region between them (Figs. 28.19*a, b*). This situation is much like that shown in Fig. 28.18. There is a very small but nonzero probability that the electrons will tunnel through the surface region and go from the material into the probe. They can tunnel in the opposite direction as well.

Suppose now that a very small electric potential difference is applied between the solid and the probe. Then electrons will move between the solid and the probe and the rate of flow, the electric current, will be proportional to the square of the wave function. Since the wave function dies out exponentially in the barrier, the effective width of the barrier and hence the current will depend critically on the distance of the probe from the surface. This is the heart of the scanning tunneling microscope.

To attain the greatest possible spatial resolution parallel to the surface, a pointed electrode is used with a single atom forming the tip. It is placed near the surface of interest and a small voltage is applied. The tip is adjusted in relation to the surface until a measurable current is observed. Then the electrode is moved horizontally along the surface. As it moves, it is brought closer to or farther from the surface as necessary to maintain the same current. As one might expect, the surface is not at all smooth. Instead it appears bumpy, with the bumps at the positions of the surface atoms. The electron wave function is largest near these atoms (Fig. 28.19*c*).

A surprising aspect of this apparatus is the ability that has been developed to move a physical probe reliably with a precision, in some case, of about 1 percent of an atomic radius, or better than 0.01 nm. The apparatus is controlled electromechanically using feedback from the measured current. Because of the exponential falloff of the wave functions in the surface region, the current changes dramatically when the electrode is moved toward or away from the surface. It is found that a motion of about 0.1 nm can change the current by a factor of 1000.

The instrument yields representations of the surface with an accuracy far greater than any previously obtainable. This is particularly important since the arrangement of atoms at surfaces plays a primary role in many phenomena. For example, it is the surface characteristics of metals and silicon that determine their electrical properties. It is often the surface characteristics of viruses and other biological structures that determine their behavior in a system. This nondestructive technique appears to be ideal for making major progress in mapping and understanding the surfaces of many important substances.

SUMMARY

The structure of atoms with more than one electron can be largely understood in terms of electronic en-

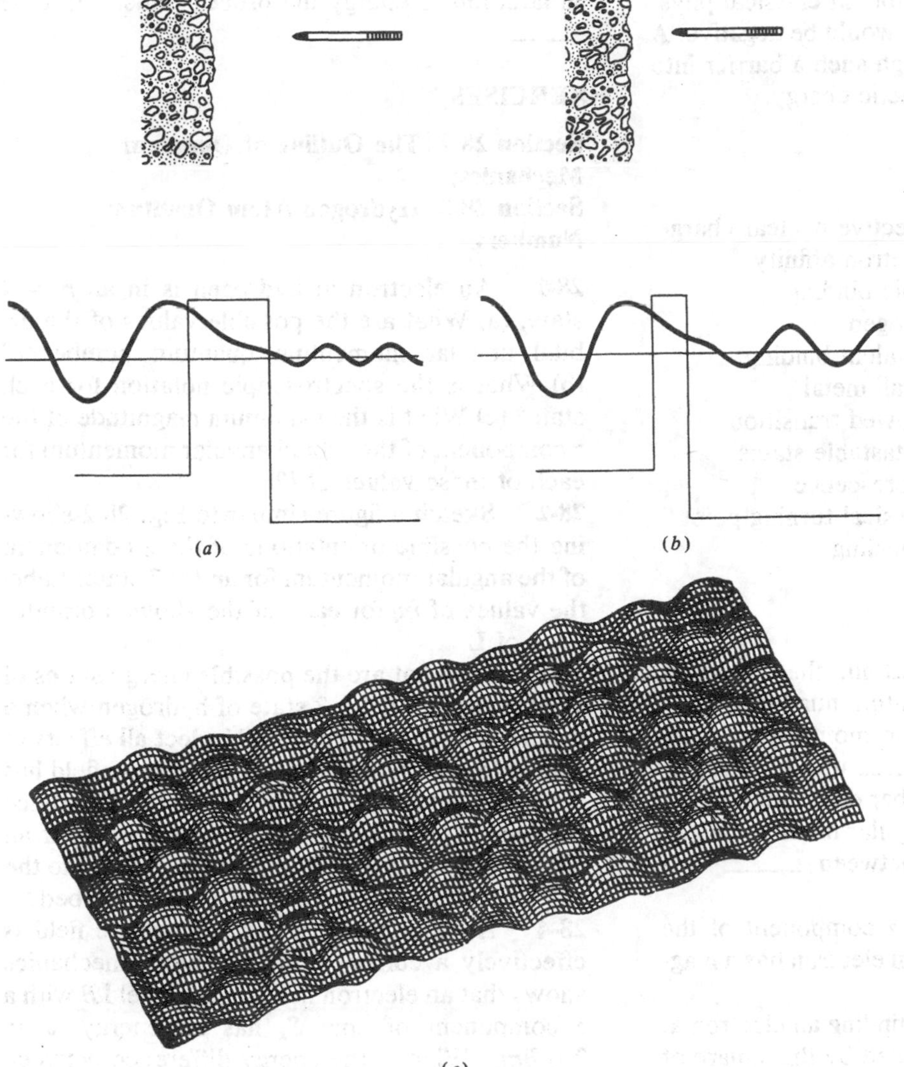

Figure 28.19. (a) The potential energy for an electron when the metal probe is relatively far from the surface. The tunneling probability is small. (b) The tip is closer to the surface, and the barrier associated with the surface region is reduced in width. This makes it easier for the electrons to tunnel through the surface into the probe and increases the current that will be observed if a potential difference is applied. (c) A typical surface map obtained by repeated scans of the probe over the surface. The plot shows the vertical position of the probe required to maintain a constant current.

ergy levels similar to those of the hydrogen atom. The positions of the electronic energy levels are determined by the attractive electric force due to the nucleus and the repulsive electric forces among the electrons.

The Pauli exclusion principle requires that only one electron can be in a given state. These states are labeled by quantum numbers that indicate the energy, orbital angular momentum, and spin angular momentum of an electron in that state. In the ground states of atoms, electrons occupy the lowest energy states available consistent with the exclusion principle.

The square of the wave function is an indication of the position probability of an electron in a given state. This probability distribution can be used to understand the screening of the nucleus by other electrons and the relatively low energy of the zero angular momentum states.

The observed atomic spectra of complex atoms depend not only on the positions of the energy levels but also on angular momentum conservation.

The wave function for a particle can penetrate into regions that are inaccessible in classical physics because the kinetic energy would be negative. A particle can also tunnel through such a barrier into another region of positive kinetic energy.

Checklist

Define or explain:

wave function	effective nuclear charge
principal quantum number	electron affinity
quantum number l	ionic binding
quantum number m_l	halogen
spin angular momentum	covalent binding
$\|\psi\|^2$	alkali metal
s states, p states	allowed transition
radial probability	metastable states
Pauli exclusion principle	fluorescence
closed electron shell	classical turning point
ionization energy	tunneling

REVIEW QUESTIONS

Q28-1 In the hydrogen atom, the energy is specified by the ______ quantum number.

Q28-2 The orbital angular momentum quantum number may be any ______ up to ______.

Q28-3 The quantum number determining the z component of the orbital angular momentum can have any integer value between ______ and ______.

Q28-4 In units of $\hbar$, the z component of the spin angular momentum of an electron has a magnitude of ______.

Q28-5 The probability of finding an electron at a certain position is determined by the square of ______.

Q28-6 The probability of finding an electron near the nucleus is greatest for an l = ______ state.

Q28-7 Two identical spin one-half particles may not be in the same ______.

Q28-8 The minimum energy needed to remove an electron from an atom in its ground state is the ______.

Q28-9 An atom with all the states corresponding to approximately the same energy filled has a closed ______ and is very ______.

Q28-10 When an excited atom emits a photon, in addition to energy the process must conserve ______.

EXERCISES

Section 28.1 | The Outline of Quantum Mechanics; Section 28.2 | Hydrogen Atom Quantum Numbers

28-1 An electron in hydrogen is in an $n = 4$ state. (a) What are the possible values of the orbital angular momentum quantum number l? (b) What is the spectroscopic notation for each state? (c) What is the maximum magnitude of the z component of the orbital angular momentum for each of these values of l?

28-2 Sketch a figure similar to Fig. 28.2 showing the possible orientations of the z component of the angular momentum for an $l = 3$ state. Label the values of m_l for each of the allowed orientations of **L**.

28-3 (a) What are the possible energy states of an electron in an $l = 2$ state of hydrogen when a magnetic field B is applied? (Neglect all effects of spin in this exercise.) (b) If the magnetic field has a magnitude of 10 T, what is the energy difference between the $m_l = 1$ and $m_l = 0$ states? (c) If an electron makes a transition from the $m_l = 0$ to the $m_l = 1$ state, is a photon emitted or absorbed?

28-4 A spinning charge in a magnetic field is effectively a current loop. Quantum mechanics shows that an electron in a magnetic field B with a z component of spin S_z has an energy $\mathcal{U} = 2\mu_B B m_s$. What is the energy difference between the spin up and spin down states of an electron in a magnetic field of magnitude 1 T?

28-5 How many $n = 4$ states are there in hydrogen? (Include spin effects.)

28-6 How many states in hydrogen have $n = 3$ and (a) $l = 0$; (b) $l = 1$; (c) $l = 2$? (Include spin effects.)

Section 28.3 | Hydrogen Atom Wave Functions

28-7 For the 2s state in hydrogen, where is (a) the wave function largest; (b) the radial probability largest; (c) the radial probability zero?

28-8 For the $2p$ state in hydrogen, where is (a) the wave function largest; (b) the radial probability largest; (c) the radial probability zero?
28-9 Atomic wave functions normally have a definite "parity." This means that comparing the wave function at x, y, z to the one at $-x, -y, -z$, the two wave functions are either equal or differ by a factor of -1. Consider the $2p$ wave functions in Fig. 28.8. (a) How are these wave functions related at x, y, z and at $-x, -y, -z$? (b) Is there any difference in the probability of finding the electron at x, y, z or at $-x, -y, -z$?

Section 28.4 | The Pauli Exclusion Principle

28-10 How many electrons can be in the $n = 3$ hydrogenlike states of an atom?
28-11 How many electrons can be in the $4f$ hydrogenlike states of an atom?
28-12 (a) Three electrons are in hydrogenlike states in an atom with $Z = 3$. List the quantum numbers for the three electrons for the atomic state with the lowest possible energy. (b) Find the corresponding energy in units of E_0. (Ignore the interactions among the electrons.) (c) If the electrons could be replaced by particles with the same mass and charge but with spin zero, what would be the lowest possible energy for the atom? (Again ignore the interactions among the electrons.)

Section 28.5 | Atomic Structure and the Periodic Table

28-13 Why is potassium chemically similar to sodium and lithium? ($Z = 19$ for potassium.)
28-14 In $Z = 56$, barium, the $n = 6$, $l = 0$ state is filled and in succeeding atoms the electrons start filling the $n = 4$, $l = 3$ subshell. How many states are available in this subshell? (These are the rare earth elements.)
28-15 Using the ideas of screening described for the helium atom, estimate the energy required to remove the second electron from lithium, leaving Li^{++}. Compare your estimate of Z_{eff} with $Z = 3$, the nuclear charge of lithium.
28-16 One of the two electrons in a helium atom is excited to an $n = 2$ state while the other electron remains in the $n = 1$ state. Will the $n = 2$ electron have the same energy in the $l = 1$ and $l = 0$ states?
28-17 The alkali metals are strongly reactive; they readily interact with other atoms, particularly those that attract electrons. Why are these metals so chemically active?
28-18 In the water molecule, H_2O, the oxygen atom shares the electrons of the hydrogen atoms. Why is this such a stable compound?
28-19 Hydrogen combines with the halogens to form such acids as HF, HCl, HBr, and HI. Why do these compounds form so readily?
28-20 The Nobel prize work of Tomonaga, Feynman, and Schwinger on quantum electrodynamics was prompted, in part, by some unexplained features of atomic spectra. Techniques developed in the late 1940s enabled experimenters to observe that the splitting of energy levels in a magnetic field B due to the electron spin is not $\Delta\mathcal{U} = 2\mu_B B$, but is instead $\Delta\mathcal{U} = 2\mu_B(1 + \alpha/2\pi)B$. ($\alpha = ke^2/\hbar c = 1/137$ is the fine structure constant.) (a) In a magnetic field of 10 T, what is the magnitude of the discrepancy in the spectrum? (b) What is the percentage of the shift from the value $\Delta\mathcal{U} = 2\mu_B B$?
28-21 What are the quantum numbers for the outer electron in the ground state of sodium ($Z = 11$)?
28-22 Estimate the energy of a $1s$ electron in a lead atom ($Z = 82$).

Section 28.6 | Atomic Emission and Absorption Spectra

28-23 The effective nuclear charge for a $3s$ ($n = 3$, $l = 0$) electron is $Z_{eff} = 3.1$, and for the same electron in an excited $3p$ state ($n = 3$, $l = 1$), it is $Z_{eff} = 1.5$. What is the energy of the photon emitted when the electron returns to the $3s$ state?
28-24 When one of the innermost electrons of an atom is captured by the nucleus, an X ray is emitted. Further X rays are emitted as electrons from higher levels drop down to fill the vacant level or hole left by the captured electron. In copper ($Z = 29$): (a) Estimate Z_{eff} for the $2p$ and $1s$ states. Explain your reasoning. (b) Estimate the wavelength of the X ray emitted when an electron drops from the $2p$ state to the $1s$ state.

Section 28.7 | Barrier Penetration and Tunneling

28-25 (a) For the $1s$ state in hydrogen, estimate the ratio of the radial probabilities at r_t and at a_0. (b) Estimate the ratio at $2r_t$ and at a_0.

28-26 Estimate the probability of finding a $1s$ electron in hydrogen at radii larger than $2r_t$.

28-27 In hydrogen, find the radius at the classical turning point for (a) the $2s$ state; (b) the $2p$ state.

28-28 The classical turning point of a hydrogen atom is $200a_0$. What is the quantum number n for this state?

PROBLEMS

28-29 The energy necessary to remove a $1s$ electron in nitrogen ($Z = 7$) is 540 eV. (a) Using $Z_{\text{eff}} = 6.5$, estimate the energy needed to remove a $1s$ electron. (b) Why does this calculation overestimate the energy required? (c) Might the presence of the $2s$ electrons affect the energy of the $1s$ state? Why?

28-30 Beryllium ($Z = 4$) has two $1s$ and two $2s$ electrons in its ground state. The ionization energy for the first $2s$ electron is 9.32 eV, and for the second it is 18.12 eV. (a) What is Z_{eff} for the single $2s$ electron of Be^+? (b) What is Z_{eff} for the two $2s$ electrons in the neutral ground state of Be?

28-31 In singly ionized neon, Ne^+ ($Z = 10$), the five outer $2p$ electrons see an effective nuclear charge as high as 6 and as low as 2, depending on the shielding due to the other four $2p$ electrons. By a simple averaging process we find $Z_{\text{eff}} = (6 + 5 + 4 + 3 + 2)/5 = 4$. (a) What is the total energy of the five outer electrons of Ne^+ using this value of Z_{eff}? (b) The measured ionization energy of neon is 21.56 eV. Assuming that the Z_{eff} of part (a) is correct, compute Z_{eff} for the six $2p$ electrons for neutral neon in its ground state.

ANSWERS TO REVIEW QUESTIONS

Q28-1, principal; **Q28-2**, integer, $n - 1$; **Q28-3**, $-l$, $+l$; **Q28-4**, $\frac{1}{2}$; **Q28-5**, absolute value of the wave function; **Q28-6**, zero; **Q28-7**, quantum state; **Q28-8**, binding energy; **Q28-9**, electron shell, stable; **Q28-10**, angular momentum.

SUPPLEMENTARY TOPICS

28.9 | MASERS AND LASERS

The ability to produce intense, coherent electromagnetic waves at nearly a single frequency has made possible much of modern communication. Masers and lasers now produce very intense coherent monochromatic microwave and visible radiation in a narrow beam. The word maser stands for *Microwave Amplification by Stimulated Emission of Radiation.* The laser, which relies on the same principles, produces visible light rather than microwaves. In this section, we consider some general features common to all masers and lasers and then describe the helium–neon gas laser.

Two important conditions must occur in any maser or laser: one is called *population inversion*, and the other is called *stimulated emission*. We describe these ideas in terms of atoms that have two energy levels E_1 and E_2 (Fig. 28.20).

Under normal conditions most of the atoms will be in the lower energy state, with a few in the upper level. Atoms that are in the excited state spontaneously emit photons and drop into the lower state. This process is random, and the emitted photons are not coherent, that is, they are not in phase with one another. In a laser, another type of emission process, called stimulated emission, plays an important role. If one atom emits a photon of energy $E_2 - E_1$, that photon may collide with a second atom that is in the state E_2. When this happens the second atom is stimulated to also emit a photon of the same energy. *These two photons are coherent with each other* (Fig. 28.21).

Stimulated emission may occur under normal conditions but is a rather minor effect because so few atoms are in the higher energy state. However,

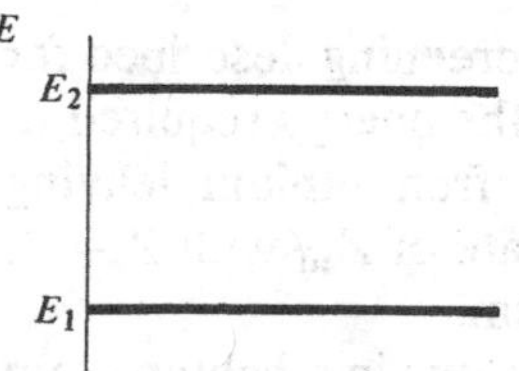

Figure 28.20. Two energy levels of an atom. Under normal conditions, a system of atoms will have more electrons in the lower energy state E_1. Heating will at best result in the nearly equal population of the two states.

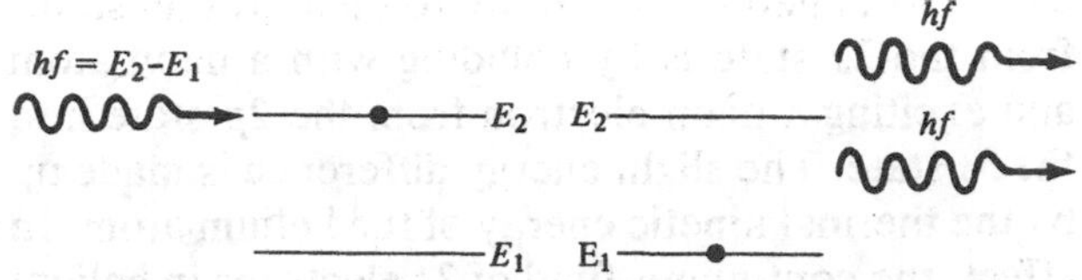

Figure 28.21. A photon with energy $hf = E_2 - E_1$ is incident on an atom in the state E_2. The incident photon stimulates the atom to drop into the lower energy state E_1, emitting a second photon with the same energy and coherent with the first.

in lasers the upper energy level is caused to be overpopulated, with more atoms in the upper than the lower state, and *population inversion* is said to occur. Under these conditions the probability that stimulated emission occurs is large, and many coherent photons can be obtained.

We can now see how intense coherent radiation may be produced. If a system of atoms or molecules can be forced into having the higher of two energy states overpopulated, the emission of a single photon during a transition to the lower state by one atom will trigger the emission of photons by many more atoms. In practice, this is achieved by an arrangement like that in Fig. 28.22.

The laser diagrammed is said to be a two-state, or pulsed, laser. After the process of stimulated emission is completed and most of the atoms in the material have been de-excited, energy must again be fed into the system to invert the population. This energy is usually supplied by electromagnetic radiation.

Lasers that produce continuous radiation rather than a pulsed beam require the presence of at least three, rather than two, energy states. In a continuous laser, atoms are continuously pumped from a low energy state to a higher one. These excited atoms then do not return to the initial state, but instead fall into and overpopulate a third state of intermediate energy. The laser action then takes place between this third level and some lower state.

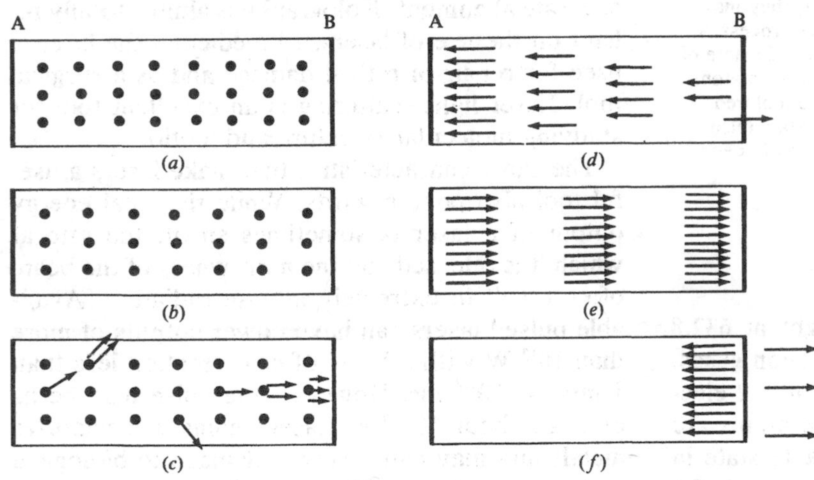

Figure 28.22. A schematic diagram of a laser. A material is placed between two parallel walls A and B. Wall A is a perfect reflector and B is 99 percent reflecting. (*a*) The material is in its normal state with most atoms (black circles) in a lower energy state and some (colored circles) in a higher energy state. (*b*) Population inversion is achieved. This is done by feeding energy into the system and is often called *pumping*. (*c*) Photons are emitted by random atoms. Some photons are lost through the sides, but one is shown initiating stimulated emission perpendicular to the ends. (*d*) After partial reflection, the buildup of coherent photons continues. (*e*) The buildup continues after total reflection from wall A; and in (*f*) 1 percent of the very large number of photons present escape through wall B. The photons inside continue to sweep back and forth until the population becomes normal and all the photons escape.

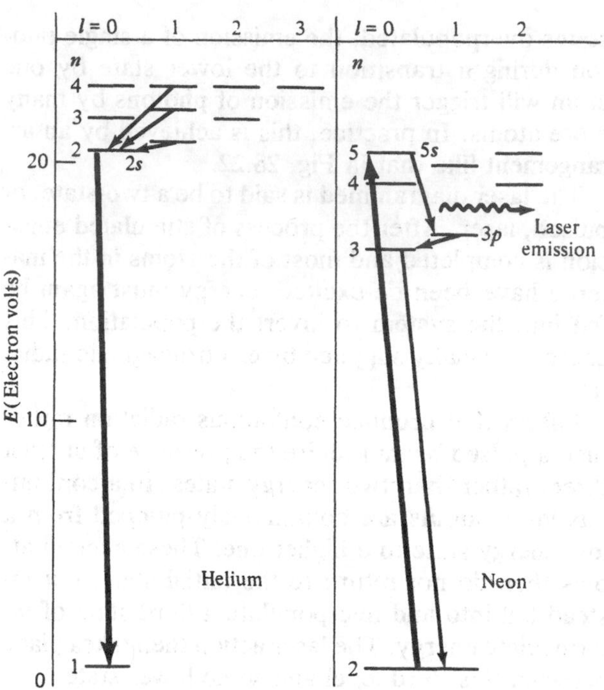

Figure 28.23. If electrons in helium are excited, they may return to the ground state emitting photons in the process. However, many electrons end up in the metastable 2*s* state of helium. When such a helium atom collides with a neon atom, the electron in helium drops into the ground state (colored line) and an electron in neon is raised into its 5*s* state (also shown colored). Laser action occurs as the electron in neon drops into the 3*p* state.

One continuous laser, producing light at 632.8 nm, contains a mixture of helium and neon gases. These two atoms have filled $n = 1$ and $n = 2$ electronic shells, respectively. When these atoms are excited, the electrons must return to a 1*s* state in helium and to a 2*p* state in neon to reestablish the ground state (Fig. 28.23).

The 2*s* ($n = 2$, $l = 0$) level in helium is 20.61 eV above the ground state and is lower in energy than the 2*p* ($n = 2$, $l = 1$) state. When an electric discharge occurs in the gas, electrons that end up in the 2*s* state in helium cannot return to the 1*s* ground state because the orbital angular momentum of the two states is the same; the 2*s* state is metastable. However, the 5*s* state of neon happens to be 20.66 eV above its ground state. Thus one way that the electrons in helium can return to their ground states from the 2*s* state is by colliding with a neon atom and exciting a neon electron from the 2*p* state into the 5*s* state. The slight energy difference is made up by the thermal kinetic energy of the helium atom. In effect, the continuous fund of 2*s* electrons in helium is pumping electrons into the 5*s* state of neon. The laser action then occurs when the electrons of the 5*s* state of neon falls into the 3*p* state, emitting photons with wavelength 632.8 nm. Other coherent transitions can also occur, but none are in the visible spectrum.

A variety of lasers and masers are now available that produce radiation in large portions of the visible, infrared, and microwave regions. Although not all wavelengths in these regions are available, some devices are tunable; that is, their output wavelengths may be changed. Masers and lasers have already found a wide range of applications and more are being developed.

In surveying and construction work the intense narrow laser beam can be used as a reference for accurate alignment. Holography is almost totally reliant on the use of lasers. In medicine, the laser is used for repair of retinal damage and as a surgical tool. Laser light scattering is an excellent tool for studying molecular structure and motion.

The same characteristics that make lasers a useful tool also pose hazards. While the total energy output of a laser is sometimes small, the rate at which it is released and the narrowness of the beam often result in extremely intense radiation. Available pulsed lasers can have power outputs of more than 10^{13} W with a beam of cross section less than 1 mm^2 = 10^{-6} m^2. However, the pulse may be as brief as about 10^{-12} s. Laser beams can vaporize metals and may cause severe damage to biological systems and tissue. For example, the retina is a strong absorber of light. Thus direct visual observation of even a relatively weak laser beam can cause severe retinal damage.

28.10 | SCHRÖDINGER'S EQUATION

Schrödinger's equation, like Newton's laws of motion or the basic laws of electricity and magnetism, cannot be derived from more fundamental concepts. Its validity rests on the successful testing of its predictions over a wide range of phenomena. We show how to construct the equation in this section, and examine its solutions for some simple situations in the following sections.

Applying Newton's laws to sound waves or waves on a string leads to a *wave equation* involving second derivatives of the displacement. Maxwell's equations lead to a similar equation for electromagnetic waves. Thus Schrödinger guessed that matter waves also satisfy a wave equation containing second derivatives of ψ.

Schrödinger developed a procedure or "recipe" for constructing the wave equation for any system. It starts from the total energy of the system written in terms of the momenta and positions of its particles. For example, suppose there is just one particle of mass m, and it can only move along the x axis. The particle has a kinetic energy $mv^2/2 = p^2/2m$ and a potential energy $\mathcal{U}(x)$ that depends on the nature of the forces acting on it. The total energy is

$$\frac{p^2}{2m} + \mathcal{U}(x) = E$$

The equation for ψ is constructed by making the replacement

$$p^2 \rightarrow -\hbar^2 \frac{d^2}{dx^2} \qquad (28.11)$$

Then Schrödinger's equation for this case is

$$\left[\frac{p^2}{2m} + \mathcal{U}(x)\right]\psi(x) = E\,\psi(x) \qquad (28.12)$$

or, with Eq. 28.11,

$$\frac{-\hbar^2}{2m}\frac{d^2}{dx^2}\psi(x) + \mathcal{U}(x)\,\psi(x) = E\,\psi(x)$$

(Schrödinger's equation) (28.13)

This equation does not contain the time, and is sometimes called the *time-independent* Schrödinger equation. A related *time-dependent* Schrödinger equation, which we will not consider, determines how the wave function evolves in time. Also, if the particle can move in two or three dimensions, or if there are more particles, the energy must include additional terms, and Schrödinger's equation is then more complicated.

28.11 | PARTICLE IN A ONE-DIMENSIONAL BOX

To see how you can solve Schrödinger's equation and interpret the resulting wave function, we consider a particle trapped in a one-dimensional "box." This idealized situation contains many of the features of more realistic but complex problems.

In Fig. 28.24, the particle experiences no force as long as it is the region between $x = 0$ and $x = a$. Thus the potential energy $\mathcal{U}$ is constant in that region, and can be set to the convenient value $\mathcal{U} = 0$. At $x = 0$ and $x = a$, infinitely large forces keep the particle in the box. If the forces were finite but large the potential energy would be rising steeply at these points. Here, since it would take an infinite amount of work to go beyond these limits, the potential energy becomes infinite at the ends of the box.

Inside the box, with $\mathcal{U} = 0$, Schrödinger's equation is

$$\frac{-\hbar^2}{2m}\frac{d^2}{dx^2}\psi(x) = E\,\psi(x) \qquad (28.14)$$

We try a solution of the form

$$\psi(x) = A \sin kx \qquad (28.15)$$

Now we saw in Chapter 21 that standing waves have an x dependence of the form sin kx. There the

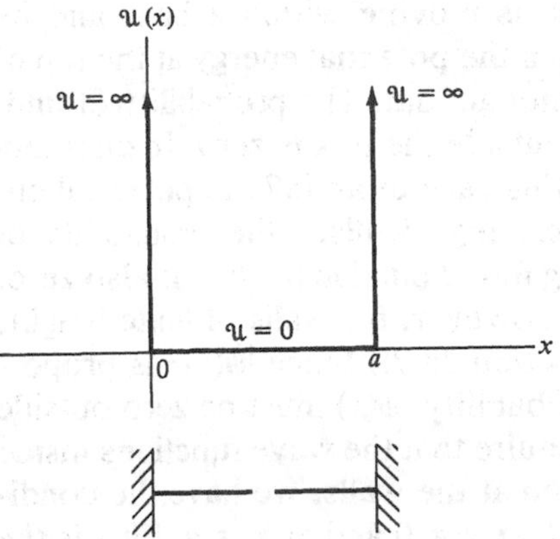

Figure 28.24. The potential energy function $\mathcal{U}(x)$ for a particle in a one-dimensional "box." There is no force on the particle inside the box, so its potential energy is constant. At the ends of the box, there are infinitely large forces, and the potential energy jumps to infinity.

wave number k was related to the wavelength λ by $k = 2\pi/\lambda$. Equation 28.15 therefore represents a standing wave with a wavelength $\lambda = 2\pi/k$.

According to Eqs. B.26 and B.27 in Appendix B, $(d/dx)\sin kx = k\cos kx$, and $(d/dx)\cos kx = -k\sin kx$. Hence substituting $\psi(x) = A\sin kx$ in Eq. 28.14 leads to

$$\frac{\hbar^2 k^2}{2m}(A\sin kx) = E(A\sin kx)$$

Since $A\sin kx$ is a common factor on both sides, it can be divided out. Thus we have a solution to Eq. 28.14 provided that the wave number k satisfies

$$\frac{\hbar^2 k^2}{2m} = E \qquad (28.16)$$

or

$$\hbar k = (2mE)^{1/2} \qquad (28.17)$$

Now $E = p^2/2m$, or $2mE = p^2$, so this equation reduces to $\hbar k = p$. Furthermore, with $\hbar = h/2\pi$ and $k = 2\pi/\lambda$, we have

$$p = \hbar k = \frac{h}{2\pi}\frac{2\pi}{\lambda} = \frac{h}{\lambda}$$

This is de Broglie's hypothesis! Schrödinger's recipe produces waves with de Broglie's wavelength. Note that if we replaced the sine by a cosine in Eq. 28.15, we would again find a solution.

Now let's consider the effect of the "walls." If a classical particle is moving within a box, and its energy is less than the potential energy at the top of the walls, it cannot get out. The probability of finding the particle outside the box is zero. In quantum mechanics, for this case of an infinite potential energy or "infinitely high walls," the probability of the particle being found outside the box is also zero. (This isn't true, however, for walls of finite height, as we saw in Section 28.7.) Since $|\psi(x)|^2$ is proportional to that probability, $\psi(x)$ must be zero outside the box. If we require that the wave functions inside and outside match at the walls, we have the condition that $\psi(x) = 0$ at $x = 0$ and at $x = a$. *This is the boundary condition for a particle in a box:* $\psi(x)$ *vanishes at the walls.*

At the point $x = 0$, $\sin kx = \sin 0 = 0$ as required. (Note that $\cos kx = \cos 0 = 1$ at $x = 0$, which rules out a cosine solution.) At $x = a$, $\sin kx = \sin ka$. This is zero only if ka equals one of the arguments for which the sine is zero. There are $0, \pi, 2\pi, \ldots$, corresponding to 0°, 180°, 360°, ... Thus $ka = n\pi$, where n is an integer. The case $ka = 0$ is uninteresting, since it implies $k = 0$ and $\psi(x) = A\sin 0 = 0$ for all x. Hence k is restricted to the values

$$k_n = \frac{n\pi}{a} \qquad n = 1, 2, 3, \ldots \qquad (28.18)$$

Using $E = \hbar^2 k^2/2m$, the corresponding energies are

$$E_n = \frac{n^2\hbar^2\pi^2}{2ma^2} \qquad n = 1, 2, 3, \ldots \qquad (28.19)$$

The energies E_n *are discrete.* There is a lowest or ground state energy $E_1 = \hbar^2\pi^2/2ma^2$, a first excited state with $E_2 = 2^2E_1$, and so on (Fig. 28.25). The *quantum number* n labels the energy levels E_n and the associated wave functions $\psi_n(x)$.

Since the wavelength λ is related to k by $\lambda = 2\pi/k$, and k can have the values $n\pi/a$, the possible wavelengths are $\lambda = 2\pi(a/n\pi) = 2a/n$. Thus $n\lambda/2 = a$, or *an integer number of half-wavelengths must "fit into the box.* This is just the condition for resonant waves on a fixed end string or in a closed pipe. Clearly we could have obtained these results without a detailed mathematical discussion by simply requiring the de Broglie waves to fit within the box.

However, our primary goal is not to solve the particle in a box problem, but rather to illustrate how we solve quantum mechanical problems in general. We construct the wave equation using Schrödinger's recipe and find solutions consistent with the boundary conditions.

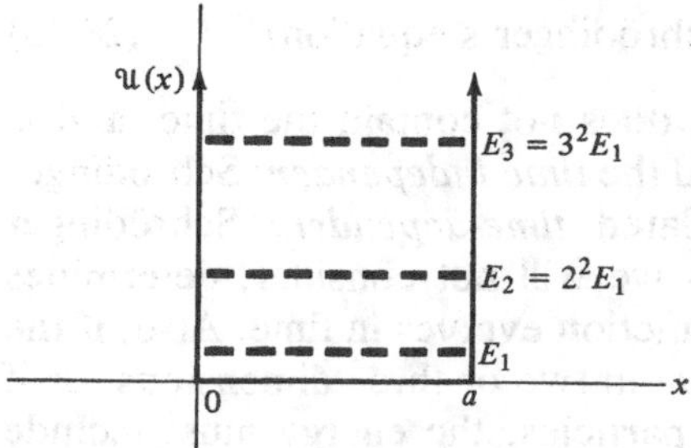

Figure 28.25. The first three energy levels for the particle in a one-dimensional box.

An atom is not a box with infinitely high walls, but an electron without sufficient energy to leave the atom is kept within the general neighborhood of the nucleus. *Thus the boundary condition for an atomic wave function is that ψ must go to zero when an electron is far from the nucleus, or when $r \to \infty$.* This requirement implies that the constants analogous to k in the wave function must have special values. The corresponding energies are then discrete.

The following example illustrates that the solutions to Schrödinger's equation are consistent with the uncertainty principle, as expected.

Example 28.6

Show that the ground state energy is consistent with the minimum energy predicted by the uncertainty principle.

If we guess that the particle is at the midpoint of the box, we cannot be off by more than $a/2$. Hence we take $\Delta x \simeq a/2$. Then the uncertainty principle requires $\Delta x\, \Delta p \geq \hbar$, so $\Delta p \geq \hbar/\Delta x = 2\hbar/a$. The momentum is at least as large as its uncertainty, so its minimum value is $p = \Delta p = 2\hbar/a$. The corresponding kinetic energy is

$$E = \frac{p^2}{2m} = \frac{4\hbar^2}{2ma^2}$$

The ground state energy is actually $\pi^2\hbar^2/2ma^2$, which is larger than this minimum by a factor of $\pi^2/4 \simeq 2.5$.

Interpretation of the Wave Function

We have noted that for matter waves, $|\psi(x)|^2$ is a measure of the probability of finding a particle at x. More precisely, $|\psi|^2$ is a *probability density*. Thus, in one dimension $P(x) = |\psi(x)|^2$ is a *probability per unit length*. The probability of finding the particle between x and $x + dx$ is

$$P(x)dx = |\psi(x)|^2\, dx \qquad (28.20)$$

In regions where ψ is large, the odds are high of finding the particle. It is less likely to be found where ψ is small.

For example, Fig. 28.26*a* shows ψ and $|\psi|^2$ for the $n = 1$ or ground state of a particle in a one-dimensional box. At the center, $x = a/2$, $|\psi|^2$ has its greatest value. We can't say where the particle is, except in a probabilistic way. However, if we measure its position, the chances are best of finding it near $a/2$. If we have many identical particles in their ground states in identical boxes, and we measure their positions, a graph of the relative frequencies of the observed positions will look like the $|\psi(x)|^2$ plot. Figure 28.26*b* shows ψ and $|\psi|^2$ for the first excited state, $n = 2$. For this state the probability density is zero at the center, and it peaks at $a/4$ and $3a/4$. The probability density $P(x)$ is very different for the $n = 1$ and $n = 2$ states.

The total probability of finding the particle somewhere in the box must be 1, since it is somewhere! This means that if we integrate $P(x)$ over all regions where the wave function is not zero, we must find $\int P dx = 1$, or

$$\int |\psi(x)|^2\, dx = 1 \quad \text{(normalization condition)} \qquad (28.21)$$

This is called the *normalization condition*. If the constant factor A in $\psi = A \sin kx$ is chosen so that Eq. 28.21 is satisfied, ψ is said to be *normalized*, and A is called the *normalization constant*. Thus we must have

$$\int_0^a |\psi(x)|^2\, dx = \int_0^a A^2 \sin^2 kx\, dx = 1 \qquad (28.22)$$

It is left as an exercise to verify that $A^2 = 2/a$, so that the normalized wave function is

$$\psi_n(x) = \left[\frac{2}{a}\right]^{1/2} \sin \frac{n\pi x}{a} \qquad \text{(particle in a box)} \qquad (28.23)$$

Since classical physics correctly describes the world at the macroscopic level, a quantum description must approach the classical predictions in suitable limiting cases. This is referred to as the *correspondence principle*. The next example shows that this occurs in the limit of large energies or quantum numbers for a particle in a box.

Example 28.7

Show that the probability distribution for a particle in a box approaches the classical distribution for large values of the quantum number n.

If a classical ball is moving back and forth within a one-dimensional box, it is equally likely to be found at any point in the box. Stated mathematically, the classical probability distribution $P_{\text{C.M.}}(x)$ is the same everywhere in the box. In the quantum mechanical case, in the ground state the probability density is greatest at the center (Fig. 28.19*a*), and

$$P(x) = |\psi(x)|^2 = \frac{2}{a} \sin^2 k_1 x = \frac{2}{a} \sin^2 \frac{\pi x}{a}$$

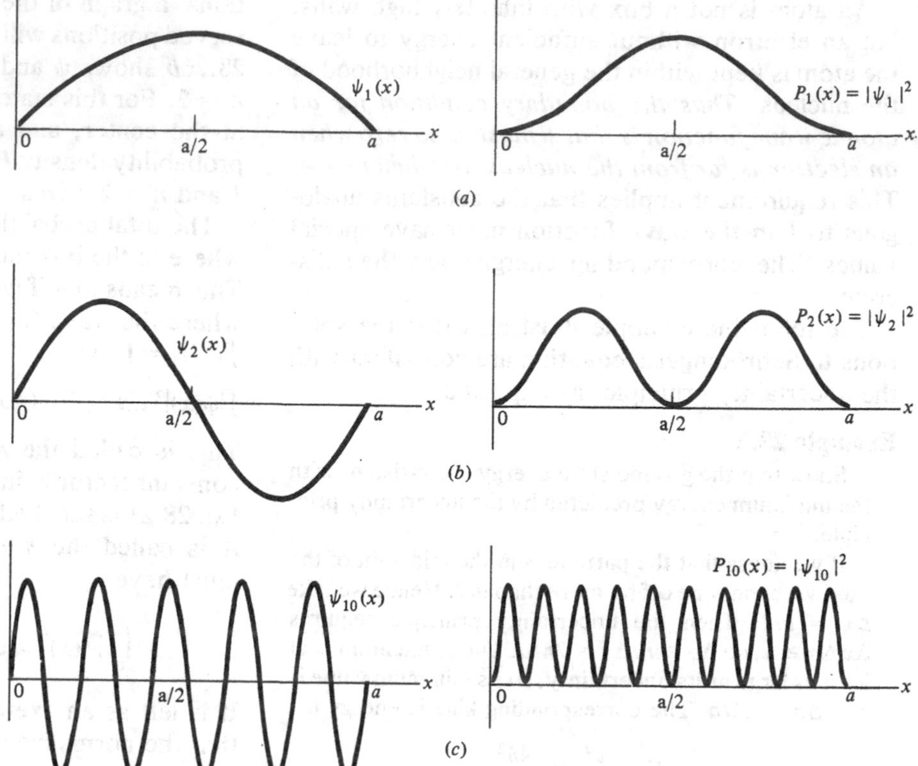

Figure 28.26. Graphs of $\psi(x)$ and $|\psi(x)|^2$ for a particle in a one-dimensional box. (*a*) Ground state ($n = 1$). (*b*) First excited state ($n = 2$). (*c*) $n = 10$ state.

Thus the classical and quantum probability distributions are very different for a particle with the ground state energy.

However, when n is large, $|\psi_n|^2 = (2/a) \sin^2 k_n x$ oscillates very rapidly (Fig. 28.26*c*). Now consider the probability of finding the particle somewhere within a narrow "bin" of x values comparable to the width of the $\sin^2 k_n x$ oscillations but still small compared to a. The odds of finding the particle are the same for the bins everywhere in the box. As the energy E_n and the quantum number n become larger, the bins become smaller. Thus for all practical purposes the probability distribution becomes constant, as in the classical case. This is what is expected from the correspondence principle.

28.12 | THE SQUARE WELL

The square well was used in Section 28.7 to illustrate the remarkable quantum mechanical phenomena of barrier penetration and tunneling. We now consider this idealized problem in a little more detail. What we shall find is that the energy levels and wave functions are similar to those we have just discussed for the particle in a box, except that the wave functions penetrate into the classically inaccessible region.

The square well is shown again in Figure 28.27*a*. The potential energy $\mathcal{U}$ equals zero inside and equals $\mathcal{U}_0$ outside. If a particle leaves the well, its potential energy increases by $\mathcal{U}_0$. Since the total energy $E = K + \mathcal{U}$ is constant, the kinetic energy K decreases by $\mathcal{U}_0$.

According to classical physics, the particle cannot leave the well if $E < \mathcal{U}_0$, since it would then have a negative kinetic energy, which is impossible. What does quantum mechanics say about this situation? Inside the well, just as in the box problem, Schrödinger's equation predicts sinusoidal waves of

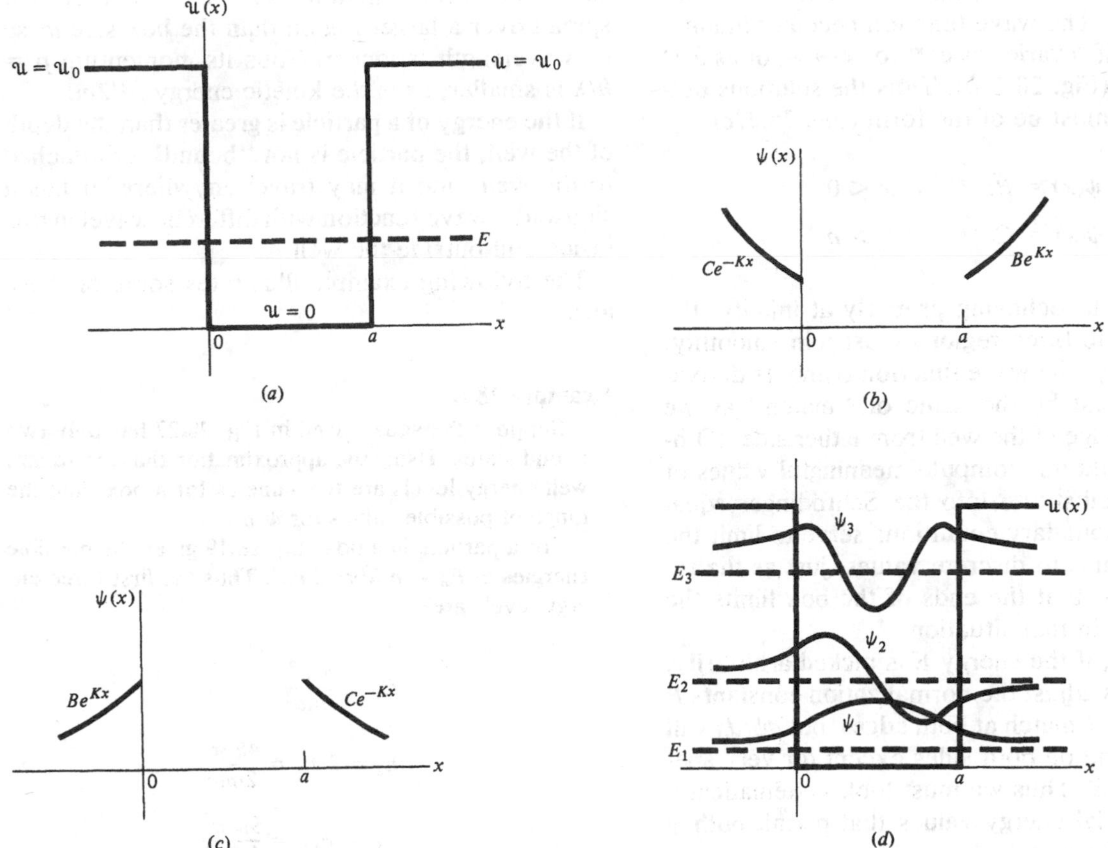

Figure 28.27. The square well. *(a)* The potential energy is $\mathcal{U}_0$ for $x < 0$ and $x > a$, or outside the well; it is zero inside the well. *(b)* Wave functions which grow rapidly as we move away from the well are not physically meaningful. *(c)* The acceptable wave functions decrease exponentially outside the well. *(d)* The first three energy levels and the corresponding wave functions.

the form sin kx or cos kx, where again $\hbar k = (2mE)^{1/2}$. Outside, we have

$$\frac{-\hbar^2}{2m}\frac{d^2}{dx^2}\psi(x) + \mathcal{U}_0\,\psi(x) = E\,\psi(x)$$

or

$$\frac{-\hbar^2}{2m}\frac{d^2}{dx^2}\psi(x) = (E - \mathcal{U}_0)\psi(x) \qquad (28.24)$$

This is similar to Eq. 28.14 for the particle in a box, but with $(E - \mathcal{U}_0)\psi$ replacing $E\psi$. However, E $E - \mathcal{U}_0$ is negative, since $E < \mathcal{U}_0$. Because of this, a sine or a cosine no longer is a solution. Instead, we need exponentials. Specifically, we can try the solutions

$$\psi(x) = Be^{+\kappa x} \quad \text{or} \quad \psi(x) = Ce^{-\kappa x}$$

(κ is the greek lowercase letter "kappa.") Using Eq. B.25 in Appendix B, $(d/dx)e^{ax} = ae^{ax}$, we find with either function $(d^2/dx^2)\psi = \kappa^2\psi$. Thus either is a solution if $-(\hbar\kappa)^2/2m = (E - \mathcal{U}_0)$ or

$$\hbar\kappa = [2m(\mathcal{U}_0 - E)]^{1/2} \qquad (28.25)$$

Just as in the box problem, boundary conditions limit the acceptable solutions of the Schrödinger equation. First, we must reject as unphysical any wave functions that become infinite as we go far from the well. The wave function becomes infinite, for example, if ψ varies as $e^{+\kappa x}$ for $x \to \infty$, or as $e^{-\kappa x}$ for $x \to -\infty$ (Fig. 28.27*b*). Thus the solutions outside the well must be of the form (Fig. 28.27*c*)

$$\psi(x) = Be^{+\kappa x} \qquad x < 0$$

$$\psi(x) = Ce^{-\kappa x} \qquad x > a$$

In addition to behaving properly at infinity, the solutions in the three regions must join smoothly. More precisely, the wave function ψ and its derivative $d\psi/dx$ must be the same or "match" as we approach an edge of the well from either side. (Otherwise we could not compute meaningful values of $(d^2/dx^2)\psi$ to substitute into the Schrödinger equation.) These boundary conditions serve to limit the possible energies to discrete values, just as the requirement $\psi = 0$ at the ends of the box limits the energy values in that situation.

Specifically, if the energy E is picked arbitrarily, we can always adjust the normalization constants B and C to make ψ match at both edges, but $d\psi/dx$ will not be the same on both sides except for very special values of E. Thus we must look systematically for those special energy values that permit both ψ and $d\psi/dx$ to be matched.

Carrying out this calculation in detail is messy, and the results can only be stated in numerical or graphical form. Some of the allowed energy values and the corresponding wave functions are sketched in Fig. 28.27*d*. The wave function is sinusoidal inside the well, but it has expontential "tails" extending outside. Thus the wave function and the probability density are not zero in the region where the kinetic energy is negative! There is a nonzero probability of finding the particle in places where it could never be according to classical physics. Note that as $\mathcal{U}_0$ becomes larger relative to the energy E, the tails become smaller; the lowest energy level has the smallest tails. In the limit of infinitely high walls, $\mathcal{U}_0 \to \infty$, the tails are zero. This is why we used the boundary condition $\psi = 0$ at the walls of a box.

The energy values for the square well correspond closely to those for the particle in a box, but they are systematically a bit lower. This happens because the wave functions for the particle is now spread over a larger region than the box size a, so its wavelength is longer. Thus its momentum $p = h/\lambda$ is smaller, as is the kinetic energy $p^2/2m$.

If the energy of a particle is greater than the depth of the well, the particle is not "bound" or attached to the well, and it may travel anywhere. It has a sinusoidal wave function with different wavelengths inside and outside the well.

The following example illustrates some of these ideas.

Example 28.8

Suppose the square well in Fig. 28.27 has only two bound states. Using the approximation that the square well energy levels are the same as for a box, find the range of possible values for $\mathcal{U}_0 a^2$.

For a particle in a box, Eq. 28.19 gives the possible energies at $E_n = n^2\hbar^2\pi^2/2ma^2$. Thus the first three energy levels are

$$E_1 = \frac{\hbar^2\pi^2}{2ma^2}$$

$$E_2 = 2^2E_1 = \frac{4\hbar^2\pi^2}{2ma^2}$$

$$E_3 = 3^2E_1 = \frac{9\hbar^2\pi^2}{2ma^2}$$

If there are only two bound states, this means that the height $\mathcal{U}_0$ of the well is more than E_2 and less than E_3. Thus

$$\frac{4\hbar^2\pi^2}{2ma^2} < \mathcal{U}_0 < \frac{9\hbar^2\pi^2}{2ma^2}$$

or

$$\frac{4\hbar^2\pi^2}{2m} < \mathcal{U}_0 a^2 < \frac{9\hbar^2\pi^2}{2m}$$

In the approximation that the square well levels are the same as those for the box, this is the range of $\mathcal{U}_0 a^2$ values for which the well has two bound states. If a^2 is small, $\mathcal{U}_0$ is large; the well is then very deep, but it extends over a small region of space. Conversely, a large value of a^2 implies a shallow well. Allowing for the fact that the actual energies for a square well are lower than for a box would slightly lower the limits.

28.13 | APPLICATION TO ATOMS, MOLECULES, AND NUCLEI

The basic ideas developed in our discussion of idealized one-dimensional problems apply to atoms, molecules, and nuclei. A Schrödinger equation is constructed and solved either exactly or approximately for the wave functions. The acceptable bound state wave functions are limited by the boundary conditions, so that only special energy values are allowed. The allowed energies and the associated wave functions are characterized by several quantum numbers, rather than by one quantum number as in the one-dimensional case. Again, the wave functions typically oscillate in classically allowed regions, and decrease rapidly in classically inaccessible regions.

Carrying out the actual calculations for even the simplest atom, hydrogen, requires more space and more advanced mathematics than is appropriate here. Textbooks on modern physics, quantum mechanics, and quantum chemistry go into these problems in detail. Some of the most basic results of these calculations for hydrogen and larger atoms were discussed earlier in this chapter. In the next section, we give explicit formulas for the hydrogen wave functions and show how to use them. Molecules and atomic nuclei are considered in later chapters.

28.14 | EXPLICIT FORM OF THE HYDROGEN WAVE FUNCTIONS

Although the Schrödinger equation for the hydrogen atom is too complicated for us to solve, we can write down and discuss the wave functions it predicts. A number of interesting and important results can be obtained in this way.

Since the electron in a hydrogen atom moves in three dimensions, its wave function depends on three coordinates. These may be chosen to be the Cartesian coordinates x, y, and z. However, the spherical symmetry of the Coulomb force between the electron and the nucleus is reflected in the wave function. Hence the spherical coordinates r, θ, and ϕ are often more convenient.

The two sets of coordinates are related by (Fig. 28.28*a*)

$$x = r \sin\theta \cos\phi$$
$$y = r \sin\theta \sin\phi \qquad (28.26)$$
$$z = r \cos\theta$$

Another useful relationship is

$$r^2 = x^2 + y^2 + z^2 \qquad (28.27)$$

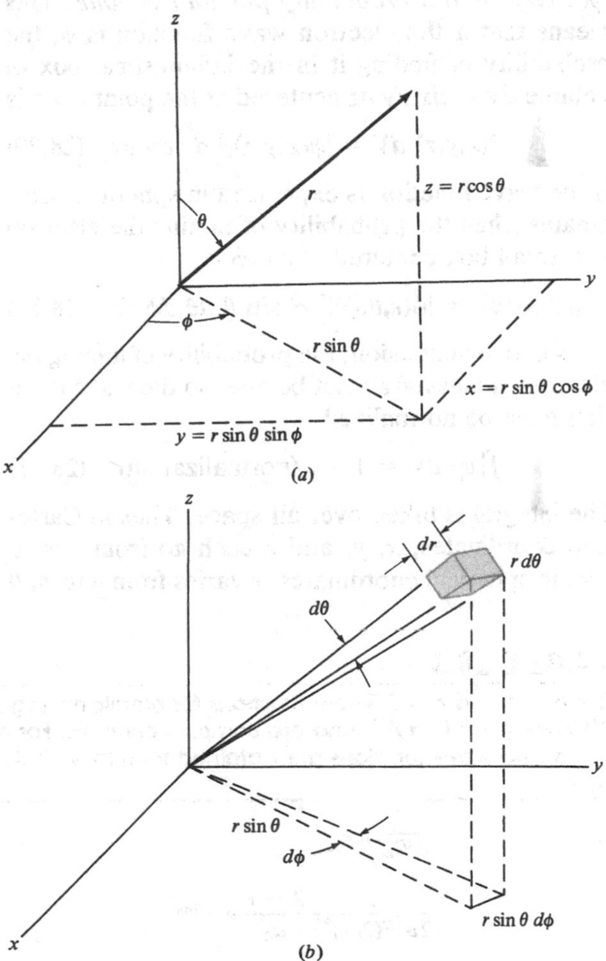

Figure 28.28. (*a*) Relation between spherical and Cartesian coordinates. (*b*) The volume element formed when the coordinates change by dr, $d\theta$, and $d\phi$.

An infinitesimal element of volume in spherical coordinates is (Fig. 28.28*b*)

$$dV = r^2 \sin\theta \, d\theta \, d\phi \, dr \quad \text{(volume element)} \quad (28.28)$$

Table 28.3 lists the $n = 1$ and $n = 2$ hydrogen atom wave functions. The ground state (1*s*) wave function is the simplest, and all the *s* states are spherically symmetric, or independent of the angles θ and ϕ. As n or l increases, the formulas contain more and more terms; these give rise to additional oscillations and nodes in the wave functions (Figs. 28.5 and 28.6).

In three dimensions, the probability density $|\psi(x,y,z)|^2$ is the *probability per unit volume.* This means that if the electron wave function is ψ, the probability of finding it in the infinitesimal box of volume $dV = dx\,dy\,dz$ centered at the point x,y,z is

$$P(x,y,z)\,dV = |\psi(x,y,z)|^2\,dx\,dy\,dz \quad (28.29)$$

If the wave function is expressed in spherical coordinates, then the probability of finding the electron in a small box centered at r,θ,ϕ is

$$P(r,\theta,\phi)dV = |\psi(r,\theta,\phi)|^2\, r^2 \sin\theta\, d\theta\, d\phi\, dr \quad (28.30)$$

As in one dimension, the probability of finding the electron *somewhere* must be one, so the wave function must be normalized:

$$\int |\psi|^2\, dV = 1 \quad \text{(normalization)} \quad (28.31)$$

The integral is taken over all space. Thus in Cartesian coordinates, x, y, and z each go from $-\infty$ to $+\infty$; in spherical coordinates, r varies from 0 to ∞, θ from 0 to π, and ϕ from 0 to 2π. The wave functions in Table 28.3 have normalization constants chosen so that this condition holds. For example, the 1*s* state normalization constant is

$$N_{1s} = \left(\frac{1}{\pi a_0^3}\right)^{1/2}$$

As we noted in Section 28.3, the *s* state wave functions are largest at $r = 0$, so there is a relatively large probability of finding an *s* electron near the nucleus. The wave functions for all $l > 0$ states are zero at the origin, so electrons in these states are less likely to be found at small values of r. The chance of finding an *s* state electron at a very small value of r is reduced, however, by the factor of r^2 in Eq. 28.30; spherical shells with small radii have very small volumes. We apply some of these ideas in the following example.

Example 28.9

For the 1*s* state, find the maximum value of the radial probability density r^2P.

From Table 28.3, the wave function can be written as

$$\psi_{1s} = N_{1s}e^{-r/a_0}$$

Thus the radial probability density is

$$r^2P = r^2|\psi_{1s}|^2 = N_{1s}^2 r^2 e^{-2r/a_0} \quad \text{(i)}$$

To find the maximum value of r^2P, we set its derivative $d(r^2P)/dr$ equal to zero:

$$N_{1s}^2 e^{-2r/a_0}\left(2r - \frac{2r^2}{a_0}\right) = 0$$

TABLE 28.3

The $n = 1$ and $n = 2$ wave functions for atomic hydrogen. Note that some of the ψ's involve $i = (-1)^{1/2}$, and are complex numbers. For one-electron atoms with $Z > 1$, the wave functions are obtained from those below if a_0 is replaced by a_0/Z.

1*s*	$\frac{1}{\pi^{1/2}a_0^{3/2}} e^{-r/a_0}$
2*s*	$\frac{1}{2\pi^{1/2}(2a_0)^{3/2}} \frac{2-r}{a_0} e^{-r/2a_0}$
2*p* ($m = 0$)	$\frac{1}{2\pi^{1/2}(2a_0)^{3/2}} \frac{r}{a_0} e^{-r/2a_0} \cos\theta$
2*p* ($m = \pm 1$)	$\frac{1}{\pi^{1/2}(4a_0)^{3/2}} \frac{r}{a_0} e^{-r/2a_0} \sin\theta (\cos\phi \pm i \sin\phi)$

This has solutions at $r = 0$ and $r = \infty$, which are not relevant since they correspond to minima, and at $r = a_0$; the last solution corresponds to the desired maximum. Thus, as stated earlier, the electron is most likely to be found at a radius equal to the Bohr radius. Substituting $r = a_0$ in Eq. i, the probability of finding the electron in that region is proportional to

$$r^2P = r^2|\psi_{1s}|^2 = N_{1s}^2 a_0^2 e^{-2}$$

If this calculation is repeated for the $2p$ states, you find that the radial probability density peaks at $4a_0 = 2^2a_0$, the radius predicted by the Bohr model for $n = 2$. The $2s$ state has its greatest radial probability density at a somewhat larger radius.

In Section 28.7, we obtained a formula for the classical turning point r_t in a hydrogen atom, the radius at which the kinetic energy is zero for the orbiting electron. In classical physics, the electron can never go beyond this point, since it cannot have a negative kinetic energy. The wave function tells us the probability of finding the electron at all values of r, including $r \geq r_t$. This is illustrated in the next example,

Example 28.10

For the $1s$ state, find the value of the radial probability density r^2P at the classical turning point r_t and at $2r_t$.

The classical turning point is at $r_t = 2n^2a_0$, so with $n = 1$,

$$r_t = 2a_0^2$$

$$r^2P = r^2|\psi_{1s}|^2 = N_{1s}^2 r^2 e^{-2r/a_0}\big|_{r=2a_0}$$

$$= 4N_{1s}^2 a_0^2 e^{-4}$$

We saw in Example 28.9 that for the $1s$ state, the maximum radial probability density occurs at a_0 and is $N_{1s}^2 a_0^2 e^{-2}$. Thus at the turning point, r^2P is smaller by a factor of $4e^{-2} = 0.54$.

In the same way, at $r = 2r_t = 4a_0$, we find

$$r^2P = 16N_{1s}^2 a_0^2 e^{-8}$$

At $r = 2r_t$, r^2P is smaller than at r_t by a factor of $4e^{-4} = 0.073$, and smaller than its maximum value at a_0 by a factor of $16e^{-6} = 0.040$. At twice the classical turning point, the chance of finding the electron is 4 percent as great as at its most probable radius.

The total probability of finding the electron at radii larger than the classical turning radius is obtained by evaluating $\int P\, dV$ over all points in space with $r \geq r_t$. For the $1s$ state, this probability turns out to be 0.24, as noted in Section 28.7. Thus the electron actually spends almost a quarter of its time in the region where it can never be found according to classical physics.

We noted in Section 28.3 that in molecular structure discussions, it is convenient to use $2p$ wave functions that are superpositions of those shown in Table 28.3. In the $2p$ wave functions, the angular factors can be rewritten with the aid of Eqs. 28.26 as follows:

$$m = 0: \qquad \cos\theta \rightarrow \frac{z}{r}$$

$$m = \pm 1: \qquad \sin\theta\,(\cos\phi \pm i\sin\phi) \rightarrow \frac{x \pm iy}{r}$$

Thus adding and subtracting the $m = +1$ and $m = -1$ wave functions yields wave functions proportional to x and to y, respectively:

$$\psi_x = \frac{\psi_{2p,m=+1} + \psi_{2p,m=-1}}{2^{1/2}} \propto \frac{x}{r} \qquad (28.32)$$

$$\psi_y = \frac{\psi_{2p,m=+1} - \psi_{2p,m=-1}}{2^{1/2}i} \propto \frac{y}{r}$$

These are the p_x and p_y wave functions, respectively. The factors in the denominators are chosen to give real, normalized wave functions. Also, we define the p_z wave function by

$$\psi_z = \psi_{p,m=0} \qquad (28.33)$$

These wave functions are illustrated in Fig. 28.8. Because of the factor of x in ψ_x, at any value of r the probability density $|\psi_x|^2$ is greatest along the x axis. Similarly, $|\psi_y|^2$ is greatest along the y axis, and $|\psi_z|^2$ is greatest along the z axis.

EXERCISES ON SUPPLEMENTARY TOPICS

Section 28.9 | Masers and Lasers

28-32 The angular spread of a particular laser beam is 10^{-5} rad. What is the diameter of the spot formed on the moon's surface if the laser is directed toward the moon from the earth? (The earth-to-moon distance is 3.8×10^5 km.)

28-33 (a) If a laser emits 10 J of energy in a pulse lasting 5×10^{-11} s, what power is emitted?

(b) What is the intensity of the beam if it is 2×10^{-6} m^2 in area?

28-34 What is the length of a laser pulse in a vacuum if it is emitted in 10^{-11} s?

Section 28.11 | Particle in a One-Dimensional Box

c28-35 Verify that the wave function in Eq. 28.23 is normalized, so that Eq. 28.22 holds.

28-36 The discreteness of energy levels is unobservably small for macroscopic objects. Illustrate this point by finding the separation in joules of the $n = 1$ and $n = 2$ levels for a 1-g object in a 1-cm box.

28-37 In atomic nuclei, the separations between energy levels decrease as the nuclei increase in size. Consider a neutron trapped in a one-dimensional box. Find the difference in energy in MeV of the $n = 1$ and $n = 2$ states if the length of the box is (a) 3 fm; (b) 8 fm. (1 MeV = 10^6 eV; 1 fm = 10^{-15} m; the neutron mass is listed on the inside rear cover. The lengths chosen correspond roughly to the sizes of carbon and lead nuclei.)

28-38 A model for an atom is an electron in a one-dimensional box of length 10^{-10} m. (a) What is the energy difference in electron volts between the ground and first excited states of this system? (b) Find the ratio of the calculated energy difference to the actual energy difference in atomic hydrogen.

Section 28.12 | The Square Well; Tunneling

28-39 The heavy hydrogen or deuterium nucleus consists of one proton and one neutron. Their mutual attraction is just barely strong enough so that there is one bound state. A simple model for this system is a neutron moving in a square well of length 3 fm = 3×10^{-15} m. Assuming that the square well energy levels are the same as in a box, what is the minimum well depth in MeV that will permit a bound state? (1 MeV = 10^6 eV; the neutron mass is listed on the inside rear cover.)

Section 28.14 | Explicit Form of the Hydrogen Wave Functions

c28-40 Verify that the $1s$ state hydrogen atom wave function is normalized.

c28-41 Verify that the $2p$, $m = 0$ hydrogen atom wave function is normalized.

c28-42 Find the radius at which the radial probability density r^2P is a maximum for the $2s$ state of hydrogen.

c28-43 (a) Find the radius at which the radial probability density r^2P is a maximum for the $2p$ states of hydrogen. (b) At what radius is P largest for these states?

28-44 What is the radial probability density for a hydrogen atom $2s$ electron at its classical turning point?

c28-45 (a) Show that since the atomic nucleus is very small compared to the Bohr radius, the wave function of a hydrogen atom $1s$ state electron is essentially constant at its $r = 0$ value within the nucleus. (b) If the nuclear radius is 1 fm = 10^{-15} m, what is the probability of finding a $1s$ hydrogen atom electron within the nucleus?

PROBLEMS ON SUPPLEMENTARY TOPICS

c28-46 A particle of mass m moves in one dimension. It is attached to a spring with spring constant k, so its potential energy is $\frac{1}{2}kx^2$. (a) What is the Schrödinger equation for this system? (b) What boundary conditions must ψ satisfy for $x \to \pm\infty$? (c) Show that

$$\psi(x) = Ae^{-\alpha x^2}$$

is a satisfactory solution of the Schrödinger equation if α is suitably chosen. (This is actually the ground state wave function.) (d) What is the energy corresponding to this wave function?

c28-47 A particle of mass m is in a one-dimensional box with its walls at $x = -a$ and $x = +a$. (a) What are the boundary conditions the wave functions must satisfy? (b) Show that both sine and cosine solutions are acceptable wave functions if k has suitable values. (c) Find the normalized wave functions and the corresponding energies.

c28-48 A particle in a one-dimensional box extending from 0 to a is in is ground state. Calculate the probability of finding it in the region $0 < x < a/4$. [*Hint:* $\int \sin^2 bx\, dx = x/2 - (\sin 2bx)/4b$.]

c28-49 Find the total probability that the electron in a hydrogen atom 1*s* state is at a radius greater than the maximum radius permitted by classical physics.

c28-50 Find the probability that a 2*s* electron in a hydrogen atom is at a radius smaller than the Bohr radius. (*Hint:* Integrate the probability density over the appropriate volume.)

c28-51 The average value of r^n is denoted by $<r^n>$. If an electron has a wave function ψ, then $<r^n> = \int r^n |\psi|^2\, dV$. For the 1*s* state in hydrogen, find the average values of (a) r; (b) $1/r$. (c) Discuss the reasons why $1/<r> \neq <1/r>$.

c28-52 The average value of z^2 is $<z^2> = \int z^2 |\psi|^2\, dV$, and the average value of r^2 is $<r^2> = \int r^2\, |\psi|^2\, dV$. Evaluate both of these quantities for the 2*s* state in hydrogen.

c28-53 Verify that the $2p_x$ hydrogen atom wave function is normalized. (Use $|a + ib|^2 = a^2 + b^2$.)

c28-54 Repeat the previous problem for the 2*p*, $m = 1$ state.

Additional Reading

Arthur L. Robinson, Quantum Jumps Seen in a Single Ion, *Science*, vol. 234, October 3, 1986, p. 24.

R. Riuker, The Safe Use of Lasers, *Physics Teacher*, vol. 11, 1973, p. 455.

Victor F. Weisskopf, Personal Memories of Pauli, *Physics Today*, December 1985, p. 36.

Calvin F. Quate, Vacuum Tunneling: A New Technique for Microscopy, *Physics Today*, August 1986, p. 26.

H. Weichel, W. A. Danne, and L. S. Pedroth, Laser Safety in the Laboratory, *American Journal of Physics*, vol. 42, 1974, p. 1006.

J. M. Coakley, Probability of Laser Injury to the Eye—Further Considerations, *Physics Teacher*, vol. 13, 1975, p. 388.

Arthur L. Schawlow, Lasers and Physics: A Pretty Good Hint, *Physics Today*, December 1982, p. 46.

Phillip Sprangle and Timothy Coffey, New Sources of High-Power Coherent Radiation, *Physics Today*, March 1984, p. 44. Free-electron lasers and cyclotron-resonance masers.

Special Issue: Lasers Now and Then, *Physics Today*, October, 1989. History, medical and other applications.

Mitja Kregar and Victor Weisskopf, Ionization Energies and Electron Affinities of Atoms up to Neon, *American Journal of Physics*, vol. 50, March 1982, p. 213.

James J. Wayne, Current Trends in Atomic Spectroscopy, *Physics Today*, November 1982, p. 52.

Bernd Crasemann and Francois Weilleumeir, Atomic Physics with Synchrotron Radiation, *Physics Today*, June 1984, p. 34.

Scientific American articles:

Leslie Holliday, Early View on Forces Between Atoms, May 1970, p. 116.

H. R. Crane, The g Factor of the Electron, January 1968, p. 77.

Vernon W. Hughes, The Muonium Atom, April 1966, p. 93.

O. R. Frisch, Molecular Beams, May 1965, p. 58.

William C. Livingston, Magnetic Fields on the Quiet Sun, November 1966, p. 54.

J. P. Gordon, The Maser, December 1958, p. 42.

Arnold L. Bloom, Optical Pumping, October 1960, p. 72.

Arthur L. Schawlow, Optical Masers, June 1961, p. 52.

Arthur L. Schawlow, Advances in Optical Masers, July 1963, p. 34.

S. E. Miller, Communication by Laser, January 1966, p. 19.

George C. Pimentel, Chemical Lasers, April 1966, p. 32.

Alexander Lempick and Harold Samelson, Liquid Lasers, June 1967, p. 80.

Donald F. Nelson, The Modulation of Laser Light, June 1968, p. 17.

C. K. N. Patel, High Power Carbon Dioxide Lasers, August 1968, p. 22.

Arthur L. Schawlow, Laser Light, September 1968, p. 120.

Donald R. Herriott, Applications of Laser Light, September 1968, p. 141.

Peter Sorokin, Organic Lasers, February 1969, p. 30.

M. W. Berus and D. E. Rounds, Cell Surgery by Laser, February 1970, p. 98.

M. S. Field and V. S. Letokhov, Laser Spectroscopy, December 1970, p. 69.

M. B. Parish and I. Hayashi, A New Class of Diode Lasers, July 1971, p. 32.

Richard N. Zare, Laser Separation of Isotopes, February 1977, p. 86.

Daniel Kleppner, Michael G. Littman, and Myron L. Zimmerman, Highly Excited Atoms, May 1981, p. 28.

R. I. G. Hughes, Quantum Logic, October 1981, p. 202.

Aldo V. La Rocca, Laser Applications in Manufacturing, March 1982, p. 94.

Jearl Walker, The Spectra of Streetlights Illuminate Basic Principles of Quantum Mechanics, *The Amateur Scientist*, January 1984, p. 138.

Isaac F. Silvera and Jook Walraven, The Stabilization of Atomic Hydrogen, January 1982, p. 66.

Marie-Anne Bouchiat and Lionel Pottier, An Atomic Preference Between Left and Right, June 1984, p. 100.

Vitalii I. Goldanskii, Quantum Mechanical Reactions in the Deep Cold, February 1986, p. 46. Tunneling.

W. T. Tsang, The C^3 Laser, November 1984, p. 148.

Gerd Binnig and Heinrich Rohrer, The Scanning Tunneling Microscope, August 1985, p. 50.

William D. Phillips and Harold J. Metcalf, Cooling and Trapping Atoms, March 1987, p. 50.

Vladilen S. Letokhov, Detecting Individual Atoms and Molecules with Lasers, September 1988, p. 54.

Dennis L. Matthews and Mordecai D. Rosen, Soft X-Ray Lasers, December 1988, p. 86.

Henry P. Freund and Robert K. Parker, Free-Electron Lasers, April 1989, p. 84.

H. Kumar Wickramasinghe, Scanned-Probe Microscopes, October 1989, p. 98

CHAPTER 29
THE STRUCTURE OF MATTER

Molecules and bulk matter are aggregates of atoms held together by electric forces. If the electrons and nuclei of a molecule have a lower energy than that of the separate neutral atoms, the molecule will be stable. Similarly in metals and semiconductors, the energy of the aggregate is less than that of its isolated constituents. The problem of understanding the structure of matter is one of finding the arrangement that has the lowest energy or greatest binding energy.

Fortunately, it is not necessary to solve Schrödinger's equation for all the electrons and nuclei of a system, because this can only be done approximately and is generally difficult. Instead, we use simplified models based on our knowledge of atoms that are very successful in accounting for the structure and properties of molecules and bulk materials. There are three models of primary interest to us here, which describe *ionic*, *covalent*, and *metallic* binding, respectively. Weaker bonds such as the *van der Waals* and *hydrogen* bonds are also important where the stronger bonding mechanisms are not effective.

29.1 | IONIC BINDING

When some molecules and crystals are formed, one or more electrons from one atom are completely transferred to another atom. The atom losing the electrons acquires a net positive charge, and the atom accepting these electrons becomes negatively charged. These two ions are then held together by the electric forces between them. This *ionic binding* usually involves one atom with one or more loosely bound electrons and a second with a nearly full outer shell. For example, the alkali metals, such as sodium and potassium with one valence electron, readily combine with the halides, such as chlorine and fluorine, which have one vacancy in their outer shells. This type of binding is responsible both for the formation of single molecules and of bulk crystals.

Ionic binding is illustrated by the ionic molecule potassium chloride, KCl. In order to understand why it is energetically favorable for potassium and chlorine atoms to form KCl molecules, we break up the formation of the molecule into three stages. These are the removal of an electron from the potassium atom, its binding to the chlorine atom, and the attraction of the resulting K^+ and Cl^- ions. These steps are not necessarily followed in the actual formation of the molecule:

1. The outer electron of potassium is removed, leaving the K^+ ion and an electron. This requires an energy equal to the ionization energy of potassium, which is 4.34 eV.
2. The extra electron binds to the neutral chlorine atom yielding Cl^-. This releases energy called the energy of formation, or *electron affinity*. For chlorine, this is 3.82 eV. The entire process of transferring one electron from potassium to chlorine then requires that $4.34 - 3.82 = 0.52$ eV of energy be supplied.
3. The oppositely charged ions approach each other. Because of their mutual attraction, their potential energy initially decreases as they approach. However, when they are so close that their electron clouds begin to overlap, there is a repulsive force and the potential energy begins to increase (Fig. 29.1). The ob-

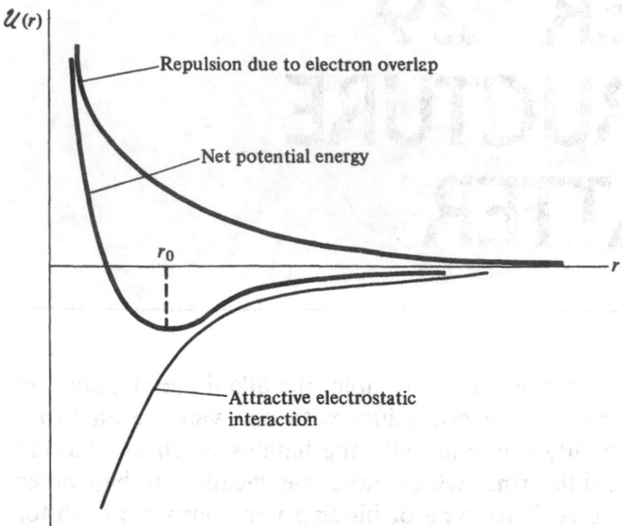

Figure 29.1. The potential energy of two ions versus the distance between their centers. The repulsive part due to the overlap of core electrons, which is positive, plus the attractive electrostatic part, which is negative, equals the net potential energy (shown colored). This energy is a minimum at a spacing r_0.

served equilibrium separation of the ions in KCl is $r_0 = 2.79 \times 10^{-10}$ m. The electric potential energy at this separation is

$$\begin{aligned} E &= -\frac{ke^2}{r_0} \\ &= -(9 \times 10^9 \text{ N m}^2 \text{ C}^{-2}) \frac{(1.6 \times 10^{-10} \text{ C})^2}{2.79 \times 10^{-10} \text{ m}} \\ &= -8.26 \times 10^{-19} \text{ J} = -5.16 \text{ eV} \end{aligned}$$

Ignoring other contributions to the potential energy momentarily, this means that the molecule has an energy of (0.52 − 5.16) eV = −4.64 eV compared to the separate neutral atoms. Conversely, 4.64 eV of energy would be required to break up the molecule into neutral potassium and chlorine. The measured value is 4.40 eV. The difference in the two results can be attributed to the repulsion of the inner electron clouds.

In ionic crystals the ions form a lattice. A number of crystal structures are possible, but the common feature of all of them is that ions of one charge have closest neighbors that are ions of the opposite charge. The electrical attraction between neighbors is responsible for the binding of the crystals.

29.2 | COVALENT BINDING

The vast majority of molecules are formed by sharing the outermost or *valence* electrons of the constituent atoms. In such *covalent* binding, the distribution of electrons in the molecule may be quite different from that in the separated atoms. These electronic distributions and other molecular properties are studied by interpreting detailed experimental results with the aid of theoretical models. These models rely on two important concepts described in the preceding chapter:

1 The square of a wave function $|\psi|^2$ indicates the relative probability of an electron being at a particular location. Equivalently, $|\psi|^2$ determines how often an electron is at a given place. When two atoms share an electron, it effectively belongs to each atom part of the time. Thus we expect that in molecules the wave functions of the electronic states should overlap so that the shared electron is favorably positioned with respect to both atoms.
2 When the atoms combine, the Pauli principle requires that each spatial state contain at most two electrons, one with spin up and one with spin down.

We can illustrate these ideas with the diatomic hydrogen molecule, H_2. Neutral hydrogen atoms have one electron in the 1*s* shell, although this state could hold two electrons if their spins were opposite (Fig. 29.2*a*). When two such atoms move together, one of two things will occur. If the electron spins are parallel, the Pauli principle prevents the electrons from being very close together since they cannot be in the same spatial state. The electrons repel each other and their wave functions are distorted (Fig. 29.2*b*). Because the electrons are far from each other most of the time, the nuclear charges also repel each other, and the whole arrangement is energetically unfavorable.

On the other hand, if the spins are opposite, each electron "fits" into the 1*s* state of the other atom.

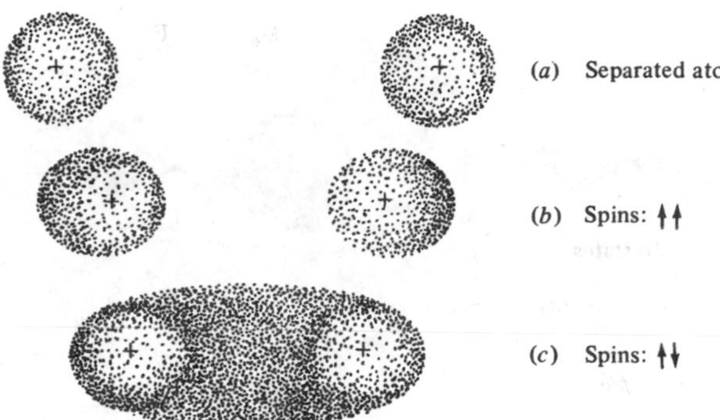

Figure 29.2. Representation of $|\psi|^2$ for the 1*s* states of two hydrogen atoms when they are far apart. (*a*) Contours representing the electron probability. (*b*) When the electrons have parallel spins, they repel each other because of the exclusion principle and the molecule does not form. (*c*) When the spins are opposite, the two 1*s* electronic wave functions add. In a sense, each atom has a filled 1*s* shell. The energy of the H_2 molecule is lower than that of two separate neutral atoms and the molecule is stable.

The electrons can now be close to each other, and the molecular wave function looks like the sum of the two 1*s* wave functions of each atom (Fig. 29.2*c*). The electrons have a high probability of being between the two nuclei where they are attracted by both protons. This reduces the total energy of the molecule below that of the separated atoms and results in a stable molecule. The characteristic elongated wave function of Fig. 29.2*c* is called a σ (Greek lowercase letter "sigma") *orbital.* This bond is said to be a σ bond.

Hybridization | An approximate approach to the structure of complex covalent molecules that has proved very useful is called *hybridization*. This method employs wave functions that are combinations or *hybrids* of atomic states, such as the 3*s* and 3*p* states of the atoms, that have slightly different energies. These energy differences can usually be ignored in molecules because they are small compared to the molecular binding energy. To illustrate the method of hybridization we describe the scheme for magnesium fluoride, MgF_2.

Magnesium ($Z = 12$) has closed $n = 1$ and $n = 2$ shells and two 3*s* valence electrons; its six 3*p* levels are empty. Fluorine ($Z = 9$) is one electron short of having a filled $n = 2$ shell and hence attracts electrons. Since the outer 3*s* wave functions of magnesium are spherically symmetric, their overlap with the 2*p* wave functions of fluorine is small (Fig. 29.3*a*). However, using combinations of magnesium wave functions, the overlap can be greatly increased, resulting in stronger binding (Fig. 29.3*b*, *c*).

We saw in the last chapter that the three *p* wave functions have pairs of lobes oriented along coordinate axes. If a *p* wave function and an *s* wave function are added and subtracted, the result is a pair of *sp hybridized* wave functions, or *orbitals*, each with a large lobe in one direction and a small lobe opposite (Fig. 29.3*b*). The two magnesium valence electrons can be thought of as being in these states, which overlap well with the single vacant *p* state of a fluorine atom. Consequently, MgF_2 is a linear molecule with the magnesium atom between two fluorine atoms. Note that the *sp* orbital is a mixture of two atomic orbitals with slightly different energies, so a free magnesium atom would not ordinarily be found in such a state. However, the energy needed to occupy this *sp* orbital is much smaller than that gained in the formation of the molecule, so in the molecule it is energetically favorable for the electrons to be in this configuration.

In sp^3 *hybridization*, we consider combinations of one *s* state and all three *p* states. We illustrate this procedure for the water molecule, H_2O. Oxygen ($Z = 8$) has two 2*s* electrons and four 2*p* electrons in its $n = 2$ shell. Thus it is two electrons short of having a closed $n = 2$ shell. Figure 29.4*a* shows the four sp^3 orbitals that can be formed from suitable combinations of the *s* and *p* states of oxygen. These states have a maximum angular separation, 109.5°. When occupied by electrons, this will minimize their repulsion.

Each sp^3 orbital can accommodate two electrons with opposite spins. In the water molecule, four of the $n = 2$ oxygen electrons fill two of the sp^3 orbitals. Each of the other two orbitals has one electron from the oxygen and one from a hydrogen atom (Figs. 29.4*b* and 29.4*c*).

A reminder that the hybridization model for water is not exact is provided by the experimental bond angle, 104.5°, which is slightly less than the predicted angle of 109.5°. The difference is due to the effects of electric forces among the bond elec-

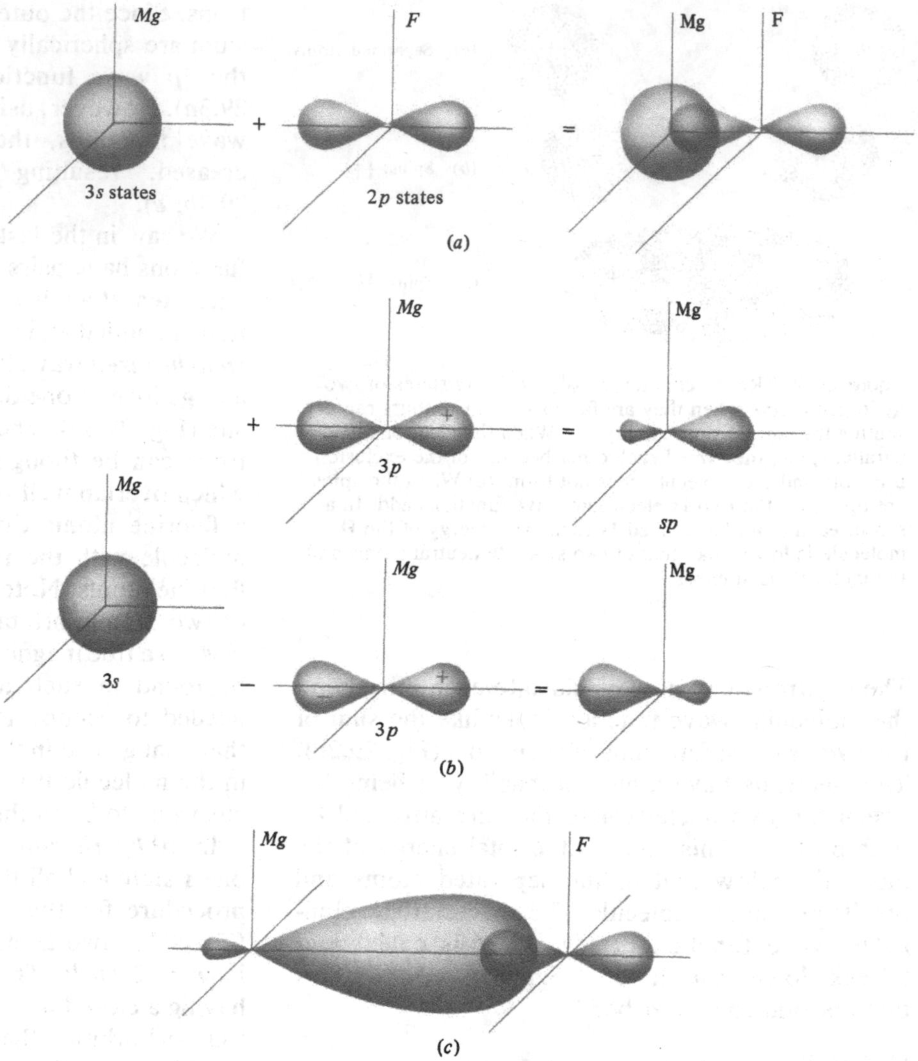

Figure 29.3. (*a*) The 3*s* wave functions in magnesium and the 2*p* wave function in fluorine have a small overlap area. (*b*) Adding and subtracting 3*s* and 2*p* magnesium wave functions produces *sp* wave functions with large lobes. (*c*) The *sp* wave function has a large overlap with the 2*p* fluorine wave function. In the MgF_2 molecule, a second fluorine atom binds on the left with the other *sp* wave function, forming a linear, symmetric molecule.

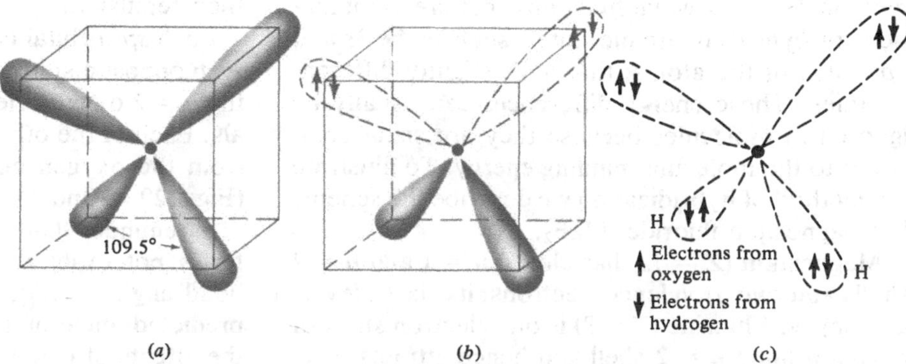

Figure 29.4. (*a*) The four sp^3 orbitals formed from combinations of *s* and *p* states of oxygen. (*b*) Two of the orbitals are full, containing a pair of electrons with opposite spins. The remaining two orbitals each have one of the oxygen electrons. (*c*) In the water molecule, the hydrogen atoms provide the electrons to fill these two orbitals. The experimentally determined angle between the two hydrogen bonds is 104.5°.

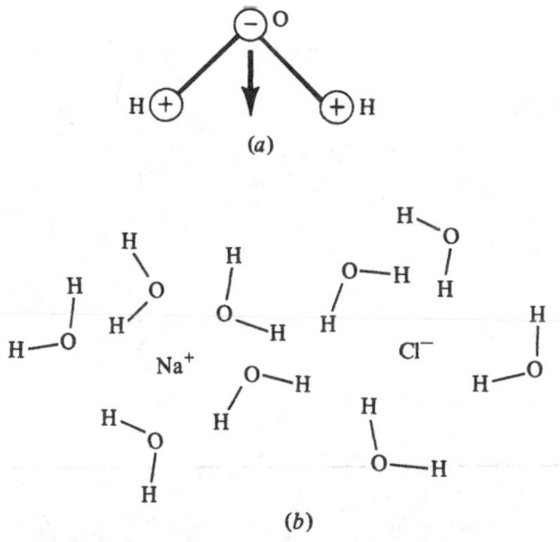

Figure 29.5. (*a*) The water molecule is electrically neutral, but the electrons are closer to the oxygen nucleus. The result is a permanent electric dipole in the molecule. Water acts as a solvent because its dipole field can weaken and break the ionic bond in molecules such as NaCl. (*b*) The water molecules tend to surround the dissociated ions so that they are nearly electrically neutral and do not recombine.

trons and the hydrogen nuclei in the asymmetric water molecule.

The structure of the water molecule makes it a *polar* molecule, one with a permanent electric dipole moment. The oxygen nucleus attracts the bond electrons somewhat more strongly than do the hydrogen nuclei. The result is an effective excess of positive charge near the hydrogen nuclei and an excess of negative charge (electrons) near the oxygen nucleus. This permanent electric dipole moment plays an important role in the properties of water. For example, water as a solvent breaks ionic salts up into ions, as in $NaCl \rightarrow Na^+ + Cl^-$ (Fig. 29.5).

Carbon | Carbon ($Z = 6$), because it has only four out of a possible eight $n = 2$ electrons, can participate in covalent bonds in a variety of ways. When the *s* and *p* states are combined to form four sp^3 orbitals, carbon can, for example, bond with four hydrogen atoms forming methane, CH_4. Each orbital has an electron from carbon and a second from a hydrogen atom. The carbon wave functions can also be hybridized to form two *sp* orbitals or three sp^2 orbitals. The sp^2 orbitals are used for molecules such as ethylene, $CH_2{=}CH_2$ (Fig. 29.6).

29.3 | THE METALLIC BOND; SUPERCONDUCTIVITY

Covalent bonds occur in molecules containing two to several thousand atoms. By contrast, metallic binding holds billions of atoms together. Usually these substances are solid, with ionized atoms

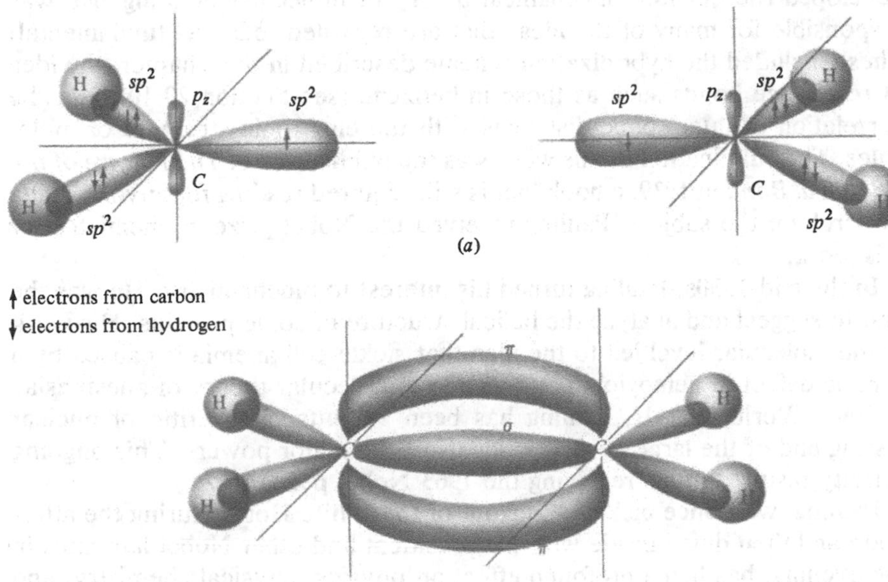

Figure 29.6. (*a*) The ethylene molecule, $CH_2 = CH_2$, is formed by attaching two hydrogen atoms along two of the three sp^2 orbitals of each carbon atom and then (*b*) bringing the two complexes together. The σ bonds are formed along the C—C and C—H directions, and a bond is also formed by the overlap of the p_z wave functions of the two carbon atoms. The overlapping p_z states of the two complexes are called a π bond.

LINUS CARL PAULING

Born: 1901

Pauling belongs to the generation that developed the methods of quantum physics and applied them to atoms and molecules. After receiving a B.S. in chemical engineering from Oregon State College, Pauling obtained his Ph.D. in Chemistry at the California Institute of Technology in 1925. He has been a professor there and at Stanford University since 1931.

By the mid-1920s the quantum theory of atoms was relatively well developed, and enough was known so that one could try to understand molecules and molecular binding. The models then existing depicted molecules as composed of atoms containing fixed charges, somewhat like knobs on the surface of a spherical nucleus. Atoms combined when these knobs fit into place, held together by the electrical attraction between the various electrons and nuclei. This model was unsatisfactory for several reasons and was completely incompatible with the wave–particle description of electrons in atoms.

From 1928 to 1932, Pauling published a series of papers in which he developed the quantum mechanical theory of molecular bonding. He was responsible for many of the ideas that are regarded today as fundamental. These included the hybridization scheme described in this chapter, the idea of resonance bonds such as those in benzene (see Section 29.10), and the correlation of interatomic distances with the electronic structure of molecules. The culmination of this work was the publication of *The Nature of the Chemical Bond* in 1939, a book that is still required reading for anyone doing research on the subject. Pauling received the Nobel prize in chemistry for this work.

In the mid-1930s, Pauling turned his interest to biochemistry. He was the first to suggest and analyze the helical structure of some proteins. His work at the molecular level led to the idea that sickle-cell anemia is caused by a genetic defect in hemoglobin and also to a molecular theory of anesthesia.

Since World War II, Pauling has been an outspoken critic of nuclear testing and of the large nuclear arsenals of the major powers. This ongoing activity resulted in his receiving the 1963 Nobel peace prize.

Pauling, who once picketed in front of the White House during the afternoon and then dined inside with the president and other Nobel laureates in the evening, has had a profound effect on physics, physical chemistry, and biochemistry. In his efforts for nuclear disarmament, Pauling has become a thoughtful and important advocate.

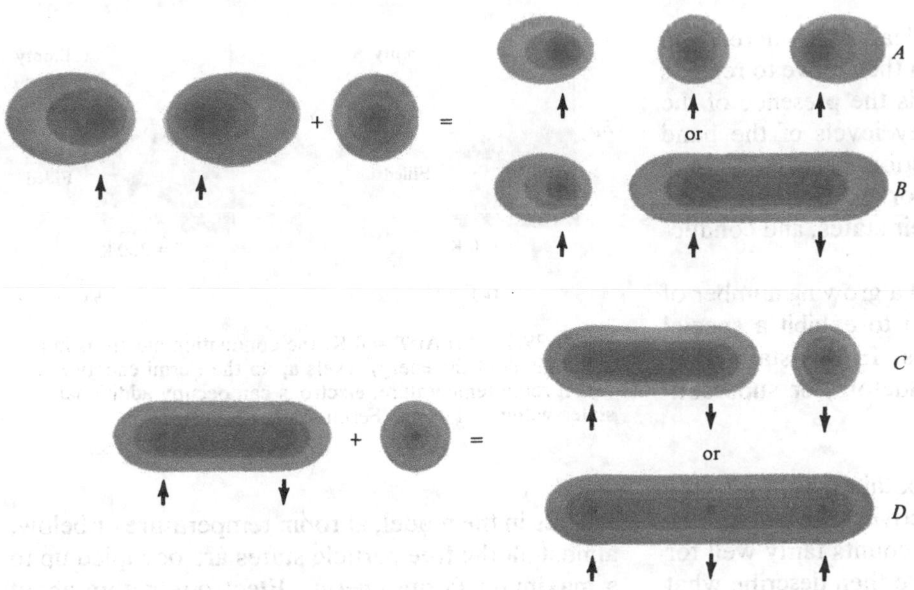

Figure 29.7. Two lithium atoms have their outer electron spins either parallel (above left) or antiparallel (below left). When a third atom is brought near, configurations like those at the right result. We expect that the configurations represented schematically as *B* and *C* would have the same energy. Reversing all the spins in *A* or *D* produces two more configurations *A′* and *D′* with the same energies as *A* and *D*. Thus the picture suggests three energy levels, each having two states. In fact, this picture is oversimplified. Combining the wave functions of several particles is complicated, and this diagram is only suggestive. Extending this type of diagram to four or more particles can lead to erroneous conclusions.

forming a rigid lattice and electrons contributed by the atoms that are free to move over the entire crystal. These delocalized electrons are the charge and energy carriers in metals and are responsible for their large electrical and thermal conductivities.

To see how the electrons become delocalized, consider lithium atoms, which have one 2*s* electron outside a filled 1*s* shell. This electron can have its spin up or down. When two lithium atoms are brought together, there are only two possible energy levels for the outer electrons. Their wave functions are similar to those for hydrogen (Fig. 29.2), the parallel spin state being higher in energy than the antiparallel state. Now, when a third atom is brought close to the first two, three separate energy levels become available for the outer electrons (Fig. 29.7). The energy levels are clustered near the original energy of the 2*s* electron in the free atom (Fig. 29.8).

Each time another atom is added, a new energy level results. However, the net effect of each new atom becomes smaller as the number of atoms already close together increases. Finally, with N atoms present, we have a *band* of N closely spaced energy levels. This band can accommodate $2N$ electrons. For example, for $N = 3$, there are three energy levels and six states (Fig. 29.8). The electronic wave functions are spread over large distances, and the electrons in this *conduction band* are free to move over the entire crystal.

Metals are good electrical and thermal conductors because of the presence of the conduction electrons. There are many unoccupied states in the conduction band into which electrons can move with only a small change in energy. Thus if a metal is heated at one end, electrons in this region move into higher energy states and transport the heat energy away from this region. Similarly, a small voltage

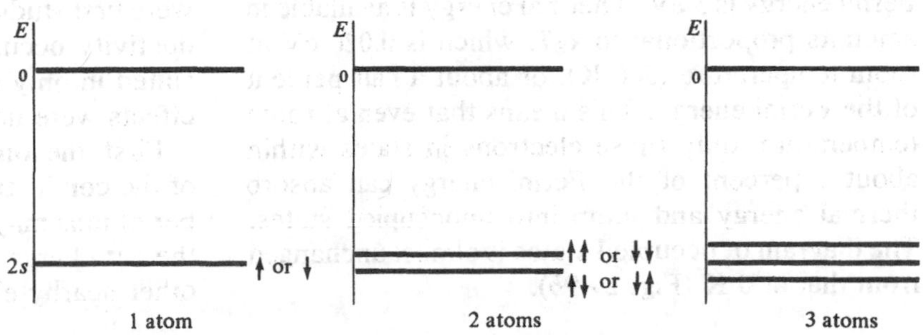

Figure 29.8. The lowest energy levels available to the outer electrons from one, two, and three lithium atoms placed close together.

difference along a metal will lead to an increase in the energy of electrons, which then move to regions of lower potential energy. It is the presence of the closely spaced unfilled energy levels of the band that facilitates these conduction processes. In a filled band in a semiconductor or insulator, electrons cannot easily change their states, and conduction is much reduced.

Many metals and alloys and a growing number of ceramic conductors are found to exhibit a special state at reduced temperatures. In this state, they become perfect electric conductors, or superconductors.

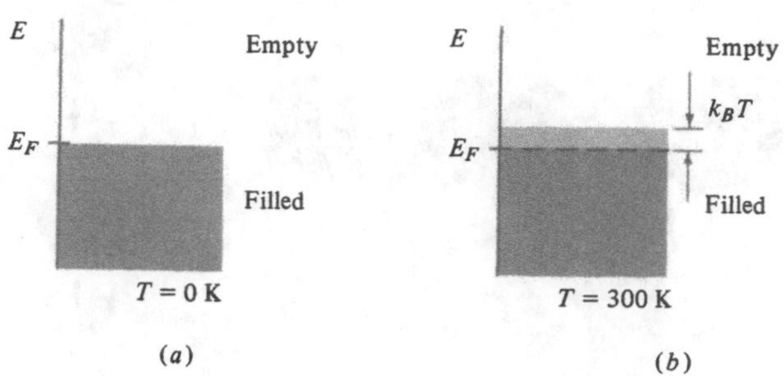

Figure 29.9. (*a*) At $T = 0$ K, the conduction electrons in a metal fill all of the energy levels up to the Fermi energy E_F. (b) At room temperature, electrons can occupy additional states within k_BT of the Fermi surface.

Superconductivity | To obtain insight into the physical origin of superconductivity, we first look in more detail at a model that accounts fairly well for the normal state of a metal. We then describe what happens at low temperatures that makes materials superconductors.

Consider a metal sample with about 10^{23} atoms. Suppose that each atom loses one election and settles as a positive ion into a regular position in the lattice structure. The released electrons occupy states in the conduction band. They move freely in the metal and behave much like noninteracting particles in a box (Section 28.7). The allowed wavelengths are those that "fit" into the box. Because electrons are spin $\frac{1}{2}$ particles, only one electron can be in a given state at any one time (Section 28.4). Thus each electronic energy state can accommodate a spin-up and a spin-down electron. The conduction electrons tend to fill the lowest electronic energy states first. In particular, at absolute zero (0 K) the lowest levels are filled up to a maximum energy called the *Fermi energy* E_F (Fig. 29.9*a*).

As the temperature is increased, thermal energy may be absorbed by electrons if there is an empty higher-energy state available. A typical value of the Fermi energy is 5 eV. Thermal energy is available in amounts proportional to k_BT, which is 0.026 eV at room temperature (300 K), or about a half percent of the Fermi energy. This means that even at room temperature, only those electrons in states within about 1 percent of the Fermi energy can absorb thermal energy and jump into unoccupied states. The diagram of occupied states is almost unchanged from that at 0 K (Fig. 29.9*b*).

Thus in the model, at room temperature or below, almost all the free particle states are occupied up to a maximum Fermi energy. Electrons within about k_BT of the Fermi energy can change their energy by absorbing thermal energy. It is these electrons that participate in electrical and thermal phenomena.

This model is not always successful in describing the properties of a metal. The problems show up most spectacularly at low temperatures. The model indicates that the number of electrons that participate in electrical transport diminishes as the temperature drops. However, the major source of electric resistance, electrons bumping into vibrating lattice ions, also diminishes at low temperatures because the ions vibrate less violently. Hence the resistance decreases gradually with temperature. But in materials that become superconducting, typically at temperatures on the order of 10 K, the metal suddenly loses *all* its resistance and becomes superconducting! What happens?

Apparently, the model is just too simple. For example, the electrons are not really free; they interact via electric forces with each other and with the vibrating ions. However, when these interactions were first studied, it was still unclear why superconductivity occurs. Their inclusion in the model resulted in only minor changes until two very subtle effects were noted.

First, the ions can produce a very weak attraction of the conduction electrons for each other. A number of ions may move toward an electron and make the net charge in that region appear positive to another nearby electron. The second electron is then attracted rather than repelled by the first. This is a weak effect since the coordinated motion of the ions is not a frequent occurrence. Furthermore, the degree to which the force becomes attractive is very small. The second important discovery is that if there is a net attractive force between electrons in states just above the Fermi surface, then two electrons can form a bound state. In such a state energy is required to break the bond.

Roughly speaking, if all other influences are ignored, and if one only takes account of the weak attractive forces between the electrons, then one can explain superconductivity in many materials. At sufficiently low temperatures, many of the electrons near the Fermi surface pair themselves up. This pairing is most effective between electrons of equal and opposite momenta. A bound pair of spin-one-half particles is a spin-zero object, if the spins are opposite as they usually are. We noted in Section 28.4 that spin-zero and spin-one objects do not obey the Pauli exclusion principle; in fact, they tend to occupy the same quantum states. So, if one pair exists, there is no reason why another pair, with exactly the same momentum and quantum numbers, cannot also exist. Indeed, calculations indicate that if n pairs are formed, then the probability that another pair will form is proportional to $\sqrt{n}$. This means that the more pairs that are formed, the more probable it becomes that more will form! It is a sort of cascade effect.

The thermal energy acts against this formation of pairs, but as the temperature is lowered, it becomes less effective in breaking pairs. The victory of the pair formation over the thermal disruption occurs very suddenly. At a critical temperature, the superconducting *transition temperature* T_c, the pairs win out. The pairing dominates and the metal becomes superconducting. An energy gap E_g emerges as the pairs form (Fig. 29.10). An energy equal to the gap energy is required to break apart an electron pair; anything less will have no effect. For typical metals, the energy gap is three to four times $k_B T_c$.

The most important part of this unusual event is that now the metal contains a very large number of objects (electron pairs) that are in a single quantum state. This state contains about 1 percent of all the conduction electrons, and these electrons behave differently from normal electrons for two reasons.

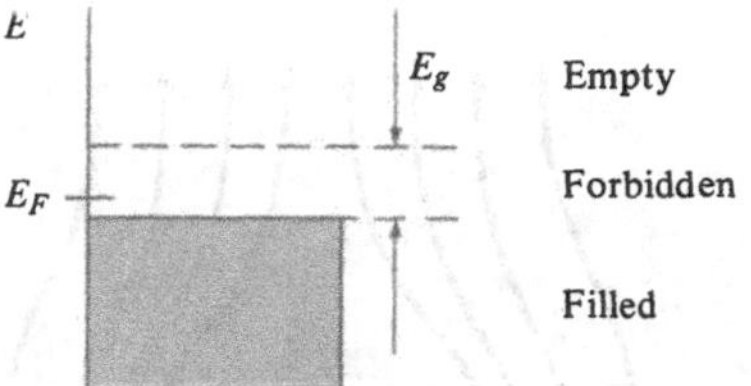

Figure 29.10. Below the transition temperature, electrons near the Fermi surface form bound-state pairs with an energy gap E_g. For electrons to behave as they do in normal metals, the pairs must be broken up by absorbing an energy greater than E_g.

One is the energy gap. The second is the enormous number of electron pairs in a single quantum mechanical state. A single wave function describes all of the pairs and extends over the entire sample.

The lack of resistance is due to the ineffectiveness of the thermal motion of the ions in deflecting moving electrons. The single wave function can describe a state in which all the paired electrons move together. This tendency for the special state wave function to stay intact is a general feature of the superconducting state. Each pair can acquire only a tiny amount of momentum and energy, but since so many pairs participate, the current can be very large.

Superconductors also exhibit unusual magnetic properties. For example, if a magnetic field is applied to a superconductor, the field is entirely excluded from the interior of the material. When the field is applied the magnetic flux in the superconductor changes, inducing an electric field inside by Faraday's law. Each electron pair changes its momentum just enough so a net current results. This current, because of the lack of resistance, produces an opposing magnetic field that cancels the applied one exactly. Furthermore, once it is started, there is nothing to stop the current. This zero interior magnetic field situation is dramatically evidenced when a metal in an external magnetic field is cooled through its superconducting transition temperature. The field lines that passed through the sample are suddenly excluded at T_c (Fig. 29.11).

The unusual features of superconductors are of more than academic interest primarily because of the zero electrical resistance. In particular, new materials are being found with much higher transition

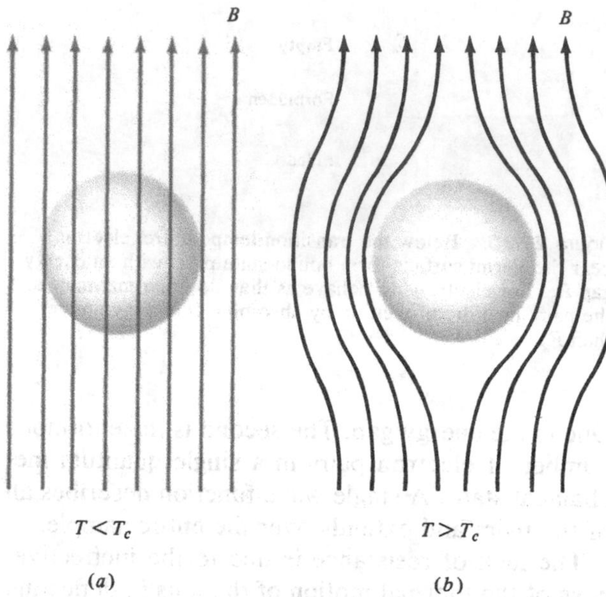

Figure 29.11. (*a*) Above the transition temperature an external magnetic field penetrates a cylindrical metal shell. (*b*) As the temperature passes down through T_c, the field is excluded from the metal by the induced current.

temperatures. The more economical it is to reach the transition temperature, the more practical the material. Recent results in this area were described earlier in Section 17.9.

29.4 | INSULATORS AND SEMICONDUCTORS

In metals, the formation of the conduction band, resulting in a decrease in the kinetic energy of the electrons, plays a vital role in the binding of atoms. In materials such as diamond, germanium, and silicon, bands are also formed when a large number of atoms are assembled. However, in these cases the valence electrons form a *band that is completely filled* at zero temperature.

Additional bands at higher energies are formed from higher atomic orbitals, but at zero temperature these are completely empty. There is an *energy gap* between the fully occupied *valence band* and the empty conduction band at a higher energy (Fig. 29.12).

In diamond the energy gap is about 6 eV. A temperature of 300 K, which is approximately room temperature, implies a mean thermal energy of $\frac{3}{2}k_BT = 0.04$ eV. Thus virtually no electrons will have enough thermal energy to be excited from the filled band into the conduction band at any reasonable temperature. The motion of electrons due to electric forces or to temperature gradients requires that they increase their kinetic energy. Since the electrons in the filled band cannot change energy states, conduction is impossible and diamond is an excellent insulator.

In germanium ($E_g = 0.72$ eV) and in silicon ($E_g = 1.1$ eV), the energy gap is much smaller, and a few electrons succeed in being thermally excited from the valence to the conduction band. Once in the conduction band they behave exactly as the conduction electrons in metals. The resistivity is higher in these *semiconductors* than in metals, because the number of electrons free to move is much smaller than in metals. For example, the room temperature resistivities of metals, semiconductors, and insulators are on the order of 10^{-8}, 10^2, and 10^{13} ohm m, respectively.

A unique feature of semiconductors is the conduction by *holes* in the filled band. When an electron is excited to the conduction band, it leaves an empty state, or hole, in the valence band with an effective positive charge. If an electric field is applied, electrons from adjacent atoms jump into the hole and the hole moves. Thus in an electric field, electrons in the conduction band move one way and holes in the valence band move the other way (Fig. 29.13).

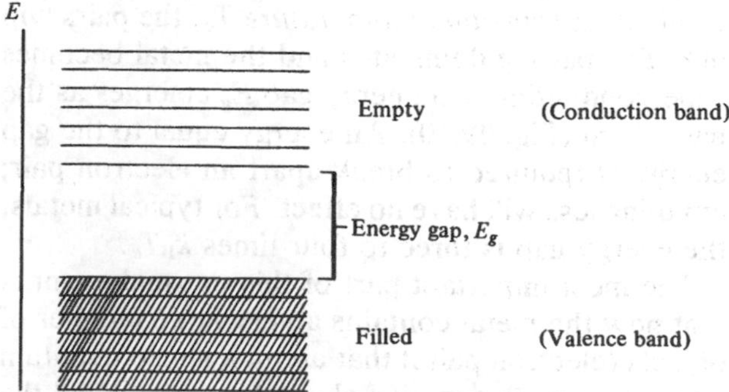

Figure 29.12. Energy bands of insulators and semiconductors.

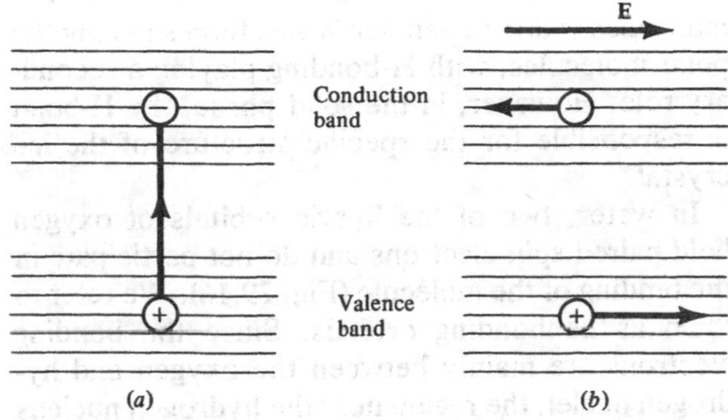

Figure 29.13. (*a*) An electron excited from the filled valence to the conduction band leaves a positively charged hole behind. (*b*) In an electric field, both move, producing a net current.

The conductivity of a semiconductor can be increased by adding impurities to the sample. For example, if a few parts per million of arsenic are added to germanium, the conductivity increases a thousandfold. Arsenic has one more electron in its outer shell than does germanium. When added as an impurity, it replaces a germanium atom, and its extra electron is freed for conduction. Similarly, gallium has one less outer electron than germanium, and when present as an impurity, it takes one electron from germanium, leaving a hole.

Semiconductors have many practical uses. A semiconductor can serve as a photocell for use in photography or in automatic door openers. The quanta of visible light have energies of about 2 or 3 eV, more than enough to excite electrons from the valence band to the conduction band. In an electric field, the semiconductor current increases greatly when the material is exposed to light and the number of charge carriers increases. Different types of semiconductors in contact are used in a wide variety of transistors and other devices. These devices have all but replaced the older vacuum tubes in electronics. They are desirable because they have low power requirements and no heating problems, are rugged, and last almost indefinitely.

29.5 | WEAKER BONDS

The bonds we have discussed typically have energies of a few electron volts. However, two bonds with energies of at most one tenth of an electron volt play an important role in nature: the *van der Waals bond* and the *hydrogen bond*. These bonds are especially important when the stronger types of bonds are not present. For example, the inert gases such as helium, neon, argon, and krypton condense to liquids and solids only because of attractive van der Waals forces among their atoms. Hydrogen bonding is often responsible for important structural features of molecules and solids such as the helical and pleated sheet structures of some organic molecules. In some instances, both types of bonding are present simultaneously.

van der Waals Attraction | The van der Waals attraction of molecules or atoms for each other is electrical in nature just as are other types of bonds. However, this attraction is due to the presence of electric dipoles, either permanent or induced.

Molecules such as water have a permanent electric dipole moment corresponding to an effective separation of charge within the molecule (Fig. 29.5). As a result these polar molecules tend to cluster together (Fig. 29.14). This clustering is opposed by the normal thermal motion of the molecules. The motion diminishes as the temperature decreases, so the van der Waals attraction becomes more effective and may cause condensation or solidification.

A polar molecule can induce an electric dipole moment in a nearby nonpolar molecule. The positive end of the polar molecule repels the nucleus and attracts the electrons of the nonpolar molecule. Once this induced dipole moment is formed, the two molecules attract each other just as do two polar molecules.

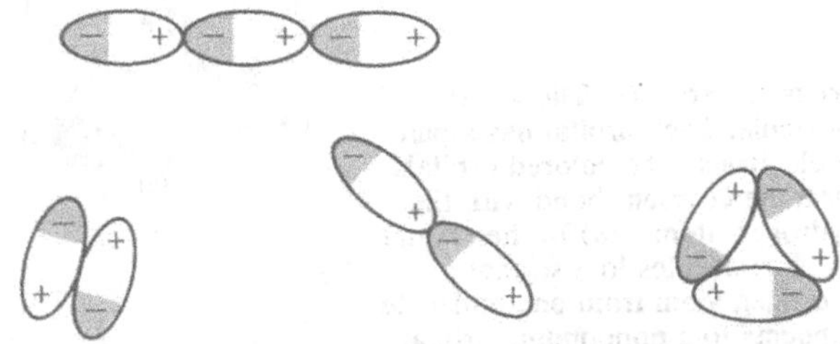

Figure 29.14. Polar molecules tend to cluster together due to the electrical attraction of the positive and negative ends of neighboring molecules.

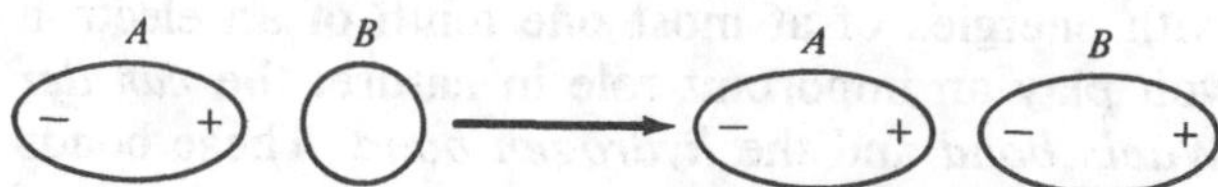

Figure 29.15. The instantaneous presence of a dipole moment in molecule A induces a dipole moment in molecule B, and the two nonpolar molecules attract one another.

A van der Waals attraction even occurs between nonpolar atoms and molecules. Although the centers of positive and negative charge are coincident on the average in a nonpolar atom, the electrons are constantly moving. At any instant, the atom may have a temporary electric dipole moment in some random direction. This moment will induce a dipole moment in a neighboring atom, and the two dipoles are always aligned, so there is a net attraction. On the average then there is a net van der Waals attraction (Fig. 29.15).

Van der Waals forces are responsible for the attraction between inert gas atoms and for the behavior of liquids in capillary tubes. For example, water rises in a glass tube because the van der Waals attraction between the water and glass molecules is stronger than that among the water molecules themselves.

The Hydrogen Bond

The hydrogen atom plays a unique role in compounds because of its small size and its single electron. A classic example of a hydrogen bond (H-bond) is found in ice. In liquid form, the primary attraction among water molecules is due to van der Waals forces among the polar molecules, with H-bonding playing a secondary role. However, in the solid phase, the H-bond is responsible for the specific structure of the ice crystal.

In water, two of the hybrid orbitals of oxygen hold paired spin electrons and do not participate in the binding of the molecule (Fig. 29.16). We refer to them as nonbonding orbitals. Since the bonding electrons are mainly between the oxygen and hydrogen nuclei, the region near the hydrogen nucleus is electrically positive. Each nonbonding orbital has a pair of electrons that is attracted to the positive hydrogen nucleus on an adjacent molecule. The hydrogen nucleus then is positioned with two electrons on either side (Fig. 29.16*b*). In ice, we find the hydrogen nuclei situated between the bonding and nonbonding orbitals of adjacent molecules. This is the hydrogen bond.

Hydrogen bonding plays an important role in the spatial arrangement of atoms in large organic molecules. For example, in DNA there are two helical strands of alternate sugars and phosphate groups. Each sugar residue has a side chain, and the side chain strands are hydrogen bonded to each other. Thus the strands of the double helix have hydrogen bonds as their weakest link (Fig. 29.17).

SUMMARY

Molecules and bulk matter represent energetically favorable configurations of electrons and nuclei held together by electric forces. Ionic bonds form

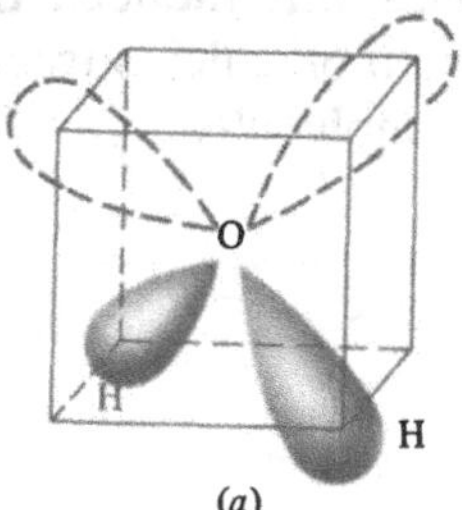

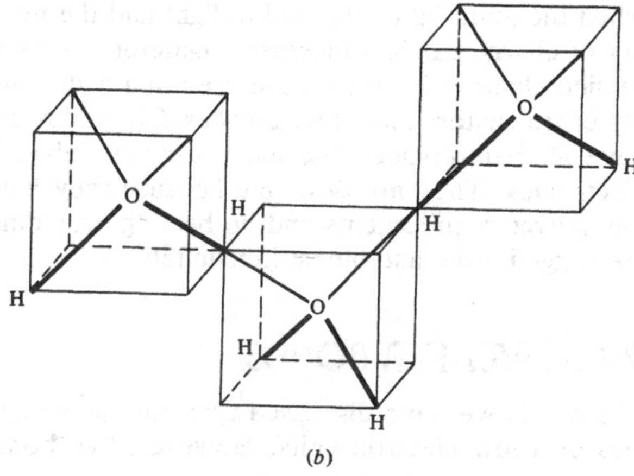

Figure 29.16. (*a*) The water molecule. Each orbital has a pair of electrons. The colored orbitals form the covalent bond with the hydrogen atoms. (*b*) In the crystal, water molecules join so that a hydrogen atom from one molecule connects to a nonbonding orbital (represented by a single black line) of an adjacent molecule. Bonding orbitals are shown as colored lines.

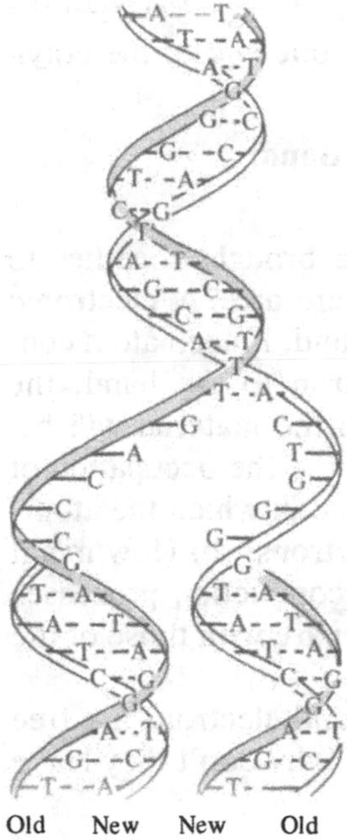

Figure 29.17. The DNA structure during replication. A, T, G, and C label side chain components attached to opposing side chains by hydrogen bonds as shown by the dashes. The double helix separates and rejoins at the hydrogen bonds.

between atoms that have completely transferred an electron. The electric potential energy gained by having the ions close together more than compensates for the energy required to transfer the electron.

In covalent bonds, electrons are shared. In general, this sharing can be understood by examining the electronic structure of the constituent atoms. The wave functions of the atoms should overlap well, so that the electrons are favorably positioned with respect to the nuclei. Usually, such bonds contain two opposite spin electrons satisfying the Pauli principle. The pairs of bonding electrons tend to be as far apart as possible so the electric repulsion between electrons in different bonds is minimized. A model of the molecular wave function treats the constituent atoms as having hybrid electronic states in covalent bonding.

In metals, the electrons become the common property of the metal as a whole. They are completely delocalized. In semiconductors in their ground state, the electrons remain bound to the nuclei, although they may be shared by neighboring atoms. An electron must increase its energy by at least a minimum amount to move into a conduction band. That is, excitation of an electron is equivalent to taking it away from an atom and allowing it to be free to move throughout the sample, just as in a metal. This excitation can be produced by heating or by the absorption of light.

Weak hydrogen bonds and van der Waals bonds often act between or within molecules. The van der Waals bond, which is caused by the mutual attraction of permanent or induced electric dipole moments, is responsible for the existence and properties of many liquids and solids. Hydrogen bonds are formed when a covalently bonded hydrogen atom attracts the electrons in a nearby orbital. This weak bond is responsible for much of the detailed structure in some solids and many organic molecules.

Checklist

Define or explain:

ionic bond	valence band
electron affinity	superconductor
covalent binding	Fermi energy
Pauli principle	electron pair
σ orbital	insulator
hybridization, sp, sp^2, sp^3	semiconductor
directional p state	energy gap
electric dipole moment	holes
conduction band	van der Waals forces
	hydrogen bond

REVIEW QUESTIONS

Q29-1 In _____ binding, one or more electrons is transferred from one atom to another.

Q29-2 In _____ binding, electrons are shared by the atoms.

Q29-3 If electron spins are parallel, the _____ prevents them from being very close to each other.

Q29-4 A combination of $3s$ and $3p$ wave functions is called a _____ wave function.

Q29-5 A polar molecule has a _____.

Q29-6 Electrons in a conduction band in a metal can move _____.

Q29-7 In an insulator, the valence electrons form a band that is _____.

Q29-8 Semiconductors have much smaller _____ than insulators.
Q29-9 A hole is a _____.
Q29-10 When a polar molecule is near a nonpolar molecule, it can induce an _____.

EXERCISES

Section 29.1 | Ionic Binding

29-1 The ionization energy of neutral sodium (Na) is 5.12 eV, and the electron affinity of chlorine (Cl) is 3.82 electron volts. (Neglect the repulsions of the core electrons.) (a) How much energy is required to transfer one electron from Na to Cl? (b) If the ionic separation in the molecule NaCl is 2.36×10^{-10} m, what is the electric potential energy of the molecule? (c) What is the predicted energy required to separate NaCl into its separate neutral constituents Na and Cl?
29-2 The ionization energy of lithium atoms is 5.39 eV, and the interatomic distance in the lithium fluoride molecule, LiF, is 1.51×10^{-10} m. The electron affinity of fluorine is 3.51 eV. (Neglect the repulsions of the core electrons.) (a) What is the potential energy of the ions Li^+ and F^- in the molecule? (b) What is the binding energy of LiF?
29-3 The binding energy of sodium bromide (NaBr) is 3.77 eV, the interatomic spacing is 2.50×10^{-10} m, and the ionization energy of Na is 5.12 eV. (Neglect the repulsions of the core electrons.) (a) What is the potential energy of the ions Na^+ and Br^- in the molecule? (b) What is the electron affinity of bromine?

Section 29.2 | Covalent binding

29-4 Describe how magnesium and chlorine form the molecule $MgCl_2$.
29-5 Does the molecule H_2 have a permanent electric dipole moment? Explain.
29-6 The distance between the protons in a singly ionized H_2^+ molecule is 1.06×10^{-10} m. If the remaining electron is midway between the protons, what is its electric potential energy?
29-7 Describe the formation and structure of the methane molecule CH_4 using the sp^3 hybridization scheme for carbon.
29-8 What is the theoretical angle between the hydrogen–carbon bonds at one end of the ethylene molecule?

Section 29.3 | The Metallic Bond; Superconductivity

29-9 When N atoms are brought together to form a certain material, there are $2N$ electronic energy levels formed in a band. If each atom contributes one valence electron to the band, the band will be half filled and the material will behave like a metal. (a) Describe the occupation of the band for another material in which the atoms contribute two valence electrons. (b) How might the electrical and thermal conduction processes of this second material compare with those of the metal? Explain.
29-10 If the conduction band electrons are free to move about in the metal, why don't they leave the metal entirely?

Section 29.4 | Insulators and Semiconductors

29-11 What is the minimum frequency of light necessary to excite electrons from the valence to the conduction band in pure silicon? (The energy gap is 1.1 eV.)
29-12 Explain how a semiconductor might be used as a thermometer.
29-13 Is energy conserved when an electron drops from the conduction band to the valence band in a semiconductor? Explain.

Section 29.5 | Weaker Bonds

29-14 In Fig. 29.15, molecule A is polar and molecule B is nonpolar. Molecule A induces an electric dipole moment in B. Explain qualitatively why the net force between the molecules is attractive. Include the effects of the positive and negative charges of both molecules in your discussion.
29-15 Draw a schematic diagram of the boundary between a horizontal water surface and a vertical piece of glass. Describe qualitatively in terms of the van der Waals forces the shape of the water surface near the boundary.
29-16 Figure 29-18 shows a methane molecule. Would you expect that hydrogen bonding is as important in solid methane as it is in ice? Explain.

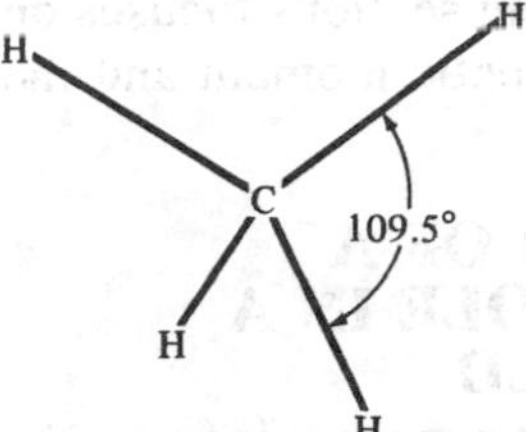

Figure 29.18. The structure of the methane molecule. Exercise 29-16.

PROBLEMS

29-17 The electric dipole moment of a molecule is the charge separation distance times the charge itself. What is the electric dipole moment of KCl? (The separation of the K^+ and Cl^- ions is 2.79×10^{-10} m.)

29-18 The neutral molecule H_3 is not stable although H_3^+ is. Using the exclusion principle, explain these results.

29-19 The ammonia molecule (NH_3) is usually described by an sp^3 hybridization of the nitrogen wave functions. Starting from the fact that the neutral nitrogen atom has two $2s$ and three $2p$ electrons in its $n = 2$ shell, describe the structure of NH_3. Do you expect this molecule to have a permanent electric dipole moment? Explain.

29-20 The hybridization model is a highly simplified one that sometimes leads to results that are not in agreement with experiment. For example, hydrogen sulfide (H_2S) might be expected to have the same shape as H_2O, since oxygen and sulfur are both two electrons short of having filled outer shells. However, the bond angle in H_2S is 92°, which is quite different from the bond angle in H_2O of 104.5°. Show that H_2S may be expected to have 90° bond angles if the hydrogen atoms overlap with the pure p states of sulfur. Sulfur has two $3s$ and four $3p$ electrons.

***29-21** Two common forms of pure solid carbon are graphite and diamond (Fig. 29.19). (a) Describe the hybridization scheme appropriate to the two structures. (b) Graphite can be used as a lubricant, while diamond is extremely hard. Can this difference in properties be explained by their difference in crystal structure?

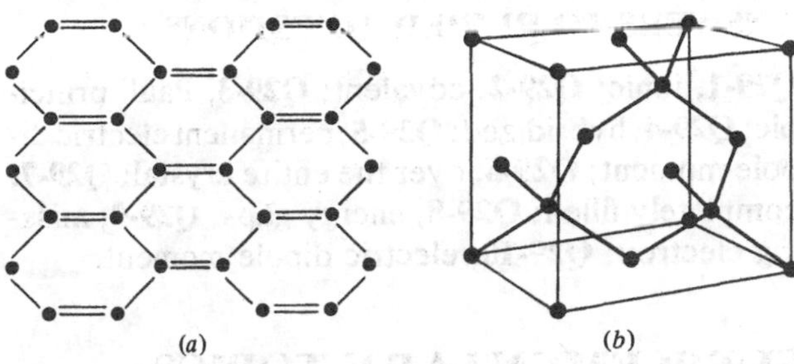

Figure 29.19. Problem 29-21. The positions of carbon atoms in (*a*) graphite; (*b*) diamond. The structure of graphite is nearly two-dimensional, with each carbon bound to three neighbors in the same plane. In diamond, each carbon atom has four equidistant nearest neighbors.

***29-22** In methane (CH_4) the carbon atom shares an electron from each of four hydrogen atoms. These four electrons would be sufficient to fill the $n = 2$ shell of carbon. Chlorine atoms need a p state electron to complete a shell. Carbon tetrachloride (CCl_4) is a covalently bound molecule. (a) What is the structure of CCl_4? (b) Does this molecule have a permanent electric dipole moment? (c) How might the positions of the bonding electrons differ from those in methane?

***29-23** Figure 29.20*a* shows a crude model of a hydrogen bond. Compute the difference between the total electric potential energy of the charges in Fig. 29.20*a* and Fig. 29.20*b*. (Do not include the repulsion between electrons that are in the same side of the hydrogen nucleus.)

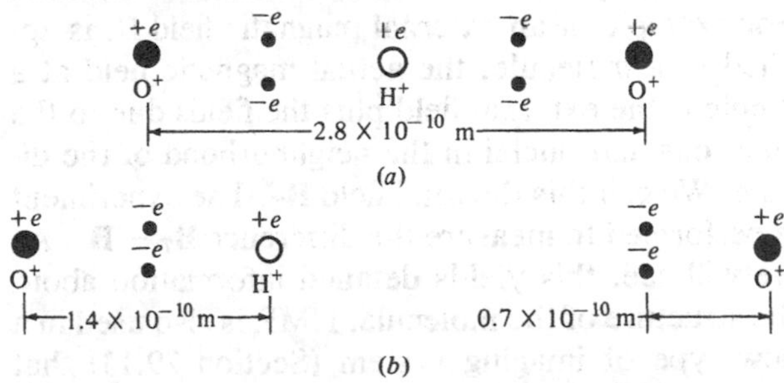

Figure 29.20. Problem 29-23. (*a*) A crude model of a hydrogen bond in ice. The oxygen nuclei (shown colored) have effective charges $+e = 1.6 \times 10^{-19}$ C. The hydrogen nucleus (open circle) is midway between with a charge $+e$. The electrons with charges $-e$ are midway between the oxygen and hydrogen nuclei. (*b*) The same charges grouped as shown but separated by a large distance.

ANSWERS TO REVIEW QUESTIONS

Q29-1, ionic; **Q29-2**, covalent; **Q29-3**, Pauli principle; **Q29-4**, hybridized; **Q29-5**, permanent electric dipole moment; **Q29-6**, over the entire crystal; **Q29-7**, completely filled; **Q29-8**, energy gaps; **Q29-9**, missing electron; **Q29-10**, electric dipole moment.

SUPPLEMENTARY TOPICS

29.6 | NUCLEAR MAGNETIC RESONANCE

A number of experimental techniques originally used by physicists are now in wide use by biochemists and others to study complex molecules. These studies yield information about the structure of molecules and their role in biological processes.

The experimental information necessary for any description of molecules includes the identification of the types of atoms present, their positions in the molecule, and the properties of the molecule as a whole. Usually the experimental evidence is acquired in bits and pieces and is very difficult to interpret, except in terms of models such as those of this chapter.

We now describe one of the most commonly applied and versatile techniques used to study molecular structure: *nuclear magnetic resonance*, or *NMR*. NMR exploits the fact that many atomic nuclei behave in magnetic fields as small magnetic dipoles. Measuring the energy needed to reorient the nuclear magnetic moments determines the magnetic fields at the positions of the nuclei in the molecule. For example, if an external magnetic field $\mathbf{B}_e$ is applied to a molecule, the actual magnetic field at a dipole is the external field plus the fields due to the electrons and nuclei in the neighborhood of the dipole. We call this the total field $\mathbf{B}_T$. The experiment is performed to measure the difference $\mathbf{B}_T - \mathbf{B}_e$. As we will see, this yields detailed information about the structure of the molecule. NMR is also used in a new type of imaging system (Section 29.13) that supplements ultrasonic scans and X rays.

NMR can be used on any molecule that has nuclei with nonzero magnetic dipole moments. The single proton in a hydrogen nucleus has such a moment, and the presence of hydrogen in so many organic molecules makes them excellent subjects for study. Our discussion in the following sections focuses on the origin of this proton magnetic moment and the methods of NMR.

29.7 | THE BEHAVIOR OF A MAGNETIC DIPOLE IN A MAGNETIC FIELD

In Section 19.5, we found that a current loop can be considered as a magnetic dipole. The magnetic dipole moment was found to be the current times the area of the loop. In the case of a particle moving in a circular orbit, this magnetic dipole moment turns out to be proportional to the particle's orbital angular momentum.

A spinning charge also has a magnetic dipole moment $\boldsymbol{\mu}$ proportional to its spin angular momentum $\mathbf{S}$. Experimentally, the relationship between these quantities for a proton is found to be

$$\boldsymbol{\mu} = 2.79 \frac{e}{m_p} \mathbf{S} \tag{29.1}$$

where m_p is the proton mass. In the remainder of this section, we describe how the energy of a proton depends on the magnetic field it experiences. We also find that the proton moment experiences a torque due to the magnetic field. This torque causes the proton moment and spin to precess. This motion is quite analogous to that of a precessing top (Section 7.8).

We saw in Section 19.5 that the energy of a dipole at an angle θ to a magnetic field $\mathbf{B}_T$ is $\mathcal{U} = -\mu B_T \cos\theta$. When the total magnetic field $\mathbf{B}_T$ is in the z direction, the potential energy of the dipole is $\mathcal{U} = -\mu_z B_T$. If S_z is the z component of the spin angular momentum, this energy is

$$\mathcal{U} = -2.79 \frac{e}{m_p} S_z B_T \tag{29.2}$$

For the proton, $S_z = +\hbar/2$ or $-\hbar/2$. It is conventional to define the *nuclear magneton* by

$$\mu_N = \frac{e\hbar}{2m_p} = 5.05 \times 10^{-27} \text{ A m}^2$$

so the potential energy becomes

$$\mathcal{U} = \pm 2.79 \mu_N B_T \tag{29.3}$$

The minus sign holds when S_z amd μ_z are parallel to the field (spin up) and the plus sign when they are opposite (spin down). The following example illustrates these energy relationships.

Example 29.1

A photon is absorbed when a proton moves from the spin-up to the spin-down state in a magnetic field of 1.4 T. (a) What is the energy of the absorbed photon in electron volts? (b) What is the photon frequency?

(a) Using $\mathcal{U} = -2.79\mu_N B_T$ for the spin-up state and $\mathcal{U} = +2.79\ \mu_N B_T$ for the spin-down state, the change in energy is

$$\begin{aligned}\Delta\mathcal{U} &= 2(2.79)\mu_N B_T \\ &= 2(2.79)(5.05 \times 10^{-27}\ \text{A m}^2)(1.4\ \text{T}) \\ &= 3.94 \times 10^{-26}\ \text{J} = 2.47 \times 10^{-7}\ \text{eV}\end{aligned}$$

We see that the energy of the photon absorbed is small compared to the changes of 1 to 10 eV usually observed in atomic and molecular processes.

(b) The photon energy is hf, so

$$f = \frac{\Delta\mathcal{U}}{h} = \frac{2.47 \times 10^{-7}\ \text{eV}}{4.14 \times 10^{-15}\ \text{eVs}} = 5.96 \times 10^7\ \text{Hz}$$

It is important to note that the spin angular momentum **S** (and also $\boldsymbol{\mu}$) is not parallel or antiparallel to $\mathbf{B}_T$. This follows from Chapter Twenty-eight where we found that the magnitude of the spin angular momentum **S** for spin $\frac{1}{2}$ particles is given by $S = \sqrt{s(s+1)}\hbar = \sqrt{\frac{1}{2}(\frac{1}{2}+1)}\hbar = \sqrt{3}\ \hbar/2$. Since $S_z = \pm\hbar/2$, **S** must always be at an angle with the z axis (Fig. 29.21*b*).

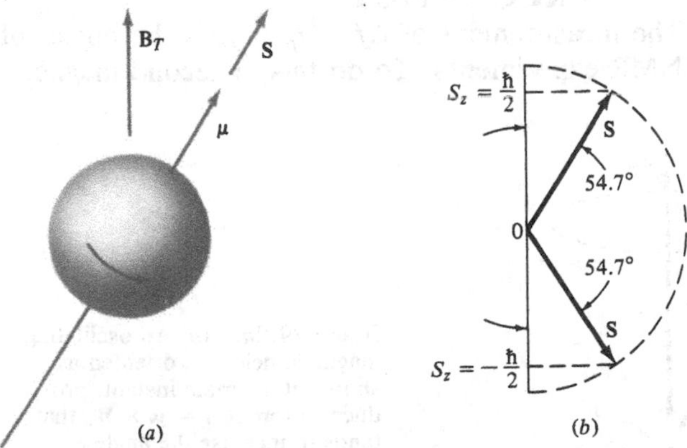

Figure 29.21. (*a*) A classical model of a spinning charge in a magnetic field $\mathbf{B}_T$. The spin angular momentum **S** and the magnetic moment $\boldsymbol{\mu}$ are parallel if the charge is positive. (*b*) The spin of a proton has a magnitude of $S = \sqrt{3}\ \hbar/2$, and the z component of **S** is $S_z = \pm\hbar/2$.

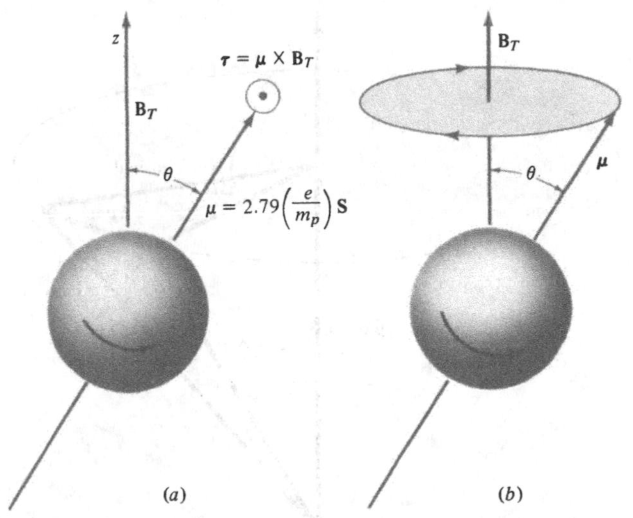

Figure 29.22. (*a*) The magnetic dipole moment $\boldsymbol{\mu}$ experiences a torque $\boldsymbol{\tau}$ due to the field $\mathbf{B}_T$. Here $\boldsymbol{\tau}$ is directed out of the page. (*b*) The magnetic moment $\boldsymbol{\mu}$ precesses around $\mathbf{B}_T$; the tip of the arrow representing $\boldsymbol{\mu}$ traces out a circle.

In a magnetic field, the proton moment experiences a torque $\boldsymbol{\tau}$ (Section 19.5) given by

$$\boldsymbol{\tau} = \boldsymbol{\mu} \times \mathbf{B}_T \tag{29.4}$$

This torque is perpendicular to $\boldsymbol{\mu}$, $\mathbf{B}_T$, and also to **S** (Fig. 29.22*a*). The torque produces a change in the angular momentum **S** according to $\boldsymbol{\tau} = \Delta\mathbf{S}/\Delta t$ (Chapter Seven) and the result is a precession of **S** and $\boldsymbol{\mu}$ around the direction of the field $\mathbf{B}_T$ (Fig. 29.22*b*). We can see this more clearly if we write $\Delta\boldsymbol{\mu} = 2.79(e/m_p)\ \Delta\mathbf{S}$, so

$$\boldsymbol{\tau}\ \Delta t = \Delta\mathbf{S} = \frac{m_p}{2.79e}\ \Delta\boldsymbol{\mu} \tag{29.5}$$

Since $\boldsymbol{\tau}$ is always perpendicular to $\boldsymbol{\mu}$, the magnitude of $\boldsymbol{\mu}$ is constant, but its direction changes. The vector $\boldsymbol{\mu}$ is "pulled" around by the torque and $\boldsymbol{\mu}$ precesses around $\mathbf{B}_T$ (Fig. 29.22*b*). This precession is analogous to the precession of a spinning top.

The rate of precession is an important parameter in a resonance experiment. From Fig. 29.23, we see that the z component of $\boldsymbol{\mu}$ is constant, but the component of $\boldsymbol{\mu}$ perpendicular to $\mathbf{B}_T$, $\mu \sin\theta$, turns through a small angle $\Delta\Omega$ in a time Δt. Since the arc AB is approximately equal to the chord $\Delta\mu$, $\Delta\mu = \mu\ (\sin\theta)\ \Delta\Omega$.

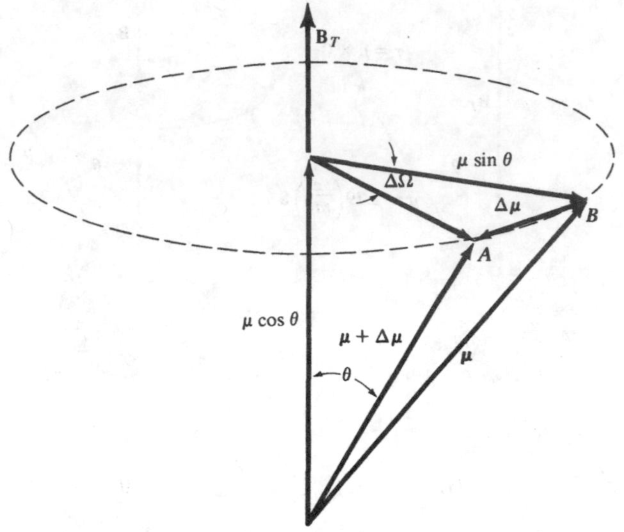

Figure 29.23. The vector $\boldsymbol{\mu}$ precesses around $\mathbf{B}_T$. The component of $\boldsymbol{\mu}$ perpendicular to $\mathbf{B}_T$ changes by an amount $\Delta\mu = \mu \sin\theta\, \Delta\Omega$ in a time Δt.

The torque is in the same direction as $\Delta\boldsymbol{\mu}$, and from Fig. 29.22 we see that its magnitude is $\tau = \mu B_T \sin\theta$. Using these results for $\Delta\mu$ and τ in Eq. 29.5, we find

$$\mu B_T (\sin\theta)\, \Delta t = \frac{m_p}{2.79e}\, \mu\, (\sin\theta)\, \Delta\Omega$$

The precession frequency f_p is defined as $\Delta\Omega/(2\pi\, \Delta t)$, so we find

$$f_p = \frac{1}{2\pi}\frac{\Delta\Omega}{\Delta t} = 0.444\, \frac{e}{m_p}\, B_T \qquad (29.6)$$

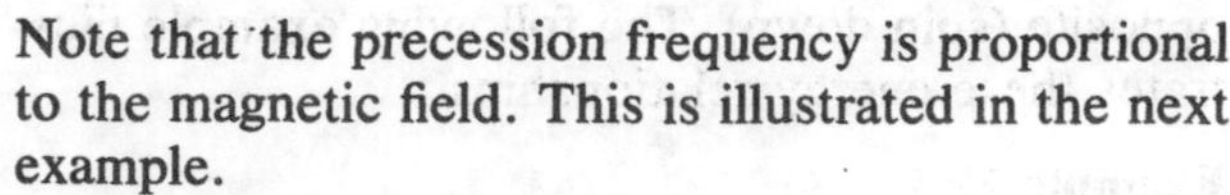
Note that the precession frequency is proportional to the magnetic field. This is illustrated in the next example.

Example 29.2

Calculate the precession frequency of a proton in a total magnetic field of 1.4 T.

Using Eq. 29.6, we have

$$\begin{aligned} f_p &= 0.444\, \frac{e}{m_p}\, B_T \\ &= (0.444)\left(\frac{1.6 \times 10^{-19}\ \text{C}}{1.67 \times 10^{-27}\ \text{kg}}\right)(1.4\ \text{T}) \\ &= 5.96 \times 10^{7}\ \text{Hz} \end{aligned}$$

This is a typical radio wave frequency.

In an NMR experiment, the proton moments of the sample precess at a frequency $f_p = 0.444eB_T/m_p$, where B_T is the total field at the position of the proton. A free proton precesses at a frequency $f_e = 0.444eB_e/m_p$, where B_e is the magnitude of the external magnetic field. The difference between the two precession frequencies is

$$\Delta f = f_p - f_e = 0.444\, \frac{e}{m_p}\, (B_T - B_e) \qquad (29.7)$$

The difference of $\mathbf{B}_T$ from the external field $\mathbf{B}_e$ indicates the effects of the surroundings. This information is obtained by measuring Δf.

29.8 | MEASURING THE PRECESSION FREQUENCY

The measurement of $\Delta f = f_p - f_e$ is the object of NMR experiments. To do this, a second magnetic

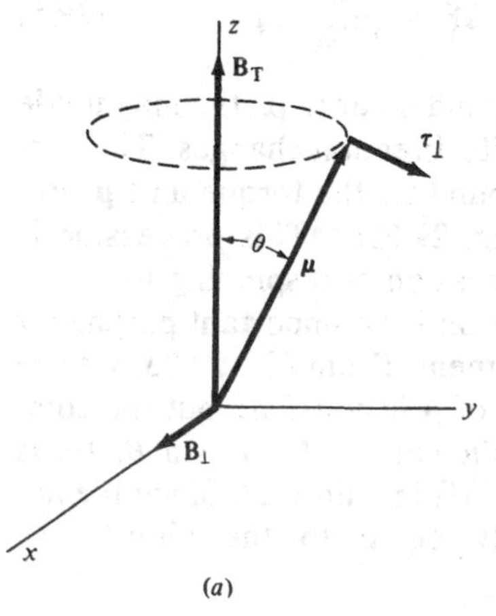

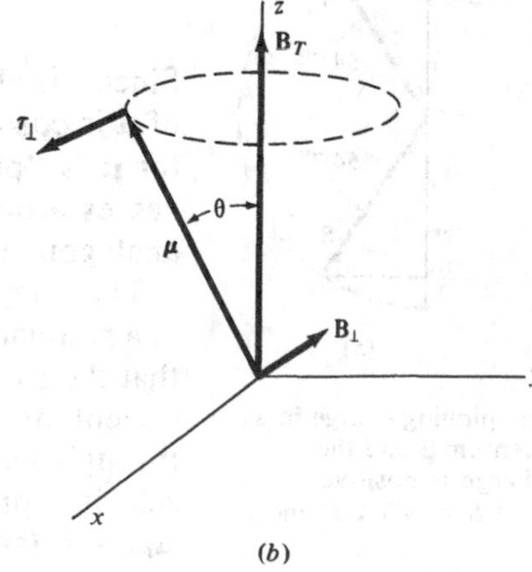

Figure 29.24. (*a*) An oscillating magnetic field $\mathbf{B}_\perp$, oriented as shown at a certain instant, produces a torque $\boldsymbol{\tau} = \boldsymbol{\mu} \times \mathbf{B}_\perp$ that tends to increase the angle θ. (*b*) If the field $\mathbf{B}_\perp$ varies at a frequency $f_\perp$, which is just equal to the precession frequency f_p, the torque $\tau_\perp$ again tends to increase θ. If $f_\perp \neq f_p$, the effect of $\mathbf{B}_\perp$ averages to zero.

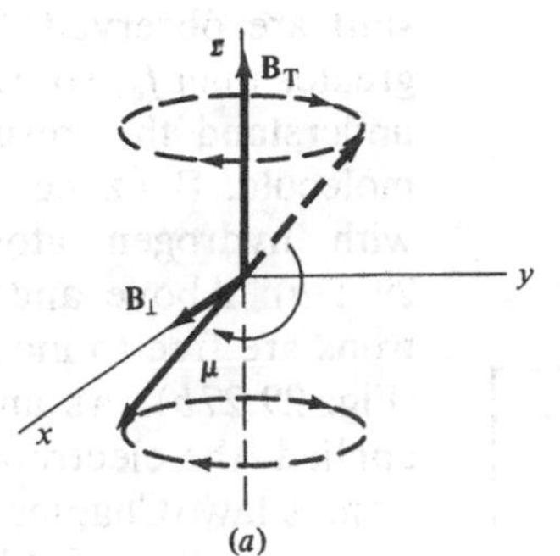

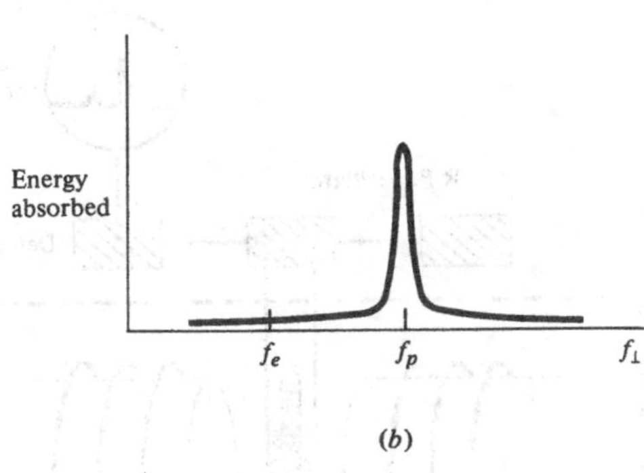

Figure 29.25. (a) A dipole precessing at a frequency f_p in a magnetic field $\mathbf{B}_T$ can absorb energy and "flip" over if a second field $\mathbf{B}_\perp$ is properly applied. (b) Absorption will occur when the frequency $f_\perp$ of $B_\perp$ is equal to f_p.

field $\mathbf{B}_\perp$ is applied perpendicular to $\mathbf{B}_e$ and $\mathbf{B}_T$ (Fig. 29.24). This field changes with time, oscillating between the positive and negative x directions with a frequency $f_\perp$, and also produces a torque on the proton. When $f_\perp = f_p$, the resulting torque $\boldsymbol{\tau}_\perp$ on the proton moment tends to increase the angle θ. At all other frequencies, the effect of $\boldsymbol{\tau}_\perp$ averages to zero.

As we noted earlier, the magnetic moment can only have two possible orientations with respect to the magnetic field $\mathbf{B}_T$. From Eq. 29.3, the energy difference between these states is $\Delta\mathcal{U} = 2(2.79)\mu_N B_T = 5.58\,\mu_N B_T$. When the magnetic field $\mathbf{B}_\perp$ is applied at the precession frequency, the torque $\boldsymbol{\tau}_\perp$ will cause the dipole to "flip" (Fig. 29.25). Energy $\Delta\mathcal{U}$ is absorbed by the dipole, and this absorption can be detected. The frequency at which energy absorption occurs determines the precession frequency. (*Note*: The magnitude of $\mathbf{B}_\perp$ is always much smaller than that of $\mathbf{B}_T$ and is thus neglected in the calculation of $\Delta\mathcal{U}$.)

To summarize, when an external magnetic field is applied to a sample, the proton moments precess at the frequency f_p. The perpendicular time varying magnetic field acts to flip the dipoles over when $f_\perp = f_p$ (Fig. 29.25*b*).

29.9 | THE NMR APPARATUS

The NMR apparatus has four fundamental components:

1 A permanent magnet or electromagnet used to produce the large external field $\mathbf{B}_e$. Standard instruments produce a field of 1.4 T with the field uniform over the region of the sample to one part in 10^8.
2 A method for varying $\mathbf{B}_e$ over a small range. In Fig. 29.23, the sweep coils fill this function.
3 A radio frequency (R.F.) oscillator that produces electromagnetic radiation at a fixed frequency, normally $f_\perp = 6 \times 10^7$ Hz. The magnetic field of this radiation plays the role of $\mathbf{B}_\perp$.
4 A radio frequency receiver used as a detector for the absorption of energy from the oscillator. Sometimes a single coil serves as both the oscillator and detector. When energy is absorbed an induced EMF is produced in the coil. This induced EMF is slightly out of phase with the oscillator voltage and can be electronically detected.

Since the R.F. oscillator has a fixed frequency, variations in f_p are produced by varying B_e. This is done by altering the current in the sweep coils in Fig. 29.26. Resonance occurs when the external field is adjusted so that $f_p = f_\perp = 6 \times 10^7$ Hz. Each time a resonance appears, energy is absorbed. As we see in the following sections, there are often many resonant frequencies for a given molecule.

The sample region is quite small, usually a tube of radius 0.2 cm filled about 3 cm deep. This is done to minimize the expense of the high-precision magnet. Liquid solutions are usually used with the solvents chosen so that their resonant absorption frequencies do not overlap with those of the sample. An internal reference is commonly employed, normally tetramethylsilane (TMS), a molecule that does not interact strongly with other molecules. It has a single resonant frequency that shows up on the absorption graph and is used to calibrate the system.

Having established the physical basis for NMR measurements, we now consider what information can be obtained.

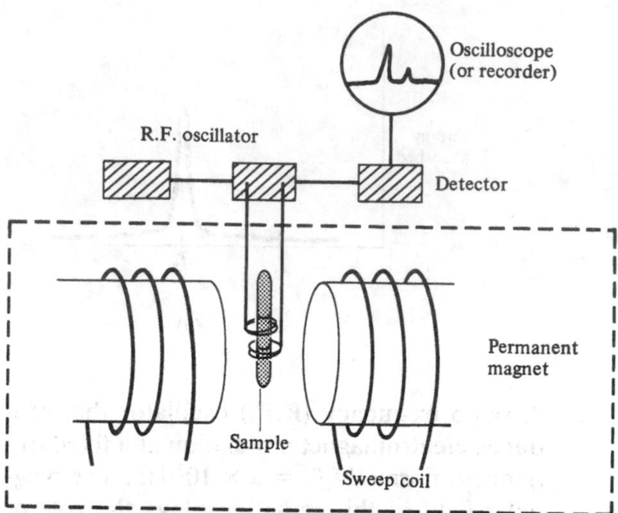

Figure 29.26. A schematic diagram of an NMR apparatus. The electronic instruments outside the box produce and monitor the energy absorbed. The sweep coils are used to make small variations in the field $\mathbf{B}_e$ produced by the permanent magnet. Other features are described in the text.

29.10 | THE CHEMICAL SHIFT

The *chemical shift* is the observed shift of the resonant frequency of protons in a given molecule from that of free protons in a field $\mathbf{B}_e$. For example, in benzene a single resonant frequency and chemical shift are observed. The measured frequency f_p is greater than f_e, so $\Delta f = f_p - f_e$ is positive. We can understand this result by examining the benzene molecule. Benzene has six carbon atoms in a ring with hydrogen atoms attached to them (Fig. 29.27*a*). Above and below the carbon ring, electrons are free to move in doughnut-shaped regions (Fig. 29.27*b*). As an external magnetic field $\mathbf{B}_e$ is applied, the electrons circulate in accordance with Lenz's law (Chapter Twenty). They form a current whose magnetic field opposes the initial increase in $\mathbf{B}_e$, reducing the flux inside the ring (Fig. 29.27). However, *outside the ring*, this induced current produces an increase in the magnetic field, and the total magnetic field there is greater than B_e by ΔB. Since the hydrogen atoms in benzene are outside the ring, they have a precession frequency that is greater than f_e by Δf.

Note that at least two qualitative pieces of information about benzene have been confirmed. First, there exists a closed path around which the electrons can circulate and second, the hydrogen nuclei are outside this path. If the hydrogen nuclei were inside the ring, the resonant frequency would be less than f_e; the chemical shift would be in the opposite direction.

Subtle differences in the positions of electrons in different bonds can be seen using NMR. When an

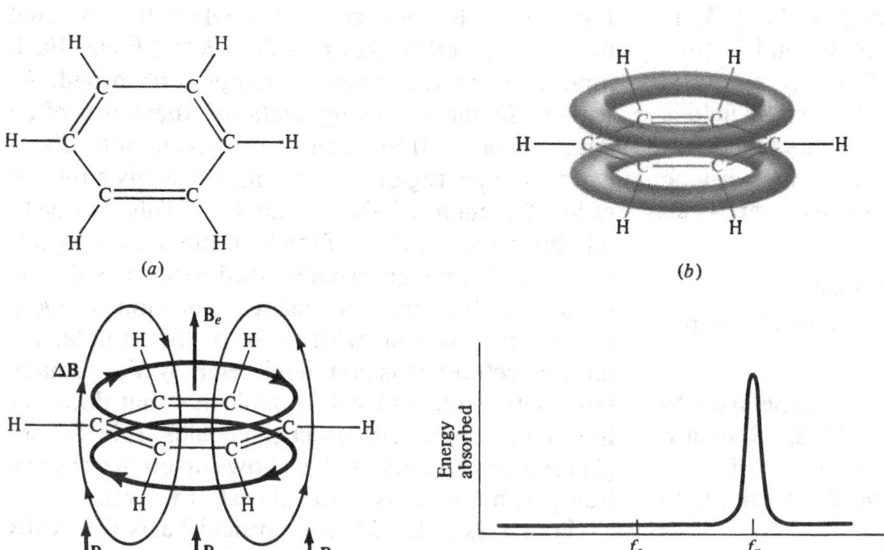

Figure 29.27. (*a*) The chemical diagram of benzene. (*b*) Electrons in benzene move freely in two rings above and below the plane of the molecule. (*c*) When $\mathbf{B}_e$ is applied, an induced electron current produces a magnetic field that opposes $\mathbf{B}_e$ inside the rings and adds to it outside the rings. (*d*) The field at the protons is larger than $\mathbf{B}_e$, so the resonant frequency is larger than f_e.

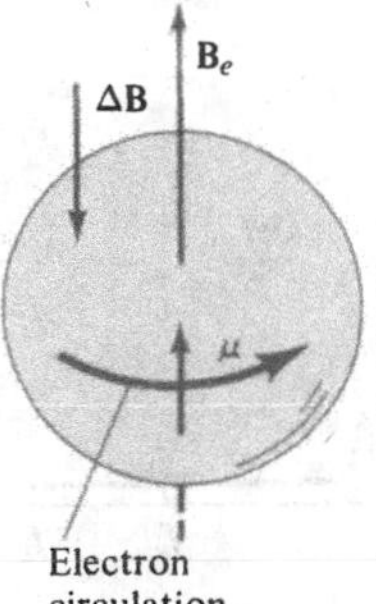

Figure 29.28. When $\mathbf{B}_e$ is applied to a hydrogen atom, the electron circulates as shown, producing the induced field $\Delta\mathbf{B}$. The field at the proton is then $B_T = B_e - \Delta B$.

external field $\mathbf{B}_e$ is applied to a neutral hydrogen atom in its ground state, the *s* electron has its energy changed slightly, and it circulates according to Lenz's law (Fig. 29.28). The local field at the proton is less than B_T, and the precession frequency is smaller than f_e. This is called the *diamagnetic* effect.

When hydrogen occurs in a covalent bond, the electron wave function is no longer symmetric about the nucleus. The more the electron is pulled away from the hydrogen nucleus, the smaller the diamagnetic effect, since its ability to produce an effective induced field at the nucleus is reduced. For example, in an OH group, the oxygen atom strongly attracts the bond electron from the hydrogen atom and the precession frequency of the proton in hydrogen is only slightly smaller than f_e. The bond electrons in CH_2 are not as far from the hydrogen as in OH. Hence the diamagnetic effect is larger and the precession frequency of these two protons is less than in OH. Finally, electrons in CH_3 are only weakly attracted by the carbon so the diamagnetic effect and chemical shifts are even larger. The precession frequency of these three protons is well below f_e. Thus in ethanol, CH_3—CH_2—OH, we see three chemical shifts (Fig. 29.29).

The identification of the three resonance peaks in ethanol is also facilitated by the fact that for every proton in an OH group that absorbs energy, there are two protons in CH_2 and three in CH_3. Energy is absorbed in the ratio of 1 to 2 to 3 in the three groups, as seen in Fig. 29.29*b*.

When an NMR experiment of higher resolution is performed on ethanol, the broad spectrum of Fig. 29.29 is resolved into a number of sharp peaks (Fig. 29.30). The explanation of these peaks is the subject of the next section.

29.11 | SPIN–SPIN SPLITTING

The same proton magnetic moments that precess and absorb energy in molecules give rise to magnetic fields within the molecule. These dipole magnetic fields produce modifications in the electronic configuration of the molecule that, in turn, affect other dipoles. The net result is that the orientation of each dipole may influence the energy of the other dipoles.

When the effects of interactions among spins within a group such as CH_3 are taken into account, the energy required to flip any one spin does not depend on the orientation of the others. On the other hand, the effect of proton spins on adjacent groups is significant and measurable. Consider first

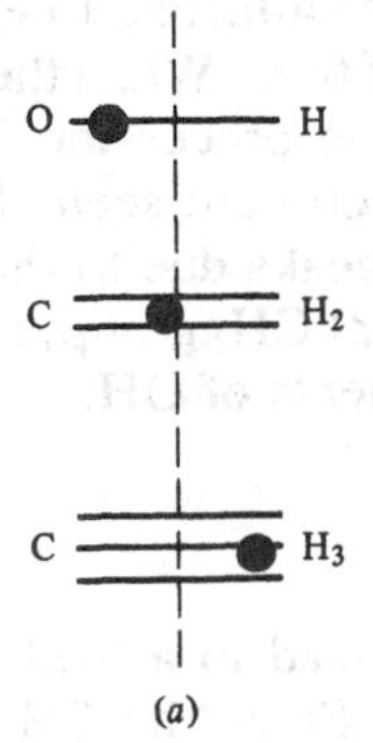

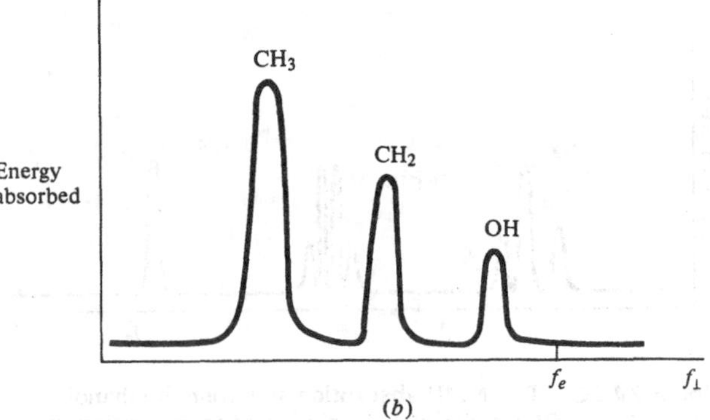

Figure 29.29. (*a*) Schematic diagram of the center of charge of bond electrons in the OH, CH_2, and CH_3 groups of ethanol. (*b*) The changes in the electron density and current at the hydrogen nucleus are evidenced by the different chemical shifts or precession frequencies of each group.

the effect of the CH_3 spins on the protons of an adjacent group.

The three proton spins in CH_3 can have four possible types of spin configurations:

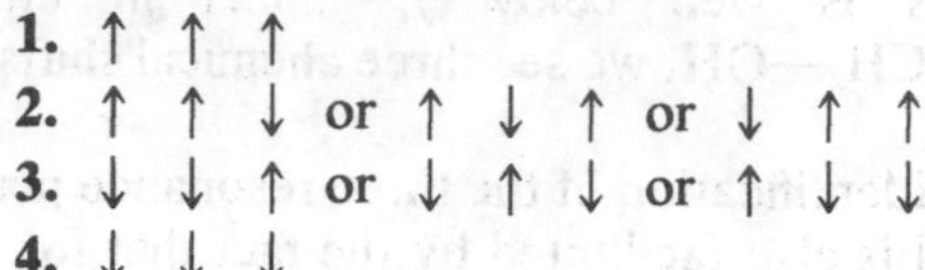

1. ↑ ↑ ↑
2. ↑ ↑ ↓ or ↑ ↓ ↑ or ↓ ↑ ↑
3. ↓ ↓ ↑ or ↓ ↑ ↓ or ↑ ↓ ↓
4. ↓ ↓ ↓

The configurations with one spin opposite to the other two are three times as probable as those where all the spins are parallel.

Each of the configurations shown produces a different effect on dipoles of a neighboring group. Thus the protons of the group adjacent to CH_3 will experience four slightly different magnetic fields and in a sample four slightly different precession frequencies will be observed. The fourfold splitting of the CH_2 line in Fig. 29.30 shows this. It is also seen that the two central peaks are about three times as high as the outermost peaks, corresponding to the relative frequency of occurrence of the spin configurations in CH_3.

The two proton spins in CH_2 can have three different configurations:

1. ↑ ↑
2. ↑ ↓ or ↓ ↑
3. ↓ ↓

These three configurations produce three different fields in adjacent groups, and the CH_3 resonance is split into three peaks. The central peak is very close to twice as intense as the two side peaks (Fig. 29.30). Using the same reasoning, we expect to see

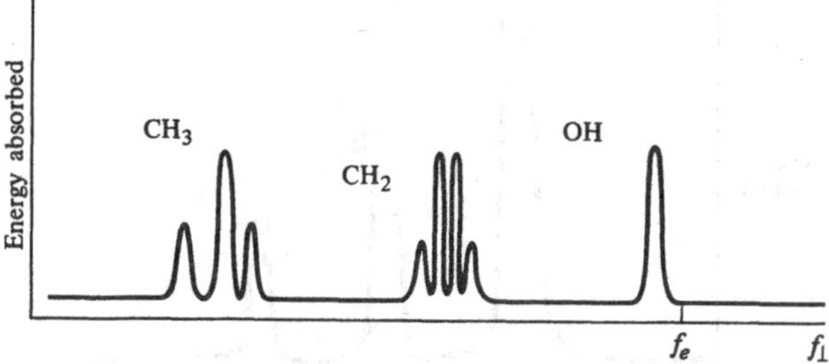

Figure 29.30. The NMR absorption spectrum of ethanol (CH_3—CH_2—OH) under high resolution at room temperature. (The effect of temperature will be discussed later.)

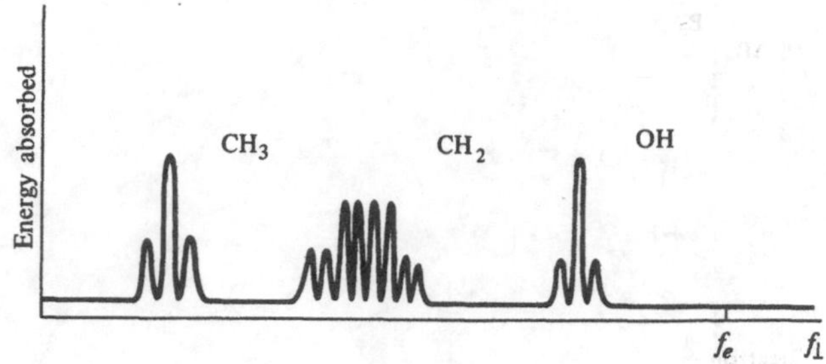

Figure 29.31. At low temperatures, further structure is observed in the spectrum of ethanol. There are eight peaks near the CH_2 resonance, and the OH line has three peaks.

a threefold splitting of the OH resonance due to the adjacent CH_2 group. This splitting is not seen in the room temperature spectrum of Fig. 29.30. However, if the temperature of the sample is lowered, the threefold splitting is finally observed (Fig. 29.31). Furthermore, the CH_2 resonance undergoes an additional splitting so that eight peaks are seen.

The disappearance of this additional structure at room temperature is explained by *chemical exchange*. The hydroxyl group OH is rather weakly bound in ethanol and can be pictured as moving from molecule to molecule, binding briefly at each site and then moving again. This process is so rapid that during the time it takes for the resonant absorption of energy to occur, about the time it takes for the dipole to precess once, several OH groups have been attached to the same molecule. Thus the resonance experiment detects an average effect from the presence of the OH groups, and the detailed structure is not seen. As the temperature is lowered, the thermal energy that facilitates this random exchange motion is decreased, and the OH group remains attached to each molecule for a longer period of time. When the exchange frequency is lower than the precession frequency, the effects of the OH group are seen. The OH resonance splits into three peaks due to the spin–spin coupling with the adjacent CH_2 group, and there are two possible spin alignments of OH:

1. ↑
2. ↓

These lead to a twofold splitting of the CH_2 resonance. Since the CH_2 resonance already had four peaks, it now has eight.

When experiments are performed on complex molecules, it may be difficult to distinguish the resonance of a given group from the spin–spin splitting of another group. In such cases, the experiment can be performed at several different values of the external field. The size of the chemical shift varies with the applied field, but the spin–spin coupling does not. The chemical shift depends on the magnitudes of induced fields, which, in turn, depend on the applied field. On the other hand, the spin–spin coupling is produced by the effects of spins on each other. Because these spins have the same magnitude, regardless of the applied field, the separation of the spin–spin splittings is always the same.

29.12 | RELAXATION TIMES

So far we have considered the effects of the molecular environment on the measured precessional frequencies, that is, the chemical shift. However, there is another type of experiment in which the magnetic dipoles in a material are briefly subjected to a transverse field, upsetting the thermal equilibrium of the material. Measurements of the *relaxation times* that characterize its return to equilibrium provide very useful information and are the basis for the biological NMR imaging systems discussed in the next section.

Consider a material that is in an external magnetic field along the z direction, $\mathbf{B}_0$. The *magnetization* $\mathbf{M}$ is defined to be the vector sum of the individual nuclear magnetic dipole moments in a unit volume of the material:

$$\mathbf{M} = \boldsymbol{\mu}_1 + \boldsymbol{\mu}_2 + \boldsymbol{\mu}_3 + \cdots \tag{29.8}$$

Since the dipoles may point in various directions, the magnetization can be small or even zero even though the individual magnetic dipole moments are not zero.

As we saw earlier, the energy of a magnetic dipole in a magnetic field is determined by the angle between the dipole moment and the field. Specifically, when $\mathbf{B}_0$ is in the z direction, $\mathcal{U} = -\mu B_0 \cos\theta = -\mu_z B_0$. In the same way, when a collection of molecules is placed in an external magnetic field $\mathbf{B}_0$ in the z direction, the energy of the collection is

$$\mathcal{U} = -M_z B_0$$

When such a system is in thermal equilibrium, the energy in the collection of spins remains constant as does the vibrational, rotational, and kinetic energy of the collection. Energy exchange among these modes does occur, but on the average, the energy in each mode is constant.

Suppose now that we briefly apply a varying transverse magnetic field $\mathbf{B}_\perp$. The magnetization has a component M_z parallel to the external field $\mathbf{B}_0$ and components M_x and M_y along the x and y axes. The magnetization vector $\mathbf{M}$ precesses just as if it were a single magnetic dipole (Fig. 29.32*a*). Note that all the transverse components line up initially because only those individual dipoles that are oriented properly can absorb energy from $\mathbf{B}_\perp$. If nothing but $\mathbf{B}_0$ acted upon the magnetization after $\mathbf{B}_\perp$ was turned off, $\mathbf{M}$ would continue to precess indefinitely.

Two processes disrupt this endless precession. First, the magnetic fields produce magnetic dipole moments in neighboring regions that cause the transverse components of the individual magnetic moments composing $\mathbf{M}$ to stop precessing in unison. As the many small dipoles precess about the z axis, they eventually begin to point in many random directions in the x–y plane. Mathematically, the vector sums defining the x and y components of the magnetization add up to zero. However, this interaction has no effect on M_z.

This smearing out of the x and y components of $\mathbf{M}$ occurs at a rate that depends on the nature of the substance and is characterized by a *transverse* or *spin–spin relaxation time* T_2. What is observed is that the transverse components of the magnetization die out exponentially, or as

$$M_x = M_{x0}e^{-t/T_2}, \qquad M_y = M_{y0}e^{-t/T_2}$$

Thus measuring the rate at which the transverse components of the magnetization die out yields information about the interaction of the dipoles in the material.

The second process that affects the precessional motion is related to the interaction of the dipoles and the vibrational motions of the molecules. If a system is disturbed from a state of thermal equilibrium by briefly applying a transverse magnetic field $\mathbf{B}_\perp$, it eventually returns to thermal equilibrium. In the process, the total energy of the system, the sum of the magnetic, vibrational, rotational, and kinetic energy, remains constant. However, the amount stored in each category changes. In particular, the

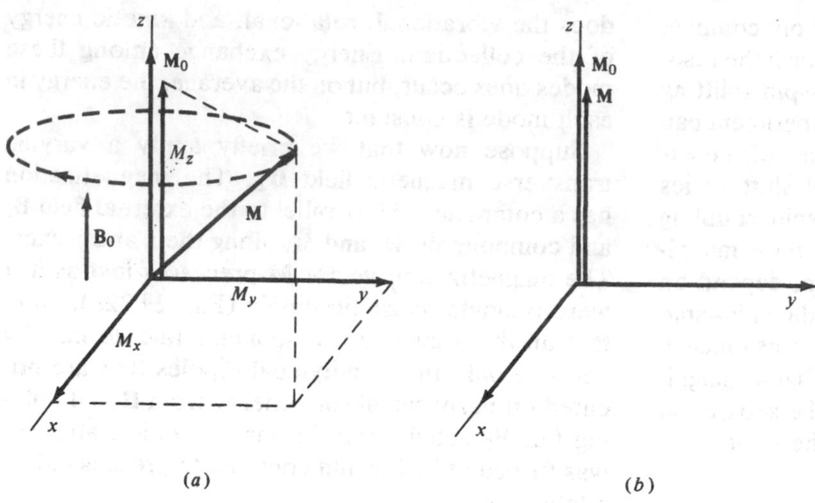

Figure 29.32. (*a*) The magnetization at an instant of time, shown precessing about $\mathbf{B}_0$. Note that M_z is smaller than M_0. (*b*) At a later time, the effects of magnetic dipoles on one another tend to smear out the contributions of the individual dipole moments so that M_x and M_y are zero. Note that M_z is still smaller than M_0.

magnetic energy absorbed by the system while $\mathbf{B}_\perp$ is present is transferred through the vibrational motion of the molecules to the other modes.

Suppose then that the system starts in a state where $\mathbf{M}$ is initially aligned with $\mathbf{B}_0$ and the longitudinal component M_z has a value M_0. After $\mathbf{B}_\perp$ is applied and turned off, the system returns gradually to thermal equilibrium with M_z again equal to M_0. The difference between M_z and M_0 also dies out exponentially, with a characteristic *longitudinal* relaxation time T_1:

$$M_0 - M_z = M_0 e^{-t/T_1}$$

Thus T_1 determines the rate at which the z or longitudinal component of the magnetization returns to M_0 after a transverse magnetic field is applied to the system. This time is a characteristic of the substance and depends on the interaction of the dipoles and the vibrational motion of the molecules. T_1 is often called the *spin–lattice* relaxation time because of this interaction of the dipoles and molecules that are at lattice positions in solids.

Measurements of T_1 and T_2 provide the basis for NMR imaging.

29.13 | NMR IMAGING

To obtain tomographic images of an object, one measures one or more of its characteristics such as the absorption of X rays and correlates the measurements with the position. The relaxation times T_1 and T_2 are the characteristics measured in NMR imaging.

In the schematic apparatus of Fig. 29.33, the external magnetic field $\mathbf{B}_0$ produces a magnetization $\mathbf{M}$ that is initially in the z direction. Then a brief time-varying current pulse is put through the transverse coils, producing $\mathbf{B}_\perp$, which acts like a rotating transverse magnetic field. This causes the magnetization to "tip" and precess about the z direction.

The same coils that produce the transverse field can also detect a current induced by the magnetization. To understand the origin of the induced current, we note that as the magnetization vector precesses, its transverse component swings completely around. Thus the magnetic field produced at the wire coil by that transverse magnetization changes with time. According to Faraday's law, this changing magnetic field produces an induced current in the coil. The frequency of $\mathbf{B}_\perp$ must be matched to the precessional frequency of the dipoles in order for energy to be absorbed in any significant amount. The induced current has the same frequency since it reverses itself with each precessional cycle.

In the previous section, we noted that the transverse magnetization disappears as the individual dipoles lose their correlation in the transverse direction. The induced current also disappears over a time characterized by T_2 (Fig. 29.33*c*). Thus a measurement of the induced current from the transverse coils yields both T_2 and the precession frequency.

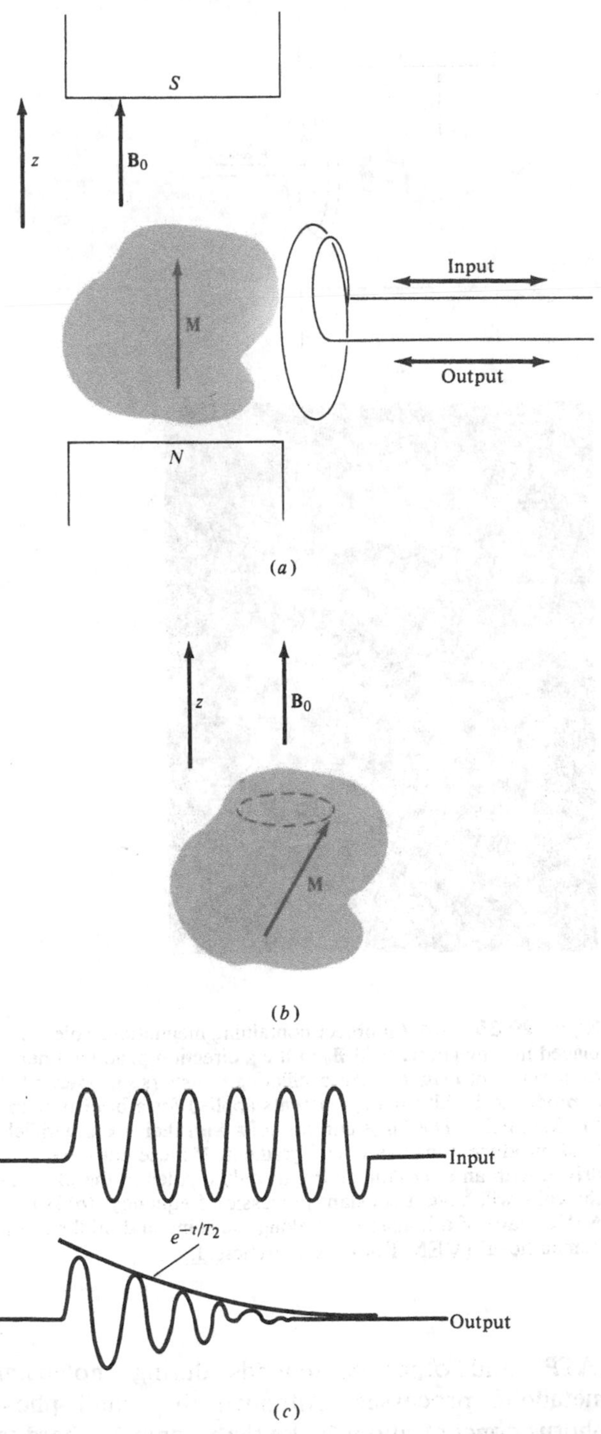

Figure 29.33. (*a*) An object containing magnetic dipoles is placed in a magnetic field $\mathbf{B}_0$ in the z direction produced here by permanent magnets. An oscillating transverse magnetic field is produced by alternating currents applied for a brief time in the coils shown. This causes the magnetization to precess as shown in (*b*). The input current is shown diagrammatically in (*c*). These same coils are used to detect the induced current produced by the precessing transverse magnetization. This induced output current dies out exponentially with a relaxation time T_2.

The precession frequency, as we have seen earlier, depends upon the external applied field $\mathbf{B}_0$ and the local magnetic field in the substance.

If a sequence of current pulses is applied to the transverse coils the induced current may appear as in Figure 29.34*a*, as long as the time t between pulses is long compared to T_1. What is happening is that the magnetization M_z is returning to its initial magnitude M_0 between each pulse. The individual dipoles return to their orientation parallel to $\mathbf{B}_0$ and each pulse affects the same number of dipoles.

If the time between pulses is shortened, not all of the dipoles will have returned to the z direction; thermal equilibrium will not have been achieved when the next pulse occurs. Thus the initial magnitude of the induced current generated by that pulse is smaller than before (Fig. 29.34*b*). (There may be a small effect from some "tipped" dipoles being tipped some more, but this can be neglected when the number of such tipped dipoles is small compared to the number in the z direction.) Comparing the initial heights for pulse sequences applied at two different time intervals determines T_1.

In practice, experimenters often use complex sequences of pulses to measure T_1 and T_2. These sequences are designed to help eliminate effects due to irregularities in the applied field $\mathbf{B}_0$ or to emphasize certain features.

The relaxation times must be correlated with the position to obtain images. There are a variety of methods available for this purpose, but they all add a field *gradient* to the static external field $\mathbf{B}_0$. In Fig. 29.35, for example, the average local magnetic field experienced by the dipoles, $\mathbf{B}_T$, gradually increases between the bottom and the top of the object. The precession frequency of the dipoles depends on $\mathbf{B}_T$, so it can be used to determine the vertical position in the object. If the coils producing the gradient are driven by an alternating current, the gradient will reverse itself periodically. Only the dipoles in the plane of the gradient coil will have a constant precession frequency, so this scheme picks out a single plane in the object. More extensive position information can be obtained with a complex system of

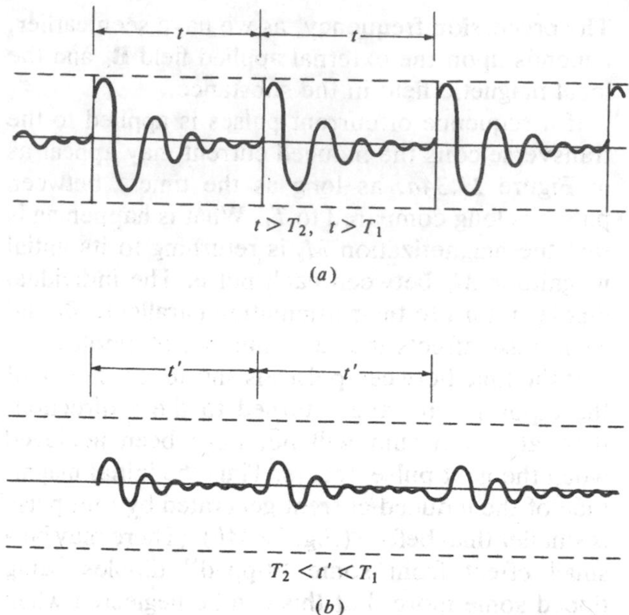

Figure 29.34. (*a*) A pulse sequence applied to a sample results in an induced current that dies out between each pulse. Furthermore, as long as $t > T_1$, the initial height of the induced pulse is a maximum. (*b*) A pulse sequence with $t' < T_1$ results in an initial induced current pulse height that is smaller than in (*a*). We assume $T_2 < T_1$.

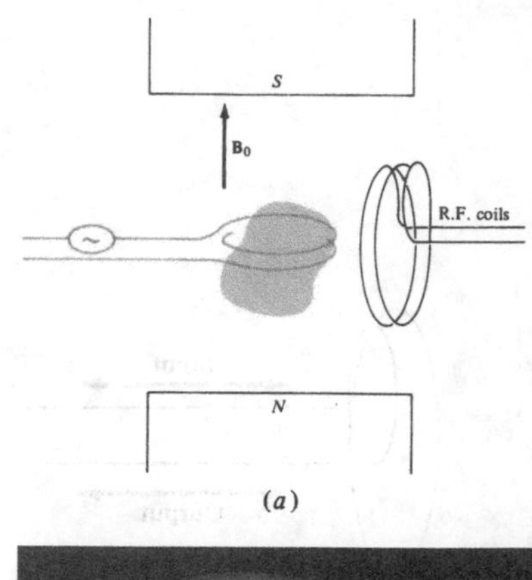

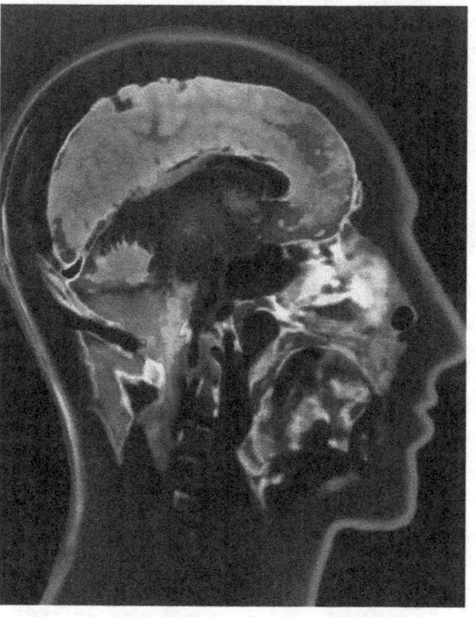
(b)

Figure 29.35. (*a*) An object containing magnetic dipoles is placed in a magnetic field $\mathbf{B}_0$ in the *z* direction produced here by permanent magnets. An oscillating transverse magnetic field is produced by alternating currents applied for a brief time in the R.F. coils. The large current coils with their axes parallel to $\mathbf{B}_0$ produce a magnetic field gradient. If these coils are driven with an alternating current, only dipoles in the plane of the coils will have a constant precession frequency. (*b*) An NMR image of a human head along the spine and midline of a human head. (VEM Photo Researchers, Inc.)

coils. Thus adding field gradients to the original setup makes it possible to produce tomographic NMR images.

NMR imaging of biological systems is of great interest for several reasons in addition to avoiding the radiation hazards associated with using X rays. At present, it primarily relies on the resonance of hydrogen nuclei. It is found, for example, that large differences occur in T_1 between tissue containing hydrogen bound in water molecules and tissue with hydrogen bound in fats or other large molecules. Thus tissues with different water content, such as normal and cancerous tissues, image well using NMR. Also, because brain gray matter has more water-bound hydrogen than does white matter, the contrast in brain scans is good. In some situations the contrast obtained at tissue boundaries is a factor of 2 with NMR and only a few percent with X rays.

An especially promising area of development derives from the fact that the NMR chemical shift from phosphorus differs in adenosine triphosphate (ATP) and other compounds during molecular metabolic processes. Although the small phosphorus concentrations make the resonances hard to detect, a great deal of attention is being given to following metabolic activity using phosphorus NMR imaging.

EXERCISES ON SUPPLEMENTARY TOPICS

Section 29.7 | The Behavior of a Magnetic Dipole in a Magnetic Field

29-24 What is the energy of a proton in a magnetic field of 1.2 T if the z component of the spin angular momentum is (a) along the field; (b) opposite to the field?

29-25 A photon of frequency 5×10^7 Hz is emitted when a proton spin flips. (a) What is the orientation of the proton spin angular momentum in the final state after the spin flips? (b) How large is the magnetic field?

29-26 Indicate the direction of the torque and the path of precession of the proton magnetic moment $\boldsymbol{\mu}$ in the field $\mathbf{B}_T$ of Fig. 29.36*a* and 29.36*b*.

29-27 What is the precession frequency f_p of a proton in a magnetic field $B_T = 1.2$ T?

29-28 When a magnetic field is applied to protons in a molecule, the difference between the precession frequencies $\Delta f = f_p - f_e$ is found to be 300 Hz. What is the difference between the actual and applied magnetic fields at the position of the dipole?

29-29 Show that the energy absorbed when a proton spin flips in a magnetic field $\mathbf{B}_T$ can be written as $\Delta\mathcal{U} = hf_p$, where f_p is the precession frequency.

29-30 (a) Using the results of Exercise 29-29, compute the frequency of the photons absorbed by protons in a magnetic field of 5 T. (b) What is the energy change when absorption occurs?

Section 29.8 | Measuring the Precession Frequency

29-31 In a typical NMR experiment the difference between the external field and the field at the position of the proton is $B_e - B_T = 1.5 \times 10^{-6}$ T. What is the measured frequency shift Δf?

29-32 A free proton precesses with a frequency f_e in an external field B_e. At resonance in a molecule the total field is $B_T > B_e$. Is the frequency at which the perpendicular magnetic field is applied greater or less than f_e?

29-33 In Fig. 29.37, the proton magnetic moment precesses with a frequency f_p. The period, the time necessary for the dipole to precess once, is $T = 1/f_p$. At resonance the perpendicular magnetic field $\mathbf{B}_\perp$ has a maximum magnitude and is oriented as shown at $t = 0$. Sketch the field $\mathbf{B}_\perp$ and show the direction of the torque on $\boldsymbol{\mu}$ due to $\mathbf{B}_\perp$ at $t = 0$, $T/4$, $T/2$, $3T/4$, and T.

Section 29.9 | The NMR Apparatus

29-34 Standard instruments produce a field $\mathbf{B}_\perp$ at a frequency of $f_\perp = 6 \times 10^7$ Hz. At what value of $\mathbf{B}_e$ will resonance occur for a free proton?

29-35 Describe briefly what might be observed if the applied field $\mathbf{B}_e$ in an NMR apparatus did not have exactly the same value everywhere in the sample.

Section 29.10 | The Chemical Shift

29-36 Sketch a graph of energy absorbed versus $f_\perp$ for a molecule shaped like benzene but with the hydrogen atom protons located inside the carbon ring.

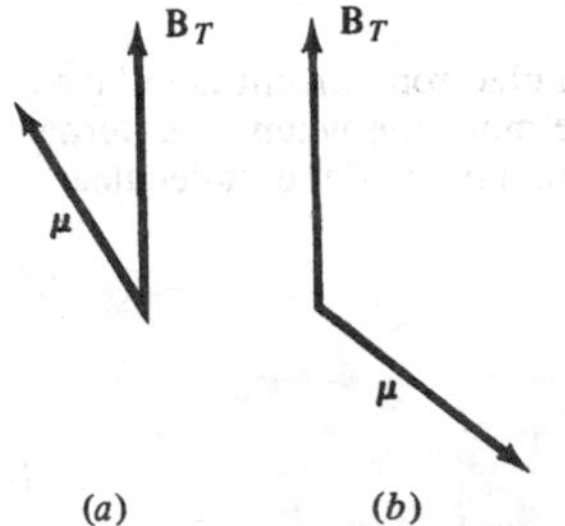

Figure 29.36. Exercise 29-26. At the instant shown, the proton magnetic moment $\boldsymbol{\mu}$ is in the plane of the page, as is $\mathbf{B}_T$.

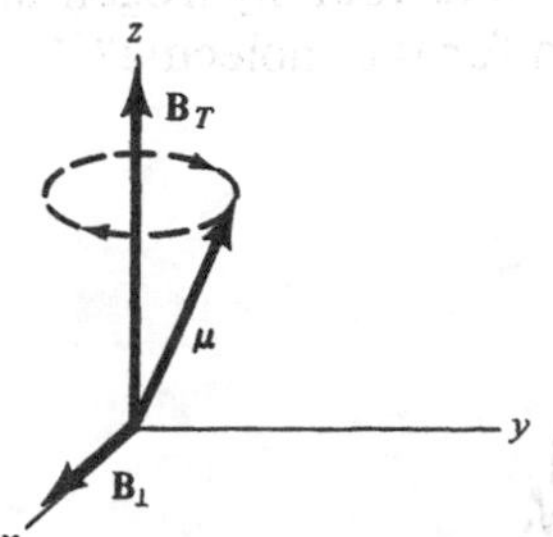

Figure 29.37. Exercise 29-33. At $t = 0$, $\boldsymbol{\mu}$ and $\mathbf{B}_T$ are in the y–z plane, and $\mathbf{B}_\perp$ is along the x axis.

29-37 In the compound $CH_3—CH_2—CH_2—I$, the two CH_2 groups experience slightly different local fields because their environments in the molecule are not identical. (a) Assuming the chemical shift in the CH_2 group beside the iodine (I) atom is smaller than in the adjacent CH_2 group, sketch a graph of energy absorbed versus $f_\perp$ for this molecule analogous to that in Fig. 29.29. Do not include the effects of spin–spin coupling. (b) What is the predicted ratio of the peak heights of the resonances that appear for this molecule?

29-38 When molecules such as ethanol, $CH_3—CH_2—OH$, are in certain solutions, the hydrogen in the OH group may form the center for a hydrogen bond with a solvent molecule. In such a bond, the hydrogen proton has four electrons near it rather than two as when the hydrogen bond is not present. The OH resonance when hydrogen bonds are present is observed to shift so that it appears between the CH_3 and CH_2 resonances in Fig. 29.29. Describe why this shift occurs in terms of the diamagnetic effect.

Section 29.11 | Spin–Spin Splitting

29-39 Sketch and explain the NMR spectrum of 1,1,2-trichloroethane,

$$Cl—CH_2—CH\begin{matrix} Cl \\ Cl \end{matrix}$$

(The chemical shift of CH is smaller than that of CH_2.)

29-40 Figure 29.38 shows the NMR absorption spectrum of a molecule containing one carbon atom, one oxygen atom, and four hydrogen atoms. What is the formula for the molecule?

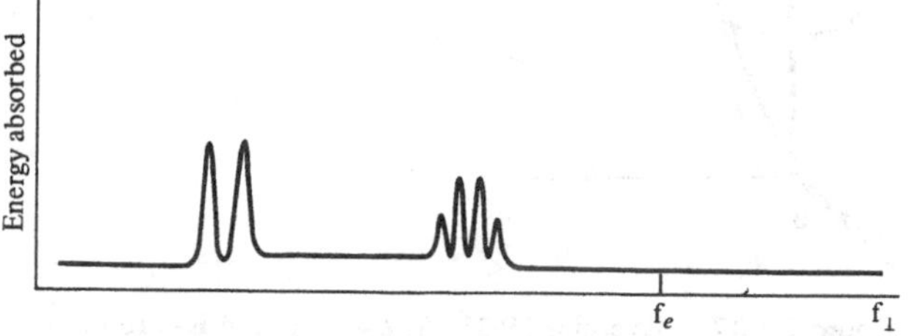

Figure 29.38. Exercise 29-40.

PROBLEMS ON SUPPLEMENTARY TOPICS

29-41 Figure 29.39 shows the circulating electron current of the C—O bond in aldehyde. What will the effect of this induced current be on the precession frequency of the proton dipole moment in the hydrogen atom?

29-42 Sketch the NMR absorption spectrum of acetaldehyde:

$$CH_3—C\begin{matrix} {/\!\!/}O \\ \backslash H \end{matrix}$$

(Use the fact that the chemical shift of the CH group is smaller than that of CH_3.)

29-43 When an external magnetic field is applied to acetylene, the electrons of the C—C bond can circulate around the surface of a cylinder (Fig. 29.40). (a) What is the direction of the induced electron current if viewed looking along the $\mathbf{B}_e$ direction? (b) What is the effect of this current on the precession frequency of the protons in the hydrogen atoms?

29-44 The NMR absorption spectrum of $CH_3—CH_2—CH_2—I$ is shown in Fig. 29.41. The

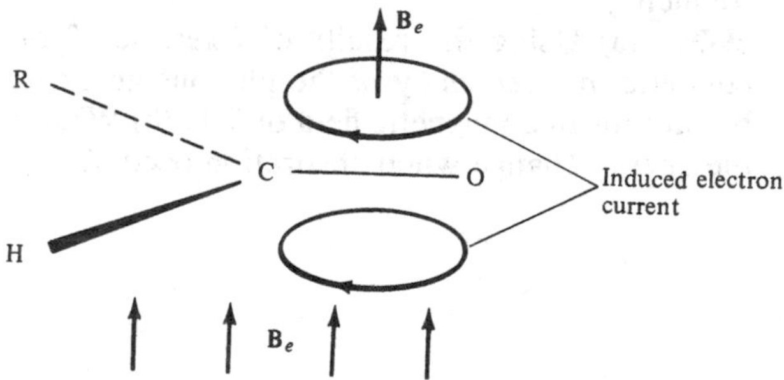

Figure 29.39. Problem 29-41. An electron current is induced in the C—O group of the aldehyde molecule when an external field is applied. *R* stands for the remainder of the molecule.

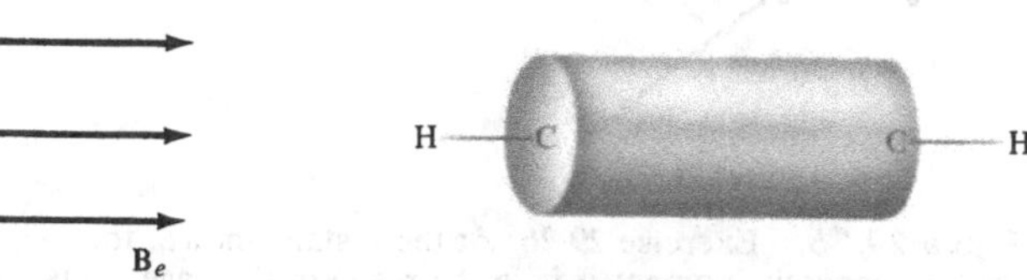

Figure 29.40. Problem 29-43.

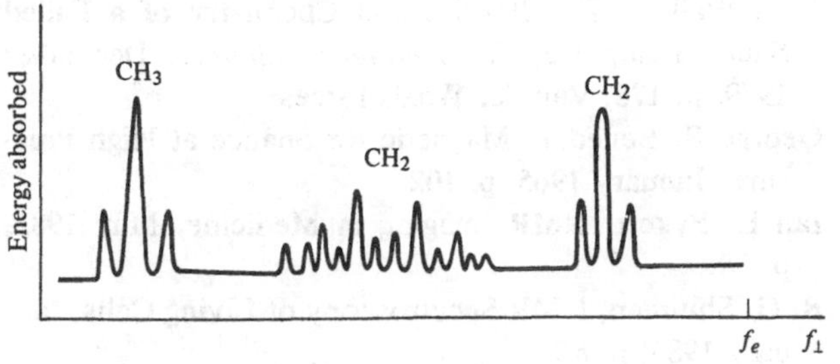

Figure 29-41. Problem 29-44.

different chemical shifts of the two CH_2 groups are due to the different environments of the two groups in the molecule. (a) Explain the threefold splitting of the CH_3 peak. (b) Why is the central CH_2 line split into 12 peaks?

Additional Reading

Linus Pauling, *The Nature of the Chemical Bond*, Cornell University Press, Ithaca, New York, 1960.

Alan Holden, *Bonds Between Atoms*, Bell Telephone Laboratories, Murray Hill, N.J., 1966.

Gordon M. Barrow, *Physical Chemistry*, 3rd ed., McGraw-Hill Book Co., New York, 1973. Schematic representations of atomic and molecular orbitals.

R. B. Setlow and E. C. Pollard, *Molecular Biophysics*, Addison-Wesley Publishing Co., Reading, Mass., 1962, Chapter 7.

John R. Dyer, *Applications of Absorption Spectroscopy of Organic Compounds*, Prentice-Hall, Inc., Englewood Cliffs, N.J., 1965. Paperback.

Dudley H. Williams and Ian Fleming, *Spectroscopic Methods in Organic Chemistry*, McGraw-Hill Book Co., London, 1966. Paperback.

Joe Demuth and Phaedon Avouris, Surface Spectroscopy, *Physics Today*, November 1982, p. 62. Information from emitted electrons.

Edward Edelson, Scanning the Body Magnetic, *Science 83*, July/August 1983, p. 60. NMR scans.

D. Chapman and P. D. Magnus, *Introduction to Practical High Resolution Nuclear Magnetic Resonance Spectroscopy*, Academic Press, London and New York, 1966. Paperback.

Stanley J. Opella, Biological Nuclear Magnetic Resonance, *Science*, vol. 198, 1977, p. 158.

Jean L. Marx, NMR Researchers Embark on New Enterprise, *Science*, vol. 213, 1981, p. 425. Clinical applications of phosphorus NMR methods.

G. C. Levy and D. J. Craik, Recent Developments in Nuclear Magnetic Resonance, *Science*, vol. 214, 1981, p. 291.

Gordon L. Brownell, Thomas F. Budinger, Paul C. Lauterbur, and Patrick L. McGreer, Positron Tomography and Nuclear Magnetic Resonance Imaging, *Science*, vol. 215, 1982, p. 619.

R. Stuart Mackay, *Medical Images and Displays*, John Wiley & Sons, Inc., New York, 1984.

J. Jonas, Nuclear Magnetic Resonance at High Pressure, *Science*, vol. 216, 1982, p. 1179. Application to the study of liquids.

Olli V. Lounasmaa, Nuclear Magnetic Ordering at Nanokelvin Temperature, *Physics Today*, October 1989, p. 26.

Scientific American articles:

Boris V. Derjaguim, The Force Between Molecules, July 1960, p. 47.

Arnold C. Wahl, Chemistry by Computer, April 1970, p. 54.

Harry Selig et al., The Chemistry of the Noble Gases, May 1964, p. 66.

Ronald Breslow, The Nature of Aromatic Molecules, August 1972, p. 32.

The entire September 1967 issue is devoted to *Materials*, with a number of articles related to this chapter.

Marvin L. Cohen, Volker Heine, and James C. Phillips, The Quantum Mechanics of Materials, June 1982, p. 82.

Gerald L. Pollack, Solid Noble Gases, October 1966, p. 64.

L. K. Rumels, Ice, December 1966, p. 118.

J. D. Bernal, The Structure of Liquids, August 1960, p. 125.

A. R. Mackintosh, The Fermi Surface of Metals, July 1963, p. 110.

N. W. Ashcroft, Liquid Metals, July 1968, p. 72.

N. Ya. Azbel', M. I. Kaganov, and I. M. Lifshitz, Conduction Electrons in Metals, January 1973, p. 88.

Robert Gomer, Surface Diffusion, August 1982, p. 98. Metallic surfaces.

Gordon A. Thomas, An Electron-Hole Liquid, June 1976, p. 28.

Bernard Bertram and Robert A. Guyer, Solid Helium, August 1967, p. 84.

James L. Fergason, Liquid Crystals, August 1964, p. 76.

Raymond Bowers, Plasmas in Solids, November 1963, p. 46.

R. D. Parks, Quantum Effects in Superconductors, October 1965, p. 57.

F. Reif, Superfluidity and "Quasi-Particles," November 1960, p. 138.

N. David Mermin and David M. Lee, Superfluid Helium 3, December 1976, p. 56.

Richard E. Dickerson, The DNA Helix and How It Is Read, December 1983, p. 94. X-ray analysis.

Klaus Bechgaard and Denis Jerome, Organic Superconductors, July 1982, p. 52.

Donald H. Levy, The Spectroscopy of Supercooled Gases, February 1984, p. 96. Molecular energy levels.

Ednor M. Rowe and John H. Weaver, The Uses of Synchrotron Radiation, June 1977, p. 32.

David Adler, Amorphous-Semiconductor Devices, May 1977, p. 36.

James L. Dye, Anions of the Alkali Metals, July 1977, p. 92.

Kurt Nassau, The Causes of Color, October 1980, p. 124. Absorption of light by molecules.

Jearl Walker, The Physics and Chemistry of a Failed Sauce Béarnaise, *The Amateur Scientist*, December 1979, p. 178, Van der Waals forces.

George B. Benedek, Magnetic Resonance at High Pressure, January 1965, p. 102.

Ian L. Pykett, NMR Imaging in Medicine, May 1982, p. 78.

R. G. Shulman, NMR Spectroscopy of Living Cells, January 1983, p. 86.

Mordehai Heilblum and Lester F. Eastman, Ballistic Electrons in Semiconductors, February 1987, p. 102.

James L. Dye, Electrides, August 1987, p. 66. A new class of crystalline materials.

Robert T. Bate, The Quantum-Effect Device: Tomorrow's Transistor?, March, 1988, p. 96.

Yoshihiro Hamakawa, Photovoltaic Power, April 1987, p. 86.

William R. Frensley, Gallium Arsenide Transistors, August 1987, p. 80.

Franck Laloë and Jack H. Freed, The Effects of Spin in Gases, April 1988, p. 94.

Alan M. Wolsky, Robert F. Giese, and Edward J. Daniels, The New Superconductors: Prospects for Applications, February 1989, p. 60.

UNIT NINE

THE ATOMIC NUCLEUS

We have seen that the development of quantum physics in the early decades of this century made possible an understanding of atomic and molecular phenomena. By the early 1930s, the frontier of physics and the search for the ultimate structure of matter had moved on to the much smaller scale of the atomic nucleus.

Until 1939, nuclear physics was a scholarly activity of little practical importance. In that year, O. Hahn (1879–1968) and F. Strassman, working in Germany, discovered that a uranium nucleus can fission into two lighter nuclei. This process releases millions of times more energy than any chemical reaction among atoms or molecules and represents an energy source of unprecedented magnitude.

The great contemporary impact of nuclear physics is demonstrated by a few examples. Nuclear weapons brought a gruesome but rapid end to World War II, and the threat of their possible use has become a central factor in international politics. The world's reserves of fossil fuels are rapidly diminishing, and of all the possible alternative energy sources, only nuclear fission reactors have as yet become available for widespread use. Many kinds of radioactive materials have been made available; their use in medicine has saved many lives, and important applications have been developed in research, agriculture, and industry. Major advances in geology and archeology have resulted from radioactive dating and other nuclear physics tools.

This unit is divided into two chapters. The first covers the fundamental physics of the nucleus, and the second deals with the effects and uses of ionizing radiation.

CHAPTER 30 NUCLEAR PHYSICS

The atomic nucleus is a very small, dense object made up of two kinds of nucleons: protons and neutrons. A proton has a positive electric charge equal in magnitude to the electron charge and a mass about 1840 times that of the electron. Neutrons are about 0.1 percent more massive than protons. As their name suggests, they bear no electric charge.

A nucleus is specified by its *atomic number Z* and its *mass number A*. Z is the number of protons, and A is the total number of nucleons, so the *neutron number N* equals $A - Z$. The standard notation for nuclei is illustrated by $^{238}_{92}U$. This nucleus has 238 nucleons, of which 92 are protons and $238 - 92 = 146$ are neutrons. U is the chemical symbol for the 92nd element, uranium. Sometimes the atomic number is omitted, since it is implicitly given by the name of the element. The notation U-238 is occasionally used when one needs to specify the isotope as well as the element.

Nuclear species, or *nuclides*, that have the same atomic number but different neutron numbers are called *isotopes*. Because the electronic structure of atoms depends mainly on the total positive charge of the nucleus, different isotopes of an element are nearly identical chemically. Slightly over 100 naturally occurring or artificially produced elements and about 300 stable nuclides are known.

Three distinct types of forces play important roles in nuclei. Nuclei are held together by very strong, short-ranged *nuclear forces* among the nucleons. *Electric forces* are smaller in magnitude, but they become progressively more important as the number of protons in the nucleus increases. The *weak interactions* are much weaker than either the strong nuclear forces or the electromagnetic interactions, but they are responsible for the *beta decay* processes in which, for example, neutrons in nuclei are converted into protons as they emit electrons and neutrinos. Gravitational forces are weaker still, and are unimportant in nuclear physics.

The detailed motions of the individual nucleons inside a nucleus are very complex. However, their average orbits and the resulting nuclear structure can be fairly well described by a nuclear shell model, which closely resembles the atomic shell model.

In this chapter, we first explore some basic properties of nuclei and then discuss nuclear forces and the nuclear shell model. We conclude with an examination of nuclear decay processes. In the supplementary topics, we discuss nuclear energy. We also examine current ideas which suggest that nucleons are not themselves elementary objects but are composed of more fundamental constituents.

30.1 | RADIOACTIVITY

Antoine Henri Becquerel (1852–1908) accidentally made the first observation of a purely nuclear phenomenon in 1896, 15 years before Rutherford inferred the existence of the nucleus. Becquerel noted that uranium compounds produce invisible rays, or *radiation*, that can penetrate an opaque container and expose a photographic emulsion. Soon thereafter, Pierre and Marie Curie showed that uranium ores also contain traces of polonium ($Z = 84$) and radium ($Z = 88$), both much more intensely *radioactive* than uranium. Many other radioactive nuclear species, or *radionuclides*, were subsequently found.

Before long, some important properties of the radiation were discovered. A lead plate an inch or so

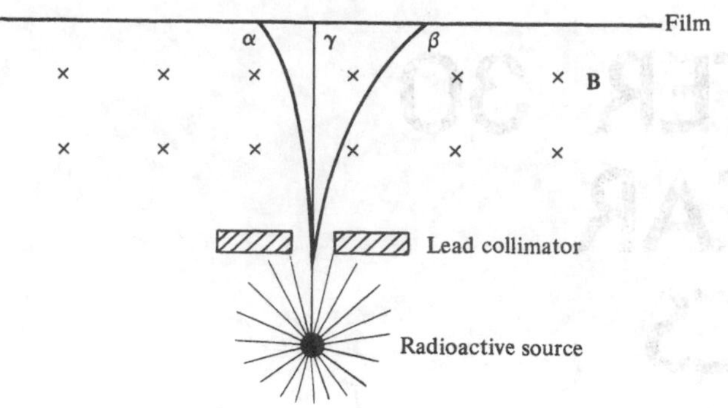

Figure 30.1. Radiation from a radioactive source splits into three components in a magnetic field. The α particles are ${}^4_2\text{He}$ nuclei, the β particles are electrons, and the uncharged γ rays are photons.

thick stops most of the radiation from a uranium source, so a plate with a small hole can be used to form a narrow collimated beam of radiation. In the presence of a magnetic field, this beam splits into three components, labeled *alpha* (α), *beta* (β), and *gamma* (γ) (Fig. 30.1). *Alpha particles* are positively charged and have a very short range in matter; they are now known to be helium nuclei (${}^4_2\text{He}$). The negatively charged *beta particles* have a longer range in matter and are electrons. The neutral *gamma rays* penetrate furthest in matter. They are photons whose energies are usually greater than those of X rays.

The energies of α, β, and γ radiation are as much as several million electron volts (MeV) per particle. Since atomic and molecular processes typically involve energies of a few electron volts, radioactivity represented a totally new kind of phenomenon and suggested the existence of forces much stronger than electric forces.

In 1903, Rutherford and Soddy showed that when a uranium nucleus emits an alpha particle, it is changed into a thorium nucleus. Symbolically,

$$ {}^{238}_{92}\text{U} \rightarrow {}^{234}_{90}\text{Th} + {}^4_2\text{He} $$

Thus a transmutation of the elements occurs in α *decay processes*. This is a change that cannot be produced by chemical means, with or without medieval incantations. Similar transmutations occur in β *decays*, but not in γ *decays*.

Along with the early discoveries of the basic physical properties of radiation, there was progress in understanding the biological effects of radiation. By the start of this century, it was realized that both X rays and nuclear radiation can cause skin burns. However, it was not then known that they also can induce cancer. Research scientists, physicians, and industrial workers often received massive radiation doses, and many developed malignancies, sometimes decades after the exposure had ceased. Not until the 1920s were the first governmental limitations on radiation exposures formulated.

30.2 | HALF-LIFE

Consider a large group of students at a dull lecture. If they all toss coins, saying "heads I stay, tails I leave," about half will remain after one toss. Roughly half of these will remain after the next toss, and so on. We cannot predict in any way when a specific student will depart, and the process is said to be *random*. Because about half the students leave after each toss, the time between tosses is called the *half-life* of the class.

A nuclear decay is a similar random process and is characterized by a half-life T, the time required for half the nuclei present to decay. If at time $t = 0$, there are N_0 nuclei, then one half-life later at $t = T$, an average of $N_0/2$ will remain. At $t = 2T$, when two half-lives have elapsed, half of these, or $N_0/4$, nuclei will be left; at $t = 3T$, $N_0/8$ will be left, and so on. Depending on the nuclide, the half-life may vary from a small fraction of a second to billions of years.

When the elapsed time is not an exact integer multiple of the half-life, we can find the number of nuclei remaining as follows. The change ΔN in the number of nuclei N present occurring in a short time Δt is proportional to N and to Δt, so

$$ \Delta N = -\lambda N \, \Delta t $$

The minus sign is needed because N is decreasing and ΔN is negative; the proportionality constant λ is called the *decay constant*. Dividing by Δt and taking the limit as Δt approaches zero, we find

$$ \frac{dN}{dt} = -\lambda N \tag{30.1} $$

We must solve Eq. 30.1 for the case where the initial number of nuclei at time $t = 0$ is a given value, N_0. The correct solution is $N = N_0 e^{-\lambda t}$, or

$$\frac{N}{N_0} = e^{-\lambda t} \tag{30.2}$$

At $t = 0$, this exponential decay formula reduces to $N = N_0$ as required; it is also a solution of Eq. 30.1, as can be verified by differentiation.

The decay constant λ is related to the half-life T. Suppose one half-life has elapsed, so $N/N_0 = \frac{1}{2}$. Substituting $t = T$ in Eq. 30.2, we have $e^{-\lambda T} = \frac{1}{2}$, or

$$e^{\lambda T} = 2$$

Taking the base e logarithm (the natural logarithm) of this equation, we find $\lambda T = \ln 2 = 0.693$, or

$$\lambda = \frac{\ln 2}{T} = \frac{0.693}{T} \tag{30.3}$$

We see that a short half-life implies a large decay constant.

The exponential decay formula is plotted versus time in Fig. 30.2. When $t = T$, $N/N_0 = \frac{1}{2}$, in accordance with our discussion of the half-life; when $t = 2T$, $N/N_0 = \frac{1}{4}$; and so forth. Values of N/N_0 for any time can be read from the graph or calculated using an electronic calculator or tabulated values of e^{-x}, as in the next example.

Example 30.1

Iodine 131 is used in the treatment of thyroid disorders. Its half-life is 8.1 days. If a patient ingests a small quantity of ^{131}I and none is excreted from the body, what fraction N/N_0 remains after 8.1 days, 16.2 days, 60 days?

Since 8.1 days is the half-life, the fraction remaining at this time is $\frac{1}{2}$. Similarly, 16.2 days is 2 T, so $(\frac{1}{2})(\frac{1}{2}) = \frac{1}{4}$ remains. Sixty days is not an exact integer multiple of the half-life, so to find the fraction remaining we use the exponential decay formula:

$$\frac{N}{N_0} = e^{-\lambda t} = e^{-0.693\, t/T}$$
$$= e^{-0.693(60\text{ d})/(8.1\text{ d})}$$
$$= e^{-5.13} = 0.0059$$

Thus only 0.59 percent of the radioactive iodine remains after 60 days.

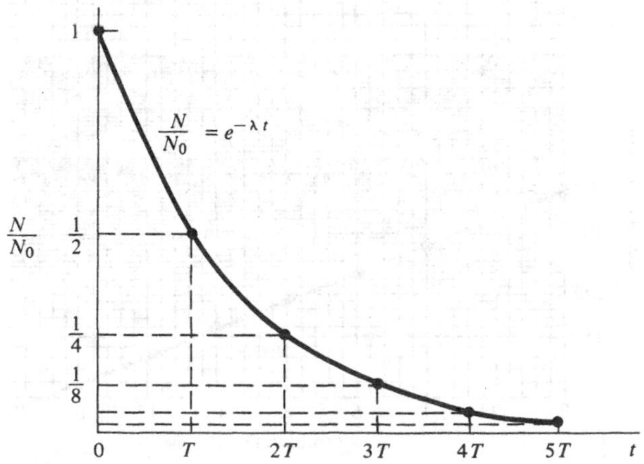

Figure 30.2. The fraction of radioactive nuclei N/N_0 remaining after time t. N_0 nuclei are present at $t = 0$, and T is the half-life.

The assumption made in the above example that no ^{131}I is lost from the body by biological processes is not quite correct; ^{131}I is excreted steadily but slowly with a biological half-life of 180 days. Thus if nonradioactive iodine were ingested, only $\frac{1}{2}$ would remain in the body after 180 days, $\frac{1}{4}$ after 360 days, and so on. The effective half-life T_{eff} is obtained by combining the biological half-life T_b and the radioactive or physical half-life T_p according to the formula

$$\frac{1}{T_{eff}} = \frac{1}{T_b} + \frac{1}{T_p} \tag{30.4}$$

Some representative half-lives are given in Table 30.1.

TABLE 30.1

Half-lives of some radionuclides used in medicine and biology

Nuclide	Organ Where Concentrated	Half-Life (days) Physical	Biological
$^{3}_{1}$H	Total body	4.6×10^3	19
$^{14}_{6}$C	Fat	2.09×10^6	35
	Bone	2.09×10^6	180
$^{24}_{11}$Na	Total body	0.62	29
$^{32}_{15}$P	Bone	14.3	1,200
$^{35}_{16}$S	Skin	87.1	22
$^{36}_{17}$Cl	Total body	1.6×10^8	29
$^{42}_{19}$K	Muscle	0.52	43
$^{45}_{20}$Ca	Bone	152	18,000
$^{59}_{26}$Fe	Blood	46.3	65
$^{64}_{29}$Cu	Liver	0.54	39
$^{131}_{51}$I	Thyroid	8.1	180

Example 30.2

^{59}Fe is administered to a patient to diagnose blood anomalies. Find its effective half-life.

Using Table 30.1, $T_b = 65$ days and $T_p = 46.3$ days. Thus

$$\frac{1}{T_{\text{eff}}} = \frac{1}{T_b} + \frac{1}{T_p} = \frac{1}{65\text{ d}} + \frac{1}{46.3\text{ d}}$$
$$= 0.037\text{ d}^{-1}$$
$$T_{\text{eff}} = 27\text{ days}$$

Note that the effective half-life is shorter than either the biological or physical half-life. This happens because both processes are depleting the supply of the radionuclide.

For many applications, it is convenient to plot ln N versus t because the resulting graph is a straight line. This result follo from taking the natural logarithm (see Appendix B.10) of

$$\frac{N}{N_0} = e^{-\lambda t}$$

to obtain

$$\ln N = \ln N_0 - \lambda t$$

This equation is of the form $\ln N = a + bt$, so ln N and t are linearly related and have a straight-line graph. If values of N versus t are plotted on semilog paper, a graph of ln N versus t is obtained directly.

This kind of graph is useful when we wish to determine the half-life of a radioactive sample. We can measure its activity with one of several detectors described in the next chapter. From Eq. 30.1, *the number of decays observed per second, the count rate $\Delta N/\Delta t$, is proportional to the number N of radioactive nuclei present and will diminish at the same rate*. Consequently, we can deduce the half-life from observations of the count rate by noting when the count rate drops to about half its initial value. However, a better value is obtained by plotting the data on semilog paper and drawing a straight line through the points. This procedure is more accurate since it uses all the observations, not just two data points. It is illustrated by the following example.

TABLE 30.2

t(min)	Count Rate (s^{-1})	t(min)	Count Rate (s^{-1})
0	400	8	194
2	336	10	162
4	280	12	131
6	230	14	110

Example 30.3

The measured count rate for a radioactive sample is given in Table 30.2. The initial count rate is 400 per second, the rate after 2 minutes is 336 per second, and so on. What is the half-life of the sample?

Inspecting the table, we can immediately estimate the half-life by noting that the count rate dropped to 200 per second, or half the initial rate of 400 per second sometime between t = 6 minutes and t = 8 minutes. Hence T is between 6 and 8 minutes. To find a more exact value, we plot the data in the table on semilog paper as in Fig. 30.3. The straight line drawn through the data points crosses 200 counts per second at 7.6 minutes, so this is the half-life.

It is worth noting that the half-life is determined without using any information about the absolute number of nuclei present. Also, one does not need to know what fraction of the radiation is observed by the detector as long as it is a constant fraction.

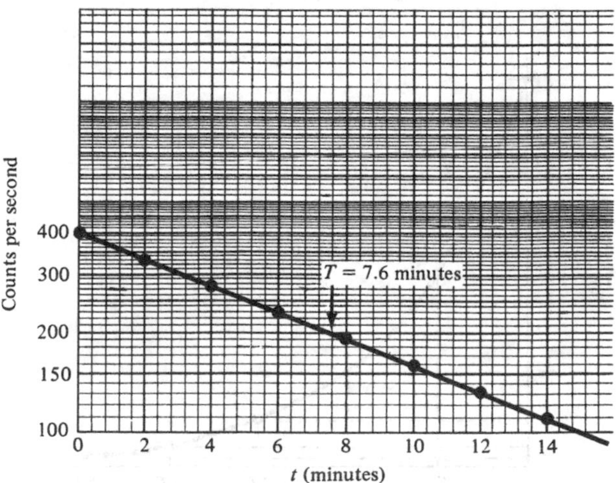

Figure 30.3. Data of Table 30.2 plotted on semilogarithmic paper.

30.3 | DATING IN ARCHAEOLOGY AND GEOLOGY

The ratio of the original and present-day quantities of a radionuclide in an object indicates the time elapsed since that object was created or formed. Whereas the present-day concentration of a radionuclide may be measured directly, the original amount of the radionuclide must be determined indirectly.

Carbon-14 Dating

Radiocarbon dating of seeds, wooden artifacts, human and animal remains, and other objects containing plant or animal materials provides a reliable way of dating events occurring within the past 60,000 to 70,000 years. Developed by Willard Libby in the 1940s, this technique has had a tremendous impact on archaeology and related fields.

Carbon-14, which has a half-life of 5730 years, is always present in the environment because of the effects of cosmic-ray particles arriving in the atmosphere from outer space. These energetic particles interact with the atomic nuclei of the upper atmosphere to produce neutrons (n) that subsequently collide with nitrogen nuclei to produce ^{14}C and protons (p) in the reaction

$$n + {}^{14}_{7}N \rightarrow {}^{14}_{6}C + p$$

The radiocarbon mixes thoroughly with the ordinary carbon in the environment and is ingested by all living organisms. Once an organism dies, the input of radioacarbon stops, and the ratio of radiocarbon to ordinary carbon decreases steadily as the ^{14}C decays. Thus the quantity of ^{14}C remaining indicates the date of death.

Although this basic concept is simple, the actual application of radiocarbon dating is complex. One reason for this is that the ^{14}C is a minute fraction of the total carbon, only about one part in 10^{12}. Consequently, the radioactivity produced by the ^{14}C as it beta decays to ^{14}N is very small compared to the total background radiation from sources normally present in the environment. To reduce this background, it is necessary to perform a careful chemical separation of the carbon and to use elaborate shielding arrangements during the counting. A second complication arises from uncertainties about the levels of radiocarbon in antiquity. The plausible assumption that radiocarbon levels have remained constant leads to predicted radioactivities that are close to the measured values for objects of known age (Fig. 30.4). However, studies made on tree rings have shown that minor variations have occurred in the ^{14}C level. These studies make use of the fact that only the outer portion of a tree is living material, so the ring formed in any one year records the radiocarbon level at that time. Using older trees that have long since fallen but whose lifetimes overlapped appropriately, tree ring chronologies have been constructed extending back some 8000 years. These data permit small corrections to be made in doing accurate work.

The fraction of ^{14}C in the atmosphere decreased by about 3 percent over the past century because of the additional carbon dioxide produced by the large-scale burning of fossil fuels that no longer contain ^{14}C. Hydrogen bomb testing, which began in 1954, reversed the trend, doubling the radiocarbon level

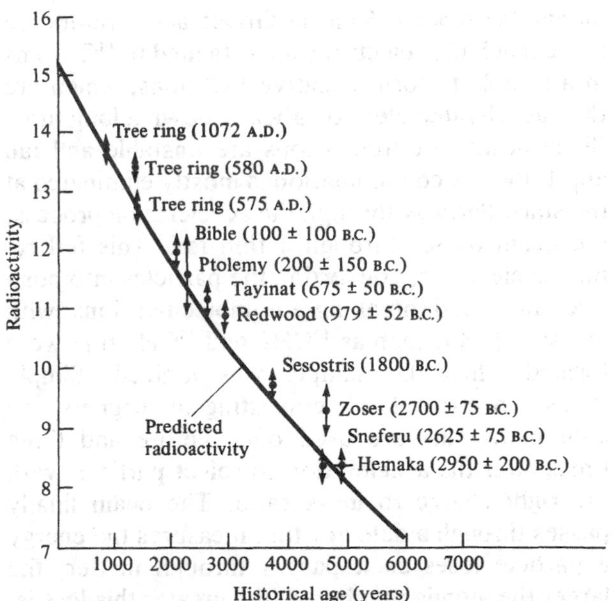

Figure 30.4. Predicted and observed radioactivities of samples of known age, assuming radiocarbon levels were constant in past centuries. "Bible" refers to Dead Sea scrolls. "Tayinat" to wood from the floor of a Syrian palace, and the other names refer to wooden objects from Egyptian tombs. (Adapted from W. F. Libby. *Radiocarbon Dating*, 2nd ed., University of Chicago Press, Chicago, 1955.)

by 1963. For example, whiskies made after 1954 can be dated accurately by their radiocarbon levels.

Direct Detection with Accelerators | An accelerator-based technique involving the direct detection of radionuclide atoms has recently opened the doors to a wide range of new dating applications. It was first applied to radiocarbon dating, but the method is being extended to other cosmic-ray-produced radionuclides.

For each decay per minute occurring in a sample containing ^{14}C, there are actually 4×10^9 such atoms present. If these could be detected directly, without waiting for them to decay, the sensitivity would be much greater. Attempts to do this with mass spectrometers, which measure the charge-to-mass ratio with magnetic fields (Chapter Nineteen), failed because the tiny quantities of ^{14}C were masked by ^{14}N, which has nearly the same mass and is always present in large amounts because it is the main constituent of the atmosphere.

Although some direct detection work is done with cyclotrons (Chapter Nineteen), most of the experiments use tandem Van de Graaff accelerators. In these machines, electrons are attached to ^{14}C atoms in a sample to form negative $^{14}C^-$ ions, which are then accelerated electrostatically down a long tube. Since negative nitrogen ions are unstable and fall apart, the ^{14}N contamination is mostly eliminated at the start. Partway through the acceleration process, the beam passes through a thin foil. This foil removes electrons, converting the particles into positive ions, and breaking up molecular ions with masses of 14 u such as $^{12}CH_2^-$ and $^{13}CH^-$ that were formed when the sample was ionized. Simple "mass spectrometers" consisting of magnets and collimating slits are used once before and three times after the acceleration to select particles with the right charge to mass ratio. The beam finally passes through a detector that measures the energy a particle loses as it passes through matter; the larger the atomic number Z, the greater this loss is. The result is a very clean separation of the ^{14}C nuclei from all others (Fig. 30.5). Several accelerators intended solely for this kind of research are under construction and should routinely give ages up to 60,000 years with just a few milligrams of material.

Minute amounts of other cosmic-ray-produced radionuclides are present in the environment and are candidates for similar dating studies. Beryllium-10 has a half-life of 1.5×10^6 years and accumulates in ocean sediments; it can be used to date sedimentary rocks. Since one decay per minute corresponds to 10^{12} atoms of ^{10}Be, direct detection offers a vast improvement over radioactive decay detection. Studies of the circulation of deep ocean layers and of underground water reservoirs have been done with ^{14}C and ^{36}Cl (half-life 30,000 years); other promising radionuclides for these applications with shorter half-lives are ^{32}Si (650 years) and ^{39}Ar (269 years).

Geochronology | Most of the radionuclides used for dating rocks have half-lives comparable to geological times (Table 30.3). The oldest rocks on the surface of the earth are 3.3 billion years old, while the earth itself is estimated to be about 4.5 billion years old.

The techniques used in geochronology depend on the particular kind of rock or mineral under study. For example, ordinary lead of nonradioactive origin is a mixture of ^{204}Pb, ^{206}Pb, ^{207}Pb, and ^{208}Pb. From Table 30.3, we see that the radioactive decays of the uranium isotopes and thorium produce all of these isotopes except ^{204}Pb. If the lead in a sample does not contain any ^{204}Pb, this indicates that the lead present was produced by radioactive decay, and the sample can be used for dating. According to the table, ^{238}U decays into ^{206}Pb with a half-life of 4.49 billion years. Suppose a sample with no ^{204}Pb contains equal numbers of ^{238}U and ^{206}Pb nuclei. Then exactly one half-life, or 4.49 billion years, must have elapsed since the specimen was formed. The ^{232}Th to ^{208}Pb ratio can be employed in the same

TABLE 30.3

Radionuclides used in geochronology

Natural Radionuclide	Stable Nuclide Produced	Half-Life (Billion Years)
^{238}U	^{206}Pb	4.49
^{235}U	^{207}Pb	0.71
^{232}Th	^{208}Pb	14.1
^{87}Rb	^{87}Sr	50
^{40}K	^{40}A	1.3

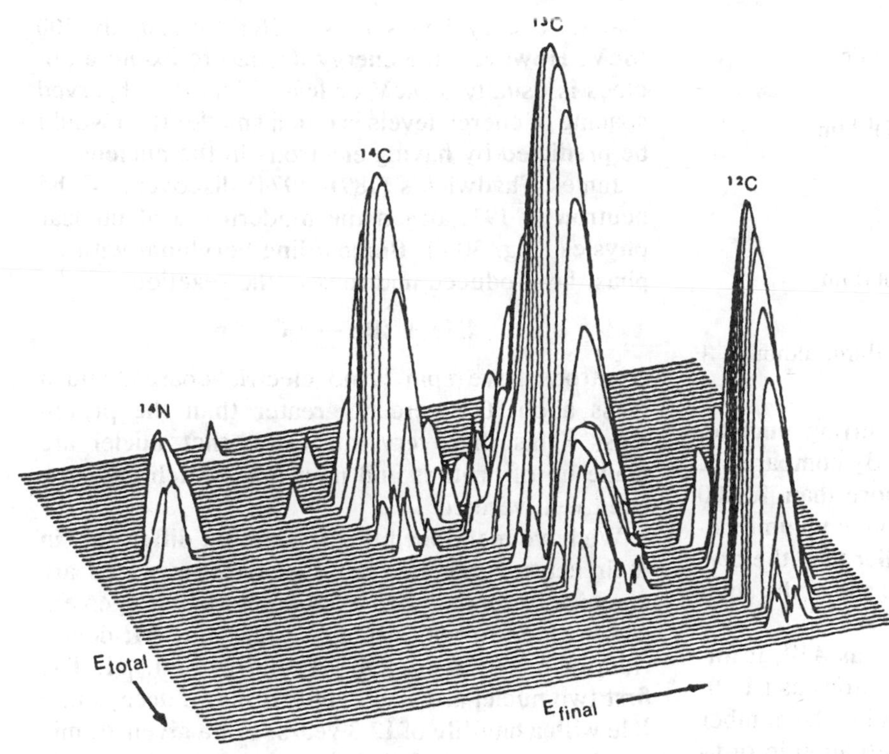

Figure 30.5. A display of the particles passing through the Van de Graaff accelerator system for direct detection of ^{14}C nuclei. E_{total} is the energy of the particles as they emerge from the last magnet. The spread in E_{final} reflects the increasing energy loss with Z as particles pass through matter. The small ^{14}N peak arises from $^{14}NH^-$ molecules. (From C. L. Bennett et al., *American Scientist*, vol. LXVII. 1979, p. 456.)

way. Alternatively, the $^{206}Pb/^{207}Pb$ ratio can be used, since ^{235}U and ^{238}U decay at different rates. The $^{87}Rb/^{87}Sr$ and $^{40}K/^{40}Ar$ ratios are also sometimes employed.

30.4 | NUCLEAR SIZES

Beginning in 1907, Rutherford conducted a series of experiments in which he bombarded various atoms with alpha particles. As we saw in Chapter Twenty-seven, he found that an atom contains a small positive nucleus with a radius of less than 10^{-14} m, which is about 10^{-4} times the radius of an atom. From further experiments with alpha particles, nucleons, and other projectiles, considerable information has emerged about the spatial distribution of matter in the nucleus.

Roughly speaking, a nucleus containing A nucleons is a uniformly dense sphere of radius (Fig. 30.6)

$$\begin{aligned} R &= 1.4A^{1/3} \times 10^{-15} \text{ m} \\ &= 1.4A^{1/3} \text{ fm} \end{aligned} \tag{30.5}$$

(1 fm = 1 femtometre = 10^{-15} m). The radius is proportional to the cube root of the mass number and therefore increases very slowly as is seen in this next example.

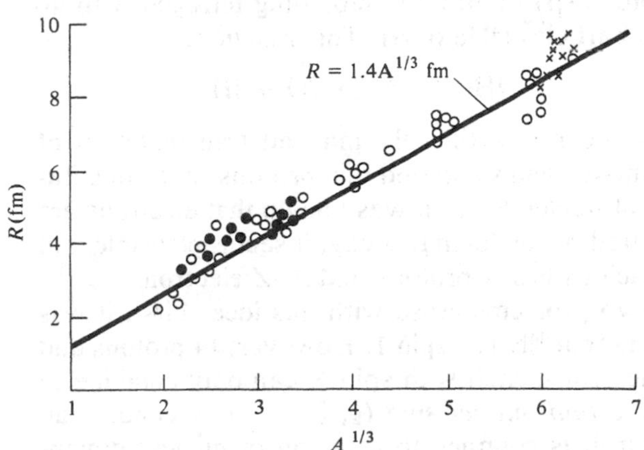

Figure 30.6. Experimental values of the radius of the nucleus versus $A^{1/3}$.

Example 30.4

Find the nuclear radii of ^{27}Al and ^{64}Zn.

The radius of ^{27}Al is

$$R = 1.4\, A^{1/3}\text{ fm} = 1.4(27)^{1/3}\text{ fm}$$
$$= (1.4)(3)\text{ fm}$$
$$= 4.2\text{ fm}$$

Similarly, the radius of ^{64}Zn is

$$R = 1.4(64)^{1/3}\text{ fm} = (1.4)(4)\text{ fm}$$
$$= 5.6\text{ fm}$$

The radius has increased only by a third, although A has more than doubled.

^{238}U is the largest naturally occurring nuclide, with a radius of about 9×10^{-15} m. By comparison, atomic radii are about 10^{-10} m, more than 10,000 times larger. The fraction of the atomic volume occupied by the nucleus is much smaller than the corresponding fraction occupied by the sun in the solar system.

Because the nuclear radius varies as $A^{1/3}$, it follows that the nuclear volume $\frac{4}{3}\pi R^3$ varies as $(A^{1/3})^3$ or A. Thus the volume is proportional to the number of nucleons. This is similar to the situation in ordinary bulk matter; if we double the number of water molecules, we double the volume of water present.

30.5 | PROTONS AND NEUTRONS

In 1921, Rutherford produced hydrogen nuclei or protons (^1_1H or p) by bombarding nitrogen with alpha particles (^4_2He or α). This reaction,

$$^4_2\text{He} + {}^{14}_7\text{N} \rightarrow {}^{17}_8\text{O} + {}^1_1\text{H}$$

was the first artificially induced transmutation of elements, and suggested that protons are a constituent of nuclei. Since it was known that electrons are emitted by nuclei in β decay, it seems plausible that a nucleus has A protons and $A-Z$ electrons.

Two problems arose with this idea. First, it was found that $^{14}_7N$ has spin 1. However, 14 protons and 7 electrons, each with spin $\frac{1}{2}$, can only combine to give a *half integer* spin ($\frac{1}{2}$, $\frac{3}{2}$, . . .). Second, if an electron is confined to a region of nuclear dimensions, the uncertainty principle can be used to show that its energy levels must differ by roughly 100 MeV. However, the energy needed to excite a nucleus is usually 5 MeV or less. Thus the observed spacing of energy levels is much smaller than would be predicted by having electrons in the nucleus.

James Chadwick's (1891–1974) discovery of the neutron in 1932 began the modern era of nuclear physics (Fig. 30.7). Bombarding beryllium with alphas, he produced neutrons in the reaction

$$^4_2\text{He} + {}^9_4\text{Be} \rightarrow {}^{12}_6\text{C} + \text{n}$$

Neutrons have spin $\frac{1}{2}$, no electric charge, and a mass about 0.1 percent greater than the proton mass. This discovery suggested that nuclei are made up of protons and neutrons, which has now been well verified.

We have mentioned that nuclei that differ only in their neutron number are called isotopes and are chemically very similar. For example, hydrogen exists in three forms: ordinary hydrogen, ^1_1H; deuterium or heavy hydrogen, ^2_1H; and tritium, ^3_1H. The first two nuclei are stable, but tritium β decays into ^3_2He with a half-life of 12.3 years. For a given atomic number, it is found that from zero to nine stable isotopes may exist, and several naturally occurring or artificially produced radioactive isotopes may also exist. Each chemical element as it is found on the earth normally contains a mixture of its stable isotopes with nearly constant relative abundances.

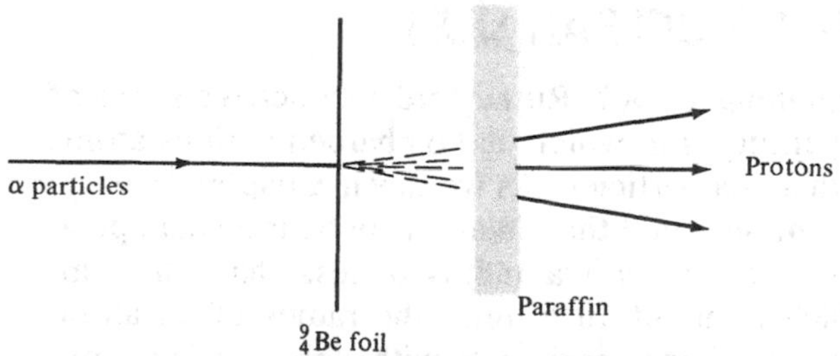

Figure 30.7. Chadwick's discovery of the neutron. A beam of α particles struck a thin beryllium foil, producing uncharged particles (shown dashed). When a block of paraffin (a hydrocarbon containing many hydrogen nuclei or protons) was placed in front of the foil, protons were ejected. From measurements of the energy and momentum of the protons, he found the velocity and mass of the neutral particles striking them. The mass of these neutral particles turned out to be slightly greater than that of the proton.

TABLE 30.4

Atomic masses in u. Except for e, p, and n, the masses given are for the neutral atom and include the electronic masses. The atomic mass unit is defined so that the mass of a ^{12}C atom is exactly 12 u.

Nuclide	Mass, m (u)	$Zm_p + Nm_n + Zm_e$ (u)	Difference (u)	Binding Energy per Nucleon (MeV)
e	5.48×10^{-4}			
p	1.00728			
n	1.00866			
$^1_1$H	1.00783			
$^2_1$H	2.0141	2.0165	0.0024	1.1
$^4_2$He	4.0026	4.0330	0.0304	7.1
$^{12}_6$C	12.0000	12.0989	0.0989	7.7
$^{13}_6$C	13.0034	13.1078	0.1044	7.5
$^{56}_{26}$Fe	55.9349	56.4633	0.5284	8.8
$^{238}_{92}$U	238.0508	239.9845	1.9337	7.6

30.6 | NUCLEAR MASSES AND BINDING ENERGIES

The masses of many nuclei have been accurately measured (Table 30.4) using mass spectrometers (Chapter Nineteen). A little arithmetic shows that the mass of a nucleus is less than the sum of the masses of its constituents. For example, $6m_p + 6m_n + 6m_e = 12.0989$ u, while a $^{12}_6$C atom has a mass of only 12.000 u. This *mass defect* tends to increase with the mass number A.

The significance of the mass defect is made clear by Einstein's principle of the equivalence of mass and energy (Chapter Twenty-five). For an object at rest,

$$E = mc^2 \tag{30.6}$$

In words, a mass m of matter can be converted into an amount of energy E; the quantity c is the speed of light in a vacuum. The mass of a ^{12}C nucleus is less than that of its constituent nucleons because it is a bound system. One must supply energy equal to the *nuclear binding energy* to pull apart the protons and neutrons. According to Einstein's principle, this energy is equal to the mass defect times c^2.

To relate the mass defect and binding energy, we first calculate the energy associated with a mass of 1 u = 1.66×10^{-27} kg:

$$\begin{aligned} E &= (1 \text{ u})(c^2) \\ &= (1.66 \times 10^{-27} \text{ kg})(3 \times 10^8 \text{ m s}^{-1})^2 \\ &= 1.49 \times 10^{-10} \text{ J} \end{aligned}$$

Since 1 eV = 1.602×10^{-19} J, this energy can be expressed in electron volts as 931×10^6 eV = 931 MeV. Effectively,

$$1 \text{ u} = 931 \text{ MeV} \tag{30.7}$$

The ^{12}C mass defect of 0.0989 u corresponds to a total binding energy of 0.0989×931 MeV = 92.1 MeV. Dividing by the mass number $A = 12$, the *binding energy per nucleon* in ^{12}C is 7.7 MeV.

The binding energy per nucleon for the stable nuclei is plotted versus A in Fig. 30.8. It is about 8 MeV per nucleon except for the lightest nuclei. There is a broad maximum in the region of medium-size nuclei, with a peak of 8.8 MeV per nucleon at ^{56}Fe. Above $A \simeq 100$, the curve gradually declines, reaching 7.6 MeV per nucleon for uranium.

The initial increase and later decrease in the binding energy per nucleon can readily be explained. The strong *nuclear forces* among the nucleons that hold the nucleus together have a very short range; these forces are zero at distances greater than a few femtometres. Accordingly, a nucleon is attracted

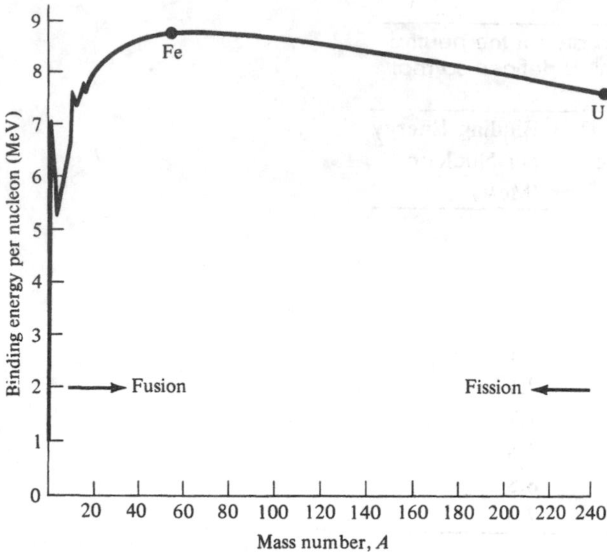

Figure 30.8. Binding energy per nucleon versus A for stable nuclei.

only to its closest neighboring nucleons. A nucleon near the surface has fewer neighbors than one in the interior of the nucleus and is less tightly bound. This *surface energy* effect implies that the binding energy per nucleon will rise as the nucleus increases in size and proportionately fewer nucleons are near the surface. This explains the initial rise in the binding energy per nucleon for the light elements.

To explain the decrease in the binding energy per nucleon for large A, we must take into account the fact that the electrical repulsions among the protons are proportional to the number of proton pairs, or to Z^2. The potential energy of two protons at a separation r is ke^2/r, so the total electric potential energy due to the proton charges varies as Z^2e^2/R, where R is the nuclear radius. This energy grows rapidly as the number of protons increases. In the region near ^{56}Fe, the changes in the surface and electrical energies are roughly equal in magnitude but opposite in sign. Above $A \simeq 100$, the electrical repulsion gradually outstrips the surface effects, leading to the observed gradual decline in the binding energy per nucleon.

The fact that intermediate-size nuclei have the greatest binding energy per nucleon has some important consequences. If a heavy nucleus splits or *fissions* into two intermediate-size nuclei, the binding energy increases by close to 1 MeV per nucleon. The extra energy is released as kinetic energy of the fission products or as γ rays. Similarly, if two very light nuclei such as ^{2}H or ^{3}H combine, this *fusion* releases several MeV. Fission and fusion will be discussed in the supplementary topics at the end of this chapter, but we can already see that both processes release large amounts of energy.

30.7 | NUCLEAR FORCES

We now discuss the strong nuclear forces that hold the nucleus together. We have seen that the nuclear volume is proportional to A; as more nucleons are added, the nucleus grows in size but its density remains constant. We also saw that the binding energy of each additional nucleon is roughly constant at 8 MeV. These properties both occur because the *nuclear forces are short ranged* and are zero at distances greater than a few femtometres. Note that if the forces were long ranged as is true for electric and gravitational forces, then every pair of nucleons would interact, leading to an increase in the density and mean binding energy with A. These do not happen because each nucleon interacts with only a few neighbors.

Complex nuclei are tightly bound despite the large electrical repulsions among the pairs of closely spaced protons. This indicates that nuclear forces are much stronger than electric forces. They must also be attractive, at least at the average internucleon separation in nuclei. However, it is found by studying collisions between nucleons that the force actually becomes repulsive at very short internucleon distances (Fig. 30.9). It has also been established that, except for the electrical repulsion between two protons, the proton–proton, proton–neutron, and neutron–neutron forces are the same; *nuclear forces do not depend on the electric charge*.

Since the nuclear radius is $1.4A^{1/3}$ fm, the average internucleon separation turns out to be over a femtometre. At this distance the nucleon-nucleon potential energy is of moderate size and slowly varying. Consequently, the nucleus should not be viewed as a rigid arrangement of nucleons. To a surprisingly good approximation, each nucleon in

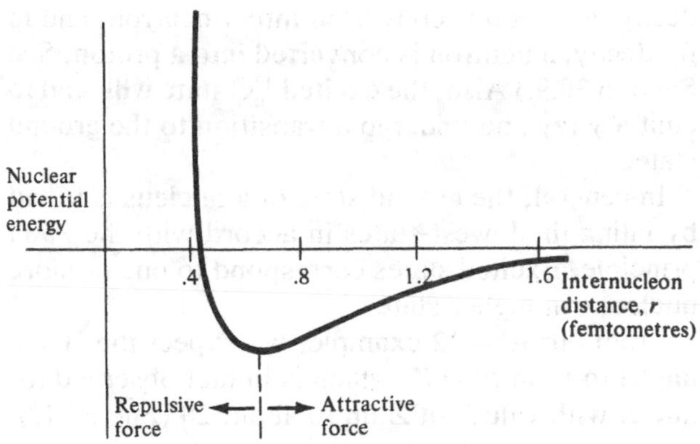

Figure 30.9. A rough graph of the nucleon–nucleon potential energy. The force becomes large and repulsive for $r \lesssim 0.4$ fm.

the interior of the nucleus can be viewed as moving fairly freely with a constant potential energy arising from the effects of its neighbors. This idea is the basis for the nuclear shell model, which is discussed in the next section.

30.8 | NUCLEAR ENERGY LEVELS AND NUCLEAR STABILITY

A nucleus, like an atom, has a ground state and excited states. These states can be studied by bombarding nuclei with energetic protons, alpha particles, and other projectiles from particle accelerators. Many of the observed energy levels and other properties of nuclei can be predicted using the *nuclear shell model.* Initially developed in 1949 by Maria Mayer (1906–1972) and J. H. Jensen, this model resembles the atomic shell model.

Successive nuclear energy levels are usually separated by a few million electron volts or less, and the average binding energy of a nucleon in a nucleus is 8 MeV. Accordingly, most nuclear physics research has been done with projectile kinetic energies from a few million electron volts up to about 1000 MeV. At the higher energies, the de Broglie wavelength is shorter, so the nucleus can be probed on a finer scale.

Nuclear processes studied with accelerators are of several types. A projectile may scatter *elastically*, so that the nucleus remains in its original state. It can scatter *inelastically*, exciting the nucleus and giving up part of its kinetic energy. In collisions, there may also be a *transfer* of one or more nucleons to or from the target, increasing or decreasing its mass number. Measurements of the kinetic energies and relative directions of the incident and outgoing particles can be used to study the processes that occur. Experiments of these and other types have yielded a great deal of information about the energies and wave functions of nuclear states.

Nuclear Shell Model | In the preceding section, we noted that when a nucleon is deep inside the nucleus, its potential energy is approximately constant. However, a nucleon near the edge of a nucleus experiences a net inward attraction, since there are fewer neighboring nucleons on the side away from the nuclear center. Thus near the edge of a nucleus, the potential energy increases as r increases (Fig. 30.10). Such a potential energy curve is referred to as a *potential well*.

The possible energy levels for a nucleon are obtained by solving the basic equation of quantum mechanics, the Schrödinger equation. As we saw in discussing similar wells in Section 28.7, its solutions are wave functions that are oscillatory inside the potential well and exponentially decreasing outside. If we ignore the small exponential tails, the solutions for stable states correspond to fitting waves into the potential well. The longest waves that fit into the potential well have nodes at $r = 0$ and at the

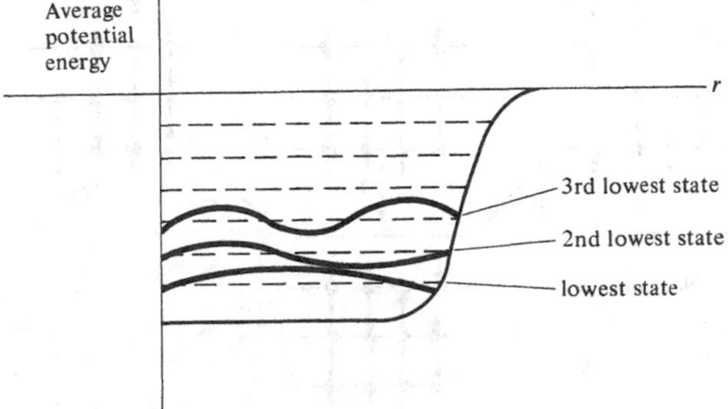

Figure 30.10. Average potential energy of a nucleon in the nucleus versus the distance r from the nuclear center. The possible nucleon energy levels are shown along with the wave functions for the lowest three states.

edge. Now using the de Broglie relation $p = h/\lambda$, the kinetic energy of a nucleon $\frac{1}{2}mv^2 = p^2/2m$ can be rewritten as $h^2/2m\lambda^2$. Thus the longest wavelength wave functions represent the lowest energy states. The longest waves fitting into the well are shown in Fig. 30.10. When angular momentum is taken into account, the level scheme is more complex, but it is found that, as in atoms, the levels fall into closely spaced groups or shells.

Nucleons are spin $\frac{1}{2}$ particles, so the Pauli principle applies, and two identical nucleons cannot occupy a single quantum state. Any energy level may contain at most two protons, one with spin up and one with spin down, the two possible orientations for a spin $\frac{1}{2}$ particle. Since there can also be spin-up and spin-down neutrons in an energy level, it can have at most four nucleons.

The lowest energy configuration for a given number of protons and neutrons is obtained by filling the lowest level with two protons and two neutrons, then the next level, and so on, until all the nucleons are used. A schematic diagram for three $A = 12$ nuclei is given in Fig. 30.11. Because of the Pauli principle, the lowest energy ground state occurs for the $Z = N$ case, $^{12}_{6}C$. Neglecting the small differences due to the electrical repulsions among the protons and to the neutron–proton mass difference, the *excited state* of $^{12}_{6}C$ and the *ground states* of $^{12}_{5}B$ and $^{12}_{7}N$ have the same energy. The latter two nuclei will tend to β decay into the ground state of $^{12}_{6}C$, since that is a state of lower total energy. (In β^+ decay, a proton is converted into a neutron; and in β^- decay, a neutron is converted into a proton. See Section 30.9.) Also, the excited $^{12}_{6}C$ state will tend to emit a γ ray and undergo a transition to the ground state.

In general, the ground state of a nucleus is found by filling the lowest states in accord with the Pauli principle. Excited states correspond to one or more nucleons in higher states.

From our $A = 12$ example, we expect the stable nuclei to have $N \simeq Z$, which is in fact observed for nuclei with values of Z up to about 20 (Fig. 30.12).

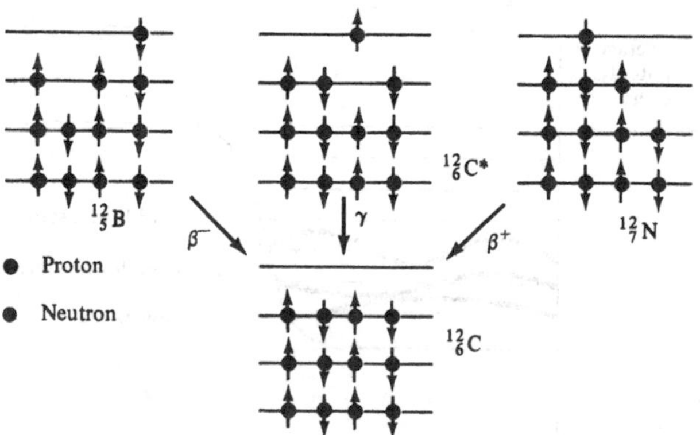

Figure 30.11. Lowest states of three $A = 12$ nuclei and the first excited state of $^{12}_{6}C$. The $^{12}_{5}B$, $^{12}_{6}C^*$, and $^{12}_{7}N$ nuclei have nearly the same energy. All three decay to the ground state of $^{12}_{6}C$ as described in the text. (*Indicates excited state.)

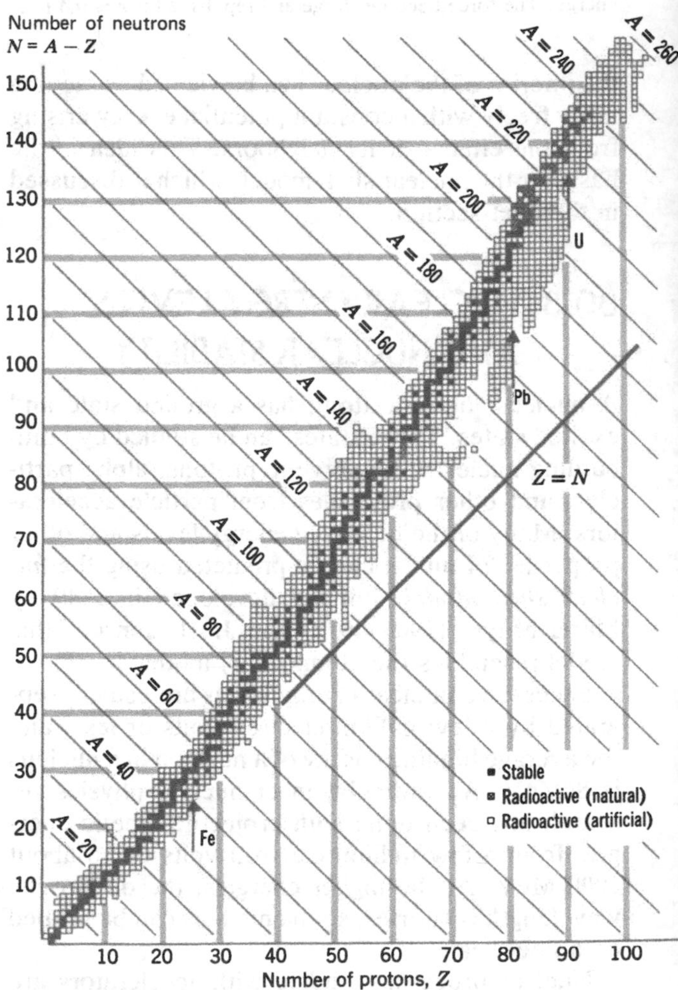

Figure 30.12. The known stable and radioactive nuclei. Nuclei beyond those shown in most cases rapidly break up into fragments.

This equality maximizes the number of nucleons in the lowest nuclear energy states. If N differs substantially from Z, the nucleus tends to β decay. As Z increases beyond 20, the known stable and radioactive nuclei tend to have increasing neutron excesses. A neutron excess occurs because the energy that would be released by converting a neutron to a proton (β^- decay) and placing it in a lower nuclear energy level is less than the increase that would occur in the electric potential energy as a result of the increase in Z. Since the electrical energy is proportional to Z^2e^2/R, it becomes increasingly important as Z becomes large. Consequently, in the heaviest nuclei there are about 50 percent more neutrons than protons.

We saw in Chapter Twenty-eight that atoms with a completely filled outermost shell are inert gases and are very stable. Similarly, nuclei with closed outer shells are more tightly bound than neighboring nuclei and are called *magic nuclei*. Nuclei with both proton and neutron shells closed are especially stable.

30.9 | RADIOACTIVE DECAYS

At the beginning of this chapter, we noted that many nuclei undergo alpha, beta, or gamma decay. In these decays, as in all nuclear processes, the following quantities must be conserved:

1 Energy (including mass energy)
2 Momentum (both linear and angular)
3 Electric charge
4 Number of nucleons

Note in particular that the total charge and number of nucleons does not change. We now discuss these decays individually.

γ Decay | Gamma rays are electromagnetic quanta or photons emitted when a nucleus undergoes a transition from a higher to a lower energy level. They are completely equivalent to the light quanta and X rays emitted by excited atoms, but their energies are usually much greater. The half-lives for γ decay are usually very short, typically 10^{-13} s. However, in a few special cases, the half-lives may be as long as several years.

Closely related to γ decay is *internal conversion*. Here an excited nucleus gives up its excess energy to an electron in one of the inner atomic shells, ejecting it from the atom. No gamma ray is emitted. Some radionuclides used in nuclear medicine decay in this fashion.

β Decay | In β decay, an electron (e^-) or in a few cases a positron (e^+) is emitted by a nucleus. In 1928, P. A. M. Dirac proposed a theory of the electron that included the effects of special relativity and accurately predicted some fine details of the hydrogen atom spectrum not given by Schrödinger's equation. Dirac's equations also had solutions corresponding to positrons, *positively* charged particles with the same mass and spin as the electron. This *antiparticle* was first discovered in the products of cosmic-ray reactions in 1932. Today, antiprotons, antineutrons, and many other antiparticles have been seen, and all particles are believed to have antiparticles. Particle–antiparticle pairs can annihilate in a burst of gamma rays, converting all their mass to energy.

Some typical β decays are listed in Table 30.5. The half-lives are very long compared to γ decay half-lives, varying from seconds to many years. This indicates that the force responsible for the β decay is weak compared to the electromagnetic forces that are responsible for γ decay.

A striking feature of β decay is that the emitted betas are variable in kinetic energy (Fig. 30.13). For example, in ${}^3_1H \to {}^3_2He + e^-$, the mass energy of the ${}^3_1H$ nucleus exceeds that of a ${}^3_2He$ nucleus plus an electron by 0.0186 MeV, the maximum electron kinetic energy. However, sometimes the electron en-

TABLE 30.5
Typical beta decays

Decay	Half-Life	Maximum Kinetic Energy (MeV)
${}^3_1H \to {}^3_2He + e^-$	12.3 years	0.186
${}^{14}_6C \to {}^{14}_7N + e^-$	5730 years	0.156
$n \to p + e^-$	11.0 minutes	0.782
${}^{34}_{15}P \to {}^{34}_{16}S + e^-$	12.4 seconds	5.1
${}^{22}_{11}Na \to {}^{22}_{10}Ne + e^+$	2.60 years	0.546
${}^{13}_7N \to {}^{13}_6C + e^+$	9.99 minutes	1.19

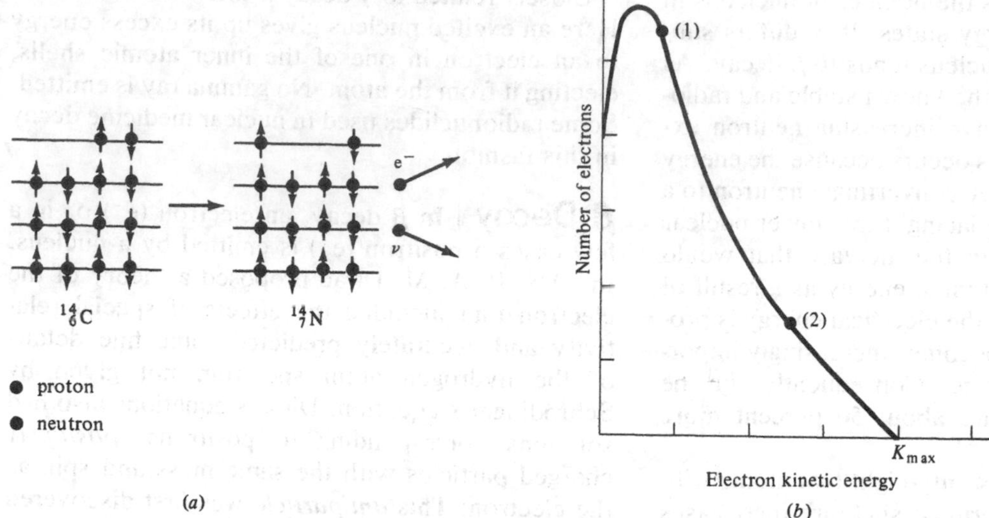

Figure 30.13. (*a*) The ground state of $^{14}_{6}C$ decays into $^{14}_{7}N$ as a neutron is converted into a proton. An electron and a neutrino are emitted, and they share the energy given up as the nucleus goes into a lower energy state. (*b*) The number of electrons emitted versus kinetic energy for a large number of decays. Point (1) represents a decay in which the electron has less energy than that represented by point (2). The total energy available is constant so the neutrino in decay (1) has correspondingly more energy than in decay (2).

ergy is less than 0.0186 MeV. What has happened to the missing energy?

Enrico Fermi (1901–1954) supplied the answer in 1933. He proposed that when a nucleus β decays, it creates not only an electron but also a *neutrino* (ν): a massless, uncharged, spin $\frac{1}{2}$ particle. Then the $^{3}_{1}H$ decay is more completely written as

$$^{3}_{1}H \rightarrow {}^{3}_{2}He + e^- + \nu$$

Since the decaying nucleus emits two particles, they can share the decay energy in various combinations.*

The $\beta^{\pm}$ decay processes *in nuclei* result in the following conversions:

$$n \rightarrow p + e^- + \nu \qquad (\beta^- \text{ decay}) \qquad (30.8)$$

$$p \rightarrow n + e^+ + \nu \qquad (\beta^+ \text{ decay}) \qquad (30.9)$$

Both processes tend to occur whenever they produce a nucleus with more binding energy. The β^+ decay can never happen for a free proton, since the proton mass is less than that of the neutron. However, the free neutron does β^- decay with a half-life of 11 minutes.

Another closely related way in which protons are changed into neutrons in some nuclei is *electron capture*. Here an atomic electron and a proton interact via

$$p + e^- \rightarrow n + \nu \qquad \text{(electron capture)} \qquad (30.10)$$

Two additional aspects of beta decay are worth noting. First, the forces responsible for the beta decay processes, including electron capture, are very weak compared both to the strong nuclear forces and to the electromagnetic forces among the nucleons. Accordingly, these β decay forces are referred to as *weak interactions*; they are the weakest of the fundamental forces in nature, except the gravitational forces. Second, as we mentioned earlier, β decay is responsible for the fact that in stable nuclei the proton and neutron levels are filled to about the same maximum energy. When electric forces are

* According to the modern form of Fermi's theory, an *antineutrino* ($\bar{\nu}$) is emitted in a β^- decay, and a *neutrino* (ν) in a β^+ decay. We will ignore the differences between the neutrino and antineutrino.

ENRICO FERMI
(1901–1954)

Physics has become sufficiently specialized so that most physicists concentrate their efforts either on experimental work or theoretical calculations. Enrico Fermi was a notable exception to this rule. He made many important contributions of both types to physics.

Born in Rome, Fermi received his doctorate in 1922 from the University of Pisa for his research on X rays. As a student he taught himself the new quantum theories that were being developed elsewhere but were not yet known in Italy. His efforts to explain these concepts to his fellow students and his professors helped to establish modern physics in Italy and also developed his abilities as a teacher.

After a brief period of further study in Germany and Holland, Fermi returned to Italy in 1924 and became a professor at the University of Rome in 1926. In that year, he developed the theory of an ideal gas whose atoms obey the exclusion principle introduced in 1925 by Pauli. He found striking departures from the behavior predicted using classical physics, particularly at low temperatures and high densities. An example of such a *Fermi gas* is provided by the conduction electrons in a metal, which are nearly free and obey the exclusion principle. Fermi showed that many previously unexplained features of the electrical and thermal properties of metals were correctly predicted by this theory.

Turning his attention to nuclear physics, Fermi proposed a theory of beta decay in 1933, which in a slightly modified form remains our present-day basis for understanding this process. In 1934, he began a series of experiments in which he systematically bombarded a variety of targets with neutrons. Soon he discovered that placing water or a hydrocarbon between the source and the target increased the rate of production of artificial radioactivity. Fermi realized that the light atoms had absorbed some of the kinetic energy of the neutrons in a series of collisions and that the resulting slow neutrons were more readily captured by the target nuclei.

When a neutron is captured by a nucleus, its mass number A is increased by 1; if a subsequent β^- decay occurs, the atomic number Z also is increased by 1. Fermi and his collaborators therefore tried, in 1934, to go beyond the last known element by bombarding uranium ($Z = 92$) with neutrons. They thought mistakenly that they succeeded in producing the first transuranic element ($Z = 93$) when in fact they had caused uranium nuclei to fission. This was not realized until further work was done by Hahn and Strassman in Germany in 1939 that conclusively identified the fission products. Shortly before this discovery, Fermi and his family had fled the Fascist regime in Italy by traveling to Stockholm, where he accepted the Nobel prize, and then proceeded to New York. It was there that he learned of the work done in Germany.

Fermi immediately realized the importance of the discovery of fission and the possibility of a nuclear chain reaction. Working initially at Columbia University and later at the University of Chicago, he supervised the construction of the first nuclear reactor. When it was first operated on December 2, 1942, a now famous but then secret telegram announced that "the Italian navigator has entered the new world."

Fermi worked on the development of the atomic bomb during World War II, and then returned to academic life at the University of Chicago. In 1949, he joined several other leading scientists in opposing the development of the hydrogen bomb on ethical grounds. His postwar research centered on neutron studies, the properties of newly discovered particles called pi mesons, and the origin of cosmic rays. Shortly after his death in 1954, the artificially produced element with atomic number 100 was named fermium in his honor.

---

taken into account, this implies $N \simeq Z$ for light nuclei and $N \simeq 1.5\,Z$ for the heaviest nuclei.

α Decay | In α decay, an alpha particle ($^4_2$He nucleus) is emitted, leaving behind a residual nucleus that has lost two protons and two neutrons. For a given nuclide, the α particle energy is always the same. This is because when a nucleus at rest emits one particle, energy and momentum conservation determine its energy. Alpha decay is usually observed in the heavier unstable nuclei. All known nuclei above $Z = 83$ are unstable; those that do not β decay have been observed to α decay with half-lives ranging from about 10^{-3} s to 10^{10} years.

In β decay, the weak interaction determines the decay time. We might expect α decay to be much faster, since it is due to the strong nuclear interaction. However, typical decay processes are much slower than β decays. Why then does α decay take so long if it is energetically favorable for the strong nuclear forces to eject four nucleons in the form of an α particle?

The explanation of why this process is so slow involves the quantum mechanical phenomenon called tunneling, discussed in Section 28.7. In classical physics, a ball bouncing elastically inside an open container can bounce over the walls and escape from the container only if its energy is great enough. Specifically, its energy must exceed the gravitational potential energy at the walls (Fig. 30.14). Quantum mechanically, if a particle reaches a region of high potential energy without sufficient energy to pass over this *barrier*, it has a small but nonzero probability of passing through the barrier (Fig. 30.15). This means that each time a particle strikes the barrier, it has a small probability of getting past the barrier. After enough impacts, the odds are that it will have passed through the barrier and escaped. It is then said to have *tunneled* through the region where, according to classical physics, it lacks sufficient energy to ever penetrate.

To see how this argument applies to α decay, we must consider the origin of the energy barrier for alpha particles. We do this by examining the poten-

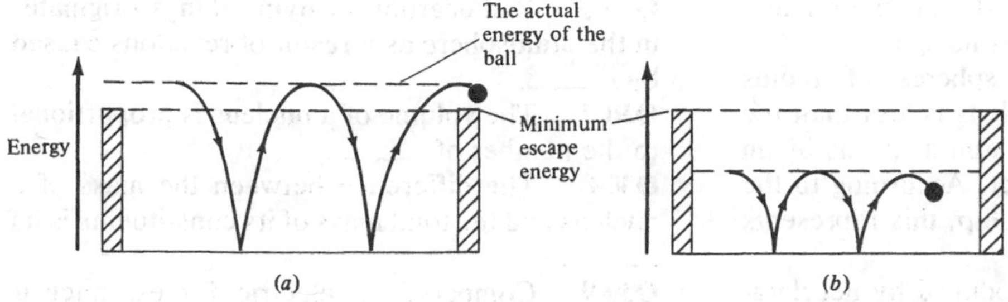

Figure 30.14. (*a*) The ball has enough energy and bounces high enough so that it can escape from the container. (*b*) The ball is trapped according to classical mechanics.

tial energy curve for an alpha particle and a nucleus (Fig. 30.16). If we bring an alpha particle up to a nucleus, we must do work to overcome the electrical repulsion. Thus the potential energy increases as the particles approach and r decreases. At the nuclear surface, the alpha particle begins to feel the attractive nuclear force, which corresponds to a negative potential energy. The sum of the two potential energies has a positive maximum value somewhere near the nuclear surface. This peak corresponds to the barrier in the preceding discussion.

Inside the nucleus, occasionally an alpha particle forms briefly when two protons and two neutrons meet. When the Schrödinger equation for the alpha particle inside this potential well is solved, it is found that the lowest alpha particle state has an energy greater than zero but below the barrier peak. Thus the alpha particle can reach a lower energy state by leaving the nucleus, and if it strikes the barrier often enough, it will eventually escape. This will take a long time if the barrier is very high or wide. Detailed calculations based on this theory are in excellent agreement with the measured α decay half-lives and energies.

SUMMARY

A nucleus is specified by its mass number A, atomic or proton number Z, and neutron number $N = A - Z$. After one half-life has elapsed, about half the unstable, or radioactive, nuclei present will remain. The decay constant is related to the half-life by $\lambda = 0.693/T$. After a time t, the fraction of radioactive nuclei remaining is

$$\frac{N}{N_0} = e^{-\lambda t}$$

The effective half-life of a radionuclide in an organism is determined by the physical and biological half-lives. If the original amount of a radioactive

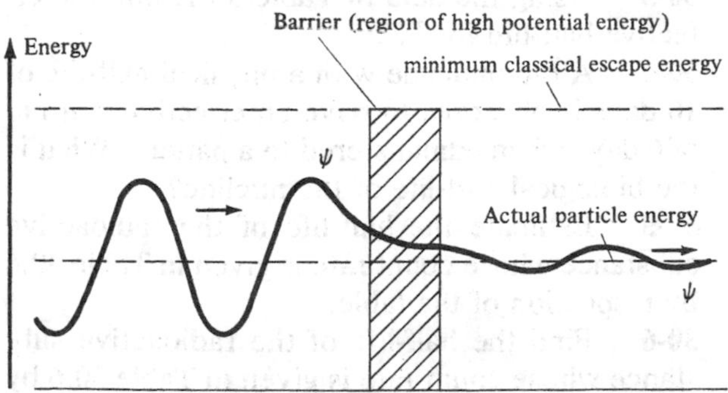

Figure 30.15. The quantum mechanical wave associated with a particle approaching a barrier, a region where the potential energy exceeds the energy of the particle. The wave function ψ is small but nonzero to the right of the barrier, so the probability $|\psi|^2$ that the particle may be found beyond the barrier is greater than zero. This probability diminishes rapidly as the barrier becomes taller or wider.

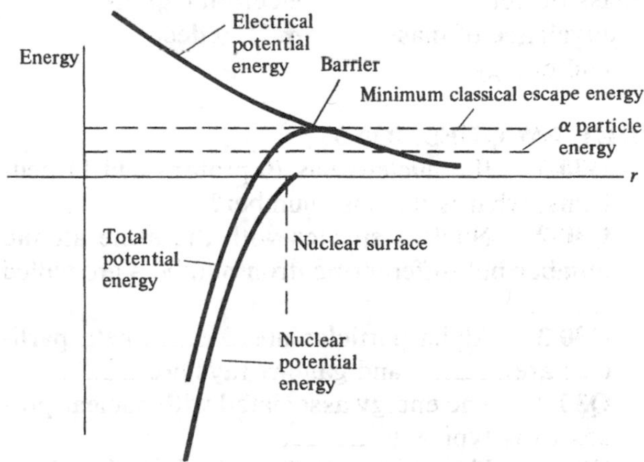

Figure 30.16. The potential energy of an α particle and a nucleus.

substance in a sample is known, the amount remaining at the present time indicates its age.

Nuclei are approximately spheres of radius $1.4A^{1/3}$ fm. The mass of a nucleus is less than the mass of its constituent protons and neutrons by an amount equal to its mass defect. According to the Einstein mass–energy relationship, this represents the nuclear binding energy.

Using beams of particles produced by accelerators, the energy levels and structure of nuclei can be studied in detail. The nuclear shell model, which is similar to the atomic shell model, accounts for much of these data. Light nuclei either have $Z = N$ or are unstable against β decay; because of electric forces, very heavy stable nuclei have $N \simeq 1.5Z$. Excited states of nuclei tend to γ decay to their ground states. All nuclei above $Z = 83$ are unstable; those that do not β decay are all alpha particle emitters, and some will also spontaneously fission.

Checklist

Define or explain:

nuclide	binding energy
mass number	fission
atomic number	fusion
neutron number	nuclear force
isotope	nuclear shell model
alpha, beta, gamma radiation	potential well
	magic nuclei
half-life	internal conversion
nuclear radius	positron
mass defect	electron capture
equivalence of mass and energy	α, β, γ decay

REVIEW QUESTIONS

Q30-1 If a nucleus has 10 protons and 11 neutrons, what is its mass number?

Q30-2 Nuclear species with the same atomic number but different neutron numbers are called ______.

Q30-3 Alpha particles are ______, beta particles are ______, and gamma rays are ______.

Q30-4 The energy associated with nuclear processes is typically ______.

Q30-5 If there are 1000 nuclei initially, about ______ remain after one half-life, and about ______ after two half-lives.

Q30-6 Radiocarbon in living things originates in the atmosphere as a result of reactions caused by ______.

Q30-7 The volume of a nucleus is proportional to the number of ______.

Q30-8 The difference between the mass of a nucleus and the total mass of its constituents is its ______.

Q30-9 Compared to electric forces, nuclear forces have a ______ magnitude and a ______ range.

Q30-10 Nucleons, like electrons, obey the Pauli principle, which prevent two protons or two neutrons from occupying the ______.

Q30-11 A positron has the same ______ as the electron, but the opposite ______.

Q30-12 An alpha particle can escape from a nucleus by ______, even though it lacks the minimum energy required according to classical physics.

EXERCISES

Section 30.2 | Half-Life

30-1 After 24 hours the radioactivity of a nuclide is one-eighth times its original level. What is its half-life?

30-2 How many half-lives are required for the activity of a radionuclide to decrease by a factor of 64?

30-3 Using the data in Table 30.1, find the effective half-life for ^{35}S.

30-4 A radionuclide with a physical half-life of 10 days is observed to have an effective half-life of 6 days when administered to a patient. What is the biological half-life of the nuclide?

30-5 Estimate the half-life of the radioactive substance whose count rate is given in Table 30.6 by inspection of the table.

30-6 Find the half-life of the radioactive substance whose count rate is given in Table 30.6 by plotting the data on semilog paper.

30-7 A radionuclide has a half-life of 10 hours. What percentage of a sample remains after 24 hours?

30-8 A patient is administered ^{35}S in a diagnostic study. (a) Using the data in Table 30.1, find the

TABLE 30.6

Time (days)	Count Rate (counts per minute)
0	455
1	402
2	356
3	315
4	278
5	246
6	218
7	193
8	171
9	151
10	133

effective half-life. (b) What percentage of this radionuclide remains in the body after 22 days?

30-9 A patient is administered ^{131}I. How long will it take for the observed radioactivity in her body to decrease to one-fourth its original magnitude?

30-10 The half-life of ^{131}I is 8.1 days. What fraction of a sample will decay in 1 minute?

30-11 A radionuclide has a half-life of 3 days. After 6 days, find (a) the fraction of the original sample that still remains; (b) the ratio of the count rate to the original count rate.

Section 30.3 | Dating in Archaeology and Geology

30-12 What fraction of the radiocarbon nuclei in a sample decay each day?

30-13 A wooden bowl has one-fourth the ^{14}C activity observed in contemporary wooden objects. Estimate its age. (Assume ^{14}C levels in the atmosphere have remained the same.)

30-14 A rock contains three ^{207}Pb nuclei for each ^{235}U nucleus. How old is the rock, assuming all the ^{207}Pb is from the uranium decay?

30-15 Why is there no radiocarbon in fossil fuels?

30-16 Carbon from living organisms contains ^{14}C at about the level of 1 part in 10^{12}. What is the corresponding number for a sample 40,000 years old?

30-17 Water taken from a deep well is found to have one-fourth the amount of ^{32}Si found in surface water. How long docs it take for the source of the water to be replenished? (The half-life of ^{32}Si is 650 years.)

Section 30.4 | Nuclear Sizes

30-18 (a) Find the nuclear radii for ^{4}He, ^{27}Al, ^{64}Cu, ^{125}I and ^{216}Po. (b) Draw a rough graph of the nuclear radius versus A.

30-19 What fraction of the volume of a helium atom is occupied by its nucleus, assuming an atomic radius of 10^{-10} m?

30-20 (a) Calculate the density of an oxygen nucleus in kilograms per cubic metre. (b) Find the ratio of this density to the density of water, 10^3 kg m^{-3}.

30-21 Neutron stars are believed to have a mass similar to that of the sun, but a density comparable to that of atomic nuclei. Estimate the radius of such a star.

30-22 Find the volume of 1 mole of carbon nuclei (1 mole = 6.02×10^{23} particles).

Section 30.5 | Protons and Neutrons

30-23 How many neutrons are there in $^{14}_{6}C$, $^{36}_{17}Cl$, $^{64}_{29}Cu$, and $^{208}_{82}Pb$?

30-24 (a) Of the nuclides $^{1}_{1}H$, $^{2}_{1}H$, $^{3}_{1}H$, $^{3}_{2}He$, and $^{4}_{2}He$, which have the same neutron numbers? (b) Which nuclides have similar chemical properties?

Section 30.6 | Nuclear Masses and Binding Energies

30-25 The atomic mass of $^{208}_{82}Pb$ is 207.9766 u. What is its average binding energy per nucleon?

30-26 The atomic mass of $^{207}_{82}Pb$ is 206.9759 u, and the atomic mass of $^{208}_{82}Pb$ is 207.9766 u. (a) Find the difference of their mass defects. (b) What is the minimum energy needed to remove a neutron from $^{208}_{82}Pb$?

30-27 A nucleus has a mass defect of 1.5 u. (a) What is its binding energy in MeV? (b) If the mass number is 200, find the binding energy per nucleon.

Section 30.7 | Nuclear Forces

30-28 (a) Find the magnitude of the electric force between two protons separated by a typical nuclear distance, 10^{-15} m. (b) A typical atomic dimension is about 10^{-10} m. How large is the electric force between a proton and an electron with this separation? (c) Calculate the ratio of the two forces in parts (a) and (b).

30-29 When a proton moves toward a nucleus, its initial kinetic energy must be great enough to overcome the electrical repulsion if it is to experience nuclear forces. For the largest naturally occurring nucleus, $^{238}_{92}U$, this minimum energy is about 15 MeV. Find the corresponding energies for incident (a) alpha particles (^4_2H nuclei); (b) neutrons.

30-30 All nuclei above $Z = 83$ are radioactive; if they do not β decay, they eventually α decay or fission. What is the origin of this instability?

30-31 (a) What is the electric potential energy in MeV of two protons separated by 1 fm? (b) How much does this contribute to the mass defect if the two protons are in a nucleus?

Section 30.8 | Nuclear Energy Levels and Nuclear Stability

30-32 What is X in the following reactions? (d = ^2_1H) (a) p + $^{12}_6C \rightarrow$ d + X. (b) ^3_2He + $^3_2He \rightarrow$ ^4_2He + p + X. (c) p + $^{14}_7N \rightarrow$ $^{12}_7N$ + X.

30-33 What is X in the following reactions? (d = ^2_1H, α = ^4_2He) (a) d + d $\rightarrow X$ + p; (b) $^6_3Li + X \rightarrow \alpha + \alpha$; (c) X + $^{16}_8O \rightarrow$ $^{19}_9F$ + p.

30-34 In Fig. 30.11, the ground states of $^{12}_5B$ and $^{12}_7N$ and an excited state of $^{12}_6C$ have the same states filled. (a) Which of these nuclides has the greatest binding energy if electric forces are taken into account? (b) What effect does the neutron–proton mass difference have on the relative energies? Explain.

Section 30.9 | Radioactive Decays

30-35 An excited nucleus decays, emitting a 2-MeV gamma ray. Find (a) the frequency of the gamma-ray photon emitted; (b) the wavelength of the photon.

30-36 Complete the following decay processes by adding the missing decay particles (α, γ, or $\beta^{\pm} + \nu$): (a) $^{11}_6C \rightarrow$ $^{11}_5B$ + ? (b) $^{32}_{15}P \rightarrow$ $^{32}_{16}S$ + ? (c) $^{12}_6C^*$ $\rightarrow$ $^{12}_6C$ + ? (d) $^{240}_{94}Pu \rightarrow$ $^{236}_{92}U$ + ?

30-37 A nucleus with 54 protons and 54 neutrons is formed in a collision of two heavy nuclei. (a) Would you expect this nucleus to be stable? Explain. (b) Which is more likely to occur, electron or positron emission? Why?

30-38 Protons incident on a target are scattered and lose energy. When they lose only a few MeV, gamma rays are emitted by the target. However, if the lost energy is 12 MeV or greater, neutrons are found to be emitted, but not gamma rays. Explain what is happening.

PROBLEMS

30-39 A piece of wood contains 1 ^{14}C atom for every 10^{12} atoms of ^{12}C. (a) If there is 1 kg of carbon in the wood, how many ^{14}C atoms does it contain? (b) How many of these will decay in 1 hour?

30-40 An alpha particle in a heavy nucleus has a velocity of 10^7 m s^{-1}. The nuclear diameter is 1.6×10^{-14} m. (a) How long does it take the alpha particle to cross the nucleus? (b) If the α decay lifetime of the nucleus is 10^9 years, find the average number of times the alpha particle crosses the nucleus before it escapes. (c) What is the escape probability each time it strikes the barrier?

30-41 How many half-lives have elapsed if the activity of a radionuclide has diminished to 1 percent of its initial value?

30-42 An excavated wooden beam has 20 percent of the ^{14}C found in atmospheric carbon. How old is it? (Assume the atmospheric ^{14}C levels have remained the same.)

30-43 ^{90}Sr has a half-life of 28 years. How many years must this material be stored before its activity drops to $1/e$ times its original value?

30-44 A radioactive material contains two radionuclides, one with a half-life of 1 day and the other with a half-life of 8 days. Initially the radioactivity of the short-lived nuclide is $2^7 = 128$ times greater than that of the long-lived nuclide. When will their activities be equal?

***30-45** In the preceding problem, suppose one cannot distinguish the radiation from the two radionuclides and plots the *total* count rate on semilog paper. (a) What is the shape of the graph for the first few days? (b) Why does the shape change when the two activities are nearly equal?

(c) What is the shape of the graph when the short-lived nuclide has largely disappeared? Is there any difference from the initial curve?

30-46 The μ meson (muon) is a short-lived particle that, like the electron, has electrical interactions with nuclei but does not experience the strong nuclear force. The muon mass is 207 times that of an electron. Both $\mu^{\pm}$ have been observed and the magnitude of their charge is equal to that of the electron. (a) What is the radius of the first Bohr orbit of a negative muon in orbit around a $^{238}_{92}U$ nucleus? (b) Find the ratio of that radius to the nuclear radius. (Actually the radii and energy levels of muonic atoms are changed somewhat from the Bohr values because a significant fraction of the wave function is inside the nucleus for low-lying atomic states. These changes provide information about the distribution of protons in the nucleus.)

30-47 The energy of the sun is derived from reactions that convert four protons into an alpha particle (^4_2He) with the emission of two positrons and two massless neutrinos. (a) How much energy in MeV is released in this process? (See Table 30.4 for the required atomic masses.) (b) When H_2 and O_2 gases combine to produce H_2O, 6.2 eV is released for each molecule formed. What mass of hydrogen would have to be burned to equal the energy released by the nuclear fusion of 1 kg of hydrogen into alpha?

30-48 How can reactions in which a projectile transfers nucleons to a target nucleus be used to find nuclear energy levels?

30-49 ^9_4Be is stable, but ^9_5B is unstable, as is ^9_3Li. (a) Draw nuclear energy-level diagrams similar to those of Fig. 30.11 for these three $A = 9$ nuclides. (b) Suggest why two of these three nuclides are unstable. (c) What decay process would be expected for ^9_3Li?

30-50 After a heavy nucleus α decays, a β^- decay often follows, but never a β^+ decay. What is the reason for this?

30-51 We can estimate the electrostatic energy converted into kinetic energy in the fission of ^{235}U with a simple model. (a) What is the radius of a ^{235}U nucleus? (b) Suppose half the 92 protons in the nucleus are, on the average, separated from the other half by a nuclear diameter. What is the potential energy in MeV corresponding to the electrical repulsion of the two groups of protons?

30-52 Just as the mass of a nucleus is less than that of its constituents because of the binding energy, the mass of an atom is less than the mass of its nucleus and its electrons. Proportionately the effect is much smaller. (a) What is the ratio of the binding energy of a typical nucleus with a binding energy of 8 MeV per nucleon to its total mass energy? (b) A hydrogen atom consists of a proton and an electron bound by electric forces with an energy of 13.6 eV. Find the corresponding ratio.

30-53 When a particle and its antiparticle meet, they can annihilate into a burst of gamma rays. However, other final products may result if they are consistent with the conservation laws. For example, pi mesons are much less massive than nucleons, and can be produced when a proton and antiproton collide. If an antiproton and proton with negligible kinetic energy annihilate forming two positive pi mesons and two negative pi mesons, how much kinetic energy is shared by the four pi mesons? (The rest energy of a positive or negative pi meson is 139.6 MeV.)

***30-54** ^3_1H is unstable; it β decays into ^3_2He, even though the electric potential energy of the two protons is present in ^3_2He and not in ^3_1H. The extra mass of the neutron that is converted into a proton is sufficiently large to make ^3_2He more stable. Use this information to find a minimum average separation of the protons in ^3_2He.

30-55 If two processes deplete the number of nuclei in a sample, then the change in the number present in a short time Δt is $\Delta N = -\lambda_1 N\,\Delta t - \lambda_2 N\,\Delta t$. Use this relationship to derive the effective half-life formula, Eq. 30.4.

ANSWERS TO REVIEW QUESTIONS

Q30-1, 21; **Q30-2**, isotopes; **Q30-3**, helium nuclei, electrons, energetic photons; **Q30-4**, several MeV; **Q30-5**, 500, 250; **Q30-6**, cosmic rays; **Q30-7**, nucleons; **Q30-8**, mass defect; **Q30-9**, greater, shorter; **Q30-10**, same quantum state; **Q30-11**, mass, charge; **Q30-12**, tunneling through a barrier.

SUPPLEMENTARY TOPICS

30.10 | NUCLEAR FISSION

We saw earlier that the binding energy per nucleon decreases gradually as A increases beyond 100. Consequently, about 1 MeV per nucleon is released if a large nucleus such as uranium splits into two smaller fragments. Such fission processes are the energy sources in nuclear power reactors and in the fission weapons first developed during World War II.

A simple model of the $^{235}_{92}U$ nucleus shows how fission occurs. The model pictures a $^{235}_{92}U$ nucleus as composed of two parts, each containing a large number of protons and neutrons. The potential energy curve for the two parts is much like that of an alpha particle and a nucleus. If the two positively charged parts are initially far apart and gradually approach, their electric potential energy rises. When they become close enough so the strong attractive nuclear forces play a role, the total potential energy begins to diminish (Fig. 30.17).

The ground state of the ^{235}U nucleus turns out to have an energy considerably greater than zero, but the system is trapped in its bound state below the

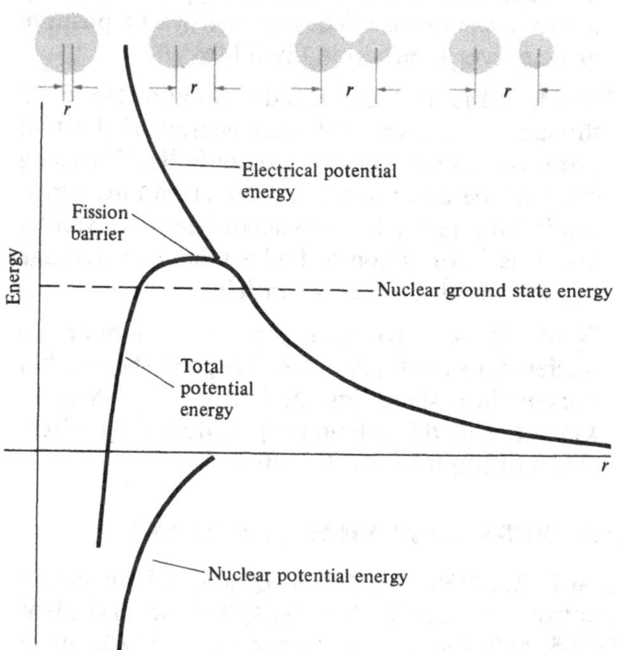

Figure 30.17. The potential energy of the uranium nucleus versus the separation r of the two parts of the nucleus. The corresponding shape of the nucleus is shown above the graph.

peak in the potential energy curve. The region that is inaccessible according to classical physics is called the *fission barrier*. As in α decay, tunneling through the barrier makes it possible for this nucleus to *spontaneously fission*. As the two parts of the nucleus separate, a large amount of electrical potential energy is converted into kinetic energy. Spontaneous fission occurs in both ^{235}U and ^{238}U, but much less frequently than α decay.

Some nuclides can also undergo *induced fission* when they are bombarded by *thermal neutrons*, very slow neutrons with kinetic energies comparable to kT (less than 1 eV). Thermal neutrons have a large de Broglie wavelength and therefore a large effective size for an interaction. Many nuclei have high probabilities (large *cross sections*) for capturing thermal neutrons that pass close by and incorporating them into their structure. When this happens, a nucleus with A nucleons is transformed into one with $A + 1$ nucleons. The average binding energy of the last nucleon in a heavy nucleus is roughly 7 MeV. Hence when the neutron is captured, the $A + 1$ particle nucleus will have an energy excess of about 7 MeV, and it will be in an excited state. If this excitation energy is sufficient to put the nucleus above the fission barrier, it will immediately fission, releasing a large amount of energy.

Precisely this happens when ^{235}U is bombarded by thermal neutrons. An excited state of ^{236}U is formed, with an energy 6.8 MeV above the ground state. Since the ^{236}U fission barrier height is also 6.8 MeV, the nucleus immediately fissions. On the other hand, ^{238}U does not fission when it captures a slow neutron, because the resulting excitation energy in the ^{239}U nucleus is 5.3 MeV, while the fission barrier is 7.1 MeV. Consequently, induced fission can occur with ^{238}U only if the incoming neutron has at least 1.8 MeV of kinetic energy. Such fast neutrons have shorter de Broglie wavelengths and smaller effective sizes and are hard to capture. The fast neutron fission cross section for ^{238}U is 1/2000 times the thermal neutron fission cross section for ^{235}U. For this reason, ^{235}U is much more useful in a fission energy source.

Natural uranium is 99.3 percent ^{238}U and only 0.7 percent ^{235}U. However, it is necessary to use nuclear fuels with a larger percentage of ^{235}U in most types of power reactors and in nuclear weapons.

Since separation of these isotopes is costly and difficult, this both retards nuclear power development and tends to stabilize some aspects of international politics.

The energy released in nuclear fission can be estimated by noting that the binding energy per nucleon is 7.6 MeV for ^{235}U and about 8.5 MeV for the two $A \simeq 100$ fission fragments (see Fig. 30.8). Consequently, the energy released is 235(8.5 MeV − 7.6 MeV) ≃ 200 MeV per nucleus. To put that in perspective, we may note that chemical reactions typically liberate about 1 eV per atom, so nuclear fission is 200 million times more powerful! If all the nuclei in one kilogram of ^{235}U fission, the energy released is equivalent to that of 20,000 tons of TNT. The World War II fission bombs released approximately this much energy.

Usually the fission fragments have proportionately too many neutrons for medium *A* nuclei, so they eject one or more *prompt neutrons* almost immediately in 10^{-13} s or less (Fig. 30.18). They then undergo a series of three or four β^- decays, each of which converts one neutron into a proton and brings the nucleus closer to stability. Accordingly, the first β^- decay proceeds in a few seconds, while the next has a half-life of minutes or hours, and the last may take days or years. It is these relatively long-lived radioactive nuclides that comprise the *radioactive wastes* produced in reactors and that must be safely stored until the radioactivity is negligible. Sometimes a *delayed neutron* is ejected after the first β^- decay. On the average, there are 2.6 prompt neutrons for each fission; about 1 percent of the fission events lead to the emission of a delayed neutron after a delay averaging some 10 s.

The neutrons released in an induced ^{235}U fission can be captured by other ^{235}U nuclei, causing them to fission in turn in a *chain reaction*. Suppose, on the average, the 2.6 neutrons from one fission induce more than one additional fission. The *fission ratio* is then greater than 1, and the reaction will grow exponentially. Before long an explosion will occur if the growth proceeds unchecked. On the other hand, if enough neutrons escape from the ^{235}U or are absorbed by other materials, the fission ratio is less than 1. The process will then not be self-sustaining and will die out after being initiated by a stray neutron. When each fission produces exactly one more fission, the fission ratio is 1 and the reaction continues at a constant rate. The ^{235}U is then said to have a *critical mass*. In a nuclear reactor, the fission ratio is controlled so that fission reactions occur at a desired rate.

30.11 | FISSION REACTORS AND EXPLOSIVES

To achieve a critical mass, explosives and most fission reactors require enriched uranium containing more than the 0.7 percent of ^{235}U found in natural uranium. In the most common reactors, enrichment to 3 percent is required, while explosives use about 90 percent enriched material. The two uranium isotopes cannot be separated chemically, since their chemical properties are almost identical. However, the average molecular kinetic energy is determined by the temperature, so molecules containing a heavier isotope move more slowly on the average. Hence physical processes, such as diffusion, that depend on the average velocity can be used to separate isotopes. The masses of the uranium isotopes are so similar that although the separation may be accomplished by diffusion, it is slow and costly. Electromagnetic separators, which are similar to mass spectrometers, are sometimes used to concentrate partially enriched uranium further.

Reactors | All the electrical power reactors in the United States and most of those in operation elsewhere employ thermal neutrons to induce fission and have several common features. They have

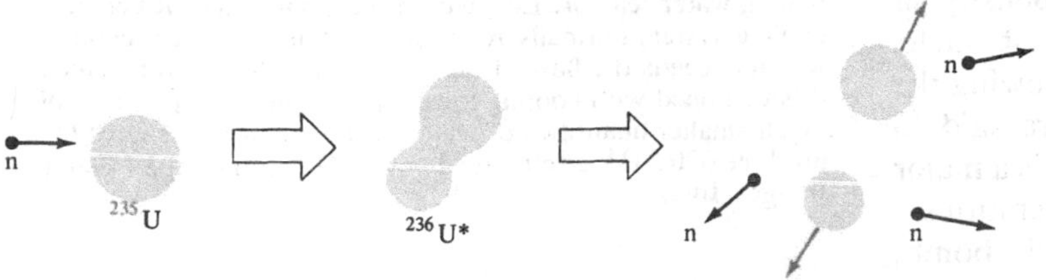

Figure 30.18. Induced fission of ^{235}U. A thermal neutron approaching a ^{235}U nucleus is captured, producing an excited ^{236}U nucleus that fissions. In this example the two fission fragments that are produced emit three prompt neutrons.

many *fuel rods*, tubes containing enriched uranium, along with a *moderator* and *control rods*. The moderator serves to slow down the neutrons. This is necessary because the neutrons are produced with an initial energy of several MeV, and the ^{235}U fission cross section is largest below 1 eV. The control rods are made of a substance such as boron, which has a large neutron capture probability, and are used to control the fission rate. As these rods are withdrawn from the reactor assembly, the chain reaction grows until the desired rate is reached. The approximately 1 percent of the neutrons that are delayed play a key role in this process. They permit the operators to gradually adjust the control rods and to make readjustments if the reaction grows too rapidly.

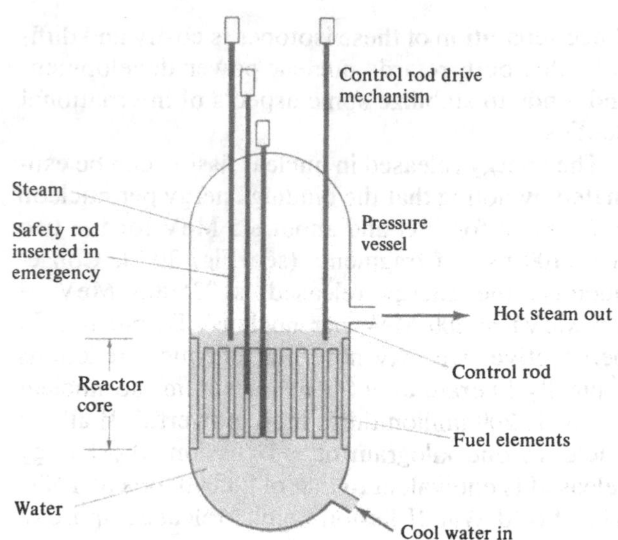

Figure 30.19. The boiling-water reactor. The water serves as the moderator and also carries off the heat energy produced. Steam heated in the reactor drives a turbine and is then condensed before returning to the reactor.

Light-Water Reactors | Most electrical power reactors in the United States, Western Europe, and Japan use ordinary light water (H_2O) as a moderator; neutrons slow down when they collide with the hydrogen nuclei. The water also serves as a coolant. Canadian reactors use *heavy water* (D_2O), in which deuterons (^2_1H) containing a proton and a neutron replace the ordinary hydrogen nuclei (protons, ^1_1H).

There are two types of light-water reactors: *boiling water* and *pressurized water*. The energy released in the fission process is converted into heat when the fast-moving fission fragments collide with other atoms in the fuel rods. In a boiling-water reactor (Figs. 30.19, 30.20), the water carries off this thermal energy in the form of steam that is then used to drive turbines and generate electricity. In a pressurized-water reactor, the pressure is kept high enough so that the water never boils. Its heat is transferred through a heat exchanger to water at a lower pressure that boils and produces the steam that drives the turbines.

Figure 30.20. The reactor at Vernon, Vermont, is a typical boiling-water reactor. Located on the Connecticut River, its cooling system normally requires 23 m³ of water per second, which exceeds the flow of the river during dry periods. Hence it is equipped with cooling towers that require evaporation of much smaller quantities of water. The reactor is designed to produce 620 MW of electrical power. (Boston Globe / Getty Images, Inc.)

Both types of light-water reactors are intrinsically stable against runaway chain reactions. Any unintended rise in temperature reduces the density of the water, thereby reducing the number of nuclei available to moderate the neutrons and slowing the reaction. Reactors with this behavior are said to have *negative temperature coefficients*. It is a major safety feature and it simplifies routine operations.

Reactors cannot explode like an atomic bomb;

only the energy equivalent to a minor chemical explosion can be released in an accident. The controversy surrounding the use of nuclear reactors centers not so much on the risk of a large-scale explosion as on the possible dispersal of radioactive material into the environment. In light-water reactors, three levels of containment are used to protect against this. The fuel is sealed in cylinders made of a high-strength alloy of zirconium. The reactor assembly is inside a massive pressure vessel. Finally, the pressure vessel and the associated piping for the heat removal system are inside a sturdy containment building designed to withstand the largest pressures that might reasonably be expected to arise in an accident.

The loss of cooling water due to a broken pipe or malfunctioning pump poses the greatest risk of a major accident. Since the water is a moderator as well as a coolant, its loss stops the chain reaction. However, just after shutdown, the fission products in the fuel elements continue to release energy at about 7 percent of the previous rate. Without cooling water, within a minute or two the temperature in the zirconium covering of the fuel rods exceeds 1600°C, and it begins to fail. Also, a chemical reaction occurs between the zirconium and the steam, which releases more heat and makes hydrogen gas. This may accumulate and explode. If cooling water is not restored to the system, before long the fuel rods melt and a radioactive pool forms on the bottom of the reactor. After some hours, the pool can melt through the bottom of the reactor and the floor below, entering the earth underneath. This "China syndrome" would presumably terminate with the material solidifying some metres into the earth.

Many active safety features protect against such a catastrophic loss of coolant. When any abnormality occurs, various systems cause the reactor to shut down automatically, stopping the chain reaction in less than 1 s. If the coolant pressure drops, high-pressure pumps inject cooling water onto the reactor core. Additional pumps are available if the pressure loss continues. Backup power systems assure electricity for the pumps.

The worst accident to date in reactors of this type occurred in March 1979 at a pressurized water reactor located at Three Mile Island in Pennsylvania. A pump failure shut off the supply of cool water to the heat exchanger. The reactor shut itself down and the backup pumps came on automatically, but their flow did not enter the heat exchanger because of a shut valve. The operators could not tell that it was shut because their view of the warning light was blocked. The reactor temperature and pressure started to rise, and a relief valve opened to relieve the pressure. However, it failed to close again, and the pressure and temperature dropped. This triggered the emergency cooling system, adding water to the core. Now the temperature stabilized, but the pressure continued to fall due to the loss of water through the stuck relief valve, and water began to boil. This forced excess water into the pressurizer, a tank used to stabilize the pressure during normal operation, so the operators cut back on the emergency cooling water. Finally, more than 2 hours after the problems started, the stuck relief valve was discovered and closed to stop the loss of water.

The reactor was finally fully shut down after several days. Its core was severely damaged, and some fuel rods had melted. A small release of radioactive gases occurred, but the containment prevented any major release of radioactive materials. Hydrogen gas formed due to the zirconium–steam reaction. The gas exploded but did not damage the containment. No injuries were received by the plant employees or by the people in the area, and the amount of radiation released was not sufficient to cause either immediate or long-term harm to anyone according to the regulatory officials.

What were the implications of this accident? According to supporters of the nuclear energy program, it showed the need for further improvements in operator training and in safety systems, but indicated that such reactors pose no significant threat to the health and safety of the general public. They continued to cite estimates of the hazards associated with every large-scale industrial activity that show that nuclear power is the safest available electric power option and much less dangerous than coal-burning power plants, automobiles, cigarette smoking, and so on. Opponents of nuclear energy pointed to the enormous emotional disturbance caused by the accident to the area residents and argued that much larger radiation releases might easily have occurred. There is no way, they reasoned, to anticipate all the possible mechanical and human failures in dealing with such complex and potentially lethal systems.

Graphite-Moderated, Water-Cooled Reactors | Several types of thermal reactors have been built or proposed that use graphite for the moderator. Reactors like those at Chernobyl, near Kiev in the Soviet Union, use light water as a coolant.

The core of this type of reactor consists of a large cylinder containing many graphite blocks. Channels in the graphite contain fuel cylinders or control rods. Water flows through these channels and removes heat, coming to a boil in the process. The graphite provides all the moderation required for the chain reaction, and the main effect of the water on the neutron flux is to absorb some of the neutrons. If the temperature of the water rises and its density decreases, or if the water is lost, this absorption diminishes and the chain reaction rate increases. Thus such a reactor has a *positive temperature coefficient*, and it is inherently less stable than the reactors discussed earlier. Also, the Chernobyl reactors had no containment structure around the core, and shutting them down required 20 s, much longer than the second required for the water-moderated reactors. Finally, they were normally operated at temperatures considered too high by many reactor experts.

Late on April 25, 1986, the operators began a test of the ability of one of the Chernobyl reactors to generate electricity under emergency conditions. Power dropped unexpectedly to very low levels, and was restored to higher levels at 1 A.M. by taking the control rods almost all the way out, in violation of regulations. At 1:03, water flow was increased as a part of the test, and it was permitted to exceed authorized rates, nearly stopping the boiling. Much of the coolant was very close to the temperature at which it would suddenly become steam. Hence small temperature fluctuations would have large effects. By 1:22, automatic controls had been turned off as part of the test, and the water flow was again reduced. Warnings from the computer about the dangerous state of the control rods and the coolant were ignored. A minute later, the operators turned off the flow of steam to the turbine. Within seconds the reactor began to heat up rapidly, the coolant density decreased, and power levels rose rapidly. Operators tried unsuccessfully to shut down the chain reaction. The water flashed to steam, and a steam explosion blew off the top and bottom plates of the reactor. The convective up-rush of air set the graphite on fire, and it continued to burn for days, carrying materials from the reactor into the atmosphere.

Clearly this accident had several causes, ranging from weak design features to procedural and operator errors. Reactor experts outside the Soviet Union were quick to point out that they had previously rejected similar reactor designs as being too unstable and that these reactors could never have been licensed in their countries. There are no comparable commercial power reactors outside the Soviet Union, although some reactors used to make plutonium for weapons bear similarities.

What were its effects? Thirty-one reactor personnel and firefighters died from radiation exposure. A large quantity of radiative material was dispersed into the atmosphere, with some of it settling nearby, some spread over much of Europe, and some sent into the upper atmosphere, where it would gradually come down over a large area. It is estimated that the radiation will cause 1000 premature cancer deaths worldwide over several decades; this will not be detectable because of the much larger normal cancer incidence. Tragic as it was, the human cost of the accident was not larger than that of many other industrial accidents, including the 1985 chemical factory accident at Bhopal, India, that killed over 2000 people and injured 200,000.

Gas-Cooled Reactors | A number of reactors have been built with graphite moderators and helium or carbon dioxide as a coolant. There are over 40 gas-cooled reactors in Great Britain and a few elsewhere in Western Europe, the United States, and Japan. They have several basic advantages over water-cooled reactors. The fuel is embedded in massive graphite blocks. The cooling gas circulates within the containment vessel and never leaves it, so the rupture of pipes outside cannot mean a loss of coolant. If the coolant is lost, the temperature rises slowly enough in the massive structure so that the operators have hours rather than seconds to react to emergencies by inserting control rods or by dumping in boron pellets to dampen the reaction.

Also, the gas is strictly a coolant, with no role in moderating the reaction, so its loss does not accelerate the generation of heat. There is no water and hence no potential hydrogen formation problem. The reactors can operate at higher temperatures, producing a greater yield of electricity per pound of uranium, and thereby reducing thermal pollution and the production of radioactive wastes.

With the increasing concern for limiting the possible effects of an accident, the U.S. Department of Energy has supported the development of a new type of helium-cooled reactor, the Modular High Temperature Gas-Cooled Reactor. This reactor shuts itself down without human help or powered systems because the ratio of uranium, thorium, and graphite is chosen so that there is a large negative temperature coefficient. The proposed power output has been limited to 150 MW, an eighth of the typical current reactor size, so that less heat must be dealt with in the event of an accident. Also, the geometry has been designed to assure that there is enough natural conduction and convection to keep the temperatures within bounds even if all the pumping systems fail. Finally, the reactor vessel is to be placed underground so that if all else fails, the earth is available as a heat sink, as a way of preventing air from entering and supporting combustion of the graphite, and as a safeguard against atmospheric dispersal of the reactor contents.

It remains to be seen whether the technical, economic, and political realities will permit this or any other type of reactor to be built in the United States. Nuclear power puts the question of the balance between the benefits and risks of our technologies squarely before us, and the answer is not simple.

Breeder Reactors | If the number of nuclear power reactors expanded rapidly, uranium supplies might be depleted in a few decades. A possible solution to this problem is the *breeder reactor*, which produces more fissionable material than it consumes. One type of breeder reactor produces ^{239}Pu, which can be fissioned like ^{235}U by thermal neutrons. In this reactor, a fast neutron causes the reaction

$$^{238}_{92}U + n \rightarrow ^{239}_{92}U + \gamma$$

This is followed by two β^- decays, which produce first neptunium and then plutonium:

$$^{239}_{92}U \rightarrow ^{239}_{93}Np + \beta^-, \qquad ^{239}_{93}Np \rightarrow ^{239}_{94}Pu + \beta^-$$

The plutonium α decays with a half-life of 24,000 years, so it is relatively stable. It is a suitable material for thermal neutron reactors as well as for bomb construction, but has the unfortunate property of being highly toxic.

Since fast neutrons are needed for breeding, a breeder reactor contains no moderator. The design currently receiving the greatest study in the United States uses liquid sodium metal, which is extremely reactive chemically, as a coolant. The reactor fuel is highly enriched, and the reactor core is very compact and hot. This places very great demands on the components and materials.

In the 1980s, research on breeder reactors in the United States was cut back along with a reduction in the construction of thermal reactors. However, in France, which has very small domestic reserves of fossil fuels, reactor construction continued at a high rate, with nuclear power plants supplying 65 percent of the country's electricity in 1985. The Phénix (250 MW) demonstration fast breeder plant was placed into operation in 1974, and the Superphénix (1200 MW) was completed in 1986.

Fission Explosives | In a fission or atomic bomb, a subcritical sphere of ^{235}U or ^{239}Pu is surrounded by a chemical explosive. When this is detonated, shock waves implode the sphere, substantially reducing its volume and increasing its density. This makes the fission ratio greater than 1, and the chain reaction grows rapidly. Because of the inertia of the imploding material, the fission ratio stays above 1 long enough for a large total energy release to occur before the bomb material disperses. Such a bomb is limited in size by the requirements that it must not be critical before it is detonated, and that it must be brought to critical size quickly and held together long enough for a substantial amount of fission to occur. The largest fission explosives are equivalent to about 250 kilotons of TNT and are about 12 times the size of the World War II atomic bombs.

30.12 | NUCLEAR FUSION

Nuclear fusion is potentially a much greater source of energy than fission because the supplies of suitable materials are nearly inexhaustible. Fusion is also attractive because its final products are stable and do not present radioactive waste disposal problems. Nevertheless, the achievement of controlled fusion and the extraction of useful power is a very difficult challenge.

The source of the difficulty is seen by considering two fusion reactions among the hydrogen isotopes, deuterium (d = $^2_1$H) and tritium (t = $^3_1$H):

$$d + d \rightarrow t + p + (4 \text{ MeV kinetic energy})$$
$$t + d \rightarrow {}^4_2\text{He} + n + (17.6 \text{ MeV kinetic energy})$$

In both reactions, there is a strong electrical repulsion keeping the two positively charged nuclei apart. Unless their total initial kinetic energy is at least 0.1 MeV, they cannot come close enough together for the nuclear force to cause them to fuse. It is easy to supply 0.1 MeV or more to a nucleus in an accelerator, but such a machine consumes much more energy than is released, since fusion occurs in only a relatively few nuclei. Thus the only practical way to attain large-scale fusion is in a *thermonuclear reaction*, that is, by heating the materials until at least a small fraction of the nuclei have enough kinetic energy to fuse. This requires temperatures of about 1 million degrees Celsius.

The necessary temperatures are attained in a fission–fusion bomb by using a fission bomb to heat the hydrogen isotopes. Tritium is desirable in a thermonuclear device, since the d–t fusion process starts at a lower temperature than does the d–d reaction. However, tritium is radioactive, with a half-life of 12 years, so it is costly to produce and difficult to work with. These problems are avoided in hydrogen bombs by effectively storing the needed hydrogen isotopes in a solid, nonradioactive form in the chemical compound ^{6}Li d, lithium deuteride. When struck by a fast neutron from the fission explosion, the ^{6}Li nuclide produces tritium in the reaction

$${}^6_3\text{Li} + n \rightarrow {}^4_2\text{He} + t + (4.8 \text{ MeV kinetic energy})$$

The tritium produced in this reaction then undergoes fusion with the deuterium. The required ^{6}Li is separated from natural lithium, which also contains the more abundant ^{7}Li, at a much lower cost than that of producing tritium.

The basic problem in achieving controlled fusion is containing the materials, since no solid can exist at the required temperatures. Since the hot deuterium or tritium gases are completely ionized, they form an electrically conducting mixture of positive and negative charges, which is called *plasma* and can be contained by magnetic fields. After the plasma is heated by bombardment from an electron gun, the magnetic field is suddenly increased. This compresses the plasma, raises its temperature still further, and cause some nuclei to fuse.

Although thermonuclear reactions have been produced in this way, it is not yet possible to produce them for a long enough time and in a large enough volume to be useful. It may turn out that an approach quite different from the magnetic containment schemes will work best. For example, considerable progress has been made recently using intense laser beams or electron beams focused on tiny spheres containing hydrogen isotopes. In general, progress has been slower than was hoped when the fusion program began in the 1950s, and practical power seems to be decades away at best. However, deuterium, unlike fossil fuels and uranium, is available in almost unlimited amounts. This is because one hydrogen nucleus out of 20,000 is a deuteron, making the oceans giant reservoirs of this fuel. Thus the potential benefits from the successful generation of power from deuterium fusion are very great.

30.13 | QUARKS

In the nineteenth century, scientists discovered that the many different substances that occur in nature or can be made in a laboratory are all composed of ninety-odd kinds of atoms. Early in this century, it was learned that atoms consist of electrons bound to nuclei containing protons and neutrons. Thus atoms are not the basic constituents of matter; rather they are built up from more elementary objects—electrons and nucleons. Now it appears that nucleons are also composites and contain objects called *quarks*.

The first evidence that nucleons might be formed from still smaller objects came with the development of high-energy accelerators and the discovery in the 1950s and 1960s of an embarrassingly large number of *hadrons*. Hadrons are particles that interact with each other via the strong nuclear forces, also known as the strong interactions. By now, physicists have observed *hundreds* of kinds of short-lived hadrons. Some of these particles are *mesons*, particles with integer spins (0, 1, . . .). The lowest-mass meson is the *pi meson* or *pion*, which has spin 0 and comes in three charge states, π^+, π^0, π^-; pion masses are about $\frac{1}{7}$ times that of a nucleon. The other new hadrons are *baryons*, with half-integer spins ($\frac{1}{2}$, $\frac{3}{2}$, . . .) and masses greater than the nucleon mass; these particles can decay into nucleons, which are the lowest-mass baryons, by emitting one or more mesons or photons. Regularities in the masses, lifetimes, magnetic moments, and other properties of the hadrons are reminiscent of the relations among the ground and excited states of molecules, atoms, and nuclei, all of which are composite structures.

Violent collisions between electrons and protons or between two protons provided additional evidence that nucleons are composite objects. In 1911, Rutherford discovered that alpha particles passing through thin foils are sometimes deflected through large angles. This was hard to understand in terms of a distributed charge model of an atom, but rather natural if most of the atomic mass is concentrated in a small nucleus. Similarly, these new experiments produced far more frequent large-angle events than would be expected with a diffuse distribution of matter in the nucleon, suggesting that the nucleon contains discrete objects.

In the early 1960s, many hadronic properties were correlated using a branch of mathematics called *group theory* and employing the concept of *broken symmetries*. To understand what this term means, think of an atom. In the absence of an externally applied magnetic field, the orientation of the atom is irrelevant, and its energy is the same for any value of the z component of the angular momentum. However, if a magnetic field is turned on, defining a special direction in space, this *removes or breaks the rotational symmetry* of the system. The energy levels now depend on the component of the angular momentum along the field, and the energy levels are split apart. In particle physics, a fairly small portion of the strong interactions is believed to lead to analogous splittings among the mass energies of related hadrons.

Murray Gell-Mann and George Zweig noted in 1964 that the mathematical relations among the hadronic properties followed very naturally if there are three *quarks* in a baryon and a quark–antiquark pair in a meson. Quarks are spin $\frac{1}{2}$ objects with electric charges equal to $2e/3$ or $-e/3$, where e is the charge on a proton. (The word "quark" is from "Three Quarks for Muster Mark," in *Finnegan's Wake* by James Joyce.) In the full quantum mechanical formulation of atomic physics, quantum electrodynamics, an atom is held together because the electrons and protons exchange photons, which are massless, electrically neutral, spin 1 particles. Coulomb's law represents a first approximation to this description. Similarly, hadrons are held together because the quarks exchange massless, electrically neutral, spin 1 particles called *gluons*.

Originally, many physicists regarded quarks as a handy mnemonic device for an abstract mathematical description of hadronic properties. This attitude was due in part to the failure to observe fractionally charged particles. However, physicists now generally feel that quarks are, in fact, real physical entities. The failure to find free quarks is an indication that they are bound by forces that do not weaken as the separation grows, so that they cannot be pulled apart with a finite amount of energy.

Flavors and Colors | All the hadrons discovered before 1974 could be built up from three kinds, or *flavors*, of quarks, labeled u, d, and s, for *up*, *down*, and *strange*. These carry electric charges $2e/3$, $-e/3$, and $-e/3$, respectively; the antiquarks, $\bar{u}$, $\bar{d}$, and $\bar{s}$, carry charges of equal magnitude and opposite sign. Thus a proton has charge e and is (uud); a neutron has no charge and is (udd); π^+ is $(u\bar{d})$; π^0 is $(u\bar{u})$ or $(d\bar{d})$; and π^- is $(d\bar{u})$. The strange quark was needed to construct *strange particles*, hadrons that can decay into nucleons or pions only via the weak interactions, and hence have comparatively long lifetimes. The discovery in 1974 of a very massive, relatively long-lived meson called the J/Ψ confirmed the suspected existence of a fourth *charmed* quark, c. A fifth quark (*bottom*, b) was discovered more recently, and it is expected that a sixth (*top*, t) will be found.

Quarks are spin $\frac{1}{2}$ particles, so only one quark can occupy a given quantum state in accordance with the Pauli principle. A given spatial state can contain at most one spin-up and one spin-down quark of a given type. However, as many as three spin-up quarks of a given flavor are found in a single spatial state. This implied that quarks have an additional quantum number that specifies their state. This quantum number has been named *color*, although, of course, it has nothing to do with color in the conventional sense. Each quark flavor comes in three colors, usually taken to be red, blue, and green. Only "colorless" or "white" combinations of quarks correspond to physically observable hadronic states.

In analogy with quantum electrodynamics (QED), the theory of the interactions of quarks and gluons is called *quantum chromodynamics* (QCD). Many exact and approximate results have been obtained from this theory, but the mathematics of QCD are quite difficult, and many questions remain. Both theoretical and experimental progress in this field are quite rapid, and many new ideas are likely to appear before long. However, the basic elements of the quark picture are likely to remain with us, just as Rutherford's ideas about the atom still have relevance today.

30.14 | SUPERSTRINGS

In recent years, many physicists have attempted to account for all the observed particles in terms of extremely small objects called *superstrings*. These theories are especially appealing because they provide the first example of a consistent quantum theory of gravity, the weakest and longest known of the fundamental forces. In so doing, they unify gravity with the other three fundamental forces: electromagnetism, the strong nuclear forces, and the weak interactions. Moreover, as became clear in the fall of 1984, they do not seem to have some mathematical inconsistencies that have plagued other quantum mechanical theories of gravity.

Essentially a new dynamical concept, superstrings are intended to replace the Newtonian concept of a point particle. Originally conceived of as a way to explain the plethora of strongly interacting particles, such as the proton and its many excited states, string theories were eclipsed around 1974 as quarks (and their underlying theory, quantum chromodynamics) became popular. While quarks proved to be a successful way of organizing the many elementary particles, the theory involved is not considered by many as very pretty. The equations that describe how a proton might be made up of quarks and gluons are, in fact, much more complicated than are those describing a nucleus in terms of protons and neutrons. It is also argued that a "fundamental" view of the world that has some three dozen "elementary particles" (quarks with various flavors and colors plus gluons) and 20 or so adjustable parameters must surely not be very fundamental.

In contrast, in superstring theory, there is just one kind of object, a one-dimensional extended "string." There is also just one kind of interaction, and that occurs when two strings touch and join to form one string or when one string splits into two. The tips of these open strings carry quantum numbers that represent identifying characteristics of that thing we observe as a "particle." Those quantum numbers include the value of its spin and its electric charge. Joining two strings, one end to another, is thus equivalent to an exchange of quantum numbers between two interacting particles. The mathematical equations for string theory even exhibit a quantum number exchange that looks like the exchange of the graviton, the presumed spin 2 mediator of gravity. (The mediators of the other three known fundamental forces are all spin 1 particles. These are the photon and gluons discussed in the preceding section and the particles associated with the weak interactions.) This feature suggested that strings might have a wider application than just that of classifying strongly interacting particles.

Strings look to us like point particles because they are minute on the scale of ordinary things, such as a proton. A string is characteristically 10^{-35} m long, whereas the proton has a radius of 10^{-15} m. But a string can oscillate in a series of harmonics, just as does the string of a violin. Which observed particle a string looks like at any moment depends on the mode in which it is oscillating. One might, in analogy to the violin string, think of the proton as lying at middle C; the first excited state of the proton might be the string vibration one octave higher.

The string theories currently of greatest interest to particle physicists are *supersymmetric*, hence the "super" in the name, superstring. Supersymmetry is something many physicists would like to see in any theory of the universe even though, so far, there is not a shred of experimental evidence that it does, in fact, exist in nature. Supersymmetry relates the particles of matter (such as quarks) to the particles that are said to embody the forces between them (such as gluons). For every low-energy particle a superstring creates, it is also said to create a massive *superpartner*, a partner differing in that it has a higher mass and a different spin. This superpartner will also obey different quantum statistics. Thus if one particle, say, the electron, has half-integer spin and obeys the Pauli exclusion principle, its superpartner will have integer spin and will not obey this principle.

Another curious feature of the theory is that the universe described by superstrings occurs in ten-dimensional space-time. The observed physics of three spatial dimensions and one time dimension emerges when the original supersymmetry is broken, that is, when the extra six dimensions spontaneously "compactify." These dimensions are said to curl up into a small ball, whose radius would be of the order of 10^{-39} m. The unseen dimensions would only "open up" if the string could be probed at energies on the order of the 10^{19} GeV energies that presumably existed only in the first 10^{-42} seconds after the Big Bang signaling the start of the universe. There is, however, no mathematical proof that these extra dimensions, needed to make the theory consistent, really do curl up. To probe such small dimensions would require an accelerator the size of the galaxy.

The best that one can thus hope for in the near future is an indirect test of superstring theories. Optimists hope that superpartners with masses of the order of 100 GeV will turn up in the forthcoming large accelerators being built at CERN near Geneva, DESY in Hamburg, Fermilab near Chicago, and SLAC in Palo Alto, California. Pessimists question the value of a theory that involves extremely high energies and that cannot therefore be directly verified experimentally.

EXERCISES ON SUPPLEMENTARY TOPICS

Section 30.10 | Nuclear Fission
Section 30.11 | Fission Reactors and Explosives

30-56 Why are β^-'s and γ's emitted in the decay of fission fragments but not β^+'s?

30-57 Geologists spend a great deal of time inspecting potential nuclear reactor sites. What do you think they are looking for?

30-58 It is easier to separate fissionable ^{239}Pu bred in a reactor from the uranium and other materials present than to separate ^{235}U from the more abundant ^{238}U. Why? (This plutonium isotope is suitable for bombmaking. One reason for international inspection of reactors sold to the nonnuclear powers is that any thermal reactor breeds a small amount of ^{239}Pu. Over a period of years, a reactor could make enough plutonium to assemble a bomb.)

30-59 Suppose an object of mass m_1 strikes a stationary object of mass m_2 squarely so that object 2 moves straight ahead. If the collision is elastic, the final and initial kinetic energies of object 1 satisfy

$$K_f = \left(\frac{m_1 - m_2}{m_1 + m_2}\right)^2 K_i$$

Use this result to explain why the hydrogen nuclei are more effective than the oxygen nuclei in water in slowing down neutrons.

Section 30.12 | Nuclear Fusion

30-60 The $^3_1$H–$^2_1$H fusion process releases 17.4 MeV, while $^{235}_{92}$U fission releases about 200 MeV. Find the energy released per nucleon for each process.

30-61 The reaction ^{6}Li + d → α + α + 22 MeV occurs in a hydrogen bomb. Why does this reaction need higher temperatures to occur than does the d + d or d + t fusion reactions? (d = $^2_1$H; t = $^3_1$H.)

30-62 2.2-MeV γ rays are produced when a proton captures a slow neutron in the reaction p + n → d + γ. (d = $^2_1$H.) Why can this fusion process occur at very low temperatures? (This process is not usable as a fusion power source since suitable neutron sources do not exist.)

PROBLEMS ON SUPPLEMENTARY TOPICS

30-63 (a) Calculate the energy released in joules when 1 kg of ^{235}U fissions, assuming 200 MeV per nucleus is released. (b) The electrical power capacity of the United States is about 6×10^{11} W. Assuming 30 percent efficiency in producing electricity from nuclear energy, at what rate must ^{235}U be consumed to provide this power?

30-64 In a pressurized water reactor, as in a boiling-water reactor, water cools the reactor core and serves as a moderator. However, the water is kept at high pressure so that it is well below its boiling point. Why is this reactor less stable than a boiling water reactor? (*Hint*: What is the effect, if any, of a local increase in the water temperature?)

30-65 (a) At what temperature is the average thermal kinetic energy of a nucleus, $\frac{3}{2}kT$, equal to 0.1 MeV? (b) Why is it not necessary to achieve this temperature to initiate a fusion reaction that requires a kinetic energy of 0.1 MeV?

Additional Reading

W. A. Blanpied, *Physics: Its Structure and Evolution*, Ginn Blaisdell, Waltham, Mass., 1969, Chapters 20–23.

W. F. Libby, *Radiocarbon Dating*, 2nd ed., University of Chicago Press, Chicago, 1955.

I. Perlman, F. Asara, and H. V. Michel, Nuclear Applications in Art and Archaeology, *Annual Reviews of Nuclear Science*, vol. 22, 1972, p. 383.

D. E. Nelson, R. G. Korteling, and W. R. Stott, Carbon 14: Direct Detection at Natural Concentrations, *Science*, vol. 198, 1977, p. 507.

L. Paul Knauth and Madhurendu B. Kumar, Uranium Series Dating of Human Skeletal Remains from the Del Mar and Sunnyvale Sites, California, *Science*, vol. 213, 1981, p. 1003.

C. L. Bennett et al., Radiocarbon Dating Using Electrostatic Accelerators: Negative Ions Provide the Key, *Science*, vol. 198, 1977, p. 508.

Richard A. Muller, Radioisotope Dating with Accelerators, *Physics Today*, vol. 32, February 1979, p. 23.

G. M. Raisbeck, F. Yiou, M. Fruneau, and J. M. Loiseaux, Beryllium-10 Mass Spectroscopy with a Cyclotron, *Science*, vol. 202, 1978, p. 215.

D. R. Inglis, *Nuclear Energy: Its Physics and its Social Challenge*, Addison-Wesley Publishing Co., Reading, Mass., 1973.

B. N. DaCosta Andrade, *Rutherford and the Nature of the Atom*, Science Study Series, Doubleday and Co., Garden City, N.Y., 1964.

Enrico Fermi, The Nucleus, *Physics Today*, vol. 5, March 1952, p. 6.

C. F. Tsang, Superheavy Elements, *Physics Teacher*, vol. 13, 1975, p. 279.

G. T. Seaborg, W. Loveland, and D. J. Morrissey, Superheavy Elements: A Crossroads, *Science*, vol. 203, 1979, p. 711.

Laurie M. Brown and Lillian Hoddeson, The Birth of Elementary-Particle Physics, *Physics Today*, vol. 35, April 1982, p. 36.

Frederick Reines, The Early Days of Neutrino Physics, *Science*, vol. 203, 1979, p. 11.

K. G. McNeill, Photonuclear Reactions in Medicine, *Physics Today*, vol. 27, April 1974, p. 75. See also the printing corrections in vol. 27, May 1974, p. 71.

R. F. Post and F. L. Ribe, Fusion Reactors as Future Energy Sources, *Science*, vol. 186, 1974, p. 397.

Robert G. Sachs, Maria Goeppert-Mayer, *Physics Today*, vol. 35, 1982, p. 46.

Tracey Kidder, Taming a Star, *Science 82*, vol. 3, 1982, p. 54.

Otto R. Frisch and John A. Wheeler, The Discovery of Fission, *Physics Today*, vol. 20, Nov. 1967, p. 43.

F. L. Culler, Jr. and W. O. Harms, Energy from Breeder Reactors, *Physics Today*, vol. 25, May 1972, p. 28.

Anthony V. Nero, Jr., *A Guidebook to Nuclear Reactors*, University of California Press, Berkeley, 1979. A detailed but highly readable description of specific reactor designs and systems.

Charles M. Koplik, Maureen F. Kaplan, and Benjamin Ross, The Safety of Repositories for Highly Radioactive Wastes, *Reviews of Modern Physics*, vol. 54, 1982, p. 269.

David J. Rose, *Learning About Energy*, Plenum Press, New York, 1986. Quantitative comparisons of energy systems.

M. M. El-Wakil, *Power Plant Technology*, McGraw-Hill Book Co., New York, 1984. Technical description of methods of energy production.

Richard Wilson, Chernobyl: Assessing the Accident, *Issues in Science and Technology*, vol. III, Fall 1986, p. 21.

Harold M. Agnew and Thomas A. Johnston, The Future of Nuclear Power, *Issues in Science and Technology*, vol. III, Fall 1986, p. 36.

Chernobyl: The Soviet Report, *Nuclear News*, September 11, 1986, p. 1.

Arthur I. Miller, Werner Heisenberg and the Beginning of Nuclear Physics, *Physics Today*, November 1985, p. 60.

Laurie M. Brown, Hideki Yukawa and the Meson Theory, *Physics Today*, December 1986, p. 55. The first theory of nuclear forces.

Karen E. Johnson, Maria Goeppert Mayer: Atoms, Molecules, and Nuclear Shells, *Physics Today*, September 1986, p. 44.

George F. Bertsch and Ricardo A. Broglia, Giant Resonances in Hot Nuclei, *Physics Today*, August 1986, p. 44.

Edward W. Kolb and Chris Quigg, Probing the Structure of the Universe from Quarks to Cosmology, *The Physics Teacher*, vol. 24, 1986, p. 528.

Ronald J. Madaras and Piermaria J. Oddone, Time-Projection Chambers, *Physics Today*, August 1984, p. 36. Huge detectors for reconstructing particle reactions.

Fred A. Donath and Robert O. Pohl, A Debate on Radioactive Waste Disposal, *Physics Today*, December 1982, p. 36.

John H. Nuckols, The Feasibility of Inertial-Confinement Fusion, *Physics Today*, September 1982, p. 24.

D. Allan Bromley, Neutrons in Science and Technology, *Physics Today*, December 1983, p. 30.

Fay Ajzenberg-Selove and Ernest K. Warburton, Nuclear Spectroscopy, *Physics Today*, November 1982, p. 26.

Sallie A. Watkins, Lise Meitner: The Making of a Physicist, *The Physics Teacher*, vol. 22, 1984, p. 12. Short biography of a pioneering nuclear scientist.

O. Lewin Keller, Jr., Darlene Hoffman, Robert A. Penneman, and Gregory R. Choppin, Accomplishments and Promise of Transplutonium Research, *Physics Today*, March 1984, p. 34.

H. E. Gove, A New Accelerator-Based Mass Spectrometry, *The Physics Teacher*, vol. 21, 1983, p. 237.

William A. Fowler, Experimental and Theoretical Nuclear Astrophysics: The Quest for the Origin of the Elements, *Reviews of Modern Physics*, vol. 56, 1984, p. 149. Nobel lecture.

Nathan Isgur and Gabriel Karl, Hadron Spectroscopy and Quarks, *Physics Today*, November 1982, p. 36.

Edward Whitten, New Ideas About Neutrino Masses, *The Physics Teacher*, vol. 21, 1983, p. 78.

Richard C. Henry, Particle Physics Meets Cosmology—The Search for Decaying Neutrinos, *The Physics Teacher*, vol. 20, 1982, p. 531.

Paul Forman, The Fall of Parity, *The Physics Teacher*, vol. 20, 1982, p. 281.

John S. Laughlin, History of Medical Physics, *Physics Today*, July 1983, p. 26.

Paul R. Moran, R. Jerome Nickles, and James A. Zagzebski, The Physics of Medical Imaging, *Physics Today*, July 1983, p. 36.

Margaret L. Silbar, A Profound Theory Lurking . . . . *Mosaic*, vol. 17, no. 4, Winter 1986–1987. A discussion of superstrings.

Henry H. Barschall, Reminiscences of the Early Days of Fission, *Physics Today,* June 1987, p. 27.

Emilio G. Segré, The Discovery of Nuclear Fission, *Physics Today,* July 1989, p. 38.

Andrew M. Sessler, New Particle Acceleration Techniques, *Physics Today,* January, 1988.

Thomas D. Cornell, Merle Antony Tuve: Pioneer Nuclear Physicist, *Physics Today,* January 1988, p. 57.

Scientific American articles:

O. Hahn, The Discovery of Fission, February 1958, p. 76.

Lawrence Bodash, How the Newer Alchemy Was Received, August 1966, p. 88.

Victor F. Weisskopf, The Three Spectroscopies, May 1968, p. 15.

G. T. Seaborg and A. R. Fritsch, The Synthetic Elements: III, April 1963, p. 68.

Glenn T. Seaborg and Justin L. Bloom, The Synthetic Elements: IV, April 1969, p. 56.

Clyde E. Wiegand, Exotic Atoms, November 1972, p. 102.

Vernon D. Barger and David B. Cline, High-Energy Scattering, December 1967, p. 76.

G. Feinberg and M. Goldhaber, Conservation Laws, October 1963, p. 36.

M. D. Kameu, Tracers, January 1949, p. 31.

C. Emiliani, Ancient Temperatures, February 1958, p. 54.

C. Renfrew, Carbon 14 and the Prehistory of Europe, October 1971, p. 63.

R. K. O'Nions, P. J. Hamilton, and Norman M. Evensen, The Chemical Evolution of the Earth's Mantle, May 1980, p. 120. Geochronology.

Stephen Moorbath, The Oldest Rocks and the Growth of Continents, March 1977, p. 92.

J. D. Macdougall, Fission-Track Dating, December 1976, p. 114.

Maria G. Mayer, The Structure of the Nucleus, March 1951, p. 228.

Hans Bethe, What Holds the Nucleus Together, September 1953, p. 201.

Victor F. Weisskopf and E. P. Rosenbaum, A Model of the Nucleus, December 1955, p. 261.

R. H. Hofstadter, The Atomic Nucleus, July 1956, p. 55.

R. B. Peierls, Models of the Nucleus, January 1959, p. 235.

Robert B. Marshak, The Nuclear Force, March 1960, p. 98.

Lawrence Cranberg, Fast-Neutron Spectroscopy, March 1964, p. 79.

Michael Baranger and Raymond A. Sorenson, The Size and Shape of Atomic Nuclei, August 1969, p. 58.

H. W. Kendall and W. Panofsky, The Structure of the Proton and the Neutron, June 1971, p. 66.

Chris D. Zafiratus, The Texture of the Nuclear Surface, October 1972, p. 100.

Alan D. Krisch, The Spin of the Proton, May 1979, p. 68.

D. Allan Bromley, Nuclear Molecules, December 1978, p. 58.

S. B. Treiman, The Weak Interactions, March 1959, p. 72.

Sheldon Penman, The Muon, July 1961, p. 46.

Leon M. Lederman, The Two-Neutrino Experiment, March 1963, p. 60.

W. B. Fowler and N. P. Samios, The Omega-Minus Experiment, October 1964, p. 36.

John N. Bahcall, Neutrinos from the Sun, July 1969, p. 29.

Steven Weinberg, Unified Theories of Elementary Particle Interactions, July 1974, p. 50.

Sidney D. Drell, Electron-Positron Annihilation and the New Particles, June 1975, p. 50.

Sheldon Lee Glashow, Quarks with Charm and Color, October 1975, p. 38.

David B. Cline, Alfred K. Mann, and Carlo Rubbia, The Search for New Families of Elementary Particles, January 1976, p. 44.

David B. Cline, Carlo Rubbia, and Simon van der Meer, The Search for Intermediate Vector Bosons, March 1982, p. 48.

John G. Learned and David Eichler, A Deep-Sea Neutrino Telescope, February 1981, p. 138.

Howard Georgi, A Unified Theory of Elementary Particles and Forces, April 1981, p. 48.

Lewis P. Fulcher, Johann Rafelski, and Abraham Klein, The Decay of the Vacuum, December 1979, p. 150.

Martin L. Perl and William T. Kirk, Heavy Leptons, March 1978, p. 50.

Gerard 't Hooft, Gauge Theories of the Forces Between Elementary Particles, June 1980, p. 104.

Frank Wilczek, The Cosmic Asymmetry Between Matter and Antimatter, December 1980, p. 82.

Kenneth A. Johnson, The Bag Model of Quark Confinement, July 1979, p. 112.

Elliot D. Bloom and Gary J. Feldman, Quarkonium, May 1982, p. 66.

D. J. Hughes, The Reactor as a Research Instrument, August 1953, p. 23.

A. M. Weinberg, Power Reactors, December 1954, p. 33.

Alvin M. Weinberg, Breeder Reactors, January 1960, p. 82.

R. B. Leachman, Nuclear Fission, August 1965, p. 49.

Glenn T. Seaborg and Justin L. Bloom, Fast Breeder Reactors, November 1970, p. 13.

Hugh C. McIntyre, Natural-Uranium Heavy-Water Reactors, October 1975, p. 17.

George A. Cowan, A Natural Fission Reactor, July 1976, p. 36.

H. A. Bethe, The Necessity of Fission Power, January 1976, p. 21. See also April 1976, pp. 8–21, for letters to the editor.

Bernard L. Cohen, The Disposal of Radioactive Wastes from Fission Reactors, June 1977, p. 21. See also October 1977, p. 7, for letters to the editor about this article.

David J. Rose and Richard K. Lester, Nuclear Power, Nuclear Weapons, and Nuclear Stability, April 1978, p. 45.

Harold W. Lewis, The Safety of Fission Reactors, March 1980, p. 53. The lessons of the Three Mile Island accident.

Harold M. Agnew, Gas-Cooled Nuclear Power Reactors, June 1981, p. 55.

Kenneth S. Deffeyes and Ian D. MacGregor, World Uranium Resources, January 1980, p. 66.

Steven A. Fetter and Kosta Tsipis, Catastrophic Releases of Radioactivity, April 1981, p. 48.

William P. Bebbington, The Reprocessing of Nuclear Fuels, December 1976, p. 30.

George A. Vendryes, Superphénix: A Full Scale Breeder Reactor, March 1977, p. 26.

R. F. Post, Fusion Power, December 1957, p. 73.

T. K. Fowler and R. F. Post, Progress Toward Fusion Power, December 1966, p. 21.

Francis F. Chen, The Leakage Problem in Fusion Reactors, July 1967, p. 76.

William C. Gough and Bernard J. Eastlund, The Prospects of Fusion Power, February 1971, p. 50.

Moshe J. Lubin and Arthur P. Fraas, Fusion by Laser, June 1971, p. 21.

Bruno Coppi and Jan Rems, The Tokamak Approach in Fusion Research, July 1972, p. 65.

John L. Emmett, John Nuckolls, and Lowell Wood, Fusion Power by Laser Implosion, July 1975, p. 24.

Gerold Yonas, Fusion Power with Particle Beams, November 1978, p. 50.

Harold P. Furth, Progress Toward a Tokamak Fusion Reactor, August 1979, p. 50.

Haim Harari, The Structure of Quarks and Leptons, April 1983, p. 56.

Kenzo Ishikawa, Glueballs, November 1982, p. 142.

Claudio Rebbi, The Lattice Theory of Quark Confinement, February 1983, p. 54.

Duane A. Dicus, John R. Letaw, Doris C. Teplitz, and Vigdor L. Teplitz, The Future of the Universe, March 1983, p. 90.

Nariman B. Mistry, Ronald A. Poling, and Edward H. Thorndike, Particles with Naked Beauty, July 1983, p. 106.

George F. Bertsch, Vibrations of the Atomic Nucleus, May 1983, p. 62.

Wm. C. McHarris and John O. Rasmussen, High Frequency Collision Between Atomic Nuclei, January 1984, p. 58.

Robert W. Conn, The Engineering of Magnetic Fusion Reactors, October 1983, p. 60.

J. M. LoSecco, Frederick Reines, and Daniel Sinclair, The Search for Proton Decay, June 1985, p. 54.

Chris Quigg, Elementary Particles and Forces, April 1985, p. 84.

Martinus J. G. Veltman, The Higgs Boson, November 1986, p. 76.

Michael B. Green, Superstrings, September 1986, p. 48. A new theory of the fundamental constituents of matter.

Daniel Z. Freedman and Peter van Nieuwenhuizen, The Hidden Dimensions of Spacetime, March 1985, p. 74.

Howard E. Haber and Gordon L. Kane, Is Nature Supersymmetric? June 1986, p. 52.

J. David Jackson, Maury Tigner, and Stanley Wojcicki, The Superconducting Supercollider, March 1986, p. 66.

J. H. Hamilton and J. A. Maruhn, Exotic Atomic Nuclei, July 1986, p. 80. Unusual numbers of protons, neutrons.

Walter Greiner and Horst Stocker, Hot Nuclear Matter, January 1985, p. 76.

Richard K. Lester, Rethinking Nuclear Power, March 1986, p. 31. Lower-powered rectors designed for inherent safety.

Robert E. M. Hedges and John A. J. Gowlett, Radiocarbon Dating by Accelerator Mass Spectrometry, January 1986, p. 100.

Lawrence Badash, The Age-of-the Earth Debate, August 1989, p. 90.

Peter Armbruster and Gottfried Münzenberg, Creating Superheavy Elements, May 1989, p. 66.

Michael K. Moe and Simon Peter Rosen, Double-Beta Decay, November 1989, p. 48.

Alan D. Krisch, Collisions Between Spinning Protons, August 1987, p. 42.

Martinus J. G. Veltman, The Higgs Boson, November 1986, p. 76.

David B. Cline, Beyond Truth and Beauty: A Fourth Family of Particles, August 1988, p. 60.

Herman Winick, Synchroton Radiation, November 1987, p. 88. New sources and uses for ultraviolet light and X rays.

Johann Rafelski and Steven E. Jones, Cold Nuclear Fusion, July 1987, p. 84.

David N. Schramm and Gary Steigman, Particle Accelerators Test Cosmological Theory, June 1988, p. 66.

John R. Rees, The Stanford Linear Collider, October 1989, p. 58.

John M. Dawson, Plasma Particle Accelerators, March 1989, p. 54.

CHAPTER 31 IONIZING RADIATION

The radioactive decay of nuclei produces several kinds of *ionizing radiation* with energies that are typically several million electron volts per particle or quantum. When this radiation passes through matter, it leaves a trail of ionized atoms along its path. Even a small amount of ionization can seriously disrupt a sensitive system such as a living cell or a transistor.

The term "ionizing radiation" includes both nuclear radiation and atomic X rays. The less energetic quanta of lower-frequency electromagnetic waves such as visible light and microwaves do not ordinarily cause appreciable ionization. In general, radiation refers only to ionizing radiation in this chapter.

Radiation is an excellent example of an area of science that has been studied intensively by physicists because of its intrinsic interest and that has also become invaluable in applications to many other fields including biology and medicine. Radiation also illustrates with unusual clarity how a scientific advance may, despite its great benefits, have a very large potential for harm. For example, X-ray pictures are often essential in diagnosing a serious illness, but even one X-ray exposure slightly increases the chance of developing cancer. Consequently, all those working with radiation, especially those in the health sciences, have an obligation to understand the physics and biology of radiation and to use it wisely and carefully.

In this chapter, we first consider the interaction of radiation with matter. We then discuss common radiation sources and the biological effects of radiation. We conclude with a discussion of some applications where radiation is used.

31.1 | THE INTERACTION OF RADIATION WITH MATTER

There are four major categories of radiation of interest to us. In order of increasing range in matter, these are

1. Positive ions, such as alpha particles
2. Electrons and positrons
3. Photons (gamma rays and X rays)
4. Neutrons

Positive Ions | Alpha particles, protons, and other positive ions have very short ranges in matter. Roughly speaking, the average range or stopping distance varies inversely with the density of the medium, so a 5-MeV alpha that can travel about 4 cm in air cannot penetrate a sheet of paper or a layer of skin (Fig. 31.1).

A fast alpha particle undergoes frequent collisions with atomic electrons as it passes through matter, leaving a wake of excited and ionized atoms. About 100 eV is transferred in a single collision, so many collisions occur as the alpha particle slows. When its kinetic energy decreases to about 1 MeV, the alpha acquires two electrons and becomes a neutral helium atom. The neutral atom comes to rest in a short distance after a few more collisions.

Because an alpha particle is so much more massive than an electron, it is scarcely deflected in the collisions, and its path is nearly a straight line. Although individual particles do not all travel exactly the same distance before stopping, the spread in

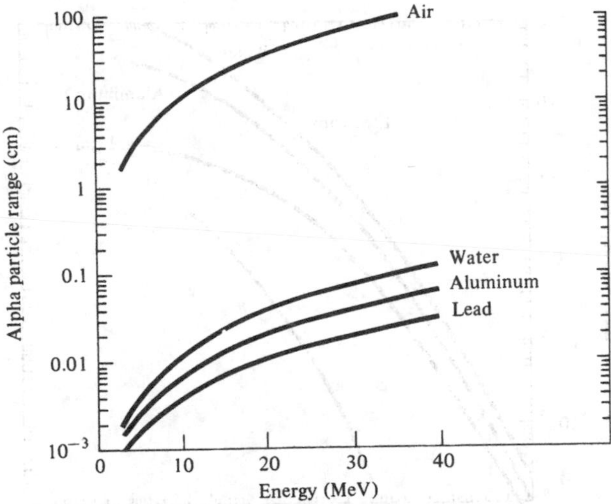

Figure 31.1. Range of alpha particles versus energy for air, water, aluminum, and lead. Water is a good approximation to soft animal tissue. (Adapted from G. S. Hurst and J. E. Turner, *Elementary Radiation Physics*, Copyright © 1970, John Wiley & Sons, New York.)

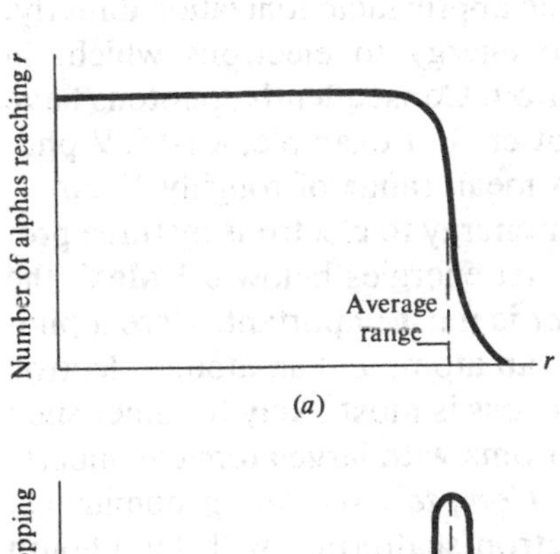

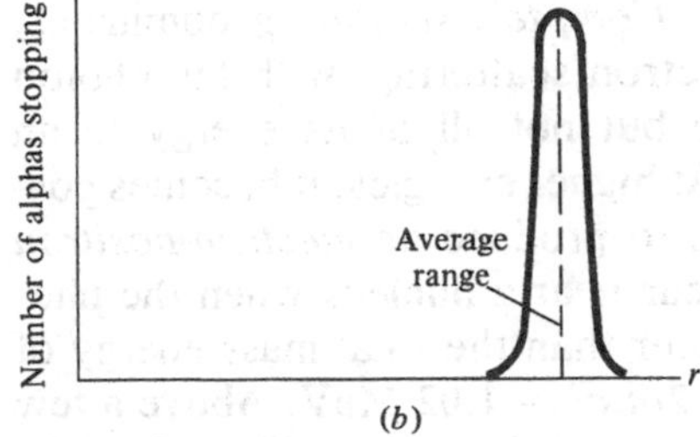

Figure 31.2. Alpha particles from a monoenergetic point source enter a medium. (*a*) The number of alphas passing a point a distance *r* into the medium. (*b*) The number of alphas stopping versus distance *r* traveled. Note that most alphas travel a distance within a few percent of the average range.

stopping distances, or *struggling*, is only a few percent of the average range (Fig. 31.2).

Energy Loss Rate | The fact that alpha particles have a short range in matter compared to electrons of the same energy can be understood from basic physical principles. An ion traveling through a medium collides repeatedly with atomic electrons and gradually loses energy (Fig. 31.3). We show in Section 31.8 that in a given medium, the energy ΔK lost per unit distance by an ion with charge q and velocity v is proportional to q^2/v^2, or

$$\Delta K \propto -\frac{q^2}{v^2} \tag{31.1}$$

The minus sign indicates that the ion is losing kinetic energy. ΔK is also approximately proportional to the density of atomic electrons in the medium. It is convenient to rewrite this result for the rate of energy loss with distance in terms of the kinetic energy instead of v^2. If the ion is moving slowly compared to the speed of light, its kinetic energy is $K = \frac{1}{2}mv^2$, where m is the mass of the ion. Thus $v^2 = 2K/m$ and Eq. 31.1 can be rewritten as

$$\Delta K \propto \frac{-mq^2}{2K} \quad (v \ll c) \tag{31.2}$$

This shows that for a given kinetic energy, the energy loss rate is proportional to ion mass, so that massive particles such as alphas lose energy rapidly and come to rest in a short distance.

These equations are in good agreement with observed energy loss rates except at very low ion velocities. They show that the rate of energy loss increases as the ion slows and is a maximum near the end of the path. To the extent that they are correct, these equations allow one to compare the energy

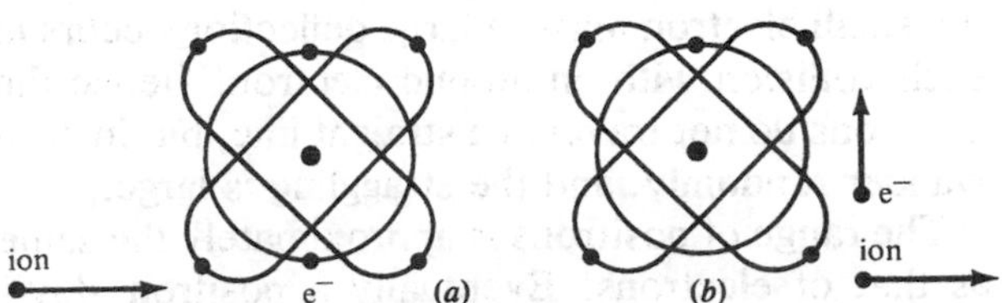

Figure 31.3. (*a*) An ion approaches an atomic electron that is moving slowly compared to the ion. (*b*) The ion collides with the electron, transferring momentum and energy to it. In this case, the electron is removed, so the atom it came from is now ionized. Collisions can also excite atoms without ionizing them.

loss rates of various ions in a given medium. This is illustrated in the following example.

Example 31.1

Compare the rates of energy loss in a given material for protons and alpha particles having the same initial kinetic energies, assuming $v \ll c$.

From Eq. 31.2, the energy loss rate for a given particle is proportional to mq^2. A proton ($^1_1$H) has a charge e, while an alpha particle ($^4_2$He) has a charge $2e$. Thus q^2 for the two particles is related by $q_p^2 = q_\alpha^2/4$. The mass of a proton is close to 1 u and that of an alpha particle is close to 4 u, so $m_p = m_\alpha/4$. The energy loss rate for the proton is then proportional to

$$m_p q_p^2 = \frac{m_\alpha}{4}\frac{q_\alpha^2}{4} = \frac{m_\alpha q_\alpha^2}{16}$$

Thus the rate of energy loss with distance for a proton is one sixteenth that of an alpha particle. This suggests that a proton has a range 16 times that of an alpha particle with the same initial energy. Experimentally, this is only roughly correct; the proton range is typically about 10 times the alpha particle range. This happens because, as noted, Eq. 31.2 does not hold for very low velocities.

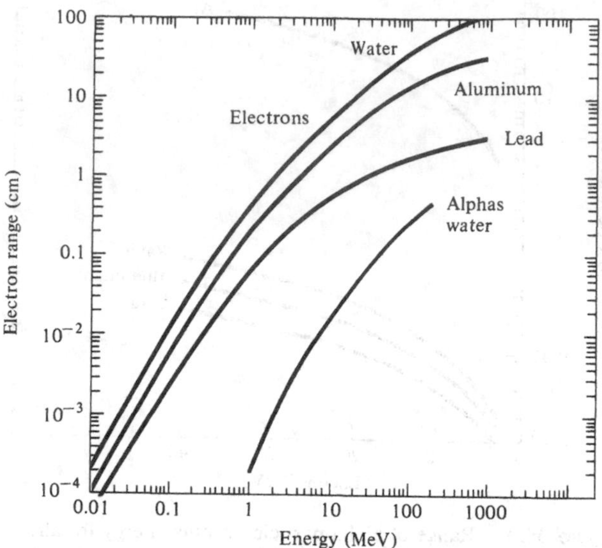

Figure 31.4. Average range of electrons in water, aluminum, and lead. The range of alpha particles in water is shown again for comparison. (Adapted form Hurst and Turner.)

Electrons and Positrons | These products of nuclear β decays have ranges that are typically a hundred times greater than those of alpha particles. For example, a 1-MeV electron has a range in water or soft tissues of 0.4 cm (Fig. 31.4). Like positive ions, electrons lose energy mainly by ionizing or exciting atoms. However, for a given kinetic energy, the velocity will be much larger than for a proton or an alpha particle, because the electron mass is so small. Thus the rate of energy loss given by Eq. 31.1 will be much smaller. This accounts for the large range of the electrons. Also, because of the small electron mass, a large deflection occurs in each collision with an atomic electron. Hence the electrons do not travel in a straight line, but instead wander randomly, and the straggling is large.

The range of positrons is approximately the same as that of electrons. Eventually a positron slows and comes close enough to an electron so that they annihilate, producing gamma rays.

Photons | Gamma rays and X rays are both electromagnetic quanta or photons, but since the gamma rays originate in nuclear rather than atomic processes, they typically have more energy. Photons do not produce appreciable ionization directly; instead, they lose energy to electrons which, in turn, cause ionization. Consequently, photons have a long range in matter. For example, a 1-MeV photon in water has a mean range of roughly 10 cm.

Photons transfer energy to electrons by three processes (Fig. 31.5). At energies below 0.1 MeV, the *photoelectric effect* is most important. Here a photon is absorbed by an atom, and an atomic electron is ejected. This process is most likely for inner shell electrons and for atoms with large atomic numbers. At about 1 MeV, *Compton scattering* dominates; this is photon-electron scattering, with the photon transferring some but not all of its energy to an atomic electron. At higher energies, it becomes possible for a photon to produce an *electron-positron pair*. This can occur near a nucleus when the photon energy is greater than the total mass energy of the two particles, $2m_ec^2 = 1.02$ MeV. Above a few million electron volts, this is the most likely fate of a photon.

Photon absorption probabilities usually diminish as the energy rises. Consequently, as the photon energy increases, the absorption becomes more

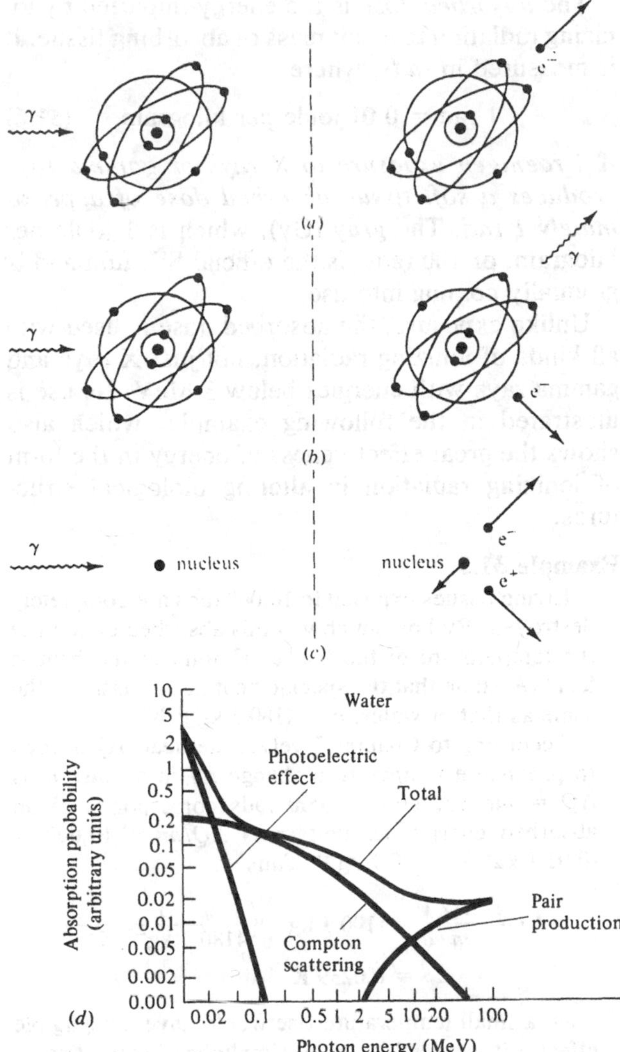

Figure 31.5. Energy loss mechanisms for photons. (*a*) Photoelectric effect. The photon is absorbed by an atom, and an inner shell electron is ejected. (*b*) Compton scattering. Some energy and momentum are transferred to an atomic electron. (*c*) Pair production. The photon disappears and an electron–positron pair is created. Some momentum is transferred to a nucleus. (*d*) Relative importance in water of the three mechanisms versus energy. [(*d*) is adapted from Gloyna and Ledbetter.]

gradual, and the radiation becomes more penetrating or *harder*.

Neutrons | Neutrons are uncharged and produce ionization only indirectly. Since they interact primarily with the small atomic nuclei rather than the atomic electrons, they have a very long range in matter. Neutrons with energies of a few million electron volts may travel a metre or so in water or in animal tissues.

Neutrons are slowed by elastic scattering from nuclei and by nuclear reactions. Some of these reactions lead to proton or gamma-ray emission; the protons, in particular, are significant in causing biological effects. Once a neutron has slowed to thermal energies—less than 1 eV—it has a high probability of being captured by a nucleus. Such a capture is often followed by gamma-ray emission.

31.2 | RADIATION UNITS

Four types of radiation measurements are used in various applications: *source activity*, *exposure*, *absorbed dose*, and *biologically equivalent dose*. We discuss each of these briefly and define their most common units.

The *source activity* $\mathcal{A}$ is the disintegration rate of a radioactive material or the rate of decrease in the number of radioactive nuclei present. It is measured in *curies*, where the curie is defined by the *exact* relationship

$$1 \text{ curie} = 1 \text{ Ci} = 3.7 \times 10^{10} \text{ disintegrations per second} \qquad (31.3)$$

One gram of radium has approximately 3.7×10^{10} disintegrations per second, so that 1 Ci of radium has a mass of about 1 g.

A curie is a fairly large unit; a 1-Ci radioactive source requires shielding and careful handling. Radioactive sources used in an introductory physics laboratory experiments have an activity measured in microcuries.

The S.I. source activity unit is the *becquerel* (Bq), which is one disintegration per second. It is expected to gradually replace the curie.

The activity of a sample is related to its half-life T. From Chapter Thirty, $\Delta N = -\lambda N \,\Delta t$ and $\lambda = 0.693/T$, so

$$\mathcal{A} = \frac{-\Delta N}{\Delta t} = \lambda N = \frac{0.693}{T} N$$

The minus sign is needed because ΔN is the change in the number of nuclei present and is negative, while the disintegration rate or activity is positive. If there are n moles in the sample, then the number of atoms is $N = nN_A$, where Avogadro's number $N_A = 6.02 \times 10^{23}$ is the number of particles in a mole. The activity of n moles of a sample is then

$$\mathcal{A} = \frac{0.693}{T} nN_A \quad (31.4)$$

Note that the activity varies inversely with the half-life. This result is used in the following example.

Example 31.2

^{60}Co beta decays with a half-life of 5.27 years = 1.66×10^8 s into ^{60}Ni, which then promptly emits two gamma rays. These gamma rays are widely used in treating cancer. What is the mass of a 1000-Ci cobalt source?

Solving Eq. 31.4 for the number of moles and using $\mathcal{A} = 1000$ Ci,

$$n = \frac{\mathcal{A}T}{0.693N_A} = \frac{1000(3.7 \times 10^{10}\ \mathrm{s}^{-1})(1.66 \times 10^8\ \mathrm{s})}{0.693(6.02 \times 10^{23}\ \mathrm{mole}^{-1})}$$
$$= 0.0147\ \mathrm{mole}$$

Since a mole of ^{60}Co has a mass of 60 g, the mass of the sample is

$$m = (0.0147\ \mathrm{mole})(60\ \mathrm{g\ mole}^{-1}) = 0.882\ \mathrm{g}$$

Exposure and Absorbed Dose

Exposure indicates the amount of radiation reaching a material, while *absorbed dose* indicates the energy absorbed in the material from the beam. Thus the absorbed dose depends on the properties of the material and the beam, while the exposure depends on the characteristics of the beam alone.

Exposure is defined only for X rays and gamma rays with energies up to 3 MeV and not for other forms of radiation. It is defined as the amount of ionization produced in a unit mass of dry air at standard temperature and pressure (STP), 1 atmosphere and 0°C. The conventional unit is

$$1\ \text{roentgen} = 1\ \mathrm{R} = 2.58 \times 10^{-4}\ \text{coulomb per kilogram} \quad (31.5)$$

Thus 1 roentgen of X rays will produce 2.58×10^{-4} C of positive ions in a kilogram of air at STP, and an equal amount of negative ions.

The *absorbed dose* is the energy imparted by ionizing radiation to a unit mass of absorbing tissue. It is measured in *rads*, where

$$1\ \text{rad} = 0.01\ \text{joule per kilogram} \quad (31.6)$$

A 1-roentgen exposure to X rays or gamma rays produces a soft tissue absorbed dose of approximately 1 rad. The *gray* (Gy), which is 1 joule per kilogram, or 100 rads, is the official S.I. unit and is gradually coming into use.

Unlike exposure, the absorbed dose is used with all kinds of ionizing radiation, not just X rays and gamma rays with energies below 3 MeV. Its use is illustrated in the following example, which also shows the great effectiveness of energy in the form of ionizing radiation in altering biological structures.

Example 31.3

Living tissues exposed to 10,000 rads are completely destroyed. By how much will this absorbed dose raise the temperature of the tissues if none of the heat is lost? (Assume that the specific heat of the tissue is the same as that of water, $c = 4180\ \mathrm{J\ kg^{-1}\ K^{-1}}$.)

According to Chapter Twelve, the heat ΔQ needed to produce a temperature change ΔT in a mass m is $\Delta Q = mc\,\Delta T$. Now 10,000 rads corresponds to an absorbed energy per unit mass $\Delta Q/m = 10{,}000 \times (0.01\ \mathrm{J\ kg^{-1}}) = 100\ \mathrm{J\ kg^{-1}}$. Thus

$$\Delta T = \frac{\Delta Q}{m}\frac{1}{c} = (100\ \mathrm{J\ kg^{-1}})\left(\frac{1}{4180\ \mathrm{J\ kg^{-1}\ K^{-1}}}\right)$$
$$= 0.0239\ \mathrm{K}$$

Such a small temperature rise would have a negligible effect if it were achieved by simply heating the tissue. Radiation is so lethal to living tissue because it does not deposit the energy uniformly at all points. Instead, it imparts energy in relatively large amounts to single atoms at random locations, and this may disrupt critical biological molecules.

Biological Quantities

The absorbed dose refers to a physical effect: the transfer of energy to a material. However, the effects of radiation on biological systems also depend on the type of radiation and its energy. The quality factor (QF) of a particular radiation is defined by comparing its effects to those of a standard kind of radiation, which is usually taken to be 200-keV X rays. For example, fast neutrons (with energies above 0.1 MeV) have a QF

TABLE 31.1

Typical QF values. By definition, the QF is exactly 1 for 200-keV X rays.

Radiation	Typical QF
^{60}Co gamma rays (1.17 and 1.33 MeV)	0.7
4-MeV gamma rays	0.6
Beta particles	1.0
Protons (1 to 10 MeV)	2
Neutrons	2–10
Alpha particles	10–20

of about 10 for causing cataracts. Hence the absorbed dose (in rads) of 200-keV X rays needed to produce cataracts is 10 times the dose required for neutrons. The QF varies with the radiation type and energy, with the animal species, and the biological effect under consideration (Table 31.1). Positive ions, which deposit more energy per unit length than beta or gamma rays, generally do more biological damage than the same absorbed dose of betas or gammas. However, their effects are often limited to the surface tissue because they have short ranges.

The *rem* and the millirem = 10^{-3} rem are the units used in discussions of biological effects. For example, in the case of cataract formation, 1 rad of 200-keV X rays and 0.1 rad of fast neutrons each produce 1 rem of damage. In any situation, the *biologically equivalent dose* (in rems) is the physical absorbed dose (in rads) times the QF. *One rem of any kind of radiation* produces the same biological effect, namely, the effect of *one rad of 200-keV X rays*. In S.I. units, the biologically equivalent dose in *sieverts* (Sv) equals the dose in grays times the QF.

A summary of various radiation units is given in Table 31.2. An illustration of the use of these units is given in the next example.

Example 31.4

A cancer is irradiated with 1000 rads of ^{60}Co gamma rays, which have a QF of 0.7. Find the exposure in roentgens and the biologically equivalent dose in rems.

For gamma rays, the soft tissue dose in rads is approximately equal to the exposure in roentgens, so the exposure is approximately 1000 R. The biologically equivalent dose is the product of the QF and the dose in rads, or (0.7)(1000) = 700 rems.

Radiation is present in our environment from many sources, both natural and man-made. As with toxic chemicals, machines, electrical devices, and automobiles, we must balance the risk of using radiation against the benefits. Small amounts of radiation are easier to detect than are trace quantities of most other toxic materials, so assessing this risk is relatively simple. The effects of various radiation doses are discussed in the following two sections. The next example illustrates how we can estimate the dose received from a radioactive material.

Example 31.5

A laboratory experiment in a physics class uses a 10-microcurie ^{137}Cs source. Each decay emits a 0.66-MeV gamma ray. (a) How many decays occur per hour? (b) A 60-kg student standing nearby absorbs 10 percent of the gamma rays. What is her absorbed dose in rads in 1 hour? (c) The quality factor is 0.8. Find her biologically equivalent dose in rems.

(a) Since 1 curie produces 3.7×10^{10} decays per second, the number of decays in an hour for a 10-microcurie source is

$$N = (10 \times 10^{-6})(3.7 \times 10^{10}\ s^{-1})(3600\ s) = 1.33 \times 10^9$$

TABLE 31.2

Radiation units

	Unit	Definition
Source activity	curie (Ci)	3.70×10^{10} disintegrations per second
	becquerel (Bq)	1 disintegration per second
Exposure (X and γ rays)	roentgen (R)	2.58×10^{-4} C kg^{-1} in dry air at STP
Absorbed dose	rad	0.01 J kg^{-1}
	gray (Gy)	1 J kg^{-1}
Biologically equivalent dose	rem	QF × (dose in rads)
	sievert (Sv)	QF × (dose in grays)

(b) Each decay produces 0.66 MeV, of which 10 percent is absorbed. Thus the total energy absorbed is

$$E = (0.1)(1.33 \times 10^9)(0.66 \text{ MeV}) \times (1.6 \times 10^{-13} \text{ J MeV}^{-1}) = 1.41 \times 10^{-5} \text{ J}$$

Dividing by her mass, the absorbed dose in rads is

$$\frac{E}{m} = \frac{(1.41 \times 10^{-5} \text{ J})(1 \text{ rad})}{(60 \text{ kg})(0.01 \text{ J kg}^{-1})} = 2.34 \times 10^{-5} \text{ rad}$$

(c) Multiplying the dose in rads by the quality factor gives the biologically equivalent dose in rems,

$$\left(\frac{E}{m}\right)(\text{QF}) = (2.34 \times 10^{-5} \text{ rad})(0.8) = 1.87 \times 10^{-5} \text{ rem} = 0.0187 \text{ mrem}$$

We see in the next section that the annual radiation dose received by an average person from all sources is about 400 mrem. The dose due to being near this source is about 0.005 percent of that annual amount and is not significant. Note, however, if someone were to swallow this source, a significant dose would result. (See Problem 31-51.) Radioactive sources used in physics laboratories are safe when used properly, but they must be handled correctly to avoid potentially serious problems.

31.3 | HARMFUL EFFECTS OF RADIATION

When radiation passes through living cells, it can alter or damage the structure of important molecules. This may lead to the malfunctioning or death of the cells and ultimately to the death of the organism.

Usually, immature cells and the cells that are growing or dividing most rapidly are the most radiosensitive. Often, cancer cells are rapidly growing; in such cases, they are highly vulnerable to radiation. Similarly, fetuses and infants are much more readily harmed by radiation than are adults. For example, in one study it was found that children whose mothers received pelvic X rays while pregnant had a 30 to 40 percent increase in the incidence of cancer.

The limited knowledge of the immediate effects on humans of large radiation doses comes from studies of victims of atomic bomb explosions and of occasional accidents. Whole body doses under 25 rems have no observable effect. As the dose increases above 100 rems, damage to the blood-forming tissues becomes evident, and above 800 rems severe gastrointestinal disorders occur. Death usually follows in a period of days or weeks if the dose is much more than about 500 rems.

Sublethal, short-term doses and doses acquired gradually over a long period may lead to cancer after a latent period of many years during which no ill effects are discernible. The chance of dying of cancer is doubled by a dose somewhere between 100 and 500 rems. Over a wide range of exposures, both in animal experiments and in human data, the increase in the cancer rate is directly proportional to the total accumulated dose.

Studies of low-level doses are difficult and inconclusive, because of the much larger incidence of cancer from other causes. Consequently, it is possible that the damage resulting from doses below some threshold is repaired, so that no increase in the cancer rate occurs. For many years, most experts favored the more conservative *linear hypothesis*, which assumes that the effects of radiation in causing cancer are proportional to the dose at all levels (Fig. 31.6). However, in 1980 the Advisory Committee on the Biological Effects of Ionizing Radiations (the BEIR committee) of the National Academy of Sciences found that the linear hypothesis probably overestimates the effects of low-level exposures. If this is correct, the public health impli-

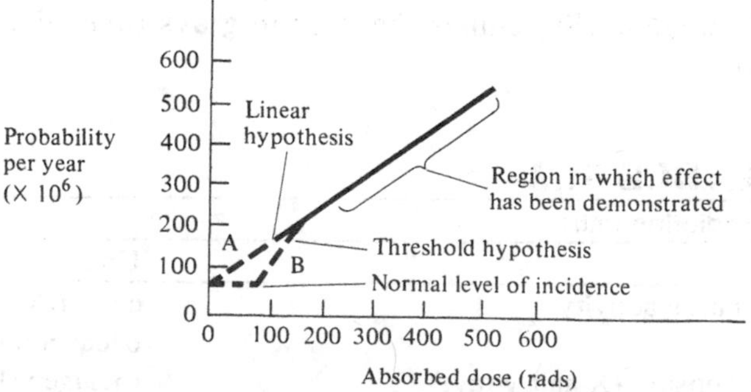

Figure 31.6. Leukemia rates in humans. Both the linear and threshold hypotheses are consistent with the high-dose data. Measurements of the very small rates at low doses such as 1 to 10 rads would require huge populations to be statistically meaningful. (Adapted from Hurst and Turner.)

cations of occupational exposures or of nuclear accidents may be less serious than previously believed. Nevertheless, since it is simple to apply and definite in its predictions, the National Council on Radiation Protection continues to use the linear hypothesis as the basis for radiation protection standards. We will also use the linear hypothesis in this chapter.

Genetic Effects | Although genetic mutations have helped humans to evolve to their present state, most mutations are harmful. Any increase in the mutation rate means more prenatal deaths and more people born with serious defects. In addition to the personal tragedy this implies, there is also the problem that the increasing ability of medical science to keep such people alive until they reproduce tends to keep defective genes in the human genetic pool.

Mutations can be increased above the normal rate by elevated temperatures, some chemicals, and by ionizing radiation. The mutations caused by radiation are similar to those occurring naturally. It is generally believed that their rate is proportional to the absorbed dose, no matter how small, and that there is no threshold or repair mechanism. The dose that will double the mutation rate is probably between 25 and 150 rems.

Figure 31.7. An example of the misuse of X rays was the shoe-fitting fluoroscopy machine, a popular selling feature of many children's shoe stores from 1946 until the late 1950s. The first machines were largely unshielded. Doses to the feet sometimes were as high as 40 rems per minute and averaged 8 rems per minute. The machines were eventually eliminated by legislation that restricted X-ray use to licensed medical practitioners. (Gary Retherford / Photo Researchers, Inc.)

31.4 | CHRONIC RADIATION EXPOSURE

Living things have always been exposed to chronic low-level radiation arising from cosmic rays and from radionuclides naturally present in the environment. To this natural background, we have added a substantial amount of artificially produced radiation, mostly from medical diagnostic X rays (Table 31.3). Some individuals receive much more than the average chronic doses from natural sources. For example, some villages in Brazil and India happened to be built on soil with a high thorium content; doses in these villages are up to 100 times the norm. Also, the water from some wells and mineral springs in Italy, Austria, and elsewhere contains up to a million times the usual radioactivity. In these localities the cancer rates are abnormally high.

The National Council on Radiation Protection establishes a *maximum permissible dose* (*MPD*) for radiation workers and the general public from all artificial radiation sources (Fig. 31.7) *except* medical diagnosis and treatment. (The council does not regulate medical exposures.) The MPD has been lowered repeatedly as the hazards of radiation have become better understood. For example, in the late 1930s the MPD was 0.1 rem per day. The current MPD for radiation workers is a seventh of this, or 5 rems per year (Table 31.4). The average permitted for the entire population averaged over all individuals is a thirtieth of the occupational MPD, or 170 millirems per year.

Since any radiation exposure implies some hazard, these standards represent a compromise involving judgments of risks versus benefits. No single radiation-producing device or activity, such as watches, TV sets, or nuclear reactors, is permitted to expose the public to more than a small fraction of the MPD. In general, the Council requires that ex-

TABLE 31.3

Chronic sources of radiation in the United States. All values are approximate or average (1 millirem = 10^{-3} rem). (The effects of indoor radon exposure are not included. See table 31.5.)

Source	Dose (Millirems per Year Except as Noted)	
Cosmic rays		
Sea level	41	
Denver (5000 ft)	70	
Leadville, Colorado, area (10,500 ft)	160	
20,000 ft	400	
Commercial jet (35,000 ft)	0.7 millirems per hour	
U.S. average from cosmic rays		44
γ rays from rocks, soil (Ra, U, Th, K, etc.)		
Atlantic Coastal Plains	22.8	
Colorado Front Range	89.7	
U.S. average from external radionuclides	40	
Calculation of gonadal dose		
Correction factor due to housing shielding	0.8	
Correction factor due to biological shielding	0.8	
U.S. average gonadal dose from external radionuclides	(40)(0.8)(0.8)	26
Internal radionuclides		
^{40}K	16	
^{14}C, Ra, and decay products	2	
Total		18
Total U.S. environmental average gonadal dose (Oakley, 1972)		88 ± 11
Fallout (1970)	4	
(1990)	1	
Nuclear power, including mining, milling, transportation (1990)	<0.1	
Medical diagnostic	72	
Medical radiopharmaceuticals	1	
Occupational	0.8	
Miscellaneous	2	

Sources: Natural Radiation Exposure in the U.S., by D. T. Oakley, U.S. Environmental Protection Agency, June 1972; National Academy of Sciences Committee on Biological Effects of Ionizing Radiation Report, November 1972; *Exposure of the Population of the United States and Canada from Natural Background Radiation*, NCRP Report No. 94, National Council on Radiation Protection and Measurements, Washington, D.C., 1987; *Public Radiation Exposure from Nuclear Power Generation in the United States*, National Council on Radiation Protection and Measurements, Washington, D.C., 1987.

TABLE 31.4

Maximum permissible doses (MPD) for whole body exposures as revised in 1972 by the National Council on Radiation Protection. Larger doses are permitted for some parts of the body.

	MPD
General population	
MPD for any individual*	500 millirems per year
Average for whole U.S. population†	170 millirems per year
Radiation workers	
Annual	5000 millirems per year
3-month period	1250 millirems per 3 months
Pregnant workers	500 millirems per 9 months

* Facilities using radiation may occasionally expose some individuals to this dose.
† This is the average for everyone, including radiation workers.

posures must be "as low as reasonably achievable." Total present-day general population exposures are much less than the limit.

Nevertheless, the 1972 National Academy of Sciences report quoted in Table 31.4 urged that the allowed doses be lowered substantially. It is estimated that *if* everyone received the present MPD from nonmedical sources, between 3000 and 15,000 *additional* U.S. cancer deaths would occur annually. To see how this estimate comes about, let us assume that 250 rems will double the cancer rate. At 170 millirems per year, the average American who is about 30 years old will have accumulated 30(170 mrem) $\simeq$ 5000 mrem = 5 rems. This dose is 5/250, or 2 percent, of the amount needed to double the cancer rate. The total death rate is roughly the U.S. population of 220 million divided by 70 years, or about 3 million, of which one tenth, or 300,000, deaths are due to cancer. A 2 percent increase would mean 6000 more deaths per year. (The range of additional deaths quoted in the Academy report corresponds to the uncertainty in the doubling dose, which is somewhere between 100 and 500 rems.) At present, nonmedical artificial radiation sources contribute about 1 percent of the MPD. Thus the actual number of deaths due to these sources is small.

Medical diagnostic X rays are currently the major source of artificial radiation exposure, and they are increasing annually. These average 40 percent of the nonmedical MPD and are estimated to cause 1500 to 3000 cancer deaths annually, plus a possibly greater number of genetic deaths in future generations via lethal mutations. It is estimated that *medical exposures could be greatly reduced* without any loss of the benefits of diagnostic X rays. Clearly, the medical and dental professions have a great responsibility to minimize exposures. This means avoiding unneeded diagnostic X rays and assuring the use of modern, well-shielded machines and high-sensitivity films. It also means educating the public, so that people do not equate diagnostic X rays with good medical practice in evaluating the care they receive.

The importance of using the proper X-ray devices and techniques is illustrated by the range of doses received from chest X rays. The best procedures give only 6 millirems, although the average is 200 millirems. By contrast, the X-ray machines used in mobile units to screen large populations for tuberculosis, which are relatively inexpensive to operate, gave about 1000 millirems to the chest area. Public health authorities no longer recommend their general use, since they believe the risks of radiation exposure outweigh those of lung diseases for the average person.

To summarize, any radiation exposure carries with it a small but very real risk. The benefits of such exposures must be weighed against the hazards, both for the individual and for society overall.

A simple way to estimate the public health implications of radiation exposure with the linear hypothesis is to calculate the total or collective dose.

For example, if a million people receive an average of 0.1 rem, the collective dose is (1,000,000 persons)(0.1 rem) = 100,000 person rems. Our calculation earlier in this section is equivalent to assuming that 5000 person rems causes one fatal cancer. A commonly used estimate is that 10,000 person rems will cause one premature cancer death. We use this estimate in the following example.

Example 31.6

Medicine and nuclear energy are the main sources of occupational radiation exposure. 1975 Environmental Protection Agency data indicated that 1,260,000 U.S. workers in these and a few other industries received measurable whole-body doses averaging 340 mrem annually. (a) What was the collective annual dose received by these workers? (b) What is the probable number of cancer deaths due to this exposure? (c) What is the reduction in the average life expectancy of a worker due to 30 years of exposure? (Assume that the cancer death occurs at age 40.)

(a) The collective dose received is the product of the number of exposed workers and the average dose received,

$$(1{,}260{,}000 \text{ persons})(0.340 \text{ rem}) = 430{,}000 \text{ person rems}$$

(b) At 1 cancer death per 10,000 person rems, the number of deaths resulting is 430,000/10,000 = 43.

(c) If the 43 workers die at an average age of 40 instead of 70, their total lost days of life is $(70 \text{ y} - 40 \text{ y})(365 \text{ day y}^{-1})(43) = 470{,}000$ days. Dividing by the number of workers, we get (470,000 days)/1,260,000 = 0.37 day. The corresponding number of 30 years of exposure is (30)(0.37) = 11 days.

By comparison, the reduction in life expectancy due to cigarette smoking is 2370 days, or 6.5 years. The reduction in life expectancy due to industrial accidents is over 200 days in mining, construction, and agriculture. Although it is little consolation to a terminally ill cancer patient, the risks faced by radiation workers are much less than are those in many other occupations.

Radon Exposure | ^{222}Rn is a radioactive noble gas. It is produced as one step in a long chain of decays that starts with ^{238}U (half-life 4.49 billion years) and terminates with ^{206}Pb (stable). Radon and its decay products emit alpha particles. It has been known for a long time that radon causes lung cancer in miners who have been heavily exposed. However, only recently has it been realized that many people receive large radon exposures in their homes.

Uranium is naturally present in small amounts in granite and many other kinds of rock. As a result, radon occurs in the soil everywhere, although there is a great deal of geographic variation. Radon also is found to some extent in water supplies and in building materials. It is very dense, so it tends to become trapped in homes and other buildings as it emerges from the ground. The tighter the building, and the less the exchange of air with the outdoors, the greater the likely radon concentration. Thus energy conservation efforts that have reduced air infiltration have aggravated the radon problem. Ironically, some solar-heated houses that use crushed granite as a heat storage medium have been discovered to have very high radon levels. Crushing the rock frees radon that would otherwise be trapped.

The average radon level in single-family houses in the United States is 1.5 pCi litre^{-1} (picocuries per litre) and represents about a 0.2 to 0.3 percent lifetime risk of developing lung cancer. About a million homes have concentrations above 8 pCi litre^{-1}. A 1986 survey of homes in Clinton, New Jersey, found 5 out of a group of 105 houses with radon concentrations above 1000 pCi litre^{-1}. The average levels in high-rise apartments are much lower. This is consistent with the fact that the largest source of the radon is the soil.

It is now clear that indoor radon produces more radiation exposure than all other sources combined. Table 31.5, which is based on a 1987 report, shows the equivalent exposure for various organs. The equivalent exposure is the whole body dose that carries the same risk as the actual dose to that organ. The sum of these exposures is the equivalent whole body radiation exposure. The rounded total of exposures due to naturally occurring background sources is 300 mrem per year, or about three times the older estimate of 88 mrem listed in Table 31.3. The difference is due entirely to inclusion of the lung damage resulting from the inhalation of radon and its decay products.

Radon is calculated to be responsible for roughly 10,000 annual lung cancer deaths out of a total of 130,000. Cigarette smoking is the principal cause and is responsible for about 108,000 lung cancer

TABLE 31.5

Background radiation effective doses, including exposure to indoor radon and its decay products, for residents of the United States. (Doses from inhaled radionuclides are about 20 percent less in Canada.)

	Dose in Millirems per Year					
Source	Lung	Gonads	Bone Surfaces	Bone Marrow	Other Tissue	Total
Cosmic rays	3	7	1	3	13	27
γ rays from rocks, soil	3	7	1	3	14	28
Inhaled radionuclides	200	—	—	—	—	200
Other internal radionuclides	4	9	3	6	17	40
Rounded totals	210	23	5	12	44	300

Source: *Exposure of the Population of the United States and Canada from Natural Background Radiation,* NCRP Report No. 94, National Council on Radiation Protection and Measurements, Washington, D.C., 1987.

deaths per year. A 200-pCi litre^{-1} radon concentration in a home exposes residents to the same cancer risk as smoking four packs of cigarettes a day.

Public health agencies are currently evaluating radon concentration levels and limits and developing practical strategies for reducing excessive levels. In several houses in Clinton, for example, a simple but effective ventilation system was successfully tested. Plastic pipes were run through cellar floors or walls into the soil, and turbine fans were used to draw radon gas out of the soil and vent it into the atmosphere. Indoor radon levels soon dropped close to or below the 4-pCi litre^{-1} limit currently recommended by the Environmental Protection Agency and were expected to drop further as the systems were adjusted. The cost of these ventilation systems averaged less than $1000.

31.5 | RADIATION IN MEDICINE

Despite its hazards, the use of ionizing radiation in medical research, diagnosis, and therapy has been invaluable and has saved many lives. Within a few weeks of their discovery by Roentgen in 1895, the value of X rays for medical diagnosis was realized. By early in this century, X rays and naturally occurring radionuclides (radium, radon) were being used in cancer therapy. Today, most hospitals have a large variety of X-ray and nuclear medicine facilities designed to diagnose or treat many ailments with a minimum of radiation exposure and risk to the patients and the staff.

In the past decade, the integration of computers into imaging and diagnostic work, the development of new imaging techniques and instrumentation, and the increased availability of radioisotopes have given the physician and researcher important new and improved tools. In this section, we describe those techniques that are specifically related to X rays and to radioactive materials. Earlier we discussed nuclear magnetic resonance (Sections 29.12 and 29.13) and ultrasound imaging (Section 22.7) and described the principles of tomographic imaging (Section 24.8).

X rays | The earliest and most familiar imaging technique uses X rays. A beam from an X-ray tube passes through the body and strikes a fluorescent screen or a sensitive film. Excellent spatial resolution can be obtained when portions of the object differ greatly in density and X-ray absorption rate. Thus bones, and bone fractures, are very easily seen because bone differs greatly from the surrounding soft tissue and body fluids. However, the contrast is much poorer when imaging soft tissues with similar characteristics. For example, the absorption rate in a 1-cm diameter brain tumor may differ by only 1 percent from that in the surrounding tissue. When X rays traverse the entire head, the difference in transmitted intensity is reduced to only about 0.2 percent. Furthermore, the skull bones are imaged strongly and significantly complicate analysis of the picture. Transmitted intensities must differ by at least 2 or 3 percent to be distinguishable.

With the advent of computerized axial tomography (CAT), X-ray resolution was considerably improved, but at considerable expense. Because the final image is the result of scanning from many directions, portions of objects with marginally different absorption characteristics are more readily resolved and the effects of bones shielding areas of interest can be reduced. That is, since the image is a slice of an object, the image of the bone itself is localized, and it does not mask other parts of the object. Nevertheless, brain scans are still difficult, because for all directions, most of the absorption is from the skull, reducing the resolution of objects in the interior of the brain. X-ray CAT scans in general can resolve tissue absorption differences of a fraction of 1 percent.

It was, and still is because of its relatively low expense and ease of use, common practice to improve normal X-ray resolution by introducing contrast agents into the systems being imaged. In general, these materials have a high atomic number and absorb X rays readily. For example, barium compounds are often used with gastrointestinal X rays and iodine compounds are common in urological studies. Since large-density changes from one place to another often enhance X-ray contrast, air is used to replace cerebrospinal fluid. Continued development of new materials that are locally accumulated in living systems and are of considerably different density from the normal constituents make this an important method both in conventional and CAT X-ray imaging.

The use of contrast agents with X rays is an example of a technique that greatly enhances the utility of many imaging methods. Originally, it was a scheme to improve the contrast between different parts of an object. However, if the substance introduced can be distinguished by itself in an image (we will discuss techniques where only the substance can be detected shortly), then the imaging method can be used to study time-dependent processes. That is, successive images can be used to detect and measure the rate at which a substance accumulates in a given region. For example, xenon can be used to study localized cerebral blood flow. Such studies of time-dependent biological processes are referred to as *dynamic function studies*.

Diagnostic Studies Using Radionuclides

Most studies done with radionuclides share some common features. A radioactive substance is introduced into the system, and detectors outside the body detect the position of the substance. These radioactive substances, called *tracers*, are usually chosen because they are absorbed in organs or tissues of interest or may be followed through particular processes such as the metabolism of starches and sugars, the building up of proteins from amino acids, and the action of hormones and drugs. Radiation doses are normally comparable to those from diagnostic X rays.

To minimize the dose, short-lived radionuclides are selected that emit gamma rays with little more than the energy required for detection. Many studies use a long-lived excited state of technicium (Z = 43) referred to as ^{99m}Tc. Formed when ^{99}Mo beta decays, this radionuclide decays to its stable ground state ^{99}Tc with a half-life of 6.0 hours by emitting a 140-keV gamma ray. Its chemical properties permit it to be incorporated into many kinds of molecules that can be targeted for specific processes and organs. For example, compounds containing ^{99m}Tc or a radioactive iodine isotope ^{123}I can be used in dynamic function studies of the thyroid. Indeed, this is a standard method of diagnosis of the common hyperthyroid condition. It allows a determination of abnormal activity and an assessment of the severity of the condition from the rate of uptake of the labeled substance. Similarly, when diuretics containing radioactive compounds are concentrated in the kidneys, alterations from the usual patterns of uptake and excretion signal possible abnormalities.

In the simplest gamma-ray scans, a picture is pro-

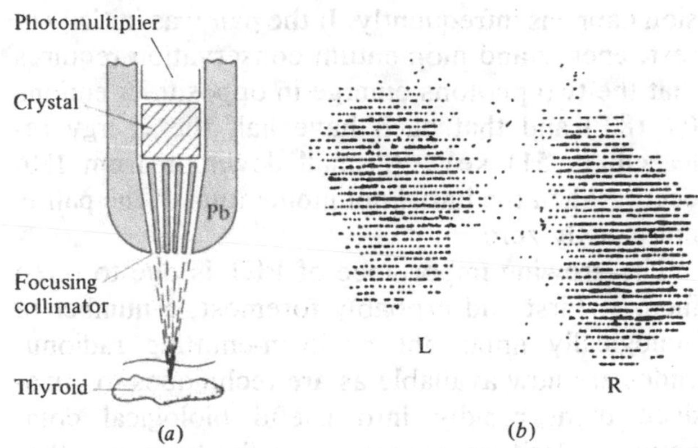

Figure 31.8. Diagnostic scans. (*a*) A scintillation counter shielded with a lead collimator. (*b*) A kidney scan. Note the difference in appearance between the healthy right kidney and the diseased left kidney.

duced by detecting the gamma radiation from a radionuclide introduced into the system. The radiation is detected with the aid of a *scintillating crystal*, which emits flashes of light when beta or gamma rays pass through it. (Scintillation detectors are discussed in more detail in the supplementary topics at the end of this chapter.) The scintillation counter is equipped with a lead collimator containing several tapered holes that transmit the gamma rays from a small region of the organ that has absorbed the radionuclide. The counter is slowly moved or *scanned* over the region of interest, and the pulses generated are amplified and recorded on paper, photographic film, or video tape (Fig. 31.8). For example, a thyroid scan is done by administering a suitable compound containing ^{99m}Tc or ^{123}I. Since nonfunctioning tissue in the thyroid does not absorb these materials, it appears as a less radioactive region in the thyroid. Areas with above-normal metabolic activity also show up with high levels of radioactivity. Other common scans include those of the liver, kidneys, and brain.

The *Anger* or *gamma camera* is an ingenious device developed by H. O. Anger in 1957. It measures the radioactivity everywhere in a large area simultaneously and displays the results on an oscilloscope screen as well as recording them on film or tape. This makes it possible to perform dynamic studies in which one observes a radionuclide enter or leave an organ. It also permits static examinations to be completed in a minute or so. For this reason, the Anger camera has largely replaced the older scanners, which required up to an hour.

The gamma camera has a single, large, thin scintillating crystal shielded by a lead collimator containing hundreds of holes (Fig. 31.9*a*). This collimator is placed over the organ under study. Nineteen light-sensitive *photomultiplier tubes* behind the crystal observe flashes of light produced when a gamma ray passes through the crystal and send signals to a small computer. The amount of light entering a particular tube depends on its distance from the point where the gamma ray passes through the crystal. The computer locates this point from the relative light intensities and sends appropriate signals to the oscilloscope plates. The oscilloscope then displays a two-dimensional picture whose intensity at each point is proportional to the level of radioactivity at the corresponding point in the organ. Gamma cameras are used to diagnose diseases of the thyroid, liver, brain, kidneys, lungs, spleen, heart, and circulatory system.

Positron Emission Tomography | Positron emission tomography, commonly referred to as PET, also forms images using gamma rays emitted from a radionuclide. However the origin of the gamma rays is different from that described above. Here radionuclides that decay through positron emission are introduced into the body; gamma rays are produced when the positrons encounter electrons and annihilate. Also, PET is used almost exclusively with apparatus that constructs pictures of slices or tomograms (Section 24.12).

When positron emission occurs, the positron does not travel far before encountering an electron. They annihilate, producing gamma rays. This is a striking example of the equivalence of mass and energy. The positron and electron are usually moving slowly at the time of annihilation so their net momentum and kinetic energy are approximately zero. Hence the energy released is almost exactly the combined rest energy of the two, 1022 keV. To conserve momentum, at least two gamma rays must be produced. Two-photon emission is, in fact, the predominant annihilation mode; three-photon emis-

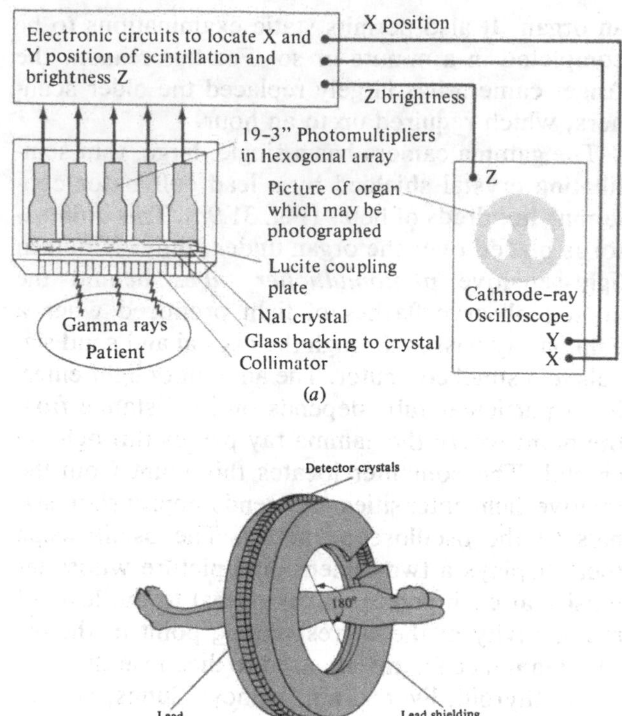

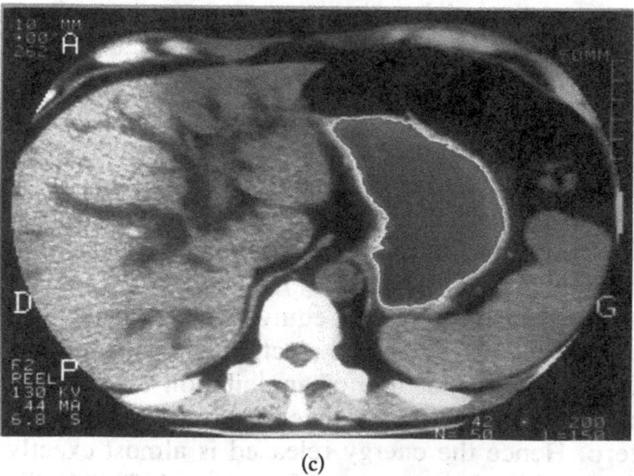

(c)

sion happens infrequently. If the pair was initially at rest, energy and momentum conservation requires that the two photons emerge in opposite directions (at 180°) and that each have half the energy released, or 511 keV. A small deviation from 180° occurs when the initial net momentum of the pair is not exactly zero.

The growing importance of PET is due to three factors. First and probably foremost, a number of biologically important positron-emitting radionuclides are now available as are techniques to introduce them rapidly into useful biological compounds. Positron emitters usually have a rather short half-life, so they are produced nearby on site by cyclotrons set up expressly for that purpose. Three such isotopes are ^{15}O, ^{13}N, and ^{11}C with half-lives of roughly 2, 10, and 20 minutes, respectively. These isotopes can be introduced as labels into compounds containing oxygen, nitrogen, and carbon without modifying the normal chemical activity of the compounds.

The second factor is the high probability of detecting the gamma rays in an arrangement such as that in Fig. 31.9*b*. By contrast, in the conventional gamma-ray imaging described, many photons are lost through collimation. Third, the ring geometry and computer-monitored coincidence checking introduced to verify that two detected photons are indeed from a single electron–positron annihilation event are ideally suited to produce tomograms. These contain considerably more information and better resolution than the conventional images.

Although gamma rays and X rays are both electromagnetic waves, the information obtainable from PET is considerably different from that from X rays and often not available from X rays at all. This is because this technique does not depend on comparing the absorbed intensity from rays passing through the object. Instead, using the fact that the observed gamma rays are 180° apart, the location of the labeled substance is easily obtained by triangulation using a number of events. This makes PET

Figure 31.9. (*a*) The Anger or gamma camera. (*b*) A schematic view of a positron emission tomography apparatus. There are several rings of gamma photon detectors that recognize coincidental events 180° apart. In some designs, the coincidences can be correlated between the rings so that data for tomograms of several planes can be collected at once. (*c*) A CAT scan, made with X rays of a plane through a human abdomen. The very white structure at the bottom of the image is the spinal column. (James Cavallini / Photo Researchers, Inc.)

very valuable, for example, in following processes in the brain. Cerebral blood volume can be determined by having a patient inhale ^{11}C-labeled carbon monoxide, CO. This compound is used because it readily binds to hemoglobin and thus labels the entire blood volume. This same tracking of labeled hemoglobin forms the basis for metabolic studies in heart muscle.

Radioimmunoassay (RIA) | A technique with increasingly widespread applications in research and in medical diagnosis, RIA can detect minute quantities of *antibodies*, hormones, and other complex molecules. An antibody is a protein molecule manufactured by the body to combat a specific *antigen*. For example, someone who inhales ragweed pollen produces a particular antibody that binds to the pollen.

In one version of RIA, a known quantity of radioactively labeled antigen is added to a sample of blood serum. (Serum is a clear yellowish fluid obtained by removing the cells in the blood with a centrifuge.) Some of the labeled antigen binds to antibodies in the serum, forming antigen–antibody complexes. These complexes are separated out using electrophoresis (Section 17.11) or other methods. The radioactivity of the separated complexes indicates the fraction of the labeled antigen that has been bound in competition with the unlabeled antigen originally in the serum. Comparison with known calibration samples then determines the amount of antigen originally present. In another RIA procedure, labeled antibodies are added to serum that bind with human growth hormone molecules. The radioactivity of the separated complexes then indicates the level of this crucial hormone.

Therapy | As we noted earlier, rapidly dividing cancer cells are highly vulnerable to radiation. Also, unlike many kinds of normal cells, they lack the ability to repair themselves. Accordingly, at least half of all cancer patients receive *radiation therapy*, often in combination with surgery and chemotherapy. Sometimes the radiation is administered externally, using ^{60}Co gamma rays, or X rays produced by an electron linear accelerator or a conventional X-ray machine (Fig. 31.10). Large medical centers frequently have facilities for irradiating patients with electron beams. Alternatively, radium-filled needles, small seeds containing radon

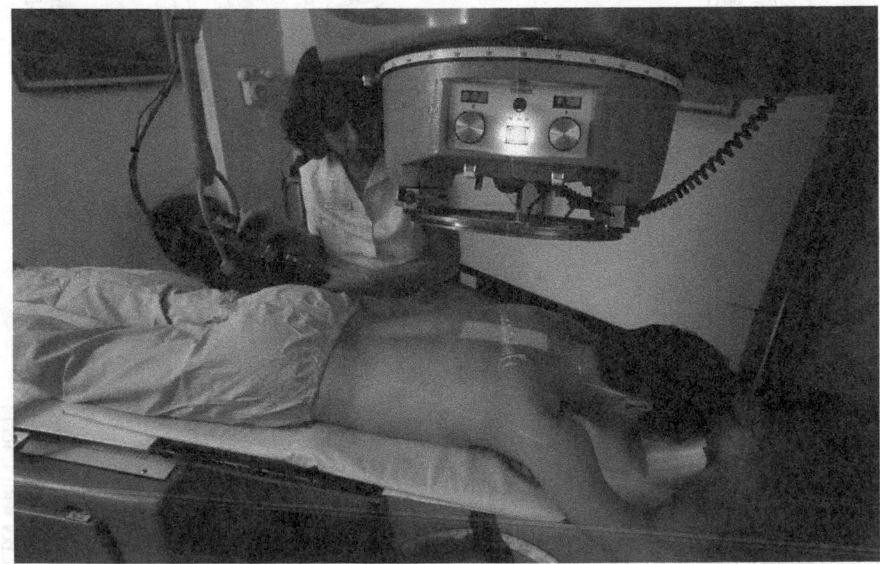

Figure 31.10. A facility for ^{60}Co radiation therapy. The cobalt is in a heavily shielded container that can be moved near various parts of the patient's body. Since the cobalt produces gamma rays that have a greater energy than is available with standard X-ray machines, they penetrate farther into the body and are more effective in treating many forms of cancer. (Martin Dohrn / Photo Researchers, Inc.)

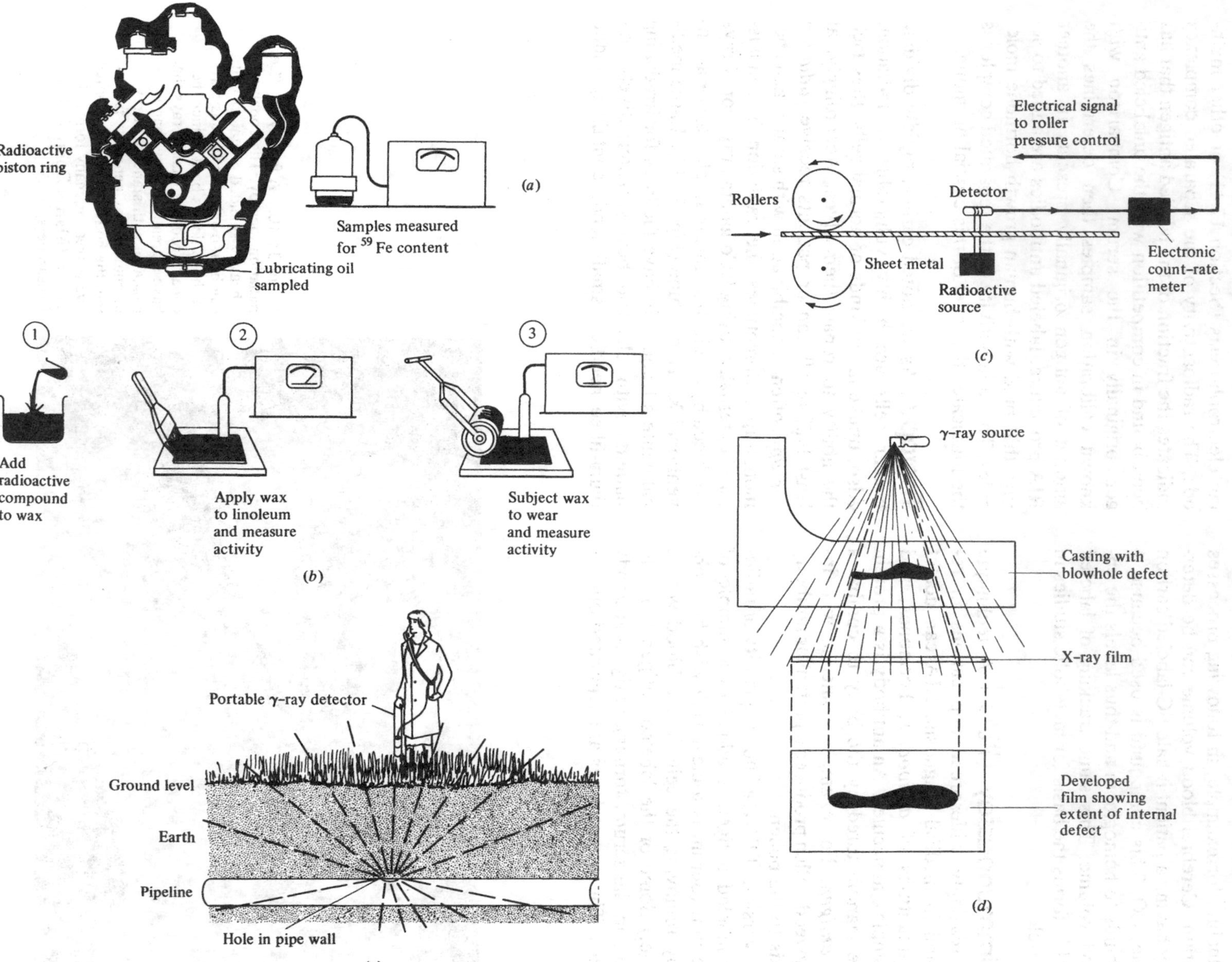

Figure 31.11. Typical industrial uses of radiation. Measurement of wear rates of (*a*) engine parts and (*b*) floor wax. (*c*) A thickness gauge. (*d*) Inspection of castings. (*e*) Locating pipeline leaks with tracers.

gas, or wires or ribbons containing artificial radionuclides may be implanted in the tumor. Occasionally, radioactive compounds are administered that are absorbed by the affected part of the body. Still in the experimental stage is the use of beams of neutrons and other particles with fairly high energies. Because these particles deposit much of their energy in a small region near the end of their range, it is hoped that they will do less damage to the tissues surrounding the cancer being irradiated and therefore permit larger doses.

31.6 | OTHER USES OF RADIATION

Radiation has hundreds of uses in agriculture and industry. Sometimes radiation offers the cheapest or most convenient way to perform some function, while in other situations, no other technique is available. For example, there is often no substitute for tracer studies of metabolic processes or complex reactions.

In agriculture, tracers have been used to study how fertilizers, hormones, weed killers, and pesticides perform their functions. With labeled growth hormones or pesticides, it is even possible to measure residues in the final food products that are too minute to be detected chemically.

Radiation has been used to induce plant mutations, which have led to improved varieties of many crops, such as wheat, peas, and beans, with higher yields and more resistance to diseases. It has also been used to eliminate a major agricultural pest, the screwworm fly, without employing pesticides. This was done by using radiation to sterilize hordes of male flies and releasing them to compete with normal males for mates. The females mate only once, and unfertilized eggs do not hatch. Hence repeatedly saturating an area with millions of sterile males soon wiped out the population completely.

The range of uses that radiation has found in industry can be seen with some typical examples (Fig. 31.11). Gamma rays or X rays are used much like medical diagnostic X rays to reveal potentially dangerous but invisible defects in metal castings and welds. The thickness of rolled sheets of plastic, paper, or metal, or of thin coatings, can be controlled by measuring the transmission of radiation. Densities and fluid levels are easily measured. Tracers are used to locate leaks in underground pipelines, to measure the rate of wear of automobile tires and engine parts, and to determine the effectiveness of detergents.

SUMMARY

Charged particles passing through matter ionize atoms along their paths by colliding with atomic electrons. For a given energy, the rate of energy loss with distance is greatest for the most massive particles. Hence at energies of a few MeV, alpha particles penetrate about 0.01 cm in water, while electrons travel about 1 cm. Photons lose energy to electrons via the photoelectric, Compton, and pair production processes; at 1 MeV, their range is about 10 cm. Neutrons lose energy only in nuclear processes, and their ranges are of the order of a metre.

The source activity refers to the number of nuclear disintegrations occurring per second in a source and is measured in curies. The exposure indicates the number of photons in an X-ray or gamma-ray beam and is measured in roentgens. The absorbed dose for any kind of radiation is the energy absorbed per unit mass of material; its unit is the rad. One roentgen of X rays or gamma rays produces a dose of about 1 rad. The biologically equivalent dose in rems is the absorbed dose in rads times the quality factor, which is defined to be 1 for 200 keV X rays.

Radiation doses from cosmic rays and naturally occurring radionuclides average about 300 millirems per year in the United States. Medical diagnostic X rays contribute almost as large a dose on the average. The effects of low-level radiation in causing cancer and inducing mutations are apparently proportional to the total dose accumulated. Immature rapidly growing cells are highly radiosensitive, so many kinds of cancer cells can be killed with radiation.

Checklist

Define or explain:

ionizing radiation	photoelectric effect
range	Compton scattering
energy loss rate	pair production

source activity	maximum permissible dose
curie, becquerel	linear hypothesis
exposure	latent period
roentgen	radon
absorbed dose	tracers
rad, gray	Anger camera
quality factor	CAT scan
rem, sievert	PET
doubling dose	

REVIEW QUESTIONS

Q31-1 The rate at which a charged particle loses energy in matter is _____ to the mass for a given kinetic energy.

Q31-2 Photons lose energy by _____, _____, and _____.

Q31-3 Which of the following has the longest range: protons, alpha particles, positrons, neutrons? Which has the shortest range?

Q31-4 The source activity varies _____ with the half-life.

Q31-5 Absorbed dose is the energy absorbed per _____.

Q31-6 A 1-roentgen exposure to X rays gives an absorbed dose of about _____.

Q31-7 Radiation is so lethal because it can disrupt critical _____.

Q31-8 The major source of artificial radiation exposure is _____.

Q31-9 Prolonged exposure to low-level radiation can cause _____ and _____.

Q31-10 Rapidly growing cells are most _____.

EXERCISES

Section 31.1 | The Interaction of Radiation with Matter

31-1 If a microwave beam is sufficiently intense, it can heat a material sufficiently to ionize some of its atoms. How does this differ qualitatively from the way gamma-ray photons cause ionization?

31-2 The rate of energy loss for a charged particle in a medium with atomic number Z is almost exactly proportional to nZ, where n is the number of atoms per unit volume. Give an argument for this.

31-3 In a laboratory experiment to study the properties of radioactive sources, a student finds that the count rate drops sharply to zero when a Geiger–Mueller counter in the air is moved from 9 cm to 10 cm from the source. (a) What is the most likely nature of the radiation? Explain. (b) Estimate the range of this radiation in aluminum, assuming the range varies inversely with the density. (The density of aluminum is 2700 kg m^{-3}, and that of air is 1.29 kg m^{-3}.)

31-4 Using Fig. 31.4, find the ranges of 10-MeV alpha particles and 10-MeV electrons in water.

31-5 In the photoelectric process, a gamma ray is absorbed and an electron is ejected from an atom. Usually, X rays are then produced. Explain why.

31-6 When a gamma ray is absorbed in a photoelectric process, an electron is ejected from an atom, and the gamma ray disappears. Is the kinetic energy of the electron equal to the gamma-ray energy? Explain your answer.

31-7 In electron–positron pair production by gamma rays, some momentum is transferred to a nearby nucleus. Why is the energy transferred to the nucleus very small?

31-8 According to Fig. 31.5, when gamma rays are absorbed in water, at what energy are pair production and Compton scattering equally important?

31-9 Protons and deuterons (^1_1H and ^2_1H) lose the same amount of energy in a thin sheet of material. How are their energies related?

31-10 If protons and deuterons (^1_1H and ^2_1H) have the same kinetic energy when they enter a thin sheet of material, how are the energies they lose related?

31-11 How could thin foils and a proton detector be used to determine the energy of a beam of protons produced by an accelerator?

31-12 Suppose ^{14}C and ^{14}N nuclei are both accelerated to an energy of 40 MeV and are then allowed to pass through a thin foil. If the ^{14}C nuclei lose 2 MeV, how much energy will the ^{14}N nuclei lose? (Some of the dating studies based on the direct detection of radioactive nuclei with accelerators use this technique to sort out the various nuclei with nearly equal masses. See Section 30.3.)

31-13 Using Fig. 31.4, estimate the range of a 10-MeV electron in (a) water; (b) lead.

Section 31.2 | Radiation Units

31-14 What is the mass of a 1-microcurie (10^{-6}-Ci) ^{131}I source? (The half-life of ^{131}I is 8.1 days.)

31-15 How many positive ions are produced in 1 kg of air at standard conditions by a 1-R X-ray exposure? (Assume each ion has one electronic charge, $+e$.)

31-16 A 10^{-6}-Ci source has a half-life of 8 h. How many moles of the radioactive material are present in the source?

31-17 When ^{99m}Tc decays, it emits a 140-keV gamma ray. (a) How many photons per second are emitted by a 10^{-6}-Ci ^{99m}Tc source? (b) How much energy, in keV, is carried by these photons? (c) Find the power in joules per second or watts associated with the photons.

31-18 Radon radioactivity levels average 1.5 pCi per litre in single-family homes in the United States. Express this activity in becquerels per cubic metre. (1 pCi = 1 picocurie = 10^{-12} curie.)

31-19 Water from a mineral spring is naturally radioactive, with an activity of 300 becquerels per litre. What is the activity in curies of a 100-litre tank of this water?

31-20 A well-insulated tank of water exposed to radiation has its temperature increased by 30 K. How many rads were absorbed?

31-21 A beam of gamma rays is found to produce 10^{16} positive ions per kilogram in dry air at STP. What is the corresponding exposure if each ion has a charge $+e$?

31-22 Treating fish or meat with 200,000 rads kills many of the bacteria present and increases the refrigerated shelf life five to seven times. (a) How much energy is absorbed per kilogram of food? (b) Neglecting heat losses, estimate the temperature rise. (Assume that the specific heat is equal to that of water.)

31-23 A ^{60}Co source produces an absorbed dose of 4000 rads per hour in tissue. The QF is 0.7 for cobalt gamma rays. (a) How much time is required for an absorbed dose of 300 rads? (b) How much time is required for a biologically equivalent dose of 300 rems?

31-24 A mouse receives an absorbed dose of 200 rads of 10-MeV protons, which have a QF of 2. What is the biologically equivalent dose?

31-25 The average radiation dose received at sea level from cosmic rays is 41 mrem per year. What is this dose in sieverts per year?

31-26 A tank of water absorbs 1000 grays. By how much does its temperature rise?

Section 31.1 | Harmful Effects of Radiation
Section 31.4 | Chronic Radiation Exposure

31-27 A nuclear radiation technologist receives a whole-body dose of 0.1 rem every time she loads a radium source. How many times is she permitted to load the source in (a) a quarter year; (b) a year?

31-28 The lethal dose of radiation for mammals and birds is under 1000 rads, while it takes about 100,000 rads to kill amoebas and over 1 million rads to kill viruses. What is the likely reason for this?

31-29 Suppose 100,000 radiation workers each receive 5 rems. Is this more or less important genetically than the entire world population of about 5 billion people receiving 5 millirems? Why?

31-30 A stewardess flies at an average height of 11 km for 20 hours per week. If she receives 0.7 millirems per hour, what is her annual biologically equivalent dose? Compare this with the MPD for the general population and for radiation workers.

31-31 Estimate the death rate due to diagnostic X rays, assuming the U.S. cancer death rate is 300,000 per year, that the doubling dose for cancer is 250 rems, and that the average person of age 30 has received 72 millirems per year.

31-32 A radiation worker accidentally receives 50 rems. Using the assumptions in the preceding exercise, estimate his chances of developing cancer because of this accident.

31-33 The earliest safety rules for radiological personnel limited their dose to the equivalent of 100 rems per year, a level low enough to avoid skin burns. Estimate the cancer risk and genetic effects of such doses.

31-34 If a man lives in Denver instead of at sea level, how much does the additional cosmic-ray exposure reduce his life expectancy? (Use the data in Table 31.3, and assume that 10,000 person rems produces one premature cancer death.)

31-35 Workers in medical fields who receive measurable doses of radiation average whole-body doses of 320 mrem per year. The collective annual dose for all medical radiation workers is 51,400 person rems. Assume 10,000 person rems produces one premature cancer death. (a) How many medical workers received a measurable radiation dose? (b) How many of these workers are likely to die of cancer caused by one year's exposure?

31-36 Show that assuming a doubling dose for cancer of 250 rems and an annual U.S. cancer death rate of 300,000 is equivalent to equating approximately 5000 person rems to one premature cancer death.

31-37 In discussing possible reduction of the maximum occupational dose from 5 rems per year to 0.5 rem per year, an NRC report notes that 2.6 million person rems would be saved in the nuclear power plant industry over a 20-year period. The estimated cost of this reduction would be $23 billion, which was considered to be excessive. How much would this cost for each premature cancer death prevented? (Assume 10,000 person rems produces one premature cancer death.)

31-38 According to one article, the 1986 accident at the Chernobyl reactor in the Soviet Union was estimated to have produced a worldwide collective dose of 10,000,000 person rems. The world population is about 5 billion people. Most of these people live near sea level. (a) Find the ratio of the total collective dose to that due to cosmic rays over a year. (b) How many deaths are likely to result worldwide from the accident? (Assume 10,000 person rems produces one premature cancer death.)

31-39 Nuclear weapons testing has exposed people to about 4 mrem per year for 30 years. Assume 10,000 person rems produces one premature cancer death. Estimate the annual number of premature deaths worldwide due to this testing. (Use a world population of 5 billion people.)

Section 31.5 | Radiation in Medicine

31-40 In *rotation therapy* the patient or the radiation source is rotated about an axis through the tumor being irradiated. What is the advantage of this procedure?

31-41 How do you explain the apparent paradox that X rays induce cancer and that X rays are used to treat cancer?

Section 31.6 | Other Uses of Radiation

31-42 How can you use radioactively labeled dirt to test the effectiveness of a detergent?

PROBLEMS

31-43 X-ray machines produce a continuous distribution of X-ray photon energies up to a maximum determined by the voltage of the machine. A thin sheet of aluminum will absorb the lowest-energy X rays without appreciably absorbing the higher-energy photons. (a) What is the reason for this? (b) What is the advantage of such an aluminum filter in medical uses of X rays?

31-44 A 1000-Ci alpha emitter is in a lead container. (a) How many disintegrations occur per second? (b) The alpha particles have an energy of 2.5 MeV, and all the alphas are stopped in the lead. At what rate is energy absorbed in the lead?

31-45 Cobalt 60 produces two gamma rays per disintegration. (a) How many gammas are emitted per second by a 10-Ci source? (b) What is the flux of gammas per square metre at a distance of 1 m from the source? (Assume the radiation is uniform in all directions.)

31-46 A 10-Ci β^- emitter is 2 m from your hand. How many electrons strike each square centimetre of your hand per second? (Neglect absorption in air.)

31-47 A radiation worker is accidentally exposed to 100 R of 200-keV X rays. Estimate the absorbed and biologically equivalent doses.

31-48 One milligram of radium produces a dose of 8.2 rads per hour at a distance of 0.01 m. The

QF for radium gamma rays is 0.965 for the tissue irradiated. (a) Explain why the exposure varies inversely with the square of the distance from the source. (b) How long is required for a 60-mg radium source to give a dose of 100 rems at a distance of 0.01 m? (c) How long would this take at 0.05 m?

31-49 A small quantity of radioactive serum albumin is administered to a patient, and an equal quantity is placed in 2000 cm^3 of water to serve as a standard. After 10 min, a blood sample is taken from the patient and the red cells removed by centrifugation, leaving the serum. The activity of 10 cm^3 of the serum is measured with a scintillation counter and found to be 2600 counts per minute. A 10-cm^3 sample from the standard gives 1892 counts per minute. In both cases, 155 counts per minute are due to background from cosmic rays and other environmental sources. What is the total volume of the patient's blood serum?

31-50 After an accident, the World Health Organization recommended banning food contaminated with radioactive material with an activity of 4000 Bq kg^{-1} (becquerels per kilogram) or greater. Suppose that a 80-kg man ingests 1 kg of food with this activity and that each disintegration produces 1 MeV of radiation that is totally absorbed in his body. If the effective half-life of the radioactive material is 1 week, estimate the total dose in rads averaged over his body.

31-51 Suppose a young child accidentally swallowed the radioactive source described in Example 31.5. (a) Assuming that half the gamma rays are absorbed by the child, how much energy does the child absorb in a year? (b) If the mass of the child is 20 kg, what is the absorbed dose in rads in a year? (c) Using a quality factor of 0.8, find the ratio of the biologically equivalent dose to the average annual dose from natural causes, 88 mrem.

31-52 After it has been in operation for a year or so, a large nuclear reactor has accumulated about 10^{10} Ci of radioactive wastes from the fission reactions. If the reactor is shut down by inserting the control rods, this radioactive material continues to emit decay products for a long time. (a) How many kilograms of radium would be needed to produce as many decays per second? (b) Assuming that a typical decay releases 1 MeV, at what rate in watts does the reactor continue to produce heat? (c) Find the ratio of this power to the rate heat is generated when the reactor is in operation, 3×10^9 watts.

31-53 (a) In March 1979, an accident occurred at the reactor at Three Mile Island near Middletown, Pennsylvania. ^{133}Xe, which has a half-life of about 5 days, was released in sufficient quantity to cause a total exposure to the public over a large region of approximately 4000 person rems. Using the 10,000 person rems per cancer ratio, how many extra cancer deaths are likely to occur because of the accident? (b) Could these predictions be verified with public health data? Explain.

31-54 Estimate the percentage of all deaths that are due to cancers caused by radiation from natural sources.

31-55 If a large population consumes milk containing radioactive ^{131}I, latent thyroid cancers will be induced at approximately 63 cancers per 10^6 person rads of thyroid dose. In 1976, fallout from nuclear explosions in the atmosphere detonated by the People's Republic of China resulted in an average thyroid dose in the United States of 3.1×10^{-4} rad. The total U.S. population is about 2.2×10^8. (a) How many extra thyroid cancers were induced in the United States by these explosions? (b) These cancers will appear over a period of 45 years. The present rate of thyroid cancers in the United States is 8400 per year. Find the fractional increase in this rate. (c) Infants received thyroid doses as large as 0.02 rad. What chance does such an infant have of developing thyroid cancer because of the fallout? (In order to carry out the calculation, assume that the risk for a given dose to an infant is the same as for the overall population. The risk is, in fact, larger.)

ANSWERS TO REVIEW QUESTIONS

Q31-1, proportional; **Q31-2**, photoelectric effect, Compton scattering, pair production; **Q31-3**, neutrons, alpha particles; **Q31-4**, inversely; **Q31-5**, unit mass; **Q31-6**, 1 rad; **Q31-7**, biological molecules;

Q31-8, diagnostic X rays; **Q31-9**, cancer, genetic mutations; **Q31-10**, radiosensitive.

SUPPLEMENTARY TOPICS

31.7 | RADIATION DETECTION AND MEASUREMENT

Radiation is detected by observing the ionization it produces in matter. In this section, we describe the radiation detectors most commonly used in biomedical applications of radiation.

Gas Ionization Counters | These detectors, which are easy to use, are very sensitive to beta particles. They can also be used for gamma rays, but are not very effective in stopping this more penetrating radiation. A typical arrangement has argon gas in a cylinder with a fine wire along its axis (Fig. 31.12). When ionization is produced by radiation, a brief current pulse results that is metered or recorded.

Depending on the applied voltage V_0, the counter operates in basically different ways (Fig. 31.13). A small voltage drives all the ions and electrons produced to the cathode or anode, causing a small current pulse. Increasing the voltage further, we reach the *proportional region*, where each electron released in the original ionization process acquires sufficient kinetic energy to ionize one or more additional atoms before it reaches the anode. The total charge in the current pulse now is proportional to the initial amount of ionization, and it indicates the

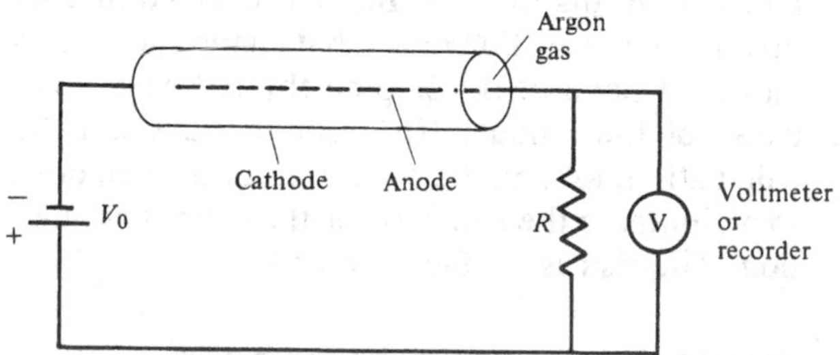

Figure 31.12. Gas ionization counter. When radiation ionizes one of the argon atoms, the electrons are attracted to the positively charged wire (anode) and the positive ions to the negatively charged outer cylinder (cathode). This produces a current through R and a voltage drop across it that is measured by the voltmeter.

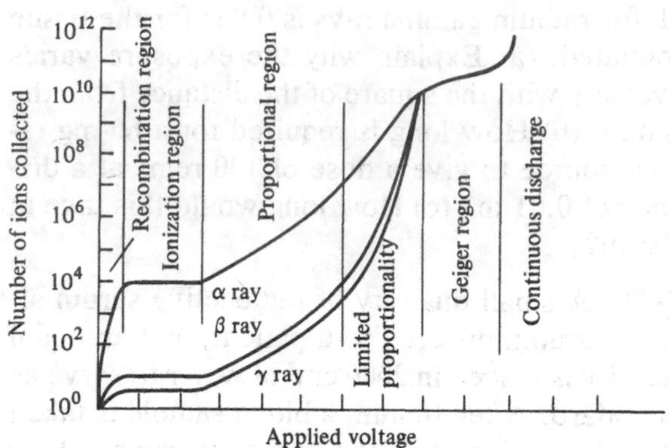

Figure 31.13. Number of ions collected versus applied voltage in a gas ionization counter.

energy of the beta particle or gamma ray that passed through the detector. Often these current pulses are fed to a *multichannel analyzer*, which records the number of pulses produced versus the total charge in the pulse. This information can be used to identify the nuclide producing the radiation (Fig. 31.14).

If the applied voltage is increased still more, the counter operates in the *Geiger region*. Here each electron produces several secondary electrons, which in turn produce others, and so on. A current pulse develops that is large enough so that it can be observed or recorded with very simple circuits. Such a detector is called a *Geiger–Müller counter*, and it can be quite compact and portable. However, the total amount of charge in a pulse is the same for any incident ionizing particle, since the tube becomes fully ionized. Consequently, a Geiger–Müller counter cannot be used to identify the nature or energy of the radiation being detected.

Scintillation Counters | These counters have relatively high efficiencies for detecting gamma rays and can be used to measure their energies. They are the detectors most widely used in biomedical applications.

A scintillation counter consists of a crystal such as sodium iodide and a *photomultiplier*. When it is irradiated, the crystal *scintillates* or emits flashes of visible light as atoms excited by the radiation emit photons. The photons enter the photomultiplier and strike a light-sensitive cathode, causing the emis-

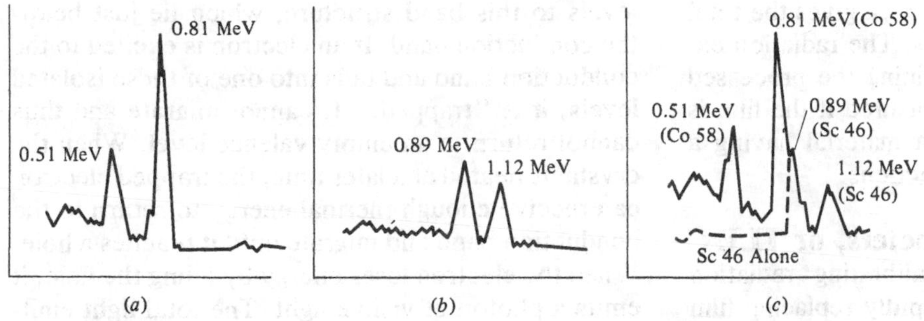

Figure 31.14. Gamma-ray spectra obtained with a multichannel analyzer. The gamma-ray energy is the horizontal coordinate, and the vertical coordinate gives the intensity at that energy. (*a*) ^{58}Co. (*b*) ^{46}Sc. (*c*) A mixture of ^{58}Co and ^{46}Sc. Mixtures of radionuclides can be analyzed if the energy resolution of the apparatus is good enough to distinguish the characteristic peaks. Sometimes, samples are made radioactive artificially by exposing them to beams of neutrons, gamma rays, or charged particles that induce various nuclear reactions. Such *activation* techniques require only small samples and can be used to detect and measure extremely small traces of many elements.

sion of electrons (Fig. 31.15). These electrons are accelerated by a potential difference and strike an electrode called a *dynode*, which emits approximately four secondary electrons for each incident electron. A series of 10 dynodes gives an amplification factor of 4^{10}, or approximately a million. As in the proportional gas counter, the total charge in the current pulse is proportional to the amount of ionization, and a multichannel analyzer can be used to identify the source.

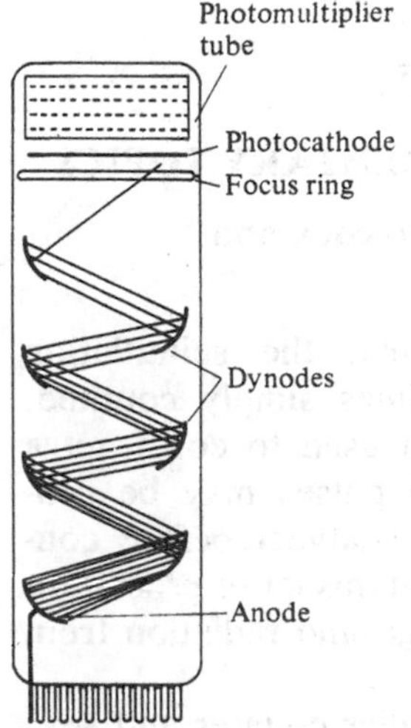

Figure 31.15. Scintillation counter.

Semiconducting Detectors | When radiation deposits energy in a semiconducting material, electrons can be excited from filled valence bands to conduction bands. This produces pairs of conduction electrons and electron vacancies, or *positive holes*. If a potential difference is maintained across the semiconductor, these charge carriers will move, and a current pulse will be observed. The energy needed to produce an electron–hole pair is typically about 1 eV, considerably less than the energy needed to ionize gas atoms or to excite atoms in a scintillating crystal. Accordingly, a relatively large number of charge carriers is produced for a given energy loss. The statistical fluctuations in the number of atoms excited or ionized limit the energy resolution of any detector. The large number of charge carriers produced in the semiconductor reduces these statistical effects and enables such a detector to determine energies very accurately when used with a multichannel analyzer.

At the present time, these detectors are expensive and difficult to make unless they are quite small. Small semiconducting detectors have the disadvantage of low-gamma-ray efficiencies.

Photographic Emulsions | Film badges are used to monitor the beta- and gamma-ray exposure of radiation personnel. Thin metal strips shield parts of the film from beta rays so that they indicate the gamma flux; the unshielded area gives the total dose from beta and gamma rays. The radiation exposure is determined by examining the processed film. Neutron doses can be measured if the film is impregnated or covered with a material having a high probability for neutron reactions.

Thermoluminescent Dosimeters, or TLDs | These are widely used in calibrating radiation sources in hospitals and are rapidly replacing film badges in personnel monitoring. A TLD is a crystal such as lithium fluoride (LiF) or calcium fluoride (CaF_2) containing trace impurities. After a TLD is exposed to radiation, it will emit visible light upon being heated. The total amount of light emitted is directly proportional to the dose received by the crystal, even if the crystal is stored for many months after exposure. TLDs are more accurate than film badges and are usable over a much larger range of radiation levels.

The principle of the TLD is illustrated in Fig. 31.16, which shows the energy levels of a LiF crystal. A perfect crystal will have a completely filled valence band and an empty conduction band. Electrons cannot be in energy levels between these bands. Electrons can be excited from the valence band to the conduction band, leaving empty valence levels or holes if they absorb enough energy from the radiation passing through the crystal. The impurity atoms present in the crystal add isolated energy levels to this band structure, which lie just below the conduction band. If an electron is excited to the conduction band and falls into one of these isolated levels, it is "trapped." It cannot migrate and thus cannot return to an empty valence level. When the crystal is heated at a later time, the trapped electron can receive enough thermal energy to return to the conduction band and migrate until it reaches a hole. When the electron loses energy by filling the hole, it emits a photon of visible light. The total light emitted as the crystal is heated is a measure of the number of trapped electrons and therefore of the total absorbed radiation.

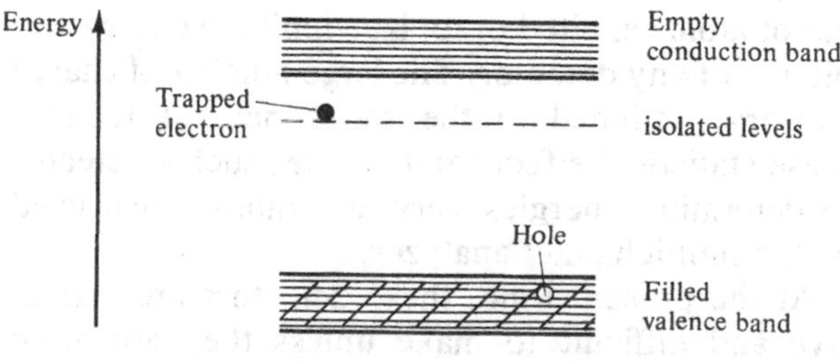

Figure 31.16. Energy levels of a LiF crystal. A perfect crystal has a filled band and an empty conduction band. Isolated levels below the conduction band are caused by impurities. If radiation excites an electron to the conduction band, leaving a valence band hole, the electron can fall into an isolated level and become trapped. Heating will provide the energy needed for the electron to return to the conduction band. It will emit visible light when it drops to the vacant valence band level.

31.8 | DERIVATION OF THE ENERGY LOSS RATE FORMULA

We now derive Eq. 31.1 for the rate of energy loss with distance for an ion in matter.

The velocity $\mathbf{v}_e$ of an atomic electron in the medium is negligible compared to its final velocity $\mathbf{v}'_e$ after it is struck by the ion. The momentum transferred by the ion to the electron is therefore $\mathbf{F}\,\Delta t = m_e(\mathbf{v}'_e - \mathbf{v}_e) \simeq m_e\mathbf{v}'_e$, where $\mathbf{F}$ is the force exerted by the ion and Δt is the time duration of the collision. The energy transferred to the electron is approximately $\frac{1}{2}m_e v_e'^2$, which is proportional to $(\mathbf{F}\,\Delta t)^2$. Now the electric force between the ion and the electron is proportional to the ion charge q, and the collision time varies inversely with the ion velocity v. Thus $\mathbf{F}\,\Delta t$ must vary as q/v, and the energy transfer as q^2/v^2, or as we stated earlier,

$$\Delta K \propto \frac{q^2}{v^2} \tag{31.1}$$

EXERCISES ON SUPPLEMENTARY TOPICS

Section 31.7 | Radiation Detection and Measurement

31-56 In gamma-ray scans, the scintillation counter pulses are sometimes simply counted, and the count rate is then used to construct a picture. Alternatively, the pulses may be processed by a multichannel analyzer before constructing a picture. How can this latter procedure reduce the effects of background radiation from other sources?

31-57 Given a Geiger–Müller counter and several thin slabs of a material containing a large amount of hydrogen, such as a hydrocarbon, how can you tell whether a given radioactive source is emitting neutrons?

Additional Reading

Steward C. Barshong, Radiation Exposure in Our Daily Lives, *The Physics Teacher*, vol. 15, 1977, p. 135. Survey of environmental, occupational, and medical exposures.

G. S. Hurst and J. E. Turner, *Elementary Radiation Physics*, John Wiley & Sons, Inc., New York, 1970. An excellent brief introduction at the level of this book.

E. F. Gloyna and J. E. Ledbetter, *Principles of Radiological Health*, Marcel Dekker, Inc., New York, 1969. Emphasis on simplified calculational methods and engineering estimates.

Louis E. Etter (ed.), *The Science of Ionizing Radiation*, Charles C Thomas, Springfield, Ill., 1965. Interesting chapters on history and on medical and other applications.

J. N. Gregory, *The World of Radioisotopes*, Angus and Robertson, Sydney, 1966. Directed at nontechnical audiences; many interesting applications.

H. E. Johns and J. R. Cunningham, *The Physics of Radiology*, 3rd ed., Charles C Thomas, Springfield, Ill., 1969.

Victor Arena, *Ionizing Radiation and Life*, The C. V. Mosby Co., St. Louis, 1971.

Bacq and Alexander, *Fundamentals of Radiobiology*, Pergamon Press, New York, 1961.

P. N. Goodwin, E. H. Quimby, and R. H. Morgan, *Physical Foundations of Radiology*, 4th ed., Harper & Row, Publishers, Inc., New York, 1970.

G. E. M. Jauncey, The Early Days of Radioactivity, *American Journal of Physics*, vol. 14, 1946, p. 226.

Gordon L. Brownell and Robert J. Shalek, Nuclear Physics of Medicine, *Physics Today*, August 1970, p. 33.

Advisory Committee on the Biological Effects of Ionizing Radiations, *The Effects on Populations of Exposure to Low Levels of Ionizing Radiation*, National Academy of Sciences, National Research Council, Washington, D.C., 1972.

Advisory Committee on the Biological Effects of Ionizing Radiation, *The Effects on Populations of Exposure to Low Levels of Ionizing Radiation*, National Research Council, National Academy of Sciences, National Academy Press, Washington, D.C., 1980.

Exposure of the Population of the United States and Canada from Natural Background Radiation, NCRP Report No. 94, National Council on Radiation Protection and Measurement, Washington, D.C., 1987.

Public Radiation Exposure from Nuclear Power Generation in the United States, National Council on Radiation Protection and Measurements, Washington, D.C., 1987.

Committee on the Biological Effects of Ionizing Radiation, *Health Effects of Exposure to Low Levels of Radiation*, National Academy Press, Washington, D.C., 1990.

Eric J. Hall, *Radiation And Life, Second Edition*, Pergamon Press, New York, 1984. A survey of radiation, its effects, uses, and hazards.

Charles M. Koplile, Maureen F. Kaplan, and Benjamin Rass, The Safety of Repositories for Highly Radioactive Wastes, *Reviews of Modern Physics*, vol. 54, 1982, p. 269.

William J. Schull, Masanori Otake, and James V. Neel, Genetic Effects of the Atomic Bombs: A Reappraisal, *Science*, vol. 213, 1981, p. 1220. Descendents of atomic bomb survivors show genetic effects at a rate indicating a doubling dose of 156 rems, some four times larger than the doubling dose suggested by experiments on mice.

J. Michael Smith, Jon A. Broadway, and Ann B. Strong, United States Population Dose Estimates for Iodine-131 in the Thyroid After the Chinese Atmospheric Nuclear Weapons Tests, *Science*, vol. 200, 1978, p. 44.

High Background Radiation Research Group, Health Survey in High Background Radiation Areas in China, *Science*, vol. 209, 1980, p. 877. Studies of people living in areas with above-average natural radioactivity showed no discernable health differences from control groups.

Charles E. Land, Estimating Cancer Risks from Low Doses of Ionizing Radiation, *Science*, vol. 209, 1980, p. 1197.

Scientific American articles:

S. A. Korff, Counters, July 1950, p. 40.

G. B. Collins, Scintillation Counters, November 1953, p. 36.

D. A. Glaser, The Bubble Chamber, February 1955, p. 46.

H. Yagoda, The Tracks of Nuclear Particles, May 1956, p. 40.

Gerard K. O'Neill, The Spark Chamber, August 1962, p. 36.

Olexa-Myron Bilamick, Semiconductor Particle Detectors, October 1962, p. 78.

Jearl Walker, A Radiation Detector Made Out of Aluminum Foil and a Tin Can, *The Amateur Scientist*, September 1979, p. 234.

R. L. Fleischer, P. B. Price, and R. M. Walker, Nuclear Tracks in Solids, June 1969, p. 30.

W. H. Wahl and H. H. Kramer, Neutron Activation Analysis, April 1967, p. 68.

The September 1959 issue was devoted to ionizing radiation.

H. J. Muller, Radiation and Human Mutations, November 1955, p. 58.

E. F. Knipling, The Eradication of the Screw-Worm Fly, October 1960, p. 54.

Theodore T. Puck, Radiation and the Human Cell, April 1960, p. 142.

Renato Baserga and W. B. Kisielski, Autobiographies of Cells, August 1963, p. 103.

Richard Gordon, Gabor T. Herman, and Steven A. Johnson, Image Reconstruction from Projection, October 1975, p. 56.

Michel M. Ter-Pogossian, Marcus E. Raichle, and Burton E. Sobel, Positron-Emission Tomography, October 1980, p. 170.

Ian L. Pykett, NMR Imaging in Medicine, May 1982, p. 78.

Harold W. Lewis, The Safety of Fission Reactors, March 1980, p. 3.

Steven A. Fetter and Kosta Tsipis, Catastrophic Releases of Radioactivity, April 1981, p. 48.

Arthur C. Upton, The Biological Effects of Low-Level Ionizing Radiation, February 1982, p. 41.

Edward R. Landa, The First Nuclear Industry, November 1982, p. 180. Radium production and uses.

Kenneth R. Foster and Arthur W. Guy, The Microwave Problem, September 1986, p. 32. Is exposure to low levels of microwaves hazardous?

Rosalyn S. Yallow, Radioimmunoassay: A Probe for the Fine Structure of Biologic Systems, *Science*, vol. 200, 1978, p. 1236.

Arthur L. Robinson, Position-Sensitive Detectors: An "Electronic Film" for X rays, *Science*, vol. 199, 1978, p. 39.

Maurice J. Cotter and Kathleen Taylor, Neutron Activation Analysis of Paintings, *The Physics Teacher*, vol. 16, May 1978, p. 263.

C. L. Melcher and D. W. Zimmerman, Thermoluminescent Determination of Prehistoric Heat Treatment of Chert Artifacts, *Science*, vol. 197, 1977, p. 1359.

The October 1978 issue of *Physics Today* is devoted to articles on new types of particle detectors.

Arthur Robinson, Image Reconstruction (I) Computerized X-ray Scanners, *Science*, vol. 190, 1975, p. 542; (II) Computerized Scanner Explosion, *Science*, vol. 190, 1975, p. 647.

Rowland W. Redington and Walter H. Berninger, Medical Imaging Systems, *Physics Today*, vol. 34, August 1981, p. 5.

G. L. Brownell et al., Positron Tomography and Nuclear Magnetic Resonance Imaging, *Science*, vol. 215, 1982, p. 619.

U.S. Nuclear Regulatory Commission, *Regulatory Guide* 8.29. Appendix: Instruction Concerning Risks from Occupational Radiation Exposure. Tables of occupational hazards and radiation exposures, discussion of radiation exposure limits.

Richard Wilson, Chernobyl: Assessing the Accident, *Issues in Science and Technology*, vol. III, Fall 1986, p. 21.

A. V. Nero, M. B. Schwehr, W. W. Nazaroff, and K. L. Revzan, Distribution of Airborne Radon-222 Concentrations in U.S. Homes, *Science*, vol. 234, 1986, p. 992.

Anthony Nero, Earth, Air, Radon, and Home, *Physics Today*, April 1989, p. 32.

David Bodansky, Maurice A. Robkin, and David R. Staller, editors, *Indoor Radon and Its Hazards*, University of Washington Press, Seattle, 1987.

Biological Effects and Medical Applications of Electromagnetic Energy, *Proceedings of the IEEE*, vol. 68, no. 1, January, 1980.

APPENDIX A

PERIODIC TABLE OF ELEMENTS

The symbol for each element is preceded by the atomic number; below is the atomic mass of the element as it occurs naturally on the earth. The atomic mass unit (u) is defined so the mass of a ^{12}C atom is exactly 12 u. The mass of carbon is listed as 12.01115 u because naturally occurring carbon is 98.89 percent ^{12}C and 1.11 percent ^{13}C. For artificially produced elements, the approximate atomic mass of the most stable isotope is given in brackets.

Group→		I	II	III	IV	V	VI	VII	VIII			O
Period	Series											
1	1	1 H 1.00797										2 He 4.0026
2	2	3 Li 6.939	4 Be 9.0122	5 B 10.811	6 C 12.01115	7 N 14.0067	8 O 15.9994	9 F 18.9984				10 Ne 20.183
3	3	11 Na 22.9898	12 Mg 24.312	13 Al 26.9815	14 Si 28.086	15 P 30.9738	16 S 32.064	17 Cl 35.453				18 A 39.948
4	4	19 K 39.102	20 Ca 40.08	21 Sc 44.956	22 Ti 47.90	23 V 50.942	24 Cr 51.996	25 Mn 54.9380	26 Fe 55.847	27 Co 58.9332	28 Ni 58.71	
	5	29 Cu 63.54	30 Zn 65.37	31 Ga 69.72	32 Ge 72.59	33 As 74.9216	34 Se 78.96	35 Br 79.909				36 Kr 83.80
5	6	37 Rb 85.47	38 Sr 87.62	39 Y 88.905	40 Zr 91.22	41 Nb 92.906	42 Mo 95.94	43 Tc [99]	44 Ru 101.07	45 Rh 102.905	46 Pd 106.4	
	7	47 Ag 107.870	48 Cd 112.40	49 In 114.82	50 Sn 118.69	51 Sb 121.75	52 Te 127.60	53 I 126.9044				54 Xe 131.30
6	8	55 Cs 132.905	56 Ba 137.34	57–71 Lanthanide series*	72 Hf 178.49	73 Ta 180.948	74 W 183.85	75 Re 186.2	76 Os 190.2	77 Ir 192.2	78 Pt 195.09	
	9	79 Au 196.967	80 Hg 200.59	81 Tl 204.37	82 Pb 207.19	83 Bi 208.980	84 Po [210]	85 At [210]				86 Rn [222]
7	10	87 Fr [223]	88 Ra [226.05]	89–Actinide series**								

* Lanthanide series:	57 La 138.91	58 Ce 140.12	59 Pr 140.907	60 Nd 144.24	61 Pm [145]	62 Sm 150.35	63 Eu 151.96	64 Gd 157.25	65 Tb 158.924	66 Dy 162.50	67 Ho 164.930	68 Er 167.26	69 Tm 168.934	70 Yb 173.04	71 Lu 174.97
** Actinide series:	89 Ac [227]	90 Th 232.038	91 Pa [231]	92 U 238.03	93 Np [237]	94 Pu [242]	95 Am [243]	96 Cm [247]	97 Bk [247]	98 Cf [249]	99 Es [254]	100 Fm [257]	101 Md [256]	102 No [253]	103 Lw [260]
	104 [261]	105 [262]	106 [263]												

APPENDIX B MATHEMATICAL REVIEW

This appendix reviews topics covered in high school or introductory college mathematics courses that are needed in various parts of this book. Students who are somewhat rusty in basic algebra, geometry, and trigonometry may find it helpful to study Sections B.1 to B.6 in detail; the remaining sections are provided mainly for reference at specific points in the book. A list of paperback mathematics review books is given at the end of the appendix for students who need additional preparation in this area. Answers to all the review problems are also given at the end of this appendix.

B.1 | POWERS AND ROOTS

A quantity x multiplied by itself n times is written as x^n. For example, $(2)(2)(2) = 2^3$; in words, this is 2 raised to the *exponent* or *power* 3. The basic rule in manipulating powers of a given number is that exponents add. For example, $(2^2)(2^3) = (2)(2) \cdot (2)(2)(2) = 2^5$. In symbols, the rule is

$$(x^n)(x^m) = x^{n+m} \qquad \text{(B.1)}$$

From this rule, we see that $x^n x^0 = x^n$, so $x^0 = 1$ for any value of x. Also, $x^n x^{-n} = x^0 = 1$, so x^{-n} is the inverse of x^n:

$$x^{-n} = \frac{1}{x^n} \qquad \text{(B.2)}$$

For example, $10^{-2} = 1/10^2 = 1/100 = 0.01$. Another useful rule is

$$(x^n)^m = x^{nm} \qquad \text{(B.3)}$$

For example, $(10^2)^3 = (10)(10) \cdot (10)(10) \cdot (10)(10) = 10^6$; similarly, $(10^2)^{-3} = 10^{-6}$.

When two numbers are raised to the same power, their products and quotients obey simple rules:

$$(x^n)(y^n) = (xy)^n \qquad \text{(B.4)}$$

$$\frac{x^n}{y^n} = \left(\frac{x}{y}\right)^n \qquad \text{(B.5)}$$

For example, $(4)^2(2)^3 = (4 \cdot 2)^3 = (8)^3$, and $(4)^3(2)^{-3} = (4/2)^3 = (2)^3$.

A fractional exponent means that a root of a number is involved. For example, $x^{1/2}x^{1/2} = x^1 = x$, so $x^{1/2}$ is the square root of x. The quantity $x^{1/n}$ is the nth root of x:

$$x^{1/n} = \sqrt[n]{x} \qquad \text{(B.6)}$$

For example, $(64)^{1/3} = \sqrt[3]{64} = 4$. More complicated fractional powers can be evaluated with the aid of Eq. B.3. For example, $(27)^{2/3} = (27^{1/3})^2 = (3)^2 = 9$. All the other rules listed above also apply to fractional powers.

REVIEW PROBLEMS

Evaluate or simplify the following quantities:

1. 2^4
2. 3^2
3. $(2^2)(2^3)$
4. $(x^5)(x^3)(x)$
5. 5^{-2}
6. $(5^{-3})(5^4)$
7. $(x^4)(x)(x^{-3})$
8. x^4/x^2
9. x^4/y^4
10. $(a^2x^4)^{1/2}$
11. $(a^3x^6)^{1/2}$
12. $(x^2y^6)^{1/2}$
13. $(x^4y^4)^{-1/2}$
14. $(1000)^{1/3}$

15. $(10{,}000)^{-1/4}$

16. $x^2(x^6)^{-1/3}$

17. $(125)^{-1/3}$

18. $\left(\frac{x^2}{64}\right)^{1/2}$

19. $(x^4y^{-8})^{1/2}$

20. $(10^4)^{3/4}$

B.2 | SCIENTIFIC NOTATION

A number is said to be in scientific notation when it is written as a number between 1 and 10 times a power of 10. For example, 376 can be written as $3.76 \times 100 = 3.76 \times 10^2$, since $10^2 = 10 \times 10 = 100$. One advantage of this notation is compactness; 376,000,000 can be written as 3.76×10^8. Note that the power of 10 is the number of places the decimal point has been shifted to the left. Similarly, $0.0000376 = 3.76 \times 0.00001 = 3.76 \times 10^{-5}$. Here the number in this negative exponent indicates how many places the decimal point has been shifted to the right.

Scientific notation facilitates many kinds of numerical calculations. It is especially useful in manipulations involving very large or small numbers. As an illustration, consider 2×10^{20} times 3×10^{-15} divided by 8×10^8:

$$\frac{(2 \times 10^{20})(3 \times 10^{-15})}{8 \times 10^8} = \frac{(2)(3)}{8} \times 10^{20-15-8}$$
$$= 0.75 \times 10^{-3} = 7.5 \times 10^{-4}$$

The use of scientific notation also aids in the evaluation of roots, as in the following illustrations:

$$(2.32 \times 10^8)^{1/2} = (2.32)^{1/2}(10^8)^{1/2} = \sqrt{2.32} \times 10^4$$
$$= 1.52 \times 10^4$$

$$(2.32 \times 10^8)^{1/3} = (232 \times 10^6)^{1/3}$$
$$= (232)^{1/3}(10^6)^{1/3}$$
$$= \sqrt[3]{232} \times 10^2 = 6.14 \times 10^2$$

$$(9.37 \times 10^{-4})^{1/3} = (937 \times 10^{-6})^{1/3}$$
$$= (937)^{1/3}(10^{-6})^{1/3}$$
$$= \sqrt[3]{937} \times 10^{-2}$$
$$= 9.79 \times 10^{-2}$$

In the last two examples, we have rewritten the power of 10 so that it leads to an integer power of 10 when the root is calculated. Notice also from the first two examples that the cube root of a number greater than 1 is less than the square root; the fourth root is smaller still. The converse statement holds for numbers less than 1.

REVIEW PROBLEMS

Write the following numbers in scientific notation:

21. 27,631

22. 2,763,100

23. 15,000

24. 0.000000034

25. 1,600

26. 4,329.76

27. 0.003902

28. 0.08002

Express the following numbers in ordinary notation:

29. 2.34×10^{-3}

30. 1.76×10^6

31. 5.799×10^{-5}

32. 4.5×10^7

33. 0.067×10^4

34. 27.2×10^5

35. 0.0272×10^8

Evaluate the following expressions:

36. $(3 \times 10^6)(5 \times 10^4)$

37. $\frac{4 \times 10^8}{8 \times 10^6}$

38. $(5 \times 10^{10})(3 \times 10^{-8})(4 \times 10^6)$

39. $\frac{(4.4 \times 10^6)(3 \times 10^3)^2}{6 \times 10^{-4}}$

40. $\frac{(8.25 \times 10^4)(3.14)(5.2 \times 10^3)^2}{(6.25 \times 10^{-3})}$

41. $(4 \times 10^4)^{1/2}$

42. $(90{,}000)^{1/2}$

43. $(2.7 \times 10^7)^{1/3}$

44. $(8{,}000)^{1/3}$

45. $(4 \times 10^{-6})^{1/2}$

46. $(160{,}000)^{1/4}$

47. $(10^{10})^{1/2}$

48. $(10^{10})^{-1/2}$

49. $(10^{10})^{1/3}$

50. $(3.2 \times 10^8)^{1/3}$

B.3 | SIGNIFICANT FIGURES

The accuracy of any measurement is limited by errors of various types (see Section 1.1). It is important to keep track of these errors at least approximately in using or manipulating experimentally determined numbers. This is accomplished most readily with the rules for significant figures.

The principle involved is illustrated by the problem of determining the area *A* of a rectangular sheet of paper using a ruler whose smallest spacing is 0.1 cm. If we place one end of the ruler at the edge of the paper, the other edge might lie between the markings indicating 8.4 and 8.5 cm. We can, at best, then judge its position to one tenth of a spacing, so we might report our reading as 8.43 cm. However, a more elaborate measuring arrangement might well give a length closer to 8.44 or 8.42 cm; the last digit we report is somewhat uncertain. The number 8.43 is said to have three *significant figures*. In the same way we might find 6.77 cm for the other dimension of the rectangle. The area is then the product

$$A = (8.43 \text{ cm})(6.77 \text{ cm}) = 57.0711 \text{ cm}^2 = 57.1 \text{ cm}^2$$

Each of the factors in the product is uncertain in the third place, so only three places on the right have any meaning. Hence A is given to three significant figures. To clarify the reason for this, suppose the first factor is found to be closer to 8.42 cm when more careful measurements are made. Then the area becomes $A = (8.42 \text{ cm})(6.77 \text{ cm}) = 57.0034 \text{ cm}^2$, and the digits beyond 57.0 are changed. Clearly, these digits in the product are meaningless, and the area A is somewhat uncertain in the third digit. Note that our answer for A has been rounded up from 57.07 . . . to 57.1; a number below 57.05 would be rounded down to 57.0.

In all computations involving multiplication and division, the factor with the fewest significant figures determines the number of significant figures in the answer. For example, in

$$\frac{(8.2239)(2.7)(98.35)\pi^2}{2764} = 7.797899\ldots$$

the first three factors in the numerator have five, two, and four significant figures, respectively; $\pi^2 = (3.1415926\ldots)^2$ is known to an arbitrarily great accuracy; and the denominator is known to four significant figures. Accordingly, the answer obtained for this expression should be rounded to two figures, that is, to 7.8. However, it is a good idea to retain one or more extra places in *intermediate steps* of the calculation in order to avoid introducing additional errors in the process of rounding off the numbers. This is important in complex multistep calculations and is easy to do with an electronic calculator.

The significant figures procedure used in addition and subtraction differs from that for multiplication and division. It is illustrated by the sum

$$\begin{array}{r} 45.76 \\ +\ 0.123 \\ \hline 45.883 \end{array}$$

Here the 6 in the first number is somewhat uncertain, and the next place is completely unknown. Accordingly, the 3 in the sum is meaningless, and the answer is rounded to 45.88. *The answer contains as many places relative to the decimal point as the "least accurate number" in the sum.* Notice that in this example the least accurate number that limits the accuracy is 45.76, which has four significant figures; 0.123 has only three significant figures but is more accurate in the sense meant here.

Since the same ideas apply to subtraction, the difference of two nearly equal numbers may have very few significant figures. For example, consider

$$\begin{array}{r} 35.179 \\ -35.17813 \\ \hline 0.001 \end{array}$$

This result has essentially no accuracy, since it is uncertain by approximately 1 in the last place. If a new set of measurements changed the numbers slightly, their difference could well be 0.002 or −0.001.

Adding or subtracting numbers expressed in scientific notation requires that they be written with the same power of 10. For example,

$$\begin{aligned} 2.25 \times 10^6 + 6.4 \times 10^7 &= 2.25 \times 10^6 + 64 \times 10^6 \\ &= 66.\not{2}\not{5} \times 10^6 \\ &= 6.6 \times 10^7 \end{aligned}$$

Note that we have rounded 66.25 to 66 in accordance with the rules.

Significant Zeros

The number 1200 may have two, three, or four significant figures, depending upon whether the zeros represent measurements or are merely used to locate the decimal point. Scientific notation avoids this ambiguity; 1.2×10^3, 1.20×10^3, and 1.200×10^3 have two, three, and four significant figures, respectively.

REVIEW PROBLEMS

Round off the following quantities to three significant figures and write them in scientific notation:

51. 27632.0
52. 0.3729
53. 4.6667
54. 3.33333
55. 2.45558×10^4
56. 0.000034567

How many significant figures are there in the final result for each of the following expressions?

57. (3.2)(8.67)/(3.008)

58. (0.0002)(45.6)

59. $(2.0 \times 10^5)(3.777 \times 10^{-4})$

60. 17.2 + 2.35 + 4.3333

61. 88.45 + 9.24 − 6.05043

62. 186.45 − 186.12

Evaluate the following expressions in accordance with the rules for significant figures:

63. $3.28 \times 10^5 + 4.25 \times 10^7$

64. $3.7 \times 10^6 + 2.91 \times 10^7$

65. $1.91 \times 10^{-3} - 1.7 \times 10^{-5}$

B.4 | SOLUTION OF ALGEBRAIC EQUATIONS

The application of physical laws often leads to one or more algebraic equations that must be solved for the desired quantities. To do this, we must have as many equations as there are unknowns; for example, if we want to find two forces acting on an object, we must have two different equations relating them.

Equations in One Unknown | The basic rule in manipulating any algebraic equation is that both sides of the equation must be treated in the same way. If we add a number to one side, or multiply it by some factor, or square it, we must do the same thing to the other side.

To illustrate how a simple equation is solved, we first consider a *linear* equation, one in which the unknown quantity x appears only to the first power:

$$5x - 10 = 30$$

To solve for x, we first add 10 to both sides, giving

$$5x = 40$$

Dividing by 5 leads to the desired solution:

$$x = 8$$

A *quadratic* equation is one in which the highest power of the unknown is 2. Quadratic equations may or may not have a term linear in the unknown. An example of the latter situation is

$$16t^2 = 64$$

Dividing by 16 gives $t^2 = 4$. Taking the square root then gives two possible answers, $t = +2$ and $t = -2$, since either of these numbers squared is equal to 4. (Quadratic equations generally have two solutions.) Since t represents some number such as a time that is measured, it can only have one correct value. The circumstances of the specific problem will indicate which is the appropriate solution. For example, in Chapter One, in determining when a ball thrown straight up is at a specific height, we encounter quadratic equations in the time variable t. The two solutions of these equations correspond to the time when the ball is at that height on the way up and on the way down.

The quadratic equation

$$t^2 - 6t + 8 = 0$$

is somewhat more complicated than the preceding one, since it contains t to the first power as well as t^2. It can be solved by *factoring*, rewriting the equation as a product of two factors that is equal to zero:

$$(t - 2)(t - 4) = 0$$

This factoring can be verified by noting that when we multiply out the two factors, we obtain four terms, $t^2 - 4t - 2t + 8 = t^2 - 6t + 8$. Clearly the product can be zero only if either the first *or* the second factor is 0. Thus

$$t - 2 = 0, \qquad t = 2$$

or

$$t - 4 = 0, \qquad t = 4$$

The two solutions of this equation are $t = 2$ and $t = 4$.

The disadvantage of factoring is that one must guess the factors somehow. The *quadratic formula* is a general solution that can always be used without any guesswork. The equation

$$at^2 + bt + c = 0$$

has two solutions,

$$t = \frac{-b + \sqrt{b^2 - 4ac}}{2a}$$

and (B.7)

$$t = \frac{-b - \sqrt{b^2 - 4ac}}{2a}$$

This can be applied to the example $t^2 - 6t + 8 = 0$ by setting $a = 1$, $b = -6$, and $c = 8$. We find then

$$t = \frac{-(-6) + \sqrt{(-6)^2 - 4(1)(8)}}{2(1)}$$

$$= \frac{6 + \sqrt{4}}{2} = 4$$

and

$$t = \frac{-(-6) - \sqrt{(-6)^2 - 4(1)(8)}}{2(1)}$$

$$= \frac{6 - \sqrt{4}}{2} = 4$$

These are the same solutions as found before.

Simultaneous Equations | Two different equations containing the same two unknowns are called *simultaneous equations*. The unknowns are found by combining the equations in such a way that a single equation is obtained that contains just one unknown. For example, consider these two equations for a force F and an acceleration a, $F - 6a = 20$ and $-F + 8a = 0$. If we add these equations, the F and $-F$ cancel:

$$\begin{array}{r} F - 6a = 20 \\ -F + 8a = 0 \\ \hline F - F - 6a + 8a = 20 + 0 \end{array}$$

This reduces to

$$2a = 20$$

or

$$a = 10$$

F is then found by substituting the value found for a into the first equation:

$$F - 6(10) = 20, \qquad F = 20 + 60 = 80$$

Sometimes one equation must be multiplied by a factor before the equations are added or subtracted in order to eliminate one unknown. For example, consider $x + 3y = 6$ and $2x - y = 5$. Neither the x's nor the y's will completely cancel if these equations are added. However, if we multiply the first equation by 2 and the second by -1, we find upon adding them

$$\begin{array}{r} 2x + 6y = 12 \\ -2x + y = -5 \\ \hline 7y = 7 \end{array}$$

and $y = 1$. Substituting this value of y into either equation then gives $x = 3$.

The procedure just used is readily extended to three simultaneous equations containing three unknowns, x, y, and z. Two of the equations are combined to yield an equation containing only two unknowns, say, x and y, and another combination of two of the original equations is formed that again contains only x and y. The problem has then been reduced to two equations in two unknowns, and one then proceeds as in the example just given to find x and y.

REVIEW PROBLEMS

Solve the following equations for the unknown quantities.

66. $x - 7 = 3$
67. $3x + 7 = 4 + 6x$
68. $1 + 0.2x = 7$
69. $x^2 + 4 = 13$
70. $x^{1/2} + 4 = 13$
71. $-4x + 7 = 2x + 15$
72. $(x/3)^{1/2} = 2$
73. $0 = 64 - 16t^2$
74. $x^3 - 1 = 63$
75. $(x + 2)(x + 4) = 0$
76. $x^2 + 3x + 2 = 0$
77. $3x^2 + 2x - 5 = 0$
78. $x^2 + 4 = -4x$
79. $2x^2 = -3x$
80. $-3x + 2x^2 - 5 = 0$
81. $x + y = 5$, $x - y = 1$
82. $2 - T = 3a$, $T = 4a$
83. $x + 3y = 9$, $x - 2y = 10$
84. $2x - y = 10$, $x + y = 6$
85. $3x - 7y = 2$, $3x - 2y = 4$

B.5 | GRAPHS

Just as pictures are often more informative than words, graphs are often more useful than algebraic formulas in understanding what is happening in a

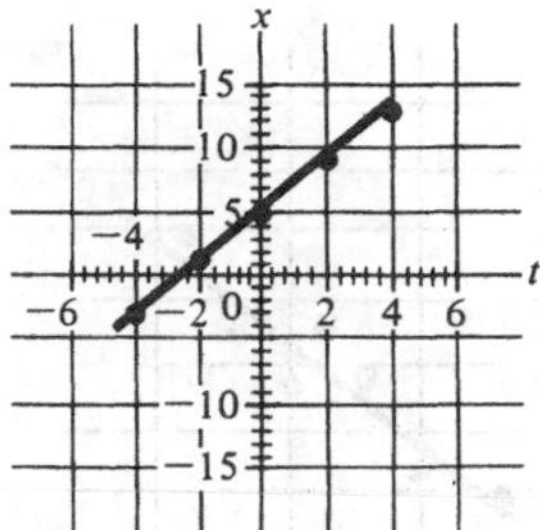

Figure B.1. The graph of $x = 5 + 2t$.

physical system. To illustrate how a graph is constructed, consider the equation for the position coordinate x of an object moving at a constant velocity at a time t:

$$x = 5 + 2t$$

We start by making a table of the values of x obtained from this equation for several values of t between −4 and +4:

time t	−4	−2	0	2	4
position x	−3	1	5	9	13

Using ordinary (Cartesian) graph paper, we draw a horizontal axis for the independent variable, t, and a vertical axis for the dependent variable, x. The tabulated values are then used to locate the points marked on the graph (Fig. B.1).

In this example, all the points fall on a single straight line because t appears only to the first power. If other powers are present, the graph of the equation will be a curve. Some examples of such curves are shown in Fig. B.2.

The choice of the dependent and independent variables is not fixed, and it depends on what one is trying to do. For example, the equation

$$x = 16t^2$$

gives the position of an object dropped from $x = 0$ at time $t = 0$. If we want to know when it will be at a position x, we must solve for t in terms of x:

$$t = \tfrac{1}{4}\sqrt{x}$$

Now x has become the independent variable. The graphs of the two forms of the equation look quite different (Fig. B.3), although both are curves rather than straight lines. We can also get a straight-line graph if we consider t^2 rather than t as a variable. This is particularly useful in analyzing experimental measurements, since it is easy to see if the data points all fall on a straight line as expected.

REVIEW PROBLEMS

Draw the graphs of the following equations:

86. $y = 3x - 7$

87. $x = 2t^2$

88. $y = 2x^4 - 3$

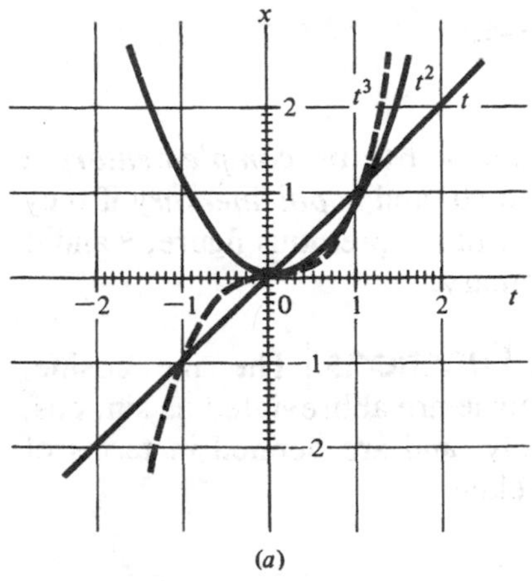

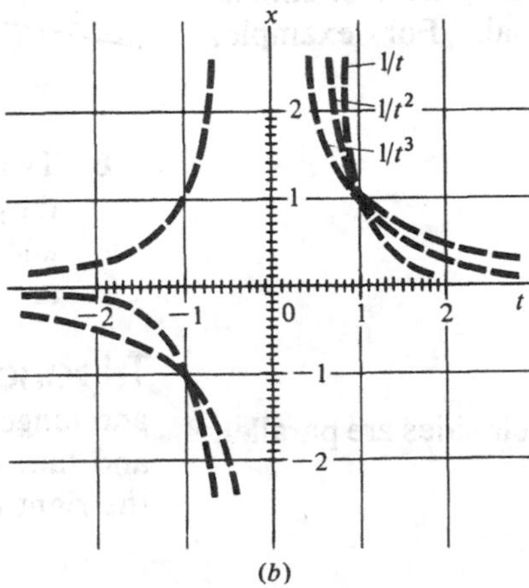

Figure B.2. (a) Graphs of $x = t$, $x = t^2$, and $x = t^3$. (b) Graphs of $x = 1/t$, $x = 1/t^2$, and $x = 1/t^3$. Note that $1/t^3$ becomes very small most rapidly as t increases and also grows most rapidly as t approaches zero.

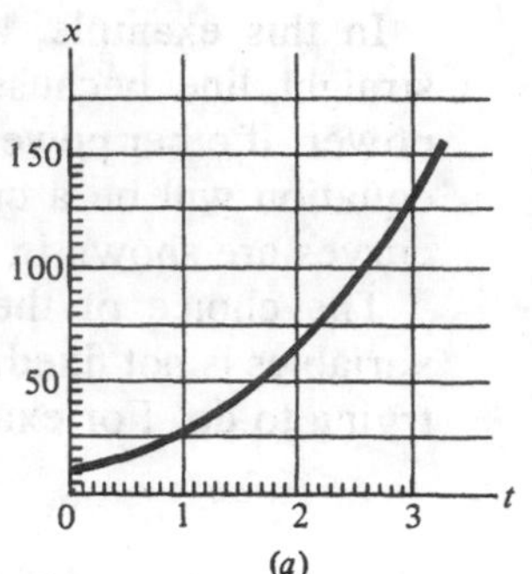

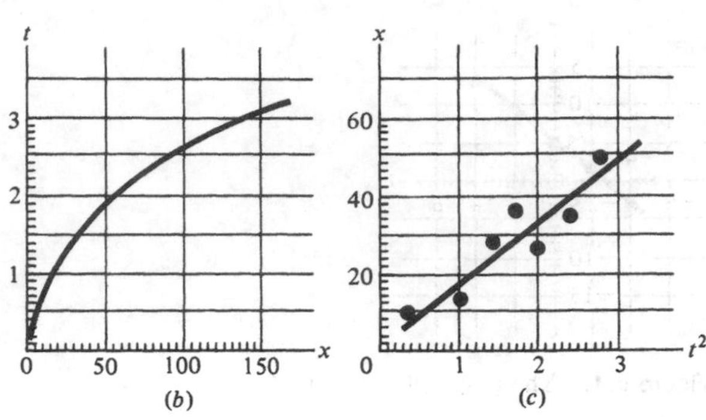

Figure B.3. (*a*) A graph of $x = 16t^2$. (*b*) A graph of $t = \frac{1}{4}\sqrt{x}$. (*c*) Measured pairs of x and t^2 values are plotted. They fall close to a straight line drawn through them with a ruler. On a plot of x versus t, they would fall near a curved line that would be harder to draw accurately and to analyze numerically.

B.6 | PLANE GEOMETRY AND TRIGONOMETRIC FUNCTIONS

Plane Geometry | The following results from plane geometry are often useful:

1 The sum of the internal angles of any triangle is 180°. In a right triangle, where one angle is 90°, the other two angles must add up to 90°.

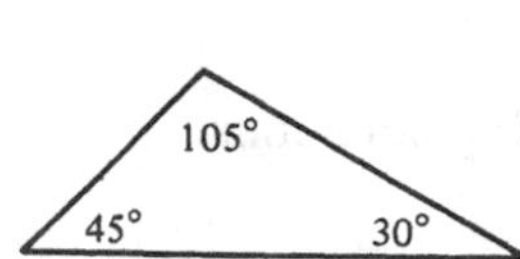

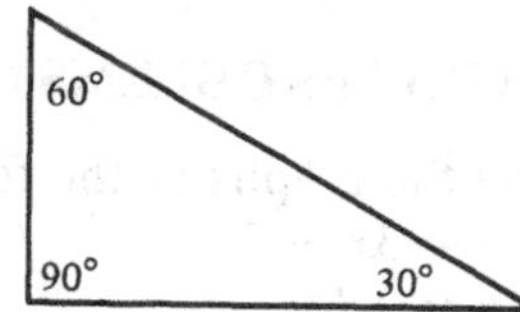

2 Two triangles are *similar* if two of their angles are equal. The corresponding sides of similar triangles are proportional. For example, $a/A = b/B$ in this figure:

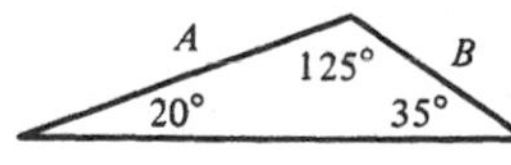

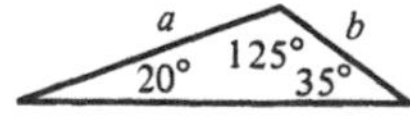

3 Two angles are equal if their sides are parallel.

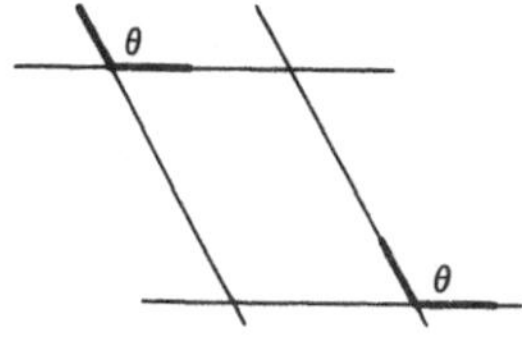

4 Two angles are equal if their sides are mutually perpendicular. For example, the angle between the weight vector **w** and the line perpendicular to the inclined plane equals the angle between the plane and the horizontal direction.

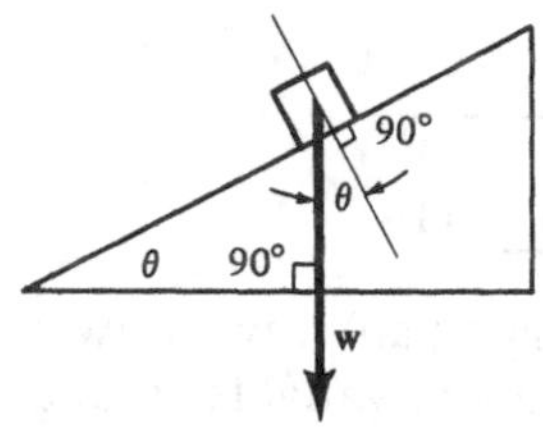

5 Two angles are equal if they are *vertical* angles.

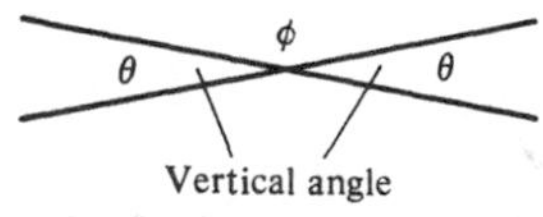

6 Two angles are said to be *complementary* if they add up to 90° and *supplementary* if they add up to 180°. In the previous figure, θ and ϕ are supplementary.

Trigonometric Functions | The sine, cosine, and tangent of an angle are abbreviated as sin, cos, and tan, respectively, and are defined in terms of the right triangle below:

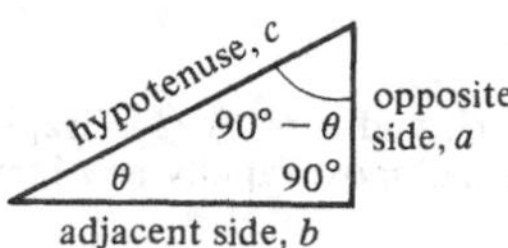

$$\sin \theta = \frac{\text{opposite side}}{\text{hypotenuse}} = \frac{a}{c} \tag{B.8}$$

$$\cos \theta = \frac{\text{adjacent side}}{\text{hypotenuse}} = \frac{b}{c} \tag{B.9}$$

$$\tan \theta = \frac{\text{opposite side}}{\text{adjacent side}} = \frac{a}{b} \tag{B.10}$$

The Pythagorean theorem states that

$$a^2 + b^2 = c^2 \tag{B.11}$$

Dividing by c^2,

$$\frac{a^2}{c^2} + \frac{b^2}{c^2} = 1$$

or

$$\sin^2 \theta + \cos^2 \theta = 1 \tag{B.12}$$

The trigonometric functions of angles larger than 90° may be either positive or negative, depending on the angle. In the notation of the diagram below, they are defined by

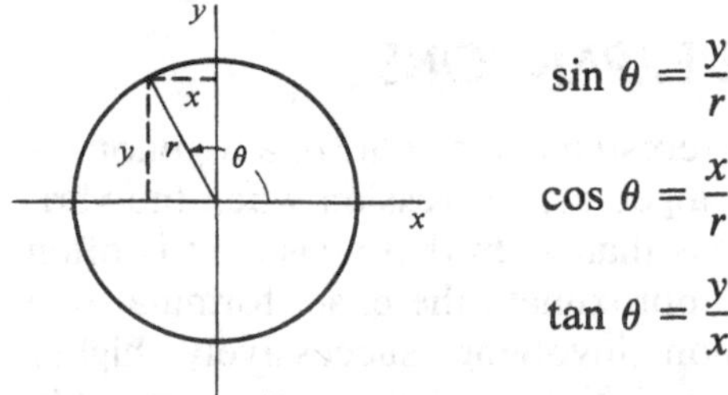

$$\sin \theta = \frac{y}{r}$$

$$\cos \theta = \frac{x}{r}$$

$$\tan \theta = \frac{y}{x}$$

By convention, r is always positive. However, for the angle shown, which is said to be in the second *quadrant*, x is negative and y is positive. Accordingly the sine is positive, and the tangent and cosine are negative. In the third quadrant, only the tangent is positive; and in the fourth, only the cosine is positive.

Many books contain a table of the trigonometric functions for angles up to 90°. For angles between 90° and 180°, one looks up the supplement, $180° - \theta$. Between 180° and 270°, one looks up $\theta - 180°$; and from 270° to 360°, one looks up $360° - \theta$. Minus signs are inserted wherever required in accordance with the discussion above. For example, $\sin 150° = \sin 30°$, $\cos 150° = -\cos 30°$, and $\tan 150° = -\tan 30°$. These rules are summarized in Fig. B.4. Many pocket calculators have these rules built in.

Graphs of the sine, cosine, and tangent (Fig. B.5) are useful in understanding the general behavior of these quantities. They all repeat after one full circle or cycle; their *period* is 360° or 2π radians. (Measuring angles in radians is discussed in Chapter Five.)

The average of the sine or cosine over a full cycle is zero, since for every positive value, there is a corresponding negative value. Notice that the $\sin \theta$ and $\cos \theta$ curves are identical if the $\cos \theta$ curve is shifted 90° to the right. The same shift also makes the $\sin^2 \theta$ and $\cos^2 \theta$ curves (Fig. B.6) identical, so the average values of these quantities over a full cycle must be equal. Denoting the average by a bar, this means

$$\overline{\sin^2 \theta} = \overline{\cos^2 \theta}$$

Since we know from Eq. B.12 that $\sin^2 \theta + \cos^2 \theta = 1$, it follows that

$$\overline{\sin^2 \theta} + \overline{\cos^2 \theta} = 1$$

Therefore,

$$\overline{\sin^2 \theta} = \overline{\cos^2 \theta} = \tfrac{1}{2} \tag{B.13}$$

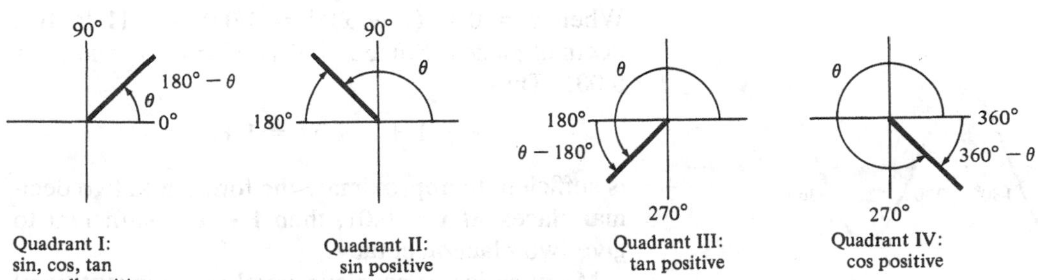

Figure B.4. A summary of the rules for finding the trigonometric functions. For example, if θ is in the third quadrant, a plus sign is used for $\tan \theta$, and a minus sign is used for $\sin \theta$ and $\cos \theta$.

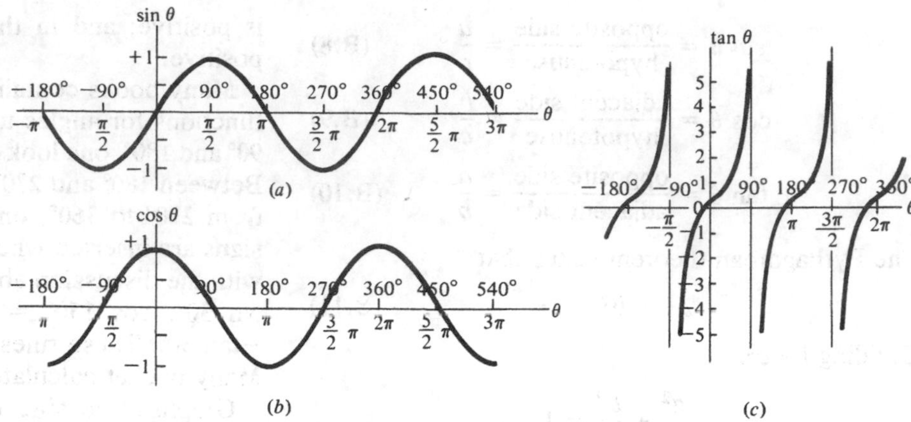

Figure B.5. Graphs of (*a*) sin θ; (*b*) cos θ; (*c*) tan θ.

Also, we can see from Fig. B.6 that the product, sin θ cos θ, has a corresponding negative value for each positive value, so averaging the product over a full cycle must give zero:

$$\overline{\sin\theta\cos\theta} = 0 \tag{B.14}$$

REVIEW PROBLEMS

89. If two angles of a triangle are 29° and 111°, what is the third angle?

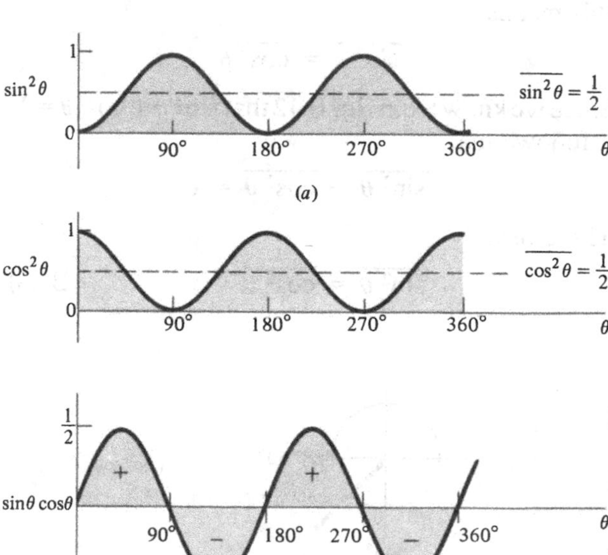

Figure B.6. (*a*) $\sin^2\theta$ and $\cos^2\theta$ have the same average value $\frac{1}{2}$. (*b*) The average value of sin θ cos θ is zero.

90. Find sin 120°; cos 120°; tan 120°.

91. Find sin 270°; cos 270°; tan 270°.

92. At what angle or angles between 0° and 360° is sin θ equal to 0, +1, −1? Give the corresponding angles for the cosine and tangent.

B.7 | SERIES EXPANSIONS

We are often interested in the value of a trigonometric function or algebraic expression when the variable is much less than 1. In these cases, it is often convenient to approximate the exact formula by a series expansion involving successively higher powers of the variable, since these terms quickly become very small.

As an example, we may consider the series expansion for $(1 - x)^{-1}$ derived in algebra texts:

$$\frac{1}{1-x} = 1 + x + x^2 + x^3 + \cdots$$

When $x = 0.1$, $(1 - x)^{-1} = 1/0.9 = 1.11$ to two decimal places. Since $x = 0.1$, $x^2 = 0.01$, and $x^3 = 0.001$. Thus

$$1 + x + x^2 = 1.11$$

is sufficient to approximate the formula to two decimal places. If $x = 0.01$, then $1 + x$ is sufficient to give two place accuracy.

Many series expansions involve the quantity $n!$ (read "n factorial") defined by

$$n! = n(n - 1)(n - 2) \ldots (2)(1)$$

For example, $4! = 4 \times 3 \times 2 \times 1 = 24$. By definition,

$$1! = 1, \qquad 0! = 1$$

The following series expansions are often useful:

$$(1 \pm x)^{-1} = 1 \mp x + x^2 \mp x^3 + \cdots \qquad (-1 < x < 1) \quad \text{(B.15)}$$

$$(1 \pm x)^n = 1 \pm nx + \frac{n(n-1)x^2}{2!} \pm \frac{n(n-1)(n-2)x^3}{3!} + \cdots \qquad (-1 < x < 1) \quad \text{(B.16)}$$

$$(1 \pm x)^{-n} = 1 \mp nx + \frac{n(n+1)x^2}{2!} \mp \frac{n(n+1)(n+2)x^3}{3!} + \cdots \qquad (-1 < x < 1) \quad \text{(B.17)}$$

$$e^x = 1 + x + \frac{x^2}{2!} + \frac{x^3}{3!} + \cdots \quad \text{(B.18)}$$

In the following series for the trigonometric functions, the angles must be measured in radians, where 1 rad = $180°/\pi = 57.3°$:

$$\sin x = x - \frac{x^3}{3!} + \frac{x^5}{5!} - \cdots \quad \text{(B.19)}$$

$$\cos x = 1 - \frac{x^2}{2!} + \frac{x^4}{4!} - \cdots \quad \text{(B.20)}$$

$$\tan x = x + \frac{x^3}{3} + \frac{2x^5}{15} + \frac{17x^7}{314} + \cdots \quad \text{(B.21)}$$

REVIEW PROBLEMS

93. What is the percentage error in using $\sin x = x$, when $x = 10° = 0.1745$ rad? What is the error at 30°?

94. For $x = 0.1$, $e^x = e^{0.1} = 1.105$. How many terms in the series expansion for e^x are needed to obtain this accuracy?

95. (a) Write out the first three terms in the series for $(1 + x)^{1/2} = \sqrt{1 + x}$. (b) What does this approximation give for $x = 0.1$? Compare this with the exact answer to five decimal places, 1.04881.

B.8 | DERIVATIVES

At the end of several chapters in this book, we present derivations of various equations that are based on arguments using differentiation. Here we list the derivatives used. Note that the derivative of a constant is zero. Also, when an expression is multiplied by a number, its derivative is multiplied by the same number. For example,

$$\frac{d}{dt}(3t^2) = 3\frac{d}{dt}(t^2)$$

In the following expressions, a and n are constants:

$$\frac{d}{dt}(t^n) = nt^{n-1} \quad \text{(B.22)}$$

$$\frac{d}{dt}\left(\frac{1}{t}\right) = -\frac{1}{t^2} \quad \text{(B.23)}$$

$$\frac{d}{dt}\left(\frac{1}{t^n}\right) = \frac{-n}{t^{n+1}} \quad \text{(B.24)}$$

$$\frac{d}{dt}(e^{at}) = ae^{at} \quad \text{(B.25)}$$

$$\frac{d}{dt}\sin at = a\cos at \quad \text{(B.26)}$$

$$\frac{d}{dt}\cos at = -a\sin at \quad \text{(B.27)}$$

If y depends on a variable u, and u depends in turn on t, then the *chain rule* states that

$$\frac{dy}{dt} = \frac{dy}{du}\frac{du}{dt} \qquad \text{(chain rule)}$$

REVIEW PROBLEMS

Find the derivatives of the following expressions:

96. $3t + 7$
97. $4t^3$
98. $1 - (1/t)$
99. $4e^{-3t}$
100. $10 \sin 2\pi t$

B.9 | AREAS AND VOLUMES

At various points in this book, we have to make use of the formulas for the areas and volumes of simple shapes. They are listed here for reference.

Circle

radius $= r$
diameter $= 2r$
circumference $= 2\pi r$
area $= \pi r^2$

Square

side $= a$
area $= a^2$

Triangle

area $= \frac{1}{2}$(base)(height)

Cube

side $= a$
surface area $= 6a^2$
volume $= a^3$

Sphere

radius $= r$
surface area $= 4\pi r^2$
volume $= 4\pi r^3/3$

Cylinder

radius $= r$, length $= l$
area of curved surface $= 2\pi rl$
area of each end $= \pi r^2$
volume $= \pi r^2 l$

B.10 | THE EXPONENTIAL FUNCTION; LOGARITHMS

Many times, the rate at which a quantity changes is proportional to the quantity present. For example, the rate at which a population of bacteria increases is directly proportional to the size of the population itself, as is the rate of growth in the funds in a savings account. Similarly, the rate of change of the charge on a capacitor is sometimes proportional to the charge present. Students of calculus will recognize these as situations where the quantity, call it y, depends on time as

$$y = Cb^{Dt}$$

where b and D are numbers and C is a constant that is determined by the conditions of the situation when $t = 0$. This is called an exponential dependence of y on t.

The choice of b is arbitrary, although it will affect the value of D when it is determined. However, there is a particular choice of b that can be made that greatly simplifies the manipulations. This choice is $b = e = 2.718. \ldots$ For this seemingly unlikely choice, the rate of change of $y = Ce^t$ with t is exactly equal to y itself. For any other choice of b, the rate of change of $y = Cb^t$ with t is proportional to but not equal to y. Thus the function $y = e^t$ is very common in many scientific studies. The decreasing function $e^{-t} = 1/e^t$ is of similar importance when the rate of *decrease* of a quantity is proportional to the present amount of that quantity. This happens, for example, in the decay of radioactive nuclei.

The exponential function e^t is built into many pocket calculators, sometimes as the inverse of the *natural logarithm*. If $x = 10^t$, then the more familiar *common logarithm* (log, or logarithm to the base 10) is the power of 10, or t in this case. Symbolically,

$$\log x = \log (10^t) = t \qquad \text{(B.28)}$$

Conversely, the inverse common logarithm of t is 10^t.

Similarly, the natural logarithm (ln, or logarithm to the base e) is defined as the power of e needed to obtain a given quantity. Thus if $y = e^t$,

$$\ln y = \ln (e^t) = t \qquad \text{(B.29)}$$

The inverse natural logarithm of t (INV ln on many calculators) is then e^t.

Some simple rules can be obtained from the definitions B.28 and B.29 for the logarithms of products, quotients, and powers. The following rules are given for natural logarithms but apply equally well to common logarithms:

$$\ln (xy) = (\ln x) + (\ln y) \qquad \text{(B.30)}$$

$$\ln (x^n) = n(\ln x) \qquad \text{(B.31)}$$

$$\ln \left(\frac{1}{x^n}\right) = -n(\ln x) \qquad \text{(B.32)}$$

$$\ln \left(\frac{x}{y}\right) = (\ln x) - (\ln y) \qquad \text{(B.33)}$$

Note that there is no simple rule for the logarithms of sums or differences of quantities.

Using either tabulated values of e^t or values found with a calculator, we can construct a plot of

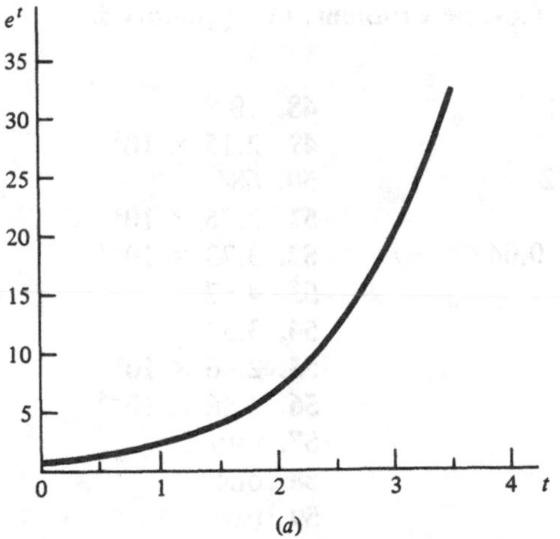

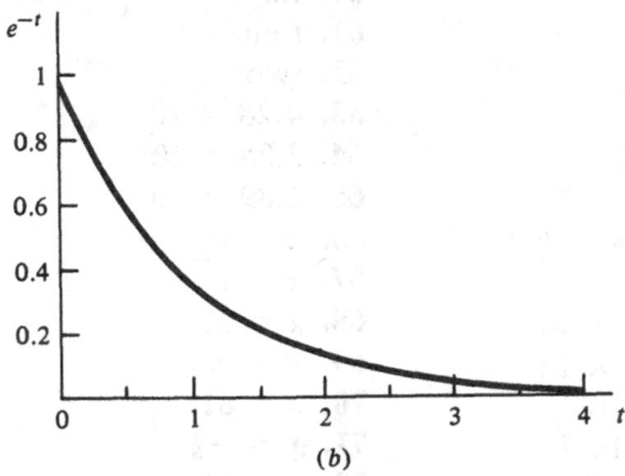

Figure B.7. (a) The graph of e^t. (b) The graph of e^{-t}. Note the difference in vertical scales in the two graphs.

e^t (Fig. B.7). Note how it grows very rapidly as t increases, much more rapidly than any power of t. Also, the plot of e^{-t} diminishes very rapidly for large t values, although it never reaches zero.

Several special values of e^{-t} are used in this book. To three significant figures, $e^{-1} = 0.368$ and $e^{-2} = 0.135$. Also, $e^{-t} = 0.500$ when $t = 0.693$.

A series expansion for e^x is given in Eq. B.18 above, and the derivative of e^x is given in Eq. B.25.

B.11 | TRIGONOMETRIC IDENTITIES

There are a variety of identities relating trigonometric quantities. The following formulas are used in this text:

$$\sin(a + b) = \sin a \cos b \pm \cos a \sin b \qquad \text{(B.34)}$$

$$\cos(a + b) = \cos a \cos b \mp \sin a \sin b \qquad \text{(B.35)}$$

$$\sin a + \sin b = 2 \sin \tfrac{1}{2}(a + b) \cos \tfrac{1}{2}(a - b) \qquad \text{(B.36)}$$

$$\cos a + \cos b = 2 \cos \tfrac{1}{2}(a + b) \cos \tfrac{1}{2}(a - b) \qquad \text{(B.37)}$$

B.12 | INTEGRALS

Integrals are used in several sections. The following brief list contains most of the *indefinite integrals* used in the text or needed for the problems. Definite integrals are discussed below.

$$\int t^n\,dt = \frac{t^{n+1}}{n+1} \quad (n \neq -1) \qquad \text{(B.38)}$$

$$\int \frac{dt}{t} = \ln t \qquad \text{(B.39)}$$

$$\int e^{at}dt = \frac{1}{a} e^{at} \qquad \text{(B.40)}$$

$$\int \sin at\,dt = -\frac{1}{a}\cos at \qquad \text{(B.41)}$$

$$\int \cos at\,dt = \frac{1}{a}\sin at \qquad \text{(B.42)}$$

$$\int \frac{t\,dt}{(a^2 + t^2)^{1/2}} = (a^2 + t^2)^{1/2} \qquad \text{(B.43)}$$

$$\int \frac{dt}{(a^2 + t^2)} = \frac{1}{a}\tan^{-1}\frac{t}{a} \qquad \text{(B.44)}$$

(Here $\tan^{-1}$ is the *arctangent;* if $y = \tan^{-1} x$, then $x = \tan y$.)

$$\int \frac{t\,dt}{(a^2 + t^2)^{3/2}} = \frac{-1}{(a^2 + t^2)^{1/2}} \qquad \text{(B.45)}$$

$$\int \frac{a^2\,dt}{(a^2 + t^2)^{3/2}} = \frac{t}{(a^2 + t^2)^{1/2}} \qquad \text{(B.46)}$$

$$\int u\,dv = uv - \int v\,du \quad \text{(integration by parts)} \qquad \text{(B.47)}$$

$$\int t^n e^{at}\,dt = \frac{t^n}{a} - \frac{n}{a}\int t^{n-1}e^{at}\,dt \qquad \text{(B.48)}$$

$$\int t^n e^{-at}\,dt = -\frac{t^n}{a} + \frac{n}{a}\int t^{n-1}e^{-at}\,dt \qquad \text{(B.49)}$$

A *definite integral* is evaluated by substituting the values of the variable at the ends of the integration range into the indefinite integral. If $g(t)$ is the indefinite integral of $f(t)$, then

$$\int_a^b f(t)dt = g(t)\Big|_a^b = g(b) - g(a) \qquad \text{(B.50)}$$

For example, according to Eq. B.38, $\int t\,dt = t^2/2$. Then

$$\int_a^b t\,dt = \frac{t^2}{2}\Big|_a^b = \frac{b^2}{2} - \frac{a^2}{2}$$

Also, repeated application of Eq. B.49 shows that

$$\int_0^\infty t^n e^{-at}\,dt = \frac{n!}{a^{n+1}} \qquad \text{(B.51)}$$

(Here $n! = n(n-1)(n-2)\ldots(2)(1)$ is *n-factorial.*)

REVIEW PROBLEMS

Evaluate the following quantities with the aid, where needed, of tables or a pocket calculator.

101. Find e^2, e^3, e^4.

102. Find $e^{0.5}$, $e^{1.5}$.

103. Find $\ln e^3$, $\ln 10$, $\ln 4$, $\ln 0.75$, $\ln 2$.

104. What is x if its natural logarithm is 0.5, 0.1, 1, −1, 2, 2.5?

105. What are the common logarithms of 10, 100, 1000, 5, 0.5, e?

106. What is x if its common logarithm is 0.5, 0, 1, −1, 2, 2.5?

Simplify the following expressions:

107. $\log(x^4)$

108. $\ln(x/y^2)$

109. $\ln(\sqrt{x})$

110. $\log(1/x^3)$

111. $\ln[x(a+b)]$

Additional Reading

Students needing additional mathematical preparation may find the following paperback books helpful:

Jerry B. Marion and Ronald C. Davidson, *Mathematical Preparation for General Physics*, W. B. Saunders Co., Philadelphia, 1972. Same level as this appendix.

Clifford E. Swartz, *Used Math*, Prentice-Hall, Inc., Englewood Cliffs, N.J., 1973. Includes more advanced material.

Michael Ram, *Essential Mathematics for College Physics*, John Wiley & Sons, New York, Inc., 1982; *Essential Mathematics for College Physics with Calculus*, John Wiley & Sons, Inc., New York, 1984.

Answers to Review Problems in Appendix B

1. 16
2. 9
3. $2^5 = 32$
4. x^9
5. $1/5^2 = 0.04$
6. 5
7. x^2
8. x^2
9. $(x/y)^4$
10. ax^2
11. $a^{3/2}x^3$
12. xy^3
13. $1/x^2y^2$
14. 10
15. 0.1
16. 1
17. $\frac{1}{5} = 0.2$
18. $x/8$
19. $x^2y^{-4} = x^2/y^4$
20. 10^3
21. 2.7631×10^4
22. 2.7631×10^6
23. 1.5×10^4
24. 3.4×10^{-8}
25. 1.6×10^3
26. 4.32976×10^3
27. 3.902×10^{-3}
28. 8.002×10^{-2}
29. 0.00234
30. 1,760,000
31. 0.00005799
32. 45,000,000
33. 670
34. 2,720,000
35. 2,720,000
36. 1.5×10^{11}
37. 50
38. 6×10^9
39. 6.6×10^{16}
40. 1.12×10^{15}
41. 200
42. 300
43. 300
44. 20
45. 2×10^{-3}
46. 20
47. 10^5
48. 10^{-5}
49. 2.15×10^3
50. 684
51. 2.76×10^4
52. 3.73×10^{-1}
53. 4.67
54. 3.33
55. 2.46×10^4
56. 3.46×10^{-5}
57. two
58. one
59. two
60. three
61. four
62. two
63. 4.28×10^7
64. 3.28×10^7
65. 1.89×10^{-3}
66. $x = 10$
67. $x = 1$
68. $x = 30$
69. $x = \pm 3$
70. $x = 81$
71. $x = -\frac{4}{3}$
72. $x = 12$
73. $t = \pm 2$
74. $x = 4$
75. $x = -2$, $x = -4$
76. $x = -1$, $x = -2$
77. $x = 1$, $x = -\frac{5}{3}$
78. $x = -2$
79. $x = -\frac{3}{2}$, $x = 0$
80. $x = -1$, $x = \frac{5}{2}$
81. $x = 3$, $y = 2$
82. $a = \frac{2}{7}$, $T = \frac{8}{7}$
83. $y = -\frac{1}{5}$, $x = 9\frac{3}{5}$
84. $x = 5\frac{1}{3}$, $y = \frac{2}{3}$
85. $y = \frac{2}{5}$, $x = 1\frac{3}{5}$
86.

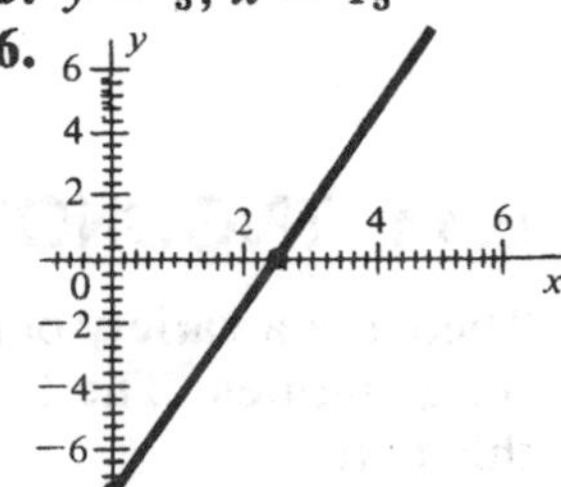

87. **88.**

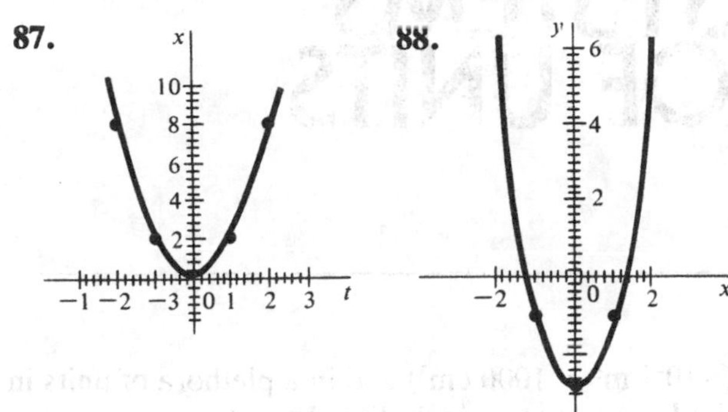

89. 40°

90. sin 120° = 0.866, cos 120° = −0.5, tan 120° = −1.732

91. sin 270° = −1, cos 270° = 0, tan 270° = ∞

92. sin θ = 0 at 0°, 180°, 360°
sin θ = 1 at 90°
sin θ = −1 at 270°
cos θ = 0 at 90°, 270°
cos θ = 1 at 0°, 360°
cos θ = −1 at 180°
tan θ = 0 at 0°, 180°, 360°
tan θ = 1 at 45°, 225°
tan θ = −1 at 135°, 315°

93. 0.52 percent at 10°, 4.7 percent at 30°

94. three items

95. (a) $1 + \frac{1}{2}x - \frac{1}{8}x^2$
(b) 1.04875, which is 0.006 percent less than the exact answer.

96. 3

97. $12t^2$

98. $1/t^2$

99. $-12e^{-3t}$

100. $20\pi \cos 2\pi t$

101. 7.39, 20.1, 54.6

102. 1.65, 4.48

103. 3, 2.30, 1.39, −0.288, 0.693

104. 1.65, 1, 2.72, 0.368, 7.39, 12.2

105. 1, 2, 3, 0.699, −0.301, 0.434

106. 3.16, 1, 10, 0.1, 100, 316

107. $4 \log x$

108. $\ln x - 2 \ln y$

109. $\frac{1}{2} \ln x$

110. $-3 \log x$

111. $\ln x + \ln (a + b)$

APPENDIX C SYSTEMS OF UNITS

In this text, we have used Système Internationale (S.I.) units almost exclusively. This is in keeping with a worldwide effort to develop a single set of units for scientific, commercial, and social use. Because this effort is far from complete and because historical material will always be important, a variety of units will be with us for a long time. In this appendix, we describe the *c.g.s.* and *British* systems of units to assist the reader in relating units in these systems to S.I. units. Some units that do not fall clearly into any of these systems are also discussed.

We assume the reader is familiar with the general scheme of conversion of units described in Chapter One of this textbook. A table of useful conversion factors can be found inside the front cover. Multiples and submultiples of S.I. units are constructed using prefixes given on the right front endpaper of this text.

C.1 | TIME, LENGTH, AND MASS

The single quantity with the same units in all systems is time. The basic unit of time is the *second*, with the *minute* and *hour* in common use. In scientific work, submultiples of the second are often convenient, and the prefixes of the S.I. system are useful for these cases.

The basic units of length are the *metre*, *centimetre*, and *foot* in the S.I., c.g.s., and British systems, respectively. There are 100 centimetres and 3.281 feet in 1 metre. Areas and volumes have the obvious units of m^2, cm^2, and ft^2 and of m^3, cm^3, and ft^3, respectively, in the three systems and require the use of conversion factors either two or three times. In the British system, the *inch* (= 1/12 foot) is often used, as is the *mile* (= 5280 feet).

Measurements of the volumes of liquids and gases are commonly expressed in the litre ($=10^{-3}$ m^3 = 1000 cm^3) and in a plethora of units in the British system including the *gallon*, *quart*, *pint*, *cup*, and various sizes of spoons. The conversions between these are most readily found in cookbooks and dictionaries. The *gallon* is equivalent to 3.786 litres.

The units of mass in the three systems are the *kilogram*, *gram*, and *slug*. The relationship between the kilogram and gram is obvious from the prefix, and the slug is equal to 14.59 kilograms. The atomic mass unit, denoted u, is accepted for use with the S.I. system; 1 u = 1.66×10^{-27} kg.

The acceleration of gravity, g, is important in all three systems:

$$g = 9.8 \text{ m s}^{-2} = 980 \text{ cm s}^{-2} = 32 \text{ ft s}^{-2}$$

Until recently, two length units were very commonly used in studies of light and in atomic physics. The *angstrom* and the *micron* are equal to 10^{-10} metres and 10^{-6} metres, respectively, and are simply names given to convenient submultiples of the metre.

In the same spirit, the *fermi*, equal to 10^{-15} metres, was used for years as the convenient length unit in nuclear studies. Similarly the *barn*, equal to 10^{-28} m^2, is a convenient measure of cross-sectional areas in subatomic particle collisions.

C.2 | UNITS OF FORCE, WEIGHT

The *newton*, the S.I. unit of force, is equivalent to 1 kg m s^{-2}, as can be seen from Newton's second law, $F = ma$. In the c.g.s. system, the force unit is the *dyne*; by the same reasoning, it is equal to 1 gm cm s^{-2}. Similarly, the *pound*, the British unit of force, is 1 slug ft s^{-2}. The numerical conversion factors are

$$1 \text{ N} = 10^5 \text{ dynes} = 0.2248 \text{ pound}$$

These can be simply obtained from $F = ma$, where $a = g$ and the force is interpreted as the weight.

Note that these units are names given to the force in the fundamental law $F = ma$. Thus the force units are derived from those for mass, length, and time given in Section C.1. In fact, with the exception of the units of electric charge, all the units of this section and those following are derived from those of mass, length, and time.

C.3 | OTHER UNITS OF MECHANICS

The derived S.I. unit of energy is the *joule*. This can be related to the units of mass, length, and time using $W = Fs$, that is work equals force times distance, or from the units of kinetic energy, $mv^2/2$. Thus the joule is equal to 1 N m = 1 kg m^2 s^{-2}. Similarly, the c.g.s. energy unit, the *erg*, is 1 dyn cm = 1 gm cm^2 s^{-2}. The British energy unit is the *foot-pound* = 1 ft lb = 1 slug ft^2 s^{-2}.

Unfortunately, the complete energy unit story is more complex. Historically, thermal energy was not recognized as the same entity as mechanical energy. Hence we have inherited a separate set of energy units from theoretical studies that are still in common use. A *calorie* is the heat necessary to raise the temperature of 1 gram of water by 1 K and is equal to 4.184 joules, or 4.184×10^7 ergs. The British Thermal Unit, the BTU, had an origin similar to the calorie, but involved raising the temperature of a pound of water by 1° F. It is equal to 777.2 ft lb = 1.054×10^3 joules.

In atomic physics, a commonly used energy unit is the *electron volt*. This is a small energy unit equal to 1.602×10^{-19} joule. It is accepted for use with the S.I. system.

There is no defined c.g.s. unit of power; it is just the erg s^{-1}. In the British system, the logical power unit is the foot-pound per second. However, the more common British unit is the *horsepower*, equal to 550 ft lb s^{-1}.

There is a wide variety of pressure units in common use. The standard units in the three systems are the *pascal*, dyn cm^{-2}, and lb in^{-2}. Atmospheric pressures are often measured in terms of the *standard atmosphere* = 1.013×10^5 pascals = 1.013×10^6 dyn cm^{-2} = 14.7 lb in^{-2}. Pressures are also often given in terms of the height of a column of liquid that is supported, usually water or mercury. In fact, the pressure of 1 mm Hg (1 millimetre of mercury) is given the name of *torr*; 1 torr = 133.3 pascals. One inch of water (1 in. H_2O) is equal to a pressure of 249.1 pascals.

In addition to the variety of systems of units, many combinations of units are used because they are numerically convenient. As an example, consider the conversion between two units of flow resistance, 1 Pa s m^{-3} = 7.50×10^{-9} torr s cm^{-3}. The smaller units are convenient in biological studies.

C.4 | ELECTRICAL UNITS

In the study of electricity and magnetism, a large number of units is introduced. However, if the unit of charge, the coulomb, is regarded as a fundamental unit, as are mass, length, and time, then all other units are derived from these four units.*

For example, the *volt* is a joule per coulomb; and, as described in the preceding section, 1 joule is equivalent to 1 kg m^2 s^{-2}. Fortunately, S.I. units are widely used in electrical and magnetic studies, and conversions from other unit systems are seldom required. One exception to this is the c.g.s. unit of magnetic field strength, the *gauss*, which equals 10^{-4} *tesla*. For example, the gauss is widely used in studies of the earth's magnetic field where the numbers are of a convenient size.

C.5 | SUMMARY

This appendix does not by any means exhaust all the systems of units or all of the combinations of units that are in use. However, if the reader will keep in mind that all units can be reduced to a combination of the units of mass, length, time, and charge, the task of relating and converting units will be greatly eased.

* If, in Coulomb's law, $F = kQ_1Q_2/r^2$, the constant k were chosen to be dimensionless, the coulomb could be expressed in terms of units of mass, length, and time. This is a perfectly valid procedure, and it is employed in some c.g.s. systems of electrical units. However, in this text (and in most other modern books), we assign units to k and regard the coulomb as a fundamental unit, and not one expressed in units of mass, length, and time.

ANSWERS TO ODD NUMBERED EXERCISES AND PROBLEMS

Chapter 1

1-1 4.05×10^3 m^2
1-3 3.79 litres
1-5 (a) 7×10^{-9} m (b) 7×10^{-3} m
1-7 40.5 hectares
1-11 \$3.51 quart^{-1}
1-13 40 km h^{-1}
1-17 80 km h^{-1}
1-19 (a) 10.2 m s^{-1}
1-21 (a) -9.8 m s^{-1} (b) -29.4 m
1-23 (a) 10 m s^{-1} (b) 5 m s^{-1} (c) 0
1-25 6.94 km h^{-1}
1-27 (a) Mary (b) 0.03 h
1-31 positive at 0, T; negative at $T/2$
1-33 $\bar{v} = 10.1$ m s^{-1}; $\bar{v} < v(\max)$
1-35 (a) -98 m s^{-1} (b) -98 m s^{-1}
1-39 (a) $T_0 < t < 3T_0$ (b) $0 < t < T_0$, $3T_0 < t < 5T_0$ (c) $t > 5T_0$
1-41 (a) $-v_0/T$ (b) $-v_0/T$ (c) equal for constant a
1-43 (a) 0.001667 s (b) 42,000 m s^{-2}
1-45 27.8 h
1-47 (a) 50 m (b) 20 m s^{-1}
1-49 (a) -0.6 m s^{-2} (b) 750 m
1-53 (a) -113 m s^{-2} (b) $-11{,}300$ m s^{-2}
1-55 400 m s^{-2}
1-57 45.9 m
1-59 (a) 400 m (b) 2440 m (c) 46.7 s
1-61 (a) 11.5 m (b) 1.53 s (c) 0.473 s, 2.59 s
1-63 (a) 39.4 m s^{-1} (b) 74.1 m
1-65 2.5 m
1-67 (a) 0.204 s (b) 38.1 m (c) 38.5 m
1-71 neither; $a = g =$ constant
1-73 (a) 0.247 s (b) ≈ 3 m s^{-1}
1-75 (a) T_1 to T_2 (b) 0 to T_0 (c) 0 to T_1 (d) T_2 to T_3 (e) none (f) T_0 to T_1, T_2 to T_3
1-77 no, it takes longer to come down
1-79 7 m s^{-1}
1-81 (a) 5 km h^{-1} (b) 1 km h^{-1}
1-87 6 s
1-89 (a) 4.52 m s^{-2} (b) 2.55 s (c) 11.5 m s^{-1} (d) 200-m, yes; 1000-m, no
1-91 closest approach is 10 m
1-93 (a) 9.7 m s^{-2} (b) 30 m s^{-2} (c) 60 m should have been 20 m
1-95 1720 m
1-97 (b) A (c) $(2\pi A/T) \cos 2\pi t/T$ (d) $-(2\pi/T)^2 A \sin 2\pi t/T$ (e) $(2\pi/T)^2$
1-99 (a) $2Bt - 3Ct^2$ (b) $2Bt - 6Ct$ (c) $2B/3t$
1-101 (a) 1.84 m (b) 1.22 s
1-103 $v = 2.42$ m s^{-1}, $a = 98.0$ m s^{-2}
1-105 62.5 m
1-107 $bT^3/3$
1-109 $v_f t + (v_f/b)(e^{-bt} - 1)$
1-111 $v_0 e^{-ct}$
1-115 (a) $(A/\omega) \sin \omega t$ (b) $(-A/\omega^2) \cos \omega t$

Chapter 2

2-1 (a) **D** (b) **G** (c) **C** (d) 0 (e) **A** (f) **G** (g) **C** (h) **D**
2-3 (b) 10.4, 17° above $-x$ axis
2-5 (a) 4.47, 63.4° above $+x$ axis (b) 4.47, 63.4° below $-x$ axis

2-7 (a) 7.21, 56° above **A** (b) 7.21, 56° above −**A** (c) 7.21, 56° below **A**
2-9 24.9, 36° above $-x$ axis
2-11 224 km, 27° N of W
2-13 (a) 8.54, 69° above **C** (b) 17.0, 28° below **A**
2-15 (a) 39.3 s (b) 12.7 m s^{-1}
2-17 v_x = 28.2 m s^{-1}, v_y = 10.3 m s^{-1}
2-19 (a) 500 km h^{-1} (b) 372.7 km h^{-1}, 63.4° south of due west
2-21 p, 2 qt
2-21 (a) 41,700 m s^{-2} (b) a_x = 36,100 m s^{-2}, a_y = 20,800 m s^{-2}
2-25 3.79 × 10^{-3} m s^{-2}
2-27 (a) just before it hits the ground (b) at the highest point reached (c) $a = g =$ constant
2-29 dropped bullet
2-31 24.75 m s^{-1}
2-33 (a) 7.50 m s^{-1} (b) g
2-35 (a) 1.79 × 10^5 m s^{-2} (b) a_x = 1.55 × 10^5 m s^{-2}, a_y = 8.93 × 10^4 m s^{-2}
2-37 (a) 1.33 s (b) 11.5 m from building
2-39 (a) 141 m (b) 4.08 s
2-41 0.0304 m s^{-2}
2-43 (a) the second (b) speeds are equal
2-45 4.47 km h^{-1} (b) 0.5 m south of starting point (c) 0.25 h
2-47 24.9 m s^{-1}
2-49 0.56 m; does not clear net
2-51 (a) 1.03 s (b) 30.8 s
2-53 v_{ox} = 6.41 m s^{-1}, v_{oy} = 15.3 m s^{-1}
2-57 (a) (50 m) sin (0.16 s^{-1})t, (50 m) cos (0.16 s^{-1})t (b) (8 m s^{-1}) cos (0.16 s^{-1})t, −(8 m s^{-1}) sin (0.16 s^{-1})t (c) (1.28 m s^{-2}) sin (0.16 s^{-1})t, −(1.28 m s^{-2}) cos (0.16 s^{-1})t
2-59 (a) $pt\hat{\mathbf{x}} + (qt^2/2)\hat{\mathbf{y}}$ (b) $\mathbf{r} = (pt^2/2)\hat{\mathbf{x}} + (qt^3/6)\hat{\mathbf{y}}$
2-61 (a) 2.04 s (b) 2.89 s (c) 3.53 s
2-63 40.8 m
2-65 8.85 m s^{-1}
2-67 20.2 m s^{-1}
2-69 26.1 m s^{-1}
2-71 71.4°
2-75 (a) 2.97 m s^{-1} (b) 0.45 m
2-77 30 m

Chapter 3

3-1 37° below the 20-N force, 25 N
3-3 15° from either force, 19.3 N
3-5 490 N
3-7 (a) 4.90 N (b) 1.10 lb
3-9 54.5 kg
3-11 0.0741
3-13 1.0595 kg
3-15 (a) 1420 kg m^{-3} (b) density near edge of sun is low compared to center
3-17 (a) 1.27 × 10^{17} kg m^{-3} (b) 1.27 × 10^{14} kg m^{-3}
3-19 1.002
3-21 127 kg
3-23 0.4515 kg
3-25 (a) 11.3 (b) 11.3 kg
3-27 no, no
3-29 (a) 0 (b) 19,600 N
3-31 w
3-33 stable, cables restore position
3-35 no, car is accelerated, net force is not zero
3-41 (a) 5 m s^{-2} (b) 0.06 s
3-43 one quarter of the original acceleration
3-45 3000 N
3-47 11,500 N
3-49 2.45 m s^{-2}
3-51 (a) 3320 m s^{-2} (b) 339
3-53 0.86 m s^{-2}
3-55 652.5 N
3-57 0.444
3-59 (a) 5500 kg m^{-1} (b) yes, if outer layers are less dense
3-61 four times as great
3-63 296 N
3-65 $m_E/8$
3-67 (a) 61.2 kg N (b) 66.2 kg (c) 99.1 N
3-69 2w, upward
3-71 (a) 3 m s^{-2} (b) 1.045 mg, 17.0° to vertical
3-73 0.867
3-75 30 N
3-77 increase maximum frictional force
3-79 (a) 300 N (b) 150 N
3-83 1125 N
3-85 (a) 81.6 kg (b) 10 m s^{-2} (c) 816 N
3-87 (a) 5122 N (b) 1914 N
3-89 (a) 1.23 m s^{-2} (b) 32,000 N (c) 16,000 N
3-91 (a) 29.4 N (b) 3.92 m s^{-2}
3-93 (a) 49 N (b) 0.5
3-95 8.85 m s^{-2}
3-97 (a) 4.105 × 10^{12} N (b) 2.93 × 10^{16} N
3-99 5.12 m s^{-2}
3-101 (a) 1.55 mg, 1.225 mg (b) 0.225 mg

3-103 (a) 23.5 N (b) 1.96 m s^{-2} (c) 0.98 m s^{-1}, 0.245 m
3-105 190 kg
3-107 (a) 6.24 m s^{-2} (b) 22.3 m s^{-1}
3-109 3.20 m s^{-2}

Chapter 4

4-1 $\mathbf{w}_1$, 0; $\mathbf{w}_2$, −6 N m; $\mathbf{w}_3$, −40 N m; $\mathbf{w}_4$, −75 N m
4-3 (a) **A × A, A × C** (b) **A × D, A × E** (c) **A × B** (d) **A × D, A × E**
4-5 equal in magnitude, opposite in direction; component of **E** perpendicular to **A** equals *D*
4-7 4 m, 1.732 m
4-9 (a) 30 N m, into page; 24 N m, into page; 21.2 N m, out of page; (b) position (*a*)
4-11 T_1 = 25.7 N, T_2 = 40.3 N
4-13 F_1 = 0.75 N, F_2 = 0.25 N
4-15 (a) $w + w_1 + w_2$ (b) w_1/w_2
4-17 3.06 m
4-19 0.175 m
4-21 1.31 m
4-23 (a) X = 0.25 m, Y = 0.25 m (b) 0.354 m
4-25 6
4-27 27°
4-31 500 N
4-33 0.667
4-37 (a) I (b) III (c) splenius
4-39 193 N
4-41 T = 3000 N, H_x = 2598 N, H_y = 500 N
4-43 24.1 N
4-45 $X = 0$, $Y = 2mL/(M + 2m)$
4-47 36°
4-49 3.33 kg
4-51 (a) T = 264 N, R_x = 251 N, R_y = 46.7 N (b) 0.133
4-55 (a) T = 2020 N, R_x = 1980 N, R_y = 70 N (b) T = 3220 N, R_x = 3150 N, R_y = −5 N
4-57 $4L/9$
4-59 $3h/4$
4-61 (a) 0.075 m (b) 3 N
4-63 3 m from scale 1
4-62 $X = 0.229h$, $Y = 0.443h$
4-67 75°
4-69 42.4 N

Chapter 5

5-1 4
5-3 0.64 m s^{-2}
5-5 367 m
5-7 (a) 19,700 N (b) 2010 kg
5-9 5100 m
5-11 0.546
5-13 31.3 m s^{-1}
5-17 14.3°
5-19 car may slide downward
5-21 up the embankment
5-23 42,300 rev min^{-1}
5-25 (a) 1.58 m s^{-2} (b) 370 N (c) 512 N
5-27 (a) 5.73° (b) 45° (c) 720°
5-29 (a) 60° (b) 135° (c) 405°
5-31 (a) up (b) down
5-33 (a) 12.5 rad s^{-1}; along axle away from us (b) 2.5 rad s^{-2}
5-35 7670 rad s^{-1}, 73,200 rev min^{-1}
5-37 (a) no (b) possibly (c) yes
5-39 (a) 66.7 rad s^{-1} (b) 4.44 rad s^{-1} (c) 500 rad
5-41 0.245 kg m^2
5-43 before, since $I \approx I_{\text{bucket}}$; water does not spin much
5-45 0.289 l
5-47 (a) 0.00640 kg m^2 (b) 0.0960 N m
5-49 $g/4$
5-51 $7ml^2/48$
5-53 $2mR^2$
5-55 6.25×10^{19}
5-57 6.25×10^{12} must be removed
5-59 3.33×10^{-6} C
5-61 (a) -9.63×10^7 C (b) $+9.63 \times 10^7$ C (c) 8.35×10^{25} N
5-63 9.22×10^{-10} N
5-65 (a) 18.9 m s^{-2} (b) 1.06
5-67 (a) 22.8 m s^{-1} (b) 57.8 m s^{-1}, 0
5-69 (a) 0.0338 m s^{-2} (b) 698 N (c) further reduces weight
5-71 16.0 s
5-73 (a) $4w$ (b) $w\sqrt{10}$
5-75 $(31/32)\pi\rho aR^4$
5-77 5.39 s
5-79 7.02 N m
5-81 (a) 0 (b) $\sqrt{3}\, kqQ/4a^2$, away from line joining $+q$ charges
5-83 25.7 mR^2
5-85 (a) $mb^2/6$ (b) $2mb^2/3$
5-89 4 AU
5-91 1.88 y
5-93 6.02×10^{24} kg

5-95 (a) 2.73×10^{-3} m s^{-2} (b) 2.71×10^{-3} m s^{-2} (c) agree within 1 percent

Chapter 6

6-1 56.4 J
6-3 76°
6-5 80 J
6-7 2.21×10^5 J
6-9 (a) $x = 0$ (b) $\frac{1}{2}ka^2$ (c) 0
6-11 12.5 J
6-13 (a) 20,000 J (b) 20,000 N
6-15 (a) 2500 J (b) 2500 J
6-17 13.1 J
6-19 4230 N
6-21 (a) 39.2 J (b) 0 (c) −117.6 J
6-23 (a) $v_0^2/2g$ (b) $v_0/\sqrt{2}$
6-25 24.2 m s^{-1}
6-27 0
6-29 31.3 m s^{-1}
6-31 35.9 m s^{-1}
6-33 8.82×10^4 J
6-35 15,000 N
6-37 0.918
6-39 0.592
6-41 19.85 m s^{-1}
6-43 (a) 2123 km h^{-1} (b) 2063 km h^{-1}
6-45 (a) 49,000 J (b) 6.45×10^{-3} kg
6-47 2.35×10^{12} J
6-49 4.32×10^{14} J
6-51 (a) 29.4 J (b) 4.85 m s^{-2}
6-53 (a) $GM_sm/2R$ (b) $GM_Em/2R_E$ (c) 14.15
6-55 -6.60×10^{-8} J
6-57 3.17×10^4 m s^{-1}
6-59 2.37×10^3 m s^{-1}
6-61 1.85×10^{19} kg m^{-3}
6-63 1.227×10^7 m s^{-1}
6-65 8464
6-67 (a) 2.915×10^{-15} J (b) 1.822×10^4 eV
6-69 400 N
6-71 (a) \$3.65 (b) 0.35
6-73 40 W
6-75 209 W
6-77 (a) 1.80 W (b) 5.14 N (c) 1080 J
6-79 (a) 200 W (b) 800 W
6-81 6.53×10^4 W
6-83 (a) 200 m^2 (b) comparable to roof of large one-story house
6-85 0.790 J
6-87 (a) 48.0 J (b) 96.0 J
6-89 (a) 1350 J (b) 2.149 N m (c) converted into thermal energy
6-91 $(4gd/5)^{1/2}$
6-93 (a) 36.3 J kg^{-1}, 132 W kg^{-1} (b) 3.23 J kg^{-1}, 131 W kg^{-1}
6-97 2.84 m s^{-1}
6-99 $mgl \sin \theta$
6-101 (a) 1.28 m (b) 0.573 m s^{-1} (c) 0.724 m (d) 3.77 ms^{-1}
6-103 (a) 6×10^{15} kg (b) 311 GW
6-105 (a) 1.529×10^{15} J (b) 3.54×10^{10} W (c) 1.77
6-107 (a) 1.25×10^{18} J (b) 1.45×10^{13} W (c) 1.45
6-109 (a) 498 N (b) 8.53 km
6-114 1.46°
6-115 earth, 11,200 m s^{-1}; sun, 42,100 m s^{-1}
6-117 (a) $GM_s^2/4R_s$ (b) 9.50×10^{40} J (c) 7.93×10^6 y
6-119 5.27×10^{-3} s
6-125 $ma^2t^2/2$
6-127 (a) 718 N (b) 5740 W
6-129 6.09 m s^{-1}
6-131 (a) 198 m (b) 58.0 s

Chapter 7

7-1 450,000 N
7-3 69.1 m s^{-1}
7-5 $2mv/\Delta t$ to left
7-7 decrease recoil velocity
7-9 change in momentum of blood
7-13 $mv_0/(m + M)$
7-15 (a) 8.26 m s^{-1} (b) 1650 *N*
7-17 0.005 m s^{-1}
7-19 $\phi = \theta$
7-21 (a) 3.34×10^{-11} m s^{-1} (b) 1.12×10^{-15}
7-23 $3\mathbf{v}/2$
7-25 (a) earth–moon center of mass (b) 4.66×10^6 m
7-27 0.932
7-29 (a) none (b) 1.33×10^5 J
7-31 1/2
7-33 no; gravity produces torque
7-35 (a) 16.7 rad s^{-1} (b) 4.33 kg m^2 s^{-1}
7-37 0.251 kg m^2 s^{-1}
7-39 to increase I, hence stability
7-43 500 s

7-45 2.05 rad s^{-1}
7-47 no; net gravitational force is not central, exerts torque
7-49 8220 m s^{-1}
7-51 no; torque about most other points is not zero
7-53 $v/2$
7-55 3.34×10^{-12} m s^{-1}
7-57 (a) car, 33.3 m s^{-1}; truck 6.67 m s^{-1} (b) 6.67 m s^{-1}
7-59 1.09×10^8 m s^{-1}
7-63 (a) 2.48 m s^{-1} (b) 0.314 m
7-65 (b) and (c)
7-67 m_2/m_1
7-69 $m/(m + M)$
7-71 (a) 18.1 m s^{-1}, 83.7° south of west (b) 3.62×10^5 J
7-73 0.2 rev s^{-1}
7-75 it will lengthen
7-77 $n^2h^2/8\pi^2I$
7-79 (a) 1.71 rad s^{-1} (b) 1.71 rad s^{-1}
7-85 1470 N
7-89 (a) 114 J (b) 55.3 J
7-97 counterclockwise
7-99 increase rate

Chapter 8

8-1 1.25×10^7 N m^{-2}
8-3 0.0125
8-5 1.56×10^{-4} m
8-7 4.84×10^{-3} m
8-9 7.07×10^4 N
8-11 1.27×10^{11} N m^{-2}
8-13 (a) 0.02 cm (b) 0.004 cm
8-15 (a) 9800 N m^{-2}, 4.90×10^{-8} (b) 9.80×10^{-8} m (c) 5.10×10^6 kg
8-17 77,400 N
8-19 (a) 3.18×10^6 N m^{-2}, 1.59×10^{-5} (b) 4.77×10^{-5} m
8-21 2.25×10^7 N m^{-1}
8-23 151 N
8-25 78.5 N m
8-27 (a) 2.13×10^{-7} m^4 (b) 8.53×10^{-7} m^4, 5.33×10^{-8} m^4 (c) board B, $\perp$ to 2-cm dimension (d) board A
8-29 (a) yes (b) weight, normal force (c) no; torques add to zero
8-31 they produce a large torque with respect to the base
8-33 8.73 m
8-35 37.6 m, compared to 8.73 m
8-37 (a) 10^6 N m^{-2}, 1.19×10^{-5} (b) 1.19×10^{-7} m
8-39 2.83×10^4 N
8-41 (a) 1.25×10^7 N m^{-2} (b) 0.125
8-43 15,700 N
8-45 (a) 205 m^3 (b) 0.005 m
8-47 (a) 3.89×10^{-3} m^2 (b) 2×10^{-4} m
8-49 16
8-51 (a) 8.80×10^{-5} m^4 (b) 7.41×10^{-7} m^4
8-53 R(solid)/R(hollow) = 0.0914
8-55 1.73 cm
8-61 areas would scale with weight
8-63 $m^{5/8}$
8-65 (a) $m^{-1/3}$ (b) $m^{-1/4}$
8-67 independent of mass, as in Chapter 6
8-69 25 m

Chapter 9

9-1 (a) 0 (b) $4R$
9-3 (a) $T/4$ to $T/2$, $3T/4$ to T (b) never (c) 0 to $T/4$, $T/2$ to $3T/4$
9-5 (a) 0.1 m, 0 (b) 0, −0.314 m s^{-1} (c) −0.1 m, 0
9-7 ±0.354 m
9-9 (a) 0 (b) $\pm R$ (maximum displacement)
9-11 −148 m s^{-2}
9-13 2.25 N m^{-1}
9-15 (a) 0.327 m (b) 1.15 s
9-17 1.36 Hz
9-19 0.248 m
9-21 12.2 m
9-23 1.49 m
9-25 4
9-27 1.050 Hz
9-29 6.35 s
9-31 2.65 m s^{-1}
9-33 8.94 m s^{-1}
9-35 (a) 4.90 N m^{-1} (b) 1.58 Hz (c) 0.635 s (d) 6.13×10^{-3} J
9-37 0.0707 m
9-39 (a) ±0.447 m s^{-1} (b) ±0.387 m s^{-1}
9-41 (a) 147 J (b) 1.176×10^5 N m^{-1} (c) 7.72 Hz
9-43 (a) 0.769 s (b) 4.61 s
9-45 1/100
9-47 (a) x_0, 0, $-4\pi^2f^2x_0$ (b) $-x_0$, 0, $4\pi^2f^2x_0$
9-49 $x = R \sin(2\pi ft)$, $v = (2\pi f)R \cos(2\pi ft)$, $a = -(2\pi f)^2 R \sin(2\pi ft)$

9-51 (a) 8.88 N m^{-1} (b) 7.5 Hz
9-53 (a) 19.7 N m^{-1} (b) 0.995 m
9-55 (a) $\simeq$ 0.7 Hz (b) $\simeq$ 4 km
9-57 5.95 m s^{-1}
9-59 (a) $7ml^2/48$, l = 1 m (b) 0.652 Hz
9-61 (a) longer (b) 14
9-69 (a) 1.31×10^{14} Hz (b) 1.32×10^{-11} m (c) 9790 m s^{-1}
9-71 2.57×10^{-6} kg m s^{-2}
9-73 (b) determines phase (point in cycle at t = 0)
9-77 $\simeq 10^5$ N m^{-1}
9-79 (a) 98,000 N m^{-1} (b) 7.05 Hz (c) yes
9-81 0.0621 m
9-83 (a) 22.2 Hz (b) well

Chapter 10

10-1 21.1° C
10-3 −40°
10-5 172.4° F
10-7 4.032 g
10-9 1.806×10^{24}
10-11 (a) 31.998 u (b) 53.15 g
10-13 2.31×10^{24}
10-15 (a) 200 kPa (b) 301.3 kPa
10-17 4.86×10^7 N
10-19 2030 N; no
10-21 (a) $\approx 10^5$ Pa (b) $\approx$1000 Pa
10-23 5
10-25 1.37
10-27 10,970 K
10-29 1.05 atm
10-31 10,100 m
10-33 393 m s^{-1}
10-35 pressure is doubled
10-37 0.9957
10-39 (a) 4.25×10^{-21} J (b) 205 K
10-41 746 s
10-43 3.74×10^6 Pa = 37.0 atm
10-45 196 moles m^{-3}
10-47 (a) −459.67° F (b) 459.67° R (c) 671.67° R
10-49 7.36×10^{22}
10-51 (a) 0.032 (b) 77,800 N
10-53 4.66 litres
10-55 9750 K
10-57 (a) 0.45 s (b) 4.5 times as large
10-59 7.88 atm
10-61 12.5 J

Chapter 11

11-1 (a) $P_1(V_3 - V_1)$ (b) $-P_1(V_3 - V_1)$
11-3 1.4 J
11-5 10^7 J
11-7 3.24×10^5 J
11-9 25 W
11-11 faster increase with piston fixed; all heat goes into internal energy change
11-13 violates second law
11-15 16.33 J K^{-1}
11-17 1.26 J K^{-1} s^{-1}
11-19 (a) no (b) increased
11-21 (a) all tails (heads) 1 way; 1 head (tail) and 5 tails (heads)—6 ways; 2 heads (tails) and 4 tails (heads)—15 ways; 3 heads and 3 tails—20 ways. (b) 3 heads and 3 tails most probable
11-25 raise it
11-27 (a) 58.1% (b) 3.3×10^6 J (c) 41.8%
11-29 500 K, 429 K
11-31 January, 1.07%; July, 6.08%
11-33 2.5
11-35 (a) 70,000 J (b) −80,000 J (c) 20,000 J
11-37 50%
11-39 (a) 2 or 12—1 way; 3 or 11—2 ways; 4 or 10—3 ways; 5 or 9—4 ways; 6 or 8—5 ways; 7—6 ways (b) 7
11-41 (a) 148 s (b) no; heat transfer from water is not efficient
11-43 (a) 43.9% (b) 1.52
11-45 (a) 0.874 (b) 11.45 kW (c) 80 kW
11-51 (a) 589 K (b) 1875 MW (c) 3.68×10^6 kg
11-53 (a) 7.43×10^{-3} litres s^{-1} (b) 214 litres
11-55 (a) 8.82 litres (b) 34.5 litres
11-57 (a) 25% (b) 231 W
11-59 1.24×10^6 J
11-61 2.68 g
11-63 no
11-65 0.375 W kg^{-1}
11-67 18.5 d

Chapter 12

12-1 5.08×10^{-3} m
12-3 4.6×10^{-4} m
12-5 lid expands more than glass
12-7 0.02991 m
12-9 different expansions would produce internal stresses

12-11 46.6 kJ
12-13 2.48 kJ kg^{-1} K^{-1}
12-15 10,000 kJ
12-17 3.54×10^3 kJ
12-19 (a) no (b) 0° C
12-21 0.25 kg
12-23 2.74 kJ
12-25 0.2 m
12-27 snow acts as insulation
12-29 384 W
12-31 53.3 W
12-33 (a) 0.263 m^2 K W^{-1} (b) 3.95 m^2 K W^{-1}
12-35 79.999°C
12-37 21.2°C
12-39 1.5
12-41 push warm air down
12-43 (a) 9×10^{-6} m (b) infrared
12-45 23.4%
12-47 (a) 895 W (b) 240 W
12-49 55.5 W
12-51 (a) 3.1×10^{-4} m (b) slow (c) 1.27×10^{-4} (d) 11.0 s
12-53 3.41×10^{-3} K^{-1}
12-55 775 W
12-57 1.2 K h^{-1}
12-59 (a) 62.4 kJ (b) 104 kJ
12-61 0.576 kg min^{-1}
12-63 (a) 127.5 J s^{-1} (b) 0.0015 m
12-65 the air does work as it expands, so it loses internal energy
12-67 (a) 102°C (b) 3200 W
12-69 100.8°C
12-71 22%
12-73 (a) 418 W m^{-2} (b) no; average sky temperature is very low
12-75 (a) 317 W (b) no
12-77 8.74×10^{-3} kg
12-79 (a) 2.65×10^6 J (b) 0.39 cents h^{-1}
12-81 (a) 79.997°C (b) 71.6 W
12-83 $0.314V_0$
12-89 0.260 kg h^{-1}

Chapter 13

13-1 0.08 m^3
13-3 0.01 m^3
13-5 25.6 m
13-7 0.21 m^3 s^{-1}
13-9 4.24 m s^{-1}
13-11 1 m s^{-1}
13-13 no; flow is turbulent
13-15 no; work is done against gravity
13-17 (a) pressure drop is greater (b) more significant; more power is dissipated
13-19 20.8 k Pa
13-21 20.4 m
13-23 1170 kg m^{-3}
13-25 9.34 k Pa = 70.1 torr
13-27 25.8 k Pa
13-29 21.6 m s^{-2}
13-31 No
13-33 (a) 1.13×10^{-3} m^3 s^{-1} (b) 2.73×10^{-4} m^3 s^{-1}
13-35 (a) 75 Pa (b) 0.4 m s^{-1}
13-39 750 kg m^{-3}
13-41 fallen
13-43 309 kg
13-45 9.8×10^4 Pa = 0.967 atm
13-49 99.986 atm
13-51 0.193 m
13-53 (a) 3.83 m s^{-1} (b) yes, until water level falls 0.25 m (c) 3.43 m s^{-1}
13-55 (a) yes, increases (b) decreases
13-59 8878 kg
13-61 high takeoff velocity
13-63 (a) 48 m s^{-1} (b) doubtful validity
13-65 yes; model predicts 66 km
13-67 7.25 km
13-69 $l^{7/2}$
13-71 $l^{3/4}$

Chapter 14

14-1 halfway
14-3 1.8 W
14-5 5.4×10^{-5} m
14-7 (a) 1.13×10^{-7} m^3 s^{-1} (b) 0.0720 m s^{-1}
14-9 (a) 0.0314 N (b) 4.71×10^{-4} W
14-11 (a) 0.354 m s^{-1} (b) 632 Pa
14-13 (a) no (b) yes (c) yes; only pressure drops due to dissipative forces are relevant
14-15 (a), (b) power dissipation is $Q \, \Delta P$
14-17 (a) 7.96 m s^{-1} (b) turbulent (c) no
14-19 (a) 0.983 m s^{-1} (b) 1.24×10^{-5} m^3 s^{-1}
14-21 $2R^2/r^2$
14-23 (a) 1.49×10^{10} kPa s m^{-3} (b) 8.72×10^{-11} m^3 s^{-1}

14-25 (a) 8.38×10^{-3} N (b) 8.33×10^{-2} N (c) oil inhibits rust
14-27 (a) 8×10^{-3} m^3 s^{-1} (b) 6.37 m s^{-1} (c) $N_R = 2.5 \times 10^5$, so flow is turbulent
14-29 900 W
14-31 $409.6P_0$
14-33 (a) 11.6 kPa, 0.873 kPa (b) right ventricle does less work than left
14-35 (a) $R_f = \Delta P/Q$ (b) increase substantially
14-37 (a) 100 kPa s m^{-3} (b) 10 W (c) no
14-39 (a) 3.32×10^{14} kPa s m^{-3} (b) 3.08×10^{10}
14-41 (a) $7\pi\,\Delta PR^4/128\eta l$ (b) 7/16 (c) 1/4
14-43 (a) 4.33×10^{-10} m s^{-1} (b) 50 m s^{-1}
14-45 4.23×10^{-8} m
14-47 $\approx$200 N
14-49 (a) 4.23 (b) 3.90 m s^{-2}, 45.8 m s^{-2}
14-51 (a) 3.25×10^{-16} N (b) 2.41×10^{-16} N
14-53 805 s
14-55 3.39×10^7 u
14-57 10^{-5} m s^{-1}
14-63 (a) 2.29×10^{-24} m^3 (b) 8.18×10^{-9} m (c) 1.54×10^{-7} m (d) no, probably flattened like a pancake
14-65 carries material to and from walls
14-67 B does 21% more work

Chapter 15

15-1 0.02 N m^{-1}
15-3 minimize film area outside
15-5 −0.0535 m
15-7 0.0703 m
15-9 0.025 N m^{-1}
15-11 (a) 6060 N m^{-1} (b) 382 N
15-13 2560 N m^{-1}
15-15 3.35×10^{-3} N m^{-1}; 7%
15-17 4 Pa
15-19 21%
15-23 yes; negative pressure situation is destroyed
15-25 −0.934 atm
15-27 $w + 4\pi r\gamma$
15-33 3.86×10^{-2} N m^{-1}
15-35 (a) 41.5 J (b) 5.03×10^{-4} J
15-37 (a) 0.514 m (b) No
15-39 0.0495 m

Chapter 16

16-1 $(2kQ^2/9b^2)\hat{\mathbf{y}}$
16-3 $-(kQ^2/2b^2)\hat{\mathbf{y}}$
16-5 4.36×10^{-9} N
16-7 (a) e (b) 640 N
16-9 (a) 1.32×10^{13} N C^{-1} outward (b) 2.11×10^{-6} N, toward nucleus
16-11 5.69×10^{-4} N C^{-1}, opposite to **a**
16-13 $-(kQ/2b^2)\hat{\mathbf{y}}$
16-15 -1.77×10^{-8} C
16-17 $x = 0$, $y = -0.243b$
16-19 no, force on a charge has a unique direction
16-21 (a) 10^{-6} C m^{-1} (b) 1.8×10^5 N C^{-1}
16-23 (a) 0.0050 (b) 0.41
16-25 (a) 86.4 V (b) -1.38×10^{-17} J
16-27 (a) 8.84×10^{-8} C m^{-2} (b) 400 V
16-29 (a) toward positive plate (b) toward negative plate (c) acquire some energy (d) 42.9
16-31 (a) 0.335 m (b) 0.335 m
16-33 (a) 16.8 MeV (b) 5.68×10^7 m s^{-1}
16-35 (a) 1.127×10^{-12} J (b) 3.67×10^7 m s^{-1}
16-37 (a) $E = 0$ (b) $\Delta V = E\ell$, where ℓ is the distance moved parallel to the field
16-39 cylinders centered on wire
16-41 3.13×10^{-11} m
16-43 $2qE$
16-45 (a) 0 (b) 1.6×10^{-23} N m (c) 0
16-47 10^{-7} F
16-49 6.25×10^{15}
16-51 3.23 m^2
16-53 4×10^8 V
16-55 (a) 0.325 m^2 (b) 1.44 cm
16-57 (a) 60 μF (b) 0.060 C
16-59 (a) 8.85×10^{-8} C (b) 4.43×10^{-5} J (c) 100 V, 4.43×10^{-6} J
16-61 (a) 1.5×10^{-6} m^2, 1.5×10^{-8} F (b) 6.075×10^{-11} F
16-63 (a) halved (b) halved (c) halved (d) halved
16-65 (a) 4.79×10^{-19} C (b) 2.99 (c) 1890 V
16-67 720 N C^{-1}, toward plate
16-69 (a) 1.76×10^{14} m s^{-2} (b) 10^{-8} s (c) 8.8×10^{-3} m (d) 5°
16-71 $0.701kQ/a^2$, 30° below $-x$ axis
16-73 (a) dark areas (b) dark (positive) areas
16-77 (a) $-2kqa\hat{\mathbf{y}}/(x^2 + a^2)^{3/2}$ (b) 1/2
16-79 $2k\lambda/R$
16-83 $mv^2/2qE$
16-85 (a) $2kp_1p_2/R^3$ (b) kp_1p_2/R^3
16-87 (b) 0.316 e
16-91 five capacitors in parallel
16-93 1.33 μF

Chapter 17

17-1 (a) 720 C (b) 4.50×10^{21}
17-3 (a) no (b) no
17-5 3.43×10^{-4} m s^{-1}
17-7 4.75×10^{-4} kg
17-9 2.5 ohms
17-11 34.2 ohms
17-13 1.05×10^{-3} m
17-15 (a) r^2 (b) $1/R$
17-17 (a) no; R decreases as I increases. (b) no
17-19 11.5 ohms
17-21 20 ohms
17-23 (a) 6 A (b) 60 C (c) −720 J (d) 720 J (e) 0 (f) 720 J (g) chemical energy in the battery
17-25 (a) 0.15 A (b) −1.5 V, 1.5 V, 1.5 V, −0.6 V, −0.9 V
17-27 (a) 3000 A, 3.6×10^4 W (b) 0.146 ohm (c) 934 W (d) 25.6 W
17-29 (a) 144 ohms (b) 0.833 A
17-31 (a) 0.4 A (b) 4.8 W, −3.2 W (c) 0.64 W, 0.96 W
17-33 64.8 cents
17-35 (a) 7.02×10^6 J (b) 8.78×10^5 J
17-37 (a) 4.17 A (b) 1.15 ohm
17-39 460
17-41 (a) 240 ohms (b) 40 ohms
17-43 1 ohm
17-45 (a) 1.5 A (b) 3 V (c) 1 A
17-47 90-ohm series resistor
17-49 (a) 0.1 ohm (b) 10^{-7} s
17-51 0.02 s
17-53 (a) 0.012 A (b) 0.005 s
17-55 (a) 0.01 C (b) 0.0037 C
17-57 (a) 10 V (b) 100 V
17-61 (a) 7200 C (b) 4.50×10^{22} (c) 6.15×10^{23}
17-63 (a) 2.09×10^{-3} ohm (b) 0.00162 m (c) $w(\text{A1})/w(\text{Cu}) = 0.462$
17-65 (a) 4600 W (b) 37.7 min
17-67 (a) 1.51×10^4 J (b) 5.16 K
17-69 (a) positive (b) 241 W (c) 12.06 V
17-71 (a) $\mathscr{E}/r$ (b) $\mathscr{E}/2r$
17-73 (a) 0.0516 ohm (b) 1.032 V (c) 20.6 W
17-75 0.00148 m = 0.148 cm
17-77 (a) 0.1 C (b) 10 ohms (c) 37 A
17-81 $\mathscr{E} = \mathscr{E}_1 R/(R + R_1)$
17-83 $\frac{1}{2} \ln 2 = 0.347$
17-85 1.295 ohm m
17-87 (a) 13.6 ohm m (b) 7.37×10^{-2} ohm^{-1} m^{-1}
17-89 (a) 1 A (b) 10 ohms (c) 14 V
17-91 3.427 W

Chapter 18

18-1 10^6
18-3 1.59×10^9 ohms
18-5 (a) 1.26×10^{-9} F (b) 1.59×10^6 ohms
18-7 (a) 1.2×10^7 N C^{-1}, into axon (b) 8.48
18-9 (a) 4.5×10^{-6} C m^{-2} (b) 9.0×10^{-4} C m^{-2}
18-11 10 μm
18-13 0.8 μm
18-15 8.17×10^{12}
18-17 74.1 mV
18-19 (a) 0.0289 A (b) 0.00260 W
18-21 1.5 mm
18-23 (a) −86.3 mV (b) −88.6 mV
18-25 (a) 0.2 s (b) 0.01 s
18-27 (a) 2.67×10^7 ohm m (b) 1.46×10^{10} m^2 (c) 8.28 μm
18-29 $\rho_a = 0.812$ ohm m, $\rho_{if} = 0.599$ ohm m
18-31 (a) 3.9×10^{-10} C (b) 2.44×10^9
18-37 (a) 75 (b) 75,000

Chapter 19

19-1 (a) P_4 (b) P_1
19-3 no; can have $\mathbf{v} \| \mathbf{B}$
19-5 (a) 0 (b) 0 (c) qvB/m, into page (d) qvB/m, out of page (e) qvB/m, $+y$ direction (f) qvB/m, $-y$ direction
19-7 (a) 5×10^{-4} N, into page (b) 0.05 m s^{-2}, into page
19-9 0.5 T
19-11 (a) 30 N
19-13 (a) 2 N, 2 N, 0 (b) 0
19-15 (a) 0.1 A m^2 (b) 0.01 N m (c) **B** in plane of loop
19-17 yes; $-x$ direction
19-19 3.77×10^{-7} T
19-21 1.257×10^{-3} T
19-23 6.28×10^{-3} T
19-25 (a) 8×10^{-6} T (b) 8×10^{-7} T
19-27 7.80×10^{-7} A
19-29 (a) 2×10^{-4} m (b) yes
19-31 0.25 A, parallel
19-33 (a) ev_dB, upward (b) v_dB, upward (c) av_dB (d) av_dB (e) 2×10^{-5} V (f) out of page (g) opposite in sign for a given current direction
19-35 (a) 0.24 A m^2 (b) 0.12 N m (c) $\boldsymbol{\mu} \| \pm\mathbf{B}$

19-37 2×10^{-6} N, toward left
19-39 (a) 10^{-5} T, into page (b) 1.67×10^{-5} T, into page (c) 2.33×10^{-5} T, out of page (d) $x = 0.0333$ m
19-41 15.9 A
19-43 (a) 1.09×10^{-3} A (b) 13.4 T
19-45 $\pi k'I/a$
19-47 (a) 9.6×10^{-20} kg m s^{-1} (b) 5.75×10^{7} m s^{-1}
19-49 5 MeV
19-51 (a) D (b) D (c) D
19-53 (a) 1.67×10^{5} m s^{-1} (b) 8.66×10^{-3} m
19-55 (a) $evB/2m$ (b) $0.866\,v$, 0 (c) $v/2$, $mv/2eB$ (d) $1.732\pi mv/eB$ (e) helix
19-59 (a) $2k'Ir/a^2$ (b) $2k'I/r$ (c) $2k'I(r^2 - b^2)/[r(c^2 - b^2)]$ (d) 0

Chapter 20

20-1 (a) yes (b) no (c) yes
20-3 (a) same (b) large in copper, almost zero in rubber
20-5 3.14 A
20-7 (a) 48 V (b) 0
20-9 clockwise
20-11 $2\omega BA/\pi$
20-13 150 V
20-15 0.075
20-17 1
20-19 induced EMF can lead to sparks
20-21 (a) clockwise (b) counterclockwise
20-27 0.32 H
20-31 (a) qvB (b) $qvB\ell$ (c) $-B\ell v$; same
20-33 Viewed from above: (a) counterclockwise (b) zero (c) clockwise
20-35 (a) proportional to ω (b) reduces it (c) increases I (d) I^2R becomes large.
20-39 (a) $4\pi K_m k'IN/\ell$ (b) $2\pi K'_m N^2 I^2/\ell^2$ (c) $1/(8\pi k')$
20-43 (a) 1.333 H (b) 6 H
20-45 (a) $(Li_0/T)e^{-t/T}$ (b) $\frac{1}{2}Li_0{}^2e^{-2t/T}$
20-47 (a) 1592 bits cm^{-1} (b) 4421 bits cm^{-1}
20-49 5.04×10^{6} bits s^{-1}
20-51 6
20-53 (a) 1.2 A (b) 0.02 s (c) 0.759 A (d) 1.2 A
20-55 2.392 J
20-59 28.3 A
20-61 (a) 200 W (b) 1.67 A (c) 2.36 A
20-63 ground plus either "hot" line
20-65 (a) 159 Hz (b) 70.7 V
20-67 (a) 39.8 μF (b) 66.7 ohms (c) 240 V
20-69 100
20-71 (a) 0.796 A (b) 1.125 A
20-73 (a) 75.4 ohms (b) 125 ohms (c) 1.92 A
20-75 (a) 101 ohms (b) 1.19 A
20-77 1.592×10^{8} Hz
20-79 250 V
20-81 (a) 13 ohms (b) 426 W
20-83 (a) 15.8 ohms (b) 2 W
20-85 R_v should be much larger to avoid altering currents and voltages significantly
20-87 9.9×10^{-3} ohm
20-91 5.77 s
20-93 (a) 1.29×10^{-9} F (b) 1.75 ohm (c) 0.452 ohm

Chapter 21

21-1 0.344 m
21-3 (a) 10^{10} Hz (b) 5×10^{9} waves (c) 1.5×10^{8} m
21-5 214 m
21-7 (a) 6×10^{14} Hz (b) 3.77×10^{15} rad s^{-1} (c) 1.257×10^{7} m^{-1}
21-11 (0.1 m) sin[(3.14 m^{-1})x − (15.7 s^{-1})t]
21-13 173 m s^{-1}
21-15 156 N
21-21 (a) $2A$ (b) $2A\cos\omega t$
21-23 (a) 0, π/k, $2\pi/k$, . . . (b) $\pi/2k$, $3\pi/2k$, . . .
21-27 (a) 435 m s^{-1} (b) 2.91×10s^{-4} kg ms^{-1}
21-29 (a) 3.5 m (b) 1.75 m
21-31 6.51 m
21-33 (a) 0.25 m (b) 0.132 m
21-37 (a) 5 Hz
21-39 0.0866 m
21-41 0.25
21-43 all kinetic energy; string is still moving
21-47 3.42 m s^{-1}
21-49 40.0 s
21-51 (a) 1.52×10s^{-3} s
21-53 (a) 80% (b) 20%
21-55 (a) ωA (b) $\omega^2A^2\,\Delta m/2$ (c) $\omega^2A^2\,\Delta m/2$
21-57 2A cos $\phi/2$
21-59 1058 Hz
21-61 29.9 m s^{-1}
21-63 8.99×10^{4} Hz
21-65 (a) +3.47 m s^{-1}, −3.41 m s^{-1} (b) No
21-67 5.28×10^{-8} m
21-69 (a) 497.1 Hz (b) 502.9 Hz (c) 5.8 Hz

21-73 0.0157 m s^{-1}
21-77 13.7 Hz
21-79 53,300 Hz

Chapter 22

22-1 $2.07 \times 10^{11} \text{ kg m}^{-1} \text{ s}^{-2}$
22-3 8.71 m
22-5 365 Hz
22-7 40.7 m
22-9 1498 m
22-11 0.0516 m
22-13 in water, c is larger, λ larger
22-15 132 Hz, 265 Hz, 397 Hz, 529 Hz
22-17 2.65 m, 0.0823 m
22-19 9.09 Pa
22-21 0.0166
22-23 4
22-25 14.7
22-27 1.73×10^{-3}·Pa
22-29 $3 \times 10^{-7} \text{ W m}^{-2}$
22-31 17,200 Hz
22-37 10
22-39 60 dB
22-41 8×10^{-13} W
22-43 no pressure differences or shielding by the head for sources overhead
22-49 (a) 0.103 m (b) 4.4×10^{-3} s
22-51 (a) 86.0 Hz (b) 1.828 m
22-53 (a) 1.26×10^4 W (b) 1.26×10^3 J
22-55 49.5 dB
22-57 (a) 10^{-8} W m^{-2} (b) 50.5 dB (c) 6.28×10^{-6} W
22-59 (a) 0.0430 m (b) 1720 Hz
22-63 (a) 99.9% (b) 0.11%
22-65 9×10^6
22-67 $\simeq$2 mm

Chapter 23

23-1 $2.25 \times 10^8 \text{ m s}^{-1}$
23-3 (a) 450 nm (b) yellow
23-5 375 nm
23-7 0.0204
23-9 0.997
23-11 1.649
23-13 (a) 15° (b) 11°
23-15 1.183
23-17 air near road is less dense, has smaller n; sunlight bends upward
23-19 57°
23-21 1.91×10^{-5} m
23-23 5.98×10^{-5} m
23-25 no, two beams are not coherent
23-27 625 nm
23-29 500
23-31 (a) to separate lines (b) to sharpen lines
23-33 693 nm
23-35 916 nm
23-37 0.258 m
23-39 0.154 m
23-41 30°
23-43 (a) 0.2 (b) 0.8
23-45 63.4°
23-47 10°
23-49 77°
23-51 11.34 m
23-53 (a) 13.4° (b) $s' = 0.74$ m
23-55 $d \sin \theta = (m + \frac{1}{2})\lambda$
23-61 (a) $(1768/m)$ nm (b) look for lines at smaller angles
23-65 2.68×10^{-3} m
23-69 (a) all of it (b) resolution is reduced in both cases
23-71 150 nm
23-75 spot is 0.117 m from plate
23-77 all wavelengths interfere destructively

Chapter 24

24-1 4 m
24-3 20 cm
24-5 −0.5 m
24-7 1.50 m
24-9 blue, 0.0775 m; red, 0.0795 m
24-11 −0.333 m
24-13 (a) −0.4 m (b) 5; erect
24-15 (a) 0.0508 m (b) −0.0169 (c) 1.42 m
24-17 four times larger
24-19 0.250 m
24-21 (a) 4.75 diopters (b) 0.211 m
24-23 (a) −0.1818 m (b) −0.286 m
24-25 10^{-3} m
24-27 0.2 m
24-29 (a) 0.133 m from objective (b) 0.00412 m (c) −277

24-31 edges of retina have most rods
24-33 (a) 510 nm, 620 nm (b) 450 nm, 560 nm
24-35 (a) 5.75×10^{-7} m (b) 5.75×10^{-6} m
24-37 real images are inverted; processing in nervous system
24-39 80.1 m
24-41 (a) 0, $-f$, ∞, $3f$, $3f/2$
24-45 -1.20 m
24-47 $2f$
24-51 6.80×10^{-3} m
24-53 0.1 m away
24-57 0.0357 m
24-59 64
24-61 (a) 1.34×10^{-6} m (b) 2.15×10^{-5} m
24-63 3.5 diopters
24-65 (a) 3.5 diopters (b) 1 m
24-67 0.1667 m
24-69 (a) 480 nm (b) 28%
24-71 (a) 0.52, 0.48, 0; 580 nm (b) 0.44, 0.13, 0.43; extraspectral
24-75 (a) 0.125 m (b) 0.5 m
24-77 -20
24-79 (a) red, blue (b) red, green (c) red

Chapter 25

25-1 2000 km h^{-1}
25-3 100 s
25-5 (a) 3.75×10^{-8} s (b) 6.75 m
25-7 0.872 m
25-9 $0.866c$
25-11 8 light-years
25-13 $0.995c$
25-15 $0.866c$
25-17 (a) 5.35×10^{-9} u (b) 1.78×10^{-10}
25-19 8.37×10^{-4} u
25-21 (a) 2150 MeV (b) 1210 MeV
25-23 (a) $0.995c$ (b) $9.95mc$
25-25 (a) 932 MeV (b) 932 MeV
25-27 (a) 1.005 y (b) 10.05 y (c) both
25-29 (a) 5 h (b) 1.25 h (c) 6.25 h (d) 4 h
25-31 3.50×10^{-7} kg
25-33 (a) 1.12 (b) 1.35×10^{8} m s^{-1} (c) 1.45×10^{8} m s^{-1}
25-37 2.25×10^{-10} m
25-41 (a) 167 m (b) *A* flashes first
25-43 (a) 0.8 h (b) 1.33 h
25-45 (a) $0.822c$ (b) 0
25-47 (a) $0.806c$ (b) $-0.263c$
25-49 (a) 4 m (b) 10^{-8} s (c) 5.8 m
25-51 $v_x = 0.8c$, $v_y = 0.54c$, $v = 0.965c$

Chapter 26

26-1 4.53×10^{14} Hz
26-3 9.65×10^{14} Hz
26-5 removal of electrons leaves positive charge
26-7 48.6 m
26-9 (a) 3.10 eV (b) 1.77 eV
26-11 (a) 6.24×10^{12} Hz (b) 1.25×10^{14} Hz (c) infrared, blue
26-13 (a) 3.08×10^{-20} J (b) 3.51×10^{-11} m
26-15 5.32×10^{20} Hz
26-17 (a) 1.21×10^{19} Hz (b) 2.48×10^{-11} m
26-19 (a) 2.42×10^{20} Hz (b) 1.24×10^{-12} nm (c) 0.00334 eV s m^{-1} = 5.35×10^{-22} kg m s^{-1}
26-21 (a) 7.95×10^{-8} W m^{-2} (b) 4.00×10^{-6} W
26-23 1995 m
26-25 (a) 1.62×10^{-27} kg (b) 13.1 N m^{-1}
26-27 (a) 277 nm (b) 0.48 eV (c) 0.48 eV
26-29 (a) 2.42×10^{19} Hz (b) 2.32×10^{19} Hz
26-31 (a) 3.34×10^{-4} eV s m^{-1} = 5.35×10^{-23} kg m s^{-1} (b) 3.93×10^{-14} J = 24.5 eV (c) 99,975.5 eV (d) 5.92×10^{15} Hz
26-33 $\Delta\lambda$ varies as $1/m$, and the nuclear mass is much larger

Chapter 27

27-1 4.73×10^{-14} m
27-3 2975 m
27-5 486 nm
27-7 151 eV
27-9 6.63×10^{-24} kg m s^{-1} (for both)
27-11 3.70×10^{-63} m
27-13 (a) 6.63×10^{-34} m (b) no, λ is too small
27-15 (a) 0.821 nm (b) 224 eV
27-17 yes
27-19 (a) 13.6 eV (b) 54.4 eV (c) 122 eV
27-21 $n = 2$
27-23 4.05×10^{-6} m
27-25 6.4 ev
27-31 1.16×10^{-3} m s^{-1}
27-33 $\gtrsim 3.52 \times 10^{-31}$ m
27-35 (a) 1.06×10^{-24} kg m s^{-1} (b) 1.16×10^{6} m s^{-1}, 5.28×10^{-24} m s^{-1}

27-37 (a) 6.8 eV (b) $2a_0 = 1.06 \times 10^{-10}$ m
27-39 (a) -7.21×10^5 eV (b) 1.60×10^{-14} m (c) 4
27-41 12.75 eV, 12.1 eV, 10.2 eV, 2.55 eV, 1.89 eV, 0.661 eV
27-43 (a) $n^2\hbar^2/2I$, $n = 0, 1, 2, \ldots$
27-45 (a) 6.17×10^4 Hz (b) 2.56 eV (c) $4 \rightarrow 2$

Chapter 28

28-1 (a) 0, 1, 2, 3 (b) 4*s*, 4*p*, 4*d*, 4*f* (c) 0, $\hbar$, $2\hbar$, $3\hbar$
28-3 (a) 0, $\pm e\hbar B/2m$, $\pm 2e\hbar B/2m$ (b) 5.79×10^{-4} eV (c) absorbed
28-5 32
28-7 (a) $r = 0$ (b) $r \approx 5a_0$ (c) $r = 0, 2a_0$
28-9 (a) equal magnitudes, opposite signs (b) no
28-11 14
28-13 all have one *s* electron outside closed shells
28-15 48 eV
28-17 small ionization energies
28-19 H electron closes shell in halogen atoms
28-21 $n = 3, l = 0, m_l = 0, s = 1/2, m_s = \pm 1/2$
28-23 11.1 eV
28-25 (a) 0.5 (b) 0.1
28-27 (a) $8a_0$ (b) $8a_0$
28-29 (a) 483 eV (b) mutual repulsion of 1s electrons (c) yes; additional shielding
28-31 (a) −272 eV (b) 3.79
28-33 (a) 2×10^{11} W (b) 10^{17} W m^{-2}
28-37 (a) 68.3 MeV (b) 9.6 Mev
28-39 22.4 MeV
28-43 (a) $4a_0$ (b) $2a_0$
28-45 (b) 9.01×10^{-15}
28-47 (a) $\psi(a) = \psi(-a) = 0$ (c) $a^{-1/2} \cos n\pi x/2a$, $n = 1, 3, 5, \ldots$; $a^{-1/2} \sin n\,\pi x/2a$, $n = 2, 4, 6, \ldots$; $E_n = n^2\hbar^2\pi^2/8ma^2$
28-49 $13e^{-4} = 0.238$
28-51 (a) 1.5 a_0 (b) $1/a_0$ (c) r and $1/r$ are large in different regions of space

Chapter 29

29-1 (a) 1.30 eV (b) −6.10 eV (c) 4.80 eV
29-3 (a) −5.76 eV (b) 3.13 eV
29-5 no; it is symmetrical
29-9 (b) 4 (c) 2
29-11 2.66×10^{14} Hz
29-13 yes; photons are emitted or lattice excited
29-17 4.46×10^{-29} C m
29-19 yes; nonbonding orbital is negative, H nuclei positive
29-21 (a) graphite, sp^2; diamond, sp^3 (b) yes; no bonding between planes in graphite
29-23 12.0 eV
29-25 1.18 T
29-27 5.11×10^7 Hz
29-31 63.8 Hz
29-35 broader peaks
29-37 3 to 2 to 2
29-41 $f_p > f_e$
29-43 (a) counterclockwise (b) reduces f_p

Chapter 30

30-1 8 h
30-3 17.6 d
30-5 5.6 to 5.7 d
30-7 18.95%
30-9 15.5 d
30-11 (a) $\frac{1}{4}$ (b) $\frac{1}{4}$
30-13 11,500 y
30-15 too old
30-17 1300 y
30-19 1.1×10^{-14}
30-21 1.48×10^4 m
30-23 8, 19, 35, 126
30-25 7.86 MeV
30-27 (a) 1397 MeV (b) 6.98 MeV
30-29 (a) 30 MeV (b) 0
30-31 (a) 1.44 MeV (b) -1.547×10^{-3} u
30-33 (a) $^3_1$H (b) $^2_1$H (c) α
30-35 (a) 4.84×10^{20} Hz (b) 6.20×10^{-13} m
30-37 (a) no, expect $N > Z$ for stable nucleus (b) positron, increase N/Z
30-39 6.93×10^6
30-41 6.64
30-43 40.4 y
30-45 (a) straight line (b) decay rate is not a simple exponential (c) straight line, less rapid decrease
30-47 (a) 24.7 MeV (b) 1.99×10^6 kg
30-49 (b) $^9_5$B and $^9_3$Li have unfilled lower levels (c) β^-
30-51 (a) 8.64 fm (b) 176.3 MeV
30-53 1319 MeV
30-57 geological stability (against earthquakes)
30-61 electrical repulsion is three times larger
30-63 (a) 8.21×10^{13} J kg^{-1} (b) 0.0203 kg s^{-1}

30-65 (a) 7.72×10^8 K (b) some atoms have above-average energies

Chapter 31

31-1 a single γ can ionize atoms; one microwave quantum cannot
31-3 (a) α particles (b) 0.0045 cm
31-7 nuclear mass is much larger than electron mass
31-9 $K(d) = 2K(p)$
31-11 determine range
31-13 (a) 5 cm (b) 0.5 cm
31-15 1.61×10^{15}
31-17 (a) 3.7×10^4 (b) 8.29×10^{-10} J (c) 8.29×10^{-10} W
31-19 8.11×10^{-7} Ci
31-21 6.20 R
31-23 (a) 4.50 min (b) 6.43 min
31-25 4.1×10^{-4} Sv y^{-1}
31-27 (a) 12 (b) 50
31-29 less important because of smaller total dose to genetic pool
31-31 2600 y^{-1}
31-33 one to 5 years doubles cancer rate, 0.25 to 1.5 years doubles mutation rate
31-35 (a) 160,000 (b) 5
31-37 $88,000,000
31-39 2000
31-43 (a) low-energy X rays have shorter ranges (b) reduce skin dose
31-45 (a) 7.40×10^{11} s^{-1} (b) 5.89×10^{10} m^{-2} s^{-1}
31-47 100 rad, 100 rem
31-49 1420 cm^3
31-51 (a) 0.616 J (b) 3.08 rad (c) 28
31-53 (a) 4 (b) 0.4 (c) no; masked by naturally occurring cancers
31-55 (a) 4.30 (b) 1.14×10^{-5} (c) 1.26×10^{-6}
31-57 count rate increases as slabs are added

INDEX

FUNDAMENTAL CONSTANTS

The numerical values of most constants have been rounded off to three significant figures for convenience.

Quantity	*Symbol*	*Numerical Value*
Speed of light (in vacuum)	c	3.00×10^{8} m s^{-1}
Gravitational constant	G	6.67×10^{-11} N m^2 kg^{-2}
Avogadro's number	N_A	6.02×10^{23} molecules mole^{-1}
Universal gas constant	R	8.31 J K^{-1} mole^{-1}
Boltzmann constant	k_B	1.38×10^{-23} J K^{-1}
		8.62×10^{-5} eV K^{-1}
Stefan's constant	σ	5.67×10^{-8} W m^{-2} K^{-4}
Atomic mass unit	u	1.66×10^{-27} kilograms
Coulomb constant	k	9.00×10^{9} N m^2 C^{-2}
	$\varepsilon_0 = 1/4\pi k$	8.85×10^{-12} C^2 N^{-1} m^{-2}
Biot-Savart constant	k'	10^{-7} T m A^{-1}
Electron charge	$-e$	-1.60×10^{-19} coulombs
Electron mass	m_e	9.11×10^{-31} kilograms
Proton charge	e	1.60×10^{-19} coulombs
Proton mass	m_p	1.673×10^{-27} kilograms
Neutron mass	m_n	1.675×10^{-27} kilograms
Planck's constant	h	6.63×10^{-34} J s
		4.14×10^{-15} eV s
	$\hbar = h/2\pi$	1.055×10^{-34} J s
		6.58×10^{-16} eV s
Rydberg constant	R_H	1.10×10^{7} metres^{-1}
Bohr radius	a_0	5.29×10^{-11} metres
Bohr magneton	μ_B	9.27×10^{-24} J T^{-1}

SOLAR AND TERRESTRIAL DATA

The numerical values given have been rounded off to three significant figures for convenience.

Standard atmospheric pressure	1 atm 1.013×10^{5} Pa 1.013 bars 760 mm Hg 760 torr
Acceleration of gravity, g	9.81 m s^{-2}
Magnetic field (Washington, D.C.)	5.7×10^{-5} teslas
Speed of sound (dry air, 20°C)	344 m s^{-1}
Mass of earth	5.98×10^{24} kilograms
Volume of earth	1.09×10^{21} m^3
Mean radius of earth	6.38×10^{6} metres
Mean density of earth	5.52×10^{3} kg m^{-3}
Mean angular rotational speed of earth	7.29×10^{-5} rad s^{-1}
Earth to sun, mean distance	1.50×10^{11} metres
Earth to moon, mean distance	3.84×10^{8} metres
Mean orbital speed of earth about the sun	2.98×10^{4} m s^{-1}
Sun, mean radius	6.95×10^{8} metres
mass	1.99×10^{30} kilograms
Moon, mean radius	1.74×10^{6} metres
volume	2.20×10^{19} m^3
mass	7.35×10^{22} kilograms
mean density	3.34×10^{3} kg m^{-3}
acceleration of gravity	1.62 m s^{-2}

ATOMIC MASSES OF THE ELEMENTS AS THEY OCCUR ON THE EARTH.

The mass of a carbon-12 atom is defined as exactly 12 u. Brackets indicate the approximate mass of the most stable isotope of artificially produced elements.

Atomic Number	Element	Symbol	Atomic Mass (u)
1	hydrogen	H	1.00797
2	helium	He	4.0026
3	lithium	Li	6.939
4	beryllium	Be	9.0122
5	boron	B	10.811
6	carbon	C	12.01115
7	nitrogen	N	14.0067
8	oxygen	O	15.9994
9	fluorine	F	18.9984
10	neon	Ne	20.183
11	sodium	Na	22.9898
12	magnesium	Mg	24.312
13	aluminum	Al	26.9815
14	silicon	Si	28.086
15	phosporus	P	30.9738
16	sulfur	S	32.064
17	chlorine	Cl	35.453
18	argon	Ar	39.948
19	potassium	K	39.102
20	calcium	Ca	40.08
21	scandium	Sc	44.956
22	titanium	Ti	47.90
23	vanadium	V	50.942
24	chromium	Cr	51.996
25	manganese	Mn	54.9380
26	iron	Fe	55.847
27	cobalt	Co	58.9332
28	nickel	Ni	58.71
29	copper	Cu	63.54
30	zinc	Zn	65.37
31	gallium	Ga	69.72
32	germanium	Ge	72.59
33	arsenic	As	74.9216
34	selenium	Se	78.96
35	bromine	Br	79.909
36	krypton	Kr	83.80
37	rubidium	Rb	85.47
38	strontium	Sr	87.62
39	yttrium	Y	88.905
40	zirconium	Zr	91.22
41	niobium	Nb	92.906
42	molybdenum	Mo	95.94
43	technetium	Tc	[99]
44	ruthenium	Ru	101.07
45	rhodium	Rh	102.905
46	palladium	Pd	106.4
47	silver	Ag	107.870
48	cadmium	Cd	112.40
49	indium	In	114.82
50	tin	Sn	118.69
51	antimony	Sb	121.75
52	tellurium	Te	127.60
53	iodine	I	126.9044
54	xenon	Xe	131.30
55	cesium	Ca	132.905
56	barium	Ba	137.34
57	lanthanum	La	138.91
58	cerium	Ce	140.12
59	praseodymium	Pr	140.907
60	neodymium	Nd	144.24
61	promethium	Pm	[145]
62	samarium	Sm	150.35
63	europium	Eu	151.96
64	gadolinium	Gd	157.25
65	terbium	Tb	158.924
66	dysprosium	Dy	162.50
67	holmium	Ho	164.930
68	erbium	Er	167.26
69	thulium	Tm	168.934
70	ytterbium	Yb	173.04
71	lutetium	Lu	174.97
72	hafnium	Hf	178.49
73	tantalum	Ta	180.948
74	tungsten	W	183.85
75	rhenium	Re	186.2
76	osmium	Os	190.2
77	iridium	Ir	192.2
78	platinum	Pt	195.09
79	gold	Au.	196.967
80	mercury	Hg	200.59
81	thallium	Tl	204.37
82	lead	Pb	207.19
83	bismuth	Bi	208.980
84	polonium	Po	[210]
85	astatine	At	[210]
86	radon	Rn	[222]
87	francium	Fr	[223]
88	radium	Ra	226.05
89	actinium	Ac	[227]
90	thorium	Th	232.038
91	protactinium	Pa	[231]
92	uranium	U	[238.03]
93	neptunium	Np	[237]
94	plutonium	Pu	[242]
95	americium	Am	[243]
96	curium	Cm	[247]
97	berkelium	Bk	[247]
98	californium	Cf	[249]
99	einsteinium	Es	[254]
100	fermium	Fm	[257]
101	mendelevium	Md	[256]
102	nobelium	No	[259]
103	lawrencium	Lw	[260]
104	Rutherfordium	Rf	[261]
105	(unnamed)		[262]
106	(unnamed)		[263]

Notes

Notes

Notes

Notes